To: Jim

For: your library and possible
use by you and your students.

Dad

26 Feb 1989

Corn and Corn Improvement
Third Edition

AGRONOMY
A Series of Monographs

The American Society of Agronomy and Academic Press published the first six books in this series. The General Editor of Monographs 1 to 6 was A. G. Norman. They are available through Academic Press, Inc., 111 Fifth Avenue, New York NY 10003.

1. C. EDMUND MARSHALL: The Colloid Chemical of the Silicate Minerals, 1949
2. BYRON T. SHAW, *Editor*: Soil Physical Conditions and Plant Growth, 1952
3. K. D. JACOB, *Editor*: Fertilizer Technology and Resources in the United States, 1953
4. W. H. PIERRE and A. G. NORMAN, *Editors*: Soil and Fertilizer Phosphate in Crop Nutrition, 1953
5. GEORGE F. SPRAGUE, *Editor*: Corn and Corn Improvement, 1955
6. J. LEVITT: The Hardiness of Plants, 1956

The Monographs published since 1957 are available from the American Society of Agronomy, 677 S. Segoe Road, Madison, WI 53711.

7. JAMES N. LUTHIN, *Editor*: Drainage of Agricultural Lands, 1957   *General Editor*, D. E. Gregg
8. FRANKLIN A. COFFMAN, *Editor*: Oats and Oat Improvement, 1961
Managing Editor, H. L. Hamilton
9. A. KLUTE, *Editor*:Methods of Soil Analysis, 1986
Part 1—Physical and Mineralogical Methods, Second Edition   *Managing Editor*,R. C. Dinauer
A. L. PAGE, *Editor*: Methods of Soil Analysis, 1982
Part 2—Chemical and Microbiological Properties, Second Edition *Managing Editor*, R. C. Dinauer
10. W. V. BARTHOLOMEW and F. E. CLARK, *Editors*: Soil Nitrogen, 1965
(Out of print; replaced by no. 22)   *Managing Editor*, H. L. Hamilton
11. R. M. HAGAN, H. R. HAISE, and T. W. EDMINSTER, *Editors*: Irrigation of Agricultural Lands, 1967   *Managing Editor*, R. C. Dinauer
12. FRED ADAMS, *Editor*: Soil Acidity and Liming, Second Edition, 1984
Managing Editor, R. C. Dinauer
13. E. G. HEYNE, *Editor*: Wheat and Wheat Improvement, Second Edition 1987
Managing Editor, S. H. Mickelson
14. A. A. HANSON and F. V. JUSKA, *Editors*: Turfgrass Science, 1969
Managing Editor, H. L. Hamilton
15. CLARENCE H. HANSON, *Editor*: Alfalfa Science and Technology, 1972
Managing Editor, H. L. Hamilton
16. J. R. WILCOX, *Editor*: Soybeans: Improvement, Production, and Uses, Second Edition, 1987
Managing Editor, D. A. Fuccillo
17. JAN VAN SCHILFGAARDE, *Editor*: Drainage for Agriculture, 1974
Managing Editor, R. C. Dinauer
18. G. F. SPRAGUE and J. W. DUDLEY, *Editors*: Corn and Corn Improvement, Third Edition, 1988
Managing Editor, S. H. Mickelson
19. JACK F. CARTER, *Editor*: Sunflower Science and Technology, 1978
Managing Editor, D. A. Fuccillo
20. ROBERT C. BUCKNER and L. P. BUSH, *Editors*: Tall Fescue, 1979
Managing Editor, D. A. Fuccillo
21. M. T. BEATTY, G. W. PETERSEN, and L. D. SWINDALE, *Editors*:
Planning the Uses and Management of Land, 1979   *Managing Editor*, R. C. Dinauer
22. F. J. STEVENSON, *Editor*: Nitrogen in Agricultural Soils, 1982
Managing Editor, R. C. Dinauer
23. H. E. DREGNE and W. O. WILLIS, *Editors*: Dryland Agriculture, 1983
Managing Editor, D. A. Fuccillo
24. R. J. KOHEL and C. F. LEWIS, *Editors*: Cotton, 1984
Managing Editor, D. A. Fuccillo
25. N. L. TAYLOR, *Editor*: Clover Science and Technology, 1985
Managing Editor, D. A. Fuccillo
26. D. C. RASMUSSON, *Editor*: Barley, 1985
Managing Editor, D. A. Fuccillo
27. M. A. TABATABAI, *Editor*: Sulfur in Agriculture, 1986
Managing Editor, R. C. Dinauer
28. R. A. OLSON and K. J. FREY, *Editors*: Nutritional Quality of Cereal Grains: Genetic and Agronomic Improvement. 1987
Managing Editor, S. H. Mickelson
29. A. A. HANSON, D. K. BARNES, and R. R. HILL, JR. *Editors*: Alfalfa and Alfalfa Improvement. 1988
Managing Editor, S. H. Mickelson

Corn and Corn Improvement
Third Edition

G. F. Sprague and J. W. Dudley, *editors*

Managing Editor: S. H. Mickelson

Editor-in-Chief ASA Publications: G. H. Heichel

Editor-in-Chief CSSA Publications: C. W. Stuber

Editor-in-Chief SSSA Publications: D. E. Kissel

Number 18 in the series
AGRONOMY

American Society of Agronomy, Inc.
Crop Science Society of America, Inc.
Soil Science Society of America, Inc.
Publishers
Madison, Wisconsin, USA

1988

American Society of Agronomy, Inc.
Crop Science Society of America, Inc.
Soil Science Society of America, Inc.
677 South Segoe Road, Madison, WI 53711 USA

Library of Congress Cataloging-in-Publication Data

Corn and corn improvement.
   (Agronomy ; no. 18)
   Includes index.
   Bibliography: p.
   1. Corn. 2. Corn—Breeding.   I. Sprague, Gretchen. II.
Dudley, J. W. (John Wesley), 1931– . III. Series.
SB191.M2C78235 1988   633.1′53   88-7954
ISBN 0-89118-099-0

Printed in the United States of America

CONTENTS

10   Climate Requirement   609

Robert H. Shaw

11   Corn Production   639

R. A. Olson and D. H. Sander

12   Diseases of Corn   687

D. R. Smith and D. G. White

13   The Most Important Corn Insects   767

F. F. Dicke and W. D. Guthrie

FOREWORD

The development of corn (*Zea mays* L.) paralleled the development of the great nations of the Western Hemisphere. Corn was a staple in the diets of the Aztecs and Incas. Its development and use by the natives and European colonists of North America and later by farmers and agricultural scientists in the USA laid a foundation of agricultural development upon which this great nation was built.

In the USA, corn emerged as a major feed crop for both domestic use and export, thus providing abundant, high-quality animal products for consumption in many nations. More recently, corn has become an important raw material for producing industrial products, such as ethanol.

Even after centuries of development, there is still great untapped potential in the corn crop. In this book, world authorities on corn describe its past development and forecast its future possibilities. The authors were chosen carefully to represent many different perspectives and areas of expertise. They represent both the seasoned veterans and the rising stars of corn research and development.

This book will serve as a valuable research and teaching reference. It provides a base of knowledge from which to launch new research efforts on corn improvement, production, and use. Hopefully, it will stimulate an expanded effort to exploit the full potential of this great species.

We particularly appreciate the efforts of Drs. George F. Sprague and John W. Dudley of the University of Illinois in performing the many duties associated with editing this book. They have made it a truly exceptional volume, one that will serve as the definitive work on corn and corn improvement for many years into the future.

D. A. Holt, *president*, 1988
American Society of Agronomy

C. J. Nelson, *president*, 1988
Crop Science Society of America

D. R. Keeney, *president*, 1988
Soil Science Society of America

ix

PREFACE

The 30 yr since the first edition of *Corn and Corn Improvement* have been years of drastic change; change in every aspect of breeding, production, and use as well as supporting basic sciences. The third edition attempts to provide an overview of the current status within each of the areas mentioned and their interrelations which, in total, have accounted for the continued steady improvement in yield and quality.

Corn (*Zea mays* L.) yields have continued to increase at a fairly constant rate conditioned by a combination of improved hybrids, parental materials, and improved breeding techniques; more efficient use of fertilizers; more selective chemicals for weed, insect, and disease control; and improved machinery permitting greater timeliness of all field operations. Changing production practices have brought with them changing problems relative to the incidence of both old and new disease and insect pests and of weed control.

Molecular biology (genetic engineering) was not recognized as having important production or breeding potential when the second edition was prepared. Since then there has been an explosive development in this broad area. Great advances have been made in understanding basic principles involved in different aspects of genetic control and regulatory mechanisms. The impact of such basic developments on breeding or production problems remains largely unexplored. Chapters have been added on cell tissue culture and in vivo manipulations and on molecular genetics of corn which survey the current state of knowledge in these areas. When controlled gene transfer becomes routinely feasible, the problem as to which genes to transfer becomes relevant. Current information is inadequate and, unfortunately the topic is receiving relatively little attention. The knowledge relative to genetic control of important physiological processes is reviewed in a new chapter on the use of physiological traits in corn improvement.

The chapters repeated from earlier editions have been extensively revised or completely rewritten by recognized authorities.

This volume, as in previous editions, was prepared to provide an authoritative overview for research workers, graduate or undergraduate students, and others interested in some aspect of breeding, production, or use. Illustrations and extensive literature citations should enhance this objective.

The editors express their deep appreciation to the authors contributing chapters and to the many others who have provided assistance during the preparation of this volume.

G. F. Sprague and John W. Dudley, *editors*

CONTRIBUTORS

D. E. Alexander
Professor of Plant Genetics, Department of Agronomy, University of Illinois, Urbana, Illinois

William L. Brown
President and CEO (Retired), Pioneer Hi-Bred International, Inc., Johnston, Iowa

Wayne R. Carlson
Chairman, University of Iowa, Iowa City, Iowa

E. H. Coe, Jr.
Geneticist, USDA-ARS, Department of Agronomy, University of Missouri, Columbia, Missouri

F. F. Dicke
Research Collaborator, USDA and Iowa State University, Corn Insect Research Unit, Ankeny, Iowa

Walton C. Galinat
Professor, University of Massachusetts, Suburban Experiment Station, Waltham, Massachusetts

Major M. Goodman
Professor, Department of Crop Science, North Carolina State University, Raleigh, North Carolina

W. D. Guthrie
Research Leader, USDA-ARS, Corn Insect Research Unit, Ankeny, Iowa

R. H. Hageman
Professor Emeritus of Crop Physiology, Department of Agronomy, University of Illinois at Urbana-Champaign, Urbana, Illinois

Arnel R. Hallauer
Research Geneticist, USDA-ARS, Department of Agronomy, Iowa State University, Ames, Iowa

K. A. Hibberd
Principal Scientist, Molecular Genetics, Inc., Minnetonka, Minnesota

D. A. Hoisington
Professor, Department of Agronomy, University of Missouri, Columbia, Missouri

R. J. Lambert
Professor of Plant Breeding and Genetics, Department of Agronomy, University of Illinois at Urbana-Champaign, Urbana, Illinois

Kendall R. Lamkey
Research Geneticist, USDA-ARS, Department of Agronomy, Iowa State University, Ames, Iowa

Joachim Messing
University Professor, Waksman Institute, Rutgers—The State University of New Jersey, Piscataway, New Jersey

M. G. Neuffer
Professor, Department of Agronomy, University of Missouri, Columbia, Missouri

R. A. Olson
Professor Emeritus (deceased), Agronomy Department, University of Nebraska, Lincoln, Nebraska

Tilden Wayne Perry
Professor, Department of Animal Science, Lilly Hall, Purdue University, West Lafayette, Indiana

R. L. Phillips
Professor, Department of Agronomy and Plant Genetics, University of Minnesota, St. Paul, Minnesota

Wilbert A. Russell
C. F. Curtiss Distinguished Professor, Department of Agronomy, Iowa State University, Ames, Iowa

D. H. Sander
Professor of Agronomy, Agronomy Department, University of Nebraska, Lincoln, Nebraska

Robert H. Shaw   C. F. Curtiss Distinguished Professor Emeritus, Iowa State University, Ames, Iowa

D. R. Smith   Area Director, Host Pest Resistance, DEKALB-PFIZER GENETICS, DeKalb, Illinois

D. A. Somers   Assistant Professor, Department of Agronomy and Plant Genetics, University of Minnesota, St. Paul, Minnesota

Virginia Walbot   Associate Professor, Department of Biological Sciences, Stanford University, Stanford, California

Stanley A. Watson   Senior Researcher (retired), Ohio Agricultural Research and Development Center, Ohio State University, Wooster, Ohio

D. G. White   Associate Professor of Plant Pathology, University of Illinois, Urbana, Illinois

Robert D. Wych   Production Research Manager, Pioneer Hi-Bred International, Inc., Johnston, Iowa

Conversion Factors for SI and non-SI Units

Conversion Factors for SI and non-SI Units

To convert Column 1 into Column 2, multiply by	Column 1 SI Unit	Column 2 non-SI Unit	To convert Column 2 into Column 1 multiply by
Length			
0.621	kilometer, km (10^3 m)	mile, mi	1.609
1.094	meter, m	yard, yd	0.914
3.28	meter, m	foot, ft	0.304
1.0	micrometer, μm (10^{-6} m)	micron, μ	1.0
3.94×10^{-2}	millimeter, mm (10^{-3} m)	inch, in	25.4
10	nanometer, nm (10^{-9} m)	Angstrom, Å	0.1
Area			
2.47	hectare, ha	acre	0.405
247	square kilometer, km^2 (10^3 m)^2	acre	4.05×10^{-3}
0.386	square kilometer, km^2 (10^3 m)^2	square mile, mi^2	2.590
2.47×10^{-4}	square meter, m^2	acre	4.05×10^3
10.76	square meter, m^2	square foot, ft^2	9.29×10^{-2}
1.55×10^{-3}	square millimeter, mm^2 (10^{-6} m)^2	square inch, in^2	645
Volume			
9.73×10^{-3}	cubic meter, m^3	acre-inch	102.8
35.3	cubic meter, m^3	cubic foot, ft^3	2.83×10^{-2}
6.10×10^4	cubic meter, m^3	cubic inch, in^3	1.64×10^{-5}
2.84×10^{-2}	liter, L (10^{-3} m^3)	bushel, bu	35.24
1.057	liter, L (10^{-3} m^3)	quart (liquid), qt	0.946
3.53×10^{-2}	liter, L (10^{-3} m^3)	cubic foot, ft^3	28.3
0.265	liter, L (10^{-3} m^3)	gallon	3.78
33.78	liter, L (10^{-3} m^3)	ounce (fluid), oz	2.96×10^{-2}
2.11	liter, L (10^{-3} m^3)	pint (fluid), pt	0.473

continued on next page

Conversion Factors for SI and non-SI Units

To convert Column 1 into Column 2, multiply by	Column 1 SI Unit	Column 2 non-SI Unit	To convert Column 2 into Column 1 multiply by
Mass			
2.20×10^{-3}	gram, g (10^{-3} kg)	pound, lb	454
3.52×10^{-2}	gram, g (10^{-3} kg)	ounce (avdp), oz	28.4
2.205	kilogram, kg	pound, lb	0.454
0.01	kilogram, kg	quintal (metric), q	100
1.10×10^{-3}	kilogram, kg	ton (2000 lb), ton	907
1.102	megagram, Mg (tonne)	ton (U.S.), ton	0.907
1.102	tonne, t	ton (U.S.), ton	0.907
Yield and Rate			
0.893	kilogram per hectare, kg ha^{-1}	pound per acre, lb acre^{-1}	1.12
7.77×10^{-2}	kilogram per cubic meter, kg m^{-3}	pound per bushel, lb bu^{-1}	12.87
1.49×10^{-2}	kilogram per hectare, kg ha^{-1}	bushel per acre, 60 lb	67.19
1.59×10^{-2}	kilogram per hectare, kg ha^{-1}	bushel per acre, 56 lb	62.71
1.86×10^{-2}	kilogram per hectare, kg ha^{-1}	bushel per acre, 48 lb	53.75
0.107	liter per hectare, L ha^{-1}	gallon per acre	9.35
893	tonnes per hectare, t ha^{-1}	pound per acre, lb acre^{-1}	1.12×10^{-3}
893	megagram per hectare, Mg ha^{-1}	pound per acre, lb acre^{-1}	1.12×10^{-3}
0.446	megagram per hectare, Mg ha^{-1}	ton (2000 lb) per acre, ton acre^{-1}	2.24
2.24	meter per second, m s^{-1}	mile per hour	0.447
Specific Surface			
10	square meter per kilogram, m^2 kg^{-1}	square centimeter per gram, cm^2 g^{-1}	0.1
1 000	square meter per kilogram, m^2 kg^{-1}	square millimeter per gram, mm^2 g^{-1}	0.001

Pressure

	SI unit	non-SI unit	
9.90	megapascal, MPa (10^6 Pa)	atmosphere	0.101
10	megapascal, MPa (10^6 Pa)	bar	0.1
1.00	megagram per cubic meter, Mg m^{-3}	gram per cubic centimeter, g cm^{-3}	1.00
2.09×10^{-2}	pascal, Pa	pound per square foot, lb ft^{-2}	47.9
1.45×10^{-4}	pascal, Pa	pound per square inch, lb in^{-2}	6.90×10^3

Temperature

	SI unit	non-SI unit	
1.00 (K − 273)	Kelvin, K	Celsius, °C	1.00 (°C + 273)
(9/5 °C) + 32	Celsius, °C	Fahrenheit, °F	5/9 (°F −32)

Energy, Work, Quantity of Heat

	SI unit	non-SI unit	
9.52×10^{-4}	joule, J	British thermal unit, Btu	1.05×10^3
0.239	joule, J	calorie, cal	4.19
10^7	joule, J	erg	10^{-7}
0.735	joule, J	foot-pound	1.36
2.387×10^{-5}	joule per square meter, J m^{-2}	calorie per square centimeter (langley)	4.19×10^4
10^5	newton, N	dyne	10^{-5}
1.43×10^{-3}	watt per square meter, W m^{-2}	calorie per square centimeter minute (irradiance), cal cm^{-2} min^{-1}	698

Transpiration and Photosynthesis

	SI unit	non-SI unit	
3.60×10^{-2}	milligram per square meter second, mg m^{-2} s^{-1}	gram per square decimeter hour, g dm^{-2} h^{-1}	27.8
5.56×10^{-3}	milligram (H_2O) per square meter second, mg m^{-2} s^{-1}	micromole (H_2O) per square centimeter second, μmol cm^{-2} s^{-1}	180
10^{-4}	milligram per square meter second, mg m^{-2} s^{-1}	milligram per square centimeter second, mg cm^{-2} s^{-1}	10^4
35.97	milligram per square meter second, mg m^{-2} s^{-1}	milligram per square decimeter hour, mg dm^{-2} h^{-1}	2.78×10^{-2}

Plane Angle

	SI unit	non-SI unit	
57.3	radian, rad	degrees (angle), °	1.75×10^{-2}

continued on next page

Conversion Factors for SI and non-SI Units

To convert Column 1 into Column 2, multiply by	Column 1 SI Unit	Column 2 non-SI Unit	To convert Column 2 into Column 1 multiply by
Electrical Conductivity, Electricity, and Magnetism			
10	siemen per meter, S m^{-1}	millimho per centimeter, mmho cm^{-1}	0.1
10^4	tesla, T	gauss, G	10^{-4}
Water Measurement			
9.73 × 10^{-3}	cubic meter, m^3	acre-inches, acre-in	102.8
9.81 × 10^{-3}	cubic meter per hour, m^3 h^{-1}	cubic feet per second, ft^3 s^{-1}	101.9
4.40	cubic meter per hour, m^3 h^{-1}	U.S. gallons per minute, gal min^{-1}	0.227
8.11	hectare-meters, ha-m	acre-feet, acre-ft	0.123
97.28	hectare-meters, ha-m	acre-inches, acre-in	1.03 × 10^{-2}
8.1 × 10^{-2}	hectare-centimeters, ha-cm	acre-feet, acre-ft	12.33
Concentrations			
1	centimole per kilogram, cmol kg^{-1} (ion exchange capacity)	milliequivalents per 100 grams, meq 100 g^{-1}	1
0.1	gram per kilogram, g kg^{-1}	percent, %	10
1	milligram per kilogram, mg kg^{-1}	parts per million, ppm	1
Radioactivity			
2.7 × 10^{-11}	bequerel, Bq	curie, Ci	3.7 × 10^{10}
2.7 × 10^{-2}	bequerel per kilogram, Bq kg^{-1}	picocurie per gram, pCi g^{-1}	37
100	gray, Gy (absorbed dose)	rad, rd	0.01
100	sievert, Sv (equivalent dose)	rem (roentgen equivalent man)	0.01
Plant Nutrient Conversion			
	Elemental	*Oxide*	
2.29	P	P_2O_5	0.437
1.20	K	K_2O	0.830
1.39	Ca	CaO	0.715
1.66	Mg	MgO	0.602

1 The Origin of Corn

WALTON C. GALINAT

Suburban Experiment Station
University of Massachusetts—Amherst
Waltham, Massachusetts

The initial steps in the origin of corn (maize) (*Zea mays* L.) were probably taken during the invention of New World agriculture more than 8000 yr ago. A contemplation of the creative power necessary for ancient man to transform the tiny spike of teosinte [*Z. mexicana* (Schrad.) Kuntze] into the magnificent ear of corn in a relatively short period of time, perhaps 100 yr, leaves the beholder with a sense of awe if not disbelief (Fig. 1-1).

The possibility of such an important achievement by America's first indigenous people has left the academic community arguing about whether man or nature was the selective agent. Some of the evidence in favor of human involvement includes the following: corn is probably younger than teosinte; the key taxonomic traits that separate corn from teosinte are agronomic rather than naturally adaptive; the differences between them are genetic rather than cytogenetic; the oldest known corn cobs are probably domestic rather than wild; evolution in this part of the grass family leads to the female spike of teosinte, with the cob of corn only possible in the most advanced position as an artifact of domestication; teosinte has greater cytological diversity than corn in the positions of its chromosome knobs; teosinte is a highly successful wild plant while corn is unknown in the wild; before the advent of corn, teosinte would be acceptable as a food plant; comparisons by chemotaxonomy (gel electrophoresis, etc.) show that corn represents only a part of the total variation that occurs within teosinte (for an earlier review, see my chapter in the previous edition of this book, Galinat, 1977b and its more recent extrapolations, Beadle, 1980; Galinat, 1983, 1985b). There are still, however, a few who do not accept all of this evidence and who continue to maintain that the corn phenotype was not derived from the teosinte phenotype by human involvement but that it stems from a wild corn (Mangelsdorf, 1983, 1986; Wilkes, 1986).

The latest version of the wild corn hypothesis now supported by Mangelsdorf and Wilkes is a modified resurrection of the old tripartite hypothesis (Mangelsdorf and Reeves, 1939). In both hypotheses, annual teosinte is proposed to have come from hybridization between corn and

1

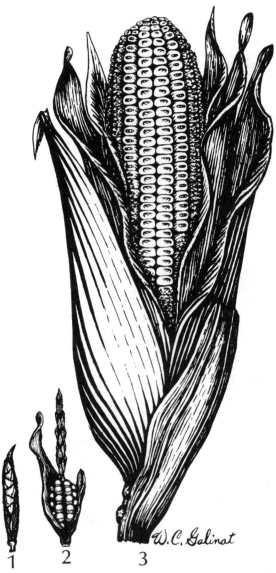

Fig. 1–1. Teosinte and its domestic derivatives. (1) Teosinte is probably corn's wild ancestor. The teosinte spike (ear) has two rows of single female spikelets that alternate between opposite sides of the rachis (cob). Each kernel is usually enclosed by the following three protective structures: The outer glume of its spikelet; the cupule of its fruitcase; and a husk enclosing the entire spike. (2) The first corn, as reconstructed from its oldest remains from Tehuacan, Mexico. It has four ranks of paired female spikelets resulting in an eight-rowed ear. The grain is exposed by rachilla elongation although the entire ear is enclosed by two or more husks. Like teosinte and modern corn, the ear may have a terminal region that is male. (3) The modern ear of corn has many ranks of paired kernels. The entire ear is enclosed in many husks. It is incapable of survival as a wild plant.

another species while cultivated corn was domesticated from a hypothetical wild corn. Initially, *Tripsacum* was suggested as being the outcross parent of annual teosinte. Now it is *Z. diploperennis*. Mangelsdorf (1974, 1986) abandoned his old hypothesis as a result of scanning electron micrograph (SEM) comparisons in pollen structure of Galinat's corn-*Tripsacum* derivatives and teosinte which seemed to exclude *Tripsacum* as a parent of teosinte. A similar conclusion was reached earlier by Galinat (1973) on a basis of comparative mapping between corn and *Tripsacum* in which it was found that *Tripsacum* did not carry the essential block of teosinte genes on chromosome four.

Mangelsdorf (1986, p. 85) states, "Even those investigators who believe corn evolved from annual teosinte generally accept the fact that the earliest corns were pod corn." While such investigators may acknowledge that the early cobs were soft, they do not all agree it was pod corn. An alternative explanation is that the pairing of the female spikelets diverted photosynthate away from an induration of the glumes and rachis. The delayed expression of induration that followed backcrossing to either teosinte or a more primitive form of corn, centuries after the emergence of soft-cob corn, occurred when corn had evolved a more elaborate vascular system in association with a high-rowed ear. If this retrogression reduced the kernel-row-number without a corresponding vascular reduction, then once again the supply system might be adequate for an expression of induration. Retention of the elaborate vascular system of an eight-rowed ear following a reduction of the ear to the four-rowed condition is known (Laubengayer, 1948, 1949).

The new wild corn hypothesis is no more valid than the old one. Both require the dismissal of annual teosinte as a redundant hybrid. Both do nothing to invalidate the overwhelming mass of data supporting annual teosinte as the wild ancestor of corn. Furthermore, the proposed new ancestors for annual teosinte would not contribute all of the chromosome knob patterns and positions now known in annual teosinte (Kato Y, 1976; McClintock et al., 1981). Speciation by domestication or by any other selective agency does not require wide cross hybridization as its main source of raw material because variability is self-generating and abundantly available in open-pollinated species such as teosinte.

When the Europeans arrived on the scene, the morphological divergence between corn and teosinte seemed to be so advanced that taxonomists erroneously placed them in separate genera (*Zea* spp. and *Euchlaena* spp.). As a result of cytogenetic comparisons, it is generally agreed that they belong in the same genus (*Zea*) (Reeves and Mangelsdorf, 1942) or consolidated further as different subspecies of the same species (*Z. mexicana*) (Iltis and Doebley, 1980).

1–1 CORN AS A PRODUCT OF SPECIATION BY DOMESTICATION

Since Darwin's time, the process of domestication has been recognized as a condensed version of the gradual type of speciation that is common in plants (Stebbins and Ayala, 1985). The underlying patterns may be similar to those in the punctuated equilibria type of speciation, i.e., a rapid rate of change and/or the isolation of certain genotypes in small colonies, as sometimes may occur in animals (Eldredge and Gould, 1972; Stebbins and Ayala, 1985). The power of selection by man in causing punctuated evolution by plant breeding lies in his mind and eye rather than in the continuous trial and error of the more gradual type of natural speciation. A common example of divergent selection under domestication is the wide range of vegetables within *Brassica oleracea* (Williams and Hill, 1986). Perhaps an even better example is the diversity represented by some 300 races of corn that have evolved since corn's initial divergence from teosinte. Since corn became taxonomically defined by the same traits that resulted in the domestication of teosinte, the transformation represents a case of speciation by domestication.

Species are separated by some form of reproductive isolation. Since the morphological integrity of a cultivar is maintained and directed by man, it does not need such a protective barrier. The wild progenitor, however, may require protection against the cultivar. Various partial isolating mechanisms may evolve in the wild form that allow it to remain sympatric with the cultivar or sometimes as a weed within populations of the cultivar, as occurs with several wild and cultivated partners (review of Pickersgill, 1981) including the teosinte-corn relationship described here.

1-2   TEOSINTE: AN ANCESTOR AND PROBABLE PROGENITOR OF CORN

Teosinte is an ancient and still flourishing wild grass from Mexico and Guatemala that has differentiated into various races, species, plant habits (annual and perennial), into two ploidies (2n and 4n), and into many cytological distributions of chromosome knobs, some of which are unknown in corn. There are some differences of opinion regarding its classification. The annual teosintes have been classified by Wilkes (1967) as six races (Nobogame, Central Plateau, Chalco, Balsas, Huehuetenango, and Guatemala) and by Doebley and Iltis (1980) and Iltis and Doebley (1980) as two subspecies of *Z. mays* L.: ssp. *mexicana* (Chalco, Central Plateau, and Nobogame) and ssp. *parviglumis*-var. *parviglumis* (Balsas) and var. *huehuetenangensis* (Huehuetenango) and as the species *Z. luxurians* (Guatemala). The perennial teosintes from Jalisco, Mexico are separated into two more species (Iltis et al., 1979) that have a ploidy difference, *Z. perennis* ($2n=40$) and *Z. diploperennis* ($2n=20$).

It is generally agreed now that teosinte is an ancestor of corn, but not all agree that teosinte is corn's progenitor in the sense that corn is a domesticated version of teosinte. That is, a few (Mangelsdorf, 1974, 1986; Wilkes, 1986) still contend that the 7000-yr-old archaeological cobs from Tehuacan, Mexico are from a now extinct wild corn. Although it is probable that these oldest known cobs were also from a cultivated plant, it is not possible to directly test hypotheses invoking extinct taxa. It has been possible to breed corn with cobs identical in appearance to those oldest ones from Tehuacan and these have no natural means of survival as successful wild plants. A reconstruction of the oldest Tehuacan ear is compared to the ear of teosinte and modern corn in Fig. 1–1.

The idea that teosinte could be the wild ancestor of corn did not firmly take hold until their cytogenetic homology was discovered. Beadle (1932a) reported that these taxa have the same chromosome number ($n =$ 10), that their Fl hybrids are fertile, and that their chromosomes pair closely at pachytene. Emerson and Beadle (1932) added that, for the loci tested, corn-teosinte hybrids have essentially the same frequencies of crossing-over as in corn itself, except in the presence of heterozygous inversions such as the one postulated on genetic grounds on chromosome 9 (Beadle, 1932b) and which was later demonstrated cytologically by O'Mara (1942). Three other inversions are known in teosinte in relation to the standard corn sequence (Ting, 1958, 1964). There is no evidence that the few inversions occasionally found in certain isolated individuals of both corn and teosinte have played any significant role in differentiating the two taxa. Longley (1937, 1941) showed that the idiograms of their chromosomes are essentially identical, although the teosinte from southern Guatemala has some terminal-knob positions unknown in both corn and the annual teosintes from Mexico. Beadle (1930) also found that the 4n hybrid between 4n corn and perennial teosinte was fertile with crossing-over apparently the same as that for 4n corn alone. The genetic ratios for segregations from such hybrids are presented by Burnham (1962, p. 219).

1–2.1   A Two-Stage Domestication Resulting in Multicenters

The concept of a multicenter origin for corn has had several advocates. Randolph (1959) thought the diversity in corn with respect to cytological, morphological, and physiological characteristics and their early widespread distribution indicated multiple domestications. McClintock (1959) suggested that the various patterns of chromosome knobs in the races of corn reflected several independent origins. Mangelsdorf (1974) proposed that there were "as many as six different geographical races of wild corn and that primitive races stemming from these still exist." Kato Y (1976, 1984), in line with McClintock's earlier suggestion, claims that the various knob patterns in the present-day races of corn stem from independent domestications of different teosintes with different knob patterns, not from different races of wild corn.

Another form of evidence supporting either two independent domestications of teosinte or early isolates from a domesticated teosinte comes from comparative kernel and cob morphology in the ancient indigenous races of corn from Mexico. Although the descriptions here agree with those of Wellhausen et al. (1952), the interpretations involving teosinte do not. An important domestic step in the origin of corn was the liberation of the kernels from confinement within the teosinte fruitcase. This was accomplished by at least two different systems that are still reflected by differences in kernel and cob morphology. In the primitive Chapalote-Nal Tel complex of corn, kernel emergence above the chaff was achieved by an elongation of the rachilla within the spikelet. In contrast, with the Palomero Toluqueño system, apparently the kernel emerged primarily by a rapid elongation of the kernel itself. As a result the kernel extended beyond the chaff while both chaff and rachilla have remained about as short as they are in teosinte (Fig. 1–2).

The present descendants with cobs based on rachilla elongation are common in U.S. corn, especially in the Northern Flints. The other system of kernel elongation with short rachillas has among its descendants White Rice Popcorn, the Gourd-Seed or Shoe-Peg types and, to lesser degrees, the Southern Dents in general. The Corn Belt Dent tends to be intermediate. It is known to be a hybrid between the Southern Dents and Northern Flints. Much of its heterosis appears to stem from combining these diverse parents (Wallace and Brown, 1956). Furtherback, the source of the heterosis may stem in part from either early isolates of domesticated teosinte or from independent domestications of two different teosintes, as suggested above.

Traditionally, sweet corn has had its evolutionary roots in the Northern Flint-long rachilla type of cob. Yet in recent years, the consumer preference has been for deep kernels and a high number of kernel rows. These are characteristics of the Palomero Toluqueño—white rice popcorn type of cob and kernel. At Waltham, we have made progress in sweet corn improvement by going directly to the source of these traits. The thick pericarp of this popcorn is easily removed by breeding (Tracy and Galinat, 1987). The vestigial glume gene may be used with this material to allow full access to its deep kernels.

The following hypothesis places a framework of such multicenters upon the scenario suggested (Galinat, 1983, 1985a, b, c) for a two-stage origin of corn. First, there was inadvertant selection within teosinte and, secondly, this was followed by the genetic construction of corn by the deliberate selection of its key traits. It is proposed here that the so-called independent domestications of different teosintes in various locations were mostly first-stage modifications of teosinte resulting from the mere act of gathering teosinte in the wild. That is, when whole teosinte plants are harvested for threshing, only those plants that still retained their seed could contribute to the crop despite random collecting. This resulted in a single tight husk enclosing each spike and a condensation of these enclosed spikes into clusters (fascicles) that usually retained their mature fruit (seed) cases even after disarticulation. These seed retention systems were not only useful in harvesting but they also acquired a survival value in the wild. Apparently they are adaptive during the dry season by de-

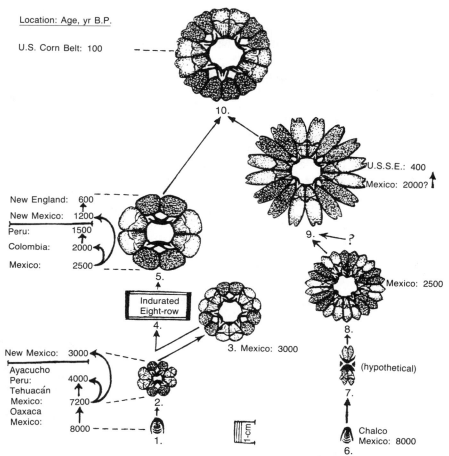

Location: Age, yr B.P.

U.S. Corn Belt: 100

10.

U.S.S.E.: 400
Mexico: 2000?

New England: 600
New Mexico: 1200
Peru: 1500
Colombia: 2000
Mexico: 2500

5.

Indurated
Eight-row

4.

3. Mexico: 3000

9. ←— ?

Mexico: 2500

8.

(hypothetical)

7.

New Mexico: 3000
Ayacucho
Peru: 4000
Tehuacán
Mexico: 7200
Oaxaca
Mexico: 8000

2.

1.

6.

Chalco
Mexico: 8000

Fig. 1–2. Cross-sectional views of corn ears representing 8000 yr of evolution after domestication. Kernel emergence from the teosinte fruitcase was accomplished by two different systems. (1) Balsas-type teosinte from Oaxaca that may be ancestral to corn with kernel emergence based on rachilla elongation. (2) String cob corn such as that from Tehuacan, Mexico (7200 yr), Ayacucho, Peru (4000 yr), New Mexico (3000 yr). (3) Chapalote with a thick cob bearing 12 rows of small kernels. The thick cob is a two-gene advance (Galinat, 1969) associated with a larger vascular supply system. A recombination of the larger supply system with the primitive four- and eight-rowed traits resulted in two new products. (4) Induration of the cob is one type of sink deposition for the larger supply when there are only eight or less rows of small kernels. (5) The evolution of larger kernels for eight-rowed maize provides a new sink outlet for increased levels of photosynthate and a new, more useful form of ear. This is a generalized view of various independent forms of Maiz de Ocho (Mexico, 2500 yr), Cabuya (Colombia, 2000 yr), Pardo and Cuzco (Peru, 1500 yr), Maiz de Ocho (New Mexico, 1200 yr) and Northern Flint (New England, 600 yr). (6) Chalco-type teosinte from the Valley of Mexico that may be ancestral to corn with kernel emergence based on kernel elongation. (7) Hypothetical domesticate based on a hybrid of Palomero Toluqueno and Chalco teosinte, (8) Palomero Toluqueno, an ancient indigenous race of corn from Mexico with short rachillas like teosinte and greatly elongate kernels. (9) Pepitilla is ancestral in varying degrees to the Southern Dents, especially to Shoe-Peg with its extremely narrow and deep kernels and Gourd-Seed with broad, deep kernels. Like teosinte, these races have short rachillas. They appear to be derived from a hybrid between Palomero Toluqueno and some unknown Dent corn. (10) The Corn-Belt Dent is known to be a hybrid between the Northern Flints (5) and the Southern Dents (9). Its kernel and rachilla types are intermediate between its parents.

laying seed dispersal until rain and wind storms heralding the onset of the growing season knock the plants down and disperse the seed. This allows a maximum population size with a relatively uniform growth stage on through flowering.

Second, when man began to harvest individual clusters of female spikes, and eventually a more productive and useful uppermost spike within the cluster, he selected deliberately for certain key variants affecting this spike that ultimately constructed the corn ear (Galinat, 1983). Once the corn ear was constructed in one or two areas (Chalco and Oaxaca), its enormous advantage as a food plant over the semidomestic teosintes and other New World cereals (e.g., *Setaria*) caused the rapid acceptance of corn as a replacement. Because the local semidomestic teosintes continued to interbreed with the alien corn introduced by man, they left their particular knob pattern like fingerprints as evidence of their major role in adapting corn to their common environment. The various knob patterns that are shared by corn and teosinte in common environments may reveal adaptive introgression from the local teosinte rather than multicenters of independent domestications.

1-2.2 Domestic Steps in the Origin of Corn

Teosinte, like the wild progenitors of many other domesticated plants, carried within its genetic load of deleterious mutations the capacity to undo its accumulation of key traits despite their essential nature for survival in the wild over millions of years. The reversal in adaptability of two key traits under the selective actions of man each doubled the grain yield per ear. That is, the reactivation of the second female spikelet doubled the yield once. This was followed by an increase from two to four ranks that doubled it again, totaling a fourfold increase. The many-ranked trait of the ear and tassel is unique to corn in the entire tribe Andropogoneae. It could only have been fixed by human selection for increased condensation leading to increased productivity. A third trait, nonshattering rachis, made harvesting more efficient.

Another domestic trait that provided easy shelling was the elevation of the grain above the chaff by an elongation of the rachilla in the Chapalote-Nal Tel derivatives described earlier. An alternative system for kernel emergence occurred in the race Palomero Toluqueño in which the rachilla remained short as in teosinte but the kernels became greatly elongated and, thereby, protruded beyond the chaff (Fig. 1-2).

These traits are not only individually nonadaptive in the wild, but their total combination is lethal to survival in the wild. They could only have been assembled and nurtured by man. In a primitive corn-teosinte background, three of these key traits segregate in a simple Mendelian fashion (Rogers, 1950; Galinat, 1978; Beadle, 1978). They are presumed to represent the first deliberate steps in the origin of corn. They have been summarized (Galinat, 1983) as follows:

1. Solitary female spikelets in teosinte in comparison with paired ones in corn.
2. Two-ranked central spike in teosinte in comparison with a many-ranked one in corn.
3. Shattering rachis (cob) in teosinte in comparison with a nonshattering one in corn.

1–2.3   The Primary Step: A Reactivation of the Second Female Spikelet

Reverse mutations that reactivate suppressed structures are sometimes adaptive in a new niche during speciation in the Gramineae (Arber, 1934). The reactivation of the suppressed second female spikelet in teosinte destroys the functional integrity of the cupulate fruitcase as a protective device in the wild, but at the same time it makes the grain more accessible to threshing and, thereby, more useful to man. The pairing of female spikelets in wild populations of teosinte occurs at a low frequency. Its significance can be questioned because, rather than being part of the natural variation in teosinte, it could just be a result of introgression from corn. Such a mutation to paired female spikelets, that is certainly not a result of corn introgression, has recently been discovered in *Tripsacum* (Dewald and Dayton, 1985), although the expression of this mutation will require some modification in that its present phenotype is too strongly female and similar to that of the tassel-seed-2 (*ts*-2) mutant of corn. Dewald and Dayton (1985) propose that it be used to domesticate *Tripsacum* as a perennial cereal in a pathway parallel to that followed during the origin of corn many thousands of years ago. This favors the reactivation hypothesis for an origin of corn.

Special importance is attached to the primary step involving a change from solitary to paired female spikelets because in this one simple change teosinte was immediately made more useful to man and less adapted to nature. It not only doubled the yield of grain per spike, but it also opened up the fruitcase, permitting easier shelling by man and easier access for grain feeding by small birds. Protection replacement came from husks (see later).

Pairing already occurs in the male spikelets and genetic variation also occurs in teosinte for an extension of this pairing to the female region. In our experimental populations of teosinte where the crop is planted, pollinated and harvested by hand, natural selection is relaxed for single female spikelets and eventually variation appears for a reactivation of the second spikelet (Galinat, 1985, unpublished data). Even if this were a consequence of introgression from corn, it still demonstrates the simple inheritance of this trait.

The genus *Tripsacum*, like teosinte, usually has solitary female spikelets and always has paired male spikelets. The more distant relatives of corn in the perfect-flowered Andropogoneae are stable for various intermediate degrees of development by the second spikelet. All that remains from an ancestral second spikelet is the sterile pedicel along one margin of a rachis depression in *Manisuris* spp. It combines with the depression to form an incipient cupule. As a result, the remaining spikelet appears to take part in forming a primitive cupulate fruitcase. This protective device became more highly specialized in teosinte with the complete reduction of the second spikelet, a deepening of the cupule with enlarged wings and an increased level of induration in both the cupule and the outer glume of the enclosed spikelet (Galinat, 1956, 1970).

1–2.4   The Inheritance of the Key Traits

When the gene (or genes, *pd* or *pd* 1 and *pd* 2) for single female spikelets is extracted directly out of teosinte, it may segregate as a single recessive in some families (Collins and Kempton, 1920), sometimes on chromosome 3 (Langham, 1940), sometimes on chromosome 7 or on both chromosomes 3 and 7 (Rogers, 1950). Mangelsdorf (1952) reported a block of teosinte genes on chromosome 3 that enhance the penetrance of the gene for single female spikelets. Mangelsdorf (1947) had also reported genes affecting *pd* expression on chromosomes 4 and 8. Apparently these are modifying genes that may operate through their effects on the vascular system. A vascular supply for a four-rowed ear that carries both the *pd* and *tr* (two-ranked) genes may developmentally switch between the two botanical types of four-rowed ears, that is, two ranks of paired spikelets and four ranks of single spikelets. This association may account for the apparent linkage of about 20 crossover units between *tr* and *pd* reported by Langham (1940) rather than true linkage due to their location on the same chromosome.

Rogers (1950) reports two different genes for two-ranking, one on chromosome 1 and one on chromosome 2. The chromosome 2 location agrees with our results with interchanges between corn chromosome 2 and its partial homeolog *Tripsacum* chromosome 9 which carries a gene that produces two-ranking in a four-ranked background as well as four other loci in common with *Zea* chromosome 2 (Galinat, 1973). Despite extensive repatterning of the *Zea* and *Tripsacum* chromosomes, this one segment is so important that its architecture has been maintained intact since the ancient divergence of these genera. The chromosome 1 location for *tr* agrees with the earlier results of Langham. The linkage data for *tr* varies in different genetic backgrounds that have different levels of condensation. The latter factor is associated with changes in kernel-row-number (Anderson and Brown, 1948). The polygenic nature of multi-ranking at the higher levels (*mr* 1, *mr* 2, *mr* 3) in the ear is well known (Emerson and Smith, 1950; Galinat, 1978).

1–2.5   The Genetic Background

After describing these taxonomic traits, it is necessary to emphasize for the benefit of the systematic biologist that their stable expression as key traits depends on the selective pressures placed upon them. Stabilizing selection assembles a background that provides the support system necessary for a conservative or uniform phenotype in varying environments.

Soon after the transformation to corn, the inheritance of these key traits became more complex. There was an enhancement and stabilization of the key traits of corn together with a suppression and destabilization of the teosinte ones. This background adjustment for multiple modifiers included selection for a larger vascular system that was necessary to supply the increased energy demands, first for paired female spikelets, then usually for their proliferation into many ranks and finally for the greatly increased kernel size in the advanced types of corn ears. The largest kernels such as in Cuzco corn are mutually exclusive with high kernel row numbers. The capacity of the vascular system to supply the photosynthate is the limiting factor.

The transitional forms now called *missing links* between teosinte and corn rapidly became extinct when corn evolved and the new form was recognized by man as a superior replacement for the old one (Galinat, 1985b). Present-day corn-teosinte hybrids representing these missing links are not only discarded by man during his selection of seed ears, but they have no natural means of seed dispersal. Weatherwax (1954, p. 181) describes it as follows: "With the one species preserved by its biological fitness and the other by man—and the hybrids between them finding no friend in either nature or man—the two species continue to live in the same area and remain more or less distinct. Some permanent interchange of germ plasm occurred between them, of course, but teosinte continued to be predominantly teosinte and maize to be maize."

The transformation of the tiny female spike of teosinte into the monstrous ear of corn is not only drastic in terms of domestication but also large when measured by the standards of speciation. This transformation appears somewhat less dramatic when viewed with the oldest type of Tehuacan cob as an intermediate form (Fig. 1-1). The development of reproductive isolation is somewhat less than the cross-sterility usually achieved during speciation. But, at least three types of partial isolation have evolved since domestication to now separate teosinte and corn. These isolating mechanisms were imposed by disruptive selection between nature and man and they may continue to elaborate. They started to evolve during man's inadvertent and then deliberate selection within his harvested crop for floral forms more useful to him, on the one hand, and by natural selection within the wild form for reproductive success on the other.

1-3 ISOLATING MECHANISMS

Speciation is not based solely on the complexity of morphological differences between the taxa, but rather on some form and degree of reproductive isolation. The barriers to interbreeding may occur at three levels. First, the taxa are unable to hybridize. Secondly, if hybrids are produced, they may be sterile. Thirdly, if the hybrids are fertile, crossing-over may be inhibited.

Although the reproductive isolation between teosinte and corn has not advanced to the level of either cross-sterility or hybrid sterility, the barrier between them is as effective as that found between other taxa in nature when based on other isolating mechanisms such as flowering time (seasonal) and geographic (spatial) factors. In addition to both of these mechanisms, teosinte and corn are separated by internal factors involving inheritance by blocks of closely linked genes that protect the genetic integrity of their distinct floral morphologies. While all three of these isolating mechanisms now separate teosinte and corn to various degrees in the different taxa of teosinte, the internal factors may still be elaborating. They will, therefore, be discussed last.

1–3.1 Isolation by Differences in Flowering Time

A common form of isolation between related taxa of plants results from the evolution of a difference in their flowering time. This is obvious in the cultivated parts of the corn fields of the Central Plateau and Valley of Mexico where both teosinte and corn start at the same time but teosinte flowers 10 d later than corn (Wilkes, 1967). Under the seasonal restrictions of this environment, only the early flowering selections of corn have sufficient time after flowering to develop and mature the large kernels preferred by man. The development of large kernels requires a long, slower filling period for the storage of photosynthate in the endosperm.

With teosinte, in contrast, where reproductive success depends upon development of a large number of small seeds that are capable of self-dispersal, natural selection is for late-flowering types as a mechanism for reproductive isolation from corn. Delayed flowering in teosinte results in a larger more competitive plant that is capable of producing a large number of seed-bearing spikes that flower over a longer period of time. Because the small seeds of teosinte mature rapidly, little time is required after flowering for their development.

Isolation between teosinte and corn by inherited differences in flowering time may be broken down at the margins of the corn field. In this area where cultivation is not clean, the teosinte may get an earlier start than the corn and then the two will flower at the same time. As a result, the other systems of isolation, especially block inheritance of the key traits, became actively important to the survival of teosinte as a wild plant.

1–3.2 Isolation by Geographic Separation

The simplest way to establish discontinuity between a divergent type and its original population is to physically separate them by geographic isolation from each other. The geographic isolation of corn and teosinte has been imposed by man from near the beginning of domestication. Man transported a primitive type of corn not far advanced from the oldest Tehuacan corn to South America some 4000 or more years ago where it freely diverged in complete isolation from teosinte. There was a delay of 2000 or more years before corn could spread into most of the area now the USA because of barriers of its own, i.e., lack of adaptation to longer daylengths and shorter growing seasons, and eventually a lack of the cultural techniques necessary for certain of the new areas, such as plowing the dense prairie sod in the area of the present-day U.S. Corn Belt (Galinat, 1985a).

The careful selection of the best corn ears as seed for planting would be made in order to ensure a good food supply for the following year, especially if their transport and introduction into a new area was contemplated. Such good founder germ plasm of corn was apparently selected elsewhere and transported into the desert environment of the Tehuacan Valley where it could grow under irrigation and also was geographically isolated from swamping by teosinte.

Agriculture by irrigation requires a sophisticated technique. The initial steps in both the invention of agriculture and the domestication of food plants would occur in a less hostile environment than the desert.

When the restricted variation within the special genetic type that was introduced in small isolated populations (Mayr, 1942) was combined with rigorous selection against lingering teosinte traits, sudden fixation (in 100 yr or less) of the new taxon called corn produced the new adaptive peak. This rigorous selection for the best seed ears must have assembled the background genes above the threshold necessary for a stable expression of the key traits of corn. This would account for the relatively abrupt shift in the archaeological record between these taxa in a punctuated manner that sometimes occurs in the fossil record of natural speciation by certain animals (Eldredge and Gould, 1972). This well-known pattern of rapid change between species such as between teosinte and corn has been misinterpreted as evidence of some novel process (Gould, 1984).

The hypothesis that the transition from teosinte to corn was of short duration in perhaps only 100 yr accounts for the present near lack of archaeological evidence for the intermediate forms (Galinat, 1983). In a paleontological record indicating punctuated evolution, Milligan (1986) has concluded that the phenotypic transition must occur in approximately 100 generations. This relatively short period of rapid change seems to apply to the origin of corn, as shown by the archaeological record.

The geographic isolation of an early type of corn in the Tehuacan Valley of Mexico has become part of a controversy on corn's origin. Here in an arid area where neither teosinte nor corn can survive without irrigation, the 7200-yr-old remains of corn cobs are about the only shred of evidence remaining for those who still favor a wild corn hypothesis (Mangelsdorf, 1974, 1986; Wilkes, 1986). Contrary to the first interpretations of the oldest Tehuacan corn in which I was involved (Mangelsdorf et al., 1967b), it now appears that corn did not occur as a wild plant either at Tehuacan or anywhere else, but after domestication from teosinte outside the Valley, it was introduced as a primitive cultivar (Galinat, 1983). The cobs were absent from the earliest phases (Ajuereado, El Riego) of collected food plants and then they suddenly appeared at a time (Coxcatlan) when other plants were being domesticated and introduced (e.g., *Phaseolus vulgaris*) into the Valley (Kaplan, 1967; Smith, 1967). The corn may have been introduced from Oaxaca which was mentioned here earlier as a possible area of teosinte domestication. Analysis of the pollen record by Schoenwetter and Smith (1986, p. 216) led them to conclude that "one or more members of the Maydeae tribe of grasses has been a cultivar in the Valley of Oaxaca at least since 10 000 B.P."

Wilkes (1986) does not believe that the first corn in the Tehuacan Valley could have been a corn-like domesticate of teosinte carried there into isolation by man because he thinks that swamping from wild teosinte would prevent such an origin for corn. But the role of man in carefully selecting the seed ears for the next generation is the answer. The best corn phenotypes were obviously the ideal ones to save as seed ears. Their attributes from domestication would not only predominate but accumulate in the progeny, especially when man planted them in isolated gardens. The most primitive known ears of corn represented by the earliest cobs of Tehuacan are beautifully designed to fulfill the demands of man for a better food plant, not the demands of nature for survival. Of the two taxa, teosinte and corn, only teosinte is in danger from swamping by the other, for it must have the morphological capacity necessary to survive on its own as a wild plant and swamping with the key traits of corn would remove this essential capacity (Galinat, 1983, 1985b).

1–3.3 Missing-link Variation at Tehuacan

A description and discussion of missing-link types from the purported homeland of wild corn is part of this section on geographic isolation. We do not at this time have archaeological evidence in the form of transitional cobs between teosinte and corn that is older than the oldest corn cobs from Tehuacan, but the fact that there were a few such connecting links contemporaneous with the assumed wild corn should not be ignored. It is known that except for their tiny size, *most* of the oldest Tehuacan cobs (5000 B.C.) were virtually identical in their botanical characteristics to the obviously cultivated corn (Mangelsdorf, 1974). It follows that these same oldest enclosed ears and their kernels would be as helpless at self-propagation by rachis disarticulation as the cultivated corn and could not, therefore, be wild. The botanical characteristics required by nature for self-propagation are distinct from those selected by man for easy harvesting for food. A mere change in morphological magnification is not related to these different structural adaptations. The key traits of teosinte and corn are mutually exclusive both genetically and functionally.

The published photographs of the oldest Tehuacan cobs concentrate on those from San Marcos TC-254 (Mangelsdorf et al., 1967b). Of the 13 oldest cobs from San Marcos shown in their Fig. 96, only one is two-ranked (four-rowed). On hindsight, these cobs should have been described as variable, as is obvious in this photograph, although the caption erroneously describes them as uniform. Of greater interest from the viewpoint of trying to identify missing link segregates are the cobs from the next-to-the-oldest phase from Coxcatlan Cave Tc-50. The earliest cobs from Coxcatlan are described (Mangelsdorf et al., 1967b, p. 194) as being both two-ranked (four-rowed) and four-ranked (eight-rowed) without mention of their frequency. At the time, the belief was that the presence of a few two-ranked cobs was insignificant because modern eight-rowed (four-ranked) corn may produce phenocopies of two-ranking under conditions of stunting or just carry a few such cobs in secondary positions on the same plant with an eight-rowed ear. But two-ranking is also a key trait of teosinte and at least some of the Tehuacan two-ranked cobs appeared to be from uppermost positions and not phenocopies. The teosinte genes controlling two-ranking have better penetrance in a corn background than the teosinte genes for single female spikelets. There is evidence from comparative morphology to be shown here that these two-ranked specimens extending down among the oldest Tehuacan cobs and other teosinte-like cobs just above them may be missing-link segregates lingering on from their teosinte ancestor. Human selection against two-ranking was probably not as strong as that against the other essential traits of teosinte such as abscission layer development and single female spikelets.

A few of these missing-link types from Tc-50 were photographed at various magnifications on 5 Oct. 1973. Two of these are illustrated here. The first and oldest of these is shown in comparison with a reasonably close match with the F1 hybrid of the primitive corn Confite Morocho crossed by Guerrero teosinte (Fig. 1–3). It illustrates full penetrance of two-ranking and weak penetrance of both single female spikelets and abscission layer development. The second photograph (Fig. 1–4) is of a two-ranked cob with paired spikelets that is relatively typical for most of the two-ranked cobs from the oldest layers. The actual specimen shown came from the Abejas Phase, aged about 5000 B.P. It compares favorably with a soft-glumed F2 segregate derived from the cross of Chapalote corn by Chalco teosinte. Modern Chapalote has soft long glumes due to the presence of a weak tunicate allele. This gene was probably also present in most of the oldest Tehuacan corn, and it may have had domestic value in terms of making teosinte easier to shell, in being freely threshable, as emphasized by Beadle (1972).

The comparisons of these archaeological missing-links with their modern counterparts are made to show that this ancient corn in complete isolation from teosinte still carried the key traits of teosinte. The assumption here is that genes for the key teosinte traits, expressed in a few

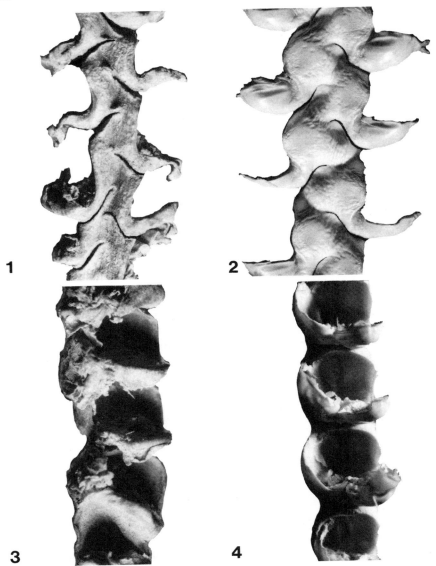

Fig. 1–3. A comparison of a Tehuacan missing link with a hybrid between primitive extant corn and teosinte. (1 and 2.) Two-ranked cob from Tehuacan, Mexico (Tc50, Coxcatlan, S2E12, Zone XI, Level 9, Feature 42, age about 6000 yr B.P.) shown in side (1.) and front (2.) views. (3 and 4.) Two-ranked cob from a recent F1 hybrid between the primitive Confite Morocho corn of Peru crossed by Guerrero (Balsas) teosinte of Mexico shown in side (3.) and front (4.) views. In comparing 1 to 3, note that they both have abscission layers that can only extend about half-way across the rachis because condensation has partially overlapped the cupules. In comparing 2. to 4., note that on the left-hand side of the cupules, they both have a partial reduction of the pedicellate spikelet. The archaeological specimen appears to have softer tissues than its modern phenotypic counterpart, possibly because of a weak tunicate allele. The cobs were photographed at ×7. The sections shown are about 1.5-cm long.

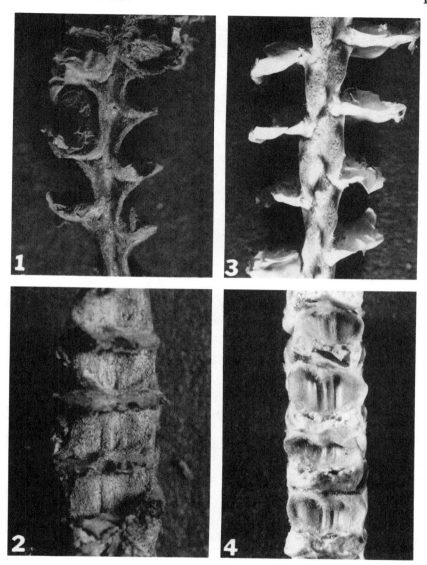

Fig. 1–4. A comparison of a Tehuacan missing link with a derivative from a hybrid between primitive extant corn and teosinte. (1 and 2.) Two-ranked cob from Tehuacan, Mexico (Tc50, Coxcatlan, S1E13, Zone IX (I), Level 8, Abejas Phase, age about 5000 yr B.P.) shown in side (1.) and front (2.) views. (3 and 4.) Two-ranked cob with soft glumes from the F2 of a cross between the primitive Chapalote corn and Chalco teosinte both from Mexico shown in side (3) and front (4) views. In comparing 1 to 3, note that they both have a slender (string cob) rachis with soft horizontal glumes. In comparing 2. to 4., note that they both have broad flat cupules with two ridges from the vascular bundles outstanding on the inner face. Both have long tufts of pulvinus notch hairs (in good focus for the central cupule of the archaeological cob) as well as an overall pubescence of short hairs. The apex of the cupule appears to be more pronounced in the modern cob, although it has better exposure due to removal of the lower glumes. The cobs were photographed at ×7. The sections shown are about 1.5-cm long.

individuals of this population, came in with the original introduction of the teosinte cultivar called corn many generations before. These genes are known to undergo dominance reversal, and they may survive in open-pollinated populations in a cryptic state despite the rigorous selection by man against them. After isolation and inbreeding, sometimes the key trait genes of teosinte became homozygous and gained the penetrance necessary for expression as shown in these specimens.

Considerable time is required in open-pollinated populations to evolve uniformity for a more productive type and at the same time to purge all remnants of inferior ancestral types. For example, selection for uniformity during the Corn Show period (1900–1920) in the U.S. Corn Belt was found to be ineffective as a means of corn improvement. The title of "grand champion" was awarded to samples of 10 ears most uniform for ear-length, row-number and kernel-type. Later (1920) it was discovered that the prize corn yielded less, rather than more than average, in comparison with ordinary corn. This ended the Corn Show era (Wallace and Brown, 1956).

Certainly the lack of uniformity for pure corn types in its oldest known remains will be interpreted differently by others, but now at least the alternative is in the record. Any claim that the exceptional teosinte-like cobs were hybrid types contaminated by teosinte and introduced from the outside admits that corn was being carried by man into the Valley at an early time (6000 B.P.). This is consistent with the contention here that the original corn in the Valley (at least 7200 B.P.) was also introduced by man.

1–3.4   Isolation by Block Inheritance

As with the other isolating mechanisms mentioned here, block inheritance is a form of incomplete isolation. In this case, the isolation is just within certain chromosome segments. The result is an inability to freely recombine the components within blocks of cooperating genes and, thereby, a discontinuity is maintained despite free interbreeding. Such clusters of linked genes have an internal balance that becomes assembled through disruptive selection increasing reproductive fitness. Their effects in segregations tend to produce either the teosinte type or corn type of female inflorescence. The intermediate forms that would result from free recombination have been eliminated by block inheritance. Thus, the integrity (internal balance) of these combinations of genes is conserved and protected against breaking-up through crossing-over and recombination with alien alleles adapted to the other niche. Contamination of one system with parts of the other would produce incongruous combinations that are nonadaptive in both environments.

Block inheritance is probably more important to the survival of teosinte as a wild plant than it is to corn as a domestic plant. Corn does not require this protection because its fitness is determined in the eye and mind of man. In a modern corn background, expression of the key-trait genes of teosinte carried by introgressed teosinte segments appears to be suppressed. Furthermore, certain dominant genes in these segments may contribute to heterosis that is adaptive to corn. But the corresponding corn segments transferred to teosinte produce nonadaptive heterosis for increased size, and they may stimulate selection for additional isolating mechanisms, as pointed out by Mather (1943) for natural species in general. In modern hybrid corn breeding, heterosis from heterozygous teosinte segments may be used to increase the yield of grain (Sehgal, 1963; Cohen and Galinat, 1984). Mangelsdorf's inbred lines of A158 corn-teosinte derivatives are less fit in terms of grain yield than their A158 controls because of an internal balance that was adapted for survival in the wild rather than domestic environments. But their hybrids with the control have significantly higher grain yields because of the block dominance of polygenes for favorable growth with good relational balance, as expected by theory (Jones, 1917; Mather, 1943; Lindstrom, 1946).

All studies of segregations from corn-teosinte hybrids so far have shown that they differ by a relatively small number of such blocks of genes, perhaps only four or five inherited units (Collins and Kempton, 1920; Mangelsdorf and Reeves, 1939; Beadle, 1980). In addition to tight linkage, the integrity of the complexes may be enhanced by inhibitors to crossing-over such as cryptic rearrangements and chromosome knobs or by close linkage with gametophyte genes. In the latter case, the Guatemalan teosintes are known to carry a gametophyte (Ga) allele within their chromosome-4 complex (J.M. Duvick, 1984, personal communication). According to the linkage data of Rogers (1950), the key traits of the Guatemalan (Florida) teosinte do not have as tight a control by block inheritance as do the Mexican teosintes. It would seem, therefore, that evolution for block inheritance may still be underway in at least the Guatemalan teosintes.

When these blocks of teosinte genes are carried as heterozygotes in corn, as represented by the Mangelsdorf A158 teosinte derivatives, they become mutagenic (Mangelsdorf, 1958). This may provide mutagenic hot spots of nonrandom raw material for continued divergence, some of which may be fortuitously suited toward structural improvements in the key traits controlled by genes within the blocks.

Mangelsdorf (1952) has attempted to transfer these essential segments separating teosinte and corn into an isogenic background of corn represented first by inbred 4R3 and then by A158. It became apparent that the genetic backgrounds of the corn used was incongruous to a penetrance by genes controlling the key traits of teosinte. Mangelsdorf developed experimental evidence that the key trait genes of teosinte were not necessarily lost during the backcrossing to corn. He observed that when the corn inbred 4R3 is crossed with Florida teosinte, the F1 control ears have the key traits of corn, namely paired female spikelets and a four-ranked spike. But, when the hybrid is made with a derived strain of 4R3 in which a block of teosinte genes on chromosome 3 has been substituted for a corresponding block of corn genes, then the key traits of teosinte are expressed, namely, single female spikelets and a two-ranked spike. Mangelsdorf concluded that, in the corn background, the teosinte genes were "concealed" or unable to have phenotypic penetrance. As a result, the selections made by Mangelsdorf during backcrossing the essential teosinte segments to corn had to be based on other effects. These involved the segment's partially dominant effects on induration of the lower glumes, reduction in kernel and ear size and reduction in the number of kernel rows (reduced condensation). In subsequent F2 linkage-test segregations from crosses between these near isogenic teosinte derivatives and a multiple marker gene stock (white multiple tester, WMT) for all corn chromosomes, Mangelsdorf determined that he had captured teosinte segments located on chromosomes 1, 3, 4, 7, and 9. Tests are underway to determine if these teosinte segments contain the key-trait genes in a cryptic state such as Mangelsdorf (1968) suggested for his "tripsacoid" isolates that he developed on an A158 background from crosses with various Latin American races of corn. Alternatively, these tripsacoid derivatives may merely act on the phenotypic stability and penetrance of the key-trait genes.

Segregation of the key-trait genes is clear in the F2 of corn-teosinte hybrids because the background level becomes sufficiently primitive to allow their penetrance. The two-gene inheritance of the key traits in such segregations is described above in this chapter.

The emergence of the kernel from the teosinte fruitcase by one or more systems made shelling easier for man but exposed the grain to depredation by birds. As a result of these selective pressures, a new protective device (the husk enclosure) evolved that was associated with pistil development becoming even more precocious than that already established in teosinte and its more distant relative, *Tripsacum*. Precocious female development in teosinte and *Tripsacum* resulted in entrapment of the female spikelet within its cupulate fruitcase. A shift in gene action during the origin of corn resulted in entrapment of the entire female inflorescence within its shoot.

1–3.5 Developmental Morphology of the Husk Enclosure of the Ear and Flowering Time

The following description of certain aspects of developmental morphology relative to the husk enclosure of the ear, flowering time, and the evolution of corn has its roots in the pioneering studies of Bonnett, 1940, 1948, 1953, 1966 as elaborated upon through the recent technologies of the SEM microscope (Cheng et al., 1983; Sundberg and Orr, 1986) and as viewed in terms of the phytomer (Galinat, 1959) and the phase change process (Galinat, 1966a, b) based primarily on studies of the corn grass and teopod mutants (Galinat, 1954a, b). Orr and Sundberg reported that in a mixed pair of male and female spikelets of diploperennis teosinte, female development is advanced beyond that of its male counterpart in the adjoining spikelet. This protogyny also occurs along a common rachis in mixed spikes of *Tripsacum*, teosinte, and corn including the tassel seed mutants of corn.

As in all plants, the primordial inflorescences of corn are enclosed within the leaves of a bud. Unlike other plants, the maturing ear of corn never emerges from its bud. Retention within its bud is just one of several secondary events resulting from a precocious thrust into rapid pistil development, as pointed out by David Galinat (1986, personal communication). The sexuality and fertility of both tassel and ear in corn are readily modified by both genetic and environmental influences (Heslop-Harrison, 1960). Apparently, the onset of pistil development sends a signal back that (i) terminates the late steps in the adult vegetative phase of the shank below the ear. Its internodes fail to elongate and its leaves fail to complete development of their blades (flags). As a result, the mature ear remains confined within the axillary bud which it terminates and, thereby, permanently protected by a husk enclosure. (ii) The early part of the female floral phase is terminated before the complete form of a tassel-type inflorescence can be differentiated. As a result, the ear represents only the central spike without the lower branches of the tassel. (iii) Precocious pistil development suppresses development of the male primordia within potentially perfect flowers. As a result, the ear is exclusively female. (iv) The internodes of the rachis fail to elongate. Because of the physical space required by the cupule and its pair of female spikelets and eventually their kernels, this factor of condensed internodes becomes associated with increases in the number of kernel rows and in the thickness of the rachis (cob).

The permanent entrapment of the corn ear within its bud as a protective device for the grain required the coevolution of associated factors. The growth of the silks (styles) in a region just above the pistils at a rate of about 2.5 cm per day forces them upward beyond the husks for exposure to pollination. In corn with a 15.0 cm husk enclosing its young ear, it would take at least 5 d for the silks from the base of the ear to reach the summit. This delay in silk emergence is compensated for by their early start from precocious pistils.

Corn had not only evolved the longest styles in the plant kingdom, but it also had to evolve the largest pollen grains in the grass family as a further accommodation to domestication. This is reflected in a relationship between ear length corresponding to style length and pollen grain size (Galinat, 1961). All of these components had a special relationship with man who had assembled them through domestication. Corn can only survive with help from man to release and disperse the seed from its protective husk enclosure.

There are correlated growth factors that tend to simultaneously increase ear length, husk length, and the number of leaves in the sterile zone between the ear shoot and the tassel all of which require the start of silk growth to become increasingly precocious relative to pollen shedding. The duration of the sterile zone varies from about two leaves or less in certain selections of Argentine popcorn and five in the Northern Flints to about 10 leaves in high-rowed U.S. Southern Dents. Shaver (1976, 1983) has reported sterile zone leaf numbers of around 14 associated with presence of a gene called leafy (Lfy) that he is exploiting to increase yields. Because the number of leaves in the sterile zone is usually similar or equal to the number of leaves in the ear shank, the leafy stocks of Shaver would be expected to have good husk coverage. The pattern of internode elongation above the ear may be unimportant to these evolutionary correlates because it takes place after their early differentiation.

The selective pressure for longer and tighter husk leaves has been applied for thousands of years by the feeding of both birds and insects at the tip of the ear. Increases in husk length must coevolve with similar increases in ear length, style length, and pollen grain size. Long husk sterility, in which the styles are unable to emerge (Singleton, 1946), is a continuing problem to corn breeding, especially with the derivatives from crosses between long- and short-eared but high kernel-rowed types. On multiple-eared varieties, silk emergence usually starts with the top ear and works down. In primitive corn and in corn-teosinte hybrids, their tiny ears are borne higher on the plant and their sexual development is less precocious. This allows time for both internode elongation and staminate development of at least the terminal portion of the ear, especially with subtassel ears. There is a tendency for higher ears to flower earlier, to have poorer husk coverage and to have tassel-tipped (mixed) ears. The poor husk coverage may be corrected by selection.

The large amount of energy (photosynthate) channeled to the corn ear, usually the only sink, has little recourse other than to expend itself on kernel development through a proliferation in the number of female spikelets and/or an increase in kernel size. If there still remains unexpended energy flowing to the ear after kernel fill, it may then be utilized through a lignification of the outer glumes, the cupule, and sometimes the pith. This capacity stems from its teosinte ancestor which depends upon a lignification of the mature fruitcase for survival.

The observation that the female inflorescence (ear) of corn acquired its husk enclosure by being even more precocious relative to male development than are the female inflorescences (spikes) of teosinte is diametrically opposite to the basic tenet of the Iltis (1983) "catastrophic sexual transmutation theory." Iltis (1983, p. 890) states "Because tassels are developmentally precocious, *Zea* is protandrous." In actuality, it is the ear that is developmentally precocious and *Zea* is protogynous. But this is not outwardly obvious to the casual observer because the leaves of the bud conceal the styles during their 7-d effort to reach above their enclosure. The resulting delay in silk emergence produces a false type of protandry that is only an artifact of selection by man for the unnatural husk enclosure that characterizes the corn ear. One can speed up the time of silk emergence by cutting back the husk of the young shoot as is a common practice by corn pollinators. But this interference may inadvertently result in long-husk sterility that becomes a seed production problem when long husk inbreds are used as the seed parent, as was the case with Connecticut inbred C95 (Singleton, 1946). The situation may be artificially simulated by extending the husk of the young ear shoot with a long tight cone of cardboard that either prevents silk emergence or requires silk extension beyond its growing capacity. Virgin silks inside a paper bag sometimes reach 90 cm in length.

In *Tripsacum*, the second closest relative of corn, discussed later, the precocious nature of pistil and style development relative to pollen shedding becomes obvious because its spike usually emerges naked above the uppermost leaf. Because one can observe the exposed style right down to the cupulate fruitcase and because another week in time must pass before pollen-shedding, it is obvious that the plant is protogynous. Except for the uppermost two or three fruitcases in the uppermost spike of a cluster (fascicle) of spikes, style exposure in teosinte is usually more modest than in *Tripsacum*. The husk enclosure system of condensed forms of teosinte includes the husks from neighboring and overlapping spikes within a cluster. Because of the time spent during the elongation of styles, their emergence above the husks of teosinte is delayed until about the same time or slightly before pollen shedding. The ultimate consequences of continuing to increase the precocious nature of the ear that began in teosinte have their fulfillment in the most advanced ears of corn, as described above. Unfortunately, this artifact of domestication has deceived some people into the delusion that the male of corn is precocious rather than the female. Understanding the nature of synchronization between tassel and ear is important to the corn breeder, but the inheritance of this false protandry cannot be treated as if it were a real sexual difference independent from husk length, as has been attempted by some (Iltis, 1983; Landi and Frascaroli, 1986).

It is silk emergence above the husk rather than the start of silk growth that now tends to become synchronous with pollen shedding (anthesis). Silk emergence usually starts at the uppermost level and works down the plant, level by level, both on the main stalk and in a lateral branch cluster from the main stalk. Selection to lower the ear to a lower level and associated increases in husk length both require the ear to become increasingly precocious relative to the tassel in order for silk emergence above longer husks to synchronize with pollen shedding. This synchronization has become important in the USA with the development of hand-pollinated inbred lines and their uniformly flowering hybrids. The raw open-pollinated varieties and races tend to have less synchronization between tassel and ear on a given plant. Nonsynchronous flowering between the sexes within a plant promotes outcrossing and heterozygosity.

Relative uniformity in flowering time for a population in which there is a potential for intercrossing between all individuals is a different factor from synchronization between sexes on an individual monoecious plant. The degree of cross pollination and its associated level of heterozygosity increase according to the size of the simultaneously flowering population. If variation in the time of seed germination resulted in isolation by flowering time, it could have harmful effects associated with inbreeding depression. Therefore, the dormancy trait became associated with another trait that ensured both uniform flowering and a maximum utilization of the growing season. This trait, involving floral induction by short daylengths continuing over a 14- to 21-d period, is now characteristic of all wild races of teosinte and, to a lesser degree, of certain subtropical and tropical races of corn.

The short-day trait of teosinte and most subtropical and tropical corn is important in delaying flowering until the short days of fall and, thereby, in allowing maximum utilization of the growing season. This time frame corresponds to the rainy season of June to September in most of teosinte's range in Mexico. When corn was carried out of this environment or grown under irrigation, short-day response became less important and the development of genetically late-flowering types became possible.

As corn spread northward from Mexico into the USA, the short-day trait lost its adaptive advantage because the growing season was cut short by earlier drops in temperatures during September that did not allow maturation of the crop. The planting of short-day corn earlier in the season such as April or May still did not allow maturation because it encountered only longer daylengths and its plants vegetated to monstrous proportions while waiting for their September floral induction. As a result, corn stayed confined to the southern-most regions of the USA until after the evolution of day-neutral flowering types. These first appeared in thick-cobbed, eight-rowed corn (Maiz de Ocho) around 700 A.D. (Galinat and Gunnerson, 1963). With selection for earlier flowering types, Maiz de Ocho spread northward and eastward to New England and Canada by 1200 A.D. Corn which stayed in the arid Southwest had to evolve other means to escape or overcome drought. One of these was the long mezocotyl of the Hopi corn of Arizona (Collins, 1914). Early flowering may also have been adaptive in escaping late season drought. Meanwhile, several thousands of years earlier, primitive short-day corn was carried by man into South America where the daylengths were short, the growing seasons long, and there was no native teosinte (Galinat, 1985a).

1–3.6 Dissemination

The structure of the cupulate fruitcase of teosinte as well as the corn cob as an extension of this structure culminate millions of years of evolutionary trends for increases in the thickness and condensation of the rachis (Galinat, 1956). The trends appear to be driven by an increasing role of birds, animals, sometimes water, and now man in dissemination, in contrast to the more ancient systems of wind dispersal. The latter system is now largely reserved for pollen dispersal except for some limited value of wind in throwing teosinte fruitcases by whiplashing the stalks.

Mature teosinte fruitcases may be disseminated in several ways, including the droppings of birds (Stadelman, 1939) and other animals (Wilkes, 1967). Of more restricted dispersal distance and probably less important would be the throwing of disarticulated fruitcases by whiplashing in the wind or just their spilling forth from the top opening of their enclosing husks following the effects of rain and/or wind storms in knocking plants down. There is evidence that the race of *T. dactyloides* from south Florida is disseminated by water and that its extra-large fruitcases will float for at least a week on water (Galinat and Craighead, 1964). Similar data are not available for teosinte.

In its new domestic niche under the mind and eye of man, allelic changes within the teosinte blocks as well as a transfer in function of the cupule have transformed this ancient product of natural selection into becoming the corn ear beautifully adapted as a food plant with man as the sole agent of seed dispersal.

1–3.7 Dormancy

The experience of everyone who has tried to grow freshly harvested teosinte seed is that it will not germinate unless its dormancy is broken by soaking in a weak solution of hydrogen peroxide for about 30 min. Seed that is held in storage for a year or more will germinate readily although precise data on the rate of germination at successive months after harvesting does not seem to have been collected.

Once fresh teosinte fruitcases reach the ground, dormancy substances in the seed appear to inhibit germination to variable degrees until sufficient time, perhaps a year or more, has passed and the moisture and temperature become favorable for sustained growth. This programmed delay protects the seed against unseasonable germination when and where continued development would probably end in premature death.

In contrast, under the semi-uniform soil conditions resulting from the agricultural practices of cultivation and irrigation, uniformity for rapid germination soon after planting is important to tending and harvesting a crop. In fact, one of the first effects of domestication would be a genetic removal of the dormancy trait except for a low level that just interrupts embryo development as the seed matures and drys down to about 13% moisture. Rehydration after planting immediately starts germination in a nondormant seed.

The dormancy trait need not be confined to seed germination. During early season drought stress, vegetative development in "latente" lines derived from the Mexican cv. Michoacan 21 appears to cease. Then these lines make a vigorous regrowth following irrigation (Castleberry and LeRette, 1979). The latente lines have elevated abscisic acid in their leaves (Larque-Saavedra and Wain, 1974, 1976) and presumably this is part of their physiological basis for drought tolerance that operates through control of stomatal opening (Munoz, 1975).

1–3.8   The Role of *Tripsacum*—Past and Future

The only other American genus, *Tripsacum*, of the corn tribe, Maydeae, includes about 16 species with chromosome numbers of 18 and 36 pairs all of which are perennials. Twelve of these are native to Mexico and Guatemala with an extension of *T. dactyloides* throughout the eastern half of USA, the tetraploids being near the East Coast and the diploids in the Central region. *Tripsacum lanceolatum* occurs in the Southwest. *Tripsacum floridanum* is native to south Florida and Cuba. Three or more species are known in South America. Taxonomic treatments include Cutler and Anderson (1941), Randolph (1970), and de Wet et al. (1981).

Although apparently all 16 species can be crossed with corn, usually it is only with extreme difficulty and the hybrids have a high degree of sterility. Nevertheless, since the classic hybrids of *T. dactyloides* 2n and corn made by Mangelsdorf and Reeves (1939), this genus has figured in past hypotheses on the origin of teosinte and the evolution of corn.

With the early introduction of primitive corn into South America, some of the ancestral traits of teosinte became isolated and upon inbreeding they gained freedom of expression. Isolates resembling cornteosinte hybrids have appeared in the race Chococeño of Columbia (Roberts et al., 1957) and cryptic genes for the key traits of teosinte (ranking and pairing of female spikelets) have been described for isolates of maize from Bolivia, Argentina, Brazil, and Paraguay (Mangelsdorf, 1968). Since teosinte is not native to South America, Mangelsdorf and Reeves (1959) concluded that such occurrences must result from hybrid introgression by *Tripsacum*, which has a wide range in South America, rather than relic teosinte germ plasm. Their former hypothesis that *Tripsacum* was one parent of teosinte (Mangelsdorf and Reeves, 1939) has now been ruled out by Mangelsdorf (1983). It seems equally improbable that *Tripsacum* has had any role in the past evolution of corn although the techniques of biotechnology to manipulate wide-cross germ plasm in certain sophisticated laboratories may produce some future benefits.

It has been demonstrated that certain segments of *Tripsacum* chromosomes can be substituted for corresponding segments of corn and in at least one case an extra pair of *Tripsacum* chromosomes (*Tr* 7) can be added to the corn genome. Benefits from such experimental introgression by *Tripsacum* are known for increased yield (Cohen and Galinat, 1984), for disease resistance—as with Ht_3, a single dominant allele for resistance to *Helminthosporium turcicum* derived from a hybrid made by Galinat between corn and *T. floridanum* (Hooker and Perkins, 1980) and for facilitating seed production of defective types of endosperm (Galinat, 1975, 1977).

Yet to be developed for corn-*Tripsacum* research are the cell culture techniques necessary for massive screening for certain recombinant phenotypes that are amenable to such manipulations. The stressful screens might involve toxins, resistance factors, nutritive values, and temperature or salt tolerances. In the last example, some of the 4n colonies of *T. dactyloides* grow along salty inlets from Florida to Massachusetts. It is not known if any of the diseases of corn can serve as vectors for gene transfer.

More than 50 homologous loci for plant and kernel traits have been identified and mapped between the chromosomes of these two genera (Galinat, 1973). The number mapped only corresponds to the number tested. Numerous other common loci would be revealed by the more sophisticated techniques of isozyme electrophoresis. In any case, it is not the number of common loci that is important in evolutionary pathways but their comparative genetic architecture. It is significant that intergenomic mapping between corn and *Tripsacum* has led to a rejection of teosinte as a corn-*Tripsacum* hybrid. The evidence is based on the absence of a block of genes in *Tripsacum* that is essential for the development of the teosinte fruitcase. This block occurs in the sugary-glossy 3 (*su-gl*3) region of corn/teosinte chromosome 4. These marked loci are on different chromosomes in *Tripsacum* with *su* on *Tr* 7 and *gl* 3 on *Tr* 13 (Galinat, 1973; Rao and Galinat, 1974).

Assuming that the wild ancestor of corn is teosinte as is now commonly agreed upon, how can this insight help the corn breeder in developing more useful and productive types? As the wild form of corn that is subjected to all of the stresses of the natural environment, teosinte should be a perfect source of genes for resistances and tolerances to all possible stresses. Unlike *Tripsacum*, in which an observed trait in the wild might have a one in a million chance of being transferred to corn by standard plant breeding, almost anything observed in teosinte can be easily transferred to corn. Some desired traits of teosinte may be controlled by genes that are locked in key trait blocks but, even so, the entire block may be manipulated in hybrid corn production and/or have its components released through rare crossovers. To accept and understand the power of human selection in transforming teosinte into corn also opens the mind to an endless array of new forms that we may selectively shape from this most amazing of food plants during an enlightened future of creative corn breeding.

REFERENCES

Anderson, E., and W.L. Brown. 1948. A morphological analysis of row number in maize. Ann. Mo. Bot. Gard. 35:323–336.

Arber, A. 1934. The Gramineae: A study of cereal, bamboo and grass. Cambridge Univ. Press, Cambridge, England.

Beadle, G.W. 1930. A fertile tetraploid hybrid between *Euchlaena perennis* and *Zea mays*. Am. Nat. 69:190–192.

―――. 1932a. Studies of *Euchlaena* and its hybrids with *Zea*. 1. Chromosome behavior in *Euchlaena mexicana* and its hybrids with *Zea mays*. Z. Abstam. Vererbungsl. 62:291–304.

―――. 1932b. The relation of crossing-over to chromosome association in *Zea-Euchlaena* hybrids. Genetics 17:481–501.

―――. 1939. Teosinte and the origin of maize. J. Hered. 30:245–247.

―――. 1972. The mystery of maize. Field Mus. Nat. Hist. Bull. 43:1–11.

―――. 1978. Teosinte and the origin of maize. p. 113–128. *In* D.B. Walden (ed.) Maize breeding and genetics. John Wiley and Sons, New York.

―――. 1980. The ancestry of corn. Sci. Am. 242:112–119.

Bonnett, O.T. 1940. Development of the staminate and pistillate inflorescences of sweet corn. J. Agric. Res. 60:25–37.

―――. 1948. Ear and tassel development in maize. Ann. Mo. Bot. Gard. 35:269–287.

―――. 1953. Development morphology of the vegetative and floral shoots of maize. Illinois Agric. Exp. Stn. Bull. 568.

―――. 1966. Inflorescences of maize, wheat, rye, barley, and oats: Their initiation and development. Illinois Agric. Exp. Stn. Bull. 721.

Burnham, C.R. 1962. Discussions on cytogenetics. Published by the author at 1539 Branston St., St. Paul.

Castleberry, R.M., and R.J. LeRette. 1979. Latente, a new type of drought tolerance? p. 46–56. *In* Proc. 34 Annu. Corn and Sorghum Conf., Chicago. 11–13 December. ASTA, Washington, DC.

Cheng, P.C., R.I. Greyson, and D.B. Walden. 1983. Organ initiation and the development of unisexual flowers in the tassel and ear of *Zea mays*. Am. J. Bot. 70:450–462.

Cohen, J.I., and W.C. Galinat. 1984. Potential use of alien germplasm for maize improvement. Crop Sci. 24:1011–1015.

Collins, G.N. 1914. A drought-resisting adaptation in seedlings of Hopi maize. J. Agric. Res. 1:293–306.

―――, and J.H. Kempton. 1920. A teosinte-maize hybrid. J. Agric. Res. 19:1–37.

Cutler, H.C., and E. Anderson. 1941. A preliminary survey of the genus *Tripsacum*. Ann. Mo. Bot. Gard. 28:249–269.

Dewald, C.L., and R.S. Dayton. 1985. A prolific sex form variant of eastern gamagrass. Phytologia 57:156.

de Wet, J.M.J., D.H. Timothy, K.W. Hilu, and G.B. Fletcher. 1981. Systematics of South American *Tripsacum* (Gramineae). Am. J. Bot. 68:269–276.

Doebley, J.F., and H.H. Iltis. 1980. Taxonomy of *Zea* (Gramineae). I. Subspecific classification with key to taxa. Am. J. Bot. 67:986–993.

Eldredge, N., and S.J. Gould. 1972. Punctuated equilibria: An alternative to phyletic gradualism. p. 82–115. *In* T.J.M. Schopf (ed.) Models in paleobiology. Freeman, Cooper, and Co., San Francisco.

Emerson, R.A., and G.W. Beadle. 1932. Studies of *Euchlaena* and its hybrids with *Zea*. II. Crossing-over between the chromosomes of *Euchlaena* and those of *Zea*. Z. Abstam. Vererbungsl. 62:305–315.

―――, and H.H. Smith. 1950. Inheritance of number of kernel rows in maize. Cornell Univ. Agric. Exp. Stn. Mem. 296:1–30.

Galinat, W.C. 1954a. Corn grass. 1. Corn grass as a prototype or a false progenitor of maize. Am. Nat. 88:101–104.

―――. 1954b. Corn grass. II. Effect of the *corngrass* gene on the development of the maize inflorescence. Am. J. Bot. 41:803–806.

―――. 1956. Evolution leading to the formation of the cupulate fruit case in the American Maydeae. Bot. Mus. Leafl. Harv. Univ. 17:217–239.

―――. 1959. The phytomer in relation to floral homologies in the American Maydeae. Bot. Mus. Leafl. Harv. Univ. 19:1–32.

―――. 1961. Corn's evolution and its significance for breeding. Econ. Bot. 15:320–325.

―――. 1963. Form and function of plant structures in the American *Maydeae* and their significance for breeding. Econ. Bot. 17:51–59.

―――. 1966a. The corngrass and teopod loci involve phase change. Maize Genet. Coop. News Lett. 40:102–103.

―――. 1966b. Somatic mosaicism in corngrass. Maize Genet. Coop. News Lett. 40:103.

————. 1969. The evolution under domestication of the maize ear: String cob maize. p. 1–19. *In* Massachusetts Agric. Exp. Stn. Bull. 577.

————. 1970. The cupule and its role in the origin and evolution of maize. p. 1–22. *In* Univ. of Massachusetts Agric. Exp. Stn. Bull. 585.

————. 1973. Intergenomic mapping of maize, teosinte and *Tripsacum*. Evolution 27:644–655.

————. 1975. The practical use of high quality but defective endosperm traits. Maize Genet. Coop. News Lett. 49:98–99.

————. 1977a. Hybrid seed production. U.S. Patent 4 051 629. Date issued: 4 October. Research Corp., New York. (The use of alien chromosomes from *Tripsacum*.)

————. 1977b. The origin of corn. *In* G.F. Sprague (ed.) Corn and corn improvement. Agronomy 18:1–47.

————. 1978. The inheritance of some traits essential to maize and teosinte. p. 93–111. *In* D.B. Walden (ed.) Maize breeding and genetics. John Wiley and Sons, New York.

————. 1983. The origin of maize as shown by key morphological traits of its ancestor, teosinte. Maydica 28:121–138.

————. 1985a. The domestication and diffusion of maize. p. 245–278. *In* R.I. Ford (ed.) Prehistoric food production in North America. Anthropology Paper 75. Univ. of Michigan, Ann Arbor.

————. 1985b. The missing links between teosinte and maize: A review. Maydica 30:137–160.

————. 1985c. Teosinte, the ancestor of maize: Perspectives for its use in maize breeding for the tropics. *In* A. Brandolini and F. Salamini (ed.) Breeding strategies for maize production improvement in the tropics. Monogr. 100:1–11, FAO, UN, and 1st Agron. per L'Oltremare, Firenze, Italy.

————, and J.H. Gunnerson. 1963. Spread of eight-rowed maize from the prehistoric southwest. Bot. Mus. Leafl. Harv. Univ. 20:117–160.

————, and F.C. Craighead. 1964. Some observations on the dissemination of Tripsacum. Rhodora 66:371–374.

Gould, S.J. 1984. A short way to corn. Nat. Hist. 93:12–20.

Heslop-Harrison, J. 1960. The experimental control of sexuality and inflorescence structure in *Zea mays* L. Symp. on the reproductive phase of seed plants. Proc. Linn. Soc. London 172:108–123.

Hooker, A.L., and J.M. Perkins. 1980. Helminthosporium leaf blights—The state of the art. p. 68–87. *In* Proc. 35 Annu. Corn Sorghum Ind. Res. Conf., Chicago. 9–11 December. ASTA, Washington, DC.

Iltis, H.H. 1983. From teosinte to maize: The catastrophic sexual transmutation. Science 22:886–894.

————, and J.F. Doebley. 1980. Taxonomy of *Zea* (Gramineae). II. Subspecific categories in the *Zea mays* complex and a generic synopsis. Am. J. Bot. 67:994–1004.

Jones, D.F. 1917. Dominance of linked factors as a means of accounting for heterosis. Genetics 2:466–479.

Kaplan, L. 1967. Archaeological *Phaseolus* from Tehuacan. p. 201–211. *In* D.S. Byers (ed.) The prehistory of the Tehuacan Valley. Univ. of Texas Press, Austin.

Kato Y, T.A. 1976. Cytological studies of maize and teosinte in relation to their origin and evolution. Massachusetts Agric. Exp. Stn. Bull. 635.

————. 1984. Chromosome morphology and the origin of maize and its races. p. 219–253. *In* M.K. Hecht et al. (ed.) Evolutionary biology 17. Plenum Publ. Corp., New York.

Landi, P., and E. Frascaroli. 1986. Inheritance of protandry in maize (*Zea mays* L.) and its relationship to yield. Genet. Agric. 40:57–64.

Langham, D.G. 1940. The inheritance of intergeneric differences in *Zea-Euchlaena* hybrids. Genetics 25:88–108.

Larque-Saavedra, A., and R.L. Wain. 1974. Abscisic acid levels in relation to drought tolerance in varieties of *Zea mays* L. Nature (London) 251:716–717.

————, and ————. 1976. Studies on plant growth-regulating substances. XLII. Abscisic acid as a genetic character related to drought tolerance. Ann. Appl. Biol. 83:291–297.

Laubengayer, R.A. 1948. The vascular anatomy of the four-rowed ear of corn. Ann. Mo. Bot. Gard. 35:337–342.

————. 1949. The vascular anatomy of the eight-rowed ear and tassel of Golden Bantam sweet corn. Am. J. Bot. 36:236–244.

Lindstrom, E.W. 1946. Block-dominance, chromosome-balance and linkage-drag in polygenic inheritance and heterosis. p. 11. *In* Agronomy abstract. ASA, Columbus, OH.

Longley, A.E. 1937. Morphological characters of teosinte chromosomes. J. Agric. Res. 54:835–
862.

————. 1941. Chromosome morphology in maize and its relatives. Bot. Rev. 7:263–289.

Mangelsdorf, P.C. 1947. The origin and evolution of maize. p. 161–207. *In* M. Demerec
(ed.) Advances in genetics. I. Academic Press, New York.

————. 1948. Teosinte derivatives. Maize Genet. Coop. News Lett. 22:19–20.

————. 1952. Hybridization in the evolution of maize. p. 175–198. *In* J.W. Gowen (ed.)
Heterosis. Iowa State College Press, Ames.

————. 1958. The mutagenic effect of hybridizing maize and teosinte. Cold Spring Harbor
Symp. Quant. Biol. 23:409–421.

————. 1968. Cryptic genes for "Tripsacoid" characteristics in *Maiz Amargo* of Argentina
and other Latin-American varieties. Bol. Soc. Argentina Bot. 12:180–187.

————. 1974. Corn, its origin, evolution and improvement. Belknap Press, Harvard Univ.
Press, Cambridge, MA.

————. 1983. The mystery of corn: New perspectives. Proc. Am. Phil. Soc. 127:215–247.

————. 1986. The origin of corn. Sci. Am. (August):72–78.

————, and J.R. Edwardson. 1953. Tests for weak alleles at the *Tu-tu* locus. Maize Genet.
Coop. News Lett. 27:24–26.

————, and W.C. Galinat. 1964. The tunicate locus in maize dissected and reconstituted.
Proc. Natl. Acad. Sci. USA 51:147–150.

————, R.S. MacNeish, and W.C. Galinat. 1967a. Prehistoric maize, teosinte and *Tripsacum*
from Tamaulipas, Mexico. Bot. Mus. Leafl. Harv. Univ. 22:33–63.

————, ————, and ————. 1967b. Prehistoric wild and cultivated maize. p. 178–200. *In* D.S.
Byers (ed.) The prehistory of the Tehuacan Valley, Vol. 1. Environment and Subsistence. Univ. of Texas Press, Austin.

————, and R.G. Reeves. 1939. The origin of Indian corn and its relatives. p. 1–315. *In* Texas
Agric. Exp. Stn. Bull. 574.

————, and ————. 1959. The origin of corn. III. Modern races, the product of teosinte introgression. Bot. Mus. Leafl. Harv. Univ. 18:389–411.

Mather, K. 1943. Polygenic inheritance and natural selection. Biol. Rev. Cambridge Philos.
Soc. 18:32–64.

Mayr, E. 1942. Populations, species and evolution. Harvard Univ. Press, Cambridge, MA.

McClintock, B. 1959. Chromosome constitutions of Mexican and Guatemalan races of
maize. Annu. Rep. Dep. Gen. Carnegie Inst. Washington 59:461–472.

————, T.A. Kato Y, and A. Blumenschein. 1981. Chromosome constitution of the races of
maize, its significance in the interpretation of relationships between races and varieties
in the Americas. Colegio de Postgraduados, Chapingo, Mexico.

Milligan, B.G. 1986. Punctuated evolution induced by ecological change. Am. Nat. 127:522–
532.

Munoz, O., A. 1975. Relaciones aqua-planta bajo sequia, en varios sinteticos de maiz
resistentes a sequia y heladas. Thesis. Natl. School of Agric. Postgraduate College.
Chapingo, Mexico.

O'Mara, J.G. 1942. A cytogenetic study of *Zea* and *Euchlaena*. p. 3–16. *In* Missouri Agric.
Stn. Bull. 341.

Pickersgill, B. 1981. Biosystematics of crop-weed complexes. Kulturpflanze 29:377–388.

Randolph, L.F. 1959. The origin of maize. Indian J. Genet. Plant Breed. 19:1–12.

————. 1970. Variation among *Tripsacum* populations of Mexico and Guatemala. Brittonia
22:305–337.

Rao, B.G.S., and W.C. Galinat. 1974. The evolution of the American Maydeae. I. The
characteristics of two *Tripsacum* chromosomes that are partial homeologs to maize
chromosome 4. J. Hered. 65:335–340.

Reeves, R.G., and P.C. Mangelsdorf. 1942. A proposed taxonomic change in the tribe
Maydeae. Am. J. Bot. 29:815–817.

Roberts, L.M., U.J. Grant, R. Ramirez-E, W.H. Hatheway, and D.L. Smith with P.C.
Mangelsdorf. 1957. Races of maize in Columbia. Pub. 510. NAS-NRC, Washington,
DC.

Rogers, J.S. 1950. The inheritance of inflorescence characters in maize-teosinte hybrids.
Genetics 35:541–558.

Schoenwetter, J., and L.D. Smith. 1986. Pollen analysis of the Oaxaca Archaic. p. 179–237. *In* K.V. Flannery (ed.) Guila naquitz: Archaic foraging and early agriculture in Oaxaca, Mexico. Academic Press, Orlando, FL.

Sehgal, S.M. 1963. Effects of teosinte and *"Tripsacum"* introgression in maize. Ph.D. diss. Bussey Inst., Harvard Univ., Cambridge, MA.

Shaver, D.L. 1976. Conversions for earliness in maize. Maize Genet. Coop. Newsl. 50:20–23.

––––. 1983. Genetics and breeding of maize with extra leaves above the ear. p. 161–180. *In* Proc. 38 Annu. Corn Sorghum Res. Conf. ASTA, Washington, DC.

Singleton, W.R. 1946. "Long husk" sterility in maize. J. Hered. 37:29–30.

Smith, C.E. Jr. 1967. Plant remains. p. 220–225. *In* D.S. Byers (ed.) The prehistory of the Tehuacan Valley. Univ. of Texas Press, Austin.

Stadelman, R. 1939. Consumption of teosinte seed by birds in Guatemala. Science 89:461–462.

Stebbins, G.L., and F.J. Ayala. 1985. The evolution of Darwinism. Sci. Am. 253–1(July):72–82.

Sundberg, M.D., and A.R. Orr. 1986. Early inflorescence and floral development in *Zea diploperennis*, diploperennial teosinte. Am. J. Bot. 73:1699–1712.

Ting, Y.C. 1958. Inversions and other characteristics of teosinte chromosomes. Cytologia 23:239–250.

––––. 1964. Chromosomes of maize-teosinte hybrids. Bussey Inst., Harvard Univ., Cambridge, MA.

Tracy, W.F., and W.C. Galinat. 1987. Thickness and cell layer number of the pericarp of sweet corn and its relatives. HortScience 22:645–647.

Wallace, H.A., and W.L. Brown. 1956. Corn and its early fathers. Michigan State Univ. Press, East Lansing.

Weatherwax, P. 1954. Indian corn in old America. Macmillan Publ. Co., New York.

Wellhausen, E.J., L.M. Roberts, E. Hernandez-Xolocotzi, and P.C. Mangelsdorf. 1952. Races of maize in Mexico. Bussey Inst., Harvard Univ., Cambridge, MA.

Wilkes, H.G. 1967. Teosinte: The closest relative of maize. Bussey Inst., Harvard Univ., Cambridge, MA.

––––. 1986. Maize: Domestication, racial evolution and spread. *In* Plant domestication and early agriculture. XI. World Archaeological Congress. Allen and Unwin, London.

Williams, P.H., and C.B. Hill. 1986. Rapid-cycling populations of *Brassica*. Science 232:1385–1389.

2 Races of Corn

MAJOR M. GOODMAN

North Carolina State University
Raleigh, North Carolina

WILLIAM L. BROWN

Pioneer Hi-Bred International, Inc.
Johnston, Iowa

More than 40 yr ago, Anderson and Cutler (1942) stated the need for a more natural classification of variability known then to exist among corn (*Zea mays* L.) varieties. In the late 1800s, Sturtevant (1899) separated corn into six main groups, five of which were based upon the composition of the endosperm. Anderson and Cutler recognized the artificial nature of Sturtevant's system and suggested that knowledge from archaeology and genetics, accumulated since Sturtevant's work, should make possible a more natural classification. They indicated that variability in corn was comparable to that found in humankind and proposed the use of a racial classification based to the extent then possible on natural relationships.

The first thorough assessment of the variation in corn had been attempted more than a decade prior to Anderson and Cutler's proposal by Vavilov's associates (Kuleshov, 1929, 1930). Although those studies were partly completed before the downfall of Vavilov, published results are not readily accessible. More limited studies by Girola (1919), Parodi (1932, 1935), and Marino (1934) also received limited distribution and little recognition.

Anderson and Cutler defined race "as a group of related individuals with enough characteristics in common to permit their recognition as a group." In genetic terms, a race according to Anderson and Cutler "is a group of individuals with a significant number of genes in common, major races having a smaller number in common than do sub-races."

In a series of publications, Anderson (1943, 1944a, 1945, 1946, 1947), Anderson and Cutler (1942), Carter and Anderson (1945), Cutler (1946), Brown and Anderson (1947, 1948), and Anderson and Brown (1952) defined further the racial concept; described morphological characters thought to be most useful in delimiting races; and classified, in a preliminary way, the corn of Mexico, Central and South America, and parts of the USA. At about the same time, Longley (1938, 1941), Mangelsdorf and Cameron (1942), and Brown (1949) described the cytological variation of corn and its relationships to varietal and regional diversity.

While much progress has been made toward a natural system of classification of corn since that time, there has been relatively little progress in determining which characters are the most definitive for the study of racial differences in corn. Anderson and Cutler (1942) suggested a number of useful tassel, ear, and kernel characters, many of which Wellhausen et al. (1951) used. More recently, Goodman and Paterniani (1969) presented data suggesting that several ear and kernel characters were superior. This study was based on a narrow sample of germ plasm and may not be representative of the species as a whole; however, work with Peruvian corn has yielded similar results (Ortiz, 1985). Limited work with Mexican races (Sanchez, 1983) suggests that ear height might be a more useful character than ear diameter. Until recently, none of the archaeologically important cob characters (Nickerson, 1953, 1954) had been tested to determine the relative importance of the genotype, the environment, their interaction, and sampling error on the expression of the characters. A recent Masters thesis, however, (Ortiz, 1985) suggests cupule width should be quite useful.

Wellhausen et al. (1951) published the results of a comprehensive study of an extensive collection of Mexican corn. The study stemmed from an attempt to organize the variation of the Mexican corn for use in a corn-breeding program (Roberts, 1950). This report, *Razas de Maiz en Mexico*, enlarged upon previous studies and set the stage for a series of race studies which followed over the next 12 yr. Procedures followed in each of these studies were similar, although they varied considerably in emphasis and detail. First, corn grown in the region under study was sampled by collectors who usually obtained from 5 to 15 ears from each farm visited. Usually several thousand collections were made per study. These ear collections were assembled, spread out on laboratory benches, and similar collections were tentatively assigned to the same race. Emphasis was placed on such characters as ear shape, row number, kernel denting, etc., which were thought to be polygenic, rather than simply inherited ones such as pericarp and aleurone colors or endosperm differences such as flint vs. floury. Collections tentatively assigned to a given race were then grown together and those collections that differed in plant and tassel characters were removed from the set. Usually three to five collections were chosen on the basis of ear and plant characteristics (and sometimes as a result of breeding true to type) as being most typical of each race. Several ears from each of the most typical collections were saved as museum specimens, while the others were shelled and later increased. Descriptions of the races, including photographs and racial averages for many plant, tassel, ear, kernel, and sometimes physiological characters, as well as chromosome knob data, were published for Mexico and Central America (Wellhausen et al., 1952, 1957); Cuba (Hatheway, 1957); the West Indies (Brown, 1960); Venezuela (Grant et al., 1963); Colombia (Roberts et al., 1957); Ecuador (Timothy et al., 1963); Peru (Grobman et al., 1961); Bolivia (Ramírez et al., 1960); Chile (Timothy et al., 1961); and eastern South America (Brieger et al., 1958). This series of "race bulletins" was followed or accompanied by similar studies on European corn races (Sanchez-Monge, 1962; Leng et al., 1962; Edwards and Leng, 1965; Pavlicic and Trifunovic, 1966; Brandolini and Mariani, 1968; Brandolini, 1969, 1970b, 1971; Costa-Rodrigues, 1969; Pavilicic, 1971; Covor, 1972) and on Asian corn (Stonor and Anderson, 1949; Anderson and Brown, 1953; Suto and Yoshida, 1956; Mochizuki, 1968), and further studies on the races of Chile (Parker and Paratori, 1965); Bolivia (Rodriguez et al., 1968; Brandolina and Avila, 1971); Mexico (Hernandez and Alanis, 1970); and Brazil and adjacent areas (Blumenschein and Deuber, 1968; Paterniani and Goodman, 1977).

The series of race bulletins, that followed *Razas de Maiz en Mexico*, stemmed from the interest and concern of the late Ralph Cleland of Indiana University. Cleland was, at that time, director of the Division of Biology and Agriculture of the National Academy of Sciences—National Research Council (NAS-NRC). Under his leadership, the Committee on Preservation of Indigenous Strains of Maize (1954, 1955) was established within NAS-NRC. The committee was charged with the responsibility for collecting, classifying, and preserving the corn germ plasm of the Western Hemisphere, a formidable task when viewed in retrospect. The committee, nonetheless, was unusually successful. Over a period of years, it provided stimulus, guidance, and direction; and obtained sufficient financial support to collect, classify, and publish the results of studies of most of the corn of the Western Hemisphere. In addition, and in cooperation with many USA and Latin American agencies, it helped to organize seed storage centers in Mexico, Colombia, and Brazil.

The classification of Western Hemisphere corn as reported in the NAS-NRC bulletins was considered by many of the authors of these reports to be of a preliminary nature. It was looked upon as a starting point and a basis for more definitive studies which it was hoped would follow. So far, this has occurred to a limited extent only. Goodman (1967, 1968, 1972) and Goodman and Bird (1977) have restudied many of the Latin American collections and, through the use of numerical taxonomy, determined more precisely racial relationships between the previously described races.

Since 1955, a large body of information has been reported on the chromosome constitutions of races of corn of the Western Hemisphere (McClintock, 1959, 1960, 1978; Longley and Kato Y, 1965; Blumenschein, 1973; McClintock et al., 1981; Kato and Blumenschein, 1967; Kato, 1975). Chromosome components that have been studied most extensively are frequency of occurrence and geographic distribution of B-type chromosomes, abnormal chromosome 10, and chromosome knobs. The knob data include not only presence or absence of a knob at each knob forming site but also information on the size of each knob (small, medium, and large) when present.

The most comprehensive study of chromosome constitutions of Western Hemisphere corn included a total of 1352 collections from the

USA, Mexico, Central America, Panama, South America, and the Caribbean Islands (McClintock, et al., 1981). Data from this study provides the student of corn with a substantial amount of additional cytological information which should be useful in determining the centers of origin of specific knob complexes, the migration routes followed by knob complexes when moved from indigenous sites to other areas, and the kinds and amounts of introgression that may have occurred during the course of racial migration.

Chromosome characteristics, unlike morphological traits subject to visual selection, have not been directly influenced by man. Those traits, therefore, provide an additional tool for use in determining more natural relationships between races. Thus, the classification process becomes more precise when information on chromosome components is used to supplement that from comparative morphology (Bretting and Goodman, 1988). The classification process is amenable to even further refinement when both chromosome components and isozyme patterns are brought to bear on the question of racial relationships (Bretting et al., 1987).

Although chromosome component information has been used in our classification, we do not intend to summarize here that body of information. We do, however, wish to refer to a few of the conclusions reached by McClintock et al. (1981) that relate to clearly recognizable knob complexes and the possible influence of those on the evolution of corn in the Americas.

Perhaps the most consistent and clearly defined knob complex is that first recognized by McClintock in her preliminary studies of indigenous races from the highlands of Ecuador, Bolivia, and Chile. This, termed the *Andean Complex*, consists of two small knobs at $6L_3$ and 7L. With very few exceptions this complex typifies all the races from the high elevations of the Andes ranging from Ecuador through Chile. The primary exceptions are found in the races Perola and Pisinkalla of Bolivia. Neither of these are representative of the typical highland phenotype and probably are not indigenous to the area. It is not surprising, therefore, that in their chromosome components they do not fit the Andean Complex.

McClintock (1978) indicates that the Andean Complex has had a major influence on the corn of eastern and central South America. It is further suggested that the complex may have been introduced from highland Guatemala, a center of small knobs and knobless chromosomes.

In addition to the knobless and small knob complex found in highland Guatemala, there is a lowland large knob complex which is somewhat scattered but tends to be concentrated in those Guatemalan departments close to the Mexican state of Chiapas. Elsewhere in Central America and Mexico certain of these knobs are widespread.

In contrast to the Andean Complex and, to a lesser degree, those of Guatemala, chromosome constitutions of the corn of Venezuela are much more complicated. A "Venezuelan Large Knob Complex" consisting of 2L, 3L, 4L, 5L, 7S, 7L, $8L_1$, 9S, and 9L seems to be the most readily recognizable knob complex of that country. A part of the distinctness of this complex relates to the infrequent occurrence of its components in the adjacent Territory of Roraima, Brazil.

The Venezuelan Large Knob Complex has been shown to have influenced the corn of the eastern Caribbean islands as well as the Guianas of northeastern South America.

Somewhat less clearly defined are two additional complexes in Venezuela. A medium size complex composed of 2S, 2L, 3L, 4L, 6L$_2$, and 7S knobs is concentrated in the northwest and, in contrast to the Large Knob Complex, is also present in the adjacent Territory of Roraima, Brazil.

The third Venezuelan complex is one of small knobs found in the western part of the country. Here again, in contrast to the Large Knob Complex, these small knobs are also present in the Territory Roraima.

Migration routes of corn germ plasm as deduced from chromosomal components is of particular interest to anthropologists and students of corn evolution. McClintock (1978), McClintock et al. (1981), and Kato (1984) have identified a number of such routes. One, described by McClintock (1978), extends along the Pacific coast of Mexico from the Guatemalan border to the state of Sonora. This involves several different knobs and a large number of races. Another route, a relatively recent one according to McClintock, extends from the Mexican Bajio into Chihuahua.

A third most interesting migration route is that extending along the east coast of Mexico from Veracruz into Tamaulipas. This route includes the highly productive race Tuxpeño which has contributed significantly to corn improvement in the lowland tropics. As Tuxpeño moved north it acquired other segments of germ plasm "without however suffering serious loss of character identity" (McClintock, 1978). This may have resulted in a heterotic response and may be the reason for the exceptional productivity of the race in its present state.

These are but a few of the numerous migration pathways that have been identified on the basis of chromosome components. The significance of these routes becomes apparent when it is realized that certain of the chromosomal components (knobs) on which they are based have not been found in the Americas outside the designated migration routes.

Although the chromosome constitution studies have dealt primarily with races of corn, Kato (1975, 1984) has extended his studies to include a fairly comprehensive collection of Mexican and Guatemalan teosinte. These investigations provide new information on the cytological relationship between corn and teosinte and possibly also on the question of origin. For example, the teosintes of Mexico exhibit the same classes of knobs that are found in corn. Moreover, all observed knob sites in the corn chromosomes are present in Mexican teosinte. However, there are a few knobs in Mexican teosinte that are not known to occur in corn. The situation is quite different in Guatemalan teosinte. Here almost all knobs are terminal, whereas most knobs in the Mexican teosintes occupy internal positions. Clearly then, many of the knob-forming sites in Guatemalan teosinte are not duplicated in corn.

The Mexican teosintes possess both B-type chromosomes and abnormal 10 chromosomes similar to those found in corn. Neither of these components are known to occur in Guatemalan teosinte.

Because corn and teosintes have long been known to intermate and produce fertile progeny where the two are sympatric in Mexico, the transfer of germ plasm and knobs would be expected to have moved reciprocally between the two. Yet, based on the preceding discussion, Kato and McClintock (McClintock et al., 1981, p. 58–60) suggest that "There are good reasons for considering that maize as we know it today, was derived, initially, from teosinte that probably was located in one specific area in Mexico but subsequently greatly influenced by other(s) located in areas between central and southwest Mexico."

A similar study based upon isoenzyme allele variation has begun (Goodman, 1978; Doebley et al., 1983, 1985, 1986; Goodman and Stuber, 1983; Bretting et al., 1987; Smith, 1988). Coverage is reasonably complete for North America, Central America, and the Caribbean. This survey has helped identify relationships between Mexican corn and related races from the USA and the Caribbean. In addition, two surveys of mitochondrial variation among Latin American accessions of corn have been completed (Kemble et al., 1983; Weissinger et al., 1983). The latter have supported several of the conclusions reached earlier and summarized in McClintock et al. (1981).

Mangelsdorf (1974) has attempted to survey the variability found among the various Latin American corn races. Rather than delineating racial groups, complexes, or "super races," he assigned races to lineages, lineage being used in the sense of "descent in a line from a common progenitor." He described six such lineages, each of which he postulates was derived from a wild race of corn. "From north to south, the still-living ancestral races of these lineages are:

1. Palomero Toluqueño, the Mexican pointed-seeded popcorn.
2. The Chapalote-Nal-Tel complex of Mexico.
3. Pira Naranja of Colombia, the progenitor of the tropical flint corn with orange-endosperm color.
4. Confite Morocho of Peru, the progenitor of eight-rowed corn.
5. Chullpi of Peru, the progenitor of all sweet corn and related starchy-seeded forms with globular ears.
6. Kculli, the Peruvian dye corn, the progenitor of all races with complexes of pericarp and aleurone colors."

The only other recent attempt at comprehensive description of the corn races is that of Brandolini (1970a), who lists a number of primary and secondary centers of differentiation and races associated with such centers.

An understanding of the variability of corn is important for several reasons. It should shed light on the history and relationships of the peoples whose lives are closely associated with corn. Corn breeding should benefit from a better understanding of the evolutionary history and genetic variability within the genus. Finally, and perhaps more importantly, increased knowledge of the racial composition of corn should point the direction to the most efficient and effective ways of minimizing the genetic vulnerability of the commercial corn of the Americas. As indicated in a recent study by the Committee on Genetic Vulnerability of Major Crops (1972) of the National Academy of Sciences, corn has undergone a gradual but continual decrease in genetic diversity over the past 50 yr. The decrease in genetic diversity has been accompanied by an increase in genetic vulnerability. As the genetic base of corn germ plasm used in commerce is diminished, the risk of economic loss of the crop due to diseases, insects, or unusual stress conditions increases correspondingly. The most recent example of the hazards associated with the widespread use of uniform genetic material is that of the southern corn leaf blight (caused by *Bipolaris maydis*) epidemic of 1970 (Sprague, 1971). That experience has brought to the fore again the realization of the hazards associated with the erosion of genetic diversity in any widely grown crop species.

Most of the corn germ plasm in use in the USA today is derived from mixtures of only two major races (Wallace and Brown, 1956). The simplest means of correcting this situation and of increasing the genetic diversity in this important crop is to introduce unrelated sources of germ plasm, most of which are found in the tropics and subtropics. To do this intelligently and efficiently is a formidable task. There is a vast store of corn germ plasm outside the USA which differs greatly in its potential usefulness within the USA. Though our knowledge of the races of corn found in the tropics and subtropics is still incomplete, the knowledge which is available should, if used, simplify the task of reducing the genetic vulnerability of our most important feed grain.

In the discussion which follows, no attempt is made to provide detailed descriptions of the races. This information is already available in the various publications cited earlier. Our objective, rather, is to recognize those earlier described races that seem still to be valid and to shed some light on apparent relationships between them. Many of these relationships are most simply indicated in the text figures. Readers interested in detailed descriptions are referred to earlier cited papers.

This report contains no reference to corn found outside the Western Hemisphere. There are many reasons for this, the foremost of which is the limited information available on the variability of corn of Europe, Africa, and Asia. In our opinion, much more information is needed before a complete and orderly classification of the corn of the Old World is possible. Supposedly, corn had its origin in the Western Hemisphere, yet it is apparent that distinct races have evolved in many areas excluded from this report.

2-1   RACES OF LATIN AMERICA

With the exception of races described by Rodriguez et al. (1968), for which no representative collections were cited, all named Latin American

Table 2-1. Races for which relationships are uncertain.

Race	Country	Reference
Conejo	Mexico	Wellhausen et al., 1952
Mushito	Mexico	Wellhausen et al., 1952
Complejo Serrano de Jalisco	Mexico	Wellhausen et al., 1952
Rosita	Mexico	Harnandez and Alanis, 1970
White Pop	Cuba	Hatheway, 1957
Yellow Pop	Cuba	Hatheway, 1957
White Dent	Cuba	Hatheway, 1957
Nal-Tel Ocho	Guatemala	Wellhausen et al., 1957
Maíz Dulce	Colombia	Roberts et al., 1957
Maíz Harinoso Dentado	Colombia	Roberts et al., 1957
Cónico Dentado	Ecuador	Timothy et al., 1963
Uchima	Ecuador	Timothy et al., 1963
Gallina	Ecuador	Timothy et al., 1963
Cholito	Ecuador	Timothy et al., 1963
Yunga	Ecuador	Timothy et al., 1963
Enano Gigante	Ecuador	Timothy et al., 1963
Yungeño	Ecuador	Timothy et al., 1963
Chuncho	Peru	Grobman et al., 1961
Jora	Peru	Grobman et al., 1961
Ajaleado	Peru	Grobman et al., 1961
Tumbesino	Peru	Grobman et al., 1961
Colorado	Peru	Grobman et al., 1961
Polulo	Chile	Timothy et al., 1961
Chutucuno Grande	Chile	Timothy et al., 1961
Harinoso Tarapaqueño	Chile	Timothy et al., 1961
Achilli	Argentina	Brieger et al., 1958
Bola Blanca	Argentina	Brieger et al., 1958
Brachytic Popcorn	Argentina	Brieger et al., 1958

corn races are included in this survey, which is largely adapted from the previous one (Brown and Goodman, 1977). For a number of races, the authors lack sufficient knowledge to accurately circumscribe racial boundaries or to correctly describe their relationships to other races. Such races are listed in Table 2-1, although such a listing does not preclude mentioning such a race elsewhere.

2-2 MEXICAN RACES

Most of the races of corn in Mexico (Wellhausen et al., 1952; Hernandez and Alanis, 1970; Ortega, 1985) can be reasonably assigned to well-defined racial groups (Goodman, 1972; Cervantes et al., 1978; Doebley et al., 1985). Figure 2-1 gives a general view of the apparent racial relationships.

The long, narrow-eared corns typical of northwestern Mexico, whether popcorns, flints, or flours, are all similar to the Indian corns of southwestern USA (Anderson, 1944b, 1946; Brown et al., 1952, Carter and Anderson, 1945). These races include Chapalote, Reventador, Harinoso de Ocho, and Tabloncillo as well as several more recently described races

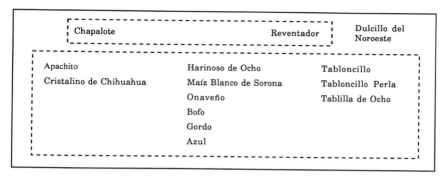

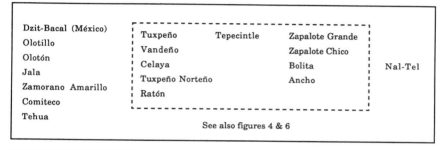

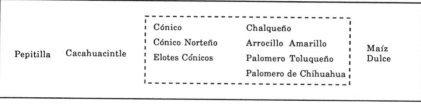

Fig. 2–1. Racial relationships of the corn of Mexico. Those races within cells outlined by solid lines are thought to be more closely related than races found in different cells. Similarly, races outlined by broken lines are assumed to be more closely related to each other than to races found outside the subcells. This method of depicting racial relationships is used in all text figures. (Fig. 2–1 through Fig. 2–10).

(Hernandez and Alanis, 1970). It appears (Nelson, 1952, 1960) that Harinoso de Ocho is one of only two Mexican races that shares the ga_1/ga_1 genotype with the most prevalent USA corn types (Northern Flints, Southern Dents, and Corn Belt Dents). Despite its geographic distribution in southern Mexico, the race Bolita, described further below, shares some isozyme and chromosome knob similarities to the races of northwestern Mexico (Doebley et al., 1985, Bretting and Goodman, 1988).

A second distinctive racial group consists of the conically eared corns with pointed kernels, mostly found at relatively high elevations in central Mexico. Endosperm varies from dented floury to pop, but the plant type—pubescent leaves; sparsely branched, thick tassels; weak roots—is consistent. Cónico, Cónico Norteño, Chalqueño, Arrocillo Amarillo, and Palomero Toluqueño each falls into this category. Pepitilla seems to be related to these races, but it may include sources of germ plasm from lower altitude races. Cacahuacintle seems to be related more closely to the Guatemalan race Salpor than to any Mexican race, yet it shares both ear shape and the general aspect of the plant with the Cónico group. It differs most by its very large floury kernels. Mushito and Ancho are two poorly described Mexican races with ear and plant similarities to the races in this group. Kato and Blumenschein (1967) suggested that Cónico, Chalqueño, Palomero Toluqueño, Cacahuacintle, and Arrocillo Amarillo share an essentially knobless karyotype whose influence they have traced to the southern USA. Blumenschein (1973) later suggested that Palomero Toluqueño was distinct from the other members in this group in its chromosome constitution. He gave no details, but this view is supported by the report by Nelson (1960) that Palomero Toluqueño, unlike most Mexican corns, possesses the ga_1/ga_1 genotype at the gametophyte locus on chromosome four. Palomero Toluqueño is the ancestral race for one of the six lineages described by Mangelsdorf (1974). He traces its influence as far as the Andean pointed popcorns and their relatives.

The remaining Mexican races fall into a set of clines or gradients between large-eared races (Jala, Olatón) and small-eared races (Zapalote Chico, Bolita, and Nal-Tel). These appear to include the widest assortment of dent races found in a single area. Included are the widely used Tuxpeño, Vandeño, and Celaya dents, as well as races such as Comiteco, Tehua, Tepecintle, and Zapalote Grande, which appear to be closely related to them. Nal-Tel appears to be related to both the small-eared dents and to Chapalote, a popcorn from northwestern Mexico. Within this group, Kato and Blumenschein (1967) found two distinct chromosome knob complexes. The Tuxpeño knob complex of many medium-sized knobs was found along the east coast of Mexico from Yucatán to the southern USA, in central and northeastern Mexico, and along the southwest coast of Mexico. Its influence reached as far as Panama and Cuba and is found in scattered parts of South America. The Zapalote Chico complex of many knobs of various sizes encompasses the races Zapalote Chico, Zapalote Grande, and Bolita, and is found from the southwest coast of Mexico to western Costa Rica. It is suspected (Blumenschein, 1973) that this complex also reached Venezuela.

Chapalote and Nal-Tel, two races which today appear to be distinct in both ear shape and plant type, are listed as the ancestral forms in one of Mangelsdorf's (1974) lineages. That lineage includes, among others, Reventador, the Mexican dents described above, and the Central American Nal-Tels.

2–3 CENTRAL AMERICAN RACES

The races from Central America have not been as carefully collected, described, or maintained as the races of Mexico. Only for Guatemala (Fig. 2–2) are the collections or descriptions reasonably thorough. The

Guatemalan races, especially those from higher altitudes, resemble South American types of corn about as closely as they resemble Mexican types. Limited tests of R alleles, which condition aleurone color, by Van der Walt and Brink (1969), however, suggest that, at least for those corn races possessing aleurone color, the corn found north of the Andes is distinct from that of the Andes. They found that all tested Andean corn possessed nonparamutable R alleles, while all Central and North American corn tested, as well as most non-Andean South American corn, has paramutable R alleles.

A number of lowland Guatemalan collections resemble Mexican Nal-Tel from Yucatán, although they are phenotypically and apparently genotypically (Nelson, 1960; McClintock, 1960) rather variable. Wellhausen et al. (1957) report that the influence of Nal-Tel extends as far south as Panama.

The Guatemalan Imbricado complex shares many features of both the ear and plant with the pointed Mexican popcorn, Palomero Toluqueño, although having larger kernels, less kernel pointing, and much less uniformity than Palomero Toluqueño. In these respects, it more closely resembles the Colombian race Imbricado. As mentioned above, the Guatemalan Salpors seem to be closely related to the Mexican race

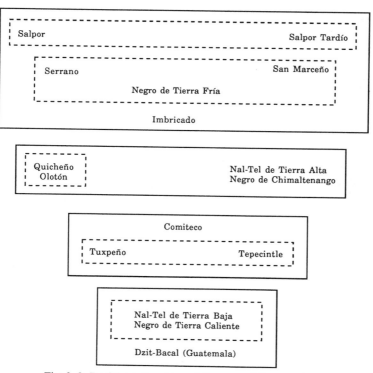

Fig. 2–2. Racial relationships of the corn of Guatemala.

Cacahuacintle. Both show great similarity in ear and plant characteristics to the Mexican Cónicos and their relatives, but have distinctive, large, floury, white kernels.

Comiteco, a medium- to high-altitude, long-eared semident, and several low-altitude dent races are common to Mexico and Guatemala. These include Tepecintle and Tuxpeño, as well as Dzit-Bacal, an eight-rowed, white dent described as a subrace of Olotillo in Mexico. Guatemalan Dzit-Bacal is much faster maturing and shorter than Olotillo and appears more closely related to the low-altitude collections of Nal-Tel than does Olotillo. Kato and Blumenschein (1967) reported that the southern Guatemala chromosome knob complex with numerous large knobs has influenced lowland corn from Panama to northern Mexico along the west coast, in the Yucatán, Chiapas, and Oaxaca. This complex, found especially in the race Nal-Tel, is reported to have reached Cuba and the Greater Antilles from Costa Rica.

Although the long-eared Guatemalan race, Olotón, is also found in the neighboring state of Chiapas, Mexico, it resembles closely a South American racial complex of medium to high altitude, large-kernelled, long-eared flints (the Montañas, Amagaceño). Two other Guatemalan races, Serrano and Quicheño, also resemble South American races. (Some of the collections of Olotón from Mexico are perhaps more similar to Quicheño of Guatemala than to Guatemalan Olotón.) There seems to be essentially continuous variation between Serrano (a small-eared flint, often with an enlarged base) and Olotón, with Quicheño being intermediate in altitudinal distribution. Olotón, and to a lesser extent, Quicheño, have long ears borne on tall, late-maturing plants. This series of clinal variants corresponds to the Pollo-Sabanero-Montaña complex found in northwestern South America. In each case, the longer eared, taller plants are found at lower elevations, usually in areas of at least high relative humidity and often in areas of much rainfall.

San Marceño seems to be basically a Serrano with eight rows of partially dented kernels, while Nal-Tel de Tierra Alta appears to have some Quicheño ancestry. A complex of small chromosome knobs is reported to be typical of high-altitude collections from Guatemala (Kato and Blumenschein, 1967). The influence of this complex extends to high elevations from southwestern Mexico to Panama. There is also an indication in Nelson's (1960) data that highland Guatemalan corn carries the ga_1 allele rather than the alleles common to tropical races. Finally, Negro de Chimaltenango, a fairly long, slender, tapering-eared, flinty flour corn with rounded kernels having deep blue aleurone, appears to be similar to Güirua and Negrito from northwestern South America. Wellhausen et al. (1957) suggest that Negro de Chimaltenango, a medium altitude race, has introgressed into both high-altitude Serrano and into several lowland races to form the subraces Negro de Tierra Fría and Negro de Tierra Caliente, respectively. Both morphology and isozyme frequencies suggest that the latter race is more likely to be a colored variant of lowland

Nal-Tel (P.K. Bretting, M.M. Goodman, and C.W. Stuber. 1988. Isozyme variation in Guatemalan races of maize. Unpublished data).

The principal commercial corn from El Salvador, Honduras, Nicaragua, and Costa Rica is a low-altitude, early maturing, flinty dent with tapering ears called Salvadoreño. In Costa Rica and Panama, a slender-eared white flint, called Clavillo by Wellhausen et al. (1957), resembles the Colombian race Clavo. Huesillo, an 8- to 10-rowed, white-capped flint resembling the Tabloncillos of Mexico, is also found in Costa Rica. It may be related to Canilla and Clavo from the Caribbean regions of South America. Two Colombian races, Chococeño (Nickerson and Covich, 1966), and Cariaco, are found in southern Panama.

2–4 WEST INDIAN RACES

The classification of West Indian corn into clearly defined races is difficult for several reasons. The area is lacking in natural barriers; because of the close proximity of the islands, one to the other, there has long been free migration of peoples between the islands. Likewise, the geographic position of certain islands relative to the South American mainland has encouraged movement of peoples from the mainland to the islands since the days of the Arawak. The free movements of peoples in the area apparently have been accompanied by transport of corn varieties and a masking of the racial differences among them. Despite these difficulties, it has been possible to identify several reasonably well-defined races in the West Indies. The validity of certain of these races has been confirmed through the subsequent discovery of similar racial counterparts in other areas of Latin America.

The first study of West Indian corn was that of Hernandez (1949), who described six provisional races from collections made primarily in Cuba. This was followed by a preliminary study by Brown (1953) of collections from 11 Caribbean islands. Brown recognized eight provisional races. Hatheway (1957) reported on a detailed analysis of Cuban corn and described seven races existing in Cuba at the time of his study. Brown (1960) did a later study of West Indian corn in which he attempted to correlate his earlier findings with those of other authors. This work included the progenies of 135 collections that were grown and studied in Trinidad. He concluded that West Indian corn consisted essentially of seven distinct races plus a number of intermediate types which presumably were products of interracial hybridization. The races recognized by Brown were Cuban Flint, Haitian Yellow, Coastal Tropical Flint, Chandelle, Early Caribbean, Tusón, and St. Croix.

This classification seems as valid today as when it was made in 1960. To our knowledge, no new, indigenous races have been reported from the West Indies since that date. On the contrary, many of the varieties formerly used as commercial corn have recently been replaced by modern hybrids. In Jamaica, for example, we estimate that 90% or more of the corn now grown consists of hybrid varieties.

The two most prominent races occupying the West Indies are Coastal Tropical Flint and Tusón. Both are widely distributed throughout the islands from Cuba to Trinidad. The two are also probably closely related. Brown (1953, 1960) postulated that Tusón arose as a hybrid between Coastal Tropical Flint and some unidentified corn maize. Even though related, Coastal Tropical Flint and Tusón are distinct. Coastal Tropical Flint is more flint-like than Tusón, has a lower number of kernel rows, and has shorter and somewhat narrower kernels. The ears of Coastal Tropical flint are distinctly tapered, whereas the ears of Tusón are cylindrical. The name Tusón, meaning large cob, seems particularly appropriate for this race, because it has distinctly larger cobs than found in any other west Indian race. Tusón is slightly earlier in maturity than Coastal Tropical Flint and has somewhat fewer primary and secondary tassel branches. Coastal Tropical Flint is tall, without tillers, and has ears placed high on the culm. Tusón is also without tillers but is somewhat shorter and has somewhat lower ear placement than Coastal Tropical Flint. Unfortunately, the most typical collections of Coastal Tropical Flint were from the island of Dominica, the last home of the Caribs, and have been completely lost from corn germplasm banks (Goodman, 1984).

Haitian Yellow seems to be more closely related to Coastal Tropical Flint than to other West Indian races. Its ears are characteristically pyramidal with conspicuously enlarged bases and with 8 to 14 rows of kernels. The pointed kernels vary from flint to slightly dented. Plants are tall and very late maturing; they usually exhibit purple anthocyanin coloration. The plants possess more extensively developed husk leaf blades, flag leaves, than do other West Indian races. The distribution of Haitian Yellow, apparently limited to Haiti, suggests relatively recent origin. Its similarity to Coastal Tropical Flint indicates it may have originated from crosses of that race with other Haitian corn.

The four remaining races found in the West Indies, Cuban Flint, Chandelle, Early Caribbean, and St. Croix, are well defined and appear not to be closely related to each other or to the three races referred to previously.

Cuban Flint is the only true flint found in the West Indies. Its distribution is limited to Cuba, and evidence is fairly clear that it was introduced from Argentina in the early 1900s (Hatheway, 1957). The ears of Cuban flint are relatively short (17 cm), are slightly compressed at the base, and are gently tapered from the base to the tip. Row numbers vary from 12 to 16, with 14 being the most frequently found number. Kernels are short and deep orange yellow in color. Tassel branches are also short in comparison with those of other West Indian races. The plants are usually without tillers, are frequently two-eared, and the leaf sheaths are usually strongly pubescent in contrast with the glabrous leaves of other races.

Although similarity between Cuban Flint and the Cateto and Cateto Sulino flints of eastern South America [described by Brieger et al. (1958) and Paterniani and Goodman (1977)] is obvious, Hatheway (1957) has suggested that Cuban Flint may be the result of accidental crossing of Argentine flint with local Cuban varieties. He feels that Argentine flints are poorly adapted to Cuba and that Cuban Flint is more similar to other Cuban varieties in plant type than to Argentine flints. Some introgression has undoubtedly occurred between introduced Argentine flint and Cuban varieties, yet the relationship between Cuban Flint and Cateto (and Camelia of Chile as well) appears to be still quite strong. Blumenschein (1973) suggested, on the basis of chromosome knob mapping, that the Cateto flints of eastern South America originated in the Antilles as a result of crosses between representatives of the Tuxpeño knob complex and the two Guatemalan knob complexes. However, there seems to be no evidence from any other source to support this hypothesis.

Chandelle is found in Cuba, Haiti, the Dominican Republic, Trinidad, and the Caicos Islands. It is a dominant race in the Dominican Republic. Two forms of Chandelle occur in Cuba and the Dominican Republic—a flint and a dent. In Haiti, Trinidad, and the Caicos Islands, it occurs only as a flint. Because of the nature of the ear, Chandelle is never confused with other races. The ears are long, slender, strongly compressed at the base, and gently tapered to the tip. Kernel rows range from 10 to 16, and the kernels are long in relation to the diameter of the cob resulting in a high-shelling percentage. The cob is slender and flexible even when mature and dry, a trait which occurs infrequently in corn and in none of the other West Indian races. Chandelle is of late maturity, and the plants are taller than those of other West Indian races; however, some early maturing tropical lines have been extracted from the race. Considerable red anthocyanin color is usually present in the leaf sheaths.

Because of its early maturity, short stature, and distinctive internode pattern, Early Caribbean is unique among West Indian corn. When grown in the lowland tropics, it flowers 46 to 48 d after planting, which is 10 to 14 d earlier than other West Indian races. It is sensitive to changes in photoperiod, however, requiring about 95 d to flower in Raleigh, NC. Early Caribbean has few condensed internodes above the ear, resulting in an internode pattern more typical of early USA varieties than of those from the tropics. The ears are relatively short (18 cm) and slightly tapered with 10 to 12 rows of relatively wide, semi-flint kernels. Pericarp color is frequently red or reddish, although colorless pericarp is not unusual. The husks are quite loose compared with other races of the area. Insofar as is known, the distribution of Early Caribbean is limited to Martinique and St. Kitts. Its characteristics are such as to suggest relationship to some of the early flint corns of North America or Europe. Yet evidence from isozyme studies (Bretting et al., 1987) do not support such a relationship. Consequently, we are inclined to consider Early Caribbean a relic of an old, indigenous race.

St. Croix apparently arose from introgression between local varieties and introductions from southeastern USA. Because many of the characteristics of St. Croix are similar to those of the old white endosperm variety, Hickory King, and because of the political connection between the USA and certain of the Virgin Islands, it seems likely that Hickory King was involved in the ancestry of St. Croix. Ears of St. Croix are the longest found in the West Indies; they are cylindrical to slightly tapered and consist of 10 to 14 rows of wide, well-dented, flat-topped kernels. Endosperm is light yellow in color, suggesting again the possibility of some white endosperm parentage. The plants of St. Croix also suggest relationships to temperate zone corn. Ear placement is low compared to other races, and the husks are relatively short and loose. The tassels have relatively few branches that are arranged more or less at right angles to the primary axis. Except for Early Caribbean, St. Croix is of earlier maturity than other West Indian races. To our knowledge, the race is limited in its distribution to the island of St. Croix. Brown (1960) suggested that St. Croix might have arisen from introgression of local varieties with Hickory King of the USA or Olotillo of Mexico. While one cannot completely rule out the possiblity of relationship to Olotillo (which is both tall and late, with relatively high ears), the phenotype of St. Croix is that which one would more reasonably expect to result from introgression with temperate varieties.

Four of the seven races found in the West Indies have similar counterparts in South America (Fig. 2–3). These are Cuban Flint, Coastal Tropical Flint, Chandelle, and Tusón. Their relationships are discussed further in the next section. The three remaining races, Haitian Yellow, Early Caribbean, and St. Croix, have not been collected from other areas and are apparently limited in their distribution to the Caribbean islands.

Kato and Blumenschein (1967) report that the corn of the West Indies appears to be influenced by three sources of chromosome knob variation. They suggest that the Tuxpeño complex of medium-sized knobs from the eastern coast of Mexico and the southern Guatemalan, mostly large-knobbed, complex were introduced to the Greater Antilles. These introductions combined to form a secondary knob complex, which they labelled Northwest Caribbean. This new, secondary complex spread southward through the Lesser Antilles to South America, then spread along the coast to Uruguay and northeastern Argentina, and inland to Paraguay and southwestern Brazil. The third chromosome knob complex found in the West Indies is Kato and Blumenschin's Venezuelan complex. This complex of large knobs apparently spread through the Lesser Antilles and along the coast of South America to Panama, Ecuador, Brazil, and Uruguay.

2–5 RACES OF SOUTH AMERICA

Much of the variation in South American corn can also be discussed on a regional basis. There are, of course, races that do not fit regional

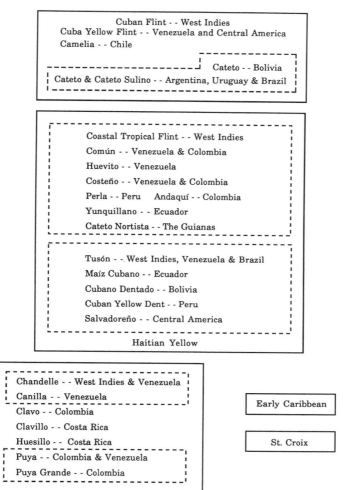

Fig. 2–3. Relationships of the races of corn of the West Indies and their Central and South American counterparts. (See also Fig. 2–4).

patterns closely, but several racial complexes, each largely confined to one of the four regions below, appear to encompass the realm of corn variation in South America. Detailed results of one set of numerical analyses of most of these races have been presented elsewhere (Goodman and Bird, 1977; Bird and Goodman, 1977). The summary presented here is largely based upon the results of those analyses tempered somewhat by field experience with the materials. We have also attempted to consider the sometimes extensive reviews of the histories and geographical distributions of the races that are included in the various race bulletins. Nevertheless, we would like to emphasize that the racial groupings presented here are, at best, working hypotheses that need much additional study.

2–5.1 Lowland Northern South America

Several of the flint and semiflint races of northern South America were discussed in the section on West Indian corn, and their relationships are presented diagrammatically in Fig. 2–3. Cuban Yellow flint of Venezuela (Grant et al., 1963), the Catetos and Cateto Sulinos of eastern South America (Brieger et al., 1958; Paterniani and Goodman, 1977), and Camelia of Chile (Timothy et al., 1961) appear to be mainland counterparts of Cuban Flint. The currently available typical collections of Cuban Flint from Venezuela are phenotypically rather variable and appear to include some Tusón and Chandelle influence.

Coastal Tropical Flint (Fig. 2–3) occurs under the names of Perla in Peru (Grobman et al., 1961), Cateto Nortista in the Guinas (Paterniani and Goodman, 1977), and Costeño and Común, both in Venezuela and Colombia (Grant et al., 1963; Roberts et al., 1957). However, the range of variation described for the latter two races seems to encompass both Coastal Tropical Flint and Tusón. The Costeño collections from Colombia are quite variable in ear shape, while the Común collections from that country have a much larger kernel size than those from Venezuela. This would appear to be the result of a higher percentage of high-altitude germplasm in Colombian Común. The Colombian race Andaquí and the similar Ecuadorian race Yunquillano, (Roberts et al., 1957; Timothy et al., 1963), also appear to belong to this racial group. Andaquí is a small-eared, white, semi-flint with many chromosome knobs. It is found at low elevations in the southern interior of Colombia. Huevito from Venezuela appears to be intermediate between the Coastal Tropical Flints and the widespread Andean Sabanero types discussed later.

Tusón is widespread in South America (Fig. 2–3). It has been described from Ecuador as Maíz Cubano (Timothy et al., 1963), from Venezuela and Brazil as Tusón (Grant et al., 1963; Paterniani and Goodman, 1977), from Bolivia as Cubano Dentado (Ramirez et al., 1960), and from Peru as Cuban Yellow Dent (Grobman et al., 1961). Salvadoreño from Central America (Wellhausen et al., 1957) and many of the collections of Tuxpeño from Venezuela and Puya Grande from Venezuela could also be classified as Tusóns. Because of its productivity, Tusón has undoubtedly been widely dispersed as a commercial corn in recent times. Whether the initial migration of Tusón was from the mainland to the islands or vice versa is still unknown. Yet, the antiquity of corn in South America suggests that Tusón probably reached the West Indies from the mainland.

Races similar to Chandelle are found in Venezuela (Grant et al., 1963), Colombia (Roberts et al., 1957), and Central America (Wellhausen et al., 1957) (Fig. 2–3). The collections from Venezuela have been given the names Canilla, Puya, and Chandelle, whereas in Colombia they are known as Clavo and Puya. Clavo seems to be less closely related to Chandelle than previously assumed (Martinez et al., 1983). Venezuelan Canilla has somewhat smaller, more flinty kernels than Chandelle. Clavillo from Costa Rica (Wellhausen et al., 1957) is apparently also a member of the same racial complex. Puya Grande from Colombia appears also to be fairly closely related to Chandelle, whereas the Puya Grande collections from Venezuela seem more closely related to the Tusóns, described above.

There is also a group of dents and semidents (Tuxpeño of Ecuador and Venezuela; Yucatán from Colombia; Alazán and Arizona from Peru; Puya Grande from Venezuela) which presumably trace back to Mexican dents of the Tuxpeño-Vandeño type (Fig. 2–4). Several Peruvian (Ale-

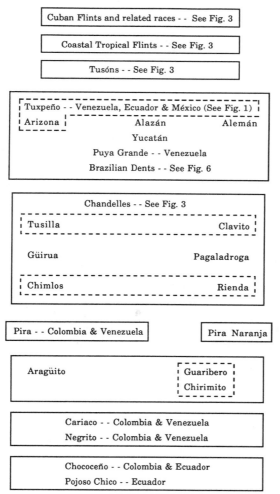

Fig. 2–4. Racial relationships of the corn of lowland northern South America.

mán, Chuncho, and Jora) and Ecuadorian (Uchima and Gallina) races have apparently arisen as a result of admixture between Caribbean flint or dent races and lower-altitude Andean races. The source of denting in all of these races presumably traces to Mexico.

The narrow-eared characteristics of Puya (see previous discussion) and Chandelle appear to trace to the Canilla-Clavo-Tusilla-Clavito group of narrow-eared flints (Fig. 2–4). The latter appear to be related to Rienda, Chimlos, and Pagaladroga (and perhaps Rabo de Zorro) of Peru and Güirua of Colombia. Güirua has elongate ears similar to the Chandelles but with blue aleurone; it is an Indian corn collected from nonSpanish-speaking Indians.

The relationships, if any, between the narrow-eared flints and flours discussed above and the phenotypically similar popcorns, such as Pira (a white, cigar-shaped popcorn with a very thin, often almost disarticulating, cob) from Venezuela and Colombia; and Pira Naranja (a yellow, cigar-shaped popcorn, which is quite late maturing and tall) from Colombia are unclear. Mangelsdorf (1974) suggests that Pira Naranja was ancestral to a lineage leading to the Cateto flints of eastern South America. Since Pira Naranja is not only extremely sensitive to photoperiod (Stevenson and Goodman, 1972), but also is quite late maturing even under short-day conditions, it, unlike Mangelsdorf's other postulated ancestral races, would appear to be highly resistant to successful adaptation to new environments, particularly those with longer days and shorter growing seasons. Both of the latter are characteristic of the environments wherein most Catetos are found.

Whether the Chirimito, Aragüito, and Guaribero small flints or popcorns (Fig. 2–4) from Venezuela are related to larger-eared races such as Pira (see above) is not yet known. The former (especially Aragüito) are quite short and very early, but lack the brittleness and upright leaf and tassel branch habit of the somewhat similar collections of Enano (see section 2–5.2 and Fig. 2–5) from Bolivia and Peru. In plant type, they more closely resemble two early maturing floury races with short, broad ears, Cariaco and Negrito of Venezuela and Colombia (Fig. 2–4). The latter especially appears to share its ear shape with the shorter-eared Caribbean tropical flints (discussed above), and both appear to share their kernel coloration with Amazonian races described in section 2–5.2. Negrito is sometimes quite flinty.

The Chococeños (Fig. 2–4) of western Colombia and Ecuador (Patiño, 1956) share the same general ear shape with Enano, Chirimito, Guaribero, and Aragüito (described just above), but the plants are tall, heavily tillered, and very late. While there are floury collections of Chococeño, it typically is a popcorn reportedly grown in an area of high rainfall by sowing rather than row planting (Roberts et al., 1957).

2–5.2 The Amazon Basin and Surrounding Lowlands

Throughout the interior lowland area east of the Central Andes, a single racial complex predominates. First described by Cutler (1946) under the name Coroico (Fig. 2–5), it has also been called Piricinco and Pojoso (Grobman et al., 1961) as well as Entrelaçado (Brieger et al., 1958). The characteristic features of this racial complex are its long, narrow ears, often with bulging butts, interlocked rows of kernels instead of the customary paired-kernel rowing, and strongly attached shanks. The very low condensation, especially near the ear tip, which is a distinctive feature of these races, has been described by Galinat (1970). The kernels are usually floury with bronze or orange-colored aleurone, although lemon-yellow aleurone is often found; there are collections with white, flinty kernels. Wolf et al. (1972) reported that many collections of this racial complex have multiple aleurone layers (see also Nelson and Chang, 1974).

Around the periphery of this region, a number of races share similar kernel coloring and/or ear shape with the Coroico types described above. Whether these features indicate genetic relationships remains to be ascertained, but the combination of geographic proximity and phenotypic similarity is suggestive. Several of these peripheral races are grouped together in the upper right of Fig. 2–5. The following races all appear to share their kernel coloring and texture with the Coroicos: Cacao and Cariaco from Colombia and Venezuela, Candela from Ecuador, Cabuya from Colombia, Morotí and Pojoso Chico from Brazil, Bolivia, Paraguay, and perhaps Marañon from Peru.

Sympatric with the Coroicos, but apparently much more limited in distribution is Enano (Fig. 2–5), a popcorn with dull, ivory-to-sand-colored kernels, short, tapering ears, strongly attached shanks, and stiff plants with erect leaves and tassel branches. The relationship between the two racial types is uncertain, but some collections of Enano approach the smaller collections of Coroico Blanco in ear size and shape.

Two types of genetic markers studied in these materials (chromosome knobs and presence of paramutable *R* alleles) present somewhat conflicting evidence for these races. With a few exceptions (Cacao, Rienda, possibly Cariaco, Montaña, and Amagaceño), these races basically have an "Andean" knob pattern with a medium to small knob in the long arm

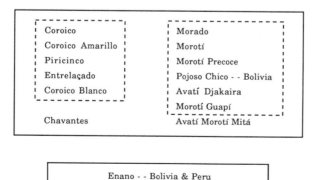

Fig. 2–5. Racial relationships of the corn of the Amazon basin and surrounding lowlands.

of the chromosome 7 and a small or no knob at the lower position on the long arm of chromosome 6 (Roberts et al., 1957; Grobman et al., 1961). Other knobs are rare (McClintock, 1959). On the other hand, the limited evidence accumulated by Van der Walt and Brink (1969) suggests that at least some of these materials (Entrelaçado, possibly Cariaco) have paramutable *R* alleles, rather than the nonparamutable *R* alleles typical of Andean maize.

2-5.3 Lowland Southern South America

Eastern and southern South America is characterized by a group of white (Cristal and Cristal Sulino from Brazil, Paraguay, Uruguay, and Argentina; Perola from Bolivia; Curagua Grande from Chile) and yellow or orange (Cateto and Cateto Sulino from Brazil, Bolivia, Uruguay, and Argentina; Cristalino and Camelia from Chile) flints with cylindrical to tapering, medium-sized ears (Fig. 2–6). In addition, floury variants of the Coroico complex (Morotí from Brazil and Paraguay; Pojoso Chico from

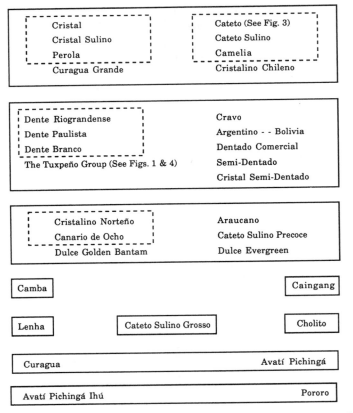

Fig. 2–6. Racial relationships of the corn of lowland southern South America.

Bolivia) discussed above were spread as far south as northern Argentina by the Guaraní Indians.

In recent years, introduction of U.S., Mexican, and Caribbean dents has resulted in a number of dent and semident races (Fig. 2–6) of hybrid origin (the dents of southern Brazil; Cubano Dentado and Argentino from Bolivia; Dentado Comerical from Chile). It also appears that flints from the northern part of the USA were introduced into both Chile (Cristalino Norteño, Araucano) and Argentina (Canario de Ocho). Similarly, U.S. sweet corns were collected and described in Chile (Timothy et al., 1961).

Several distinct floury races (Camba, a large, tapering white dent from Bolivia; Caingang, a long-eared, cylindrical, white dent from Brazil; Cholito, a short-eared, cylindrical to tapering, predominantly white dent segregating for purple or dotted aleurone, from Bolivia; Lenha, a stubby-eared, white-kernelled race with soft cobs, from Brazil) are found along the northern edge of the region. (Fig. 2–6). Cateto Sulino Grosso from Uruguay is quite unlike most of the Catetos. It has thick ears with high row numbers, sharing its ear shape with Lenha and Cravo, both found in southern Brazil, and Cateto Nortista (a variant of coastal Tropical Flint) from the Guianas.

Several cigar-shaped popcorn (Fig. 2–6) races (Avatí Pichingá Ihú from Brazil and Paraguay; Pororo from Bolivia) with predominantly white, rounded kernels (sometimes with red pericarp) are scattered throughout the region. Neighboring races with predominantly white, pointed kernels and more conical ear shape (Avatí Pichingá from Brazil and Paraguay; Curagua from Chile) may be related to higher altitude Andean pointed popcorns (see section 2–5.5). These races tend to have multiple ears, flag leaves, and several tillers.

2–5.4 The Andean Region

The geographic diversity found in the region and the isolation imposed by the terrain has, in conjunction with trading and migration, resulted in a diverse set of mostly interrelated corn races. Figure 2–7 illustrates the sort of variation that is most commonly encountered in mid- to high-altitude Andean corn. Sabanero from Venezuela, Colombia, Ecuador, and Peru and, to a lesser extent, Morocho from Peru are races that are central to a number of clines of variation throughout the north Andean region. Sabanero is a tapering, conical-eared flint or flour race with an enlarged base. It typically has large yellow kernels, but both white and colored forms are common. Morocho Cajabambino has smaller kernels and higher row numbers.

Pollo from Venezuela and Colombia, and Patillo and Kcello from Ecuador (Fig. 2–7) have smaller ears than does Sabanero (see above). These small-eared flints have relatively large, rounded kernels.

Cacao from Colombia and Venezuela appears to be a brown or bronze variant of floury Sabanero (Fig. 2–7). Cabuya from Colombia and Huan-

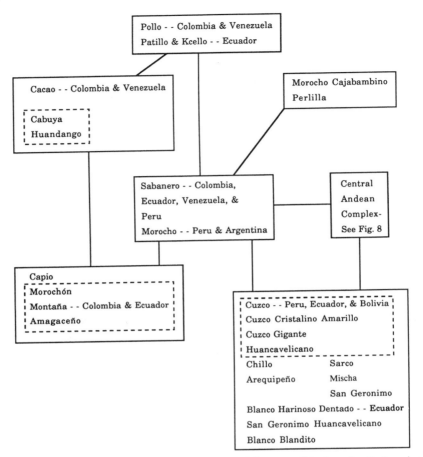

Fig. 2–7. Racial relationships of the major portion of the corn of Andean South America. Lines joining cells indicate closer relationships (often essentially continuous gradients) between racial groups.

dango from Ecuador tend to have lower row numbers than Sabanero; Huandango especially seems to lack the enlarged ear base and conical shape common to Sabanero. Both Cabuya and Huandango appear to share common aleurone coloration with Cacao [and with the lowland Colombian and Venezuelan race Cariaco (discussed in section 2–5.1) as well (Mangelsdorf, 1974)].

Montaña from Colombia and Ecuador, Morochón from Ecuador, and Amagaceño from Colombia have larger (especially longer) ears than Sabanero. Capio from Colombia seems to be essentially a floury form of the Montañas.

In the Central Andes, the Cuzcos from Peru, Ecuador, and Bolivia; Huancavelicano and Arequipeño from Peru; and Blanco Harinoso Dentado and Blanco Blandito from Ecuador (Fig. 2–7) generally have wider, more floury kernels and lower row numbers than Sabanero. These races appear to have been spread northward as a consequence of the agriculture of the Incas and/or their predecessors. The Huancavelicano kernels are pointed as are the kernels of Chillo and Mishca from Ecuador, which may be yellow, floury variants of the same group.

Most of the races of the Central Andean complex in Fig. 2–8 basically have grenade-shaped ears, the size of which varies inversely with the altitude to which they are adapted. Plant height follows a similar pattern. Additional distinctions among these races are based upon kernel coloring (Kulli from Bolivia, Racimo de Uva from Ecuador, and Morado Canteño and Kculli from Peru are essentially black; Piscorrunto from Peru and Checchi from Bolivia are speckled); row numbering (the Chulpis, Capia from Argentina, Paro from Peru, etc., tend to have high row numbers); or combinations of these two features with geographic distribution and kernel shape and texture.

In Fig. 2–8 the races are divided, perhaps somewhat artificially, into four groups. The second group from the top consists of races having relatively low row numbers (and often highly colored kernels). The third group consists largely of those races having high row numbers. This group includes essentially all of the indigenous South American sweet corns

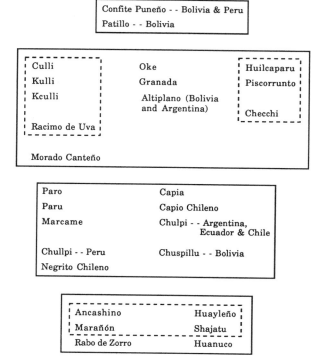

Fig. 2–8. Racial relationships of the corn of the Central Andean Complex.

(the various Chulpi, Chullpi, and Chuspillu races from Ecuador, Chile, and Argentina; Peru; and Bolivia, respectively). The bottom group has larger ears, often with larger kernels, than the groups above it in Fig. 2–8. The races with larger ears are usually later in maturity and adapted to lower elevations than the other groups in the figure. The upper group consists of the high-altitude races Patillo from Bolivia and Confite Puneño from Bolivia and Peru. The latter are adapted to altitudes of about 3.50 km above sea level. They are probably ecologically specialized relatives of the third group in Fig. 2–8, having reduced ear and plant size as a result of their adaptation to extremely high elevations. Some of the collections having low row numbers, however, may be more closely related to members of either the second group in Fig. 2–8 or to the Uchuquilla group of 8- to 10-rowed flints to be described next.

Ancestral races for two of Mangelsdorf's (1974) postulated lineage relationships are included in Fig. 2–8. Mangelsdorf suggests (based mostly on ear shape, row number, and the deleterious nature of the *su* locus) that most, if not all, sweet corns trace their source of the *su* gene to the Andean Chulpi. While the argument weakens as the distance from the Andes increases, it appears to hold for most of the indigenous South American sweet corns. He also suggests that many of the races possessing dark red pericarp and/or bronze, orange, or brown aleurone in addition to floury endosperm are descended from Kculli of Peru.

A group of 8- to 10-rowed, knobby-kernelled flints (Fig. 2–9) is found in southern Peru and Bolivia in the east central Andes. Representative

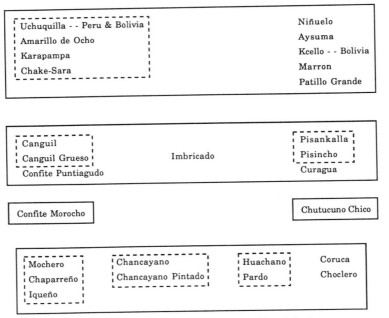

Fig. 2–9. Racial relationships among some additional Andean races.

races include Uchuquilla from Peru and Bolivia, and Karapampa, Chake-Sara, Patillo Grande, and Kcello from Bolivia. Aysuma, Niñuelo, and some of the Patillo-Confite Puneño types from Bolivia also seem to belong to or intergrade into this group. All tend to have broad, flat, flinty kernels that easily shell off the rather narrow cobs.

Two Andean popcorns with white, pointed kernels, Canguil from Ecuador and Confite Puntiagudo from Peru, have ears that are similar to those of Pisankalla and Pisincho of Bolivia and Argentina (Fig. 2–9). The Colombian-pointed popcorn Imbricado also appears to be related to these races (as does the Chilean popcorn, Curagua), but Imbricado often has large kernels similar in size to the flinty Sabaneros (Fig. 2–7 and adjacent text). Both McClintock (1960) and Mangelsdorf (1974) present evidence that at least some of these Andean pointed popcorns are related to similar Mexican materials.

A third Andean popcorn, Confite Morocho of central Peru (Fig. 2–9), has yellow kernels, often arranged in eight rows on a thin cob. It has been hypothesized to be a primitive ancestor to a number of more productive races (Grobman et al., 1961). In what appears to be Mangelsdorf's (1974) most speculative lineage, Confite Morocho is regarded as the ancestral race of a lineage leading to Harinoso de Ocho of Mexico and the Northern Flints of the USA, the so-called "Maíz de Ocho" of Galinat and Gunnerson (1963). Chutucuno Chico, a small, yellow, pearl popcorn from Chile appears to be distinct.

At lower elevations along the west coast, a series of small-eared, early, mostly white, floury corns (Fig. 2–9) is often found. These include races such as Mochero, Chaparreño, and Huachano from Peru. Large-eared Chancayano from Peru also appears to belong with this group, but several collections of this race may also have Caribbean flint germ plasm.

With only a few exceptions (the Montañas, Amagaceño, Capio, possibly Pollo, Pisankalla, and Canguil, and especially Cacao) the races included in Fig. 2–7, 2–8, and 2–9 basically appear to have the "Andean" chromosome knob pattern described on the basis of McClintock's work (Ramírez et al., 1960). In addition, the results obtained by Van der Walt and Brink (1969) suggest that Andean corn is also unique in possessing nonparamutable R alleles.

2–6 RACES OF THE USA

Unlike that of most other countries, much of the indigenous corn of the USA was replaced by hybrids prior to the implementation of an organized program of germplasm preservation.

A significant factor in the success of hybrid corn was the availability of highly selected, adapted varieties as sources of the first inbred lines. Many of these varieties had undergone selection for almost a century in the hands of intelligent and ingenious farmers. Progress in population improvement by Robert and James Reid, Isaac Hershey, George Krug,

Chester Leaming, and others gave the early U.S. developers of hybrid corn a source of elite germ plasm not duplicated elsewhere in the world.

Unfortunately, after usable inbred lines were developed, these original sources of germ plasm were largely ignored. Even less attention was given to the numerous Indian varieties and minor land races found outside the central Corn Belt. Consequently, when, at a later date, interest developed in preserving the corn germ plasm of the USA, much of it had long since disappeared.

The literature, beginning with *The History and Present State of Virginia* (Beverly, 1705), contains descriptions of numerous varieties of corn found in specified geographic areas of the USA. Among the more comprehensive treatments are those of Atkinson and Wilson (1914), Will and Hyde (1917), Carter and Anderson (1945), and Brown and Anderson (1947, 1948). Yet, to date, there have been no attempts to identify all of the major races of corn known to have existed in this country prior to the advent of hybrid corn. While much of this germ plasm has disappeared from cultivation, some of it is still available, albeit frequently in a modified form, in germplasm banks, breeder's collections, etc.

The bulk of U.S. corn, exclusive of popcorn and sweet corn, can be assigned to 1 of 10 broad racial complexes (Fig. 2–10) as follows:

  1. Northern Flints and Flours.
  2. Great Plains Flints and Flours.
  3. Pima-Papago.
  4. Southwestern Semidents.
  5. Southwestern 12 Row.
  6. Southeastern Flours.

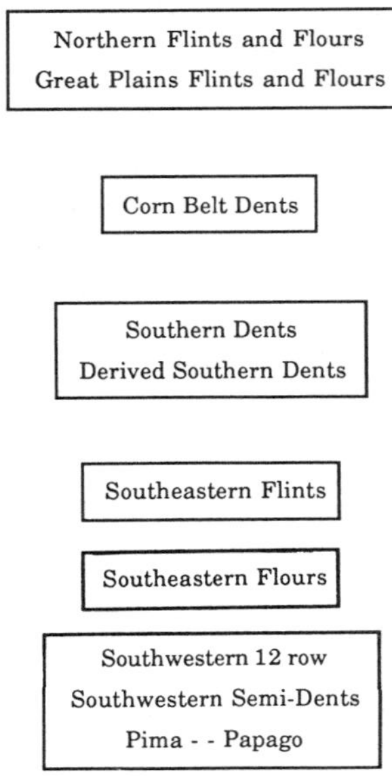

Fig. 2–10. Racial relationships of U.S. corn.

7. Southern Dents.
8. Derived Southern Dents.
9. Southeastern Flints.
10. Corn Belt Dents.

There is considerable variation within each of these racial groups, yet to split them into additional entities seems unjustified on the basis of present knowledge.

2–6.1   Northern Flints

The Northern Flints, which also include floury endosperm types, are characterized by ears possessing 8 to 10 rows of crescent-shaped kernels; relatively short, highly tillered, frequently two-eared plants with narrow leaves, well-developed husk-leaf blades, and slender culms. The ear shanks tend to be both long and thick, and the ears are frequently enlarged at the base.

The Northern Flints were, until the early 1800s, the dominant type of corn of eastern North America. Detailed descriptions, illustrations, and the geographic distribution of this racial complex have been given by Brown and Anderson (1947).

Based on the archaeological record, it has been assumed that the Northern Flints and Flours reached as far south as the southern Appalachians in preColombian times (Brown and Anderson, 1947). A recent study of Cherokee Flour corn suggests that this assumption may be in error and that archaeological collections from the southern Appalachians may represent Cherokee Flour corn rather than Northern Flints and Flours. The former is derived from Harinoso de Ocho of northwestern Mexico and, except for kernel phenotype, is quite distinct from Northern Flints and Flours. Unfortunately, the phenotypes of the carbonized kernels of the two are indistinguishable.

The origin of the Northern Flints is still unclear. Galinat and Gunnerson (1963) trace the eight-rowed flint and flour corn of North America to the Mexican race Harinoso de Ocho. Yet, the only important trait the two races seem to have in common are eight rows of kernels. Mangelsdorf and Reeves (1939) suggested the Northern Flints reached eastern North America from the southwestern USA where corns with similar ear types are found. The latter, derived primarily from western Mexico and from the Central Mesa of Mexico, differ from the Northern Flints in several traits including internode and chromosome knob patterns. Most southwestern U.S. corns possess many knobs in contrast to the knobless or nearly knobless Northern Flints (Longley, 1938; McClintock, et al., 1981).

Races which are quite similar in ear morphology to the Northern Flints are found in the highlands of Guatemala (Brown and Anderson, 1947). Within the races San Marceño and Serrano, from highland Guatemala, ear types are found that are quite similar to the Northern Flints. These are eight-rowed ears with crescent-shaped, flint kernels and distinctly enlarged butts. In contrast, Harinoso de Ocho typically possesses flat-topped kernels, distinct husk striations, and compressed butts. However, the route or routes by which these Guatemalan materials may have reached eastern North America is not clear, if indeed they do represent the origin of this race.

Mangelsdorf (1974) has postulated that Confite Morocho, an Andean popcorn of Peru, is ancestral to the Northern Flints, as well as to Harinoso de Ocho of Mexico. Although interesting, this hypothesis appears to be based on weak evidence.

The role of the Northern Flints in the evolution of Corn Belt Dents has been described in detail by Anderson and Brown (1952) and Wallace and Brown (1956). The mixing of Northern Flints with the later, higher-yielding dents of the South by Colonial farmers resulted in a new race that later completely dominated the corn-producing areas of the USA.

Some of the common varieties of Northern Flints and Flours are Longfellow, Dutton, Smut Nose, Canada Flint, Mammouth Yellow, Wilbur's Flint, Parker's Flint, Thompson Flint, New England Flint, and New York Council Flour Corn.

2–6.2 Great Plains Flints and Flours

Whereas practically all the corn found east of the Mississippi and north of Virginia in pre-Colonial times was typical Northern Flint, that found in the Northern Great Plains was much more variable. The flints and flours of this region are obviously related to the Northern Flints. Many of the varieties suggest mixtures between Northern Flints and varieties from the American Southwest. Apparently this mixing is not recent, because specimens from three village sites in South Dakota thought to have been occupied in the mid-1400s also show evidence of similar mixing (Cutler and Agogino, 1960).

Although much of this corn has 8- to 10-rowed ears and wide, crescent-shaped kernels, the frequency of 12- to 14-rowed ears with small, square kernels is much higher than that found east of the Mississippi. Also, the Great Plains Flints and Flours have shorter and more highly tillered plants and shorter tassel branches than do the Northern Flints. They also have a larger number of chromosome knobs than the Northern Flints, although the range of chromosome knob numbers in the two races overlap.

One of the best descriptions of the Great Plains Flints and Flours is that of Will and Hyde (1917). These authors describe a large number of Indian varieties in considerable detail and also give a wealth of information on corn culture by the various tribes, the uses of corn as food, and the place of corn in the Indian ceremonial organization.

Among the more important varieties included in this racial complex are Pawnee White, Mandan Yellow Flour, Arikara Flints, Rhee Flint, Omaha Flour, Otoe White Flour, Ponca Red Flour, Winnebago White, Winnebago Blue, Gehu, Assiniboine, Dakota Squaw, and Santee.

2–6.3   Pima-Papago

Because of the archaeological and ethnological interest in the southwestern USA, corn of the area has been extensively collected. Both prehistoric and modern cultivars are reasonably well represented in museum collections, yet only a small part of the historic corn of the area is still available in viable form.

Corn of the southwestern USA has apparently undergone a complicated history and includes germ plasm and mixtures of germ plasm from at least three geographic areas.

Apparently, one of the earliest types of corn in the area was that of the prehistoric "Basketmakers" (Carter and Anderson, 1945). Some of the modern varieties showing strong Basketmaker influence have been designated Pima-Papago by Anderson and Cutler (1942). This race is characterized by ears which are strongly compressed at the base and which gently taper from a subbasal position to the tip. Row numbers range from 10 to 16, with 10 rows being most common (Carter, 1945). The tessellate kernels frequently exhibit strong husk striation. The ears are small (about 12 cm in length and 2.5 cm in diameter).

Endosperm can be either flinty or floury, with the latter being more frequent. Plants usually possess two or more well-developed tillers. Leaves are narrow and the leaf sheaths frequently exhibit purple anthocyanin coloration. Tassels are not particularly distinctive compared with other southwestern U.S. races. The race is most frequently found among the corn of the Pima, Papago, and Yuma tribes (Carter and Anderson, 1945) and is also represented by the var. Kokoma of the Hopi (Brown et al., 1952).

Pima-Papago or its progenitor probably reached the American Southwest from western Mexico where similar types (Chapalote, Reventador) are still grown. When or how it migrated to southwestern USA is still not clear. Mangelsdorf (1954, 1974) has suggested that Chapalote reached New Mexico (Bat Cave) as early as 1500 B.C. Pima-Papago, while undoubtedly related to prehistoric Chapalote, has apparently undergone considerable introgression with other races (Galinat and Gunnerson, 1963). Cutler and Blake (1988) suggest that a form of Pima-Papago spread eastward through Oklahoma and Arkansas and up the Mississippi River to northern Illinois by 100 A.D., and to the Gulf Coast of Georgia even earlier.

2–6.4   Southwestern Semidents

This racial complex is apparently the product of the introgression of Tuxpeño-type dent germ plasm from Mexico into the typical 12- to 14-row flint and flour corns of the area. Except for a slight degree of denting, higher number of kernel rows, and more pronounced tassel condensation, the racial complex is quite similar to the Southwestern 12 Row described later. While we have indicated the genes for denting found in Southwestern Semidents probably came from Mexico, the source could have been the Northern Periphery (central and northern Utah, western Colorado) where prehistoric dents have been found (Carter, 1945; Anderson, 1959, n.d.).

Although we feel Southwestern Semidents merit a racial recognition, our experience suggests that such material is not recognized as a distinct variety by the tribes who grow it. As an example, typical ears of this race are usually present in collections of Hopi White Flour corn. Yet, to our knowledge, the Hopi, who place considerable emphasis on maintaining varietal purity, make no effort to separate the semident and flour forms of their white corn.

For an excellent illustration of Southwestern Semident, the reader is referred to Plate 3 of Carter and Anderson (1945). Those authors suggest that this race is found at highest frequency near the four corners region of the states of Arizona, New Mexico, Colorado, and Utah.

2–6.5   Southwestern 12 Row

This race of southwestern corn is synonymous with the Eastern Complex of Carter and Anderson (1945). Although these corns are morphologically similar to the Northern Flints of eastern North America, they differ in several important traits. Furthermore, the name Eastern Complex implies an eastern origin, which is questionable.

The plants are short (105–120 cm), highly tillered, and the tassels are characterized by long central spikes that average >30 cm in length. The ears are usually enlarged at the base and are attached to large, indurated shanks. The kernels are wide (though not as strongly crescent-shaped as the Northern Flints) and are arranged in long straight rows. Endosperm is either flinty or floury. Row numbers are usually 12 to 14.

As indicated by Carter and Anderson (1945), Southwestern 12 Row corn is more prevalent among the easternmost Pueblos (mostly east of the Rio Grande River of central New Mexico) than among those in the westernmost part of the area. This lends some credence to the notion that this kind of corn germ plasm reached the Southwest from the East, rather than having migrated from the Southwest to the East.

The morphological similarities between Southwestern 12 row and Northern Flints are great, suggesting a common origin or at least a close phylogenetic relationship. Yet, the two races differ markedly in two important traits, that of number of kernel rows and chromosome knob numbers and pattern. The Northern Flints possess few knobs. Many varieties are knobless and only a few varieties are known to possess as many as four to five knobs. In contrast, corn of the southwestern USA, including the Southwestern 12 Row, has many knobs (Longley, 1938; Brown, 1949). Furthermore, the chromosome knob patterns characterizing the Northern Flints and the Southwestern 12 Row are distinctly different (McClintock, et al., 1981).

2–6.6 Southern Dents

This racial complex, prior to its replacement by hybrids, was concentrated in the southeastern USA. In Colonial times, it reached as far north as northern Virginia and Maryland. The western limits of its distribution are not clear, yet it is known to have been present in central Texas.

The Southern Dent complex was described and illustrated by Brown and Anderson (1948). The plants are consistently taller than other U.S. races. Internodes are condensed above the ear in contrast to the long upper internodes of the Northern and Great Plains Flints. Ears are enveloped in many tight, thick husks, which are usually without flag leaves. The plants are usually without tillers. Tassels are highly branched and condensed in contrast to the sparsely branched, noncondensed tassels of the Northern Flints. Numbers of rows of kernels are variable, ranging from 8 to 10 rows in the var. Hickory King to 24 to 26 rows in some selections of Gourdseed. Kernels are usually well dented and endosperm color is usually white.

Many varieties of Southern Dents appear to be closely related to the Mexican dent Tuxpeño. Shoepeg is much like Pepitilla, and Hickory King is quite similar to Tabloncillo and Olotillo. Consequently, certain of the Southern Dents seem simply to be northern counterparts of Mexican races still prevalent in Mexico. The time at which these corns reached the southern USA is still unknown and so are the route or routes by which they migrated northward and eastward from Mexico. We know they were widely grown in southern and southeastern USA in Colonial times, but little is known of their pre-Colombian history. That they provided at least one-half of the parentage of the more recently evolved Corn Belt Dents is well documented (Brown and Anderson, 1948; Anderson and Brown, 1952; Doebley et al., 1988).

Some of the better known varieties of Southern Dents are Gourdseed, Shoepeg, Tuxpan, Hickory King, Jellicorse, and Mexican June.

2–6.7 Southeastern Flints and Flours

This complex consists of two subraces, the Caribbean Flints and Cherokee Flour Corn. Caribbean Flints are a Northern extension of similar corn from the West Indian islands and eastern South America. The names usually applied to this race in the Southeast are Creole Flint, Cuban Flint, Spanish, St. Antoine, and Jarvis Golden Prolific. The latter is a modified form of Creole Flint that has introgressed with an unknown dent. Morphologically, the race is similar to Cuban Flint or to the Catetos of Argentina, Uruguay, and Brazil. The ears, consisting of 12 to 14 rows of kernels, are slightly compressed at the base and gently tapered toward the tip. Cobs are usually white; the kernels are flinty, and endosperm color varies from deep yellow to orange.

Cherokee Flour is an 8- to 10-rowed, white flour corn whose current distribution is limited to the Reservation of the Eastern Bank of the Cherokee at Qualla (Cherokee), NC. This race has been selected over a period of several centuries by the Cherokee and is still the primary source of corn meal and corn flour for these people. There is no evidence to indicate that this corn has ever been adopted and cultivated by the non-Indian farmers of the southern Appalachians.

Cherokee Flour produces tall, high-eared, late-maturing plants. Typically, the plants have few, if any, tillers. Tassels are variable, ranging form those with many short, upright secondary branches subtending a short central spike to others with relatively few long, horizontal to drooping, secondary branches and long central spikes. Ears ranging in length from 18 to 26 cm are attached by relatively short shanks of modest diameter. Ears consist of 8 to 10 straight rows of wide, crescent-shaped kernels consisting of soft, floury endosperm.

2–6.8   Derived Southern Dents

This complex, although closely related to the Southern Dents, has apparently arisen through the hybridization of the latter with other races. The gross morphology of the ears and plants of the Derived Southern Dents suggests that, in addition to Southern Dents, at least two other races may be involved in the ancestry of this complex. These are the Southeastern Flints and Corn Belt Dents.

The Derived Southern Dents tend, on the average, to have somewhat less dented kernels, to have fewer chromosome knobs, and to be more prolific than the Southern Dents. Some varieties have many traits in common with the Southeastern Flints and others suggest admixture with Corn Belt Dents. As a group, the Derived Southern Dents represent the primary source of the genes for prolificacy present in southern corn which has found its way into many modern hybrids grown in that area.

A number of the more prominent varieties of Derived Southern Dents are Caraway's Prolific, Giant Yellow Dent, Horsetooth, Latham's Double, Mosby's Prolific, Neal's Paymaster, Southern Snowflake, and Whatley's Prolific.

2–6.9   Corn Belt Dents

This racial complex dominated the major areas of corn production in the USA for more than half a century preceding the advent of hybrid corn. Although variable, the race is a well-defined entity and easily distinguished from other types of North American corn. The ears are slightly tapered or cylindrical and consist of 14 to 22 straight rows of kernels that are distinctly dented at the tip. Cobs are usually red in color, although white cob varieties are known. Yellow endosperm is predominant, but included in the race are a number of white endosperm varieties. The plant typically has a single stem with strong arching leaves and a heavy, many-branched tassel.

The Corn Belt Dents are of recent origin, having arisen in the 19th century in the eastern part of the U.S. Corn Belt. They are largely the product of crosses of white Southern Dents with long-eared Northern Flints of eastern USA. The historical literature is quite clear as to how Corn Belt Dents were developed. Some of the mixing of Southern Dents with Northern Flints was, undoubtedly, accidental and occurred when fields with poor stands of Southern Dents were partially replanted with early flints. However, much of it was the result of deliberate, controlled hybridizing on the part of Colonial farmers who recognized and documented the superior yield of the hybrid populations (Anderson and Brown, 1952; Wallace and Brown, 1956).

Even though Corn Belt Dents did not exist prior to the 19th century, they have provided the basic germ plasm for virtually all of the corn now produced in the USA as well as in most other temperate regions of the world. Their contribution, therefore, to total corn production in the world is unparalleled.

Hundreds of varieties of Corn Belt Dents have been described, most of which, unfortunately, have long since disappeared. A few of the more prominent varieties were Reid's Yellow Dent, Lancaster Sure Crop, Krug Yellow Dent, Boone County White, Leaming, Osterland Yellow Dent, and Midland Yellow Dent.

2–6.10 Excluded Races

As indicated earlier, no attempt has been made in this brief treatment of U.S. corn to include the various sweet corns and popcorns. To date, we have not had an opportunity to study these two types of corn sufficiently to feel confident in assigning them to meaningful racial groups. Many of the sweet corns of the USA are simply sugary counterparts of Northern Flints or higher-row-number dents (Galinat, 1971). These two types, which encompass most of the Bantam and Evergreen varieties, and a third type, Country Gentleman, comprise the bulk of U.S. sweet corn. Yet, there are other older sorts that do not fit these categories, among which are the sweet corns of the Southwestern Indians.

The U.S. popcorns are far more complex than the U.S. flint, flour, and dent corns and will require much more study before their relationships are understood.

In addition to popcorn and sweet corn, we have excluded two other corn groups—the existence of which we should at least recognize. These are the corns of the Seminole of Florida and the "tamale" corns of southern California. The Seminole corns are quite distinct from the flints and flours of the northeastern USA. But here again, our experience with these corns does not permit us to attempt to classify them. Neither have the tamale corns of the southern West Coast of the USA been studied in detail, yet these appear to represent northern counterparts of western Mexican varieties, which probably reached southern California by way of Arizona.

2-7 EFFECTIVE SOURCES OF GERM PLASM AMONG LOWLAND TROPICAL RACES

Among the collections of corn germ plasm of the Western Hemisphere now existing in the various seed banks, there is undoubtedly much material that should be useful to the breeder. However, to date, little of this material has been systematically evaluated with respect to its usefulness. It is primarily for this reason that breeders have not made full use of the germ plasm that is available. Most breeding programs are operated in such a way as to make impractical for the individual breeder the screening of vast numbers of accessions in order to identify the few genotypes of interest or value at the moment.

A major problem encountered in evaluating tropical materials for possible use in temperate regions is the late maturity that these materials often exhibit. One reason for this is that almost all corn flowers more rapidly under short-day growing conditions given equivalent temperatures. Tropical varieties adapted to 12- to 13-h daylengths flower much later under the longer days typical of temperate regions. It is for this reason that use of these materials in the USA has generally either been confined to the South or limited to very early (hence inherently low yielding) types such as Zapalote Chico of Mexico.

While extreme response to daylength is probably fairly simply inherited, it effectively blocks most evaluation of tropical materials in temperate regions. For example, most collections of the closely related races Tuxpeño and Vandeño have about equally late maturity under temperate, long-day conditions. However, most typical Tuxpeño collections from Mexico are later than Vandeño collections under short-day conditions; and, thus, Tuxpeño is probably less adaptable for use in temperate regions despite its favorable yield potential. The daylength response may totally mask the true maturity of the material. One collection of Pepitilla flowers in <65 short d (south Florida, winter) while requiring about 150 long days (North Carolina, summer). (A widely used, adapted commercial hybrid flowers in about 75 and 77 d, respectively, under the same conditions.)

Such responses to daylength suggest that the degrees of apparent adaptation of tropical materials to a temperate environment are probably negatively correlated (if correlated at all) with their breeding potentials for that region. This conflicts with the conclusions reached by Kramer and Ullstrup (1959), although their data can be interpreted to support this viewpoint. They showed that yields of topcrosses of semiadapted exotics onto adapted materials were closely correlated with maturity. In fact, almost all exotics offering potential yield improvement are late maturing under U.S. conditions (regardless of their maturities in the tropics), while a number of low-yielding exotics (often popcorns) are much earlier. Thus, such a correlation of exotic topcross yields with later maturity would be expected for both developmental and genetic reasons.

Some recent work (Gerrish, 1980, 1983; Goodman, 1985a; Holley and Goodman, 1988) suggests that adaptation of tropical materials to long-day temperate conditions is possible, even while retaining 90 to 100% tropical or semitropical germ plasm. Once elite materials have been converted to eliminate extreme daylength sensitivity, incorporation into either temperate or subtropical breeding programs should be greatly facilitated (Brewbaker, 1985; Salamini, 1985; FAO, 1985).

Limited published work with synthetics in the USA adds support for the view that "preadapted" tropical materials (i.e., those that are very early in the tropics) are not good candidates for yield improvement in temperate regions. Troyer and Brown (1972) have shown that a synthetic involving the early maturing Mexican races Zapalote Chico and Zapalote Grande initially outyielded two other synthetics involving other, later Mexican materials and West Indies materials, respectively. (These synthetics also included germ plasm from elite U.S. inbreds.) Selection for earliness in all three composites appears to have lowered the yield of the Zapalote Chico synthetic to the point where the other synthetics (involving late Mexican and West Indian materials) have higher yields. In contrast, Hallauer and Sears (1972) (also Hallauer, 1978) have shown that late-maturing but variable tropical materials—in this case ETO, a synthetic described later—can effectively be selected for much earlier maturity and lower ear height, using relatively few cycles of mass selection or by a single generation of crossing with early maturing elite lines. In addition, Eberhart (1971) and Hallauer (1972) have shown that several synthetics containing large proportions of tropical germ plasm (which in itself would largely be poorly adapted) do show promise as source materials for breeding programs in the USA.

A second major problem often encountered in the use of tropical germ plasm in temperate regions is the propensity for derivatives of exotic by adapted crosses to undergo severe inbreeding depression (Hallauer, 1978). Little published data often result from such experiments, but virtually every breeder who has seriously attempted to utilize much exotic germ plasm has encountered the problem. For this reason, Goodman (1985a) and Holley and Goodman (1988) have suggested use of tropical hybrids as sources of breeding materials, on the premise that the component lines of such hybrids have undergone at least some inbreeding.

Much work with exotics has been conducted with composites or synthetics, whose ancestry often cannot be clearly traced. While this work has apparently been successful, we have learned less from it than from earlier corn breeding efforts with open-pollinated varieties. In the earlier work, specific sources (such as the varieties Lancaster and Reid's) of successful inbred lines were fairly quickly identified. Such identification has occurred to a lesser extent with the exotic races, in part due to the emphasis on synthetics (Wellhausen, 1978). A notable recent exception is the outstanding work done in Nigeria by Kim et al. (1985) who have incorporated outstanding disease resistance (Buddenhagen, 1985) and identified both tropical × tropical and temperate × tropical heterotic combinations.

Despite the lack of a systematic evaluation of the so-called *exotic* corn germ plasm, some information has been obtained on the relative usefulness in breeding of a number of races, varieties, composites, etc. Furthermore, there is considerable work currently underway attempting to systematically evaluate the Latin American races and accessions of corn (Stuber, 1978, 1986, and unpublished; Goodman, 1983, 1985; Goodman and Castillo, 1984; Castillo, 1987; Quentin Jones cited in Smith and Duvick, 1988). If FAO (1985) recommendations are followed, much more rapid progress should be possible. We have attempted to summarize the accessible published information below; much, of course, remains unpublished.

Wellhausen (1965) has reported on the yield potential of a number of Mexican and Caribbean races and populations which he feels merit additional use in breeding. Considerable information on yields of Mexican races comes from the results of a yield test of all possible crosses of 25 races of Mexico. This test was conducted near Celaya in Central Mexico. The interracial crosses were compared with an adapted hybrid, H352. Sixteen of the interracial crosses yielded more than the check hybrid. More importantly, 15 different races were represented among the 16 highest yielding interracial crosses. Among the highest yielding crosses were Pepitilla × Chalqueño, Pepitilla × Tuxpeño, Maíz Dulce × Comiteco, Comiteco × Celaya, and Pepitilla × Maíz Dulce.

The data reported by Wellhausen (1965) did not include many important agronomic traits, and, for this reason, it is not possible to assess from these data the practical usefulness of this obviously high-yielding germ plasm. (Chalqueño and Pepitilla have weak roots, while Tuxpeño and Comiteco tend to have late maturity even when grown under short-day conditions.) However, such work is fairly typical of what needs to be done in many tropical regions; wide-scale testing of crosses among a diverse set of materials. For example, Darrah et al. (1972) found that crosses between a local Kenyan variety and a collection of the Ecuadorian race Montaña were suitable for production as one of Kenya's first hybrids. Similarly, in Brazil, Paterniani (1970, 1972) has reported that intervarietal and topcross hybrids involving Caribbean germ plasm (mostly Cuban and Caribbean Tropical Flints) with Tuxpeño derivatives outyield the local H6999B double cross check by as much as 20% with improved agronomic traits as a bonus.

Among the Caribbean germ plasm evaluated by Wellhausen (1965), a collection belonging to the race Tusón and designated Antigua 2D and a composite of collections called Antigua Group 2 have been shown to combine well with Tuxeño and with Corn Belt Dents. This material is relatively early and short in stature as compared to most other tropical varieties.

The Cuban Flints are reported by Wellhausen (1965) to combine well with the Mexican dents, especially Tuxeño. Timothy (1963) reported that the Cuban Flints have been widely used in Colombian corn breeding programs along with Tuxeño, Costeño, Puya Grande, and the synthetics ETO and Venezuela I, discussed later.

Our experience in tropical corn breeding supports, in general, Wellhausen and Timothy's conclusions relative to the usefulness of the germ plasm discussed above. [We might note that the evaluation of germplasm utility would be greatly facilitated if a program such as the former International Maize Adaptation Nurseries (IMAN) program (CIMMYT 1972a, 1972b, 1974) were expanded and publicized. Those trials included materials from 13 countries tested in 47 countries in 1971. Outstanding materials in the 1970 trials were from Australia, Jamaica, Kenya, Brazil, Mexico, and Peru.] The sections that follow include additional observations relative to the performance of the races mentioned earlier and refer also to other sources of germ plasm which we believe to be of interest.

2–7.1 Mexican Dents

The most outstanding single source of Mexican Dents is the race Tuxeño. This race, widely distributed on the east coast of Mexico, possesses excellent combining ability, good stalk quality, and good resistance to *Bipolaris* spp. Its principal disadvantages are late maturity, tall plants with high ear placement, poor roots, and susceptibility to sugarcane mosaic.

There are several derivatives of Tuxeño, both white and yellow. Some of these have given excellent performance in crosses with lines derived from Coastal Tropical Flint and Tusón. Some Tuxeño lines have also exhibited good combining ability with material derived from Cuban Flint and the var. Tiquisate, Mayorbela, and Venezuela I described later.

One of the major faults of Tuxeño is its excessive height which encourages lodging. A much shorter selection, Tuxeñito, developed by Dr. Elmer Johnson has much more acceptable plant height and is reported to yield about as well as Tuxeño of normal height.

Tuxeño germ plasm is now widespread throughout the tropical world and is an important constituent of many improved varieties and hybrids.

2–7.2 Tusón

Tusón is likely one of the best sources of tropical corn germ plasm known today. Lines derived from this race combine well with lines from Tuxeño, Cuban Flint, Chandelle, and southern U.S. dents. The race possesses excellent ear type, good grain quality, and a high degree of tolerance to sugarcane mosaic. It is relatively short for tropical material.

2–7.3 Coastal Tropical Flint

This race is widely spread throughout the lowland tropics, and its influence is apparent whenever tropical corn is grown on a commercial scale. Among the many outstanding tropical varieties which have Coastal Tropical Flint in their background are ETO, Tiquisate Golden Yellow, Metro, Mayorbela, Suwan 1, and Venezuela I. Tiquisate was developed in the 1940s by Dr. I. E. Melhus and his co-workers at the Iowa State University Tropical Research Station in Guatemala. It was derived from two Cuban varieties (probably Cuban Flint and Coastal Tropical Flint) to which were added some local varieties from coastal Guatemala. The plants and ears of Tiquisate resemble Cuban Flint. A selection of Tiquisate, developed at Bogor, Indonesia, and known as Metro, was once used extensively as a commercial variety in that country. Mayorbela was developed in Puerto Rico in the 1930s. It traces back to the Mayor farm and the Isabela substation of the Mayaguez Experiment Station. In the late 1930s, this source of material was outcrossed to an inbred line (probably from the USA) followed by selection within the resulting population. Mayorbela is a reasonably good source of earliness, stalk strength, low ear placement, and grain quality. Venezuela I was developed by Langham (1942) in Venezuela primarily from Caribbean races and varieties.

Coastal Tropical Flint has been a productive source of elite tropical lines. In addition to combining ability, these lines contribute to excellent grain quality, good husk cover, stalk quality, good roots, and resistance to *Bipolaris* spp.

2–7.4 Cuban Flint-Cateto

This racial complex, known as Cuban Flint in the Caribbean Islands, as Cateto in Brazil, and Argentine Flint in Argentina, is particularly useful in hybrid combinations with dents. The race and lines derived from it combine well with Tusón, Tuxpeño, and Coastal Tropical Flint. Cuban Flint is susceptible to virus diseases and must therefore be combined with virus-resistant lines, if it is to be used in areas where corn virus diseases are prevalent.

2–7.5 Chandelle

Among tropical germ plasms, Chandelle is an excellent source of prolificacy, low ear placement, and virus resistance. It combines well with Coastal Tropical Flint and Haitian Yellow. The race and lines derived from it tend to have poor roots.

2-7.6   Haitian Yellow

Collections of this race from the vicinity of Jeremie, Haiti, have proven to be an excellent source of root and stalk strength, traits that are not easy to find in tropical corn. Because of its outstanding stalk and root qualities, Haitan Yellow should play an increasingly important role in tropical corn improvement. It has extremely late maturity.

2-7.7   The Variety ETO

This synthetic variety, developed in Colombia in the 1940s by Chavarriaga (1966), has contributed significantly to corn improvement in the tropics and subtropics. The variety has a broad genetic base, which includes the Colombian races Común and Chococeño and the synthetic Venezuela I. The latter consists primarily of Caribbean races and varieties. To this broad mixture, known as Colombia I, were later added numerous lines and varieties from Mexico, Puerto Rico, Cuba, Venezuela, Brazil, Argentina, and the USA. Selection over a period of years resulted in the new var. ETO. The abbreviation represents "Estación Tulio Ospina," the station at Medellin where the selection work was done.

Variety ETO is available in both white and yellow endosperm forms. It is high yielding and combines well with the Tuxpeños. The variety includes a wide range of maturities, the earliest of which are no later than some lines in use in the central U.S. Corn Belt.

Despite the excellent performance of ETO in many tropical areas, it appears to have generally poor adaptation to conditions in the Caribbean (Sehgal, 1966). It is also quite susceptible to sugarcane mosaic.

2-7.8   Suwan 1 and 2

The population now known as Suwan 1 was developed at Farm Suwan in Thailand. Its initial designation was Thai composite #1 DMR [DMR = Downy Mildew Resistant]. Suwan 2 is an early, white endosperm derivative of the same population. The development of these two populations was done under the leadership of Dr. Sujin Jinahyon.

The Suwan populations are derived from composites of mostly flint and semi-flint varieties from the Caribbean, Argentina, Mexico, the Philippines, India, and the USA. Races introduced into the mixture included, among others, Tusón, Coastal Tropical Flint, Cuban Flint, Argentine Flint, Tuxpeño, and Salvadoreño. In addition, the populations included several synthetics and composites (see also comments by Renfro in Brandolini and Salamini, 1985).

Suwan 1 and 2 have some downy mildew resistance that came from DMR1 and DMR5. DMR1 is a selection out of progeny of matings of a variety from Midanao and Cuba GRP1 [GRP1 = Group 1]. DMR5 is out of a cross of the same Mindanao variety and Cupurico.

Suwan 1 is now used extensively by farmers in Thailand. Approximately 10 000 t of seed of Suwan 1 were sold in 1986. Suwan 2, although first released in Thailand, has not been accepted by Thai farmers. Its lack of popularity in Thailand is probably due to its low yield. It is also earlier than Suwan 1. Suwan 2 has also been introduced into Indonesia under the name Arjuna.

ACKNOWLEDGMENT

Paper no. 11027 of the Journal Series of the North Carolina Agric. Exp. Stn., Raleigh, NC 27695–7601.

REFERENCES

Anderson, E. 1943. Races of *Zea mays*. II. A general survey of the problem. Acta Americana 1:58–68.

––––. 1944a. Homologies of the ear and tassel in *Zea mays*. Ann. Mo. Bot. Gard. 31:325–344.

––––. 1944b. Maiz reventador. Ann. Mo. Bot. Gard. 31:301–316.

––––. 1945. Maize in the New World. p. 27–42. *In* C.M. Wilson (ed.) New crops for the New World. Macmillan Publ. Co., New York.

––––. 1946. Maize in Mexico—A preliminary survey. Ann. Mo. Bot. Gard. 33:147–247.

––––. 1947. Field studies of Guatemalan maize. Ann. Mo. Bot. Gard. 34:433–467.

––––. 1959. Zapalote Chico: An important chapter in the history of maize and man. Proc. Actas Congr. Int. Americanistas/San Jose, Costa Rica 33:230–237.

––––. n.d. Corn before Columbus. Pioneer Hi-Bred Corn Co., Des Moines, IA.

––––, and W.L. Brown. 1952. Origin of Corn Belt maize and its genetic significance. p. 124–148. *In* J.W. Gowen (ed.) Heterosis. Iowa State College Press, Ames.

––––, and ––––. 1953. The popcorns of Turkey. Ann. Mo. Bot. Gard. 40:33–48.

––––, and H.C. Cutler. 1942. Races of *Zea mays*: I. Their recognition and classification. Ann. Mo. Bot. Gard. 29:69–89.

Atkinson, Alfred, and M.L. Wilson. 1914. Corn in Montana—history, characteristics, and adaptation. Montana Agric. College Exp. Stn. Bull. 107.

Beverly, R. 1705. The history and present state of Virginia. London. (Republished 1947. Univ. of North Carolina Press, Chapel Hill.)

Bird, R. McK., and M.M. Goodman. 1977. The races of maize. V. Grouping maize races on the basis of ear morphology. Econ. Bot. 31:471–481.

Blumenschein, A. 1973. Chromosome knob patterns in Latin American maize. p. 271–277. *In* A.M. Srb (ed.) Genes, enzymes and populations. Plenum Publ. Corp., New York.

––––, and R. Deuber. 1968. Milhos cultivados no Nordeste Brasileiro. O Solo 60(2):15–27.

Brandolini, A. 1969. European races of maize. Proc. Annu. Corn Sorghum Ind. Res. Conf. 24:36–49.

––––. 1970a. Maize. p. 273–309. *In* O.H. Frankel and E. Bennett (ed.) Genetic resources in plants—their exploration and conservation. F.A. Davis Co., Philadelphia.

––––. 1970b. Rasse Europee di maiz. Maydica 15:5–27.

––––. 1971. Preliminary report on South European and Mediterranean maize germ plasm. p. 108–116. *In* I. Kovacs (ed.) Proc. of the Fifth Meet. of the Maize and Sorghum Section of EUCARPIA. Akadèmiai Kiadò, Budapest.

––––, and G. Avila. 1971. Effects of Bolivian maize germ plasm in South European maize breeding. p. 117–135. *In* I. Kovàcs (ed.) Proc. of the Fifth Meet. of the Maize and Sorghum Section of EUCARPIA. Akadèmiai Kiadò, Budapest.

––––, and G. Mariani. 1968. Il germplasma italiano nela fase attuale del miglioramento genetico del mais. Genet. Agric. 22:189–206.

----, and F. Salamini (ed.) 1985. Breeding strategies for maize production improvement in the tropics. FAO and Istituto Agron. per l'Oltremare. Relazioni e Monogr. Agrar. Subtrop. e Trop. N.S. 100. Florence, Italy.

Bretting, P.K., and M.M. Goodman. 1988. Karyological variation in Mesoamerican races of maize and its systematic significance. Econ. Bot. (In press.)

----, ----, and C.W. Stuber. 1987. Karyological and isozyme variation in West Indian and allied mainland American races of maize. Am. J. Bot. 74:1601–1613.

Brewbaker, J.L. 1985. The tropical environment for maize cultivation. p. 47–77. In A. Brandolini and F. Salamini (ed.) Breeding strategies for maize production improvement in the tropics. FAO and Istituto Agron. per l'Oltremare. Relazioni e Monografie Subtrop. e Trop. N. S. 100. Florence, Italy.

Brieger, F.G., J.T.A. Gurgel, E. Paterniani, A. Blumenschein, and M.R. Alleoni. 1958. Races of maize in Brazil and other eastern South American countries. Pub. 593, NAS-NRC, Washington, DC.

Brown, W.L. 1949. Numbers and distribution of chromosome knobs in United States maize. Genetics 34:524–536.

----. 1953. Maize of the West Indies. Trop. Agric. 30:141–170.

----. 1960. Races of maize in the West Indies. Pub. 792. NAS-NRC, Washington, DC.

----, and E. Anderson. 1947. The northern flint corns. Ann. Mo. Bot. Gard. 34:1–29.

----, and ----. 1948. The southern dent corns. Ann. Mo. Bot. Gard. 35:255–268.

----, E.G. Anderson, and R. Tuchawena, Jr. 1952. Observations on three varieties of Hopi maize. Am. J. Bot. 39:597–609.

----, and M.M. Goodman. 1977. Races of corn. In G.F. Sprague (ed.) Corn and corn improvement. Agronomy 18:49–88.

Buddenhagen, I. 1985. Maize diseases in relation to maize improvement in the tropics. p. 243–275. In A. Brandolini and F. Salamini (ed.) Breeding strategies for maize production improvement in the tropics. FAO and Istituto Agron. per l'Oltremare. Relazioni e Monografie Subtrop. e Trop. N. S. 100. Florence, Italy.

Carter, G.F. 1945. Plant geography and culture history in the American Southwest. Viking Fund. Pub. in Anthropol. No. 5, New York.

----, and E. Anderson. 1945. A preliminary survey of maize in the southwestern United States. Ann. Mo. Bot. Gard. 32:297–322.

Castillo G., F. 1987. Agronomic evaluation of Latin American maize populations. Ph.D. diss., North Carolina State Univ., Raleigh.

Cervantes S., T., M.M. Goodman, E. Casas D., and J.O. Rawlings. 1978. Use of genetic effects and genotype by environmental interactions for the classification of Mexican races of maize. Genetics 90:339–348.

Chavarriaga, E. 1966. Maíz ETO, una variedad producida en Colombia. Rev. Inst. Colomb. Agropec. 1(1):5–30.

Centro Internacional de Mejoramiento de Maiz y Trigo. 1972a. International maize adaptation nurseries (IMAN). Annu. Rep. (Mexico City) 1970–71:96–98.

----. 1972b. Results of the first international maize adaptation nursery (IMAN) 1970–71. Info. Bull. 7. CIMMYT, Mexico City.

----. 1974. Results of the second and third international maize adaptation nursery (IMAN) (1971–72, 1972–73). Info. Bull. 12. CIMMYT, Mexico City.

Committee on Genetic Vulnerability of Major Crops. 1972. Genetic vulnerability of major crops. NAS, Washington, DC.

Committee on Preservation of Indigenous Strains of Maize. 1954. Collections of original strains of corn, I. NAS-NRC, Washington, DC.

----. 1955. Collections of original strains of corn, II. NAS-NRC, Washington, DC.

Costa-Rodrigues, L. 1969. Races of maize in Portugal. Agron. Lusit. 31:239–284.

Covor, Alexandru. 1972. Rasele de Porumb din Romania. Acad. de Stunte Agricole si Silvice, Bucuresti.

Cutler, H.C. 1946. Races of maize in South America. Bot. Mus. Leafl. Harv. Univ. 12:257–299.

----, and G.A. Agogino. 1960. Analysis of maize from the Four Bear Site and two other Arikara locations in South Dakota. Southwest. J. Anthropol. 16:312–316.

----, and L.W. Blake. 1988. North American Indian corn. Handbook of North American Indians, Vol. 3. Smithsonian Inst., Washington, DC. (In press.)

Darrah, L.L., S.A. Eberhart, and L.H. Penny. 1972. A maize breeding methods study in Kenya. Crop Sci. 12:605–608.

Doebley, J.F., M.M. Goodman, and C.W. Stuber. 1983. Isozyme variation in maize from the southwestern United States: Taxonomic and anthropological implications. Maydica 28:94–120.

————, ————, and ————. 1985. Isozyme variation in the races of maize from Mexico. Am. J. Bot. 72:629–639.

————, ————, and ————. 1986. Exceptional genetic divergence of Northern Flint corn. Am. J. Bot. 73:64–69.

————, J.D. Wendel, J.S.C. Smith, C.W. Stuber, and M.M. Goodman. 1988. The origin of Cornbelt maize: The isozyme evidence. Econ. Bot. 42:120–131.

Eberhart, S.A. 1971. Regional maize diallels with U.S. and semi-exotic varieties. Crop Sci. 11:911–914.

Edwards, R.J., and E.R. Leng. 1965. Classification of some indigenous maize collections from southern and southeastern Europe. Euphytica 14:161–169.

FAO. 1985. Germplasm use in maize breeding. p. 452–453. In A. Brandolini and F. Salamini (ed.) Breeding strategies for maize production improvement in the tropics. FAO and Istituto Agron. per l'Oltremare. Relazioni e Monografie Subtrop. e Trop. N. S. 100. Florence, Italy.

Galinat, W.C. 1970. The cupule and its role in the origin and evolution of maize. Massachusetts Agric. Exp. Stn. Bull. 585.

————. 1971. The evolution of sweet corn. Massachusetts Agric. Exp. Stn. Bull. 591.

————, and J.H. Gunnerson. 1963. Spread of eight-rowed maize from the prehistoric Southwest. Bot. Mus. Leafl. Harvard Univ. 20:117–160.

Gerrish, E.E. 1980. Non-Corn Belt dent populations. Maize Genet. Coop. News Lett. 54:49–52.

————. 1983. Indications from a diallel study for interracial hybridization in the Corn Belt. Crop Sci. 23:1082–1084.

Girola, C.D. 1919. Variedades de maiz cultivadas en Argentina: Maices Argentinos y aclimatados. Talleres Graficos J. Weiss y Preusche, Buenos Aires.

Goodman, M.M. 1967. The races of maize; I. The use of Mahalanobis' generalized distances to measure morphological similarity. Filtotec. Latinoam. 4(1):1–22.

————. 1968. The races of maize: II. Use of multivariate analysis of variance to measure morphological similarity. Crop. Sci. 8:693–698.

————. 1972. Distance analysis in biology. Syst. Zool. 21:174–186.

————. 1978. A brief survey of the races of maize and current attempts to infer racial relationships. p. 143–158. In D.B. Walden (ed.) Maize breeding and genetics. John Wiley and Sons, New York.

————. 1983. Racial diversity in maize. p. 29–40. In D.T. Gordon et al. (ed.) Proc. Int. Maize Virus Disease Colloq. and Workshop. Ohio Agric. Res. Dev. Ctr., Wooster.

————. 1984. An evaluation and critique of current germplasm programs. p. 197–249. In Report 1983, Plant breeding research forum. Conservation and utilization of exotic germplasm to improve varieties. Pioneer Hi-Bred Int., Des Moines.

————. 1985a. Exotic maize germplasm: Status, prospects, and remedies. Iowa State J. Res. 59:497–527.

————. 1985b. Use of tropical and subtropical maize and teosinte germplasm in temperate conditions. p. 93–103. In A. Brandolini and F. Salamini (ed.) Breeding strategies for maize production improvement in the tropics. FAO and Istituto Agron. per l'Oltremare. Relazioni e Monografie Subtrop. e Trop. N. S. 100. Florence, Italy.

————, and R. McK. Bird. 1977. The races of maize. IV. Tentative grouping of 219 Latin American races. Econ. Bot. 31:204–221.

————, and F. Castillo G. 1984. Conservación y evaluación de razas de maíz en América Latina. p. 67–84. In Memorias II Reunión Latinoamericano del maíz. ICA, Palmira, Colombia.

————, and E. Paterniani. 1969. The races of maize. III. Choices of appropriate characters for racial classification. Econ. Bot. 23:265–273.

————, and C.W. Stuber. 1983. Races of maize. VI. Isozyme variation among races of maize in Bolivia. Maydica 28:169–187.

Grant, U.J., W.H. Hatheway, D.H. Timothy, C. Cassalett D., and L.M. Roberts. 1963. Races of maize in Venezuela. Pub. 1136. NAS-NRC, Washington, DC.

Grobman, A., W. Salhuana, and R. Sevilla, with P.C. Mangelsdorf. 1961. Races of maize in Peru. Pub. 915. NAS-NRC, Washington, DC.

Hallauer, A.R. 1972. Third phase in the yield evaluation of synthetic varieties of maize. Crop Sci. 12:16–18.

————. 1978. Potential of exotic germplasm for maize improvement. p. 229–247. *In* D.B. Walden (ed.) Maize breeding and genetics. John Wiley and Sons, New York.

————, and J.H. Sears. 1972. Integrating exotic germplasm into Corn Belt maize breeding programs. Crop Sci. 12:203–206.

Hatheway, W.H. 1957. Races of maize in Cuba. Pub. 453. NAS-NRC, Washington, DC.

Hernandez X., E. 1949. Plant exploration in Cuba. (Report to Dr. J.G. Harrar, director of the Rockefeller Agric. Program in Mexico, Mexico City.)

————, and G. Alanis F. 1970. Estudio morfologico de cinco nuevas razas de maiz de la Sierra Madre Occidental de Mexico: Implicaciones filogeneticas y fitogeograficas. Agrociencia 5:3–30.

Holley, R.N., and M.M. Goodman. 1988. Yield potential of tropical hybrid maize derivatives. Crop Sci. 28:213–218.

Kato Y., T.A. 1975. Cytological studies of maize (*Zea mays* L.) and teosinte (*Zea mexicana* Schrader Kuntze) in relation to their origin and evolution. Massachusetts Agric. Exp. Stn. Bull. 635.

————. 1984. Chromosome morphology and the origin of maize and its races. Evol. Biol. 17:219–253.

————, and A. Blumenschein. 1967. Complejos de nudos cromosómicos en los maices de América. Flitotec. Latinoam. 4(2):13–24.

Kemble, R.J., R.E. Gunn, and R.B. Flavell. 1983. Mitochondrial DNA variation in races of maize indigenous to Mexico. Theor. Appl. Genet. 65:129–144.

Kim, S.K., Y. Efron, J. Fajemisin, and F.H. Khadr. 1985. Evolution and progress of hybrid maize project at IITA. p. 367–384. *In* A. Brandolini and F. Salamini (ed.) Breeding strategies for maize production improvement in the tropics. FAO and Ist. Agron. per l'Oltremare. Relazioni e Monografie Subtrop. e Trop. N. S. 100. Florence, Italy.

Kramer, H.H., and A.J. Ullstrup. 1959. Preliminary evaluation of exotic maize germ plasm. Agron. J. 51:687–689.

Kuleshov, N.N. 1929. The geographical distribution of the varietal diversity of maize in the world. Tr. Prikl. Bot. Genet. Sel. (Bull. Appl. Bot., Genet. and Plant Breed. Lenin Acad. Agric. Sci., USSR) 20:506–510.

————. 1930. The maize of Mexico, Guatemala, Cuba, Panama, and Colombia. p. 492–502. *In* S.M. Bukasov (ed.) The cultivated plants of Mexico, Guatemala and Colombia. Tr. Prikl. Bot. Genet. Sel. (Bull. Appl. Bot., Genet. and Plant Breed. Lenin Acad. Agric. Sci. USSR) Prilozhenie (Suppl.) 47. [Republished in 1981 in Spanish as Las Plantas Cultivadas de Mexico, Guatemala y Colombia. CATIE, Turrialba, Costa Rica.]

Langham, D.C. 1942. Venezuela I, una seleccion de maiz recomendable. Cir. 2. Ministerio de Agricultura y Cria., Caracas, Venezuela.

Leng, E.R., A. Tavcar, and V. Trifunovic. 1962. Maize of southeastern Europe and its potential value in breeding programs elsewhere. Euphytica 11:263–272.

Longley, A.E. 1938. Chromosomes of maize from North American Indians. J. Agric. Res. 56:177–195.

————. 1941. Chromosome morphology in maize and its relatives. Bot. Rev. 7:263–289.

————, and T.A. Kato Y. 1965. Chromosome morphology of certain races of maize in Latin America. Res. Bull. 1. CIMMYT, Chapingo, Mexico.

Mangelsdorf, P.C. 1954. New evidence on the origin and ancestry of maize. Am. Antiq. 19:409–410.

————. 1974. Corn, its origin, evolution, and improvement. Harvard Univ. Press, Cambridge, MA.

————, and J.W. Cameron. 1942. Western Guatemala—A secondary center of origin of cultivated maize varieties. Bot. Mus. Leafl. Harv. Univ. 10:217–252.

————, and R.G. Reeves. 1939. The origin of Indian corn and its relatives. Texas Agric. Exp. Stn. Bull. 574.

Marino, A.E. 1934. La agricultura en la Quebrada de Humahuaca (Jujuy). Lab. de Bot. de la Fac. de Agron. y Vet., Buenos Aires.

Martinez W., O.J., M.M. Goodman, and D.H. Timothy. 1983. Measuring racial differentiation in maize using multivariate distance measures standardized by variation in F_2 populations. Crop. Sci. 23:775–781.

McClintock, B. 1959. Genetic and cytological studies of maize. Carnegie Inst. Washington Year Book 58:452–456.

————. 1960. Chromosome constitutions of Mexican and Guatemalan races of maize. Carnegie Inst. Washington Year Book 59:461–472.

————. 1978. Significance of chromosome constitutions in tracing the origin and migration of races of maize in the Americas. p. 159–184. *In* D.B. Walden (ed.) Maize breeding and genetics. John Wiley and Sons, New York.

————, T.A. Kato Y., and A. Blumenshein. 1981. Chromosome constitution of races of maize. Colegio de Postgraduados, Chapingo, Mexico.

Mochizuki, N. 1968. Classification of local strains of maize in Japan and selection of breeding materials by application of principal component analysis. p. 173–178. *In* Symposium on maize production in southeast Asia. Agriculture, Forestry, and Fisheries Res. Counc., Ministry of Agric. and Forestry, Kasumigaseki, Chiyoda-ku, Tokyo, Japan.

Nelson, Jr., O.E. 1952. Non-reciprocal cross sterility in maize. Genetics 37:101–124.

————. 1960. The fourth chromosome gametophyte factor in some Central and South American races. Maize Genet. Coop. News Lett. 34:114–116.

————, and M.I. Chang. 1974. Effect of multiple aleurone layers on the protein and amino acid content of maize endosperm. Crop Sci. 14:374–380.

Nickerson, N.H. 1953. Variation in cob morphology among certain archaeological and ethnological races in maize. Ann. Mo. Bot. Gard. 40:79–111.

————, 1954. Morphological analysis of the maize ear. Am. J. Bot. 41:87–92.

————, and A.P. Covich. 1966. A collection of maize from Darien, Panama. Econ. Bot. 20:434–440.

Ortega P., R. 1985. Variedades y razas mexicanas de maíz y su evaluación en el cruzamiento con lineas de clima templado como material de partida para fitomejoramiento. Abbreviated Spanish translation of Ph.D. diss. N. I. Vavilov Nat. Inst. of Plants; Leningrad, USSR.

Ortiz R., R.O. 1985. Efecto ambiental interacción genotipo-medio ambiente y heredabilidad de las características morphológicas usadas en la clasificación racial de maíz en la Sierra del Perú. Tesis Magister Scientiae, Univ. Nacional Agraria, La Molína, Peru.

Parker V., I., and O. Paratori B. 1965. Distribución geográfica, clasificación, y estudio del maíz (*Zea mays*) en Chile. Agric. Técnica 25(2):70–86.

Parodi, L.R. 1932. Notas preliminares sobre plantas sudamericanas cultivadas en la provincia de Jujuy. Gaea 4(1):19–28.

————. 1935. Relaciones de la agricultura prehispanica con la agricultura Argentina actual. An. Acad. Nac. Agron. Vet. Buenos Aires 1:115–167.

Paterniani, E. 1970. Heterose em cruzamentos intervarietais de milho. Univ. de São Paulo, Escola Superior de Agricultura "Luiz de Queiroz," Departmento e Instituto de Genetica Relatorio Cientifico 1970:95–100. Piracicaba, S.P., Brazil.

————. 1972. Capacidade de combinacao de linhagens exoticas em cruzamento intervarietal. Univ. de São Paulo, Escola Superior de Agricultura "Luiz de Queiroz," Departmento e Instituto de Genetica Relatorio Cientifico 1972:83–85. Piracicaba, S.P., Brazil.

————, and M.M. Goodman. 1977. Races of maize in Brazil and adjacent areas. CIMMYT, Mexico City.

Patiño, V.M. 1956. El maíz Chococito, noticia sobre su cultivo en América Ecuatorial. Am. Indígena 16:309–346.

Pavlicic, J. 1971. Contribution to a preliminary classification of European open-pollinated maize varieties. p. 93–107. *In* I. Kovàcs (ed.) Proc. Fifth Meet. of the Maize and Sorghum Section of EUCARPIA. Akadèmiai Kiadò, Budapest.

————, and V. Trifunovic. 1966. A study of some important ecologic corn types grown in Yugoslavia and their classification. J. Sci. Agric. Res. 19(66):45–63. [Also in Arh. Poljopr. Nauke 19(66):44–62.]

Ramírez E., R., D.H. Timothy, E. Díaz B., and U.J. Grant, with G.E. Nicholson Calle, Edgar Anderson, and W.L. Brown. 1960. Races of maize in Bolivia. Pub. 747. NAS-NRC, Washington, DC.

Roberts, L.M. 1950. Las razas mexicanas de maiz mas utiles como material basico para su mejoramiento. p. 71–84. *In* La Primera Asamblea Latinoamericana de Fitogeneticistas. Oficina de Estudios Especiales, Sec. Agric. y Ganad. Folleto Misc. 3. Mexico City.

————, U.J. Grant, R. Ramírez E., W.H. Hatheway, and D.L. Smith, with P.C. Mangelsdorf. 1957. Races of maize in Colombia. Pub. 510. NAS-NRC, Washington, DC.

Rodriguez, A., M. Robero, J. Quiroga, G. Avila, and A. Brandolini. 1968. Maices bolivianos. FAO, Rome, Italy.

Salamini, F. 1985. Photosensitivity in maize: Evaluation, genetics, and breeding for insensitivity. p. 143–157. *In* A. Brandolini and F. Salamini (ed.) Breeding strategies for maize production improvement in the tropics. FAO and Ist. Agron. per l'Oltremare. Relazioni e Monografie Subtrop. e Trop. N. S. 100. Florence, Italy.

Sanchez P., P. 1983. Estudio de estabilidad de caracteres y razas de maiz de Mexico. Tesis Maestro en Ciencias, Colegio de Postgraduados, Chapingo, Mexico.

Sanchez-Monge, E. 1962. Razas de maíz en España. Ministerio de Agricultura Monografias 13. Madrid.

Sehgal, S.M. 1966. Inbred-hybrid method of maize improvement. Proc. Caribbean Foods Crops Soc. 4:45–51.

Smith, J.S.C. 1988. Genetic diversity within the Corn Belt Dent racial complex of maize (*Zea mays* L.). Maydica (In press).

————, and D.N. Duvick. 1988. Germplasm collections and the private plant breeder. *In* J.T. Williams et al. (ed.) The use of plant genetic resources. Cambridge Univ. Press, Cambridge, England. (In press).

Sprague, G.F. 1971. Genetic vulnerability in corn and sorghum. Proc. Annu. Corn Sorghum Ind. Res. Conf. 26:96–104.

Stevenson, J.C., and M.M. Goodman. 1972. Ecology of exotic races of maize. I. Leaf number and tillering of 16 races under four temperatures and two photoperiods. Crop Sci. 12:864–868.

Stonor, C.R., and E. Anderson. 1949. Maize among the hill peoples of Assam. Ann. Mo. Bot. Gard. 36:355–404.

Stuber, C.W. 1978. Exotic sources for broadening genetic diversity in corn breeding programs. Proc. Annu. Corn Sorghum Ind. Res. Conf. 33:34–47.

————. 1986. Use of exotic sources of germplasm for maize improvement. EUCARPIA Maize Sorghum Congr. Proc. 13:19–31.

Sturtevant, E.L. 1899. Varieties of corn. USDA Office of Exp. Stn. Bull. 57. U.S. Gov. Print. Office, Washington, DC.

Suto, T., and Y. Yoshida. 1956. Characteristics of the oriental maize. p. 375–530. *In* H. Kihara (ed.) Land and crops of Nepal Himalaya. Vol. 2. Fauna and Flora Res. Soc., Kyoto Univ., Kyoto, Japan.

Timothy, D.H. 1963. Genetic diversity, heterosis, and the use of exotic stocks in maize in Colombia. p. 581–593. *In* Statistical genetics and plant breeding. Pub. 982. NAS-NRC, Washington, DC.

————, W.H. Hatheway, U.J. Grant, M. Torregroza C., D. Sarria V., and Daniel Varela A. 1963. Races of maize in Ecuador. Pub. 975. NAS-NRC, Washington, DC.

————, B. Peña V., and R. Ramírez E., with W.L. Brown and E. Anderson. 1961. Races of maize in Chile. Pub. 847. NAS-NRC, Washington, DC.

Troyer, A.F., and W.L. Brown. 1972. Selection for early flowering in corn. Crop Sci. 12:301–304.

Van der Walt, W.J., and R.A. Brink. 1969. Geographic distribution of paramutable and paramutagenic *R* alleles in maize. Genetics 61:677–695.

Wallace, H.A., and W.L. Brown. 1956. Corn and its early fathers. Michigan State Univ. Press, East Lansing.

Weissinger, A.K., D.H. Timothy, C.S. Levings, III, and M.M. Goodman. 1983. Patterns of mitochondrial DNA variation in indigenous maize races of Latin America. Genetics 104:365–379.

Wellhausen, E.J. 1965. Exotic germ plasm for improvement of Corn Belt maize. Proc. Annu. Hybrid Corn Ind. Res. Conf. 20:31–50.

————. 1978. Recent developments in maize breeding in the tropics. p. 59–84. *In* D.B. Walden (ed.) Maize breeding and genetics. John Wiley and Sons, New York.

————, A. Fuentes O., and A.H. Corzo, with P.C. Mangelsdorf. 1957. Races of maize in Central America. Pub. 511. NAS-NRC, Washington, DC.

————, L.M. Roberts, and E. Hernández X., with P.C. Mangelsdorf. 1951. Razas de maíz en México. Su origen, características, y distribución. Folleto Técnico Secretaria de Agricultura y Ganadería 5, Mexico City.

————, L.M. Roberts, and E. Hernández X., with P.C. Mangelsdorf. 1952. Races of maize in Mexico. The Bussey Inst., Harvard Univ., Cambridge, MA.

Will, G.F., and G.E. Hyde. 1917. Corn among the Indians of the Upper Missouri, St. Louis. (Republished 1964, Univ. of Nebraska Press, Lincoln.)

Wolf, M.J., H.C. Cutler, M.S. Zuber, and U. Khoo. 1972. Maize with multilayer aleurone of high protein content. Crop Sci. 12:440–442.

3 The Genetics of Corn

E. H. COE, JR.

USDA-ARS
University of Missouri
Columbia, Missouri

M. G. NEUFFER

University of Missouri
Columbia, Missouri

D. A. HOISINGTON

University of Missouri
Columbia, Missouri

Corn is genetically the most accessible and the most characterized among the higher plants, whether for study of biological phenomena in general or toward understanding and manipulating germ plasm for increased productivity and utility. The species is easy to culture systematically on any scale from single plants or small nurseries to hundreds of hectares; the pollen-bearing inflorescence (tassel) atop the plant is handily separated from the female inflorescence (ear) along the culm, such that both can be easily manipulated, removed, or bagged; and the harvested ear, though bulky, is readily labelled, scanned, and stored as a progeny unit. Pollen production is so prodigious (as many as 10^7 grains/day for a plant in the peak of a 7-d flowering period) and pollination is so convenient that it is often possible to pollinate 50 or more ears with a single day's collection of pollen from one plant. An experienced person can complete 300 to 500 individual controlled pollinations in a single day under excellent conditions, each ear yielding several hundred kernel progeny. The very bulk and robust stature of the corn plant, tassel, ear, and seed contribute greatly to the ease with which these manipulations can be done and to the ease of observation of traits, especially in the kernel. In addition, precise cytological and cytogenetic experimentation can be carried out efficiently on key stages of meiosis (Carlson, Chapter 2); various tissues and developmental stages can be defined, dissected and explored systematically; and molecular studies in corn have advanced to the point that many genes have been cloned, several parts of the genome have been characterized or sequenced in detail, and the occurrence of a remarkable degree of polymorphism in the DNA has opened even greater potential for experimental analysis and manipulation (Walbot and Messing, Chapter 6). "No other plant has been studied from the cytogenetic point of view so intensively as has maize, and the purpose of this article is to present some of the more pertinent facts which have been discovered." (Rhoades and McClintock, 1935).

Uncommonly great genetic variability is present in and among the diverse lines, varieties, and races of corn in the world. Although only part of this variability has been examined systematically, unit factors have been identified determining colors, forms, structures, constituents, or processes in every part and tissue. While the cataloguing of these factors and their relationships is of interest in itself, we aspire also to assist in the analysis of the challenging practical and theoretical problems of today by providing an organized introduction to the detailed genetics of corn, along with organized aids for the practicing research worker.

The debt the authors of this summary owe to those who have contributed to it, intentionally or unintentionally, is enormous. We could not have proceeded without a tacit assumption that whatever special knowledge we may have absorbed unlabelled from colleagues was acceptable for us to include in the compilation; that our understandings, when flawed, might be tolerated; and that corrections would be communicated to us in due course. This assumption is founded in the happy tradition, among corn research workers, of free and generous exchange of information, ideas, techniques, materials, and, above all, critiques.

This tradition is furthered in the *Maize Genetics Cooperation Newsletter* (MNL), an informal route by which unpublished notes, data, information and ideas are shared among workers in corn genetics. The authors are aware that items of linkage data, genetic expressions, and other detailed information drawn from the MNL are properly cited and attributed only by permission of the writers. In the face of the volume of literature to be selected and attributed, that propriety must be foregone in this summary. We have, in fact, attempted to avoid citations to the MNL and to prefer formal publications. We hope, as Emerson, Beadle and Fraser (1935) expressed it in introducing their classic compilation, "that this summary presentation will prove to be sufficiently helpful to the contributors to compensate them in some measure for their aid in its preparation."

The comprehensive summary by Emerson, Beadle and Fraser, covering corn genetics, linkage data and interactions, is not paralleled by any recent treatment. There also are detailed descriptions of types and their interactions, accompanied by unequalled plates and photographs, in Correns (1901), East and Hayes (1911), Emerson (1918), and Emerson (1921). Nonetheless, several aids to research that contain compilations and summarized information are available. The present chapter is a revision of Coe and Neuffer (1977) in the 2nd edition of Corn and Corn Improvement; a number of the figures, in particular, presented in that chapter have not been repeated here. The MNL, edited by Coe, contains annual compilations of the published literature, digests of mapping and other genetic data, stocklists, maps, and indexes to symbols and authors. The 170-odd photographs, mostly in color, in the book *The Mutants of Maize* (Neuffer et al., 1968) complement the present paper and convey information that is not possible to express in brief phrases. The cytogenetic studies and techniques that defined the chromosomes with the genetic linkage groups, and chromosome segments with genes, are summarized by Rhoades and McClintock (1935) and by Rhoades (1955). *Maize for Biological Research* (Sheridan, 1982) provides research information on the botany, culture, pollination, pedigree-keeping, genetic and cytogenetic and cytological materials and methodologies, biochemical systems, genetic systems, breeding, and tissue culture, among many others. The review of literature for the present chapter was completed in December, 1986.

3–1 THE GENETIC FACTORS OF CORN

Studies in corn have identified genetic variation attributable to unitary factors at perhaps 1000 or more loci, loosely defined; if rigorous criteria were applied with regard to supporting data, tests for allelism, and pleiotropisms, perhaps 575 loci could be documented unequivocally. Because of losses of strains, pending work, and preliminary reports in the MNL that have not been carried further, it has not been possible to include some factors. Aids to systematic description and cataloguing of genetic variation presented below include the nomenclatural conventions, listings of the known factors, and linkage maps. Brief consideration is also given here to dosage effects and codominance; duplicate factors; cell autonomy and auxotrophy; sporophyte-determined traits, induction and imprinting; and pleiotropisms.

3–1.1 Nomenclatural Conventions

As symbolization of genetic factors has developed, systematic conventions have formed, based on recommendations accepted by consensus. These recommendations were substantially revised in 1974 and the present summary follows the new conventions. Briefly, the significant conventions used in literature published before the revision were as follows: A one or two-letter symbol designated a locus. For different members of an allelic series, superscripts composed of numerals or letters or both were used (e.g., R^r, R^g, r^r, r^g; A, A^b, A^d, a^{m-1}, a^{m-2}, etc.). For different loci having the same class symbol, numerical subscripts were used (e.g., a_1, a_2; v_1, v_2, v_3, etc.). Normal alleles of a recessive offtype were represented with a + sign or capitalized symbol (e.g., An), while normal alleles of a dominant offtype were represented with + or a lower case symbol (e.g., tu). Nonconforming symbols have occasionally been used in the literature. The revised nomenclatural conventions adopted in 1974 by the annual Maize Genetics Conference are reproduced here.

3–1.2   Revised Genetic Nomenclature for Maize

Recommendation 1. Each locus be designated by a lower case italicized symbol. Traditionally, this has been a one or two letter symbol, but some three letter symbols have been used. We recommend that all newly assigned symbols have three letters in the future.

Recommendation 2. As previously, different loci at which mutations produce the same general phenotype are distinguished by italicized numbers following the gene symbol, but the number one will be omitted in the designation of the first locus identified, i.e., the first locus identified would be *sh* and the second *sh2*. The number will appear on the line both when the gene name is written out and when the symbol is used: e.g., *brittle-2* and *bt2*.

Recommendation 3. A mutational site or event is designated by an isolation number, laboratory number, or previous designation following the gene symbol and set off by a dash: e.g., *sh2-6801.*

The dominant allele at a locus should be designated by the gene symbol with a capital letter, *Sh2.* Where it is desirable to designate a particular dominant, this can be done as *Sh2-W22.*

The mutation by which a locus was first detected should be designated by a capital *R* or *Ref,* as *sh2-R,* to indicate the reference allele.

The superscripts that currently indicate different alleles at a locus will be written after the dash following the locus designation. As examples, *R^r* would become *R-r* and *P^rr* would become *P-rr.*

Recommendation 4. A mutation at an unknown locus conditioning a phenotype similar to that conditioned by mutations at one or more known loci can be designated by an appropriate gene symbol, an * to indicate that the locus is unknown and a laboratory number as *bt*-7011.* After tests establish allelism with mutations at a given locus, the number of that locus can be substituted for the * but the laboratory isolation number retained, as *bt2-7011.* It would be preferable if the mutations within the locus that appear to represent independent mutational events were designated only by isolation numbers that do not purport to furnish any information about the characteristics of the allele.

For the designation of loci defined by restriction fragment length polymorphisms (RFLPs), Coe and Hoisington (MNL 61:49, 1987) have proposed that numbered symbols be used to designate the locus of the segregating variation. A distinctive 3-letter upper-case symbol is chosen by the mapping laboratory and is followed by the locus number (e.g., *NPI1, NPI2,* etc.; *UMC1, UMC2,* etc.). For loci that are defined by a probe for a functional product, each laboratory that defines and maps the polymorphism assigns their laboratory symbol and a unique number rather than the functional symbol of the product. Any locus may, if desired, be specified by a hyphenated addition to the numbered symbol, e.g., *NPI227-ssu.*

The omission of the number one specified in Recommendation 2 is frequently overridden in cases of potential ambiguity or in indexing, for clarity. Thus *sh1, a1*. At times, even when no higher-numbered locus with the same letter symbol has been designated, the number one is used, e.g., *wx1*.

Since these recommendations provide only a framework for changes, uncertainties in application are certain to arise. Queries may be directed to E. H. Coe, USDA-ARS and Dep. of Agronomy, Curtis Hall, University of Missouri, Columbia, MO 65211, who has agreed to act as a clearinghouse for questions and for assignment of new symbols.

3–1.3 Genetic Loci and Their Map Locations

The accompanying list of documented loci (Table 3–1) includes, in addition to map locations, descriptions of one or more characteristic alleles at each locus. Usually the "type" allele—i.e., the unusual, non-normal or mutant variant by which the locus was first identified—is given for the symbol and for the description. Gaps in the list, for loci that are listed in Emerson et al. (1935) but not here, are either the result of corrections following findings of allelism (a few of which are specifically entered) or were excluded to avoid ambiguity because authentic stocks with which to test allelism are no longer in existence. The location tabulated includes the chromosome (L=long arm, S=short arm) and map position or approximate location. Listings of genetic and cytogenetic strains available from the Stock Center (noted by S in a column in the table) are given regularly in the *Newsletter*; copies of the listings or small quantities (20 to 50 kernels) of specific strains may be obtained from the Maize Genetics Stock Center, Department of Agronomy, Turner Hall, 1102 S. Goodwin Ave., Univ. of Illinois, Urbana, IL 61801. Not all of the listed factors, however, are available in the stocks maintained by the Stock Center; some may or may not be in current collections of individual investigators. P in a column in the table indicates that a photograph is presented in Neuffer et al. (1968). References cited in Table 3–1 identify the original description of the variant. A few symbols in Table 3–1 are those used or designated for transposable elements, chromosomal rearrangements, chromosomal components, organellar and "cytoplasmic" traits, loci showing restriction fragment polymorphisms, certain quantitative traits, or locus subunits.

Factors are known that affect any tissue type—in the kernel including the aleurone tissue, starchy portion of the endosperm, embryo axis, scutellum, and pericarp; in the seedling and plant including the roots, mesocotyl, coleoptile, coleorhiza, leaves, sheaths, culm, tassel, anther, pollen grain, husks, ear, ovules, silks, and cob. There are factors that influence form, stature, surfaces, textures, odors, and colors, including red, purple, yellow, green, brown, white, red (chlorophyll) fluorescence, blue fluorescence, and yellow fluorescence. On the other hand, "Students of genetics are well aware of the fact that the expression of the given gene varies

Table 3-1. Genelist of maize (*Zea mays* L.).

The following list, arranged by gene symbol, identifies the unit factors for which stocks are available in the Maize Genetics Stock Center (Department of Agronomy, University of Illinois, Urbana, Illinois 61801), those for which variants exist in generally available strains (e.g. isozyme variants), and those upon which current or recent research studies have been reported in the Maize Genetics Cooperation News Letter. The information tabulated includes the chromosome (L=long arm, S=short arm) and map position or approximate location, the name and phenotype, availability from the Stock Center (S), a photograph (P) in *The Mutants of Maize* (Neuffer, M.G., et al. 1968. Crop Sci. Soc. Amer., Madison, Wis.), and references to the original descriptions.

SYMBOL	LOCATION	NAME, PHENOTYPE	S	P	REF
a1	3L-149.0	anthocyaninless: colorless aleurone, green or brown plant, brown pericarp with *P1-RR*	S	P	74
a2	5S-35	anthocyaninless: like *a1*, but red pericarp with *P1-RR*	S	P	142
a3	3L-132	anthocyanin: recessive intensifier of expression of *R1* and *B1* in plant tissues	S	P	181
Ac	-	activator: designator for autonomous transposable elements; regulates *Ds* transposition and dissociation; ex. *Ac9*		P	201
		designates element isolated from *ux1-m9*			60
Ac2		activator: similar to *Ac*			
Aco1	4S	aconitase: electrophoretic mobility; monomeric			347
Aco2	-	aconitase: electrophoretic mobility			347
Aco3	-	aconitase: electrophoretic mobility			347
Aco4	9	aconitase: electrophoretic mobility; monomeric			347
Acp1	-	acid phosphatase (was *Ap1, Acph1, Phos*): electrophoretic mobility; cytosolic; dimeric			116
Acp2	-	acid phosphatase (was *Ap2*): electrophoretic mobility; dimeric			116
Acp4	1L-176	acid phosphatase: electrophoretic mobility; monomeric			152
ad1	1L-108	adherent: seedling leaves, tassel branches, and occasionally top leaves adhere	S		155
Adh1	1L-128	alcohol dehydrogenase: electrophoretic mobility; null allele is known; dimeric; intra/interlocus hybrid bands occur	S		302
Adh2	4S-46	alcohol dehydrogenase: electrophoretic mobility; null allele is known; dimeric; intra/interlocus hybrid bands occur			300
Adk1	6S-0	adenylate kinase: electrophoretic mobility; plastidial			348
Adr1	-	alcohol dehydrogenase regulator			166
ae1	5L-57	amylose extender: glassy, tarnished endosperm; high amylose content; starch branching enzyme IIb	S	P	346
afd1	-	absence of first division: male and female sterility; anaphase I equatorial			112
agt1	-	ageotropic: primary root unresponsive to gravity			67
al1	2S-4	albescent plant: erratic development of chlorophyll; pale yellow endosperm, some alleles viviparous	S	P	257
adh1	1L-near bm2	histone Ia (was *H1a*): electrophoretic mobility			332
Alpha		*A1* locus component (see *Beta*): determines reduced aleurone and plant color, brown pericarp			170
am1	5S-20	ameiotic: male and female sterility; anaphase I equatorial	S	P	248 271
Amp1	1L-near f1	aminopeptidase: electrophoretic mobility; cytosolic; monomeric			246
Amp2	1-near hm1	aminopeptidase: electrophoretic mobility; monomeric			246
Amp3	5S-near a2	aminopeptidase: electrophoretic mobility; monomeric			246
Amp4	-	aminopeptidase: electrophoretic mobility; monomeric			246

SYMBOL	LOCATION	NAME, PHENOTYPE	S	P	REF
Amy1	-	alpha amylase: electrophoretic mobility; monomeric			38
Amy2	5S-near Mdh5	beta amylase: electrophoretic mobility; monomeric			37
an1	1L-104	anther ear: andromonoecious dwarf, intermediate stature; few tassel branches; responds to gibberellins; *an1-6923* includes deletion of Bz2	S	P	71 81
anl1	5S-near lu1	anthocyaninless lethal: colorless aleurone; small kernels; embryo lethal			44
aph1	-	aphid resistance			36
ar1	9L-62	argentia: virescent seedling, greens rapidly; husk leaf tips striped	S	P	85
as1	1-56	asynaptic: synaptic failure in male and female	S	P	15
Asr1	4S-19	absence of seminal roots			212
Atc1		(see Zb8)			
ats1	8	atrazine susceptible: lacks glutathione S-transferase			119
B1	2S-49	colored plant: anthocyanin in major plant tissues; some alleles affect aleurone and embryo color	S	P	77
B chr		B chromosome: supernumerary chromosome		P	265
ba1	3L-102	barren stalk: ear shoots and most tassel branches and spikelets absent	S	P	128
ba2	2-near ts1	barren stalk: like *ba1*, but tassel more normal	S		128
baf1	9S-near w11	barren stalk fastigiate (was *ba*-s*): ear shoots often absent; tassel branches erect			45
bd1	7L-109	branched silkless: branched ear and tassel; silks absent	S	P	158
beta	9L-137	A1 locus component (see alpha): determines aleurone and plant color, red pericarp			170
Bf1		blue fluorescent: homozygous seedlings (homozygous or heterozygous anthers) fluoresce blue under ultraviolet; anthranilic acid present	S	P	338
bf2	10L-30	blue fluorescent: similar to *Bf1* in expression; shows earlier, stronger seedling fluorescence than *Bf1*	S		2
Bg		Bergamo: regulatory element mediating *o2-mr*			286
Bh1	6L-50	blotched: colored patches on colorless (*c1*) aleurone	S	P	76
Bif1	8	barren inflorescence (was *Bif*-1440*): spikelets absent from ear and tassel; tassel branching reduced			237
bk2	9L-82	brittle stalk: brittle plant parts after 4-leaf stage	S	P	169
bm1	5S-41	brown midrib: brown pigment over vascular bundles of leaf sheath, midrib, and blade	S	P	84
bm2	1L-161	brown midrib: like *bm1*	S		34
bm3	4-near bt2	brown midrib: like *bm1* (C.R. Burnham, 1935, unpublished data)	S		82 164
bm4	9L-141	brown midrib: like *bm1*	S		31
Bn1	7L-71	brown aleurone: yellowish brown aleurone color	S		162
BNL		Brookhaven National Laboratory: designator for loci defined by restriction fragment polymorphisms			
br1	1L-81	brachytic: short internodes, short plant; no response to gibberellins	S	P	154 157
br2	1L-near hm1	brachytic: like *br1*	S		172
br3	5	brachytic: like *br1*	S		313
brn1	3S-near cr1	brown aleurone: brown kernel, brown embryo; seedling lethal	S		284
bs1	-	barren sterile	S		205
bt1	5L-42	brittle endosperm: mature kernel collapsed, angular, often translucent and brittle; affects starch-granule-bound phospho-oligosaccharide synthase	S	P	192 350

(continued on next page)

Table 3-1. Continued.

SYMBOL	LOCATION	NAME, PHENOTYPE	S	P	REF
bt2	4S-67	brittle endosperm: like bt1; ADP glucose pyrophosphorylase electrophoretic mobility; (compare sh2) (G.F. Sprague, 1935, unpublished data)	S		82 339
btn1	-	brittle node			153
bu1	-	leaf burn: leaves show burning, sometimes horizontal bands, accentuated by high temperature			99
bv1	5L-47	brevis plant: short internodes, short plant	S		174
bv2	-	brevis plant: plant height 30-50% of normal			258
Bx1	4S	benzoxazin: blue color reaction of crushed root tip with FeCl3, indicating cyclic hydroxamates present; inhibits growth of Helminthosporium turcicum, correlated with resistance to ECB (Ostrinia nubilalis)			52
bz1	9S-31	bronze: modifies purple aleurone and plant color to pale or reddish brown; anthers yellow-fluorescent; UDPG-flavonol 3-O-glucosyl transferase; allele bz1-m4 = sh1-bz1-m4	S	P	270
bz2	1L-106	bronze: like bz1; anthers not fluorescent; an1-6923 mutation includes deletion for Bz2	S	P	244
C1	9S-26	colored aleurone: c1 colorless; C1-I dominant colorless; c1-p pigment inducible by light (see text)	S	P	69
c2	4L-117	colorless: colorless aleurone, reduced plant color; chalcone synthase; C2-Idf dominant inhibitor (see text)	S	P	42
Car1	1S	catalase regulator: enzyme activity level increased			292
Cat1	5S-near Mdh5	catalase: electrophoretic mobility; cytosolic/glyoxysomal; tetrameric; intra/interlocus hybrid bands occur			18
Cat2	1S	catalase: electrophoretic mobility; null allele is known; cytosolic/glyoxysomal; tetrameric; intra/interlocus hybrid bands occur			289
Cat3	-	catalase: electrophoretic mobility; null allele is known; mitochondrial; tetrameric; no hybrid bands			291
Cdh1	-	cinnamyl alcohol dehydrogenase: electrophoretic mobility			93
Cel	-	curled entangled: rolled entangled leaves tend to be entangled			39 249
cfl2	-	complementary to fl2			247
Cg1	3S-35	corngrass: narrow leaves, extreme tillering	S	P	312
Cg2	-	corngrass: like Cg1; mutable			186
Ch1	2L-155	chocolate pericarp: dark brown pericarp	S	P	5
Cin	-	Cinteotl corn insert: repetitive sequences dispersed in the genome			305
cl1	3S-60	chlorophyll: white to green seedlings, depending upon Clm1; pale yellow endosperm	S		83
dh1	-	histone Ic: electrophoretic mobility			332
Clm1	8	modifier of cl1: greens cl1 seedlings; does not restore endosperm carotenoids	S		83
Clt1	8	clumped tassel (was Clt*-985): variable dwarfing, developmental anomalies			102 236
cm1	10L-near R1	chloroplast mutator: like ij1	S		334
cms-C		cytoplasmic male sterility: female-transmitted male sterility, C type; restored by Rf4			16
cms-S		cytoplasmic male sterility: female-transmitted male sterility, S type; restored by Rf3			149 151
cms-T		cytoplasmic male sterility: female-transmitted male sterility, Texas type; restored by Rf1 Rf2			149 151
cp1	7S-near vp9	collapsed: endosperm collapsed and partially defective			184
cp2	7S-near vp9	collapsed: endosperm rough, collapsed, partially defective; seedling very light green with darker streaks; lethal			240
cr1	3S-26	crinkly leaves: plant short; leaves broad, crinkled	S	P	78
Css1	9	sucrose synthase: sucrose synthase-2 of embryo and other tissues; (compare sh1)			198
ct1	8	compact plant: semi-dwarf plant, ear furcated			228

SYMBOL	LOCATION	NAME, PHENOTYPE	S	P	REF
ct2	1S	compact plant: semi-dwarf plant with club tassel			105
ctDNA		chloroplast DNA: sequences or loci in chloroplast genome			
cto1	-	cob turned out: ear inverted to a sheet or tube, kernels internally placed; variable expression			345
Cx1	10L-near bf2	catechol oxidase: electrophoretic mobility; null allele is known; monomeric; no hybrid bands			264
Cy	5L-near pr1	regulatory element mediating bz1-rcy			294
d1	3S-44	dwarf plant: plant andromonoecious, short, compact; responds to gibberellins; d1-t intermediate in height	S	P	71
d2	3	dwarf plant: like d1	S		336
d3	9S-59	dwarf plant: like d1	S		57
d5	2S-34	dwarf plant: like d1	S		336
D8	1L-133	dwarf plant: dominant, resembles d1; not responsive to gibberellins; (compare Mpl1)	S	P	255
da1	9	dilute aleurone: aleurone color diluted	S		89
db1	-	dichotomously branching plants (= dib): variable location of dichotomy, usually at 4-8th node (possible association with aneuploidy)	S		204 205
dek1	1S-27	defective kernel (was clf1,gcy1, clf*-792): germless; floury endosperm; anthocyanins and carotenoids absent; cultured embryos not obtained	S		238 239
dek2	1L	defective kernel (was dsc*-1315A): discolored, scarred endosperm; lethal; cultured embryos green			238 239
dek3	2S	defective kernel (was gm*-1289): germless; cultured embryos white with green stripe			238 239
dek4	2L	defective kernel (was clf*-1024A): germless; floury endosperm; cultured embryos green, narrow leaved			238 239
dek5	3S	defective kernel (was sh*-874A): shrunken endosperm; white seedling with green stripes			238 239
dek6	3L	defective kernel (was sh*-627D): shrunken endosperm; lethal; cultured embryos normal			238 239
dek7	4S	defective kernel (was su*-211C): shrunken sugary endosperm; white seedling with green stripes			238 239
dek8	4L	defective kernel (was sh*-1156A): shrunken endosperm; lethal; cultured embryos green, small			238 239
dek9	5L	defective kernel (was crp*-1365): crumpled endosperm; lethal; anthocyanins and carotenoids reduced; cultured embryos not obtained			238 239
dek10	4L	defective kernel (was cp*-1176A): collapsed endosperm; lethal; cultured embryos green, curled, stubby			238 239
dek11	7L	defective kernel (was et*-788): etched endosperm; lethal; cultured embryos white with green stripes			238 239
dek12	9S	defective kernel (was cp*-873): collapsed endosperm; lethal; cultured embryos green, narrow-leaved, curled			238 239
dek13	9L	defective kernel (was o*-744): defective opaque endosperm; lethal; cultured embryos pale green with green stripes			238 239
dek14	10S	defective kernel (was cp*-1435): collapsed endosperm; lethal; cultured embryos yellow-green			238 239
dek15	10L	defective kernel (was cp*-1427A): collapsed floury endosperm; lethal; cultured embryos green			238 239
dek16	2L	defective kernel (was fl*-1414): floury endosperm; lethal; cultured embryos normal			238 239
dek17	3L	defective kernel (was cp*-330D): collapsed endosperm; lethal; cultured embryos not obtained			306
dek18	5S	defective kernel (was cp*-931A): collapsed endosperm; lethal; cultured embryos green, narrow-leaved			306
dek19	6L	defective kernel (was o*-1296A): collapsed opaque endosperm; lethal; cultured embryos green			306
dek20	8L	defective kernel (was cp*-1392A): collapsed endosperm; lethal; cultured embryos green			306
dek21	10L	defective kernel (was msc*-1330): aleurone mosaic of reduced anthocyanins; reduced carotenoids; lethal; cultured embryos white; (compare u2)			306
dek22	1L	defective kernel (was cp*-1113A): collapsed endosperm; lethal; cultured embryos not obtained			41 307

(continued on next page)

Table 3-1. Continued.

SYMBOL	LOCATION	NAME, PHENOTYPE	S	P	REF
dek23	2L	defective kernel (was dcr*-1428): defective crown; lethal; cultured embryos not obtained			41 307
dek24	3S	defective kernel (was cp*-1283): collapsed endosperm; lethal; cultured embryos normal			307
dek25	4S	defective kernel (was sh*-1167A): shrunken endosperm; lethal; cultured embryos normal			307
dek26	5L	defective kernel (was cp*-1331): collapsed endosperm; lethal; cultured embryos normal			307
dek27	5L	defective kernel (was cp*-1380A): collapsed endosperm; lethal; cultured embryos green			307
dek28	6S	defective kernel (was o*-1307A): opaque endosperm			307
dek29	8L	defective kernel (was cp*-1387A): collapsed endosperm; viable; cultured embryos green, narrow-leaved			307
dek30	9L	defective kernel (was fl*-1391): floury endosperm; lethal; cultured embryos green, narrow-leaved			307
dep1	6	defective pistils			206
Df		deficiency: general symbol for loss of segments of chromosome			
Dia1	2S	diaphorase: electrophoretic mobility; cytosolic; monomeric			347
Dia2	1L-near bm2	diaphorase: electrophoretic mobility, cytosolic; dimeric			347
dp1	4L-137	distal pale: seedling leaf tip virescent (E.G. Anderson, unpublished)	S		
Ds		dissociation: designator for transposable factors regulated by Ac; modifies gene function and/or chromosome breakage (termed "Ds-2"); ex. Ds2 designates element isolated from Adh1-2F11	S	P	201
dSpm		defective suppressor-mutator: designator for transposable factors regulated by Spm			293
dsy1	-	desynaptic: male and female sterility: synaptic failure			110
dsy2	-	desynaptic: like dsy1			109
Dt1	9S-0	dotted: regulated controlling element at A1; responding a1-m alleles express colored dots on colorless kernels and purple sectors on brown plants	S	P	266
Dt2	6L-44	dotted: like Dt1	S		245
Dt3	7L	dotted: like Dt1, but expression variable	S		245
Dt4	4	dotted: like Dt1, but dots chiefly on crown of kernel	S		61
Dt5	9S-near yg2	dotted: like Dt1	S		61
Dt6	4-near su1	dotted: like Dt1	S		324
du1	10L-28	dull endosperm: glassy, tarnished endosperm; affects soluble starch synthase and branching enzyme IIa (P.C. Mangelsdorf, 1935, unpublished data)	S		82 193
dv1	-	divergent spindle: chromosomes unoriented at metaphase I; partial male and female sterility	S		40
dy1	-	desynaptic: chromosomes unpaired in microsporocytes; partial male and female sterility	S		227
E1	7L	esterase: electrophoretic mobility; null allele is known; dimeric; intralocus hybrid bands occur			297
E2	-	esterase: presence-absence			299
E3	3S	esterase: electrophoretic mobility; dimeric; intralocus hybrid bands occur			298
E4	3S-near cl1	esterase (was Est4): electrophoretic mobility; null allele is known; monomeric			123
E5-I	-	esterase (duplicate factor with E5-II): electrophoretic mobility			188
E5-II	-	esterase (duplicate factor with E5-I): electrophoretic mobility			188
E6	-	esterase: presence-absence			188
E7	-	esterase: presence-absence			188
E8	3S-14	esterase: electrophoretic mobility; null allele is known; dimeric; intralocus hybrid bands occur			188

SYMBOL	LOCATION	NAME, PHENOTYPE	S	P	REF
E9	-	esterase: electrophoretic mobility; null allele is known	S	P	188
E10	-	esterase: electrophoretic mobility			188
eg1	5L	expanded glumes: glumes open at right angle (= *lsr1*)	S		32
Ej1					
el1	8L	elongate: chromosomes uncoiled during meiotic metaphase and anaphase in male and female; frequent unreduced gametes	S	P	271
En		enhancer: transposable element (equivalent to *Spm*); autonomous, regulates *I* transposition (e.g. at *g2-m* = *pg-m* = *pg14-m*)		P	253
Enp1	6L-near *y1*	endopeptidase: electrophoretic mobility; null allele is known; monomeric			203
et1	3L-161	etched: pitted, scarred endosperm; virescent seedling	S	P	328
f1	1L-86	fine stripe: virescent seedling, fine white stripes on base and margin of older leaves	S	P	178
Fcu		factor Cuna: controlling element of *r1-cu*			114
fl1	2S-68	floury endosperm (= *o4*): endosperm opaque, soft; dosage effect	S	P	127
fl2	4S-58	floury: endosperm opaque, soft; dosage effect (W.J. Mumm, 1935, unpublished data)	S		82 231
fl3	8L-0	floury: endosperm opaque, soft; dosage effect	S		224
Flt		flint: designator for factors determining flint endosperm type			216
g1	10L-47	golden plant: seedling and plant with distinct yellow cast	S	P	7173
g2	3S-0	golden plant (= *g5* = *pg14* = *v19*): like *g1*, but more extreme; sheaths whitish yellow-green (= *g2*)	S		139
g5					
G6	9S-near *l7*	golden plant (was *G*-1585*): like *g1*; lighter yellowish sheaths			241
Ga1	4S-32	gametophyte factor (= *ga9*). *Ga1* pollen grains competitively superior to *ga1* on *Ga1* silks; *Ga1-S* super-gametophyte	S		150
ga2	5L-55	gametophyte factor: *Ga2* pollen grains competitively superior to *ga2*			30
ga7	3L-167	gametophyte factor: *ga7* pollen from heterozygotes 10-15% functional regardless of silk genotype			268
ga8	9S-near *lo2*	gametophyte factor: *Ga8* pollen grains competitively superior to *ga8* on *Ga8* silks (= *ga1*)			296
ga9					
ga10	5	gametophyte factor			
Gdh1	1L-near *vp8*	glutamic dehydrogenase: electrophoretic mobility; null allele is known; intra/interlocus hybrid bands occur			113
Gdh2	10	glutamic dehydrogenase: electrophoretic mobility; intralocus hybrid bands occur			262
Ger		glucoside earworm resistance: designator for earworm resistance factors from Cateto Palha Roxa			115
gl1	7L-36	glossy: cuticle wax altered; leaf surface bright, water adheres			216
gl2	2S-30	glossy: like *gl1*	S	P	162
gl3	4L-112	glossy: like *gl1*	S	P	125
gl4	4L-81	glossy (= *gl16*): like *gl1* (G.F. Sprague, unpublished)	S		125
gl5	-	glossy (was *gl5-1*, duplicate factor with *gl20*): like *gl1* (G.F. Sprague, 1935, unpublished data)	S		82 325
gl6	3L-69	glossy: like *gl1* (G.F. Sprague, 1935, unpublished data)			82
gl7	3L	glossy (= *gl12*): like *gl1* (G.F. Sprague, 1935, unpublished data)			82
gl8	5L-68	glossy (= *gl10*): like *gl1* (G.F. Sprague, 1935, unpublished data)	S		82
gl9	-	glossy: expression poor (G.F. Sprague, 1935, unpublished data) (= *gl8*)			82
gl10					
gl11	2S-near *B1*	glossy: like *gl1*; abnormal seedling morphology	S		321

(continued on next page)

Table 3-1. Continued.

SYMBOL	LOCATION	NAME, PHENOTYPE	S	P	REF
gl12		(= gl7)			
gl14	2	glossy: like gl1			323
gl15	9L-66	glossy: like gl1; expressed after 3rd leaf (G.F. Sprague, 1955, unpublished data)	S	P	3
gl16		(= gl4)			
gl17	5S-34	glossy: like gl1, but semi-dwarf with necrotic crossbands on leaves	S		272
gl18	8L-near fl3	glossy: like gl1; expression poor	S		4
gl19	3S	glossy (was gl*-169): like gl1; lethal			233
gl20	-	glossy (was gl5-2, duplicate factor with gl5): like gl1 (G.F. Sprague, 1987, unpublished data)			325
gl21	10S	glossy (was gl*-4786B): like gl1			233
Glu1	10L-near bf2	beta glucosidase: electrophoretic mobility; null allele is known; cytosolic; dimeric; intralocus hybrid bands occur			263
Go1	3L-near Me1	glutamate-oxaloacetate transaminase (possibly = Ta1): electrophoretic mobility; null allele is known; glyoxysomal; dimeric; intralocus hybrid bands occur			290
Got2	5L-96	glutamate-oxaloacetate transaminase: electrophoretic mobility; null allele is known; plastidial; dimeric; intralocus hybrid bands occur			117
Got3	5S-near a2	glutamate-oxaloacetic transaminase: electrophoretic mobility; null allele is known; mitochondrial; dimeric; intralocus hybrid bands occur			117
grt1	5L	green tip (was grt*-1308B): pale yellow seedling with green first leaf tip; lethal			233
gs1	1L-135	green stripe: grayish green stripes between vascular bundles on leaves; tissue wilts	S	P	76 210
gs2	2S-54	green stripe: like gs1, but pale green stripes; no wilting (G.F. Sprague, 1935, unpublished data)	S	P	82
gs3	6L	green stripe (was gs*-268): like gs2			233
gt1	1	grassy tillers: numerous basal branches; vegetatively totipotent in combination with id1 and pe1			303
h1	3	soft starch: endosperm soft, opaque	S		223
hcf1	2L	high chlorophyll fluorescence: affects NADP+ oxidoreductase; green seedling			207
hcf2	1L	high chlorophyll fluorescence: missing cytochrome f/b6 complex; yellow-green seedling			207
hcf3	1S	high chlorophyll fluorescence (= hcf9): missing PSII thylakoid membrane core complex; green seedling			207
hcf4	1L	high chlorophyll fluorescence: affects CO2 fixation; green seedling			208
hcf5	6S	high chlorophyll fluorescence: affects PSII reaction; green seedling			209
hcf6	1S	high chlorophyll fluorescence: missing cytochrome f/b6 complex; green seedling			173
hcf9		(= hcf3)			
hcf12	1L	high chlorophyll fluorescence			173
hcf13	1L	high chlorophyll fluorescence: affects CO2 fixation; green seedling			173 208
hcf15	2L	high chlorophyll fluorescence: affects photophosphorylation; yellow-green seedling			173
hcf18	5L-near pr1	high chlorophyll fluorescence (= hcf43): major loss of PSI; other thylakoid complexes reduced; yellow-green seedling			208
hcf19	3L	high chlorophyll fluorescence: affects PSII thylakoid membrane core complex; green/yellow-green seedling			173 208
hcf21	5L	high chlorophyll fluorescence: affects CO2 fixation, Rubisco; green seedling			208
hcf23	4S	high chlorophyll fluorescence: affects photophosphorylation; green seedling			173 208
hcf26	6S	high chlorophyll fluorescence: affects electron transport; yellow-green, viable seedling			173 208
hcf28	10L	high chlorophyll fluorescence: affects CO2 fixation; green seedling			209

SYMBOL	LOCATION	NAME, PHENOTYPE	S	P	REF
hcf31	1S	high chlorophyll fluorescence: missing chlorophyll a/b binding protein; yellow-green seedling			209
hcf34	6L	high chlorophyll fluorescence: affects photophosphorylation; yellow-green seedling			173 208
hcf36	6L	high chlorophyll fluorescence: affects electron transport; green seedling			209
hcf38	5L	high chlorophyll fluorescence: affects cytochrome f/b6 complex, alpha and beta components of CF1; green seedling			173
hcf41	1L	high chlorophyll fluorescence: affects PSII thylakoid membrane core complex; green seedling			173 208
hcf42	9L	high chlorophyll fluorescence: affects Rubisco; green/yellow-green seedling			208
hcf43		(= hcf18)			
hcf44	1L	high chlorophyll fluorescence: affects PSI membrane core complex; pale-green seedling			208
hcf46	3L	high chlorophyll fluorescence			173
hcf47	10S	high chlorophyll fluorescence: affects cytochromes; yellow-green seedling			209
hcf48	6L	high chlorophyll fluorescence: affects electron transport; yellow-green seedling			209
hcf50	1L	high chlorophyll fluorescence: missing PSI thylakoid membrane core complex; green seedling			208
hcf101	7L	high chlorophyll fluorescence (was Mu-5*): affects PSI thylakoid membrane core complex			209
hcf102	8L	high chlorophyll fluorescence: affects cytochrome f/b6 complex (D. Miles, unpublished)			
hcf316	10S	high chlorophyll fluorescence: affects chlorophyll a/b binding protein; yellow-green seedling			209
hcf323	6S	high chlorophyll fluorescence: affects photophosphorylation, coupling factor; green seedling			209
hcf408	6L	high chlorophyll fluorescence: affects chlorophyll a/b binding protein; yellow-green seedling			209
Hex1	3S-near cg1	hexokinase: electrophoretic mobility; null allele is known; cytosolic; monomeric			349
Hex2	6L-near Pl1	hexokinase: electrophoretic mobility; null allele is known; cytosolic; monomeric			349
hm1	1L-64	Helminthosporium carbonum susceptibility: disease lesions vs. yellowish flecks (resistant) on leaves with race 1	S	P	343
hm2	9L-near bk2	Helminthosporium carbonum susceptibility: electrophoretic mobility; like hm1; masked by Hm1			230
Hs1	7S-0	hairy sheath: abundant hairs on leaf sheath	S	P	337
Hsf1	5	hairy sheath frayed (was Hsf*-1595): pubescent sheaths and leaf margins; liguled enations at leaf margins			20
H1	2L-121	Helminthosporium turcicum resistance			132
H2	-	Helminthosporium turcicum resistance	S		133
H3	-	Helminthosporium turcicum resistance: (from Tripsacum floridanum)			134
I		inhibitor (= C1-I, inhibitor allele at C1 locus): also commonly used as a general symbol for inhibition and for the controlling elements responding to En			65
id1	1L-near an1	indeterminate growth: requires extended growth and short days for flowering; vegetatively totipotent with gl1 and pe1			311
Idh1	8L	isocitrate dehydrogenase: electrophoretic mobility; null allele is known; cytosolic; dimeric; intra/interlocus hybrid bands occur	S		117
Idh2	6L-near w14	isocitrate dehydrogenase: electrophoretic mobility; null allele is known; cytosolic; dimeric; intra/interlocus hybrid bands occur			117
ig1	3L-90	indeterminate gametophyte: polyembryony, heterofertilization, polyploidy, androgenesis (male and female affected)			159
ij1	7L-52	iojap striping: many variable white stripes on leaves; conditions chloroplast defects that are cytoplasmically inherited	S	P	138
ij2	1L	iojap striping: like ij1; chloroplast inheritance unknown			233
In1	7S-20	intensifier: intensifies aleurone anthocyanin pigments; In1-D dominant dilute	S	P	91
Inv		Inversion: general symbol for inversion of a segment of chromosome	S	P	

(continued on next page)

Table 3–1. Continued.

SYMBOL	LOCATION	NAME, PHENOTYPE	S	P	REF
is1	-	cupulate interspace			96
Isr1	10L-near R1	inhibitor of striate (was Ej1): reduces expression of sr2 and other leaf-striping factors	S		160
j1	8L-42	japonica striping: white stripes on leaf and sheath; not expressed in seedling	S	P	73
j2	4L-106	japonica striping: extreme white striping of leaves, etc. (R.A. Emerson, 1935, unpublished data)	S	P	82
K		knob: general symbol for constitutive heterochromatic elements			
K3L	3L-115	knob: constitutive heterochromatic element			59
K10	10L-near sr2	abnormal-10: heterochromatic appendage on long arm of chromosome 10; neocentric activity distorts segregation of linked genes	S	P	183
Kn1	1L-near Adh1	knotted: localized proliferation of tissue at vascular bundles on leaf	S	P	28
Krn		kernel row number: designator for factors determining kernel row number			216
l1	10L-near R1	luteus: yellow pigment in white tissue of chlorophyll mutants w1, u2, j1, ij1, etc.	S	P	176 177
l4	-	luteus: lethal yellow seedling	S		144
l6	9S-near bz1	luteus: like l4 (W.H. Eyster, 1935, unpublished data)	S		82
l7	9S-42	luteus: yellow seedling and plant; lethal	S		89
l10	6L-19	luteus: like l4; fails to convert protochlorophyllide to chlorophyllide	S		279
l11	6S	luteus (was l*-4120): yellow seedling with green leaf tips; lethal	S		8
l12	6L-16	luteus (was l*-4902): like l11	S		53
l13	10L-91	luteus (was l*-59A, l*-Neuffer2): dark yellow, lethal seedling; fails to convert protoporphyrin IX to Mg-protoporphyrin			194 233
l15	6L-30	luteus (was l*-Blandy3, l*-Brawn): like l4			283
l16	1S	luteus (was l*-515): like l4; leaves bleach to paler yellow in patches			233
l17	1L	luteus (was l*-544): like l4; leaves with lighter yellow crossbands			233
l18	2L	luteus (was l*-1940): like l4			233
l19	10S	luteus (was l*-425): like l4			233
la1	4S-55	lazy plant: prostrate growth habit	S	P	145
Lc1	10L-65	red leaf color: anthocyanin in coleoptile, nodes, auricle, leaf blade, etc.; (compare Sn1)	S		66
Lcs1	1S	thylakoid membrane polypeptide: electrophoretic mobility			219
Lct1	1L	thylakoid membrane polypeptide: electrophoretic mobility			219
lct2	-	thylakoid membrane polypeptide: presence-absence			219
Les1	2S-58	lesion (was Les*-843): large necrotic lesions resembling disease lesions formed by fungal infections on susceptible lines	S		234
Les2	1S-near sr1	lesion (was Les*-845A): small white lesions resembling disease lesions formed by fungal infections on resistant lines	S		234
Les3	10	lesion: like Les1			7
Les4	2L	lesion (was Les*-1375): late expression of large necrotic lesions			130
Les5	1S	lesion (was Les*-1449): like Les2			130
Les6	10S	lesion (was Les*-1451): like Les4			130
Les7	?	lesion (was Les*-1461): late expression of small chlorotic lesions			130
Les8	9S-near lo2	lesion (was Les*-2005): late expression of small, pale green lesions			130
Les9	7L-near ra1	lesion (was Les*-2008): late expression of small necrotic lesions			130

SYMBOL	LOCATION	NAME, PHENOTYPE	S	P	REF
Les10	2-near v4	lesion (was Les*-A607): like Les1			131
Lfy1	-	leafy: increased number of leaves			304
lg1	2S-11	liguleless: ligule and auricle missing; leaves upright, enveloping	S	P	71 72
lg2	3L-101	liguleless: like lg1, less extreme	S	P	23
Lg3	3-65	liguleless: dominant, no ligule; leaves upright, broad, often concave and pleated	S	P	250
li1	10L-near bf2	lineate leaves: fine, white striations on basal half of mature leaves	S	P	50
lls1	1S	lethal leaf spot: chlorotic-necrotic lesions resembling Helminthosporium carbonum infection	S		344
ln1	6	linoleic acid: lower ratio of oleate to linoleate in kernel			54
lo2	9S-50	lethal ovule: ovules containing lo2 gametophyte abort	S		227
loc1		low oil content in kernel: associated with albino seedlings			259
lp1	4	lethal pollen: lp1 pollen fails in competition with Lp1			226
lte1	2	latente: drought, heat, aluminum tolerance; frost resistance; from Michoacan 21; dominance varies			213
Lte2	10L-near g1	latente: drought, heat, aluminum tolerance; from Cateto; epistatic to lte1			214
lty1		light yellow endosperm			63
lty2		light yellow endosperm			63
lu1	5S-29	lutescent: pale yellow green leaves	S		309
lw1	1L-near Adh1	lemon white: white seedling, pale yellow endosperm	S		341
lw2	5L-near pr1	lemon white: like lw1	S	P	341
lw3	5L-near v2	lemon white (duplicate factor with lw4): like lw1			341
lw4	4-near zb6	lemon white (duplicate factor with lw3): like lw1 (= ps1-lyc)			341
lye1					
mal1	9	multiple aleurone layering: recessive interacts with two complementary dominants Mal2 and an unnamed factor, giving multiple cell layers			211
Mal2	4	multiple aleurone layering: (see mal1)			211
Mc1	-	mucronate: opaque endosperm			287
Mdh1	8	malate dehydrogenase: electrophoretic mobility; null allele is known; mitochondrial; dimeric; intra/interlocus hybrid bands occur			242
Mdh2	6L-near w14	malate dehydrogenase: electrophoretic mobility; null allele is known; mitochondrial; dimeric; intra/interlocus hybrid bands occur			242
Mdh3	3L-146	malate dehydrogenase: electrophoretic mobility; null allele is known; mitochondrial; dimeric; intra/interlocus hybrid bands occur			242
Mdh4	1L-near an1	malate dehydrogenase: electrophoretic mobility; null allele is known; cytosolic; dimeric; intra/interlocus hybrid bands occur			242
Mdh5	5S-17	malate dehydrogenase: electrophoretic mobility; null allele is known; cytosolic; dimeric; intra/interlocus hybrid bands occur			242
Me1	3L-125	malic enzyme: electrophoretic mobility; null allele is known; tetrameric			117
Mei1	-	meiosis: chromosomes sticky in metaphase I; male sterile			107 108
mep1	5L	modifier of endosperm protein: affects quantities of Prot1 protein forms			301

(continued on next page)

Table 3-1. Continued.

SYMBOL	LOCATION	NAME, PHENOTYPE	S	P	REF
Mer		Maya earworm resistance: designator for earworm resistance factors from IAC Maya			215
mg1	-	miniature germ (replaces mg of Wentz): germ 1/4 to 1/3 of normal; viable			167
mi1	1	midget plant: small plant (H.S. Perry, 1935, unpublished data)	S		82
mmm1	1L-near an1	modifier of mitochondrial malate dehydrogenases: mobilities			242
mn1	2-near fl1	miniature seed: small, somewhat defective kernel; fully viable	S	P	185
mn2	7	miniature seed: small kernel, loose pericarp; extremely defective but will germinate (R.J. Lambert, unpublished)	S		25
Mp	1L-near Adh1	modulator of pericarp: transposable factor affecting P1 locus; parallel to Ac-Ds			121
Mpl1		miniplant: dominant, andromonoecious, intermediate dwarf; probable allele of D8; not responsive to gibberellins (M. Freeling, 1987, unpublished data)			
Mr	9S-near l7	mutator of R-m: transposable factor, regulates R1-m mutation		P	35
Mrh		mutator: controlling element of a1-m-rh			273
ms1	6L-near si1	male sterile: anthers shriveled, not usually exserted; affected at microspore vacuolation	S		314
ms2	9L-64	male sterile: like ms1; affected between vacuolation and pore formation	S		87 89
ms3	3	male sterile: anthers shrivelled; not usually exserted (= po1)			87 89
ms4		male sterile: anthers not exserted; affected at microspore mitosis	S		13
ms5	5-near v3	male sterile: like ms2	S		13
ms7	7L-near ra1	male sterile: like ms5; affected in meiosis	S	P	13
ms8	8L-28	male sterile: like ms5; affected in meiosis	S		13
ms9	1S-near P1	male sterile: like ms5; affected at microspore vacuolation	S		13
ms10	10L-near bf2	male sterile: like ms5; affected at microspore mitosis	S		13
ms11	10	male sterile: like ms1; affected at microspore vacuolation	S		13
ms12	1	male sterile: like ms5; affected at microspore vacuolation	S		13
ms13	5S	male sterile: like ms5; affected at microspore mitosis	S		13
ms14	1-near as1	male sterile: like ms1; affected variably in meiosis	S		79
ms17	1S-23	male sterile	S		89
ms20		male sterile: pollen grains developing in presence of Ms21 are defective and nonfunctional if sks1, normal if Sks1			
Ms21	6	male sterile: affected in meiosis			171 295
ms22	-	male sterile (allelic to ms*-Bear7): affected in meiosis			351
ms23	3L	male sterile: like ms1; affected in microspore mitosis			351
ms24	-	male sterile: anaphase I disturbed, spindle persists			108
ms28		male sterile (was Ms*-1995)			241
Ms41	4L	male sterile: anaphase I impaired			107 108
ms43	8L	mosaic (was Msc*-791A): aleurone mosaic for anthocyanin color			241
Msc1	1L	mosaic (was Msc*-1124B): aleurone mosaic for anthocyanin color			241
Msc2	5S	modifier of R-st: affects expression of R1-st	S		6
Mst1	10L-67	mitochondrial DNA: sequences or loci in the mitochondrial genome			282
mtDNA		mutator: freely transposable element; Mu1 designates element isolated from Adh1-S3034			
Mu					

SYMBOL	LOCATION	NAME, PHENOTYPE	S	P	REF
Mut	2S-near gl2	mutator: controlling element for bz1-m-rh			274
Mo1	-	resistance to maize mosaic virus I ("corn stripe")			21
na1	3L-113	nana plant: short, erect dwarf; no response to gibberellins	S	P	137 175
na2	5S-near b1	nana plant: like na1 (H.S. Perry, unpublished)	S		
NCS1		nonchromosomal stripe: maternally inherited light green leaf striping			310
NCS2		nonchromosomal stripe: maternally inherited pale green and depressed striping; mitochondrial	S		43
NCS3		nonchromosomal stripe: maternally inherited striations, distorted plants; mitochondrial	S		43
nec1	8L-near fl3	necrotic (was nec*-6697, sienna*-7748): chlorotic seedling that stays rolled, wilts and dies	S		195
nec2	1S-34	necrotic (was nec*-8147, olive-necrotic-8147, ON-8147): green seedling develops necrotic lesions at 2-3 leaf stage; lethal (E.G. Anderson, 1952, unpublished data)			
nec3	5-near b1	necrotic (was nec*-409): seedling emerge with tightly rolled leaves that turn brown and die without unrolling; manually unrolled leaves tan with dark brown crossbands	S		232
nec4	2S-near d5	necrotic (was nec*-516B): seedling yellow, leaf tips necrotic; lethal			129
nec5	4L	necrotic (was nec*-642A): pale green seedling becoming necrotic; dark brown exudate; lethal			233
nec6	5S-near a2	necrotic (was nec*-493): like nec3			233
nec7	5L	necrotic (was nec*-756B): seedling becoming necrotic in crossbands; lethal			233
nl1	10L-near b/2	narrow leaf: leaf blade narrow, some white streaks (R.A. Emerson, 1935, unpublished data)	S	P	82
NOR	6S	nucleolus organizer: codes for ribosomal RNA	S		199
NPI		Native Plants, Inc.: designator for loci defined by restriction fragment polymorphisms			
o1	4L-near gl3	opaque endosperm: endosperm starch soft, opaque (W.R. Singleton and D.F. Jones, 1935, unpublished data)	S		82 231
o2	7S-16	opaque endosperm: like o1; high lysine content; regulates b32 protein (see pro); reduced lysine degradation (lysine-ketoglutaric reductase) (W.R. Singleton and D.F. Jones, 1935, unpublished data) (= fl1)	S	P	82 231
o4		opaque endosperm: like o1; virescent to yellow or white seedlings			
o5		opaque endosperm: like o1; high lysine content (= pro1)			
o6	7L-near ra1	opaque endosperm: crown opaque and light in color, frequently with a cavity; base or abgerminal side of kernel often corneous	S		278
o7	10L-87	opaque endosperm: like o1	S		217
o9		opaque endosperm: high lysine content	S		225
o10		opaque endosperm: like o1	S		225
o11		opaque endosperm: thin, opaque, somewhat shrunken kernels with greyish cast	S		225
o12		opaque endosperm: thin, etched or scarred kernels, variable in size; plants chlorophyll deficient and small, with pollen but few ears	S		225
o13		opaque endosperm: opaque, etched kernels with rim of corneous starch on abgerminal side	S		225
Og1	10S-16	old gold stripe: variable bright yellow stripes on leaf blade	S	P	181
ora2	-	orange endosperm			62
ora3	-	orange endosperm			63
oro1	6S	orobanche: yellow to tan necrotic with cross-banding when grown under light-dark cycle; some chlorophyll with Oro1; fails to convert Mg-protoporphyrin monomethyl ester to protochlorophyllide	S		194

(continued on next page)

Table 3-1. Continued.

SYMBOL	LOCATION	NAME, PHENOTYPE	S	P	REF
oro2	-	orobanche: like oro1			194
Orom1	-	orobanche modifier: partially corrects chlorophyll loss in oro1			194
orp1	4S	orange pericarp (duplicate factor with orp2): pericarp orange over orp1 orp2 kernels; lethal			235
orp2	10L	orange pericarp (duplicate factor with orp1)			235
oy1	10S-12	oil yellow: seedling oily greenish-yellow; viable; fails to convert protoporphyrin IX to Mg-protoporphyrin; oy1-t tinged green; oy1-1039, oy1-1040 lethal; Oy1-700 dominant yellow-green	S	P	88
P		plant color component at R1: anthocyanin pigmentation in seedling leaf tip, coleoptile, anthers			329 330
P1	1S-26	pericarp color: red pigment in cob and pericarp	S	P	70 182
pam1	-	plural abnormalities of meiosis: desynchronized meiotic divisions and premeiotic mitosis; male sterile, incompletely female sterile			111
pam2	-	plural abnormalities of meiosis: like pam1			109
pb1	6L-near y1	piebald leaves: very light, irregular green bands on leaf		P	58
pb4	6L-near y1	piebald leaves: like pb1		S	58
pd1	-	paired rows: single vs. paired pistillate spikelets; pd1 is found in teosinte also			168
Pdf1	-	thylakoid membrane polypeptide: dominant increase in electrophoretic mobility			220
pe1	-	perennialism: vegetatively totipotent in combinations with gt1 and id1			303
pg11	6L-38	pale green (duplicate factor with pg12): seedling light yellowish green; mature plant pale and vigorous	S	P	269
pg12	9-61	pale green (duplicate factor with pg11)	S		269
pg13	-	pale green: seedling light yellowish green; stunted growth (= g2)			308
pg14					
pg15	1S	pale green (was ppg*-340B): seedling light yellowish green; bleaches to near white in patches; lethal	S	P	253
pg16	1L	pale green (was pg*-219): seedling light yellowish green			233
Pgd1	6-near rgd1	6-phosphogluconate dehydrogenase: electrophoretic mobility; null allele is known; cytosolic; dimeric; intra/interlocus hybrid bands occur			233
Pgd2	3L-near ts4	6-phosphogluconate dehydrogenase: electrophoretic mobility; null allele is known; cytosolic; dimeric; intra/interlocus hybrid bands occur			117
Pgm1	1L-near Prot1	phosphoglucomutase: electrophoretic mobility; null allele is known; cytosolic; monomeric			117
Pgm2	5S-0	phosphoglucomutase: electrophoretic mobility; null allele is known; cytosolic; monomeric			117
Ph1	4S-0	pith abscission: cob disarticulation			97
Phi1	1L-149	phosphohexose isomerase: electrophoretic mobility; null allele is known; cytosolic; dimeric; intralocus hybrid bands occur			117
pi1	-	pistillate florets (duplicate factor with pi2): secondary florets develop ("Country Gentlemen" or "Shoe Peg" expression) in pi1 pi2 ears			135
pi2	-	pistillate florets (duplicate factor with pi1)			135
PIO		Pioneer Hi-Bred, International: designator for loci defined by restriction fragment polymorphisms			
Pl1	6L-49	purple plant: sunlight-independent purple pigment in plant	S	P	77
pm1	3L-near ts4	pale midrib: midrib and adjacent tissue lighter green	S	P	24
Pn1	7L-112	papyrescent glumes: long, thin papery glumes on ear and tassel	S	P	98

SYMBOL	LOCATION	NAME, PHENOTYPE	S	P	REF
po1	6S-4	polymitotic (= ms4): repeats 2nd meiotic division in male and female	S	P	11
ppg1	5L	pale pale green (was cb*-199A): white seedling with faint green; white necrotic crossbands; lethal			233
pr1	5L-67	red aleurone: changes purple aleurone to red; flavonoid 3'-hydroxylase	S	P	69
pro1	8L-near fl3	proline requiring (= o6): crumpled opaque kernel; b32 protein isoforms and null; green-striped lethal seedling			100
Prot1	1L-121	protein: embryo protein mobility variations; null allele is known			301
ps1	5S-39	pink scutellum (= vp7): viviparous; endosperm and scutellum pink, seedling white with pink flush; ps1-lyc not viviparous	S	P	320
Pt1	6L-60	polytypic ear: proliferation produces irregular growth on ear and tassel	S	P	229
Px1	2L	peroxidase: electrophoretic mobility; null allele is known; monomeric			120
Px2		peroxidase: electrophoretic mobility; monomeric			187
Px3	7L-near Pn1	peroxidase: electrophoretic mobility; monomeric			187
Px4	-	peroxidase: electrophoretic mobility; null allele is known; monomeric			187
Px5	-	peroxidase: presence-absence			187
Px6	-	peroxidase: presence-absence			187
Px7	-	peroxidase: electrophoretic mobility; null allele is known; monomeric			187
Px8	-	peroxidase: electrophoretic mobility; monomeric			22
Px9	-	peroxidase: electrophoretic mobility; null allele is known; monomeric			22
py1	6L-69	pigmy plant: leaves short, pointed; fine white streaks	S	P	336
py2	1L	pigmy: like py1			233
pyd1	9S-near yg2	pale yellow deficiency: pale yellow seedling; deficiency for short terminal segment of chromosome arm; lethal			200
R1	10L-61	colored: red or purple color in aleurone and/or anthers, leaf tip, brace roots, etc.; (for alleles, see text)	S	P	69
ra1	7L-32	ramosa: ear branched, tassel conical	S	P	13 103
ra2	3S-49	ramosa: irregular kernel placement; tassel many-branched, upright (R.A. Brink, 1935, unpublished data)	S	P	82 243
ra3	4	ramosa: (H.S. Perry, 1954, unpublished data)	S		228
rd1	1L-near Adh1	reduced plant: semi-dwarf plant			106
rd2	6L	reduced plant: like rd1, but not as extreme			
rDNA		ribosomal DNA: rDNA5.8S, rDNA18S and rDNA25S located in NOR on 6S; rDNA5S on 2L near H1			318
rDt		receptor of Dotted			
Rf1	3S-near Lg3	fertility restorer: restores fertility to cms-T; complementary to Rf2			148
Rf2	9-near wx1	fertility restorer: see Rf1			68
Rf3	2L	fertility restorer: restores fertility to cms-S	S		29
Rf4	2	fertility restorer: restores fertility to cms-C	S		118
Rg1	3-67	ragged leaves: defective tissue between veins of older leaves, causing holes and tearing	S	P	26
rgd1	6-8	ragged seedling: seedling leaves narrow, thread-like, have difficulty in emerging	S	P	163
Rgd2	5	ragged leaves (was Rgd*-1445): leaves narrow and distorted; tillering			237
rgo1		reversed germ orientation: embryo faces base of ear; variable frequency, maternal trait			285
rhm1	6-near rgd1	resistance to Helminthosporium maydis: chloretic-lesion reaction with race O	S		315
Ri1	4S-27	rind abscission: cob disarticulation			97
Rp1	10S-0	resistance to Puccinia sorghi		P	189 190

(continued on next page)

Table 3-1. Continued.

SYMBOL	LOCATION	NAME, PHENOTYPE	S	P	REF
Rp3	3-near gl6	resistance to Puccinia sorghi	S		352
Rp4	4S-24	resistance to Puccinia sorghi	S		352
Rp5	10S-near Rp1	resistance to Puccinia sorghi			288
Rp6	10S-near Rp1	resistance to Puccinia sorghi			352
Rpp9	10S-near Rp1	resistance to Puccinia polysora and P. sorghi			342
Rs1	1-near as1	rough sheath: extreme ligule disorganization	S		161
rs2		rough sheath	S		161
rt1	3S-near Cg1	rootless: secondary roots few or absent	S	P	141
S		seed color component at R1: anthocyanin pigmentation in aleurone			329
Sad1	10L-near bf2	shikimate dehydrogenase: electrophoretic mobility; plastidial; monomeric			347
Sdw1	8	semi-dwarf plant (was Sdw*-1592): shortened internodes, erect leaves			19
se1	4L	sugary-enhancer: high sugar content with su1; light yellow endosperm; freely wrinkled in Il677a			90
sen1	3	soft endosperm (duplicate factor with sen2): endosperm soft, opaque			331
sen2	7	soft endosperm (duplicate factor with sen1)			331
sen3	1	soft endosperm (duplicate factor with sen1): like sen1			331
sen4		soft endosperm (duplicate factor with sen3)			331
sen5	2	soft endosperm (duplicate factor with sen6): like sen1			331
sen6	5	soft endosperm (duplicate factor with sen5)			331
sfl1		small flint type: ears on sfl1 plants produce only small flint endosperms; +/sfl1 ears are normal			64
Sg1	-	string cob: reduced pedicels	S	P	95
sh1	9S-29	shrunken: inflated endosperm collapses on drying, forming smoothly indented kernels; sucrose synthase-1 of endosperm (compare Css1); homotetramer	S	P	136
sh2	3L-149.2	shrunken: inflated, transparent, sweet kernels collapse on drying, becoming angular and brittle; ADPG pyrophosphorylase (compare bt2)	S	P	191
sh4	5L	shrunken: collapsed, chalky endosperm	S		340
si1	6L-20	silky (= ms-si): multiple silks in ear; sterile tassel with silks	S		92
sk1	2S-56	silkless ears: pistils abort, no silks	S		147
Sks1	2L-near v4	suppressor of sterility: pollen grains developing in presence of Ms21 are defective and nonfunctional if sks1, normal if Sks1			171 295
sl1	7L-50	slashed leaves: leaves slit longitudinally by necrotic streaks	S		125
sm1	6L-59	salmon silks: silks salmon color with P1-RR, brown in P1-WW	S	P	1
Sn1	10L-near R1	scutellar node color: anthocyanin in coleoptile, nodes, auricle, leaf blade, etc. (compare Lc1)			101
Sod1	-	superoxide dismutase: electrophoretic mobility; plastidial; dimeric; intralocus hybrid bands occur			9
Sod2	-	superoxide dismutase: electrophoretic mobility; mitochondrial; tetrameric; intralocus hybrid bands occur			9
Sod4		superoxide dismutase: electrophoretic mobility; cytosolic; dimeric; intralocus hybrid bands occur			9
Spc1	3L-near ig1	speckled (was Spc*-1376, Les*-1376): brown speckling on leaves and sheath at flowering; supporting tissues weak			237
spc2	1L	speckled (was spc*-262A): green seedling with light green speckles			233
spc3	3L	speckled (was pg*-553C): green seedling with dark and light green speckles			233

SYMBOL	LOCATION	NAME, PHENOTYPE	S	P	REF
Spm	2L	suppressor-mutator: autonomous transposable element (equivalent to En); regulates dSpm transposition and function at a1-m1, a1-m2, b21-m13, etc.			202
spt1	4S	spotted (was spt*-464): pale green seedling with dark green spots			233
spt2	1S-0	spotted (was pg spt*-1269A): like spt1			233
sr1	10L-95	striate leaves: many white striations or stripes on leaves (A.M. Brunson, 1935, unpublished data)	S		82
sr2	10S	striate leaves: white stripes on leaf and sheath	S	P	146
sr3		striate leaves: virescent and striate to striped	S	P	105
Ss2		(see Css1)			
st1	4S-62	sticky chromosome: small plant, striate leaves, pitted kernels resulting from sticky chromosomes; st1-e heightened by high temperature	S	P	14
su1	4S-66	sugary: endosperm wrinkled and translucent when dry; sweet at milk stage; starch debranching enzyme 1; su1-am	S	P	51
su2	6L-58	sugary-amylaceous; su1-st recessive starchy	S		89
Sup1	-	sugary: endosperm glassy, translucent, sometimes wrinkled			196
sy1	-	suppressor: modifies o2 kernels to semi-transparent			319
		yellow scutellum			
T		reciprocal translocation: general symbol for exchange of parts between two nonhomologous chromosomes			
Ta1	1L-near Adh1	transaminase (possibly = Got1): electrophoretic mobility; dimeric; intralocus hybrid bands occur	S	P	187
tb1	5-near bt1	teosinte branched: many tillers; ear branches tassel-like	S		33
td1	3	thick tassel dwarf: (E.G. Anderson, unpublished)	S		197
te1		terminal ear: ears replace tassel or tassel parts; mixed terminal inflorescences	S		254
Thc1	-	thiocarbamate sensitive: sensitive to Eradicane	S		205
tl1	1L	tasselless			241
Tr1	7L-46	tillered (was Tr*-1590): extreme tillering	S	P	180
Tp1	10L-45	teopod: many tillers, narrow leaves, many small partially podded ears, tassel simple	S	P	252
Tp2	-	teopod: like Tp1			
Tpi1		triose phosphate isomerase: electrophoretic mobility; plastidial; dimeric			347
Tpi2	8	triose phosphate isomerase: electrophoretic mobility; plastidial; dimeric			347
Tpi3	3L-near Rg1	triose phosphate isomerase: electrophoretic mobility; cytosolic; monomeric			347
Tpi4		triose phosphate isomerase: electrophoretic mobility; cytosolic; monomeric			349
tpm1	-	thylakoid peptide modifier: dominant decrease in electrophoretic mobility			218
tr1	2S-74	two-ranked ear: distichous vs. decussate phyllotaxy in ear axis			168
ts1	1S-24	tassel seed: tassel pistillate and pendant; if removed, small ear with irregular kernel placement develops	S		75
ts2	3L-73	tassel seed: like ts1, but branches pendant rather than whole tassel	S	P	75
ts4	4S-53	tassel seed: tassel compact, upright, with pistillate and staminate florets	S	P	256
Ts5	1L-158	tassel seed: nearly normal tassel with scattered, short silks	S		80
Ts6	4L-101	tassel seed: tassel pistillate to mixed, compact, ear with irregular kernel placement	S	P	243
Tu1	-	tunicate: kernels enclosed in long glumes; tassel glumes large, coarse	S	P	48 49
ub1		unbranched: tassel with one spike	S	P	240

(continued on next page)

Table 3-1. Continued.

SYMBOL	LOCATION	NAME, PHENOTYPE	S	P	REF
Ufo1	-	unstable factor for orange: anthers, silks, and most other plant parts orange with *P1-WR* or *P1-RR*; growth retarded			335
UMC		University of Missouri, Columbia: designator for loci defined by restriction fragment polymorphisms			
Uq		ubiquitous: controlling element mediating *a1-ruq*			
v1	9L-63	virescent: yellowish white seedling, greens rapidly; low temperature exaggerates	S	P	94
v2	5L-107	virescent: like *v1*, but greens slowly; low temperature exaggerates	S	P	56
v3	5L-45	virescent: light yellow seedling, greens rapidly; low temperature exaggerates	S	P	73
v4	2L-83	virescent: like *v2*	S	P	56
v5	7S-24	virescent: like *v1*, but older leaves have white stripes	S	P	56
v8	4L-near *Tu1*	virescent: like *v2*; lethal	S		57
v12	5L-near *ys1*	virescent: like *v3*	S		257
v13	-	virescent: first leaf with green tip; greens slowly	S		257
v16	8L-14	virescent: like *v2*	S		257
v17	4	virescent: like *v1*, but greening from base to tip	S		257
v18	10	virescent: like *v1*	S		257
v19		(= *g2*)			
v21	8L	virescent (was *v*-25, v*-A562*): grainy virescent, greening from tips and margins inward	S		17
v22	1L-near *an1*	virescent (was *v*-18983*): like *v1* (E.G. Anderson, unpublished)	S		
v23	4-near *su1*	virescent (was *v*-8914*): like *v1* (E.G. Anderson, unpublished)	S		
v24	2L	virescent (was *v*-424*): like *v1*			233
v25	1S	virescent (was *v*-17*): greenish white seedling; greens from base upward			233
v26	2S	virescent (was *v*-453*): yellowish white seedling with green leaf tip and midrib			233
v27	7L	virescent (was *v*-590A*): like *v1*			233
v28	9S	virescent (was *v*-27*): like *v1*			233
v29	10L	virescent (was *v*-418*): grainy virescent			233
v30	9L-87	virescent (was *v*-8587*): like *v1*			233
va1	7L-near *ij1*	variable sterile: variable male and female fertility; cytokinesis fails in anaphase I			44
Vg1	1L-85	vestigial glume: glumes very small, cob and anthers exposed	S	P	12
vp1	3L-near *ts4*	viviparous: embryo fails to become dormant, viable if transplanted; some alleles dormant; chlorophyll and carotenoids unaffected; anthocyanins in aleurone suppressed	S		322
vp2	5S-38	viviparous: embryo fails to become dormant; white endosperm, white seedling; anthocyanins unaffected	S	P	86
vp5	1S-1	viviparous: like *vp2*	S	P	275
vp7		(= *ps1*)			
vp8	1L-154	viviparous: embryo fails to become dormant; chlorophyll and carotenoids unaffected; small, pointed-leaf seedlings			276
vp9	7S-25	viviparous (also known as *y7*): like *vp2*; *vp9-4889* dormant, pale aleurone, pale green seedling			276
Vsr1	10L	virescent striped (was *Vsr*-1446*): virescent seedling; greens to white and yellow striped plant	S		241
w1	6L-near *w14*	white: white seedling	S		71 72 17
w2	10L-77	white: white seedling; endosperm pitted and spotted (compare *dek21*)	S		179
w3	2L-111	white: like *vp2*; *w3-8686* dominant, pale endosperm, pale green seedling in dim light	S	P	179

SYMBOL	LOCATION	NAME, PHENOTYPE	S	P	REF
w11	9S-54	white: like w1	S		57
w14	6L-78	white (was w*-8657): like w1	S		53
w15	6L-13	white (was w*-8896): like w1; fails to convert protochlorophyllide to chlorophyllide	S		53
w16	7S-near vp9	white: like w1			221
w17	7S-near Hs1	white: like w1			221
Wc1	9L-107	white cap: kernel with white crown and pale yellow endosperm	S		165
wd1	9S-near yg2	white deficiency: white seedling: deficiency for distal half of first chromomere of short arm	S	P	200
wgs1	5L	white green sectors (was sct*-206B): white seedling with green sectors			233
whp1	2L	white pollen: duplicate factor with c2 for yellow pollen and for anthocyanins			46
wil	6L-near y1	wilted: chronic wilting, delayed differentiation of metaxylem vessels	S		261
wlu1	3L	white luteus (was wl*-28): pale yellow seedling; lethal			233
wlu2	7L	white luteus (was wl*-543A): like wlu1			233
wlu3	8L	white luteus (was wl*-203A): like wlu1			233
wlu4	9L	white luteus (was wl*-41A): like wlu1			233
Wrk1	3S	wrinkled kernel (was Wr*-1020): kernels small and wrinkled			241
ws1	-	white sheath: light yellow leaf sheaths; duplicate factor with ws2	S		156
ws2	-	white sheath: see ws1	S		156
ws3	2S-0	white sheath: white leaf sheath, culm, husks	S	P	267
wsp		weak striped plant: maternally inherited pale striping			27
wt1	2S-60	white tip: tip of first leaf white and blunt	S		327
wt2	4S	white tip (was cb*-10): seedling with white leaf tip and crossbands on first 2 leaves			233
ux1	9S-56	waxy: amylopectin (stained red by iodine) replaces amylose (blue staining) in endosperm and pollen; starch-granule-bound NDP-starch glucosyl transferase	S	P	47
wyg1	7L-near ra1	white yellow green			221
y1	6L-17	white endosperm: reduced carotenoid pigments in endosperm; some alleles affect chlorophyll in seedlings (e.g. y1-8549)	S	P	51
y3	2S-near d1	white endosperm: like y1			251
y7		(= vp9-y7)			
y8	7S-18	white endosperm: pale yellow endosperm	S		143
y9	10S-24	white endosperm: pale yellow endosperm, slightly viviparous; green to pale green seedlings and plants	S		281
y10	3L	white endosperm (was w*-7748): pale yellow endosperm; white seedling; lethal	S		277
y11		white endosperm: pale yellow endosperm; green seedling			326
y12		white endosperm: like y11			326
yd2	3L-near lg2	yellow dwarf			280
yg1	5L-near v2	yellow-green: yellow-green seedling and plant			84
yg2	9S-7	yellow-green: like yg1	S	P	140
ys1	5L-75	yellow stripe: yellow tissue between leaf veins, reflects iron deficiency symptoms	S	P	10
ys2	1S	yellow stripe: yellow tissue between leaf veins	S		260
ys3	3L-near Rg1	yellow stripe: like ys1	S		353

(continued on next page)

Table 3-1. Continued.

SYMBOL	LOCATION	NAME, PHENOTYPE	S	P	REF
Ysk1	4-near su1	yellow streaked (was Ysk*-844): longitudinal yellow streaks top 3rd of mature leaves			237
z1	-	(= vp9-z = y7-z)			
zb1	-	zebra crossbands: yellowish crossbands on older leaves	S		55
zb2	-	zebra crossbands: crossbands on seedling leaves	S		333
zb3	5L-near v2	zebra crossbands: yellowish crossbands on older leaves (M. Demerec, 1935, unpublished data)	S		82
zb4	1S-19	zebra crossbands: regularly spaced crossbands on earlier leaves; enhanced by cool temperatures	S	P	124
zb6	4-79	zebra crossbands: regularly spaced crossbands on earlier leaves; enhanced by cool temperatures	S		126
zb7	1L-near Adh1	zebra crossbands (was zb*-101): lighter green crossbands on seedlings; glossy			233
Zb8	9-near ux1	zebra crossbands (was Atc1, Cb*-1443): yellow-green crossbands on older leaves; strong anthocyanin expression in leaf tip and blade			237 241
Zer		Zapalote Chico earworm resistance: designator for earworm resistance factors from Zapalote Chico			215
zn1	10L-26	zebra necrotic: necrotic tissue appears between veins in transverse leaf bands on half-grown or older plants	S	P	122
zn2	-	zebra necrotic: like zn1	S		104
Zp		zein polypeptide: designator for loci determining zein polypeptides			316 317
zpg1	-	zebra-stripe pale green			63

REFERENCES TO ORIGINAL DESCRIPTIONS AND DESIGNATIONS

(gene symbols referenced are included within brackets)
(MNL = Maize Genetics Cooperation News Letter)

1. Anderson, E.G. 1921. Cornell Univ. Agric. Exp. Stn. Memoir 48:533-554. (sm1)
2. Anderson, E.G. 1953. MNL 27:5. (bf2)
3. Anderson, E.G. 1955. MNL 29:5. (gl15)
4. Anderson, E.G. 1955. MNL 29:6. (gl18)
5. Anderson, E.G. and R.A. Emerson. 1931. Am. Nat. 65:253-257. (Ch1)
6. Ashman, R.B. 1960. Genetics 45:19-34. (Mst1)
7. Ashman, R.B. and A.J. Ullstrup. 1976. J. Hered. 67:220-222. (Les3)
8. Bachmann, M.D., et al. 1973. J. Ultrastruct. Res. 45:384-406. (l1)
9. Baum, J.A. and J.G. Scandalios. 1982. J. Hered. 73:95-100. (Sod1 Sod3 Sod4)
10. Beadle, G.W. 1929. Am. Nat. 63:189-192. (ys1)
11. Beadle, G.W. 1931. Cornell Univ. Agric. Exp. Stn. Memoir 135:1-12. (po1)
12. Beadle, G.W. 1932. Cytologia 3:142-155. (va1)
13. Beadle, G.W. 1932. Genetics 17:413-431. (ms5 ms7 ms8 ms9 ms10 ms11 ms12 ms13 ms14 ra1)
14. Beadle, G.W. 1932. Ztschr. ind. Abst. Vererbungsl. 63:195-217. (st1)

15. Beadle, G.W. and B. McClintock. 1928. Science 68:433. (as1)
16. Beckett, J.B. 1971. Crop Sci. 11:724-727. (cms-C)
17. Beckett, J.B. and M.G. Neuffer. 1973. MNL 47:147. (v21)
18. Beckman, L., et al. 1964. Science 146:1174-1175. (Cat1)
19. Bird, R.M. and M.G. Neuffer. 1985. MNL 59:42. (Sdw1)
20. Bird, R.M. and M.G. Neuffer. 1986. p. 818-822.In M. Freeling (ed.) Plant genetics.Alan R. Liss, New York. (Hsf1)
21. Brewbaker, J.L. 1974. Proc. 29th Ann. Corn and Sorghum Res. Conf. p. 118-133. (Mv1)
22. Brewbaker, J.L. and Y. Hasegawa. 1974. MNL 48:35-37. (Px8 Px9)
23. Brink, R.A. 1933. J. Hered. 24:325-326. (lg2)
24. Brink, R.A. 1935. J. Hered. 26:249-251. (pm1)
25. Brink, R.A. and R.A. Nilan. 1952. Genetics 37:519-544. (Mp)
26. Brink, R.A. and P.H. Senn. 1931. J. Hered. 22:155-161. (Rg1)
27. Brown, W.L. and D.N. Duvick. 1958. MNL 32:120-121. (wsp)
28. Bryan, A.A. and J.E. Sass. 1941. J. Hered. 32:342-346. (Kn1)
29. Buchert, J.G. 1961. Proc. Natl. Acad. Sci. 47:1436-1440. (Rf3)
30. Burnham, C.R. 1936. J. Am. Soc. Agron. 28:968-975. (ga2)
31. Burnham, C.R. 1947. MNL 21:36. (bm4)
32. Burnham, C.R. 1958. MNL 32:93. (eg1)
33. Burnham, C.R. 1961. MNL 35:87. (tb1)
34. Burnham, C.R. and R.A. Brink. 1932. J. Am. Soc. Agron. 24:960-963. (bm2)
35. Chang, M.T. and M.G. Neuffer. 1987. J. Hered. 78:163-170. (Mr)
36. Chang, S-H. and J.L. Brewbaker. 1976. MNL 50:31-32. (aph1)
37. Chao, S.E. and J.G. Scandalios. 1969. Biochem. Genet. 3:537-547. (Amy2)
38. Chao, S.E. and J.G. Scandalios. 1971. Genetics 69:47-61. (Amy1)
39. Chourey, P.S. and C. Mouli. 1975. Genetics 77:s11. (Ce1)
40. Clark, F.J. 1940. Am. J. Bot. 27:547-559. (ab1)
41. Clark, J.K. and W.F. Sheridan. 1985. J. Hered. 77:83-92. (dek22 dek23)
42. Coe, E.H., Jr. 1958. MNL 32:102. (c2)
43. Coe, E.H. 1983. Maydica 28:151-168. (NCS2 NCS3)
44. Coe, E.H. 1987. MNL 61:47. (anl1 v30)
45. Coe, E.H. and J.B. Beckett. 1987. MNL 61:46-47. (baf1)
46. Coe, E.H., et al. 1981. J. Hered. 72:318-320. (whp1)
47. Collins, G.N. 1909. USDA, Plant Indus. Bur. Bull. 161:1-30. (wx1)
48. Collins, G.N. 1917. J. Agric. Res. 9:383-395. (Tu1)
49. Collins, G.N. 1917. Proc. Natl. Acad. Sci. 3:345-349. (Tu1)
50. Collins, G.N. and J.H. Kempton. 1920. J. Hered. 11:3-6. (ii1)
51. Correns, C. 1901. Bibliotheca Bot. 53:1-161. (su1 y1)
52. Couture, R.M., et al. 1971. Phys. Plant Pathol. 1:515-521. (Bx1)
53. Cox, E.L. and D.B. Dickinson. 1971. Biochem. Genet. 5:15-25. (l12 w14 w15)

(continued on next page)

Table 3-1. Continued.

54. de la Roche, I.A., et al. 1971. Crop Sci. 11:856-859. (*In1*)
55. Demeree, M. 1921. J. Hered. 12:406-407. (*zb1*)
56. Demeree, M. 1924. Cornell Univ. Agric. Exp. Stn. Memoir 84. (*v1 v3 v4 v5*)
57. Demeree, M. 1926. Am. Nat. 60:172-176. (*d3 v8 w11*)
58. Demeree, M. 1926. J. Hered. 17:301-306. (*pb1 pb4*)
59. Dempsey, E.D. 1971. MNL 45:58. (K3L)
60. Dempsey, E.D. 1985. p. 311-316.In M. Freeling (ed.) Plant genetics.Alan R. Liss, New York. (*Ac2*)
61. Doerschug, E.B. 1973. Theor. Appl. Genet. 43:182-189. (*Dt4 Dt5*)
62. Dollinger, E.J. 1984. MNL 58:209-210. (*ora2*)
63. Dollinger, E.J. 1985. Crop Sci. 25:819-821. (*lty1 lty2 ora3 zpg1*)
64. Dollinger, E.J. 1987. MNL 61:103. (*sft1*)
65. Dooner, H.K. and J.L. Kermicle. 1971. Genetics 67:427-436. (*I*)
66. Dooner, H.K. and J.L. Kermicle. 1976. Genetics 93:309-322. (*Lc1*)
67. Doyle, G.G. 1978. MNL 52:77. (*agt1*)
68. Duvick, D.N. 1965. Adv. Genet. 13:1-56. (*Rf2*)
69. East, E.M. and H.K. Hayes. 1911. Conn. Agric. Exp. Stn. Bull. 167. (*C1 pr1 R1*)
70. Emerson, R.A. 1911. Nebr. Agric. Exp. Stn. Ann. Rep. 24:59-90. (*P1*)
71. Emerson, R.A. 1912. Am. Breeders Assoc. Ann. Rep. 8:385-399. (*an1 d1 g1 lg1 w1*)
72. Emerson, R.A. 1912. Nebr. Agric. Exp. Stn. Ann. Rep. 25:81-88. (*lg1 w1*)
73. Emerson, R.A. 1912. Nebr. Agric. Exp. Stn. Ann. Rep. 25:89-105. (*g1 j1 v2*)
74. Emerson, R.A. 1918. Cornell Univ. Agric. Exp. Stn. Memoir 16. (*a1*)
75. Emerson, R.A. 1920. J. Hered. 11:65-76. (*ts1 ts2*)
76. Emerson, R.A. 1921. Am. J. Bot. 8:411-424. (*Bh1 gs1*)
77. Emerson, R.A. 1921. Cornell Univ. Agric. Exp. Stn. Memoir 39. (*B1 Pl1*)
78. Emerson, R.A. 1921. J. Hered. 12:267-270. (*cr1*)
79. Emerson, R.A. 1932. Science 75:566. (*ms17*)
80. Emerson, R.A. 1932. Sixth Int. Congress Genet. Proc. 1:141-152. (*Ts5*)
81. Emerson, R.A. and S.H. Emerson. 1922. Genetics 7:203-236. (*an1*)
82. Emerson, R.A., et al. 1935. Cornell Univ. Agric. Exp. Stn. Memoir 180. (*j2*)
83. Everett, H.L. 1949. Proc. Natl. Acad. Sci. 35:628-634. (*cl1 Clm1*)
84. Eyster, W.H. 1926. Science 64:22. (*bm1 yg1*)
85. Eyster, W.H. 1929. Ztschr. ind. Abst. Vererbungsl. 49:105-130. (*ar1*)
86. Eyster, W.H. 1931. Genetics 16:574-590. (*vp1 vp2*)
87. Eyster, W.H. 1931. J. Hered. 22:99-102. (*ms2 ms3*)
88. Eyster, W.H. 1933. Am. Nat. 67:75. (*oy1*)
89. Eyster, W.H. 1934. Bibliographia Genetica. 11:187-392. (*da1 l7 ms2 ms3 ms20 su2*)
90. Ferguson, J.E., et al. 1978. J. Hered. 69:377-380. (*se1*)
91. Fraser, A.C. 1924. J. Hered. 15:119-123. (*in1*)
92. Fraser, A.C. 1933. J. Hered. 24:41-46. (*si1*)

93. Freeling, M. and J.C. Woodman. 1978. MNL 52:9-10. (*Cdh1*)
94. Friedemann, P. and P.A. Peterson. 1982. Mol. Gen. Genet. 187:19-29. (*Uq*)
95. Galinat, W.C. 1969. Mass. Agric. Exp. Stn. Bull. 577:1-19. (*Sg1*)
96. Galinat, W.C. 1971. MNL 45:98-99. (*is1*)
97. Galinat, W.C. 1975. MNL 49:100-102. (*Pt1 Ri1*)
98. Galinat, W.C. and P.C. Mangelsdorf. 1957. MNL 31:67. (*Pn1*)
99. Galinat, W.C., et al. 1978. MNL 52:58. (*bu1*)
100. Gavazzi, G., et al. 1975. Theor. Appl. Genet. 46:339-346. (*pro1*)
101. Gavazzi, G., et al. 1986. p. 91-103 *In* G.M. Reddy and E.H. Coe (ed.) Gene structure and function in higher plants Oxford-IBH, New Delhi. (*Sn1*)
102. Gelinas, D.A., et al. 1966. Am. J. Bot. 53:615. (*Clt1*)
103. Gernert, W.B. 1912. Am. Nat. 46:616-622. (*ra1*)
104. Giesbrecht, J. 1965. J. Hered. 56:118, 130. (*zn2*)
105. Glover, D.V. 1968. MNL 42:151. (*ct2 sr3*)
106. Glover, D.V. 1970. Crop Sci. 10:611-612. (*rd2*)
107. Golubovskaya, I.N. 1979. Int. Rev. Cytol. 58:247-290. (*Mei1 ms43*)
108. Golubovskaya, I.N. and D.V. Sitnikova. 1980. Genetika 16:656-666. (*Mei1 ms28 ms43*)
109. Golubovskaya, I.N. and N.B. Khristolyubova. 1986. p. 723-738 *In* M. Freeling (ed.) Plant genetics Alan R. Liss, New York. (*dsy2 pam2*)
110. Golubovskaya, I.N. and A.S. Mashnenkov. 1976. Genetika 12:7-14. (*dsy1*)
111. Golubovskaya, I.N. and A.S. Mashnenkov. 1977. Genetika 13:1910-1921. (*pam1*)
112. Golubovskaya, I.N., et al 1975. Genetika 11:11-17. (*afd1*)
113. Gonella, J.A. and P.A. Peterson. 1975. MNL 49:71-73. (*ga10*)
114. Gonella, J.A. and P.A. Peterson. 1977. Genetics 85:629-645. (*Fcu*)
115. Goodman, M.M. and C.W. Stuber. 1982. MNL 56:125. (*Gdh2*)
116. Goodman, M.M. and C.W. Stuber. 1983. Maydica 28:169-188. (*Acp1 Acp2*)
117. Goodman, M.M., et al. 1980. Genetics 96:697-700. (*Got2 Got3 Idh1 Idh2 Me1 Pgd1 Pgd2 Pgm1 Pgm2 Phi1*)
118. Gracen, V.E., et al. 1979. Proc. 34th Ann. Corn and Sorghum Res. Conf. p. 76-91. (*R/4*)
119. Grogan, C.O., et al. 1963. Crop Sci. 3:451. (*ats1*)
120. Hamill, D.E. 1968. MNL 42:36-37. (*Px1*)
121. Harberd, N., et al. 1987. MNL61:23-24. (*Mpl1*)
122. Harovitz, S. 1948. MNL 22:42. (*zn1*)
123. Harris, J.W. 1968. Genetics 60:186-187. (*E4*)
124. Hayes, H.K. 1932. J. Hered. 23:415-419. (*zb4*)
125. Hayes, H.K. and H.E. Brewbaker. 1928. Am. Nat. 62:228-235. (*gl2 gl3 sl1*)
126. Hayes, H.K. and M.S. Chang. 1938. MNL 12:8. (*zb6*)
127. Hayes, H.K. and E.M. East. 1915. Conn. Agric. Exp. Stn. Bull. 188:1-31. (*fl1*)
128. Hofmeyr, J.D.J. 1930. Unpub. thesis, Cornell. (*ba1 ba2*)
129. Hoisington, D.A. 1983. MNL 57:159-160. (*nec4*)
130. Hoisington, D.A. 1985. MNL 60:50-51. (*Les4 Les5 Les6 Les7 Les8 Les9*)

(continued on next page)

Table 3-1. Continued.

131. Hoisington, D.A. 1987. MNL 61:48-49. *(Les10)*
132. Hooker, A.L. 1963. Crop Sci. 3:381-383. *(Ht1)*
133. Hooker, A.L. 1977. Crop Sci. 17:132-135. *(Ht2)*
134. Hooker, A.L. 1981. MNL 55:87-88. *(Ht3)*
135. Huelsen, W.A. and M.C. Gillis. 1929. Ill. Agric. Exp. Stn. Bull. 320. *(pi1 pi2)*
136. Hutchison, C.B. 1921. J. Hered. 12:76-83. *(sh1)*
137. Hutchison, C.B. 1922. Cornell Univ. Agric. Exp. Stn. Memoir 60:1419-1473. *(na1)*
138. Jenkins, M.T. 1924. J. Hered. 15:467-472. *(ij1)*
139. Jenkins, M.T. 1926. Am. Nat. 60:484-488. *(g2)*
140. Jenkins, M.T. 1927. Genetics 12:492-518. *(yg2)*
141. Jenkins, M.T. 1930. J. Hered. 21:79-80. *(rt1)*
142. Jenkins, M.T. 1932. J. Agric. Res. 44:495-502. *(a2)*
143. Jenkins, M.T. 1947. MNL 21:33. *(y8)*
144. Jenkins, M.T. and M.A. Bell. 1930. Genetics 15:253-282. *(l4)*
145. Jenkins, M.T. and F. Gerhardt. 1931. Iowa Agric. Exp. Stn. Res. Bull. 138:121-151. *(la1)*
146. Joachim, G. and C.R. Burnham. 1953. MNL 27:66. *(sr2)*
147. Jones, D.F. 1925. J. Hered. 16:339-341. *(sk1)*
148. Jones, D.F. 1951. Proc. Natl. Acad. Sci. 37:408-410. *(Rf1)*
149. Jones, D.F. 1954. Proc. IX Int. Genet. Cong. 1225-1237. (cms-S cms-T)
150. Jones, D.F. and P.C. Mangelsdorf. 1925. Anat. Rec. 31:351. *(Ga1)*
151. Josephson, L.M. 1955. Empire J. Exp. Agric. 23(89):1-10 (cms-S cms-T)
152. Kahler, A.L. 1983. J. Hered. 74:239-246. *(Acp4)*
153. Kang, M.S. 1981. MNL 55:26. *(bln1)*
154. Kempton, J.H. 1920. J. Hered. 11:111-115. *(br1)*
155. Kempton, J.H. 1920. J. Hered. 11:317-322. *(ad1)*
156. Kempton, J.H. 1921. Am. Nat. 56:461-464. *(ws1 ws2)*
157. Kempton, J.H. 1921. USDA Bull. 925:1-28. *(br1)*
158. Kempton, J.H. 1934. J. Hered. 25:29-32. *(bd1)*
159. Kermicle, J.L. 1969. Science 166:1422-1424. *(ig1)*
160. Kermicle, J.L. and J.D. Axtell. 1981. Maydica 26:185-197. *(Isr1)*
161. Khadzhinov, M.I. 1937. Bull. Appl. Bot. Gen. Plant Breed. Ser. II. 7:247-258. *(Rs1 rs2)*
162. Kvakan, P. 1924. Cornell Univ. Agric. Exp. Stn. Memoir 83:1-22. *(Bn1 gl1)*
163. Kramer, H.H. 1957. MNL 31:120. *(rgd1)*
164. Kuc, J., et al. 1968. Phytochemistry 7:1435-1436. *(bm3)*
165. Kulkarni, C.G. 1927. Mich. Acad. Sci. Arts and Letters Papers. 6:253-273. *(Wc1)*
166. Lai, Y-K. and J.G. Scandalios. 1980. Devel. Genet. 1:311-324. *(Adr1)*
167. Lambert, R.J. and G.F. Sprague. 1987. MNL61:96. *(mg1)*
168. Langham, D.G. 1940. Genetics 25:88-107. *(pd1 tr1)*
169. Langham, D.G. 1940. MNL 14:21. *(bk2)*

170. Laughnan, J.R. 1949. Proc. Natl. Acad. Sci. 35:167-178. (*Alpha Beta*)

171. Leng, E.R. and L.F. Bauman. 1955. Agron. J. 47:189-191. (*Ms21 Sks1*)

172. Leng, E.R. and M.L. Vineyard. 1951. MNL 25:31-32. (*br2*)

173. Leto, K.J. 1982. p. 317-325.*In* W.F. Sheridan (ed.) Maize for biological research.Plant Mol. Biol. Assoc., Charlottesville, VA. (*hcf6 hcf12 hcf13 hcf15 hcf19 hcf23 hcf26 hcf34 hcf38 hcf41 hcf46*)

174. Li, H.W. 1931. J. Hered. 22:14-16. (*b1*)

175. Li, H.W. 1937. J. Hered. 24:279-281. (*na1*)

176. Lindstrom, E.W. 1917. Am. Nat. 51:225-237. (*l1*)

177. Lindstrom, E.W. 1918. Cornell Univ. Agric. Exp. Stn. Memoir 13:1-68. (*l1 w1*)

178. Lindstrom, E.W. 1921. Genetics 6:91-110. (*f1*)

179. Lindstrom, E.W. 1924. Genetics 9:305-326. (*w2 w3*)

180. Lindstrom, E.W. 1925. J. Hered. 16:135-140. (*Tp1*)

181. Lindstrom, E.W. 1935. Iowa St. Coll. J. Sci. 9:451-459. (*a3 Og1*)

182. Lock, R.H. 1906. Roy. Bot. Gard. Annals 3:95-184. (*P1*)

183. Longley, A.E. 1932. J. Agric. Res. 54:835-862. (*K10*)

184. Lorenzoni, C., et al. 1974. MNL 48:19-20. (*cp1*)

185. Lowe, J. and O.E. Nelson, Jr. 1946. Genetics 31:525-533. (*mn1*)

186. Lysikov, V.N., et al. 1984. Sov. Genet. 20:72-80. (*Cg2*)

187. MacDonald, T. and J.L. Brewbaker. 1972. J. Hered. 63:11-14. (*Px2 Px3 Px4 Px5 Px6 Px7 Ta1*)

188. MacDonald, T. and J.L. Brewbaker. 1974. J. Hered. 65:37-42. (*E5-I E5-II E6 E7 E8 E9 E10*)

189. Mains, E.B. 1926. J Hered. 17:313-325. (*Rp1*)

190. Mains, E.B. 1931. J. Agric. Res. 43:419-430. (*Rp1*)

191. Mains, E.B. 1949. J. Hered. 40:21-24. (*sh2*)

192. Mangelsdorf, P.C. 1926. Conn. Agric. Exp. Stn. Bull. 279:509-614. (*bt1*)

193. Mangelsdorf, P.C. 1947. Genetics 32:448-458. (*du1*)

194. Mascia, P.N. 1978. Molec. Gen. Genet. 161:237-244. (*l13 oro1 oro2 Orom1*)

195. Mascia, P.N. and D.S. Robertson. 1980. J. Hered. 71:19-24. (*nec1*)

196. Mashnenkov, A.S. and M.I. Khadjinov. 1979. Proc. IX Eucarpia Corn and Sorghum Sect. p. 447-450. (*Sup1*)

197. Matthews, D.L., et al. 1974. J. Agric. Sci. 82:433-435. (*te1*)

198. McCarty, D.P., et al. 1986. Proc. Natl. Acad. Sci. 83:9099-9103. (*Css1*)

199. McClintock, B. 1934. Z. Zellforsch. Mikrosk. Anat. 21:294-328. (NOR)

200. McClintock, B. 1944. Genetics 29:478-502. (*pyd1 wd1*)

201. McClintock, B. 1950. Proc. Natl. Acad. Sci. 36:344-355. (*Ac Ds*)

202. McClintock, B. 1956. Brookhaven Symp. Biol. 8:58-74. (*Spm*)

203. Melville, J.C. and J.G. Scandalios, J.G. 1972. Biochem. Genet. 7:15-31. (*Enp1*)

204. Micu, V. 1980. MNL 54:63-64. (*db1*)

205. Micu, V. 1981. Genetical Studies of Maize. Shtiintsa, Kishinev, Mold. SSR (*bs1 db1 tl1*)

206. Micu, V. and S.I. Mustyatsa. 1978. Genetika 14:365-368. (*dep1*)

207. Miles, C.D. and D.J. Daniel. 1974. Plant Phys. 53:589-595. (*hcf1 hcf2 hcf3*)

(continued on next page)

Table 3-1. Continued.

208. Miles, D. 1982. p. 75-107. *In* M. Edelman, et al. (ed.) Methods in chloroplast molecular biology. Elsevier, Amsterdam. (*hcf4 hcf13 hcf18 hcf19 hcf21 hcf23 hcf26 hcf34 hcf41 hcf42 hcf44 hcf50*)

209. Miles, D., et al. 1986. p. 361-365 *In* K.E. Steinbeck, et al. (ed.) Molecular biology of the photosynthetic apparatus Cold Spring Harbor Laboratory. (*hcf5 hcf28 hcf31 hcf36 hcf47 hcf48 hcf101 hcf316 hcf323 hcf408*)

210. Miles, F.C. 1915. J. Genetics 4:193-214. (*gs1*)

211. Miranda, L.T. de. 1980. MNL 54:15-18. (*ma1 Ma2*)

212. Miranda, L.T. de. 1980. MNL 54:19. (*Asr1*)

213. Miranda, L.T. de. 1981. MNL 55:18-19. (*Ite1*)

214. Miranda, L.T. de, et al. 1982. MNL 56:28-30. (*Ite2*)

215. Miranda, L.T. de, et al. 1982. MNL 56:30-32. (Mer Zer)

216. Miranda, L.T. de, et al. 1984. MNL 58:38-46. (Ger Flt Krn)

217. Misra, P.S., et al. 1972. Science 176:1425-1427. (*o7*)

218. Modena, S.A. 1983. MNL 57:38. (*tpm1*)

219. Modena, S.A. 1984. MNL 58:79-82. (*Lcs1 Lct1 lct2*)

220. Modena, S.A. 1984. MNL 58:211-212. (*Pdf1*)

221. Motto, M., et al. 1983. Theor. Appl. Genet. 64:41-46. (*w16 w17 wvg1*)

222. Muller, L.D., et al. 1971. Crop Sci. 11:413-415. (*bm3*)

223. Mumm, W.J. 1929. Anat. Rec. 44:279. (*h1*)

224. Nelson, O.E. 1976. MNL 50:114. (*fl3*)

225. Nelson, O.E. 1981. MNL 55:68. (*o9 o10 o11 o12 o13*)

226. Nelson, O.E. 1981. MNL 55:73. (*lp1*)

227. Nelson, O.E. and G.B. Clary. 1952. J. Hered. 43:205-210. (*dy1 lo2*)

228. Nelson, O.E. and A.J. Ohlrogge. 1957. Science 125:1200. (*ct1 rd1*)

229. Nelson, O.E. and S.N. Postlethwait. 1954. Am. J. Bot. 41:739-748. (*Pt1*)

230. Nelson, O.E. and A.J. Ullstrup. 1964. J. Hered. 55:194-199. (*hm2*)

231. Nelson, O.E., et al. 1965. Science 150:1469-1470. (*fl2*)

232. Neuffer, M.G. 1973. MNL 47:150. (*nec3*)

233. Neuffer, M.G. and J.B. Beckett. 1987. MNL 61:50. (*gl19 gl21 gr*1 gs3 ij2 l13 l16 l17 l18 l19 nec5 nec6 nec7 pg15 pg16 ppg1 py2 spc2 spc3 spt1 spt2 v24 v25 v26 v27 v28 v29 wgs1 wlu1 wlu2 wlu3 wlu4 wt2 zb7*)

234. Neuffer, M.G. and O.H. Calvert. 1975. J. Hered. 66:265-270. (*Les1 Les2*)

235. Neuffer, M.G. and M.T. Chang. 1986. MNL 60:55. (*orp1 orp2*)

236. Neuffer, M.G. and D.England. 1984. MNL 58:77-78. (*Clt1*)

237. Neuffer, M.G. and K.A. Sheridan. 1977. MNL 51:60. (*Bif1 Fgd2 Spc1 Ysk1 Zb8*)

238. Neuffer, M.G. and W.F. Sheridan. 1980. Genetics 95:929-944. (*dek1 dek2 dek3 dek4 dek5 dek6 dek7 dek8 dek9 dek10 dek11 dek12 dek13 dek14 dek15*)

239. Neuffer, M.G. and W.F. Sheridan. 1980. MNL 55:29-30. (*dek1 dek2 dek3 dek4 dek5 dek6 dek7 dek8 dek9 dek10 dek11 dek12 dek13 dek14 dek15*)

240. Neuffer, M.G., et al. 1968. The mutants of maize. Crop Sci. Soc. Amer., Madison, Wisc. (*cp2 ub1*)

241. Neuffer, M.G., et al. 1987. MNL 61:50-51. (*G6 Ms41 Mscl Msc2 TTr1 Vsr1 Wrk1 Zb8*)

242. Newton, K.J. and D. Schwartz. 1980. Genetics 95:425-442. (*Mdh1 Mdh2 Mdh3 Mdh4 Mdh5 mmm1*)

243. Nickerson, N.H. and E.E. Dale. 1955. Ann. Mo. Bot. Gard. 42:195-212. (*Ts6*)
244. Nuffer, M.G. 1954. MNL 28:63-64. (*bz2*)
245. Nuffer, M.G. 1955. Science 121:399-400. (*Dt2 Dt3*)
246. Ott, L. and J.G. Scandalios. 1978. Genetics 89:137-146. (*Amp1 Amp2 Amp3 Amp4*)
247. Paliy, A.F. and A.I. Rotar. 1979. Genetika 15:478-481. (*cfl2*)
248. Palmer, R.G. 1971. Chromosoma 35:233-246. (*am1*)
249. Pawar, S.E. and C. Mouli. 1973. MNL 47:17. (*Ce1*)
250. Perry, H.S. 1939. MNL 13:7. (*Lg3*)
251. Perry, H.S. and G.F. Sprague. 1936. J. Am. Soc. Agron. 28:990-996. (*y3*)
252. Peterson, H. 1959. MNL 33:41. (*Tp2*)
253. Peterson, P.A. 1960. Genetics 45:115-133. (*En pg14*)
254. Pfund, J.H. and C.W. Crum. 1977. Agron. Abstr. p. 66. (*Thc1*)
255. Phinney, B.O. 1956. Proc. Natl. Acad. Sci. 42:185-189. (*D8*)
256. Phipps, I.F. 1928. J. Hered. 19:399-404. (*ts4*)
257. Phipps, I.F. 1929. Cornell Univ. Agric. Exp. Stn. Memoir 125:1-63. (*al1 v12 v13 v16 v17 v18*)
258. Piovarci, A. 1982. MNL 56:157. (*bo2*)
259. Plewa, M. 1979. MNL 53:93-96. (*loc1*)
260. Pogna, N.E., et al. 1982. MNL 56:153. (*ys2*)
261. Postlethwait, S.N. and O.E. Nelson, Jr. 1957. Am. J. Bot. 44:628-633. (*wi1*)
262. Pryor, A.J. 1974. Heredity 32:397-401. (*Gdh1*)
263. Pryor, A.J. 1976. MNL 50:15-16. (*Glu1*)
264. Pryor, T. and D. Schwartz. 1973. Genetics 75:75-92. (*Cx1*)
265. Randolph, L.F. 1928. Anat. Rec. 41:102. (B chr)
266. Rhoades, M.M. 1935. Am. Nat. 69:74-75. (*Dt1*)
267. Rhoades, M.M. 1939. Genetics 24:62. (*ws3*)
268. Rhoades, M.M. 1948. MNL 22:9. (*ga7*)
269. Rhoades, M.M. 1951. Am. Nat. 85:105-110. (*pg11 pg12*)
270. Rhoades, M.M. 1952. Am. Nat. 86:105-106. (*bz1*)
271. Rhoades, M.M. 1956. MNL 30:38-42. (*am1 el1*)
272. Rhoades, M.M. and E. Dempsey. 1954. MNL 28:58. (*gl17*)
273. Rhoades, M.M. and E. Dempsey. 1982. MNL 56:21. (*Mrh*)
274. Rhoades, M.M. and E. Dempsey. 1982. MNL 56:22. (*Mut*)
275. Robertson, D.S. 1952. Proc. Natl. Acad. Sci. 38:580-583. (*vp5*)
276. Robertson, D.S. 1955. Genetics 40:745-760. (*vp8 vp9*)
277. Robertson, D.S. 1961. Genetics 46:649-662. (*y10*)
278. Robertson, D.S. 1967. MNL 41:94. (*o5*)
279. Robertson, D.S. 1973. MNL 47:82. (*l10*)
280. Robertson, D.S. 1974. MNL 48:70. (*yd2*)
281. Robertson, D.S. 1975. J. Hered. 66:127-130. (*y9*)

(continued on next page)

Table 3-1. Continued.

282. Robertson, D.S. 1978. Mutat. Res. 51:21-28. (*Mu*)
283. Robertson, D.S. 1981. MNL 55:115. (*Il5*)
284. Robertson, D.S. 1984. MNL 58:18. (*brn1*)
285. Sachan, J.K. and K.R. Sarkar. 1978. MNL 52:119-120. (*rgo1*)
286. Salamini, F. 1980. Cold Spr. Harb. Symp. 45:467-476. (*Bg*)
287. Salamini, F., et al. 1983. Theor. Appl. Genet. 65:123-128. (*Mc1*)
288. Saxena, K.M.S. and A.L. Hooker. 1968. Proc. Natl. Acad. Sci. 61:1300-1305. (*Rp5*)
289. Scandalios, J.G., et al. 1972. Arch. Biochem. Biophys. 153:695-705. (*Cat2*)
290. Scandalios, J.G., et al. 1975. Biochem. Genet. 13:759-769. (*Got1*)
291. Scandalios, J.G., et al. 1980. Mol. Gen. Genet. 179:33-41. (*Cat3*)
292. Scandalios, J.G., et al. 1980. Proc. Natl. Acad. Sci. 77:5360-5364. (*Car1*)
293. Schiefelbein, J.W., et al. 1985. Proc. Natl. Acad. Sci. 82:4783-4787. (*dSpm*)
294. Schnable, P.S. and P.A. Peterson. 1986. Maydica 31:59-82. (*Cy*)
295. Schwartz, D. 1951. Genetics 36:676-696. (*Ms21 Sks1*)
296. Schwartz, D. 1951. MNL 25:30. (*ga8*)
297. Schwartz, D. 1960. Proc. Natl. Acad. Sci. 46:1210-1215. (*E1*)
298. Schwartz, D. 1964. Proc. Natl. Acad. Sci. 51:602-605. (*E3*)
299. Schwartz, D. 1965. Proc. XI Int. Genet. Cong. 2:131-135. (*E2*)
300. Schwartz, D. 1966. Proc. Natl. Acad. Sci. 56:1431-1436. (*Adh2*)
301. Schwartz, D. 1979. Mol. Gen. Genet. 174:233-240. (*mep1 Prot1*)
302. Schwartz, D. and T. Endo. 1966. Genetics 53:709-715. (*Adh1*)
303. Shaver, D.L. 1967. J. Hered. 58:270-273. (*gt1 pe1*)
304. Shaver, D. 1983. Proc. Annu. Corn Sorghum Res. Conf. 38:161-180. (*Lfy1*)
305. Shepherd, N.S., et al. 1982. Mol. Gen. Genet. 188:266-271. (*Cin*)
306. Sheridan, W.F., et al. 1984. MNL 58:98-99. (*dek16 dek17 dek18 dek19 dek20 dek21*)
307. Sheridan, W.F., et al. 1986. MNL 60:64. (*dek22 dek23 dek24 dek25 dek26 dek27 dek28 dek29 dek30*)
308. Shortess, D.K. and R.P. Amby. 1979. Maydica 24:215-221. (*pg13*)
309. Shortess, D.K., et al. 1968. Genetics 58:227-235. (*lu1*)
310. Shumway, L.K. and L.F. Bauman. 1967. Genetics 55:33-38. (*NCS1*)
311. Singleton, W.R. 1946. J. Hered. 37:61-64. (*id1*)
312. Singleton, W.R. 1951. Am. Nat. 85:81-96. (*Cg1*)
313. Singleton, W.R. 1959. MNL 33:3. (*br3*)
314. Singleton, W.R. and D.F. Jones. 1930. J. Hered. 21:266-268. (*ms1*)
315. Smith, D.R. and A.L. Hooker. 1973. Crop Sci. 13:330-331. (*rhm1*)
316. Soave, C., et al. 1978. Theor. Appl. Genet. 52:263-267. (*Zp*)
317. Soave, C., et al. 1981. Genetics 97:363-377. (*Zp*)
318. Sorrentino, J.J., et al. 1987. MNL 61:103. (*rDt*)
319. Sprague, G.F. 1932. U.S. Tech. Bull. 292:1-43. (*sy1*)
320. Sprague, G.F. 1936. J. Am. Soc. Agron. 28:472-478. (*ps1*)

321. Sprague, G.F. 1938. MNL 12:2. (*gl11*)
322. Sprague, G.F. 1939. J. Hered. 30:143-145. (*Vg1*)
323. Sprague, G.F. 1955. MNL 29:6. (*gl14*)
324. Sprague, G.F. 1984. MNL 58:197. (*Dt6*)
325. Sprague, G.F. 1987. MNL 61:96. (*gl5 gl20*)
326. Sprague, G.F. 1987. MNL 61:96. (*yl1,y12*)
327. Sprague, G.F., et al. 1965. MNL 39:164. (*wt1*)
328. Stadler, L.J. 1940. MNL 14:26. (*et1*)
329. Stadler, L.J. and M.H. Emmerling. 1956. Genetics 41:124-137. (*P S*)
330. Stadler, L.J. and M.G. Nuffer. 1953. Science 117:471-472. (*P*)
331. Stierwalt, T.R. and P.L. Crane. 1974. MNL 48:139. (*sen1 sen2 sen3 sen4 sen5 sen6*)
332. Stout, J.T. and R.L. Phillips. 1973. Proc. Natl. Acad. Sci. 70:3043-3047. (*alh1 clh1*)
333. Stroman, G.N. 1924. Genetics 9:493-512. (*zb2*)
334. Stroup, D. 1970. J. Hered. 61:139-141. (*cm1*)
335. Styles, E.D., et al. 1987. MNL 61:100. (*Ufo1*)
336. Suttle, A.D. . 1924. Unpub. thesis, Cornell. (*d2 d5 py1*)
337. Tavcar, A. 1932. Jugoslav. Akad. Znanosti i Umjetnosti Prestampo. 244:74-93. (*Hs1*)
338. Teas, H.J. and E.G. Anderson. 1951. Proc. Natl. Acad. Sci. 37:645-649. (*Bf1*)
339. Teas, H.J. and A.N. Teas. 1953. J.Hered. 44:156-158. (*bt2*)
340. Tsai, C. and O.E. Nelson. 1968. Genetics 61:813-821. (*sh4*)
341. Tulpule, S.H. 1954. Am. J. Bot. 41:294-301. (*lw1 lw2 lw3 lw4*)
342. Ullstrup, A.J. 1965. Phytopathology 55:425-428. (*Rpp9*)
343. Ullstrup, A.J. and A.M. Brunson. 1947. J. Am. Soc. Agron. 39:606-609. (*hm1*)
344. Ullstrup, A.J. and A.F. Troyer. 1968. Phytopathology 57:1252-1283. (*lls1*)
345. Vahrusheva, E.I. 1975. MNL 49:95-96. (*cto1*)
346. Vineyard, M.L. and R.P. Bear. 1952. MNL 26:5. (*ae1*)
347. Wendel, J.F., et al. 1985. MNL 59:87-88. (*Aco1 Aco2 Aco3 Aco4 Dia1 Dia2 Sad1 Tpi1 Tpi2 Tpi3*)
348. Wendel, J.F., et al. 1986. MNL 60:109. (*Adk1*)
349. Wendel, J.F., et al. 1986. Theor. Appl. Genet. 72:178-185. (*Hex1 Hex2 Tpi4*)
350. Wentz, J.B. 1926. J. Hered. 17:327-329. (*bt1*)
351. West, D.P. and M.C. Albertsen. 1985. MNL 59:87. (*ms22 ms23 ms24*)
352. Wilkinson, D.R. and A.L. Hooker. 1968. Phytopathology 58:605-608. (*Rp3 Rp4 Rp6*)
353. Wright, J.E. 1961. MNL 35:111. (*ys3*)

widely in different genetic and physical environments. Many characters, for example, are sharply differentiated from the normal in certain stocks, whereas in other stocks it may be impossible to distinguish between the mutant type and normal. Similarly, environmental factors may play an important role in determining the characteristics of a mutant type. For example, virescent seedlings are markedly affected by conditions of light and temperature. To describe in detail the many variations of certain characters would be entirely outside the limits set up by the writers for this summary. The writers have attempted to set down, for each of the characters listed, the more constant deviations from normal. Individual investigators must necessarily learn the peculiarities of a given character under the particular conditions in which they work." (Emerson et al., 1935).

Figure 3–1 shows loci placed (i) on an ordered map, (ii) in a specific region (first column to right), or (iii) to chromosome or arm (far right). Each map begins with the most distal gene in the short arm. Genetic locations of centromeres are shown according to cytogenetic studies. Genetic locations of B-A translocations (TB-...) shown with spanning lines signify uncertain coverage. The diagram to the left of the linkage map gives approximate cytological locations; the chromosomes and arm ratios are proportioned to chromosome 1. Leftmost is a combined map of RFLP loci defined by T. Helentjaris, B. and F. Burr, D. Grant, and D. Hoisington, based on an optimized mathematical treatment (Hoisington, 1987; Hoisington and Lander, 1988, unpublished data).

3–1.4 Dosage Effects and Codominance

Noteworthy examples of dosage effects are found at several loci. Dosage effects for $Y1$ with $y1$ in the endosperm, where triploidy permits four different constitutions (triplex, duplex, simplex, and nulliplex for $Y1$), can often be distinguished visually; correspondingly, a linear relationship between $Y1$ dosage and vitamin A content has been demonstrated (Mangelsdorf and Fraps, 1931). Comparable dosage effects, at least to the eye, are found for anthocyanin intensity in the aleurone tissue under control of some alleles at the $A1$, $C1$, $C2$, and In loci; and for floury endosperm with $Fl1$. An exponential relationship of dosage to mutation frequency is found for the dotted (Dt) controlling elements (Rhoades, 1936; Nuffer, 1955); for Ac, however, increased frequency is accompanied by a delay in the time of mutational events (McClintock, 1951; Brink and Nilan, 1952). Some enzymatic activities and protein levels are inversely affected by dosage of certain regions of the genome (Birchler, 1979, 1981; Birchler and Newton, 1981).

Each functional allele is expressed (i.e., the locus shows codominance) in heterozygotes for virtually every locus whose protein product has been recognized. Thus codominance is now recognized as the rule rather than the exception, once sufficient biochemical criteria are available. In ad-

Fig. 3–1. Linkage map of maize (*Zea mays* L). The linkage map represents the order and recombinational distances, in centimorgans (1% recombination = 1 cM), for those genes for which sufficient information is available to make a reasonable judgment of their location. Each chromosome is arranged beginning with the most distal gene in the short arm. Locations of the centromeres are indicated according to the best available data from cytogenetic studies. The physical map of each chromosome, to the left of each linkage map, is drawn with the length of each arm in proportion to the ratio of the length of that arm to the length of the linkage map, is drawn with the length of each arm in proportion to the ratio of . . ; placement on the physical map is in accordance with observed breakpoints; placement on the linkage map is in relation to genes uncovered or not uncovered. The vertical line associated with simple B-A translocations represents the segment within which the breakpoint is located (genes distal to the line on that arm should be uncovered). In the case of compound translocations, the associated vertical line on the linkage map for the first arm involved (e.g., 1L of TB-1La-5S8041) defines the segment within which the second breakpoint is located (genes distal to the line are not uncovered). On the map of the second arm involved (5S, in the example), genes distal to the associated line are uncovered (as they are with simple B-A translocations). TB's shown as spanning one or more genes may or may not uncover the indicated gene or genes. Immediately to the right of the linkage map are those genes that have some information leading to a "rough" placement on the map, either near a gene already on the map or to a region of the map. Further to the right are those genes which have been placed to the chromosome (represented by the vertical line with arrows at both ends) or to one arm (represented by a vertical line running from near the centromere to the end of the arm).

To the left of each chromosome's linkage map is the current version of the restriction fragment length polymorphism map being developed by D. Hoisington at the University of Missouri. Distances between each locus are expressed in centimorgans with Haldane's mapping function being applied to the determined recombination value. Additional RFLP maps are being developed in other laboratories and efforts are underway to compile and analyze the data necessary to produce an integrated map of RFLP loci and other markers. **Figure is continued on next page.**

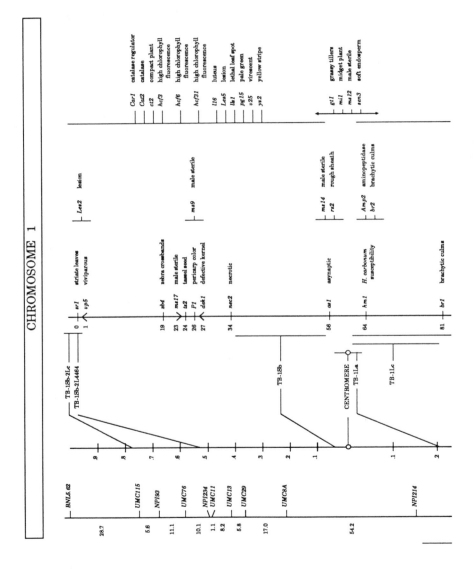

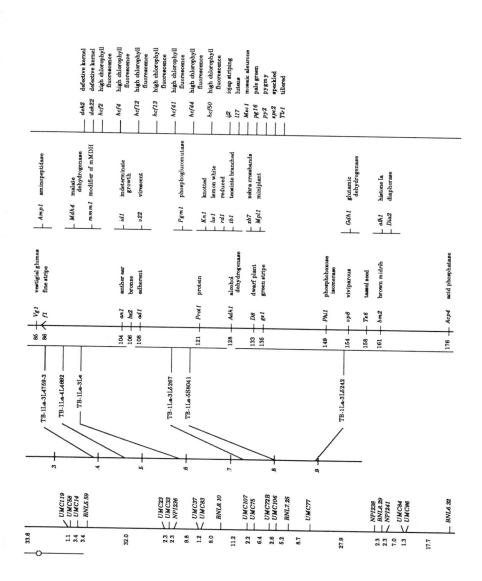

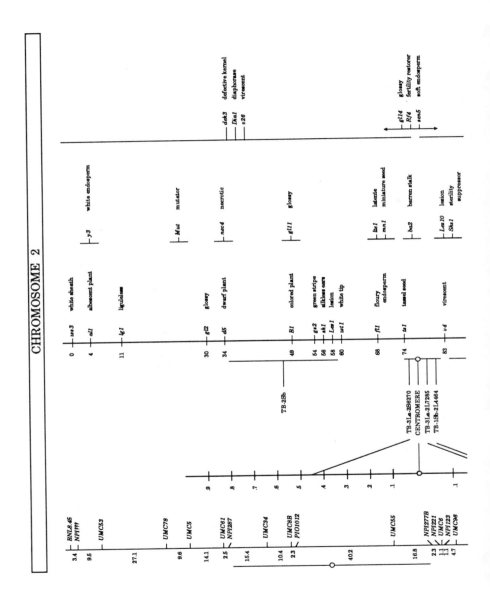

CHROMOSOME 2

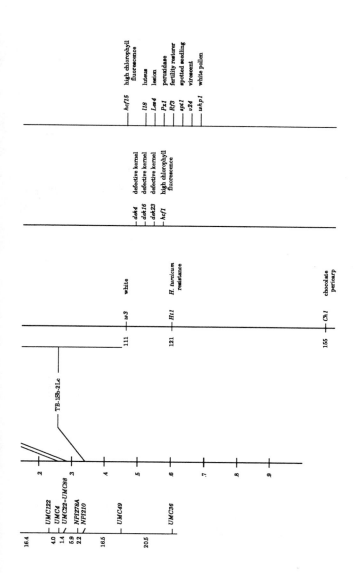

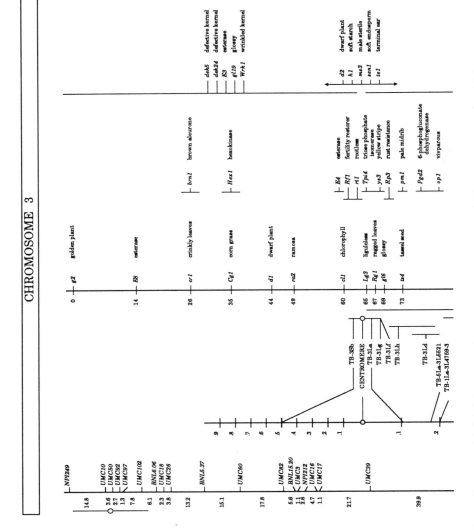

CHROMOSOME 3

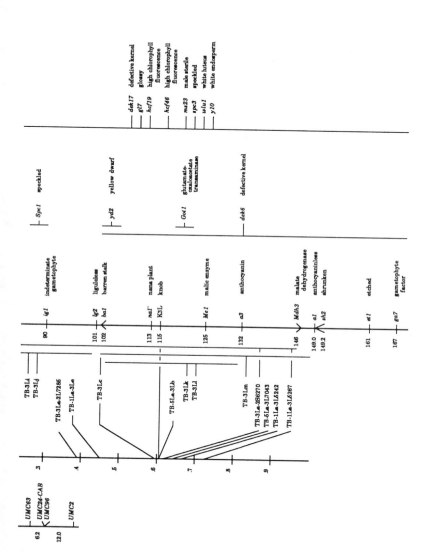

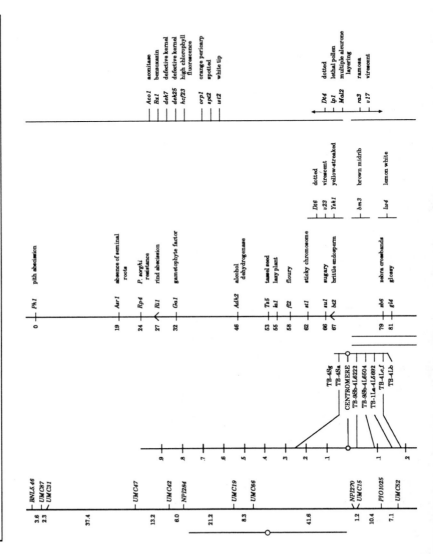

CHROMOSOME 4

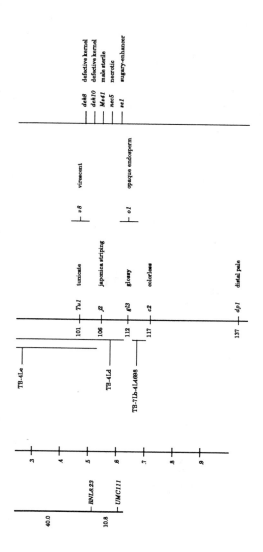

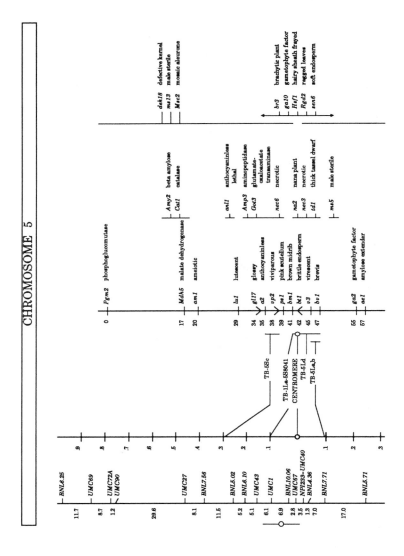

CHROMOSOME 5

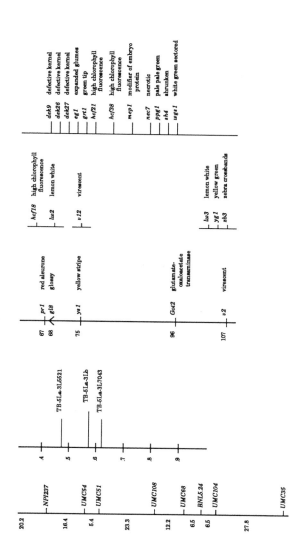

CHROMOSOME 6

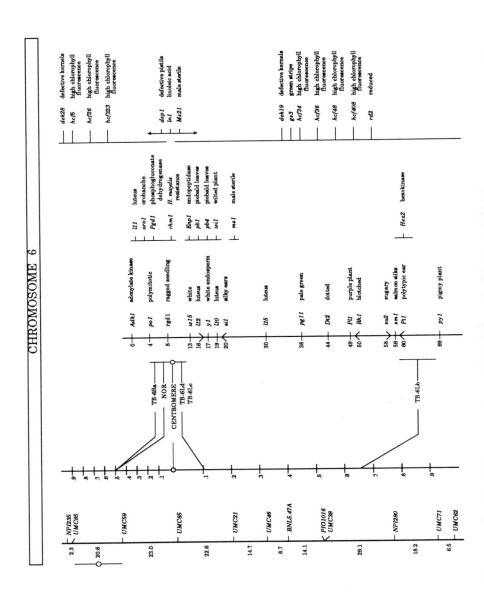

14.6 — UMC28

78 — u14 white

u1 white

Idh2 isocitrate dehydrogenase

Mdh2 malate dehydrogenase

CHROMOSOME 7

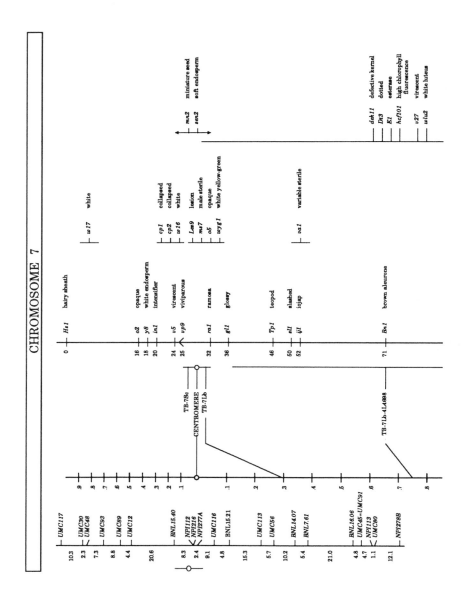

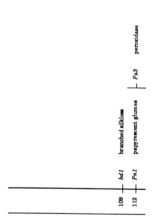

CHROMOSOME 8

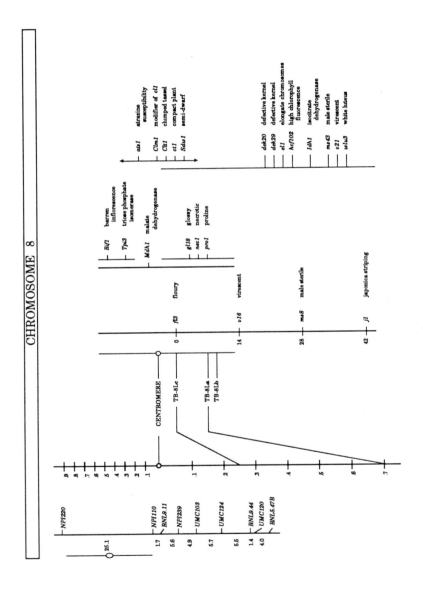

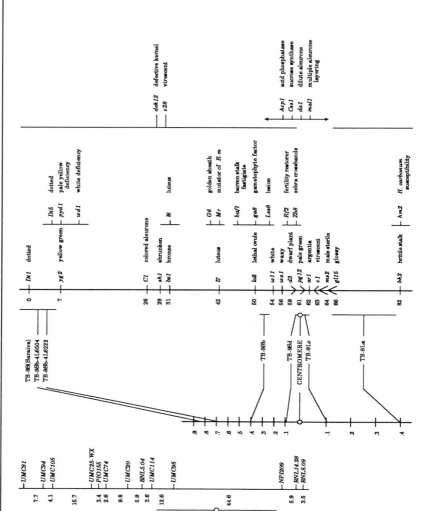

CHROMOSOME 9

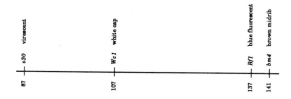

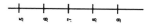

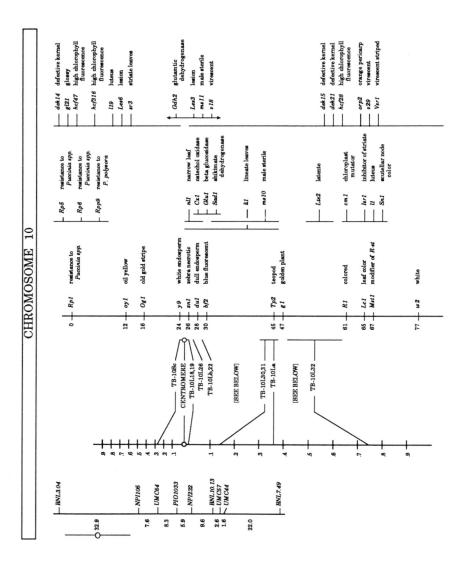

CHROMOSOME 10

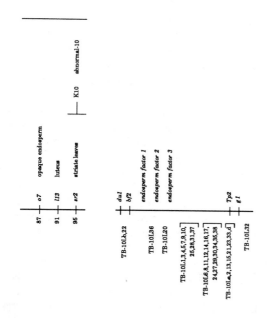

dition, many isozymes form multimeric proteins whose properties in heterozygotes can be new—that is, different from either homo-multimer (Schwartz, 1960). This can, in principle and in fact, give an enzyme with properties of overdominance (Schwartz and Laughner, 1969). Several mutants with heterozygote-specific effects on vigor have been identified (Dollinger, 1985). Modification of the product of one allele by that of its partner allele is by no means common; an intermediate mobility expression for *Gdh1* heterozygotes, suggestive of modification, appears to be attributable to multimer formation (Pryor, 1974). Among notable examples of dominant-recessive gene action, in contrast to codominance, are *mmm*, *Pdf*, *Prot* and *tpm*, each of which influences electrophoretic mobility of specific proteins in a dominant-recessive fashion, presumably by acting through protein processing or modification.

3–1.5   Duplicate Factors

Effects attributable to duplicate factors are difficult enough to analyze that they at times may not be carried through to full demonstration; stocks of several appear to have been lost. Among the factors in the locus list, 15:1 (duplicate factor) interactions are found for certain alleles at the *B* locus with certain ones at *R* (the symbol *R2* was applied at one time); for *C1* with *Pl*; *C2* with *Whp*; *cl* with *Clm,*; *E5-I* with *E5-II*; *Gl5* with *Gl20*; *Lw3* with *Lw4*; *Orp1* with *Orp2*; *Pg11* with *Pg12* (*Au1* and *Au2*, formerly thought to be a similar duplicate pair, are allelic to *Pg11* and *Pg12*); *Pi1* with *Pi2*; *Sen1* with *Sen2*; *Sen3* with *Sen4*; *Sen5* with *Sen6*; and *Ws1* with *Ws2*. The possible significance of duplicate factors in identifying large duplicated segments in the corn genome and potential origin of maize from an ancient allopolyploidization involving 5-chromosome parents has been discussed by Rhoades (1951) and by Weber and Alexander (1972).

Multiple isoenzymes coded by separate loci are frequent, especially for key functions that are effective in different cell compartments or different tissues, or at different stages. Multiple isoenzymes tend even to display parallel linkages (synteny) in their respective chromosomes (Goodman et al., 1980; Wendel et al., 1986), as though they retained phylogenetic footprints of duplication origins or were maintained in functionally significant groups on common chromosomes. Consistently with these observations, cloned genes for key functions often probe a "family" of two or more homoeologous sequences in the genome, and mapping with probes for restriction fragment length polymorphisms shows a notable degree of duplication of sequences, especially in common order for chromosomes 2 and 7, chromosomes 3 and 8, and chromosomes 6 and 8 (Helentjaris et al., 1988). The full evidence, however, indicates such extensive restructuring of the genome that origin of maize through allopolyploidization is not strongly supported.

3–1.6   Cell Autonomy and Auxotrophy

For the majority of factors it appears that the effects of their action are virtually cell-autonomous—that is, in the presence of sectoring for the function, either through chromosome loss or through mutation, little or no cross-feeding occurs to adjacent tissues, indicating that no easily diffusible product is responsible for the effects of that factor. From both the literature and the authors' experience, virtual autonomy at the cell level is characteristic of the following factors: *A1, A2, Ac, B, Bk2, Bm1, Bm4, Bt1, Bz1, Bz2, C1, C2, Ch, cms-S, D8, dek1, Dt1, Dt2, Dt3, En, G2, Gl1, Gl2, Gl15, Ij, Les1, Lg1, Lg2, O2, Oy, P, Pl, Pr, Pyd, R, Ra1, Rf3, Rp1, Sh1, Sh2, Spm, Su1, Ts6, Tu, V1, V4, Vg, Vp1, W3, Wd, Wt1, Wx, Y1,* and *Yg2.* Possible interactions between the embryo and endosperm beyond the supply of carbohydrates and other metabolites have been studied by deriving genetically mutant embryos with genetically normal endosperms and vice versa through the use of B-A chromosome translocations (Robertson, 1955, 1961; Neuffer and Sheridan, 1980; Neuffer et al., 1986a). The results generally show organ autonomy and are consistent with cell autonomy as seen in chimeral sectors, with an occasional exception in which mutant embryos are helped by non-mutant endosperms, and one case where a normal embryo was actually inhibited by the mutant endosperm. Isozymes that form heterodimers have been shown to have autonomy in pollen grains individually, forming only homodimers unless two alleles are both present in individual pollen grains (Frova et al., 1983). The diffusion and cross-feeding found for the anthocyanin system, discussed in the section on these factors, is limited in extent to only one or a few cells in the aleurone tissue. Very few factors are found to be nonautonomous: *Kn* and *Tp1* have been shown to express their effects on associated cells and tissues in sectored plants (Hake and Freeling, 1986; Poethig, MNL 61:84, 1987). Hormone-responding types, both recessives (e.g., the gibberellin-responding dwarfs, *an, d1, d2, d3, d5*) and some dominants (e.g., the "grassy" types *Tp1* and *Cg*), reflect nonautonomy as well.

Few mutants have been found to be auxotrophic, i.e., to be correctable with artificially supplied nutrients. The *pro* mutant is corrected by proline (Gavazzi et al., 1975; Racchi et al., 1978). Of 110 defective-kernel mutants that were tested by Neuffer et al. (1986a) for response to basal and enriched media, 5 were proline-requiring alleles of *pro*; 90 produced seedlings when cultured at immature stages but were not "rescued" by supplemented media. Albinos have been supplied sugars through cut leaf ends, feeding plants as far as maturity (Spoehr, 1942; Sayed, 1955). Externally supplied ferrous iron corrects the iron-deficiency-like expression of *ys* (Bell et al., 1958), in which mechanisms for transport of iron appear to be inefficient (Clark et al., 1973).

3–1.7   Sporophyte-determined Traits, Induction, and Imprinting

The sporophyte (i.e., the mother plant) can have major influences on expression and development, beyond the obvious supply of photosynthate and other constituents. Typically the flint vs. dent expression is determined by the sporophyte multifactorially, though a case of single-factor sporophytic control, by *sft* (small flint type), has been described (Dollinger, MNL 61:103, 1987). Sporophytic influence has been demonstrated for induction of flowering (Brawn, MNL 37:90-91, 1963) and for kernel maturation parameters (Alexander and Cross, 1983), among many other characters. Plants homozygous for the indeterminate factor, *id*, in typical strains require short days for induction of flowering but are pre-induced in the background of the cultivar Gaspe, an extremely early-flowering strain. The induction presumably represents either a transmittal of flowering signals from the mother plant to the developing embryo, which would be a true sporophytic effect, or alternatively a direct response of the embryo to the external daylength regime during its development. An example of the latter type is the induction of future anthocyanin pigmenting capability by light received during kernel development in the aleurone tissue of *cl-p* kernels (Chen and Coe, 1977). By way of contrast, induction of anthocyanin pigmentation by light, in *B pl* husks, sheaths, culm, roots, anthers and many other plant parts, termed sun-red expression, is very direct and prompt, displaying response in exposed tissue only, within 24 h of exposure to light.

"Imprinting" of functional expression by transmission through the male vs. female parent has been shown for some factors. Schwartz (1965) suggested, as an alternative to simple dosages and thresholds for endosperm factors, that the sex lineage through which a factor is transmitted may affect the expression of factors differentially. That just such differential effects occur has been demonstrated by Kermicle (1970b, 1978) with experiments showing pollen-transmitted *R* to be in a less active state than maternally transmitted *R*. Lin (1975, 1982) and Birchler (1981) have shown that endosperm development is differentially affected by "imprinting" via male vs. female transmission, under the influence of four defined segments in the long arm of chromosome 10 and multiple factors in the long arm of chromosome 1; the implication is that factors subject to differential expression may be distributed throughout the genome.

3–1.8   Pleiotropisms

Inasmuch as pleiotropism is always arbitrarily defined, awaiting further genetic or physiological knowledge, a listing of factors that show disconnected physiological effects may reveal more the state of knowledge or the particular biases of the compiler than any inherent validity as a listing. Among notable pleiotropisms are those involving anthocyanins, chlorophylls and carotenoids, and seed dormancy, including *al*, *cl*, *dek1*, *lw1, lw2, lw3, lw4, o5, ps, vp1, vp2, vp5, vp9,* and *w3*. The andromon-oecious dwarfs, *an, d1, d2, d3, d5,* and *D8,* all show both reduced stature and modifications in sexual development. Some other factors show dou-ble effects that might be considered to be disconnected in origin: *cp2,* several of the *dek* mutants, *et, o5, o12,* and *w2* (endosperm form and pigments; seedling chlorophyll—*et,* among others, has arisen several times as a mutation with double effects); *gl17* (cuticle waxes, plant stature, leaf necrosis); *ij* and *Isr* (chlorophyll, developmental modifications) and *loc* (oil content in kernel, seedling chlorophyll). Pleiotropisms in heterozy-gotes, affecting parameters of vigor negatively or positively, have been identified in a selection of mutants that were induced in an inbred line by chemical mutagens (Dollinger, 1985). The mutants identified with these pleiotropic effects are *bt1-4, lty1-16, lty2-20, ora3-14* and *zpg-3.* Double effects of the following mutations are known to be due to two-gene mutations or deficiencies: *a1-x1, a1-x2 (a1,* sh2, albinism, male transmission defects); *an-6923 (an, bz2); bz1-m4, sh1-bz1-x2* and *sh1-bz1-x3 (sh1, bz1,* male transmission defects); *r-x1 (r,* nondisjunction, male transmission defects).

3–2 GENETIC SYSTEMS

Much genetic information is available on unit factors controlling characteristics that are directly visible, especially in the kernel and the plant body: form, color, size and developmental progression.

The corn kernel is one of the most remarkable platforms on which genetic expressions can be studied. Because the kernels are of considerable size and are borne in compact clusters of several hundred individuals, most segregating traits can be recognized at a glance and ratios can be estimated by scanning or counting with little or no magnification or other aids, and without shelling and sorting unless necessary. Part of the reason for this visual convenience is the transparentness of the outer maternal tissue, the pericarp, often dubbed the "hull" in popped corn. The sub-stantial triploid endosperm and the shield-shaped germ (the cotyledon and the embryo), both derived as the new generation through meiosis and the sexual process, are conspicuous and are surveyed directly without dissection. With as little as 10X magnification it is possible to resolve the individual cells of the aleurone tissue (the one-cell-thick outer layer of the endosperm) and to recognize mutations or other differential expres-sions on a field of 150 000 to 250 000 cells representing 15 to 20 mitotic divisions that occurred in sequence and in contiguity (see Coe, 1978; McClintock, 1978a). This field of aleurone cells is the "petri dish" of many of the genetic analyses that are conducted. The anthocyanin pig-ments in the aleurone tissue and carotenoid pigments throughout the endosperm, discussed in separate sections, are particularly distinctive visible traits. Only slightly less conspicuously, the starchy internal portion of the endosperm can change in translucency, detectable with the naked eye or with the aid of a light box. Many factors that affect form of the kernel, e.g., collapsed or developmentally altered types, are easily distinguished from each other and from normal as well.

The plant, too, is of such substantial size and proliferation that modifications in height, proportions, reproductive organs, branching, leaf angle, leaf surface, etc., can be clearly evident and, at times, dramatic.

Other significant genetic systems include ones affecting biochemically defined properties, enzyme variations, reaction to pests, and several unique or precedent-setting systems of inheritance that have been explored in some depth.

3–2.1   Kernel Properties, Starch, and Proteins

Many simple genetic factors affect endosperm constituents so drastically that the kernel becomes distorted or collapsed and the change in form itself is recognizable; other factors affect the appearance of the kernel in other ways less dramatically, including hardness, transparency, and specific starch or protein constituents. The "dent" morphology that typifies field corn of the U.S. Corn Belt, however, is a genetically complex trait, determined by the sporophyte, and has been difficult to study. Because the dented form tends to interfere with discernment and classification of simpler traits, most strains used for study of endosperm phenotypes are the solid, hard (flinty) endosperm types characteristic of popcorns or the round to flat-topped flints of the northeastern U.S. and certain meal corn strains, in which the expressions of most endosperm traits are recognized more reliably. The genetic descriptions for visible kernel characteristics, in any event, are so specific to the strain ("background") in which they have been studied that a caution is warranted against over-generalizing on the expressions. The systems of kernel colors (anthocyanins and related compounds, red-blue-orange-yellow pigmentations; carotenoids, yellow-orange-red) are discussed in separate sections.

A somewhat arbitrary grouping of kernel morphology types, following common laboratory practice and terminology, separates them into *brittle*; *shrunken*; *sugary* or *glassy*; *waxy*; *defective, etched* or *pitted*; *opaque* or *floury*; and *viviparous*. The roles of the genes determining these morphologies, in the systems of biosynthesis and deposition of polysaccharides and storage proteins, and in the developmental steps of the endosperm and embryo, are briefly summarized here.

In the *brittle* type of kernel the endosperm is greatly collapsed. Kernels of *bt1*, *bt2*, and *sh2* have closely similar phenotypes. The endosperm before drying is like a fluid-filled sac (in *sh2* distended, balloon-like, and partially transparent) that develops little starch. On drying, the kernel shrinks and collapses into an angular structure with marked concavities and brittle texture (Fig. 3–2C). Because the sugar content of *sh2* kernels remains high longer than that of *su1* kernels, Laughnan (1953) proposed that *sh2* be used as an alternative factor for sweet corn. The "super-sweet"

Fig. 3–2. Phenotypes of the sweet corn factors. (A) normal, *Su1 Sh2*; (B) sugary, *su1 Sh2*; (C) supersweet, *Su1 sh2*; (D) sugary-supersweet, *su1 sh2*. (From Laughnan, 1953)

varieties now in widespread use, which Galinat (1971b) described as having "found a niche with those who like honey-sweet sweet corn," are homozygous for *sh2* in place of *su1*. Boyer and Shannon (1983) review the usage of *sh2*, *bt1* and *bt2* in sweet corn cultivars, and discuss the progress in development of adequate germination capability for the high-sugar kernels. In studies of phenotypic interactions, Laughnan (1953) found that *sh2 su1* kernels display the compounded effects of both factors (Fig. 3–2D). Alleles identified at the *Sh2* locus include inviable deficiencies for both *A1* and *Sh2*, isolated by Stadler and Roman (1948). Alleles at the *bt1* locus include *bt1-4*, which shows significant pleiotropic effects in heterozygous condition in a hybrid, including increased kernel weight and decreased plant height and days to silk (Dollinger, 1985).

The *shrunken* kernel characteristic of *sh1* is less severely collapsed than the brittle type. The endosperm before drying is fluid-filled and distended and has a reduced quantity of solids, which are confined to the periphery surrounding a cavity. Upon drying, the kernel usually collapses variably from the top, sides, or bottom, producing smooth, soft-line indentations that may leave a few residual pockets and seams detectable by dissection; if collapse does not occur a hollow cavity remains, rounded in outline and distinct from the small, angular cavity found in dent forms. Interactions with other factors (Garwood and Creech, 1972) indicate that the effects of *sh1* are not expressed in the presence of *bt1*, *bt2* or *sh2* (suggesting that these factors might act in sequence in starch synthesis), and that *sh1 su1* kernels express compounded effects of the two defects. Although no effects of the *sh1* genotype on plant growth or development have been found, the gene *Sh1* is expressed in roots and in etiolated shoots (but is repressed in greening tissues), and is induced by anaerobic conditions (Springer et al., 1986). Alleles identified at this locus include *sh1-S*, which complements other alleles phenotypically (Chourey, 1971); the *sh1-bz1-x* deficiencies induced by X-rays (Mottinger, 1970); and *bz1-m4* (*sh1-bz1-m4*), a mutant carrying an inserted *Ds* element that reverts to *Bz1* but does not yield *Sh1* revertants (Chourey, 1981).

Sugary and *glassy* are phenotypic terms that identify the appearance of a group of kernel types in which the endosperm shows increased transparency, not unlike crude glass or crystal sugar. The expression of sugary factor, *su1*, is familiar to anyone who has planted garden sweet corn. Dry *su1* kernels have a glassy, gumlike appearance, and a wrinkled, irregular form that is characteristic and unmistakable (Fig. 3–2B). The mature endosperm just before drying is distended and cohesive. The *su1* varieties grown for table use have been selected for a number of quantitatively measurable traits, including tenderness of pericarp, desirable flavor and aroma, and resistance to pests, but homozygosity for the *su1* factor is responsible for the primary effects of sweetness and creamy texture in sweet corn (Boyer and Shannon, 1983). The sugary enhancer factor, *se*, heightens flavor and increases the period of retention of sweetness and high palatability. The evolution of sweet corn under human selection and some of the modern potentials and implications are discussed by Galinat (1971b) and by Boyer and Shannon (1983). Alleles identified at the *Su1* locus (Brink, 1984) include some recognizable by their intermediate wrinkled phenotypes (*su1-Bn2*; *su1-cr*, crown) and some that are smooth-seeded and recognizable only by their effects in combination with *du* (*su1-am*, amylaceous; *su1-66*). Another allele, *su1-st*, determines starchy endosperm recessive to *su1* (Dahlstrom and Lonnquist, 1964). Kernels homozygous for *su2*, though similar to *su1* in appearance, generally are less deviant from normal in all respects. Two other glassy types, *ae* and *du*, tend to be a little collapsed but only slightly wrinkled. The term "tarnished" has been used to identify the dull glassiness of *su2*, *ae*, and *du* kernels. Their expressions and interactions display certain new or unique expressions in the endosperm of combinations involving this group of factors, specifically for *ae* when homozygous recessive with *su1*, *du*, or *wx*, and for *du* with *su2* and *wx* (Garwood and Creech, 1972). Specialized industrial applications for the starch from hybrids homozygous for *ae* have become significant because of their higher content of amylose, the straight-chain unbranched starch type (Watson, Chapter 15).

The *waxy* type of kernel is so unique and its expression so unconfounded that this trait is used as a universal marker in many experimental systems (e.g., as a marker, through reciprocal translocations, for linkages with each other chromosome, as described by Anderson, 1956). Recessive *wx* kernels display a uniform, marble-like opacity, and a hardness similar to that of normal kernels, except when in combination with floury mutants. Cut with a blade, *wx* endosperm chips away evenly, leaving a smooth, opaque surface, while normal endosperm (in the corneous side portions of dent kernels, for example) breaks unevenly and leaves an irregular, translucent surface. The starch in the cut surface of nonwaxy endosperm, whether flinty, floury, opaque, glassy, or brittle, will stain blue, turning quickly to black, with iodine (I_2) potassium iodide (KI) solution, while that of homozygous *wx* (waxy) will stain reddish brown, turning soon to dark brown. A drop of dilute solution (light amber solution prepared as needed by dilution from a stock solution of, for example, 10 g KI and 5 g I_2 or less in 100 mL of water) is sufficient. *Wx* can equally well be classified in pollen grains, and 1:1 segregation is found in pollen from heterozygous plants (Demerec, 1924a; Brink and MacGillivray, 1924; Longley, 1925), making a very satisfying classroom demonstration of gametic ratios. Precise staining of starch in pollen for mutation or recombination analysis at the *wx* locus (e.g., Nelson, 1968) requires more exacting preparations and procedures. Alleles that have been identified at the *Wx* locus include *wx-a* (Argentine), which has intermediate starch constitution and staining properties, and a number of recombinationally distinct stable and mutable alleles (Nelson, 1959, 1968). Interaction of *wx* in combination with either *ae* or *du* (Garwood and Creech, 1972) is striking, as double recessive kernels are shrunken or brittle-like, an expression quite distinct from the phenotypic effects of these factors singly. In callus cultures, endosperm explants of *wx* genotype continued to deposit amylose-free starch, characteristic of *wx* endosperm, rather than starch characteristic of the embryo and plant tissues; *ae* endosperm explants also retained their character to a considerable degree (Saravitz and Boyer, 1987). Though derived from a "laboratory curiosity" originally recognized in corn varieties from China, there is considerable industrial use of the pure amylopectin (branched-chain starch) milled from *wx* hybrids, as a thickening or gelling agent in foods (e.g., puddings) and in nonfood applications; *ae* hybrids are grown to a limited extent for high-amylose starch (Watson, Chapter 15).

Biochemical modifications in kernel starch biosynthesis that result from genetic changes are complex (Boyer and Shannon, 1983), yet are informative about the main program of carbohydrate transformation and deposition in the endosperm. The complexity lies in the fact that there is a dynamic interplay of inbound transport with possible transformations before, during and after entry (Tsai et al., 1970); cell pools and compartmentation; initiation of starch granule formation (Jones et al., 1985); transport into the starch granules; oligosaccharide chain initiation; primer-dependent chain lengthening; chain branching and chain de-branching. The phenotypic similarity among the brittle and shrunken types implies that the end consequences of each mutation are the same (namely gross reduction in normal starch deposition within the kernel). *Sh1* encodes sucrose synthase (SS1), which catalyzes the conversion of incoming sucrose to UDPglucose and fructose (Chourey and Nelson, 1976). Yet *sh1* mutants deposit as much as 25-30% of normal starch levels, and even homozygous viable deficiencies for the *Sh1* locus (*sh1-bz1-x* mutants) contain residual sucrose synthase activity (SS2), encoded by a second, separate locus (Chourey, 1981; Chourey et al., 1986; McCarty et al., 1986). *Bt1* affects and very possibly encodes an enzyme for short-chain initiation (D. Pan and O. E. Nelson, 1986, personal communication) with glucose-1-phosphate, without primer. *Bt2* and *Sh2* apparently encode monomers of the enzyme(s) catalyzing interconversion of ADPglucose and glucose-1-phosphate (Hannah et al., 1980), prior to polysaccharide formation. *Wx* encodes a starch synthase (ADPG + starch primer, and/or UDPG + primer), bound to the starch granule, catalyzing chain lengthening. *Ae* apparently encodes a branching enzyme leading to amylopectin starch (Hedman and Boyer, 1983), and on grounds of phenotypes and interactions *Du* and *Su2* may serve similar roles. The *Su1* locus apparently encodes a debranching enzyme that reduces the number of branches in normally deposited amylopectin (Pan and Nelson, 1984); when *sul* is recessive, a highly branched polymer, phytoglycogen, accumulates.

Defective kernel types include various poorly filled, collapsed, crumpled, small, miniature, rough, etched, pitted, germless, loose-pericarped, and wrinkled phenotypes (summarized by Neuffer et al., 1986a). In mutagenized material, defective kernel mutants are frequent (as many as 855 segregating ears were found among 3172 self-pollinated ears following treatment of pollen with ethyl methane sulfonate). An estimated 350 loci affect the development of the endosperm, of which over 40 have been located to chromosome and have been designated. The mutants *dek1* through *dek30* range across most of the variety and diversity of defective phenotypes; several otherwise-designated loci have been defined, including *cp1*, *cp2*, *mg*, *mn1*, *mn2* and *pro*. An estimated 250 of the 300 endosperm loci also affect embryo development, and a further, undetermined number of loci affect only the embryo (the symbol *gm* has historically been used for germless mutants of this type, but there are no currently available designated mutants). Several of the *dek* mutants when cultured produce seedlings that live long enough to express a plant phenotype: *dek1* produces roots but no shoots; *dek3*, *dek5* and *dek7* white seedlings with green stripes; *dek11* and *dek21* white; *dek4*, *dek12*, *dek18*, *dek29* and *dek30* narrow-leaf; *dek14* yellow-green; *dek28* necrotic; and *dek10* and *dek12* curled morphology (Sheridan and Neuffer, 1980; Neuffer et al., 1986a). Although a nutritional requirement (in contrast to a developmental one) is suggested by their ability to germinate, mutants at only one locus, *pro*, have been found to be auxotrophic, responding to proline but not to its precursor (Racchi et al., 1978). Of 110 mutants tested as immature kernels on basal or enriched media, 90 were able to germinate in culture despite the fact that most were unable to germinate from mature kernels (Neuffer et al., 1986a). Cytogenetically devised tests for interaction between embryos and endosperms in mutant/mutant vs. mutant/normal vs. normal/mutant constitutions almost always show autonomy rather than cross-feeding between the kernel parts (Sheridan and Neuffer, 1986). Developmental failures in embryo-lethal mutants are specific to stage of embryo development, and several have been studied in detail (Clark and Sheridan, 1986; Sheridan and Thorstenson, 1986). Defective kernels are associated with the anthocyaninless-lethal mutant, *anl*, with *ol1*, *ol2* and *ol3*, with *orp1 orp2*, and with *pro*. Etched, pitted, wrinkled, and aleurone-mosaic expressions are commonly associated with defective kernels (e.g., *dek2*, *dek11*). Particularly striking, however, is the finely etched and fissured surface of *et* kernels (Fig. 3–3). *Msc1*, *Msc2*, *st*, *w2* and *Wrk* also notably affect the structure of the endosperm surface. Both *et* and *w2* affect seedling pigmentation as well as the endosperm, suggesting that they are altered in functions basic to development. Pitted areas develop occasionally in kernels homozygous for intense purple aleurone color (with *in*) but these appear to be composed of disordered, burst

Fig. 3–3. Portion of ear homozygous for *et* (etched). In kernels with colored aleurone tissue, the fissured endosperm may be especially distinct. (From Neuffer et al., 1968.)

cells rather than of fissured areas. Multiple layers of aleurone cells develop in the endosperm of *mal1 Mal2* kernels; a multiple-aleurone type in combination with *o2* was studied by Nelson and Chang (1974).

Factors that can determine *opaque* appearance or *floury* texture in the endosperm include *cfl2, fl1, fl2, fl3, h, Mc, o1, o2, o5, o7, o9, o10, o11, o12, o13, pro, sen1* through *sen6, sh4,* and *Sup1*. Floury kernels are chalk-like in appearance and in hardness throughout all or most of the endosperm, the tissue crumbling away loosely when cut. Opaque kernels are normally classified with the aid of a light box arranged to observe transmission of light through the endosperm. Some of the floury and opaque types are difficult to classify in segregating material, especially in diverse backgrounds, and their penetrance and expressivity can be highly variable. The expressions of *fl1, fl2* and *fl3* are dosage-dependent, and display segregation most clearly through the female side, in accord with the two-dose contribution from the female parent to the endosperm. In contrast, recessiveness is characteristic of *h, o1, o2, o5, o7, o9, o10, o11, o12, o13,* and *pro; Mc* is a dominant opaque. Anthocyanin pigmentation in the aleurone tissue is reduced and irregular in *o1* kernels. Seedlings of *o5* genotype may be virescent, yellow or white, depending upon the particular allele. A group of duplicate factors (15:1 interaction) of the floury class, designated *sen1* through *sen6,* has been identified. The flour and meal corns, used by natives of the Americas for hand grinding and for parching, are strains that had been selected to carry *fl1* or one or more of the other factors of this class. Changes in protein composition have been identified for *o2* (Mertz et al., 1964), *fl2* (Nelson et al., 1965), *o7* (Misra et al., 1972), and *fl3* (Ma and Nelson, 1975), with important potential impact toward designed improvement in the nutritional balance (for humans and nonruminant domestic animals) of amino acids, especially lysine and tryptophan, in corn proteins.

The expressions of opaque and floury factors are a consequence of changes in the major class of storage proteins of the corn kernel, zeins (reviewed by Rubenstein and Geraghty, 1986; Soave and Salamini, 1984; Tsai, 1983). These proteins occur in two groups, one of 19-20 kDa and the other of 21-22 kDa, encoded by multigene families. The mechanism by which single-gene changes with opaque or floury phenotype result in alterations in the balance of the spectrum of proteins stored in the endosperm has attracted intensive experimentation. That some changes may be indirect in their origin is suggested by the studies of Misra et al. (1972), which demonstrate that not only opaques and flouries, but also carbohydrate-modifying factors (*su*, *sh2*, *sh4*, *bt*, *bt2*) elicit altered protein balances. Accumulation of zein polypeptides in the endosperm is reduced more in *o7* than in *o2*, and more in *o2* than in *fl2* kernels (Salamini et al., 1983). In *o7* kernels the 19 to 20 kDa family of zeins and their mRNAs are more reduced than the 21 to 22 kDa and the reverse is true of *o2*; the *o2 o7* double mutant shows additive reductions in both families, and the seeds seldom germinate. The *fl2* allele reduces both classes of zein (and the mRNA of a 27 kDa protein), but in combination with either *o2* or *o7*, *fl2* has no further effect. A protein of 32 000 molecular weight, b-32, is encoded by *o6* (= *pro*, per Manzocchi et al., 1986). The activity of the *pro* locus in concert with other storage protein loci is regulated by the *o2* locus (Di Fonzo et al., 1986). A dominant mutant temporarily designated *De*-B30* reduces 22 kDa zeins. *Mc* reduces all zein families moderately; in double mutant *Mc o2*, zeins are reduced to < 10% of normal, yet the combination is viable. The deficiency of proline in *pro* kernels apparently is due to increased proline catabolism rather than to reduced synthesis; *pro* kernels display a general reduction of major zein polypeptides (Dierks-Ventling and Tonelli, 1982). Map locations for loci controlling polymorphisms in zein polypeptides have been defined on chromosome 4 (long arm and short arm), chromosome 7 (short arm) and chromosome 10 (long arm) (Soave and Salamini, 1984; Ottoboni and Steffensen, 1987).

In *viviparous* kernels the embryos, instead of maturing into the normal dormant state, tend to grow into plantlets while still on the maturing ear. Even if a plantlet does not become discernible, moderate to severe distortion and irregular translucency in the endosperm are common, presumably due to partial digestion during premature germination. Alleles at the loci *al*, *ps*, *vp1*, *vp2*, *vp5*, *vp8*, *vp9*, *w3*, and *y9* display vivipary to various degrees. Robertson (1952, 1955, 1961, 1975) has shown that vivipary is determined by the embryo genotype independently of the endosperm genotype, and that effects on endosperm color (anthocyanins and carotenoids) are determined specifically by the endosperm genotype. Effects of diverse alleles at these loci, and the relationships of vivipary factors to the carotenoid pathway, are considered in the section on factors affecting chlorophylls and carotenoids. Except for *vp1*, which has normal levels of carotenoids and abscisic acid (ABA), the carotenoid biosynthetic pathway is blocked at locus-specific steps, and ABA is absent or greatly reduced in embryos of each viviparous type (Fong et al., 1983; Moore and Smith, 1985; Neill et al., 1986).

3–2.2   Anthocyanins and Related Pigments

The red and blue colors of the kernels and plant parts have attracted such attention that they are used not only as harvest-time decorations but as targets and aids in cloning of genes. According to East and Hayes (1911), segregations for colors in corn kernels had led plant hybridizers before the rediscovery of Mendel's work in 1900 to conduct some anticipatory counting of proportions; ultimately these segregations contributed strongly to the rediscovery, especially in the work of Correns (1901). Color factors are frequently used as markers in genetic studies: they are nonvital and are easily observed and classified. Moreover, because the genetics of pigment control is more fully elaborated than that of any other character or constituent, and because virtually every tissue can form anthocyanins under specified genetic conditions, color markers contribute to versatility and flexibility in research designs. The following is a survey of the genetics of these factors and a guide to the basic literature on the state of research into their action and nature, as they determine the red, blue, brown, yellow, and colorless compounds of the phenolic and flavonoid pathways.

Adequate description of the genetics of pigment control requires consideration of i) the loci involved and the allelic diversity found at each locus; ii) the tissues affected, which can be diverse yet very explicit, iii) the interactions among the effects of the different loci, and iv) the biosynthetic pathways through which they arise.

Some 20 loci directly affect the qualitative, quantitative, and distributional array of anthocyanin pigments and their relatives; only the smallest linkage group, number 8, lacks a member of this class. There is an interactive dependence of genotype with effectors (position, time, place, stage, conditions, history), collectively termed the ambience (Coe, 1985). Well over 20 tissues can be recognized to show differential pigmentation under genetic control. The loci are listed with the expressions of selected alleles and combinations, according to the tissues affected, in the accompanying chart (Table 3–2). Each locus has its own particular effects: some, like $A1$, are essential to anthocyanin formation in virtually every tissue; while others, like $C1$ and Pl, are essential in only a few tissues. The factors $A1$, $A2$, $Bz1$, and $Bz2$ are complementary to each other in most tissues. A few factors, such as B and certain alleles at R, have duplicate-like effects on pigmentation in particular tissues—e.g., pigment is present in the coleoptile, roots, and tassel glume faces with B $R-r$, B $r-g$, and b $R-r$, but not with b $r-g$. For designing of experiments, the chart shows which tissues express the effects of a selected locus, and which factors express genetic variation in a selected tissue. For diagnosis of genotype, the chart shows which loci are presently known to be required for pigmentation in each tissue; thus, by observing whether pigment is present or absent in specific tissues of an individual or strain under study, the genotypic constitution for known factors can be derived.

More detailed studies of expressions, alleles, structure, and action have been carried out on many of the loci, and the briefs below outline supplemental information. Interactions and the expressions of selected constitutions (some of which are presented in Table 3–2) are outlined as well.

Table 3-2. Expressions of anthocyanins in various tissues with specific genotypes.†

al	sc	pm	co	rt	au	lt	lb	hk	tg	tb	an	po	sk	sw	pc	cb	Genotype
P	()	()	R	R	R	R	P	P	P	P	P	Y	MR	B	L	P	A1 A2 A3 Anl B bh bn Brn Bz1 Bz2 C1 C2 ch Da Dek1 In lc orp1 orp2 P-rr Pl Pr R-r Sm sn Ufo Vp1 Whp
C	()	()	MT	C	G	G	G	T	T	T	G	Y		B	B	T	a1 (others as above)
C	R	()	MT	C	G	G	G	T	T	T	G	Y		B	B	T	a1 R-sc
CB	C	C	MB	C	G	G	G	Bn	B	B	P	Y		B	L	RB	a2
P			R	R	G	R	P	P	B	B	P	Y				P	a3 B-b
P			R	R	G	R	MP	MP	MP	G	MP	Y				MP	a3 b
C			G	C	G	G	G	G	G	G	G	Y				RB	a3 b r-g
C		X	X	X													anl
P	()	()	R	R	G	R	G	MP	P	G	P	Y	MR	B	L	RB	b
P	()	()	s	s	G	R	G	G	s	G	s	Y	S	B	L	RB	b pl
C	C	C	G	C	G	G	G	G	G	G	G	Y	G	B	L	RB	b pl r-g
C	C	C	G	C	G	G	G	G	G	G	G	Y	G	G	C	C	b pl P-ww r-g
P	()	C	MR	MR	G	G	G	MP	MP	P	G	Y	G	B	L	RB	B-b R-g
P	P	C	MR	MR	G	G	G	MP	MP	MP	G	Y	G	B	L	MP	B-Peru r-g
mt	()		MR	MR	G	G	G	MP	MP	P	G	Y	G	B	L	MP	B-Bolivia r-g
mt			R	R	R	R	P	P	P	P	P	Y	MR	B	L	P	Bh c1
B																	Bn c1
P	B	B	X	X		MB	B	Bn	B	B	BF	Y					brn
B	B	B	X	X		MB	B	Bn	B	B	B	Y					brn c1 r-
B	C	C	MB	C	G	R	P	P	P	P	P	Y	B	B	L	B	bz1
B	C	C	MB	C	G	R	P	P	P	P	P	Y	B	B	L	B	bz2
B	C	C	R	R	R	R	P	P	P	P	P	Y	B	B	L	P	c1-n
C	C	C	R	R	R	R	P	P	P	P	P	Y	B	B	L	P	c1-p (germ. in light)
MR	C	C	MR	R	G	G	MP	MP	MP	P	MP	Y	MR	B	L		C1-I
C	C	C	MR	R	G	G	MP	MP	MP	P	MP	Y	G	B	ML	MP	c2
MP	C	C	MR	C	G	G	MP	MP	MP	P	MP	Y	G	B	ML	MP	c2 in
MP	C	C	MR	C	G	G	MP	MP	MP	P	MP	Y	G	B	ML	MP	c2 su

Table 3–2. Continued.

								Tissue									Genotype
al	sc	pm	co	rt	au	lt	lb	hk	tg	tb	an	po	sk	sw	pc	cb	
C	C	C	G	C	G	G	G	G	G	G	G	W	G			MB	c2 whp
C	C	C	G	C	G	G	G	G	G	G	G	W	G			MB	c2 in whp
C	C	C	G	C	G	G	G	G	G	G	G	Y	G		ML	C	C2-Idf
P			R	R	G	R	G	MP	P	G	P	Y	MR		B	B	Ch b P-ww
MP			X	X					X	MP							da
C	( )		R	R	R	R	P	P	P	P	P	Y	MR	B	L	P	dek1
IP	( )		R	R	R	R	P	P	P	P	P	Y	MR	B	L	P	in
MP	( )		R	R	R	R	P	PR	PR	P	P	Y	MR	B	L	P	In-D
IR	( )		MR	MR	MR	R	P	MP	PR	P	PR	Y	MR	B	L	P	in pr
C	MP		MR	MR	MR	R	P	X	X	MP			P		P	P	Lc (or Sn) b r-g
P	( )	( )	R	R	G	R	G	MP	P	G	P	Y	MR	B	O	RB	orp1 orp2 P-wr
P	( )	( )	R	R	G	R	G	MP	P	G	P	Y	MR		C	C	P-wr b
P	( )	( )	R	R	G	R	G	MP	P	G	P	Y	MR	G	L	C	P-rw b
P	( )	( )	S	S	R	R	S	S	S	S	S	Y	S	B	MR	RB	P-ww b
R	( )	( )	R	R	R	G	P	PR	PR	P	PR	Y	MR	B	L	P	pl
P	( )	( )	R	R	G	G	P	G	P	P	G	Y	G	B	L	P	pr
P	( )	( )	G	C	R	R	P	P	P	P	G	Y	G	B	L	RB	R-g
C	( )	( )	R	R	R	R	G	P	P	P	G	Y	G	B	L	P	R-g b
C	( )	( )	R	R	G	R	P	MP	P	P	P	Y	MR	G	L	RB	r-r
C	( )	( )	R	R	R	G	G	P	G	G	G	Y	MR	B	L	P	r-r b P-ww
C	( )	( )	G	G	R	R	G	G	G	G	G	Y	G	B	L	C	r-g
C	( )	( )	G	G	G	G	G	G	G	G	G	Y	G	B	C	C	r-g b
C	( )		G	C	G	R	P	P	G	P	P	Y	G	B	L	RB	r-g b P-ww
P	P	C	R	R	G		G					Y	Sm	B	L	P	sm
P		( )		R	R		P	P	P	P	P	Y	B		C	C	sm P-ww

(continued on next page)

Table 3-2. Continued

						Tissue											Genotype
al	sc	pm	co	rt	au	lt	lb	hk	tg	tb	an	po	sk	sw	pc	cb	
P				R	R	G	R	O	O	O	O	O	Y	O	G	O	O	*Ufo*
																		Ufo b P-vv
mt			vp	R	R	R		G	MP	P	G	P	Y	MR	G	C	C	*vp1*
P		()	()	R	R	R	R	P	P	P	P	P	Y	MR	B	L	P	*whp*

† Expressions

B	Brown	L	Lacquer-red	vp	Viviparous
Bn	Brown-necrotic	M	Medium color	W	White (not Y)
C	Colorless	mt	Mottled color	X	Dies
F	Fluoresces yellow	nj	Navajo crown color	Y	Yellow
G	Green (not P or R)	O	Orange	()	Depends on genotype
I	Intense color	P	Purple		
		R	Red		
		RB	Brick-red		
		S	Sun-dependent red		
		Sm	Salmon		
		T	Tan		
		vg	Variegated		

Tissues and properties

al	Aleurone tissue	hk	Husks	pc	Pericarp
al 1d	Aleurone tissue, one dose from male	in en	Inner endosperm	pm	Plumule
an	Anthers	lb	Leaf blade	Pmbl	Paramutable
au	Seedling auricle	lt	Leaf tips	Pmgc	Paramutagenic
cb	Cob	mb	Marbled-variegated	po	Pollen
cm	Culm	me	Mesocotyl	rt	Roots
co	Coleoptile	nd 1	First node	sc	Scutellum
		Npmbl	Not paramutable	sc nd	Scutellar node
sh 1	First sheath				
sk	Silks				
st	Stippled-variegated				
sw	Silks when wounded				
tb	Tassel glume bars				
tg	Tassel glume faces				

al   Expressions of the allele types at the *A1* locus reported and analyzed by Laughnan (1948, 1955) and Nuffer (1961), with a few additions, are given in Table 3–3. There are alleles with several intermediate levels of expression; the faintest, *al-b*, can be distinguished from *al* in the aleurone tissue only with difficulty even by testing for anthocyanin with dilute acid (4% hydrogen chloride applied to cut cells containing anthocyanin causes a characteristic bright pink color change). Pericarp color determined by *A1* (*A-st*) and some other alleles in the presence of *P-rr* is lacquer-red (non-anthocyanin pigments); other alleles determine brown color that is dominant to red, and others determine recessive brown color. Laughnan (1952) has shown that *A1-b* consists of separable components *alpha* (*A-d*) and *beta* (like *A1-st*). Dots of color in *al* aleurone tissue and stripes in *al* plant tissues are mutations of *al* to *A1* and intermediate alleles, caused by *Dt* (Rhoades 1941); *Dt* can also induce changes in the direction of *A1* to *al* (Nuffer, 1961). There are a number of other mutable alleles, controlled by *Dt* or by other transposable-element systems. The locus has been cloned through cross-screening of sequences from alleles containing insertions of the *En* element and alleles containing the *Mu* element, with probes for the element sequences (O'Reilly et al., 1985; Schwarz-Sommer et al., 1987). The anthocyanins in purple aleurone tissue, cyanidin and pelargonidin glucosides, accompanied in husks by traces of peonidin glucosides (Chen, 1973; Harborne and Gavazzi, 1969; Kirby and Styles, 1970; Sando et al., 1935; Styles and Ceska, 1972), are absent in *al* tissues, but glycosides of closely related flavonols, quercetin and kaempferol, are increased (Kirby and Styles, 1970; Laughnan, 1950), and some light brown pigments (presumably oxidized polyphenolic compounds) are deposited. In three respects the functional effects of the *A1* locus stand apart from those of the other loci. For example, while purple pigment is found in the aleurone and the scutellum of *R-scm* kernels carrying *A1 A2 Bz1 Bz2 C1 C2* and *R*, none is found in either tissue if any one of these factors is recessive except in *al R-scm* kernels, where the aleurone is colorless but the scutellum is red (i. e., not purple and not colorless). Second, the light brown pigmentation of *al B Pl* husks is distinctive, more caramel-yellow in tone than the brown pigments of *a2*, *bz1*, *bz2* or *c2* husks, and the vascular bundles of *al B Pl* husks, leaves and stems contain red anthocyanins despite the total loss of anthocyanins from all other tissues (except the scutellum, as indicated above). Third, the *A1* locus, unlike *A2*, *Bz1* and *Bz2*, determines red-brown cob color and lacquer-red pericarp color with appropriate *P* alleles; with recessive *al* or with dominant *A1-b*, these colors are

Table 3–3. Types of alleles at the *A1* locus and their effects on aleurone, plant, and pericarp color. After Laughnan (1948, 1955) and Nuffer (1961).

Allele type	Aleurone color with all color factors present	Plant color with *B Pl*	Pericarp color with *P-RR*	Pericarp with *P-WW b Pl r-ch*	Notes
A1-st	Purple	Purple	Red	Cherry	Common N. Am. allele
(β)	Purple	Purple	Red	Cherry	Derived from *A1-b*
A1-b (α β)	Purple	Purple	Dominant brown	Cherry	Collected from Ecuador
A1-b:P (β α')	Purple	Purple	Dominant brown	Cherry	Collected from Peru
A1-r	Purple	Purple	Red	Cherry	From *a1* by *Dt* action
A1-rb	Purple	Purple	Red-brown	Cherry	From *a1* by *Dt* action
A1-br	Purple	Purple	Recessive brown	Cherry	From *a1* by *Dt*; dosage effect
A1-lt	Dilute purple	Deep red-brown	Recessive brown	Red-brown	From *a1* by *Dt*; dosage effect
A1-w	Dilute purple	Deep red-brown	Red-brown	Red-brown	From *a1* by *Dt* or UV; dosage effect
A1-d (α)	Dilute purple	Deep red-brown	Dominant brown	Red-brown	Derived from *A1-b*; competes with most *A1* alleles
a1-p (α')	Pale purple	Red-brown	Dominant brown	Brown	Collected from Peru; competes with most *A1* alleles
a1-b	Faint purple	Red-brown	Dominant brown	Brown	Standard; responds to *Dt*
a1	Colorless	Brown	Recessive brown	Brown	Stable with *Dt*; from *a1* by *Dt* action
a1-s	Colorless	Brown	Recessive brown	Brown	From *A1* by x-rays; deficiencies including *Sh2*
a1-X	Colorless	Brown	Recessive brown	Brown	

changed to brown. The *A1* locus is reported to encode an enzyme that catalyzes reduction of the carbonyl group at the 4-position of the flavanonol dihydroquercetin (3-hydroxy, 4-keto) to form a 3,4-dihydroxy leucoanthocyanidin (Schwarz-Sommer et al., 1987), as predicted from studies of intermediates, accumulated compounds and interactions (Sando et al., 1935; Laughnan, 1950; Styles and Ceska, 1977, 1981a). Parallel action is implied by similar evidence for flavonoids that are not 3-hydroxylated (Styles and Ceska, 1977).

a2   In husks and sheaths, dark chocolate-brown *a2 B Pl* tissues develop necrotic areas that may expand until the entire plant collapses, but if either *B* or *Pl* is absent necrosis does not occur (Laughnan, 1951). Mutable variants controlled by transposable elements at *A2* are known. Flavonols (Kirby and Styles, 1970) and leucoanthocyanidins (Reddy and Reddy, 1971) accumulate in *a2* aleurone tissue. As *a2* kernels age in storage, brown pigments tend to accumulate, presumably through slow oxidation of phenolic compounds, paralleling the rapid browning in the husks. Evidence from accumulated compounds, intermediates and interactions indicates that *A2* determines the conversion of leucoanthocyanidin (formed from *A1* action) to anthocyanidin (Coe, 1955; Styles and Ceska, 1977, 1981a).

a3   In the presence of weak *B* alleles (e.g., *B-b*), the recessive intensifier *a3* results in a dramatic increase in pigmentation (Styles and Coe, 1986), approaching or equalling that with *B* (i.e., *A3 B*). The combination *a3 B* may be still more strongly pigmented. Simply viewed, *a3* may regulate the level of expression of *B* alleles, and of certain *R* alleles (Styles and Coe, 1986).

anl   The anthocyaninless-lethal factor determines loss of anthocyanin from the aleurone in kernels that possess a normal-appearing but inviable embryo. Kernel size reduction is characteristic of at least some alleles at this locus, and pale-aleurone alleles are known. Whether the effects on pigmentation are direct in the pathway, or are through indirect physiological causes, remains to be defined.

B   The *B* locus historically was defined as a "booster" of plant color, but it is now recognized as a determiner of pigmentation. *B* plant tissues are strongly pigmented (purple, sun-red, or brown) even when no color is present in the aleurone (with *a1*, *a2*, *c1*, *C1-I*, *c2*, *C2-Idf*, or *r*) or in the anther (with *a1*, *a2*, *c2*, *C2-Idf*, *R-g* or *r-g*). Expressions of *B* alleles are best distinguished in *Pl* plants that are dominant for the factors *A1*, *A2*, *Bz1*, *Bz2*, and *C2*, but with *r-g*, as the expressions of pigmenting alleles of the *R* region (e.g., *R-r*, *r-r*, *Lc*, or *Sn*) overlap and duplicate (Styles, 1970) the expressions of *B* alleles in many tissues (Table 3–2). Coe (1966b, 1979, 1985), Styles et al. (1973), and Styles (1986) have defined expressions of alleles at the *B* locus as related to *R* expressions, summarized in Table 3–4. Particularly instructive are the rare alleles at *B* that confer aleurone and scutellum color (*B-Bolivia* and *B-Peru*, both originally referred-to as *R2*), which duplicate and replace the *R* function. Similarly, determinants near the *R* locus (*Lc* and *Sn*) have *B*- and *R*-like effects and have recombinational homology with components of the *R* locus (Dooner and Kermicle, 1976; Dooner, 1979b). The locus may, in duplicate function with *R* alleles (Styles et al., 1973; Styles and Ceska, 1977, 1981a), determine 3-hydroxylation of flavonoids, leading to anthocyanins and flavonols.

Bh   The blotching factor confers irregular, mottled anthocyanin color in the aleurone of *c1* kernels, hardly distinguishable in appearance from the mottling characteristic of *R* alleles in one paternally derived dose. *Bh* is not recognizable except in *c1* kernels that carry *A1*, *A2*, *C2* and *R*. Blotching can lead to extremely strong pigmentation approaching full color, but uniformly pigmented progeny are not derived through selection. The supplanting of *C1* function by *Bh*, however irregular, is suggestive of duplicate gene action, and the very close linkage of *Bh* and *Pl*, considered along with the light-specific control of pigmentation at both loci, may indicate a functional parallel between *C1* and *Pl-Bh* (Coe, 1985).

bm1, bm2, bm3, bm4   The brown-midrib factors condition brown pigmentation that is prominent in the leaf midrib and is strongly evident along the vascular bundles of the leaf sheath, husks, and culm, and in the cob and other parts to varying degrees, in lignified tissues. The brown pigments are visually similar to those accumulated in *a1 B Pl* plant tissues. McClintock (1938) has demonstrated that tissues homozygous deficient for *Bm1* have the same expression as the homozygous recessive for *bm1*. Lignin content is lower in all four brown-midrib types and in their double-recessive combinations (Gee et al., 1968; Kuc and Nelson, 1964; Kuc et al., 1968). The color of alkali lignin (the de-esterified "core"), which is greyish-tan from normal plants, is reddish-brown from brown-midrib plants, and differences in methylation and in proportions are found among the four types in phenolic acids released during de-esterification, as well as in other measures of the constituents and properties of lignin. The possibility that improved digestibility of livestock silage might derive from lowered lignin content and from altered lignin properties has been studied by Muller et al. (1971) and Gallais et al. (1980). Grand et al. (1985) report activity of a methyl transferase in *bm3* plants depressed to only 10% of normal levels.

Table 3–4. Expressions of alleles at the *B* and *R* loci in various tissues, in the presence of *Pl* and of the other factors necessary for pigmentation.†

Genotype		en (in)	al	ld	sc	pm	nd	me (nd)	co	l (sh)	rt	au	lt	cm	lb	hk	tg	tb	an	po	sk	pc	cb	Notes
r-g	*B*	–	–	–	–	–	–	R	R	R	R	R	–	P	P	P	P	P	–	–	–	MP	P	Pmbl
r-g	*B-b*	–	–	–	–	–	–	MR	MR	MR	MR	MR	–	MP	–	MP	MP	P	–	–	–	MP	MP	Npmbl
r-g	*B-Bolivia*	–	mt	mt	–	–	–	MR	MR	MR	MR	MR	–	P	P	P	P	P	–	–	–	MP	P	Npmbl
r-g	*B-Peru*	P	P	P	P	–	–	MR	MR	MR	MR	MR	–	MP	–	MP	MP	P	–	–	–	MP	MP	Npmbl
r-g	*B'*	–	–	–	–	–	–	MR	MR	MR	MR	MR	–	MP	MP	MP	MP	P	–	–	–	–	MP	Pmgc
r-g	*B-v*	–	–	–	–	–	–	vg	vg	vg	vg	vg	–	vg	vg	vg	vg	vg	–	–	–	vg	vg	Pmbl
r-g	*b-v*	–	–	–	–	–	–	–	–	–	–	–	–	–	–	–	–	–	–	–	–	–	–	Pmbl
r-g	*b*	–	–	–	–	–	–	–	–	–	–	–	–	–	–	–	–	–	–	–	–	–	–	Npmbl
R-r	*B*	P	P	mt	–	–	–	R	R	R	R	R	R	P	P	P	P	P	P	–	MR	MR	MP	P	Pmbl
R-r	*b*	P	P	mt	–	–	–	R	R	R	R	R	R	MP	–	MP	P	P	P	–	MR	MR	MP	MP	Pmbl
R-g	*b*	P	P	mt	–	–	–	–	–	–	–	–	–	–	–	–	P	–	–	–	–	–	–	Pmbl
r-r	*b*	–	–	–	–	–	–	R	R	R	R	R	R	MP	–	MP	P	P	P	–	MR	MR	MP	MP	Npmbl
r-g	*b*	–	–	–	–	–	–	–	–	–	–	–	–	–	–	–	–	–	–	–	–	–	–	Npmbl
R-mb	*b*	mb	mb	–	–	–	–																		Pmgc
R-nj	*b*	nj	nj	–	–	–	–		R		R		MR		–	–	MP	–	MP	MP	–				Npmbl
r-r:Pu	*b*	–	P	–	P	–	–						R		–	–	–	–	P	–					
R-scm	*b*	P	P	P	–	–	–		MR				MR												Pmgc
R-st	*b*	st	st	P	–	–	–																		Pmgc

(continued on next page)

Table 3-4. Continued.

		Tissues																	
Genotype		in en	al 1d	al sc	pm nd	co sh 1	rt	au	lt	cm	lb	hk	tg	tb	an	po	sk	pc	cb	Notes
r-xl	b	--																		
Lc r-g	b	--	--	MP	R	MR	MR	R	R	P	P	MP	MP	MP	--	--	P	P	P	
Sn r-g	b	--	--	MP	R	MR	MR	R	R	P	P	MP	MP	MP	--	--	P	P	P	

† Expressions

B	Brown
Bn	Brown-necrotic
C	Colorless
F	Fluoresces yellow
G	Green (not P or R)
I	Intense color
L	Lacquer-red
M	Medium color
mt	Mottled color
nj	Navajo crown color
O	Orange
P	Purple
R	Red
RB	Brick-red
S	Sun-dependent red
Sm	Salmon
T	Tan
vg	Variegated

Tissues and properties

al	Aleurone tissue
al 1d	Aleurone tissue, one dose from male
an	Anthers
au	Seedling auricle
cb	Cob
cm	Culm
co	Coleoptile
hk	Husks
in en	Inner endosperm
lb	Leaf blade
lt	Leaf tips
mb	Marbled-variegated
me	Mesocotyl
nd 1	First node
Npmbl	Not paramutable
pc	Pericarp
pm	Plumule
Pmbl	Paramutable
Pmgc	Paramutagenic
po	Pollen
rt	Roots
sc	Scutellum
sc nd	Scutellar node
sh 1	First sheath
sk	Silks
st	Stippled-variegated
sw	Silks when wounded
tb	Tassel glume bars
tg	Tassel glume faces
vp	Viviparous
W	White (not Y)
X	Dies
Y	Yellow
( )	Depends on genotype

Bn   Dominant brown color develops in the aleurone of colorless kernels (e.g., *c1*) and is not recognizable in purple aleurone. The pigment has not been defined and genetic interactions with other genes have not been detailed.

brn   Recessive brown color is conferred by *brn* in the aleurone and the embryo; brown is not recognizable in purple aleurone. The factor is lethal in the seedling.

bz1   The aleurone tissue of *bz1* kernels in different backgrounds can range from virtually colorless to dark brown or purple-brown approaching *Bz1* in phenotype; dilute acid (4% hydrogen chloride) applied to cut cells results in a bright pink color change characteristic of anthocyanins, showing most strongly in fresh kernels and deriving from gray-brown vacuolar pigments. Brown wall pigments are evident in *bz1* aleurone cells in some backgrounds. Plant tissues develop considerable anthocyanin, soon browning and becoming necrotic. In addition to a detailed description of the expression of *bz1*, Rhoades (1952) points out McClintock's (1951) observation of anthocyanin borders at the interface between colorless *C1-I Bz1* and bronze *C1 bz1* sectors in aleurone tissue (Fig. 3–4). The implication is that diffusion of precursors across one to three cell widths between genotypes overcomes a block in biosynthesis. The flavonol quercetin and its glucoside isoquercitrin are present in *Bz1* pollen, but the glucoside and the enzyme coded by *Bz1*, UDPglucose flavonol 3-O-glucosyl transferase, which catalyzes its formation from quercetin, are absent in *bz1* plants, pollen and kernels (Larson and Coe, 1968, 1977; Dooner and Nelson, 1977a). Other glycosides are accumulated instead, and

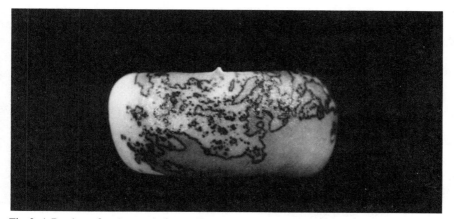

Fig. 3–4. Borders of anthocyanin formed by complementary interaction of products diffusing between cells of aleurone tissue carrying the inhibitor *C1-I* with *Bz1* (background of upper portion), and cells carrying *C1* with *bz1* (lower right, and the lightly colored central regions of small sectors). (From McClintock, 1951.)

intermediates are diverted to other flavonoids (Dooner, 1979a; Styles and Ceska, 1981a, b). Anthers of *bz1* plants are brilliantly yellow-fluorescent under ultraviolet light, regardless of genotype for any other factors except with *c2 whp* (in which all anthocyanins and other 15-carbon flavonoids are absent). The accumulation of quercetin, which is yellow-fluorescent in contrast to its glucoside, presumably becomes a contributor and a substrate toward the striking yellow fluorescence of *bz1* anthers. Mutants from *Bz1* isolated by Mottinger (1970, 1973) following x-irradiation include variants that are small deletions (at least one including *Sh1*). Alleles have been identified that show altered timing of action and altered properties of the enzyme (Dooner and Nelson, 1977b; Dooner et al., 1985). From mutable alleles containing *Ac* and *Ds* insertions, the locus has been cloned by probing with *Ac* sequences (Fedoroff et al., 1984; Dooner et al., 1985).

bz2   Aleurone and plant expression of *bz2* is closely similar to that of *bz1* (but lacking the yellow-fluorescent anthers); originally found as a mutable allele, *bz2-m*, a *Ds*-containing allele from which stable alleles have been isolated. The mutant *an1-6923*, isolated from material irradiated in nuclear bomb tests, is allelic to both *an1* and *bz2* and is viable when homozygous.

c1   Three types of alleles, inhibitor (*C1-I*), color-determining (*C1*), and colorless (*c1*), have long been known. The expressions in the endosperm are dosage-dependent: *C1 C1 C1* and *C1 C1 c1* kernels are purple while *C1 c1 c1* are pale; *C1-I C1-I C1-I* and *C1-I C1-I C1* are colorless while *C1-I C1 C1* are colorless to light pale with a few purple dots due to loss of the dominant inhibitor; heterozygotes of *C1-I* with *c1* are completely colorless. Cone et al. (1986) describe dosage effects of alleles, including those of a strongly colored allele, *C1-S*, which confers stronger color in *C1-I C1-S C1-S* kernels. A large test for recombination between *C1-I* and *c1* yielded no recombinants (Coe, 1964), supporting allelism as defined by Hutchison (1922). Kirby and Styles (1970) demonstrated light-dependent pigment synthesis during germination of *c1* kernels, which Chen (1973) and Hsu-Chen and Coe (1973) found to be specific to particular conditional alleles, designated *c1-p* (positive) in contrast to *c1-n* (negative). The dominant factor *Bh*, as described under notes for this factor above, causes variable, diffuse blotches of color in the aleurone tissue of *c1* kernels; a duplicate-function relationship of *C1* with *Bh* and *Pl*, as described under notes for each, is suggested by allelic variants that are light-dependent and by this functional duplication (Coe, 1985).

c2   Recessive *c2* plant tissues develop substantial anthocyanin (especially in the auricles, sheath edges, and glumes), but the aleurone tissue contains no detectable pigment except in the presence of homozygous intensifier (*in*) or sugary (*su1*). The dominant dilute alleles (*C2-Idf*), which have shown no recombination with *c2*, include one with virtually complete loss of pigmentation and one with intermediate color that is mutable (Brink and Greenblatt, 1954). In all tissues of plants recessive for *c2* and *whp*, anthocyanins and red-brown cob colors are absent, and flavonols and all other flavonoids are absent from the pollen; the cob and husks in *c2 whp B Pl* plants, however, deposit light gray-brown pigment. With respect to pollen color and anthocyanin, *C2* and *Whp* act as if they are duplicate in function (Coe et al., 1981). The *C2* locus has been cloned by probing for *Spm* inserts in mutable alleles (Wienand et al., 1986). *C2* encodes chalcone synthase, the enzyme that catalyzes the formation of the 15-carbon flavonoid skeleton from a 9-carbon cinnamic acid moiety (CoA-activated p-coumaric acid), joined with three 2-carbon segments from malonyl CoA (Dooner, 1983).

Ch   Chocolate brown color in the cob and pericarp, independent of constitution for factors of the flavonoid pathway, is conferred by *Ch*.

da   Dilute aleurone color is determined by recessive *da*.

dek1   The defective-kernel factor *dek1*, also known as *clf* or *gay*, results in near to complete absence of anthocyanin in the aleurone, in addition to its effects on endosperm and embryo development. Dooner (1983) has shown that the enzymes encoded by *Bz1* and *C2* are absent or very low in mutant endosperms. Whether the effects of this factor are direct in the pathway or are through indirect physiological effects on pigment deposition remains to be determined.

in   In addition to intensifying anthocyanin pigmentation specifically in the aleurone layer, *in* conditions a metallic gold-to-brown sheen in the pericarp over aleurone tissue that is homozygous recessive for *in*, implying a transfer of constituents or signals from one tissue to the other. A dominant dilute factor, *In-D*, does not recombine with *in* and may be presumed to be allelic. Reddy and Peterson (1978) have shown that *in* results in increases in quantities of anthocyanins and related compounds but does not affect them qualitatively.

Lc   The dominant expression of *Lc* (and of *Sn*) includes pigmentation in the leaves (under cool conditions) and in many other plant parts. Resemblance to the *R* and *B* loci, and duplication of their functions, is evident (Table 3–4). *Lc* and *Sn* are very likely equivalent determinants, both derived from sources of the historical "cherry alleles" *r-ch* and *R-ch*, and are sufficient to confer the unique expressions of the cherry class of alleles. Dooner and Kermicle (1976) and Dooner (1979b) have shown that *Lc* has the properties of a duplication of the *R* region, placed in tandem order a few units distal to *R*, and that this duplicated region undergoes occasional synapsis and exchange with *R* alleles. In several respects the *Lc* factor has effects beyond those of *r-r* alone (i.e., beyond those of the P element at the *R* locus), conferring pigmentation in the bar at the base of the tassel glumes (a regular property of *B* alleles), husk and cob color similar to fairly strong *B* alleles, and pericarp and silk pigmentation beyond that conferred by strongly expressed alleles at *R* and *B*.

orp1, orp2   Orange pigmentation expressed in the double recessive is located in the pericarp overlying homozygous endosperms. As with *in*, an effect of the genotype of the endosperm and embryo on the maternal tissue of the pericarp implies transfer of constituents or signals from one tissue into the other. The nature of the orange pigment or changes in potentially affected constituents remain to be determined. Aleurone anthocyanin is unaffected.

P   The allele types at the *P* locus defined by Anderson (1924) are symbolized with two letters, the first pertaining to the pericarp color and the second to the cob color, with r designating lacquer-red pericarp or brick-red cob; o, orange; w, white (clear) pericarp or white cob; c, white-cap pericarp; and v, variegated, as follows: *P-rr*, *P-or*, *P-wr*, *P-ow*, *P-cw*, *P-cr*, *P-ww*, and *P-vv*. The symbol *p* is used interchangeably with *P-ww*. The mutability due to *P-vv* results in the widely admired "candy-striped" kernel markings that arise from mutations occurring during development of the pericarp, occasionally occurring earlier and giving rise to single kernels or adjacent groups of kernels with solid lacquer-red color, usually associated with twin sectors of low-frequency events (light variegated). These events are due to removal of the inserted element *Mp* (*Ac*-equivalent) from its location within the *P-rr* gene sequence, accompanied in the twin by a gain in dosage of the *Mp* element. Silk color with recessive *sm* is salmon with *P-rr* or *P-wr*, brown with *P-ww*. The browning reaction that occurs at the ends of cut silks is dominant to non-browning and is dependent on the presence of ortho-dihydroxy flavones (Levings and Stuber, 1971), which are determined by *P-rr* or *P-wr* (Styles and Ceska, 1977) or by certain white-cob alleles, designated *P-wwb* in contrast to *P-www*, white-cob nonbrowning (Coe and Han, unpublished data). A compound of this flavone type, the C-glycosyl flavone called maysin, has been shown to inhibit the growth of earworm, *Heliothis zea* Boddie (Wiseman et al., 1983). "Dingy" colors in the pericarp of the kernel, an undesirable quality for food corn, may be contributed by flavone compounds. Styles and Ceska (1981a) propose from accumulated compounds and intermediates that the *P* locus is necessary to the initiation of the pathway leading to compounds of the flavone type (compounds not hydroxylated at the 3 position of the 15-carbon flavonoid skeleton). The locus has been cloned by probing for *Ac* sequences inserted in *P-vv*.

pl   Recessive *pl* is the allele most widely present in Corn Belt hybrids and varieties, determining a requirement of light exposure for the induction of pigment synthesis in tissues of the seedling and plant ("sun-red" pigmentation). Anthocyanins or brown pigments (*a1, a2, bz1, bz2*) are light-dependent in all tissues, so that only exposed roots, leaf parts, stem, husks, tassel parts, silks, pericarp, and cob become pigmented; the brick-red cob colors and lacquer-red pericarp colors (*P* locus-controlled), however, are not limited by light. "Sun-red" pigmentation in the pericarp of the kernel, an undesirable quality in food corns, is anthocyanin and is probably the result of light exposure to kernels having a genotype that confers anthocyanin potential (e.g., some *r-r* alleles; *Lc* or *Sn*; some *B-b* alleles). Induction of pigment in previously unexposed husks can be recognized in less than 24 hours after brief light exposure, and "windows" of light or cut patterns can be used to induce deliberately localized pigment synthesis. In the presence of *Pl*, pigmentation is independent of light exposure ("purple"). The difference between *pl* and *Pl* is dramatic, as sun-red (*B pl*) sheaths show shaded bands of color from daily growth cycles (Fig. 3–5) while purple (*B Pl*) sheaths are uniformly and intensely purple, approaching black; sun-red anthers may be no more than slightly pink, while purple anthers are very dark. Gerats et al. (1984) found that the glucosyltransferase encoded by *Bz1* is reduced in sun-red sheaths. The close linkage of the *Pl* factor, influencing light-dependent plant pigmentation, with the *Bh* factor, which confers blotched pigmentation with *c1*, a locus at which light-dependent kernel pigmentation is allele specific, has led to a suggestion that *C1* and *Pl* may be duplicate in function, albeit in different tissue types (Coe, 1985).

pr   In aleurone tissue and anthers the expressions of *Pr* vs. *pr* are usually clear-cut purple vs. red. In other tissues the differences in color tone are evident but are not unambiguously distinct. *Pr* determines mostly cyanidin glucoside with small amounts of pelargonidin glucoside, while *pr* determines reverse proportions of these two pigments (Chen, 1973; Harborne and Gavazzi, 1969; Kirby and Styles, 1970; Larson et al., 1986). The parallel leucoanthocyanidins have been identified by Reddy

Fig. 3–5. Expression of sun-red (*B pl*) in husks. *Left:* Drawing showing banding due to daily cycles of exposure during growth of husks (reproduced with permission from Emerson, 1921). *Right:* Photograph of sun-red ear showing response to light exposure: husks were pulled back, a black paper shield with cutout letters was placed over the exposed surface, and the stencil was removed 3 days later, just prior to photography.

(1964) in *a2* kernels; the homologous flavonols, quercetin and kaempferol, in several genotypes by Kirby and Styles (1970), and the homologous flavones by Styles and Ceska (1975). Activity of an enzyme controlling this hydroxylation, NADPH:flavonoid 3'-hydroxylase, has been shown to be dependent upon dosage of *Pr* (Larson et al., 1986).

More diverse varieties of expression are known at the *R* locus and in the *R* region than at any other locus, and its variants affect over 20 tissue types differentially. Expressions of the types of *R* alleles are given in Table 3–4, drawn in part from the descriptions given by Brink (1958) and by Styles et al. (1973). The four basic types (*R-r*, *R-g*, *r-r*, *r-g*) designated by Emerson (1921) are symbolized according to effects on aleurone color (*R* vs. *r*) and on anther color (*-r* vs. *-g*, red vs. green). Studies by Fogel (1946), summarized by Stadler (1951), showed that *R-r* alleles can be arranged in a series according to very fine increments in level of expression in various tissues, but an increment of difference in one tissue does not necessarily presage a parallel increment in another. The "pattern" alleles are each specific in the distribution of pigmented areas in the aleurone tissue: *R-mb* (marbled) confers large blotches of color with well-defined borders; *R-st* (stippled) confers small, sharply defined colored sectors (Fig. 3–6); *R-nj* (Navajo crown) confers color with diffuse, graded borders in the crown portion of the kernel. The designations *R-sc* and *R-scm* are applied to self-colored alleles (i.e., those that are uniformly colored rather than mottled when present in one male-derived dose); mutants with self-colored expression arise by mutation from *R-st* (*R-sc*) and *R-mb* (*R-scm*) (Ashman, 1960; Weyers, 1961). Mottling expression (irregular, scattered color) typical of *r r R* kernels is determined by transmission of *R* through the male rather than by dosage of *R* (Kermicle 1970b; Fig. 3–7). Silk color determined by *R-r* or *r-r* alleles is bright pink, localized mostly in the silk hairs but developing in the shaft of the silk with time. Mutation of plant color and seed color independently (Stadler, 1951; Fig. 3–8), and crossing over between components (Emmerling, 1958; Stadler and Emmerling, 1956; Stadler and Nuffer, 1953) have shown that the locus is compound and contains two determinants, designated P for plant color and S for seed color. These determinants are displaced from each other in a tandem duplication, and recombine after oblique

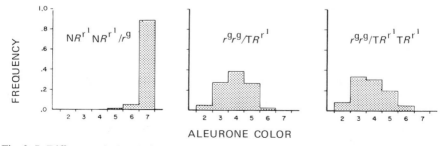

Fig. 3–6. Region of stippled (*R-st*) aleurone tissue, showing sectors (clones) of cells resulting from mutations of *R-st* to *R-sc* (self-colored) during development (25X).

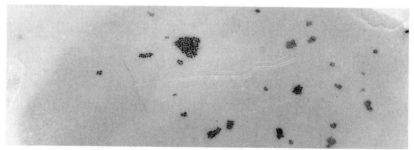

Fig. 3–7. Differences in level of expression of male-transmitted vs. female-transmitted *R'*. Kernels receiving two doses of *R'* from the male (right) show the low levels typical of kernels receiving one dose from the male (center) rather than the high level typical of kernels receiving two doses from the female (left). (From Kermicle, 1970b.)

synapsis to yield single determinants (Emmerling, 1958; Kermicle, 1974, 1985). The locus probably is even more complex in structure, according to indications from studies of various allele types and their recombinational products (Sastry, 1970; Dooner and Kermicle, 1976; Dooner, 1979b; Kermicle and Axtell, 1981; Kermicle, 1985). The picture is confounded, however, by the existence of *R-g* alleles (colored aleurone, green anthers) that condition color in certain plant tissues (coleoptile, mesocotyl, roots) and mutate to colorless in both aleurone and plant tissues in one step (Bray and Brink, 1966; Stadler, 1951). Styles et al. (1973) and Styles and Ceska (1977, 1981a) conclude from studies of tissue specificity, intermediates and accumulated compounds that the *R* locus and the *B* locus behave as if they are functionally duplicate in determining the occurrence of 3-hydroxylated anthocyanins in all tissues, except in the pollen (Styles and Ceska, 1981b). Enzymatic catalysis of 3-hydroxylation, under explicit tissue-by-tissue definition according to the alleles at each locus, is a candidate function for these two loci. The specific expressions of *R-nj:Cudu* in the endosperm (Navajo crown) and the embryo provide differential expression that identifies kernels in which exceptional ("noncorresponding") embryos can be selected that are potentially haploids or diploids of maternal or paternal origin (Greenblatt and Bock, 1967; Kermicle, 1969; Nanda and Chase, 1966; Fig. 3–9). *R-nj* expression levels have been shown

Fig. 3–8. Mutational sequences for *R-r*, in which *r-g* (lacking both plant and aleurone color) arises either through *r-r* (lacking aleurone color) or through *R-g* (lacking plant color), but not in a single step from *R-r*. (After Stadler, 1951)

A   B   C   D

Fig. 3–9. Expression of *R-nj* in endosperm and embryo and exceptional fertilizations recognized by non-correspondence. A. Endosperm *R-nj*, colored crown; embryo *R-nj*, colored scutellum: Expected kernel type in homozygous *R-nj* stock or from crosses of *r* with *R-nj* where both sperm correspond in genotype. B. Endosperm *r*, colorless; embryo *R-nj*, colored: Non-corresponding kernel type resulting from heterofertilization (frequency typically 1%) in cross of *r r* female parent by *R-nj r* male, or from mutation in one of the two sperm in a pollen grain. If the polar nuclei are not fertilized, the embryo and endosperm abort and consequently do not contribute kernels to this type of non-corresponding event. C. Endosperm *R-nj*, colored crown; embryo *r*, colorless: Non-corresponding kernel type resulting from heterofertilization (complementary to that in B), or from mutation in one of the two sperm in a pollen grain, or from haploid parthenogenetic development of the embryo accompanying fertilization of the polar nuclei. Maternal haploids from the cross of *r r* x *R-nj R-nj*, or paternal haploids from the reciprocal cross, will be of this non-corresponding kernel type. D. Endosperm and embryo *r*, colorless.

to be maternally determined (sporophytic), correlated with parameters of kernel maturation (Alexander and Cross, 1983). A deficiency, *r-x1*, was derived by L. J. Stadler in 1944 from *R-r* following X-irradiation (the deficiency termed *r-x2* is the same one as *r-x1*, accidentally misidentified). Unlike X-1 (Stadler, 1933), which was a cytologically visible terminal deficiency, *r-x1* is intercalary and is cytologically undetectable; it is transmitted only through the female and lacks aleurone and plant color effects. It has been found to induce nondisjunctional events in the megagametophyte that result in high frequencies of aneuploid eggs, generating monosomes, trisomes, segmental monosomes, and more-complex aneuploids (Weber, 1973, 1986; Carlson, Chapter 4). Among factors mapping in the *R* region whose functional relationships are curiously confounded are *Lc* (leaf color), *Mst* (modifier of *R-st*), *Isr* (inhibitor of striate and other striping factors) and *cm* (chloroplast mutator).

sm   Orange-pink salmon color develops in silks recessive for *sm* in the presence of red cob (*P-wr*) or red pericarp (*P-rr*) factors. *P-ww sm* silks are brown. The salmon color is distinct from the pink color conferred by *R-r* or *r-r*, and is localized in the silk shaft rather than in the hairs. Styles and Ceska (1977) have shown that 3-deoxyanthocyanins are increased in the presence of *sm*.

Sn   The factor for scutellar node color, like *Lc*, was derived from "cherry" sources and is very probably equivalent to *Lc*.

Ufo   Strong orange pigmentation, similar to the colors conferred by *P-rr* or *P-wr* in the cob and pericarp, is formed in all tissues of the plant in the presence of *Ufo* with red cob or red pericarp (*P-rr* or *P-wr*) factors. Like brick-red cob and lacquer-red pericarp, orange pigmentation is inhibited by *C2-Idf* and is expressed as brown rather than orange in the presence of recessive *a1*. The silks of *P-wr Ufo/+ Sm/sm* plants are salmon, displaying a dominant effect of the salmon factor in this constitution.

vp1   This one viviparous factor, unlike the others, results in near to complete absence of anthocyanin in the aleurone, in addition to failure of dormancy. Dooner and Nelson (1979) and Dooner (1983, 1985) have shown that enzymes of the flavonoid pathway are deficient, as are some other, unrelated enzymes, in the aleurone of *vp1* kernels. Plants homozygous for *vp1* develop normally if viviparous seeds are planted without drying, and anthocyanins are formed in plant parts in typical fashion according to the genotypes of other factors. The effects of the viviparous factor may be through indirect physiological control of dormancy and of the aleurone maturation process

whp

rather than through direct participation in the biosynthetic pathway (Dooner, 1985).

In plants homozygous for *c2 whp*, the bright yellow pigments of the pollen are absent. All other heterozygous or homozygous constitutions produce yellow pollen—i.e., the pigment is determined by the genotype of the sporophyte, presumably by the anther wall. For pollen color and anthocyanin, *C2* and *Whp* may be viewed as duplicate factors (Coe et al., 1981). No 15-carbon flavonoids appear to be present in white pollen. Anthocyanin pigmentation and cob and pericarp colors are absent in *c2 whp* plants and kernels, except for late-forming, gray-brown pigment in the cob and husks in the presence of *B Pl*.

Field corn lines and hybrids of the U.S. Corn Belt consistently are of the constitution *r-r* (pink anthers, leaf tips, and plant base) or *r-g* (green); usually these strains are *c1* and *pl*; usually *A1*, *A2*, *b* or *B-b*, *Bz1*, *Bz2*, *C2*, and *Pr*. Lines with red cobs are *P-wr* while ones with white cobs are *P-ww*, some of which have browning silks (*P-wwb*) in contrast to non-browning (*P-www*). Inbred lines that carry *C1* rather than *c1* include 38-11, FR35, H100, K44, K61, K302, Ky27 and N28. Both 38-11 and Ky27 have purple plumules, determined by *r-r:Pu* in the presence of *C1*. Some field corn inbreds and hybrids carry dominant dilution or inhibition factors, *C1-I*, *C2-Idf*, *In-D* or others, which may reduce either aleurone color or plant color substantially. Sweet corn and popcorn lines are quite diverse in aleurone color factors, often carrying *C1-I*; super-sweet hybrids carry *a1*, derived from the source of *sh2*, to which it is closely linked.

In the aleurone tissue the formation of strong purple anthocyanin pigmentation (Table 3–5) requires *A1*, *A2*, *Anl*, *Bz1*, *Bz2*, *C1*, *C2*, *Dek1*, *In*, *Pr*, *R* or certain rare alleles at the *B* locus, and *Vp1*. With homozygous *pr*, the aleurone is red. If any one or more of *a1*, *a2*, *anl*, *c1*, *c2*, *dek1*, *r* or *vp1* is homozygous recessive color is absent. If *bz1* or *bz2* is homozygous, little purple pigment develops and brown pigment is formed instead (as long as *A1*, *A2*, *Anl*, *C1*, *C2*, *Dek1*, *R*, and *Vp1* are present), while if *bz1* and *bz2* are both homozygous color is virtually absent. All pigmentations, whether purple, red or brown, are intensified if *in* is recessive. Kernels homozygous for *c2 in* or *c2 su* develop faint purple color except when *whp* is also homozygous. East and Hayes (1911) identified the 9:7 ratio resulting from complementary interactions in F_2 from *C1 c1 R r*, the 9:3:4 from epistatic interactions of *C1 c1* or *R r* with *Pr pr*, and ratios involving the color inhibitor, *C1-I*; Emerson (1918) identified the 27:37 complementary ratio from *A1 a1 C1 c1 R r*.

In plant tissues (e.g., husks) the formation of strong anthocyanin pigmentation requires *A1*, *A2*, *B*, *Bz1*, *Bz2*, *C2*, and either *Pl* (purple) or exposure to light if *pl* (sun-red) (Table 3–6). With homozygous *b*, plant tissues generally contain no purple, red or brown pigments, although limited pigmentation in some tissues is conditioned by *R-r* or *r-r* alleles

Table 3-5. Aleurone color expressions of factors controlling anthocyanins and related pigments. Aleurone color is given for kernels homozygous or heterozygous for the factors specified in the left column (in the presence of all other factors) with the four possible combinations of the modifying factors *Pr, pr* and *In, in*. The pericarp color given is expressed in otherwise clear pericarp tissue over aleurone tissue of the indicated genotype.

Factor	*Pr In*	*Pr in*	*pr In*	*pr in*
All color factors present	Purple	Deep purple; pericarp brown	Red	Deep red
a1	Colorless	Faint brown; pericarp brown	Colorless	Colorless; pericarp faint brown
a2	Colorless	Faint brown; pericarp brown	Colorless	Colorless; pericarp faint brown
bz1	Purple bronze	Brownish purple; pericarp brown	Red bronze	Pink; pericarp yellow brown
bz2	Purple bronze	Brownish purple; pericarp brown	Red bronze	Pink; pericarp yellow brown
bz1 bz2	Near colorless	Not seen	Colorless	Not seen
C1-n	Colorless	Colorless	Colorless	Colorless
C1/c1/c1	Pale purple	Purple	Pale red	Red
c1-p	Colorless; purple when germinated in light	Colorless; deep purple when germinated in light	Colorless; red when germinated in light	Colorless; deep red when germinated in light
C1-I	Colorless	Colorless	Colorless	Colorless
C1-I/c1/c1	Colorless	Colorless	Colorless	Colorless
C1-I/C1/C1	Colorless; few purple dots	Pale; few deep purple dots	Colorless; few red dots	Pale; few deep red dots
C1-I/C1-S/C1-S	Pale purple	Purple	Pale red	Red
c2	Colorless	Pale purple	Colorless	Pale red
c2/c2/c2	Pale purple	Purple	Pale red	Red
c2 whp	Colorless	Colorless	Colorless	Colorless
C2-Idf	Colorless	Not seen	Colorless	Colorless
C2-Idf/C2/C2	Pale purple	Purple	Pale red	Red
C2-Idf/c2/c2	Colorless	Colorless	Colorless	Colorless
In-D	Pale lavender	--	Pale violet	--
In-D/In/In	Pale purple	--	Pale red	--
r	Colorless	Colorless	Colorless	Colorless
R/R/r	Purple	Deep purple	Red	Deep red
R/r/r	Mottled purple	Mottled deep purple	Mottled red	Mottled deep red

or by *Lc*, each of whose effects can partially duplicate the action of *B*. With *B* and homozygous *pl*, red or brown pigments develop only in exposed tissues. If *a1* or *a2* is homozygous with *B Pl*, purple anthocyanins are not formed but are replaced, respectively, by light caramel brown or by dark chocolate brown and tissue necrosis. With *bz1* or *bz2*, purple anthocyanins form but soon are replaced by dark chocolate brown, accompanied in *bz1 B Pl* plants by severe necrosis and brittle nodes. With *c2*, purple is reduced and is confined mostly to the auricles, sheath edges, and glumes, eventually followed by brown pigmentation. If *c2* and *whp* are both homozygous, purple is absent and late-forming gray-brown pig-

Table 3–6. Plant color expressions of the factors controlling anthocyanins and related pigments. Color of plant tissues is given for plants bearing the factors specified in the left column (in the presence of all other factors) with the four possible combinations of the factors B, b and Pl, pl.

Factor	B Pl	B pl	b Pl	b pl
All dominant including R-r or r-r	Purple†	Sun-red in exposed tissues; pink anthers†	Green plant; purple anthers, glumes, base, and brace roots	Green plant; pink anthers, red glumes, base, and brace roots
a1	Brown	Faint brown, especially glume base; sun-dependent	Green; brown base and brace roots	Green
a2	Brown; brown tissues deteriorate†	Faint brown, especially glume base; sun-dependent	Green; brown base and brace roots	Green
a3 B-b			Purple plant	Sun-red
bz1	Red brown; some deterioration†	Weak red brown; sun-dependent	Green; red brown anthers, base, and brace roots	Green
bz2	Red brown; some deterioration†	Weak red brown; sun-dependent	Green; red-brown anthers, base, and brace roots	Green
c2	Purple auricles and glumes; faint elsewhere	Sun-red auricles and glumes	Green	Green
Lc b r-g			Dilute purple	Dilute sun-red
pr	Deep maroon†	Sun-red in exposed tissues; pink anthers	Green plant; maroon anthers, glumes, base, and brace roots	Green plant; pink anthers, glumes, base, and brace roots
R-g or r-g	Purple plant; green anthers†	Sun-red plant; green anthers†	Green	Green

† Expressed in leaf sheaths, auricles and blades, culm, cob, husks, glumes, anthers, coleoptile, seedling base, and brace roots. Same applies where indicated in B pl column only if tissue is exposed to sunlight.

mentation develops. With weak *B* alleles, e.g., *B-b*, plant pigmentation is greatly reduced; with *a3*, weak *B* expressions are intensified to nearly full levels (Styles and Coe, 1986). Emerson (1921) identified the interactions of *A1*, *B*, *Pl*, *Pr*, and *R*, including the sun-dependent synthesis of pigment with *pl*.

In cobs the formation of brick-red pigment ("phlobaphenes") requires *A1*, *C2* or *Whp* and either a *P-rr* or *P-wr* allele. If *a1* is recessive the cob is light tan; if *c2 Whp*, light red; if *c2 whp* or *P-ww*, white. Purple anthocyanin pigments (conferred by *B Pl*) or browns (due to *a1*, *a2*, *bz1*, *bz2*, or *c2*) hide the brick-red color.

In silks the formation of true pink anthocyanin color (in contrast to salmon) requires an allele of the *R-r* or *r-r* type, or *Lc*, with *A1*, *A2*, *Bz1*, *Bz2*, *C2* and *Pl* (light-independent) or *pl* (light-dependent). Salmon color (deoxyanthocyanin), on the other hand, is controlled by the same factors as brick-red cob color, requiring *A1*, *C2*, and a *P-rr* or *P-wr* allele, with recessive *sm*.

In anthers the formation of anthocyanins requires either *R-r* or *r-r* and *A1*, *A2*, *Bz1*, *Bz2*, *C2*, and *Pl* (strong purple) or exposure to light if *pl* (sun-red or pink). With *a1* or *a2* recessive, color is absent; with *bz1*, *bz2* or *c2* color may be brown to faintly tan (colorless if *c2 whp*). Anther walls of *bz1* constitution are brilliantly yellow fluorescent under ultraviolet light with all genotypes except when homozygous recessive for both *c2* and *whp*.

Information on the sequence of action of the factors, and on the relationships of factors to specific biosynthetic steps, has been summarized by Styles and Ceska (1977, 1981a). A striking and instructive complementary interaction in vivo, forming distinct borders of anthocyanin at the interface between cells of *C1-I Bz1* (colorless) and *C1 bz1* (bronze) genotype, was recognized by McClintock (1951; Fig. 4). The cells of one genotype appear to "feed" the other: Rhoades (1952) determined that the most intensely pigmented cells are the edgemost *C1 bz1* cells, indicating that *C1-I Bz1* tissue supplies intermediates across the boundary to them. This is not as would be expected from simple consideration of the probable order of action (*C1* preceding *Bz1*), but is consistent with evidence that *C1-I* tissue cannot carry out pigment synthesis functions because some of the pathway enzymes are regulated "off" by *C1-I* (Dooner and Nelson, 1979). Laughnan (1951) determined that the brown plant phenotypes of the double-recessive combinations *a1 bz1* and *a1 a2* resemble that of recessive *a1* alone, and suggested that the action of *A1* could precede that of *A2* and *Bz1*. Because the *a2 bz1* combination, on the other hand, resembles neither *a2* or *bz1* alone, the sequence of action of *A2* and *Bz1* could not be inferred. The pericarp over homozygous *in* aleurone develops a brassy metallic sheen if the aleurone tissue is colored, or if homozygous *a1*, *a2*, *bz1*, or *bz2*, but not if *c1*, *C1-I*, *c2* or *r* (Coe, 1957). The latter group of factors was suggested to precede the former in order of action. Cross-feeding interactions form pigment in pairwise combinations of aleurone tissue fragments of blocked genotypes (Reddy and Coe, 1962). The sequence of action of the factors (according to the order, receiver blocked first in order of action, donor blocked second) was suggested to be as follows: *C1-I, C1, C2, R, In, A1, A2, Bz1, Bz2*. The leucoanthocyanidins that accumulate in *a2* aleurone tissue require *C1, C2, R*, and *A1*, but not *Bz1* or *Bz2*, as expected from the proposed sequence of action (Reddy, 1964). The leucoanthocyanidin quantity is influenced by *in*, and the hydroxylation pattern by *pr*, indicating that the action of *In* and *Pr* could precede the action of *A2* (Coe, 1955). Flavonols accumulate in *A1* aleurone tissue and are affected by *Pr* vs. *pr*, indicating that the action of *Pr* could precede that of *A1* (Kirby and Styles, 1970). When appropriate intermediates (flavanones or flavanonols) are supplied to aleurone tissues recessive for *c2* they are converted to anthocyanins, demonstrating that the *c2* block precedes these intermediates and that each of the enzymatic functions subsequent to the intermediates can be present in this genotype (McCormick, 1978). *Pr* action is also carried out on the intermediates, indicating that the action of *Pr* can follow that of *C2*.

Composite perspectives on the pathway and the probable steps at which specific genes act have been developed by Styles and Ceska (1977, 1981a), Dooner (1982), and Styles (1986). Styles and Ceska (1977) comprehensively describe the individual loci and the occurrence of end products and intermediates in the different genotypes. Chalcone synthase, encoded by the *C2* locus (Dooner, 1983), forms the 15-carbon skeleton of the flavonoids by joining a 9-carbon moiety (coumaroyl CoA) derived from phenylalanine with three 2-carbon residues from malonyl CoA. The 15-carbon intermediate must become hydroxylated at the 3 position (the second carbon of the coumaroyl moiety) toward anthocyanins in a step whose genetic basis is unknown but may involve *B* or *R*, leading to flavanonol. Reduction of the carbonyl at the 4 position presumably is encoded by *A1*, leading to a flavan-3,4-diol (leucoanthocyanidin), which evidently is converted to anthocyanidin by the action of *A2*. The sugar-free anthocyanidin is unstable under oxidizing conditions (yielding brown polymers) but is stabilized by glucosylation through the action of the enzyme encoded by *Bz1*. Anthocyanins and other flavonoids also are found to undergo glycosylation at other sites, and methylation at the 3'-position (Styles and Ceska, 1977, 1981b; Larson and Bussard, 1982), for which genetic loci have not been defined. Toward flavonols, hydroxylation must occur and a reduction step is necessary, both of which are of unknown genetic basis, followed by glucosylation by the *Bz1* enzyme. Toward 3-deoxyanthocyanins (e.g., salmon silk color) and red-cob phlobaphenes, action by both *A1* and *P* appears to be necessary.

3–2.3 The Photosynthetic Pigments and Photosynthetic Machinery

About 200 loci are known that influence the pigments and processes related to photosynthesis and to carotenoids. Mutations that visibly alter chlorophyll in the seedling and plant (albino, pale green, delayed greening) are at least as frequent in occurrence as any other variation; among these are many mutations whose primary effect is actually on carotenoid content (carotenoids being essential to stable chloroplast membranes). Mutations that affect carotenoids in the kernel (yellow vs. lemon vs. white endosperm) affect chlorophyll in some instances and not in others; dormancy vs. vivipary of the embryo is affected by some of the carotenoid-affecting mutations but not others. The multiple dimensions of analysis (genetic, developmental, physiological, biochemical, molecular) necessary to characterize this class of factors and to define primary lesions have been carried out on only part of the factors, allowing only limited definition of the sites of specific defects, pathways and mechanisms (Robertson, 1982). Alleles at one locus, for example, may differ among themselves in their effects and in their response to environmental or genetic modifiers, altering specific expressions markedly.

The keyed tabulation in Table 3–7 compares effects of the factors with each other. The yellow-orange carotenoid color of the endosperm (with *Y1* and other factors) may be reduced to white or to pale yellow or orange-pink by any of 20 factors, a few of which affect endosperm morphology as well. Embryo dormancy fails to occur with mutation at any of nine loci, resulting in a viviparous ("rampant") embryo. Seedling colors may be green to pale green, yellow-green, yellow, pale yellow, tan, orange-pink, or white; seedling expressions include virescent, albescent, striped, cross-banded, piebald, speckled, finely streaked, and necrotic. Plant colors, when viable, may be green to pale green, yellow-green, or yellow; they may be albescent, striped, cross-banded, finely streaked, or they may display lighter color only between the vascular bundles. A few of the factors affect the morphology of seedlings and plants. Temperature (high or low) and light intensity dramatically influence the expressions of many of these variants.

One large group of factors includes those that condition reduced chlorophyll in the seedling, but have normal, green mature plants. This expression is termed *virescent* (becoming green—Demerec, 1924b), and is keyed by V in Table 3–7. The term is often used without distinction between the broad sense (the organism at first having reduced chlorophyll and later becoming green) and the narrow sense (cells with reduced chlorophyll becoming green). Mutants with this expression include all of the *v* group except *v8* (which dies), and *ar, dp, et, f, ij1, ij2, pg2, su1, tn, wt1,* and *wt2*. Many are only conditionally viable, depending upon temperature or other conditions; this is specifically the case for *ar, et, f, pg2, v2, v4, v12,* and *v16*. Some virescents (e.g., *ar, f, v4, v5,* and *wt1*) may be finely streaked (F) or may continue to show virescence in the young leaves of older plants; *ij1* and *ij2* plants are japonica-striped (displaying stripes predominantly near the margins of the leaves). Although *su1* (sugary endosperm) is not ordinarily included among the chlorophyll factors, pale yellow-virescent seedlings very commonly develop from homozygous

Table 3-7. Chlorophyll and carotenoid factors: Comparative effects (see key below) on endosperm, embryo, seedling, and plant.

Genotype	Endosperm color (with *Y1*)	Embryo dormancy	Seedling	Plant
al	W/PY	D/R	G/WAC	G/WAC
al-Brawn	W/PY		PGA	G/PGA
ar	Y	D	WVC	G/FC
cl clm	W/PY	D	WC	X
cl Clm-2	W/PY	D	PG	X
cl Clm-3	W/PY	D	G	G
cm	Y	D	SW	SW†
cp2	M	D	PGU	X
dp	Y	D	WV	G
et	YM	D	WV	G
f	Y	D	JVC	F/J
g1	Y	D	YGH	YGH
g2	Y	D	YG	YG
g5 (= *g2*)				
G6	Y	D	YG	YG
grt		D	V	X
gs1		D	G	LP
gs2		D	G	LP
gs3		D	G	LP
hcf1		D	G	M
hcf2		D	YG	X
hcf3		D	G	X
hcf4		D	G	X
hcf5		D	G	X
hcf6		D	G	X
hcf9 (allele of *hcf3*)				
hcf12		D		X
hcf13		D	G	X
hcf15		D	YG	X
hcf18		D	YG	X
hcf19		D	G/YG	X
hcf21		D	G	X
hcf23		D	G	X
hcf26		D	YG	YG
hcf28		D	G	X
hcf31		D	YG	X
hcf34		D	YG	X
hcf36		D	G	X
hcf38		D	G	X
hcf41		D	G	X
hcf42		D	YG	X
hcf43 (allele of *hcf18*)				
hcf44		D	PG	X
hcf46		D		X
hcf47		D	YG	X
hcf48		D	YG	X
hcf50		D	G	X
hcf101		D		X
hcf102		D		X
hcf316		D	YG	X
hcf323		D	G	X
hcf408		D	YG	X

(continued on next page)

Table 3-7. Continued.

Genotype	Endosperm color (with *Y1*)	Embryo dormancy	Seedling	Plant
ij1	Y	D	JV	J†
ij2		D	J	J
Isr	Y	D	U	U
j1	Y	D	G/J	J‡
j2	Y	D	G/J	J‡
l1	Y	D	U	U
l4		D	PY	X
l6		D	Y	X
l7		D	PYG	X
l10	Y	D	Y	X
l11		D	YU	X
l12		D	YU	X
l13		D	Y	X
l15		D	Y	X
l16		D	YB	X
l17		D	YZ	X
l18		D	Y	X
l19		D	Y	X
li			G	F
loc			W	X
lty1	PY			
lty2	PY			
lu			YGH	YGH
lw1	W/PY	D	W	X
lw2	W/PY	D	W	X
lw3 lw4	W/PY	D	W	X
ly (allele of *ps*)				
(*NCS*)			SP	SP
nec1		D	PGN	X
nec2		D	GN	X
nec3		D	TNZ	X
nec4		D	YN	X
nec5		D	PGN	X
nec6		D	TN	X
nec7		D	NZ	X
Og		D	G	SY‡
ora2	O			
ora3	O			
oro1			TNZ	X
oro2			TNZ	X
Orom			U	
orp1 orp2			PGU	X
oy oy	Y	D	Y	YG
oy-t oy-t	Y	D	YG	YG
Oy-700 Oy-700	Y	D	PY	X
Oy Oy-700	Y	D	YG	YG
oy Oy-700	Y	D	Y	X
oy-t Oy-700	Y	D	Y	X
pb1	W/PY	D	PGBZH	PGBZ
pb4	Y	D	YGBVC	ZU
pg2			PGC	GM
pg11 pg12	Y		YG	YG
pg13			PG	PG

(continued on next page)

Table 3–7. Continued.

Genotype	Endosperm color (with *Y1*)	Embryo dormancy	Seedling	Plant
pg14		D	PGU	PGU
pg15		D	PGB	X
pg16		D	PG	
pm				FU
ppg		D	PGNZ	X
ps	OP	R	OP	X
ps-lyc	OP	D	OP	X
py1	Y	D	FM	FU
pyd	Y	D	PY	X
Spc1		D	G	K
spc2		D	GK	GK
spc3		D	PGK	PGK
spt1		D	PGK	PGK
spt2		D	PGK	PGK
sr1		D	J	J
sr2		D	J	J
sr3		D	J	J
st	YM	D	FM	FM
st-e	MH	D		
su1	YM	D	PGVC	G
sy	U			
tn			PGV	G
v1	Y	D	WV	G
v2	Y	D	WVC	G
v3	Y	D	PYVC	G
v4	Y	D	YVC	G/V
v5		D	YGVC	GF
v8		D	WV	X
v12		D	WVC	G
v13		D	WV	G
v16	Y	D	WVC	G
v17		D	WV	
v18		D	PYVC	G
v21		D	WVU	G
v22		D	WV	G
v23		D	WV	G
v24		D	YGV	PG
v25		D	WV	G
v26		D	WV	G
v27		D	YV	G
v28		D	YG	PG
v29		D	PG	G
vp1	YUM	R	G	G
vp2	W/PYM	R	W	X
vp5	W/PY	R	W	X
vp7 (= *ps*)				
vp8	YM	R	GM	GM
vp9	W/PY	R	W	X
vp9-4889	PY	D	PGC	X
Vsr			V	GS
wl	Y	D	W	X
w2	YM	D	W	X
w3	W/PY	R	W	X

(continued on next page)

Table 3-7. Continued.

Genotype	Endosperm color (with $Y1$)	Embryo dormancy	Seedling	Plant
$w3$-8686	W/PY	D	PGC	X
$w11$		D	W	X
$w13$	Y	D	WSG	X
$w14$	Y	D	W	X
$w15$	Y	D	PY	X
$w16$			W	X
$w17$			W	X
Wc	PY	D	G	G
wd	Y	D	W	X
wgs		D	WGS	
wl			U	GU
$wlu1$		D	Y	X
$wlu2$		D	Y	X
$wlu3$		D	Y	X
$wlu4$		D	Y	X
$ws1\ ws2$				U
$ws3$	Y			U
$wt1$	Y	D	WVFM	G/V
$wt2$			WV	G
wyg			WYG	
$y1$	W/PY	D	G	G
$y1$-8549	W/PY	D	PGZH	PGZ
$y1$-$wmut$	W or Y	D	PG/GZH	PG/GZ
$y3$	W/PY	D	G	G
$y7$ (allele of $vp9$)				
$y8$	PY		G	G
$y9$	PY	R	PGH	G
$y10$	W/PY	D	W	X
$y10$-8624	W and Y	D	W/G	X
$y11$	PY		G	G
$y12$	PY		G	G
$yd2$			YM	
$yg1$			YG	YG
$yg2$	Y	D	YGC	YG
$ys1$			G	LY
$ys2$			G	LY
$ys3$		D	G	LY
Ysk		D	G	LYU
z (allele of $vp9$)				
$zb1$				Z
$zb2$				Z
$zb3$				Z
$zb4$				ZC
$zb6$				ZC
$zb7$		D	PGZU	
$Zb8$		D	G	ZU
$zn1$				ZN
$zn2$				ZN
zpg			PGZ	PGZ

† Sectorial loss of chlorophyll is maternally inherited.
‡ Sectorial loss of chlorophyll appears not to be inherited.

(continued on next page)

Table 3–7. Continued.

Key
A   Albescent; tending to white in later-developing tissues
B   Bleached or pale in piebald patches
C   Cool temperature (e.g., 20 °C) exaggerates expression
D   Dormant embryo
F   Finely streaked with white linear markings on leaves
G   Green
H   High temperature (e.g., 35 °C) exaggerates expression
J   Japonica striping (margins of leaves white-striped)
K   Speckled (e.g., green with pale foci or pale with green foci)
L   Linearly marked with different color between vascular strands
M   Morphologically affected; see descriptions in the locus list and text
N   Necrotic (tissues die in part or all of a plant)
O   Orange
OP Orange-pink (pink endosperm, pink-albino seedling)
P   Pale
R   Rampant embryo (not dormant)
S   Striped in morphogenetic pattern
T   Tan
U   Unique effects on phenotype; see descriptions in the locus list and text
V   Virescent seedling; white or yellow portions may remain as such or may become
        green, but later-developing tissues are green
W   White
X   Dies
Y   Yellow
Z   Zebra-banded across the width of the leaf

kernels. The studies of Demerec (1924b) found high temperatures to
stimulate development of green color (i.e., low temperatures heighten
expression) in seedlings of *v1*, *v2*, *v3*, *v4*, *v5*, and *f*. Eyster (1933) showed
that *ar* seedlings are similarly affected and that initial development of
plastids and green pigment occurs adjacent to the vascular bundles. Hopkins and Walden (1977) and Hopkins (1982) have defined temperature
dependence for *v3*, *v12*, *v16* and *v18*, but independence of temperature
for *v1* expression. Hopkins and Elfman (1984) find plastid ribosomal
RNA and ribosomes absent in *v3*, *v12*, and *v16* plants grown at restrictive
(low) temperatures, and reduced in *v1* and *v18* plants. In *v18* seedlings,
Chollet and Paolillo (1972) and Chollet and Ogren (1972) found irregular
plastid morphology and greatly reduced photosynthetic capacities before
greening, and associations between greening and key plastid enzymes,
especially RuBP carboxylase. Harpster et al. (1984) determined that chlorophyll synthesis and thylakoid protein accumulation are coordinated
during leaf development and greening in a selection of virescent mutants
(*ar*, *et*, *gs3*, *v1*, and five temporarily designated mutants). In *v24*, on the
other hand, there is an uncoupling of the integrated processes during
greening: assembly of the chlorophyll a/b light-harvesting complex is not
delayed as in other virescents, and high chlorophyll fluorescence is displayed—i.e., light energy is captured by the complex but not utilized
(Polacco et al., 1985).

   Albino (white) or *luteus* (yellow) seedlings constitute another common
group of mutations, lacking chlorophyll and unable to survive beyond

exhaustion of endosperm carbohydrate reserves. Absence of chlorophyll can be due to failure of formation of the pigment, or to a failure of stabilization of chlorophyll; because stable deposition of chlorophyll requires carotenoids, many chlorophyll-deficient mutants are actually blocked directly in leaf carotenoid formation (and may show loss of carotenoids in the endosperm as well). The difference between white and yellow residual colors can be inherent to the mutation, specific to light or temperature regimes, or specific to modifier genes (in particular the recessive gene *ll*, which has no obvious phenotypic effect in green plants but confers yellow color in many types of albino or white-striped tissues). Chlorophyll-deficient lethals include *cl*, the *luteus* group (the *l* factors except *ll*), *loc*, the *lemon-white* (*lw*) factors, certain of the *necrotic* factors (*nec3*, *nec4* and *nec6*), *oro1*, *oro2*, *oy*, *ps*, *pyd*, *vp2*, *vp5*, the *white albino* (*w*) factors, *wd*, the *white luteus* (*wlu*) factors, and *y10*. A grouping of factors is indicated on the short arm of chromosome 9, where McClintock (1944) identified *pyd* and *wd* cytologically as terminal deficiencies, with *pyd* control located distally to *yg2* and *wd* proximally, such that *pyd* and *yg2* are "allelic" to *wd* but not to each other (see Fig. 3–10). A larger grouping of six nonallelic mutants on chromosome 6 has been defined by Robertson et al. (1978). Spoehr (1942) and Sayed (1955) supplied sugars to albino seedlings through cut leaf ends and were able to maintain the plants through the flowering stage; etiolated green plants also could be grown in the dark for long periods by supplying sugar. On supplying glucose to etiolated leaf segments in the dark, Cox and Dickinson (1971) found detectable uptake and starch deposition in *cl1*, *l3*, *l4*, *l7*, *l12*, *lw1*, *lw2*, *lw3 lw4*, *w1*, *w2*, *w3*, *w11*, *w14*, and *w15* despite the absence of chlorophyll. The ultrastructure of the plastids and the pigment contents in *l3*, *l4*, *l11*, *w3-8686*, and *w15* are pictured and tabulated in detail by Bachmann et al. (1973).

Robertson (1975) summarized the genetics and expressions of the chlorophyll-deficient mutants in two groups (class I affecting endosperm carotenoids, class II not). Among the class II mutants are yellow seedling types (carotene-retaining) that are blocked at particular steps in the chlo-

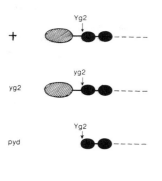

Fig. 3–10. Cytological constitutions and allelic relationships of three chlorophyll factors located at the end of the short arm of chromosome 9. The large, terminal heterochromatic knob and adjacent short chromatin thread, present with *Yg2* and *yg2*, are absent in *pyd*. The distal part of the first distinct chromomere is also absent in *wd*. Because *pyd* carries *Yg2*, and *wd* does not, the *Yg2* locus must be in the chromomere segment between the two breakpoints. If the cytology were not known, the allelic relationships would be difficult to interpret. (From McClintock, 1944)

rophyll biosynthetic pathway. Studies by Mascia (1978) and Mascia and Robertson (1978) have defined biosynthetic blocks and chlorophyll development in a selection of yellow mutants. Oil yellow (*oy*), *l13*, and *l*-Blandy4* (temporary symbol) apparently are blocked in conversion of protoporphyrin IX to Mg-protoporphyrin and its methyl ester; the two orobanche factors (*oro1*, *oro2*) are blocked in the next step, conversion to protochlorophyllide; *l10* is blocked in the conversion of protochlorophyllide to chlorophyllide. The *Orom* factor partially corrects the defect of *oro1*. There remain a considerable number of other yellow mutants yet to be defined (Robertson et al., 1978; Mascia and Robertson, 1980; see Table 3–7 for a list of all known mutants). Mayfield and Taylor (1984) have shown that the messenger RNA for the chlorophyll a/b binding protein is present in *l13* and *oy* seedlings, although chlorophyll and the protein are absent. Hopkins et al. (1980a, b) and Polacco and Walden (1987) have defined the effects of light regimes on the constituents and photosynthetic machinery of plants with *Oy-700*, a dominant yellow-green allele at the *oy* locus. The olive necrotic *nec2* mutant lacks the normal form of chlorophyll b (Wu and Rebeiz, 1985).

Class I mutants include *al* (albescent, in which the albinism is incomplete and condition-dependent and the plants may be viable), *cl*, *lw1*, *lw2*, *lw3* *lw4*, *pb1* (viable), *ps*, *vp2*, *vp5*, *vp9*, *w3*, *y1-8549* (a pale green allele), *y9* and *y10*. Summaries of expressions and genetics, biochemistry and development are presented by Robertson (1975) and Robertson et al. (1978). Photooxidative bleaching of chlorophyll by light in the absence of carotene is characteristic of a number of members of this class, e.g., *al* (Sander et al., 1968), *cl* (Robertson et al., 1966) and *w3* (Anderson and Robertson, 1960). Intensive studies on *w3* (Bachmann et al., 1967, 1969, 1973; Richardson et al., 1962) have characterized pigment stabilization and plastid ultrastructure in detail. Steps affected in the pathway of carotenoid biosynthesis have been presented by Fong et al. (1983) as follows: phytoene, *vp2*, *vp5*, phytofluene, *w3*, zeta-carotene, *vp9*, neurosporene, delta-, gamma-carotene, *ps*, alpha-, beta-carotene, *al*, alpha-, beta-cryptoxanthin, *y9*, zeaxanthin, lutein. Many of the alleles that have been derived are "leaky", forming some carotenoids, depositing some chlorophyll, and permitting survival. Each of these loci has alleles that display *viviparous* embryos, the embryo failing to become dormant and developing as a seedling on the ear. The vivipary is a consequence of failure of formation of abscisic acid from carotenoids, or failure of response to abscisic acid (Robichaud et al., 1980). Two of the vivipary factors, *vp1* and *vp8*, are not blocked in carotenoid formation; *vp1* plants are green and develop normally if the seedlings are removed from the ear and transplanted, while *vp8* seedlings are green but abnormal. Uniquely among the vivipary factors, *vp1* partially or completely blocks anthocyanin synthesis in the aleurone tissue (but not in plant tissues); this effect may be indirect, due to modified physiology of the non-dormant kernel. Neill et al. (1986) and Moore and Smith (1985) have determined contents of abscisic acid and carotenoids in viviparous kernels, seedlings and roots. Mayfield and Taylor (1984) and Mayfield et al. (1986) have shown that the messenger RNA for the chlorophyll a/b binding protein is greatly reduced in *lw1*, *vp7*, and *w3* seedlings.

White or pale yellow endosperm factors that do not affect embryo dormancy or chlorophyll pigmentation are known at the three loci *Wc*, *y1*, and *y8*. *Wc* conditions dominant white crown and pale yellow endosperm in the presence of *Y1* (white with homozygous *y1*); a somewhat lighter allele, *Wc-wh*, is known, but homozygotes for either allele are faint yellow, not white. *Y1* conditions orange-yellow endosperm in the absence of *Wc*, while homozygous *y1* conditions pure white endosperm in most backgrounds. Dosage levels for *Y1* are often visually distinguishable, and Mangelsdorf and Fraps (1931) established that these visible differences are paralleled by increases in vitamin A content in proportions closely approximating 0:1:2:3 for the four dosage levels. There are alleles at *Y1* that affect both carotenoids and chlorophyll, *y1-8549* and *y1-wmut* (Robertson and Anderson, 1961), and the factors *l10*, *l12*, *ms1*, *pb1*, *pb4*, *si*, and *w15* are also closely associated with this locus. The *y8* factor is a simple recessive that conditions pale yellow in the presence of *Y1*.

Miles and Daniel (1974), Miles (1982), and Miles et al. (1985) have isolated a large number of mutants that are blocked in the steps or processes of light energy transformation in photosynthesis. The trait used for selection is high chlorophyll fluorescence, the light energy absorbed in the chloroplast being released as red fluorescence due to blockage of electron transport. Most are unaffected in chlorophyll content but die as seedlings. These mutants have been characterized for the steps in electron transport that are blocked, for proteins in the affected complexes and for messenger RNAs (Miles and Metz, 1985; Barkan et al., 1986). Many have been shown to be affected in the functioning of specific steps, or in specific components or complexes as indicated in Table 3–1. Polacco et al. (1985) have shown that the virescent mutant *v24* has high chlorophyll fluorescence in the virescent seedling, unlike other virescents, having assembled the light-capturing chlorophyll a/b complex before greening occurs. The olive-necrotic *nec2* mutant, which accumulates an abnormal amount of a minor form of chlorophyll b (Bazzaz, 1981; Wu and Rebeiz, 1985), does not display high chlorophyll fluorescence.

Leaf striping in a lengthwise pattern (J), like sectors of mutation from green to white, is conditioned by *cm*, *f*, *ij1*, *ij2*, *j1*, *j2*, *sr1*, *sr2*, *sr3* and *v5*. Despite the impression from the striping in these mutants that they are generating mutations in sectors, the following facts contradict this assumption: (i) the sectoring is not randomly distributed over the leaves, but is mostly confined to the leaf and sheath margins in a patterned fashion, unlike the sectoring found with established mutable factors; (ii) the genes are recessive, and would not be expected to lose the greening function in both alleles at high frequencies in localized patterns; and (iii) stable mutated progeny, either white or green, are not obtained from them. The phenotypic similarity among members of the group suggests a common basis, perhaps dependent upon developmental effects and localized changes in plastid greening capability. Two of these factors, *cm* and *ij1*, exhibit maternal transmission of altered plastids (the others, as far as they have been tested, do not). Rhoades (1943) demonstrated that *ij1* induces irreversible changes in plastid greening ability. Stroup (1970) found similar mutations from *cm*. Shumway and Weier (1967) found that aberrant plastids in *ij1* plants lack normal internal structures and components, including ribosomes. Walbot and Coe (1979) and Siemenroth et al. (1980) were unable to detect RNAs and protein synthesizing machinery in white tissues of iojap plants and in maternal white seedlings. The widely diverse effects of background genotype on expression in iojap plants, ranging from pure white seedlings to nearly normal green, have been studied by Coe et al. (1988).

The linearly marked factors (L) include *gs1*, *gs2*, *gs3*, *ys1*, *ys2*, *ys3*, and *Ysk*. Their pattern of darker color at the vascular strands with lighter color between can be taken to indicate limited uptake or transport of some nutrient, in view of the demonstration by Bell et al. (1958) that ferrous iron (Fe^{2+}) can correct the *ys1* phenotype through the roots, and that either Fe^{3+} or Fe^{2+} can correct the phenotype in floated leaf sections. Clark et al. (1973) found altered contents of organic acids in the roots of *ys1* plants, perhaps limiting transport of iron.

Zebra-banded leaves (Z) are characteristic of *l17*, *nec3*, *nec7*, *oro1*, *oro2*, *pb1*, *pb4*, *ppg*, *zb1*, *zb2*, *zb3*, *zb4*, *zb6*, *zb7*, *Zb8*, *zn1*, *zn2*, and *zpg*. In addition, two alleles at the *Y1* locus, *y1-8549* and *y1-wmut*, tend to develop zebra-banding, possibly related to the expression of *pb1*, which is located at *Y1*. The cause of this particular pattern type is presumably related to the effects of diurnal light or temperature patterns, either through induction or through photooxidative bleaching, as suggested for *zb4* by Hayes (1932) and for *al* by Sander et al. (1968).

3–2.4 Plant Form

An impressive range of variation in the morphology of vegetative and reproductive structures is found among races, lines, and varieties. While casual observation might suggest that this variation could only be controlled by the overlapping effects of very large numbers of factors whose effects are expressed in small increments, straightforward genetic analysis has established more than 100 loci conditioning genetically simple morphological variations in plant stature and in the form and structure of vegetative and reproductive parts. Studies on continuous or measured variation in agronomic and other traits, analysis of which is not attempted here, suggest that unit factors with very much smaller effects could be extracted systematically and could be manipulated by choice.

Reduced plant stature controlled by single factors ranges from moderate differences that can be classified only in very uniform backgrounds to extremely shortened or morphologically deviant types that are unmistakable. Semidwarf or compact plants that show relatively little other morphological alteration are conditioned by *br1*, *br2*, *br3*, *bv1*, *bv2*, *cr*, *ct1*, *ct2*, *mi*, *na1*, *na2*, *rd1*, *rd2*, and *td*. Kempton (1921) observed that *br1* plants have shortened internodes especially below the ear, but that leaf size and attitude are essentially unaffected. Kempton suggested that brachytic plants might be advantageous because they have sturdy culms and show relatively modest reduction in grain yield. Semidwarfs *br2*, *ct1*, and *rd* may have a yield advantage, especially in high-density plantings (Nelson and Ohlrogge, 1957, 1961). The shortening of *na1* plants apparently results from lowered auxin levels due to higher rates of destruction (van Overbeek, 1935). Leaf initiation rates in developing *br2* embryos are slightly lower than normal (Stein, 1955), and *br2* plants develop fewer internodes below the ear and shorter internodes throughout the plant (Scott and Campbell, 1969). Several pleiotropic factors condition reduced stature in association with other effects (e.g., *Clt*, *gl11*, *gl17*, *py1*, *py2*, *Sdw*, *yd2*), at least some of which may be due to indirect metabolic effects or limited nutrition.

The andromonoecious dwarfs (*an*, *d1*, *d2*, *d3*, *d5*, and *D8*) form a distinctive group with reduced stature and a common morphological syndrome. The ears bear perfect (monoclinous) flowers, although the anthers in the ear generally do not shed pollen and remain nested among the kernels. With *d1*, *d2*, *d3*, *d5*, and *D8* the plants are characteristically shortened and compressed, forming "cabbage-like" rosettes with broad, crinkled, and foreshortened leaves, and more tillers than normal. With *an* or an intermediate allele at *d1* (*d1-t*) or *Mpl* (which is likely an intermediate allele at *D8*), shortening is less extreme. Stein (1955) found the leaf initiation rate in the embryo and the final leaf number in the plant to be reduced in *d1* relative to normal. Phinney (1956) and Phinney and West (1960) determined that each of the recessive andromonoecious dwarfs responds to small amounts of gibberellins (e.g., 0.1 μg) with a prompt, brief spurt of growth (Fig. 3–11); if hormone is supplied regularly in appropriate quantities, normal stature, normal habit, and normal ears (without anthers) develop. The dominant dwarf, *D8*, shows no gibberellin response, and others of the reduced-stature types that have been tested (e.g., *br1*, *bv1*, *na1*, *na2*) show little or no response. Studies on the pathway of gibberellin biosynthesis, intermediates and enzymes have defined the blocks for each of the recessive dwarfs (Phinney and Spray, 1982, 1985). The order of steps is: mevalonic acid, *d5*, *ent*-kaurene, *d3*, GA_{53}-aldehyde, *d1*, GA_1 (gibberellic acid). The fact that GA_1 is the only biologically active compound in the pathway suggests that there are several steps for which no dwarf mutant has yet been identified.

Form and structure of the plant body are affected, apart from stature, in diverse ways. Leaves are foreshortened in the andromonoecious dwarfs and in *py1* and *py2*; are narrower in *Cg1*, *Cg2*, *Isr* (with striping factors), *nl*, *rgd1*, *Rgd2*, *Tp1*, *Tp2* and *vp8*; are crinkled or have outgrowths in *cr*,

Fig. 3–11. Growth response of dwarf seedlings to a single application of gibberellic acid ranging from 0.001 to 100 µg per plant. (From Phinney and West, 1960.)

Hsf, Kn, and *Lg3*; and lose integrity by tearing or slashing in *Rg, rgd1, Rgd2,* and *sl* plants. For *Kn,* Gelinas et al. (1969) determined that the outgrowths, occurring along vascular strands, are anatomically similar to the intercalary meristem at the transition between leaf sheath and blade. Anatomically the knots are like the leaf sheath and auricle, and may form displaced ligules (Hake et al., 1985; Hake and Freeling, 1985). According to results from dosage and aneuploidy studies *Kn* is neomorphic, either encoding a new function or overproducing a normal product (Freeling and Hake, 1985). By deletion analysis and fate mapping of differential cell layers in the leaf, Hake and Freeling (1986) have shown that *Kn* genotype in internal leaf cells induces normal (*kn*) epidermal cells to develop into knots. Gelinas and Postlethwait (1969) found higher levels of compounds that inhibit the auxin-inactivating enzyme, IAA oxidase, in *Kn* seedlings. Knots were increased on *Kn* leaves by an auxin, indole butyric acid, and were decreased by gibberellic acid (Nickerson and Hewitson, 1963). *Hsf* plants show pubescence accompanied by sheath-like enations of the leaf margin and displaced ligules (Bird and Neuffer, 1985). The course of cell and tissue breakdown in leaves of *Rg* plants has been studied by Mericle (1950). Leaves adhere at the surface and fail to unroll in *ad, Ce, nec1* and *nec3* seedlings and plants.

Leaf attitude is affected by *lg1, lg2,* and *Lg3,* while *phyllotaxy* is altered by *Cg, Lfy, Tp1,* and *Tp2.* Distichous phyllotaxis (opposite leaves), common in certain strains, has been studied by Greyson and Walden (1972). The basis for upright leaf attitude in *lg1, lg2,* and *Lg3* plants is a change in the transition zone between leaf sheath and blade, in which the smooth, auriculate tissue forming the angle is reduced or supplanted and the filmy, collar-like ligule is reduced or absent. Ligules are disorganized, altered or in displaced positions with *Hsf, Kn,* and *Rs1* (Bird and Neuffer, 1985; Hake et al., 1985). *Lfy* confers an increase in leaf number: *Lfy* lines vs. normal counterparts produce a few more leaves below the ear and approach double the number above the ear; the net result is that *Lfy* plants have a dramatic increase in production-significant leaf area at the time of maturity (Shaver, 1983). Wilting and tissue survival are affected by *bu*, *gs*, *lte1*, *Lte2*, *nec1*, and *wi*; *wi* plants have imperfectly developed vascular elements (Postlethwait and Nelson, 1957). Pilosity and integrity of the surface of the leaf sheath are affected by *Hs*, *Hsf1*, *Rs1*, and *rs2*. Basal branching increases the number of tillers in the andromonoecious dwarfs and in *Cg1*, *Cg2*, *gt*, *Rgd2*, *tb*, *Tlr*, *Tp1*, and *Tp2* plants. Dichotomy of the main meristem occurs with *db*.

Several loci have been identified that condition the formation of discrete necrotic and chlorotic *lesions* on the leaves of seedlings and mature plants, in contrast to general leaf chlorosis and necrosis. Ten dominants and one recessive have been distinguished and mapped and can be grouped according to the time and type of lesion expression: early expression of necrotic lesions (*Les1*, *Les3*, *Les10*, and *lls*); late expression of necrotic lesions (*Les4*, *Les6*, and *Les9*); and late expression of small white, chlorotic, or pale-green lesions (*Les2*, *Les5*, *Les7*, and *Les8*). *Les1* and *Les2* have been shown to be temperature-sensitive and modified by genetic background (Hoisington et al., 1982). The fact that no repeat mutations have been found at any of the loci suggests the existence of additional loci that can cause lesion formation (Walbot et al., 1983). The exact cellular defect that results in the lesion phenotype has not been determined.

Prostrate culms lacking normal *geotropic response* are found with *la*, in which van Overbeek (1938) found high auxin content in the upper side of nodes and internodes, in contrast to the usual auxin distribution in normal plants placed in a horizontal position. Lazy plants can be recognized as young plants by failure of response to gravity when tipped to the side. Hertel et al. (1969) found that seedlings homozygous for *ae*, in which the starch grains are smaller than normal, have less efficient geotropic responses in the coleoptile, supporting a statolith model for these responses. Moore (1986) has presented evidence that geotropism in *ae* roots, however, is related to reduced polar transport of calcium rather than to statolith properties. In *agt* seedlings, roots fail to show geotropism; Pilet (1983) has presented evidence that growth inhibitors are reduced in the elongation region. Root branching is greatly reduced in *rt* plants, to such an extent that support is necessary in order to grow the plants to maturity; *Asr* seedlings fail to develop normal seminal roots. Treatment of *rt* plants with tri-iodo benzoic acid tends to increase brace roots (Nickerson, MNL 43:179-181, 1969, and preceding reports).

Brittle parts of the plant body (stalks, leaves, tassels, silks, cobs, and others) are conditioned by *bk2*, effects of which can be recognized as early as the 5-leaf stage; plants are difficult to bring to maturity in windy or stormy locations, even with support. The nodes of *btn* plants are brittle breaking at the node under moderate bending pressure; the breakage is localized, not unlike the break at an abscission layer. The *btn* factor in

B73 inbred line causes the unusually brittle tassel in this line. Abscission and disarticulation in the female inflorescence are affected by two factors on chromosome 4, *Ph* and *Ri*.

Reproductive structures are subject to genetically and physiologically determined presence or absence, changes in the degree of proliferation and branching, and to alterations of sexual determination (i.e., development of flower parts that are normally suppressed, such as anthers in the florets of the ear and pistils in the florets of the tassel). Initiation or completion of the ear branch fails with *ba1, ba2, baf, Bif,* or *bs*; initiation of the tassel fails with *tl*. Mustyatsa and Miku (1975) describe the overcoming of barrenness, in barren plants in which normal ear formation fails, by late-forming ears at the ground level in the lower nodes. In late, barrenness-induced ears, double recessive combinations of *ba2* with *bd, ra1, ra2, sk, ts2,* or *ts4* display the ear characteristics of the second factor. The combination of *ts2* with *sk*, however, bears essentially normal tassels and ears (Galinat, MNL 60:130, 1986).

Although *sexual alterations* are not common in strains grown under conditions to which they are adapted, most strains can show pistil-bearing parts or even small ears in the tassel, particularly on tillers. Stamen-bearing parts are also common in or on the conventional ear, including fertile tassel-like extensions from the tip. These types of alterations are highly dependent upon adaptation and growing conditions (Weatherwax, 1955; Peterson, 1976). Genetic factors that condition alterations include, among others, the andromonoecious dwarfs, in which anthers develop in the ear florets among the kernels, each of which can be normalized with gibberellins, as previously indicated, except for *D8*.

The *tassel-seed* factors (*ts1, ts2, Ts3, ts4, Ts5, Ts6*), whose comparative morphology has been described by Nickerson and Dale (1955), and *si*, result in monoclinism or partial to total sex reversal in the tassel. In addition, the spikelets tend to show proliferation, branching, and similar changes. In *tb* plants the ear branches develop into tassels with only a few pistillate spikelets at the base, a teosinte-like trait. The homeotic transformations of floral structures into differing sexuality, or to vegetative structures, can be considered to be due to release of the complex of suppressions characteristic of "normal" maize development (Coe and Poethig, 1982; Poethig, 1985).

Proliferation and branching of inflorescences without sex alteration is characteristic of tassels and ears of *ra1* and *ra2*, and ears of *bd* plants. Nickerson and Dale (1955) and Postlethwait and Nelson (1964) have shown that initiation of spikelets in *ra1* ears is replaced by initiation of branches, which then bear spikelets. Nickerson (1960a) found that *ra1* tassels, but not ears, could be normalized by gibberellin treatments, while several other tassel types could not. Orr (1969) found *ra1* ears to be normalized by gibberellins. Polytypic (*Pt*) ears and tassels show variably proliferated branches, spikelets, glumes, and pistils (Postlethwait and Nelson, 1964).

Additional alterations of form and function in the ear include inside-out ears (*cto*, *te*), pistil developmental changes (*dep*, *pi1*, *pi2*), dichotomy (*db*), reversed germ orientation (*rgo*), and changes in spatial relationships of specific parts (*is*, *pd*, *Krn* factors, *Sg*, *te*, *tr*) (Galinat, 1971a, 1975, 1978). Multiplied silk initiation is brought about by *si*, and silk growth failure by *bd* and *sk*. Glumes become exceptionally extended in ears and tassels under the influence of *Pn* or *Tu*, but do not extend normally with *Vg*. Intermediate, "half-tunicate" alleles at *Tu* are known, and the locus has been shown to undergo recombinational exchanges that yield intermediate derivatives, *tu-1* and *tu-d* (Mangelsdorf and Galinat, 1964). The tassel does not expand normally with *ad*, *Clt*, *ct2*, or *td*. Glumes in *eg* tassels open to an unusually wide angle. Branching in the tassel is altered by *an*, *ba1*, *baf*, *Bif*, *ra1*, *ra2*, *ra3*, and *ub*. Additional effects include clumped and compact tassels (*Clt*, *ct2*, *td*) and dichotomy (*db*). Fasciation (flattening of the ear tip; "bear's foot" or "bear paw"), furcation (clefted branching), basal branching and other anomalies of ear development are occasional to common, depending upon strain or variety (Weatherwax, 1955; Pego and Hallauer, 1984). Ears of *ct* plants tend to be fasciated or furcated; ears of *ra1* are multiply branched. The combination of *Tu* with *ra1* leads to "cauliflower ears" (Collins, 1917) that cannot be propagated through either female or male. Intermediate alleles such as *tu-1* in combination with *ra1* result in cauliflower ears but fertile tassels (Galinat, MNL 61:101, 1987).

Factors that affect the inflorescences and plant body morphologically in a *teosintoid* direction (showing characteristics of the teosintes) include *Cg1*, *Cg2*, *tb*, *Tlr*, *Tp1*, and *Tp2*. The effects of *Cg1*, *Tlr*, and *Tp1* include free tillering, narrow leaves, greatly increased leaf number, long bracts or spathes in both inflorescences, and variable monoclinism (Weatherwax, 1929, 1955; Neuffer, Hoisington and Bird, MNL 61:50, 1987). Nickerson (1960b) found that *Tp1* plants could be normalized by gibberellin treatments. With *tb*, the plants are also more freely tillered, and the ear branches (but not the tassel) are teosintoid, with a few female spikelets at the base. For the ear, teosinte- and *Tripsacum*-like factors include *is*, *pd*, *Ph*, *Ri*, *Sg*, and *tr*, although the linkages and expressions of these and other variations arising within maize vs. ones derived from relatives may or may not agree (Galinat, 1978). *Cg1* plants, though very similar to *Tp1* plants, characteristically branch very heavily at the tiller level, have many narrow leaves, and form bracts in the poorly developed ears; vegetative propagation has been done by division of basal branches or by adventitious shoot and root formation at nodes or in the tassel (Galinat and Andrew, 1953). *Cg1* plants are reversibly normalized by gibberellin (Nickerson, 1960b), or by autumn or winter conditions, which is presumably caused by shortened daylengths or cooler temperatures (Singleton, 1951). Heterozygous *Tlr* plants have increased tillers and ear number, and homozygous plants are more teosintoid. Angeles (see Stebbins, 1967) showed that mitotic frequency in the flank of the apical meristem of *Cg1* plants is much higher than in normal, leading to increased leaf initiations. *Tp1* and *Tp2*, according to dosage and aneuploidy analysis, involve gain of function; *Tp2*, on the one hand, is expressed equally severely with two, one or no doses of +, while *Tp1* expression is reduced by + doses (Poethig, 1985).

Initiation and development of *flowering* has been shown to be affected by a recessive factor, *id* (Singleton, 1946). Galinat and Naylor (1951) found that a definite size, age, or number of leaves is prerequisite to floral initiation, which is short-day dependent in *id* plants; vegetative reversal occurs if long days follow floral initiation. The factors for short day dependence in Latin American and other tropical strains may or may not be related to *id*. Shaver (1967) identified three recessive factors, *gt* (grassy tillers), *id*, and *pe* (perennialism), necessary for perennial habit, in derivatives from hybrids between corn and perennial teosinte.

3–2.5   Leaf Cuticle Waxes

In normal seedlings the first five or six leaves form a bluish-white waxy "bloom", consisting of minute wax projections from the cuticle on the upper and lower epidermis. In *glossy* seedlings (*gl* group), little or no bloom forms; in bright light a "glossy" effect results, in which the surface of the leaf reflects as if polished in contrast to the dull appearance of normal leaves. If a normal leaf is rubbed lightly with the fingers, the bloom rubs away and the surface becomes glossy. Because leaves with bloom are water repellent whereas glossy leaves retain water droplets, water can be sprinkled or sprayed on the seedlings for clearer discrimination (Hayes and Brewbaker, 1928). Bianchi and Marchesi (1960) point out that the water-repellency of normal leaves results in a reflective interface between water and the leaf surface so that immersed leaves or retained droplets have a mirror-like reflectance on normal seedlings but not on glossy. Most of the glossy types are classifiable beginning with the first two leaves. In *gl15* seedlings, however, the first two leaves usually have normal appearance, the third leaf is often variable but usually glossy, and the fourth and later leaves are glossy. In contrast, normal plants discontinue the heavy juvenile wax deposition at about the sixth leaf and begin to show glossy patches and mostly glossy leaf blades in subsequent leaves. The leaf sheaths continue to develop bloom in older plants, and *gl15* plants are markedly glossy in later sheaths. Conditions of seedling development that may detract from the development of bloom on normal leaves include suboptimal light, infections, injury, and weak genetic types; some of the glossy factors are associated with weak seedlings and may be glossy for indirect reasons. The electron microscope studies of Bianchi and Marchesi (1960) demonstrate that the bloom is composed of minute projections from the cuticle on the first five leaves of normal seedlings. In *gl1* seedlings there are virtually no projections, in *gl2* a few on the first three leaves but none on the fourth and fifth, in *gl3* intermediate amounts on the first five leaves, and in *gl15* normal amounts on the first two leaves, decreasing for the next three leaves. Comprehensive data on cuticle constituents in the series of glossy mutants and double mutants, summarized by Bianchi et al. (1985), place them in one or the other of two proposed pathways of chain elongation leading to fatty acids, aldehydes, alcohols, esters, and alkanes. For juvenile wax, both pathways are operative, the first involving steps as follows: (*gl8*, *gl1*, *gl7*, *gl18*), C_{16}, C_{18}, *gl11*, C_{28}, *gl3*, C_{30}, (*gl2*, *gl4*, *gl16*), C_{32}, C_{32}-aldehyde, *gl5*, C_{32}-alcohol. The second pathway involves: C_{16}, *gl15*, C_{18}, C_{20}, C_{22}, C_{24}, C_{26}. The first pathway presumably is not operative in forming adult wax. Intracistron recombination at *Gl1* has been reported by Salamini and Lorenzoni (1970).

3–2.6 Kernel Lipids

The fatty acids in corn oil, derived from embryo storage lipids, consist primarily of linoleic (18-carbon:2 double bonds, 40-60%) and oleic (18:1, 20-50%) acids, with palmitic (16:0, 10-15%), stearic (18:0, 2-3%) and linolenic (18:3, 1-2%). Higher linoleic acid is preferred for human nutrition. The inbred line R84, which has a higher ratio of linoleic to oleic than does Illinois High Oil (IHO), carries a single recessive factor on chromosome 6, *ln*, conferring a higher ratio without greatly altering the total of the two fatty acids (Poneleit and Alexander, 1965). Differences in fatty acid contents between IHO and inbred C103, however, are determined by two loci (de la Roche et al., 1971). Plewa and Weber (1973, 1975) found that embryos monosomic for chromosome 2 had higher oleic and palmitic with lower linoleic compared to normal; for chromosome 7, higher palmitic; for chromosome 8, lower stearic; and for chromosome 10, higher stearic. Shadley and Weber (1980, 1986) found embryos trisomic for chromosome 4, or hyperploid (tri-segmental) for the long arm, had higher palmitic and lower oleic; for the long arm of chromosome 5, lower oleic and higher linoleic; and for the long arm of chromosome 10, lower palmitic and higher stearic. Jellum and Widstrom (1983) found that higher stearic (9-12%) derivatives from PI175334 differed from other strains mainly by a single major recessive gene.

3–2.7 Fluorescent Seedlings and Anthers

Routine screening of seedling cultures under an ultraviolet lamp led to recognition (Teas and Anderson, 1951) of a factor conditioning strong blue-white fluorescence of the seedling leaves (rather than the typical dull reddish-purple) and blue-fluorescent anther walls. Because the factor showed dominant expression in the anther walls (though recessive in the seedling), the designation *Bf1* was used. Teas and Anderson found three chromatographically distinct blue-fluorescent compounds in *Bf1* anthers and seedlings, one of which could be identified as anthranilic acid and all of which supported growth of tryptophan-requiring (anthranilate-utilizing) *Lactobacillus* and *Neurospora crassa*. Anthranilate synthetase, the enzyme responsible for converting chorismate to anthranilic acid, was present at much higher activity levels in *Bfl* plants and was more resistant to feedback inhibition by tryptophan than the enzyme from normal plants. In addition, PR transferase, the enzyme which usually utilizes anthranilate in the tryptophan pathway, was inhibited by accumulated anthranilate, all presumably leading to accumulation of anthranilate (Singh and Widholm, 1975). In full-grown *Bfl Bfl* plants, anthranilate is detectable by odor emanating from the leaves in bright sunlight. A second factor, *bf2*, has phenotypic effects similar to *Bfl* in seedling and anther fluorescence. Brilliantly yellow-fluorescent anthers are conditioned by *bz1*, and this recessive expression is independent of all of the other known factors that influence anthocyanins and related pigments, except the *c2 whp* (white pollen) constitution. The ultraviolet-lamp screenings done by Anderson in the 1940's, from which the blue-fluorescent mutants were recovered, were intended to seek modifications in chlorophyll (red) fluorescence, but were not fruitful. Mutants with high chlorophyll fluorescence, blocked in photosynthesis, which were subsequently found by Miles (1982), are discussed in section 3–2.3 on Photosynthetic Pigments and Photosynthetic Machinery (page 170).

3–2.8 Polymorphisms in Proteins, Enzymes, and DNA Restriction Fragments

Numerous loci have been identified and mapped in corn that are detected on the basis of segregation of polymorphic alleles under electrophoretic conditions. These include phenotypes detected by general protein stains, by enzymatic reactions (isozymes), and by Southern blot hybridizations (restriction fragment length polymorphisms, RFLPs).

Several loci have been defined by detection of proteins of different mobilities with nonspecific protein stains. Schwartz (1979) described *Prot* (originally termed *Pro*, but renamed due to the existence of the proline locus by the same name), which is polymorphic and specifies two major proteins in the embryo. Specific size alleles and null alleles were identified and mapped. A second locus, *Mep*, which appears to be involved in the processing of the *Prot* protein, was also identified and mapped. Modena (MNL 57:38, 1983, MNL 58:79-82, 211-212, 1984; 1985) reported five genes affecting polypeptides of the chloroplast thylakoid membrane. *Lcs* and *Lct1* determine electrophoretic mobility of particular thylakoid polypeptides, *lct2* conditions presence/absence of what is apparently the polypeptide determined by *Lct1*, and *Pdf* and *Tpm* affect mobility of particular polypeptides in a dominant-recessive fashion. Some of the opaque and floury genes are involved in the formation of zein polypeptides (see section 3–2.1 on Kernel Properties, Starch, and Proteins, page 140), and appear to code for polymorphisms. For the many other polymorphisms found in the different zein fractions, multiple loci have been proposed; because of the complexity of the patterns the exact numbers, linkage relationships, and types of loci involved in zein formation are still under study and remain to be fully defined (Ottoboni and Steffensen, 1987; Rubenstein and Geraghty, 1986; Wilson and Larkins, 1984).

Since the finding by Schwartz (1960) that three variants of one of the esterases in young endosperms are determined by three alleles at a single locus, genetically controlled variation in electrophoretic properties of enzymes has been reported at 77 loci (Table 3–8). The physiological and theoretical implications of several of these variations have been reviewed by Nelson (1967) and by Nelson and Burr (1973). More recent reviews present the techniques in isozyme analysis (Goodman and Stuber, 1983; Stuber et al., 1988) and genotypes for a number of important inbred lines, races, and related species (Doebley et al., 1985; Smith et al., 1985c; Stuber and Goodman, 1983). Applications include cultivar characterization (Smith, 1986) and evaluation of variability, prediction of performance, and selection (Frei et al., 1986a, 1986b; Kahler et al., 1986; Kahler and Wehrhahn, 1986; Price et al., 1986; Smith, 1984; Smith et al., 1985a, 1985b).

Isozyme variants differing in mobility during electrophoresis normally will differ in charge properties of the enzyme molecule, due to differences in one to a few amino acids. In most cases the variants found in corn are codominant—that is, heterozygotes produce both of the variants rather than only one. A finding of codominance is generally considered strong evidence that the locus is coding for the enzyme and is the "structural gene."

With a number of isozymes, the heterozygote shows not only codominance but also a unique band not present in either homozygous type. The hybrid between a strain homozygous for $E1$-F (an esterase allele determining a fast-migrating band) and one homozygous for $E1$-S (slow) shows an intermediate band as well as both parental bands. Schwartz (1960) demonstrated codominance, hybrid bands, and gene dosage effects in the endosperm, all consistent with the random formation of dimeric enzymes (FF,FS,SS) from F and S units coded by each allele. Similar identification of intralocus heterodimers has led to the same interpretation of dimeric structure for 26 additional loci (see Table 3–8). In addition to the formation of intralocus heterodimers, several multi-locus isozyme systems also form interlocus heterodimers. Interlocus interactions have not been detected between loci whose products are localized in different cellular compartments, even though mixing experiments in vitro indicate that such dimers are possible (Scandalios et al., 1980; Sorenson, 1982). A tetrameric structure was defined for the catalase controlled by $Cat1$, in which three hybrid bands are found along with the parental bands in heterozygotes—i.e., homozygous $Cat1$-F X $Cat1$-S produces endosperms with FFFF, FFFS, FFSS, FSSS, and SSSS units, in proportions according to gene dosage (Beckman et al., 1964). Similar evidence supports a tetrameric structure for $Cat2$, $Cat3$, Me, and $Sod3$ (Goodman and Stuber, 1983). Definitive evidence for tetrameric structure

Table 3–8. Enzyme polymorphisms, allele types known, cellular location, and multimer formation. EM, electrophoretic mobility; +/−, presence/absence; CYTO, cytosolic; GLY, glyoxysomal; MITO, mitochondrial; MONO, monomeric; DI, dimeric; TETRA, tetrameric; INTRA, intralocus; INTER, interlocus.

Gene	Chr	Name	Type	Null allele	Cellular location	Structure	Heteropolymer formed
Aco1	4S	Aconitase	EM			MONO	
Aco2	?	Aconitase	EM				
Aco3	?	Aconitase	EM				
Aco4	?	Aconitase	EM		CYTO	MONO	
Acp1	9	Acid phosphatase	EM			DI	
Acp2	?	Acid phosphatase	EM			DI	
Acp4	1L	Acid phosphatase	EM			MONO	
Adh1	1L	Alcohol dehydrogenase	EM	YES		DI	INTRA/INTER
Adh2	4S	Alcohol dehydrogenase	EM	YES		DI	INTRA/INTER
Adk1	6S	Adenylate kinase	EM		PLASTID		
Adr1	?	Alcohol dehydrogenase regulator	EM				
Amp1	1L	Aminopeptidase	EM		CYTO	MONO	
Amp2	1	Aminopeptidase	EM			MONO	
Amp3	5S	Aminopeptidase	EM			MONO	
Amp4	?	Aminopeptidase	EM			MONO	
Amy1	?	Alpha amylase	EM			MONO	
Amy2	5S	Beta amylase	EM			MONO	
Car1	1S	Catalase regulator	EM				
Cat1	5S	Catalase	EM	YES	CYTO/GLY	TETRA	INTRA/INTER
Cat2	1S	Catalase	EM	YES	CYTO/GLY	TETRA	INTRA/INTER
Cat3	?	Catalase	EM		MITO	TETRA	NONE
Cdh1	?	Cinnamyl alcohol dehydrogenase	EM				
Cx1	10L	Catechol oxidase	EM	YES		MONO	
Dia1	2S	Diaphorase	EM		CYTO	MONO	
Dia2	1L	Diaphorase	EM		CYTO	DI	
E1	7L	Esterase	+/−	YES		DI	INTRA
E2	?	Esterase	EM				
E3	3S	Esterase	EM			DI	INTRA
E4	3S	Esterase	EM	YES		MONO	
E5-1	?	Esterase	EM				

Locus	Enzyme						
E5-II	Esterase	?	EM				
E6	Esterase	?	+/−				
E7	Esterase	?	+/−				
E8	Esterase	3S	EM	YES		DI	INTRA
E9	Esterase	?	EM	YES			
E10	Esterase	?	EM				
Enp1	Endopeptidase	6L	EM	YES			
Gdh1	Glutamic dehydrogenase	1L	EM	YES		MONO	INTRA/INTER
Gdh2	Glutamic dehydrogenase	10	EM	YES			INTRA
Glu1	Beta glucosidase	10L	EM	YES			INTRA
Got1	Glutamate-oxaloacetate transaminase	3L	EM	YES	CYTO	DI	INTRA
Got2	Glutamate-oxaloacetate transaminase	5L	EM	YES	GLY	DI	INTRA
Got3	Glutamate-oxaloacetate transaminase	5S	EM	YES	PLASTID	DI	INTRA
Hex1	Hexokinase	3S	EM	YES	MITO	DI	
Hex2	Hexokinase	6L	EM	YES	CYTO	MONO	
Idh1	Isocitrate dehydrogenase	8L	EM	YES	CYTO	MONO	INTRA/INTER
Idh2	Isocitrate dehydrogenase	6L	EM	YES	CYTO	DI	INTRA/INTER
Mdh1	Malate dehydrogenase	8	EM	YES	CYTO	DI	INTRA/INTER
Mdh2	Malate dehydrogenase	6L	EM	YES	MITO	DI	INTRA/INTER
Mdh3	Malate dehydrogenase	3L	EM	YES	MITO	DI	INTRA/INTER
Mdh4	Malate dehydrogenase	1L	EM	YES	MITO	DI	INTRA/INTER
Mdh5	Malate dehydrogenase	5S	EM	YES	CYTO	DI	INTRA/INTER
Me1	Malic enzyme	3L	EM	YES	CYTO	TETRA	
mmm1	Modifier of malate dehydrogenase	1L	EM	YES			
Pgd1	6-Phosphogluconate dehydrogenase	6	EM	YES	CYTO	DI	INTRA/INTER
Pgd2	6-Phosphogluconate dehydrogenase	3L	EM	YES	CYTO	DI	INTRA/INTER
Pgm1	Phosphoglucomutase	1L	EM	YES	CYTO	MONO	
Pgm2	Phosphoglucomutase	5S	EM	YES	CYTO	MONO	
Phi1	Phosphohexose isomerase	1L	EM	YES	CYTO	DI	INTRA
Px1	Peroxidase	?	EM	YES		MONO	
Px2	Peroxidase	?	EM			MONO	
Px3	Peroxidase	7L	EM			MONO	
Px4	Peroxidase	?	EM	YES		MONO	

(continued on next page)

Table 3–8. Continued.

Gene	Chr	Name	Type	Null allele	Cellular location	Structure	Heteropolymer formed
Px5	?	Peroxidase	+/–			MONO	
Px6	?	Peroxidase	+/–			MONO	
Px7	?	Peroxidase	EM	YES		MONO	
Px8	?	Peroxidase	EM			MONO	
Px9	?	Peroxidase	EM	YES		MONO	
Sad1	10L	Shikimate dehydrogenase	EM		PLASTID	MONO	
Sod1	?	Superoxide dismutase	EM		PLASTID	DI	INTRA
Sod3	?	Superoxide dismutase	EM		MITO	TETRA	INTRA
Sod4	?	Superoxide dismutase	EM		CYTO	DI	INTRA
Ta1	?	Transaminase	EM			DI	INTRA
Tpi1	?	Triose phosphate isomerase	EM		PLASTID	DI	
Tpi2	?	Triose phosphate isomerase	EM		PLASTID	DI	
Tpi3	8	Triose phosphate isomerase	EM		CYTO	MONO	
Tpi4	3L	Triose phosphate isomerase	EM		CYTO	MONO	

of catalase was deduced by Scandalios (1965) from the formation of hybrid bands in vitro following dissociation and reassociation of the subunits. Dissociation and reassociation experiments also demonstrated a dimeric structure for alcohol dehydrogenase, involving both intralocus and interlocus associations (Fischer and Schwartz, 1973; Freeling, 1974).

Exceptions to codominance exist at a few loci: *E2*, *E6*, *E7*, *Px5*, and *Px6* have so far shown only presence vs. absence of bands of catalytic activity. In addition, *Adr1*, *Car*, *lct2*, *mmm*, *Pdf*, and *Tpm* regulate or modify their corresponding isozymes or polypeptides. Lacking codominant variants differing in mobility, there is a strong likelihood that such loci may be indirectly regulating the synthesis or processing of the enzyme or protein rather than coding for it (MacDonald and Brewbaker, 1972). The remaining loci condition variations in electrophoretic mobility, and several have null alleles as well, which is in keeping with the range of variants anticipated for a coding locus. Presence of an immunologically cross-reacting material (CRM) that lacks catalytic activity was demonstrated for some of the null alleles of *Adh1* (Schwartz, 1971b, 1973), showing that an inactive molecular product is formed in these instances. One system, *E5-I* and *E5-II*, appears to determine the presence of a fast set of bands, in contrast to a slow set, through a duplicate-factor (15:1) interaction (MacDonald and Brewbaker, 1974).

Schwartz (1960a) suggested that the occurrence of hybrid enzymes for the *E* esterase might be relevant to hybrid vigor—specifically that a hybrid molecular complex (heterodimer) might be more active than its parental counterparts (homodimers), conferring potential vegetative advantage on the hybrid organism. Relevant to the populational aspect of this suggestion, however, Brown (1971) has examined the distribution of alleles at *E1*, *E3*, *E4*, *Adh1*, and *Px1* in strains that have been subjected to long-term selection for high and low oil and protein, and has found Hardy-Weinberg (i.e., random) distributions for each, including the three (*E1*, *E3*, *Adh1*) that form hybrid bands. That *Adh1* function is important to survival and growth in germination under flooding (anaerobic) conditions has been demonstrated by the survival of *Adh1-S* seedlings under conditions in which *Adh1-O* (null) seedlings die (Schwartz, 1969), and by faster growth rates in flooded *Adh1-S* than in flooded *Adh1-F* seedlings (Marshall et al., 1973). For the enzyme alcohol dehydrogenase, a heterodimer (Cm F) composed of one unit (Cm) that is relatively insensitive to alkaline pH but low in activity coupled with one (F) that is sensitive but highly active, results in a complemented, stable and active enzyme (Schwartz and Laughner, 1969). With two other alleles, the specific activity of FF, FS, and SS dimers falls in that order, while the stability to heat of FF and FS is similar and exceeds that of SS (Felder and Scandalios, 1971). Negative complementation (i.e., loss of stability) is found for the heterodimer between a temperature-sensitive subunit (S1108) and a typical one (Ct) following dialysis (Schwartz, 1971a), in spite of stabilization of the heterodimer in the absence of dialysis.

Numerous loci, potentially unlimited in number, are being identified in maize based on segregation of RFLPs. These loci, detected by hybridization with cloned sequences (Walbot and Messing, Chapter 6) are co-dominant, virtually always neutral in phenotypic effect, and more or less randomly located throughout the genome. Loci have been detected by random genomic clones, cDNA clones, and clones isolated by methyl-sensitive enzymes (e.g., *Pst*1), and there appears to be no selection for one type over another in specific areas of the genome. An extensive map of RFLP loci and several morphologicals, which was developed by T. Helentjaris, is presented by Walbot and Messing (Chapter 6). A combined map for a selection of the same loci with ones defined by probes of B. and F. Burr, D. Grant, and D. Hoisington, currently under development at the University of Missouri based on an optimized mathematical treatment, is given with the maps in this chapter. There is considerable potential for application of these markers across the entire genome for genetic and cytogenetic analysis, and particularly for the marking and analysis of multifactorial traits and quantitative trait loci (QTLs) (Burr et al., 1983; Burr and Burr, 1985; Evola et al., 1986; Helentjaris et al., 1985, 1986a).

3–2.9   Reaction to Pests and to Adverse Conditions

Simple genetic control of reaction with pathogens, insects, herbicides, flooding and stresses has been identified in several cases. Numerous analyses have also defined multiple-factor control of reaction with viruses, rusts, smut, wilts, blights, and other infectious diseases; with the European corn borer (*Ostrinia nubilalis* Hubner) and the earworm (*Heliothis zea* Boddie), and with various adverse conditions. Some studies have succeeded in localizing one to several differential factors to chromosomes (e.g., Ibrahim, 1954; Scott et al., 1966), but unit factors have not been designated. The reader is referred to comprehensive perspectives on corn diseases and insects, including especially genetic information and natural history, presented by Ullstrup (1977, 1978), Dicke (1977), Hooker (1978), Ford and Mikel (1984), Renfro (1984), Smith and White (Chapter 12), and Dicke and Guthrie (Chapter 13).

Common leaf rust resulting from infection with *Puccinia sorghi* Schw. (properly speaking, with particular races or genotypes of the fungus) is under monogenic control by *Rp1*, the first such gene recognized. *Rp1* was localized to chromosome 10 by V.H. Rhoades (1935) by induction of deficiencies and association of loss of the factor with cytological losses. Studies with a number of races and diverse germplasm sources have identified two other closely linked loci in the same region, *Rp5* and *Rp6*, and two independent loci with several alleles, *Rp3* (chromosome 3) and *Rp4* (chromosome 4). *Rp1-Td*, derived from *Tripsacum dactyloides* L., recombines (0.3%) with *Rp1-d* (Bergquist, 1981). Also on chromosome 10, in the same region as *Rp1* is *Rpp9*, affecting southern leaf rust due to infection with a different fungus, *Puccinia polysora* Underw. (Ullstrup,

1965). As many as 11 factors for race-specific resistance affecting southern leaf rust reaction have been designated, but which of these are genetically distinct is still under study (e.g., Scott et al., 1984).

Reaction with *Cochliobolus carbonum* Nelson (*Helminthosporium carbonum* Ullstrup) (leaf spot) is determined by two factors: *Hm1* confers full resistance (although some alleles are intermediate), while *Hm2* in the presence of homozygous recessive *hm1* confers lower resistance that becomes progressively stronger as the plants develop (Nelson and Ullstrup, 1964; see also Hamid et al., 1982). With *Bipolaris maydis* (Nisik.) Shoemaker (*Helminthosporium maydis* Nisik. and Miy.) (southern corn leaf blight) chlorotic-lesion resistance with race O is conferred by *rhm* in seedlings and can contribute to resistance in mature plants (e.g., Faluyi and Olorode, 1984; Thompson and Bergquist, 1984; see also Burnette and White, 1985); plants with the mitochondrial genotype *cms-T*, cytoplasmic male sterile, are sensitive to race T and its pathotoxin, discussed further in the section on extrachromosomal inheritance. With *Helminthosoporium turcicum* Pass. (northern corn leaf blight), *Ht1*, *Ht2*, or *Ht3* confers hypersensitive resistance in the form of chlorotic lesions (in contrast to wilt-type lesions), specifically with particular races of the fungus (e.g., Hooker and Tsung, 1980). *Ht3* was transferred into corn from *Tripsacum floridanum* Porter ex Vasey, while *Ht1* (from inbred GE440 and Ladyfinger popcorn) and *Ht2* (from Australian inbred NN14) were identified by screening of varieties and inbreds. Another chlorotic-fleck factor, *Ht*-N*, derived from Mexican inbred Gto59-272-1-7 and Pepitilla, has been reported. Calub et al. (1974) have shown that leaf diffusates from infected *Ht1* plants are inhibitory to spore germination in vitro, and that diffusates from strains with multiple-factor resistance are substantially more inhibitory. In the presence of *Bx*, a dominant factor that determines occurrence of cyclic hydroxamate ("DIMBOA") in the roots and other plant parts, *H. turcicum* infection levels are substantially reduced, either in *ht ht Bx Bx* or *Ht Ht Bx Bx*, relative to their *bx bx* counterparts (Couture et al., 1971).

A recessive factor identified by Horovitz and Marchioni (1942) in Amargo (bitter) maize and mapped to chromosome 1, conferred resistance to leaf feeding by grasshoppers and to leaf feeding by European corn borer. Authentic stocks of the Amargo factor are no longer extant. Penny and Dicke (1957) reported a dominant factor conferring resistance to European corn borer in a chromosome-3 marker stock carrying *gl7* and showing linkage to it, in segregations from crosses with susceptible WF9 inbred. Linkage analyses are in progress on genome segments affecting earworm resistance in three different germplasm sources (Miranda et al., MNL 56:28-32, 1982; MNL 58:38-46, 1984), using three-letter designators (Ger, Mer, Zer) for the multiple factors involved; these studies set the stage for definition of other quantitative factors, as mapping with markers (e.g., restriction fragment length polymorphisms) is advanced. DIMBOA content is correlated negatively with leaf feeding by the first-generation European corn borer (Klun et al., 1970; see also Tseng et al., 1984) and with aphid infestation (Beck et al., 1983). Guthrie et al. (1986) have shown that, despite correlations of DIMBOA content with resistance to both European corn borer and northern corn leaf blight, selection for resistance to corn borer does not select for resistance to northern corn leaf blight, and vice versa. The recessive gene *aph* determines resistance to the corn leaf aphid (*Rhopalosiphum maidis* Fitch).

Monogenic resistance (*Mv*) to maize mosaic virus I, derived from Caribbean races, has been identified and incorporated into breeding materials (Brewbaker and Aquilizan, 1965; Brewbaker, 1974).

A recessive factor, *ats*, in one particular derivative of the inbred line GT112 determines susceptibility to the widely used herbicide Atrazine (2-chloro 4-ethylamino 6-isopropylamino-S-triazine). The factor has been located to chromosome 8 (Scott and Grogan, 1969). The enzyme glutathione-S-transferase is controlled by this locus (Shimabukuro et al., 1971), and a clone has been isolated (Moore et al., 1986) and sequenced (Shah et al., 1986); induction of its mRNA by a safener compound has been demonstrated by Wiegand et al. (1986). Tolerance to Eradicane (S-ethyl dipropylthiocarbamate + R25788 safener) in inbred C103, relative to a sensitive inbred, H4101, is conferred by *Thc*.

Flooding has been shown to be differentially injurious to plants with specific genotypes for factors determining alcohol dehydrogenase (Schwartz, 1969; Marshall et al., 1973).

Factors *lte1* and *Lte2* have been defined that affect heat tolerance. Frost resistance is conditioned by *lte1*. Heat tolerance and drought tolerance are related to abscisic acid levels (Larque-Saavedra and Wain, 1974).

3–2.10   Gametogenesis and Development of the Gametophyte

The high fecundity of most strains makes sterility or deviant ratios easily recognizable. A wide range of genetic alterations has been identified in the processes of formation of sporogenous tissues, gametogenesis, and the functioning of the gametes.

Types termed *male sterile*, which fail to generate normal, functional pollen grains but are female-fertile, include the recessive *ms* factors, two dominant male steriles (*Ms21, Ms41*), and several other mutants defined by their effects in the meiotic process. The dominant *Rf* factors, which restore fertility to cytoplasmic male steriles (see section 3–2.14 on Extrachromosomal Inheritance, page 206), are genes whose recessive alleles condition male sterility in the appropriate cytoplasm. Studies show abnormalities and breakdown in early meiosis with *dv, dy, ms8, ms9*, and *ms22*; after meiotic prophase with *Mei, ms17, ms23, ms28*, and *ms43*; during vacuolation of the microspore with *ms1, ms2, ms7, ms10, ms12*, and *ms13*; during late vacuolation and microspore mitosis with *ms14*; and during or after microspore mitosis with *ms5, ms11*, and *ms24*; in some cases the tapetum develops abnormalities (Beadle, 1932; Clark, 1940; Nelson and Clary, 1952; Madjolelo et al., 1966; Cheng et al., 1979; Golubovskaya, 1979; Greyson et al., 1980; Albertsen and Phillips, 1981). Because the recessive male sterility factors are expressed only in homozygous plants, the gene action must affect the pollen through sporophytic (i.e., mother plant) processes rather than autonomously in the gametophyte. In this respect the control of white pollen, which is defined by *c2 c2 whp whp* genotype in the plant (Coe et al., 1981), specifically is determined by the sporophyte and results in functional failure of the pollen. The normal mechanisms of the anther (expansion, exsertion from the glumes, opening of the operculum) fail increasingly if 50% or less of the pollen grains within the anther develop (e.g., due to chromosomal aberrations). *Ms41* plants produce a few shriveled anthers from which a small amount of functional pollen can be coaxed. Double recessives of *ms28* or *ms43* with *ts2*, interestingly, produce sterile tassel-seed inflorescences (Golubovskaya and Khristolyubova, 1985).

Application of nuclear male sterility factors in hybrid seed production has been proposed through the use of cytogenetic devices (Phillips et al., 1971a) and through chemical correction (Greyson et al., 1980).

Factors that affect both male and female fertility in homozygous recessive plants include *afd, am, as, dsy1, dsy2, el, pam1*, and *pam2*, each of which results in defects in parts of the meiotic process. Golubovskaya and Khristolyubova (1985) and Curtis (1985) have compared and tabulated the meiotic mutants and have characterized the stages of their effects. Aneuploid progeny are produced on the female side by *as, dsy, pam1, st*, and *va*; telocentrics and isochromosomes by *st* and *va*; and diploid eggs by *am, as, dsy, el*, and *pam1* (Curtis, 1985). Combinations of recessives show *am* to be epistatic over *afd* and *afd* over *dsy* (Golubovskaya and Khristolyubova, 1985). Two factors, *ig* (Kermicle, 1969, 1971) and *po* (Beadle, 1932), affect both male and female fertility by altering gametophyte development per se.

In the male gametophyte, virtually any substantial deficiency results in functional failure or abortion of the pollen grain, and to a lesser degree the same is true of the female gametophyte. In over 850 reciprocal translocations, representing over 1700 terminal chromosome segments, deficiency-bearing gametophytes are generated that result in pollen abortion, accompanied in 85–95% of the segments by embryo sac abortion (Patterson, 1978). Only a fraction of these deficiencies are transmissible through the egg. From this it is clear that a large number of loci influence vital functions required for normal development of the gametophyte, of which most are required in both gametophytes, and mutants consequently cannot be maintained. Microspores deficient for different arm segments show differences in the stage at which development fails or becomes abnormal (Kindiger, 1986).

Sks is a gametophyte-specific factor that conditions normal development and functioning of *Sks* pollen grains (in contrast to *sks* grains) when they are produced on plants bearing the dominant male sterility factor *Ms21* (Schwartz, 1951; Leng and Bauman, 1955). The inbred line Kys is the only source that has been identified in which both of the factors are recessive. *Rf3*, the restorer factor for *cms-S*, is gametophytic in its action (Buchert, 1961). Pollen carrying *lp* is unable to function in the presence of *Lp* pollen. In the female, ovules carrying *lo2* gametophytes abort. Artificially influencing transmission, Mangelsdorf (1932) separated pollen grains segregating for large and small sizes by sieving, and completed pollinations with the separated samples.

A few factors have been found to affect biochemical constituents of the pollen grain. The most commonly used of these for genetic studies or for classroom demonstrations is the starch variation conditioned by the *wx* locus. Pollen grains carrying *Wx* accumulate enough amylose starch to stain black with I_2-KI solution, while *wx* pollen grains contain amylopectin starch alone and stain light brown, with the result that heterozygous *Wx wx* plants produce pollen composed of equal numbers of easily distinguishable grains. Slightly lowered transmission (about 48% instead of 50%) of *wx* relative to *Wx* is due to slower germination and establishment of *wx* pollen grains, followed by equal growth rates (Sprague, 1933). The differences between normal and *wx* grains are even more pronounced for pollen grains produced in *su su* plants. Nelson (1959, 1968) has used the *Wx wx* pollen character to survey large numbers of meiotic products as an aid to the study of genetic fine structure at the *wx* locus. With homozygous *wx* the effects of the *ae* locus also can be distinguished in the pollen, and fine structure of the *ae* locus has been studied accordingly (Moore and Creech, 1972). Schwartz (1971c) and Freeling (1976) have shown that *Adh1* is expressed in the male gametophyte (i.e., pollen grains segregate for activity). Null mutants of *Adh1* have been selected by an "enrichment" technique (Schwartz and Osterman, 1976), in which pollen that has active enzyme dies on exposure to allyl alcohol when the alcohol is converted to a toxic product. Stinson and Mascarenhas (1985) have shown that expression of *Adh1* in haploid microspores is delayed until the spores begin to separate from the tetrads, showing that there is a period of discontinuation of the sporophyte function before the gametophyte begins to show expression. The relationship between functioning of genes in the sporophyte vs. gametophyte has been examined by Frova et al. (1987): Among 34 isozyme loci, 2 are expressed only in the pollen, 7 only in the sporophyte, and 25 in both.

Effects of factors of the *Ga* group, which affect the functioning of pollen grains individually, are detected by differential transmission of marker factors linked to them. For the original factor on chromosome 4, pollen tubes carrying *Ga1* function equally with *ga1* in competition on *ga1* silks but function in 90 to 100% of fertilizations on *Ga1* silks (Mangelsdorf and Jones, 1926; Emerson, 1934). A stronger allele, *Ga1-s*, is more effective in competition against *ga1* in silks, to the point of near exclusion (Schwartz, 1950). House and Nelson (1958) demonstrated by ^{32}P labelling of pollen that *ga1* tubes grow slowly and stop in a few hours on *Ga1-s* silks. *Ga2* pollen out-competes *ga2* pollen on *Ga2* silks (Burnham, 1936). The *Ga8* factor on chromosome 9 also is dependent on *Ga8* in the silks (Bianchi et al., 1969). These factors, present in popcorns, maintain isolation of the strains from outcrossing. They have potential use as systems by which to reduce outcrossing in specialized strains (e.g., sweet corn; waxy; white; high amylose; high lysine).

Selection for competitive efficiency in pollen tube growth can affect the kernel and the sporophyte heritably (Mulcahy, 1971; Ottaviano et al., 1980, 1982, 1985). Kumar and Sarkar (1980, 1985) reported that pollen diameter and pollen tube growth rate were correlated when grown in vitro but not in vivo, and that differences among hybrids were probably multifactorial in basis. Distorted ratios in a large F2 family (but not in backcrosses produced under different environmental conditions nor in an F2 from different parentage) were found by Wendel et al. (1987) for factors on chromosomes 1, 2, 3, 6, and 8.

3–2.11   Transposable Elements

A milestone in genetics has come from the analyses of McClintock and others on genetically controlled variegation and its relationship to gene mutation, chromosome breakage, mobile genetic elements, and gene regulation. It has led to an expanding series of molecular studies, beginning with cloning of the mobile genetic elements and followed by cloning of genes for which no gene product even has been identified, and it promises to contribute to molecular definitions of gene regulation in development. These advances follow from the behavior of transposable elements, whose molecular properties are described in this volume by Walbot and Messing (Chapter 6). A comprehensive review is not attempted in the present chapter, as excellent reviews are available (Fedoroff, 1983, especially for the genetic behavior of these systems; Doring and Starlinger, 1984; Freeling, 1984; Nevers et al., 1986; Walbot et al., 1987).

The elements exhibit some properties that are Mendelian in that they are consistently associated with the chromosomes and are transmitted, despite frequent exceptions, from parent to progeny as genetic material. Apparently their only phenotypic expression is their effect on the action of known genetic markers or on chromosomes. They express some distinctly non-Mendelian properties by transposing from site to site on the chromosomes, by regulating other factors, and by changing in numbers and in properties.

Historically, the first-described system was that of the somatic variegations and mutations in "calico corn" expressed by an allele at the *P* locus (Emerson, 1914, 1917, 1929), for which a model was offered of a genetic factor, *V*, viewed "as a sort of temporary, recessive inhibitor that sooner or later permanently loses its power to inhibit color development... The cause of any such change in factors is beyond intelligent discussion at present" (Emerson, 1914). The proposal is clearly suggesting, in today's context, a component added to the gene whose effect is to block its function and to release function frequently. When Rhoades (1938, 1941, 1945) showed that a heritable factor, *Dt* on chromosome 9, controlled mutation from *a1* to *A1* on chromosome 3, not only mutable genes but genes that can control that mutability were demonstrated. The mobile nature of mutation-controlling factors first became evident when McClintock (1950, 1951) discovered and incisively analyzed the elements *Ds* and *Ac*, termed *controlling elements* in recognition of their ability to affect and control any of a number of genes. Two categories of elements, *autonomous* (determining its own transposition) and *non-autonomous* (requiring a separate determinant), were recognized from these studies; so was the property of chromosome breakage at some sites of insertion of *Ds*, which was the phenomenon actually found first (McClintock, 1947). The *Spm* system of McClintock (1952, 1956) and its equivalent, the *I En* system of Peterson (1953, 1965), defined in parallel studies, showed that there are distinct, separately regulated families of these determinants, and that not only transposition but function at the locus of insertion also was under their control. Nelson (1968) showed by recombinational analysis that the elements of *wx-m8* of the *Spm* system and *wx-m6* of the *Ac Ds* system were located at distinguishable sites within the *wx* locus.

The families of transposable elements that have been defined and distinguished by genetic tests inter se are (i) the Activator family, including *Ac*, *Ac2*, *Ds*, and *Mp*; (ii) *Bg*; (iii) the Dotted family, *Dt1*, *Dt2*, *Dt3*, *Dt4*, *Dt5*, *Dt6*, and *rDt*; (iv) *Fcu*; (v) *Mr*; (vi) *Mrh*; (vii) *Mst* and *I-R*; (viii) *Mut*; (ix) *Mu* and *Cy*; (x) the Suppressor-mutator and Enhancer family, *Spm*, *En*, and *I*; and (xi) *Uq*. A selection of the systems that have been most studied can be considered in the following briefs.

The *Ac Ds* family, discovered by McClintock (1950), is the foundation on which the present level of understanding of transposable elements is built; the review of Fedoroff (1983) gives a full genetic description of the system. McClintock (1951) showed in classic demonstrations that the active system appeared under conditions of chromosome breakage and rearrangement in the short arm of chromosome 9. *Ac* is autonomous, requiring no other factor for its own transposition; *Ds* is non-autonomous, requiring *Ac* for transposition, and has been shown to occur in several molecular modifications that are defective products from *Ac* elements. *Ac* carries the functional code for the enzyme (transposase) that effects its own transposition or that of *Ds* at separate locations (trans-activation). *Ac* and *Ds* carry an inverted-repeat base sequence structure at both ends that is specific for transposase action. The complex molecular structure of a *Ds* element representing the "original location" (chromosome-breakage) type shows a compound duplication of its ends, which may cause breakage (Doring et al., 1985). If *Ac* becomes inserted in a recognizable gene the phenotypic expression becomes variegated, mutating from the inactive or recessive expression to active in sectors that follow cell lineages. If *Ds* becomes inserted in a new gene the expression is blocked, usually completely, and becomes variegated only if *Ac* is present somewhere in the genome. Increase in dosage of *Ac* elements delays events markedly (Emerson, 1929; McClintock, 1950); in strains with very high numbers of elements mutation events can appear to be vanishing. Change in state of the *Ac* element can result in changes in the rate, timing, or locale of mutation; at least some of these changes are apparently due to change of position of the element where it is inserted. When the *Mp* (*Ac*) element leaves a site, it reinserts preferentially at a point nearby, and is replicated at the new site in that cell cycle (Greenblatt, 1974). Removal may be complete or may leave a deficiency or a molecular "footprint", a base sequence that represents incomplete excision and that may or may not have effects on the phenotype (Saedler et al., 1985; Schiefelbein et al., 1985; Starlinger et al., 1985). Brink and Nilan (1952) and Barclay and Brink (1954) showed that the *P-vv* variegation of Emerson was an expression of an *Ac* element (*Mp*) operating at the *P* locus. Nuffer (MNL 29:59, 1955) found the mutable factor *bz2-m* and its mutator (*M*) due to *Ds* and *Ac* elements, respectively. Dempsey (1985) defined an activator element, *Ac2*, whose dosage effect is to increase mutation rather than to decrease it. Schwartz (1985) has characterized genetically a number of transposed activators (*Ac-w*) from one progenitor. The *Ac* element was cloned (Fedoroff et al., 1983) from inserts at the *Wx* locus by isolation of the *Wx* protein, antiserum, cDNA, and hybridizable sequences from insertion mutants. Use of transposable elements as probes to clone genes in which an element has become inserted, even when the functional product of the target gene is unknown ("transposon tagging"), was demonstrated with *Ac* probes by Fedoroff et al. (1984). The strategy, starting with an insertion mutant of the target gene, is to define and clone DNA fragments that include element-homologous sequences along with a portion of the target gene, and to use these fragments as probes to analyze the DNA of various mutants of the target gene (whether insertion-containing or not), thus identifying the mutational changes with changes in the sequences specific to the target gene.

The Dotted family, discovered in Black Mexican sweet corn by Rhoades (1936), has been reviewed recently (Pryor, 1985). It consists of an activating element, *Dt*, and a non-autonomous element, *rDt*, that controls the action of *A1* and responds to *Dt* by removal. Transpositions of *Dt* have been found by Doerschug (1976) and by Pryor (1985), but no locus other than *A1* has been recognized to be affected. Mutations are induced by *Dt* from *A1* to recessive, inactive alleles (*a1-m*) that are stable in the absence of *Dt* but revert back to different levels of *A1* activity if *Dt* is present. In the aleurone tissue reversion sectors appear as dots (hence the designation *dotted*), which may be of variable sizes due to early and late events, or may be of a particular size class due to a restricted developmental time of reversion. Each *Dt*-controlled *A1* to *a1* event may produce a different *al-m* with regard to the type and frequency of response to *Dt*, while each *al-m* to *Al* event may produce a different allele with regard to its anthocyanin producing ability and its response to *Dt*; alleles with pale expression and mutability are found (Nuffer, 1961). Changes also occur from *al-m* to *al-s* (stable, not responsive to *Dt*). Increases in dosage of the responding allele (*al-Ref* or *al-m*) show a linear increase in the frequency of dots with no evident change in the time, type, or location of events. Increases in dosage of *Dt* show an exponential increase in frequency with no evident change in time, type, or location (Rhoades, 1941; Nuffer, 1955). A group of diverse strains was found to carry *Dt* elements at other sites than the original (Nuffer, 1955), and new *Dt* elements have been induced by chromosome breakage (Doerschug, 1973; McClintock, 1950, 1965; Neuffer, 1966).

The *Spm* family, discovered and described independently by McClintock (1952) and Peterson (1953), possesses many of the characteristics of the *Ac Ds* system, including autonomous and non-autonomous elements, blockage of expression of the gene at the site of insertion, and chromosome breakage. Fedoroff (1983) comprehensively reviews the genetics of *Spm*, and Peterson (1985) that of *En*. A special property of this family is the "suppressor" function, in which *Spm* causes intermediate alleles (e.g., ones that express pale color in the absence of *Spm*) to show no expression. The result is stable, pale expression in the absence of *Spm* and colorless expression with mutability in its presence (thus, Suppressor-mutator). The element is subject to great diversity of changes in its properties, including activation and inactivation of both the suppressor and the mutator functions, and changes affecting rate, time, locale, and level of function. Transposition to new target loci has succeeded repeatedly, indicating that there is less "distance" restriction than pertains for *Ac*. Stable alleles that may be null, intermediate, or normal in function are produced upon departure of the element from an affected locus. The epigenetic phenomenon of "presetting" (see discussion by Fedoroff, 1983) is one in which an affected allele is defined to function at a future time by the element after the element leaves (by loss or by segregation). The molecular structure of the *Spm* element and its defective derivatives (*dSpm*) shows characteristic inverted-repeat base sequences at the ends (Fedoroff et al., 1984; Pereira et al., 1985).

The Mutator (*Mu*) family of elements was discovered by Robertson (1978); reviews have been presented by Robertson et al. (1985) and Walbot et al. (1987). The properties of this system include high numbers of elements and remarkable rates of dispersion in the genome (90% of progeny from outcrosses, in contrast to 50%, carry the Mutator properties); non-mendelian regulation of frequency of events associated with numbers of elements (Robertson et al., 1985) and with molecular modification (e.g., methylation) in the genome (Bennetzen, 1985; Chandler and Walbot, 1986; Walbot et al., 1985, 1987). The system is attractive for transposon tagging because of the high frequency of transposition, 10 to 15 per gamete per generation (Alleman and Freeling, 1986), and the apparent lack of restrictions on distance or sites, although the complexities of regulation and the irregularities of transmission must be considered as limitations in this application.

McClintock (1978b, 1984) has pointed to the role that systems of this kind might serve, with the capability of responding to "shocks" to the genome by leading to reorganization of the genetic material and to speciation. Transposable elements no doubt are present in the genomes of all organisms (McClintock, 1968), and evidence indicates that many such elements are cryptic because they are not active. Their place in regulation of normal developmental processes and in evolution, considered by numerous authors, remains to be elaborated. The discovery and analysis of these systems has added a new dimension to the study of inheritance and to the tools for molecular analysis and manipulation of the genetic material.

3–2.12 Paramutation

Brink (1956) discovered a form of unorthodox inheritance at the R locus in which the functional capacity of an allele is heritably altered by its genetic history. Coe (1959) found similar behavior at the B locus. As defined by Brink (1973), paramutation is "an interaction between alleles that leads to directed, heritable changes at the locus." A full, referenced survey of the extensive genetic analyses that have been done on these systems and on related conventional genetic and physicochemical terms for the paramutation phenomena at both R and B is given in the review by Brink (1973). The basis in conventional genetic or physicochemical terms is not known, but may involve some form of specifically controlled DNA modification.

In brief, paramutation at the R locus consists of an inherited reduction in the functional capacity of a sensitive (paramutable) allele after it has passed through a heterozygote with a paramutagenic allele, which remains unchanged (Fig. 3–12). Paramutable alleles include R-st, R-mb, certain of their mutational derivatives, and a number of other naturally occurring alleles. When the paramutant allele, R', is maintained for several generations in the homozygous state, it progressively regains part of its original functional capacity; when maintained heterozygous with r or with a deficiency, R' regains nearly all of its original level of function (Styles and Brink, 1969). Inasmuch as parallel changes in level of function of R are found without prior exposure to a paramutagenic allele, R alleles may be considered metastable, capable of change (small increases or decreases) in particular passages without the necessity of an "inducing" allele (Styles and Brink, 1966), although the effects of R-st in decreasing R function are much more dramatic and are unidirectional. The spontaneous mutation (primarily recombination) rate of paramutant R' is usually lower than that of its nonparamutant counterpart (Bray and Brink,

r r x R-r'/R-r'   r r x R-r'/R-st   r r x R-st/R-st

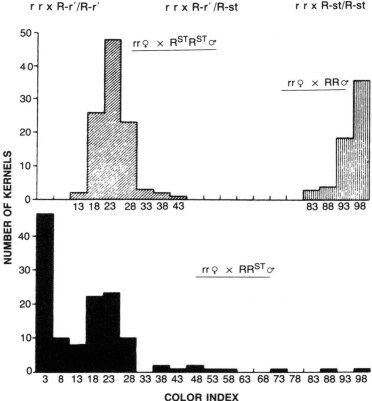

COLOR INDEX

Fig. 3–12. Paramutation of *R-r*. *Top:* ears from testcrosses of sibling plants of the three genotypes derived from the self-fertilization of *R-r/R-st*, showing (left) the medium mottled expression of *R-r'/R-r'* (*R-r* once-exposed to *R-st* and partially returned to standard *R-r* level in passage through homozygosity); (center) the dramatically reduced expression of *R-r'/R-st* (*R-r* twice-exposed to *R-st*); and (right) the standard expression of *R-st*. *Bottom:* graph showing the color grade distributions of the kernels from the three ears pictured above. (From Brink, 1956.)

1966). Mutagens such as X-rays tend to reduce the paramutability of R, to partially restore function in R', and to reduce the paramutagenicity of R-st (Shih, 1969; Shih and Brink, 1969). R' is progressively reduced by repeated passages with a paramutagenic allele to near-absence of function (Mikula, 1961). R-st has been shown to be fractionable by recombination into several units, including multiple determiners of its paramutagenicity (Ashman, 1965; Kermicle, 1970a, 1974).

Paramutation at the B locus consists of a uniform, inherited change in the level of functional capacity of B after it has passed through a heterozygote with a paramutagenic allele, B', or with certain other alleles that have been exposed to B' previously (Coe, 1966b). Once changed, B' becomes uniformly paramutagenic and retains a constant level of functional capacity, not subject to further reduction or to mutagen-induced alterations. X-ray induced losses of the B' chromosome segment during development in B' B individuals reveal B to be unchanged during most or all of the life cycle. The color level of tissues of B' B plants, including the tassels and cobs, is darker than that on B' B' and B' b, showing that B is not reduced all the way to B' level of functioning during the course of vegetative growth, even though all gametes formed on B' B plants are uniformly reduced. Mutations to B' occur spontaneously in B B plants at variable frequencies. B-$Peru$ and B-$Bolivia$, alleles that confer both aleurone color and plant color, are not affected in either expression by exposure to B' or to R-st.

3–2.13 Aberrant Ratio

In progenies derived from plants infected with barley stripe mosaic virus (BSMV), Sprague and McKinney (1966) found distortions of segregation ratios. The distorting effect, termed Aberrant Ratio (AR), was specific to infected plants and was systematically inherited, raising the suspicion that the conventional genetic system had been supplemented or altered by the infectious agent.

AR was found in rather high frequency (1 in 200) in F2 progenies from crosses of pollen from infected multiple-dominant plants on multiple-recessive ($a1$ $su1$ pr wx) ear parents. Ratio distortions ranging from small deviations close to the expected (i.e., 60:40 vs. 50:50) to extremes as deviant as 95:5 were found for any one of the factors in either direction (e.g., low $A1$ or low $a1$). Deviations were equal via male and female, in contrast to the behavior of other known systems that affect segregation pattern or transmission. Occasional changes were seen in direction or degree of distortion. Testcrosses to controls showed no distortion (Sprague and McKinney, 1971). In a 3-point testcross, Sprague and McKinney (1971) found that AR at the C locus (low C) did not affect ratios for two other factors closely linked to c, and that the pattern of crossing over fit expectations calculated on the basis that C expression was modified to that of c by an independent factor.

Brakke et al. (1981), Brakke (1984), and Nelson (1981, 1985) have determined that distorted ratios in a selection of Sprague's materials are attributable to (i) segregations for other complementary genes for aleurone color, (ii) factors probably affecting gametophyte transmission, and (iii) linked factors for zygotic lethality within the AR materials. Sprague (1987, personal communication) questions whether these materials carried the unique AR properties of equal male and female deviations and general homogeneity of deviations in a culture. Mottinger, Dellaporta, and Keller (1984a) recovered unstable *sh1* mutations from AR stocks and found various DNA arrangements in the locus. Mottinger, Johns, and Freeling (1984b) found an insertion, not homologous to the virus, in an *Adh1* mutation that arose in BSMV-infected plants. BSMV infection apparently causes mutations (Sprague et al., 1963), but the mechanism evidently is not by insertion or other direct modification of the genetic material.

3–2.14   Extrachromosomal Inheritance

Variants have been recognized that affect chlorophyll pigmentation, male fertility, or plant growth, and show non-Mendelian inheritance in being transmitted entirely through the maternal parent. The practical utilization of cytoplasmic male sterility has been one of the triumphs of genetics as applied to seed production, but it also taught a challenging lesson in crop ecology and germplasm vulnerability. Rapid and comprehensive advancements in the molecular biology of the chloroplasts and mitochondria (Walbot and Messing, Chapter 6) have been considerably stimulated by the genetics of the male sterility systems (mitochondrial), while variants of the chloroplast are limited and have been little explored. Overall, in fact, the genetics of the organelles is only scantily developed, and the following are not known: (i) whether rare transmission through the pollen can occur, particularly under special conditions, notwithstanding that fact that neither the chloroplasts nor the mitochondria are normally transmitted through the pollen; (ii) the mechanism of exclusion of organelles through the pollen; (iii) the degree to which genetically mixed organelles may undergo conjugation and recombination; (iv) the processes of distribution of the organelles during cell divisions, especially in the zygote and early embryo or at key points in development and differentiation of the plant and its parts; (v) the role of genetic communication and coordination among the nucleus and the organelles; and (vi) the potential for genetic exploitation of the organelles, whether as targets of selection, of mutagenesis, or of genetically engineered modifications. The primary genetic methods for study of the organelles have been analysis of mutations and examination of cell lineages revealing sorting-out of what appear to be mixed organelles.

A variant reported by Anderson (1923) showed stripes of green and pale green in the leaves. Striped plants transmitted striped or entirely pale green character to progeny through the maternal parent only, along with variable proportions of entirely green individuals. Pale green seedlings were lethal, and green plants remained stable in progeny tests. "Ear map" plantings (see section 3–3.3 on Developmental Analysis, page 218) from striped individuals showed clustering of types, suggesting sorting-out of determinants, presumably plastids or mitochondria. A number of variants with similar expression have been found, and these have been summarized and compared by Coe (1983). The mitochondrion has been specifically defined as the site of genetic alteration in the NCS2 and NCS3 variants (Newton and Coe, 1986), where changes in the mitochondrial genome, apparently insertions in the DNA, are found. The somatic sectoring and inheritance patterns suggest that the striping is due to sorting out of an effectively small number of mixed organelles (Coe, 1983).

A variant from Peru affecting male fertility was shown by Rhoades (1931, 1933) to be transmitted only through the maternal parent, with some irregularity in phenotype (i.e., "fertile" maternal progeny when tested yielded male-sterile products). Whether this variant is related in any way to subsequently discovered ones has not been tested, and pedigreed material is no longer extant. Duvick (1965) and Beckett (1971) defined, among a large group of male-sterile collections that show maternal inheritance, three types (*cms-C*, *cms-S*, *cms-T*) according to restoration of fertility by nuclear factors in crosses with a group of inbred lines. Duvick (1972) notes that 108 collections of cytoplasmic male steriles from widely diverse parts of the world were either type C, type S, or type T. The review by Laughnan and Gabay-Laughnan (1983) encompasses the variants and the genetic properties of the cytoplasmic male sterile systems in corn.

Plants with *cms-T* exhibit extreme sensitivity of the mitochondria to the pathotoxin produced by *Bipolaris maydis* (Nisik.) Shoemaker (*Helminthosporium maydis* Nisik. and Miy.) and several other agents (Gengenbach et al., 1973; Miller and Koeppe, 1971), sensitivity of pollen tubes to the pathotoxin (Laughnan and Gabay, 1973b), and sensitivity of plants to the insecticide Methomyl (Humaydan and Scott, 1977). In tissue culture, mutations to resistance, never reported from conventional propagation, arise either in the presence of toxin (Gengenbach et al., 1977) or in its absence (Brettell and Thomas, 1980). The mutations are accompanied in each case by recovery of male fertility. Abbott and Fauron (1986) and Wise et al. (1987) define mutational changes in the mitochondrial DNA that result in changes in the transcription of a particular open reading frame (coding for a 13 kDa protein) that is specific to *cms-T*. Synthesis of the T polypeptide is suppressed by nuclear fertility restorers (Forde and Leaver, 1979).

Over the period from 1950 to 1970, *cms-T* came into increasing use as a major aid in crossing to produce hybrid seed corn by virtue of its reliability as a male-sterile parent that could be returned genetically to the male-fertile condition in the final stage of grain production. In 1970 a nation-wide epidemic of *B. maydis* race T (a new race specifically virulent with *cms-T*) spread across host fields estimated to contain *cms-T* in 75 to 90% of plantings, causing severe losses in yield on a national scale (National Research Council, 1972). A group of 30 sources, tested for reaction to race T, were all resistant except for the four identified as *cms-T* by the fertility criteria (Smith et al., 1971). Current seed production concentrates on increasing the diversity of cytoplasmic and nuclear sources (Duvick and Noble, 1978). According to the germplasm survey conducted by Darrah and Zuber (1986), *cms-C* constituted 8% and *cms-S* 3% of total U.S. seed corn production for 1985; *cms-T* was entirely out of use, and exotic cytoplasm sources contributed only around 1% of the total.

Restoration of fertility to cytoplasmic male steriles is under the control of conventional nuclear factors, which overcome (more precisely, suppress) the sterility but do not change the maternally inherited modification that leads to male sterility when the nuclear gene is absent. Restoration of full fertility to *cms-T* is controlled by two complementary dominant factors, *Rf1* and *Rf2*, but susceptibility to *B. maydis* remains. These restorer factors are sporophytic in action—i.e., all pollen grains borne on *cms-T* plants carrying the factors are viable, even when the factors are segregating in the pollen. Suppression of a T-specific polypeptide by restorers has been shown by Forde and Leaver (1979). In addition to these factors for full fertility, Beckett (1966) has found that partial restoration of fertility to *cms-T* is conferred by several other, ill-defined factors, at least some of which are distinct from *Rf1* and *Rf2*. Restoration of fertility to *cms-S*, conferred by *Rf3*, is gametophytic—i.e., pollen grains carrying *Rf3* develop normally, while *rf3* grains abort if they are derived on *cms-S* plants (Buchert, 1961). Pollen from *cms-S* plants of *Rf3 rf3* constitution is half aborted and half normal. Restoration of *cms-C* by *Rf4* is sporophytic; other restorer factors are indicated by genetic tests (Laughnan and Gabay-Laughnan, 1983).

Singh and Laughnan (1972) identified exceptional fertile progeny in *cms-S* plants, especially in certain genetic backgrounds. Crossing analyses indicated that the exceptions resulted from instances either of mutation to normal cytoplasm, or conceivably of transfer of normal cytoplasm through the pollen. Analysis of further events in the same strains (Laughnan and Gabay, 1973a) reveals the occurrence of tassel and ear chimeras for cytoplasmically inherited changes, indicating that these are mutation-like events occurring in the cytoplasm rather than transfers through the pollen. The cytoplasmic revertants display loss of two plasmids, S1 and S2, characteristic of *cms-S* mitochondria (Levings et al., 1980), possibly by integration into the main genome, although S1 and S2 do not invariably disappear (Escote et al., 1985; Ishige et al., 1985). Nuclear reversions are also found (Laughnan et al., 1981), most of which are lethal or semi-lethal in homozygotes and are subject to transposition to new sites in the nuclear genome (Laughnan and Gabay-Laughnan, 1983). Several S-specific proteins are found in *cms-S* mitochondria (Forde and Leaver, 1979), and disappear in cytoplasmic revertants (Leaver et al., 1983). Rearrangements in *cms-S* mitochondria include a modification in the region upstream of the gene encoding cytochrome *c* oxidase subunit I (Isaac et al., 1985).

The recessive nuclear factor *ij1*, which conditions loss of chlorophyll in stripes, was shown in a now-classic study (Rhoades, 1946) to produce maternal progeny without chlorophyll. Although some striping tendency continues to be inherited, suggesting mixed determinants that are sorting out, the majority of striped individuals transmit entirely green or entirely white progeny. Stroup (1970) identified a second factor, *chloroplast mutator* (*cm*), very similar to *ij1* in its effects. Shumway and Weier (1967) found that plastids in white tissue of homozygous *ij1* plants have abnormal granal and lamellar organization and lack ribosomes. Walbot and Coe (1979) and Siemenroth et al. (1980) confirmed the absence of ribosomes in maternal white plants as well, and found no detectable alteration in the chloroplast DNA. Rhoades (1950) reported occurrence of cytoplasmic male sterility in progenies from *ij1* plants (which would bear importantly on the nature of determinants), but Duvick (1965) deduces evidence indicating that the sterility may have been derived from pre-existing *cms-S* in the *iojap* strains. Lemke et al. (1985) report occurrence of *cms-S* in progeny from an *ij1* plant, based on genetic restoration behavior and molecular evidence, for which it must be assumed that a very complex rearrangement of the genetic material of the mitochondrion, including advent of the plasmids special to *cms-S*, has occurred. Analysis of the further cases indicated by Lemke et al. (1985), along with studies of the progenitor genomes and of the genetics of restorers in these materials, will be needed to clarify whether *ij1* does cause such mutations. The somatic chlorophyll sectoring in maternal sectorial exceptions from crosses of *iojap* ear parents by normal have been interpreted to indicate that effectively there is a small number of mixed plastids sorting out during early embryogenesis (Coe et al., 1983), as with the mitochondria in NCS2 and NCS3.

Pring and Levings (1978) have examined chloroplast DNA from T, S and C cytoplasms by restriction endonuclease digestion and find that T and C are indistinguishable from each other and from normals (N type), but that S chloroplasts are distinguishable from the others. Kemble et al. (1983), McNay et al. (1983), and Weissinger et al. (1983) have shown mitochondrial diversity among lines and races, in low-molecular-weight components and in restriction fragments. Members of the S type (25 isolates) show differences among themselves in fertility restoration patterns and in restriction fragment patterns (Sisco et al., 1985). C mitochondria also show differences among members (Pring et al., 1987). Conde et al. (1979) have shown that mitochondrial and plastid DNAs from reciprocal crosses between corn and *Zea perennis* are distinguishable and that both organelles display maternal inheritance. Differences among chloroplast and mitochondrial genomes of *Zea* species have been identified by Timothy et al. (1979) and by Doebley et al. (1987).

Evidence summarized by Lonsdale et al. (1983) shows that the mitochondrial genome consists of a collection of molecules, probably arranged in large circles, which intercombine at recombination sites, along with small plasmids, linear episomes, and double-stranded RNA (Pring and Lonsdale, 1985). The occurrence of substantial sequences of chloroplast DNA in the mitochondrial DNA (Stern and Lonsdale, 1982; Lonsdale, 1985) suggests that there may have been recombinational events between the two different genomes.

Atrazine resistance has been found in other plant species to result from a conformational change in a chloroplast-encoded protein; resistance in maize, however, is determined by a nucleus-encoded detoxifying enzyme (locus *ats*).

3–3   METHODS OF GENETIC ANALYSIS

The art of designing and conducting experiments in any organism is dependent upon traits and properties peculiar to that organism. Most specific methodologies can be adapted to other organisms by modifications appropriate to their biological differences, and research methods with corn have contributed significantly to (and have appropriated significantly from) the total fund of genetic methodologies for analysis of genetic behavior, mapping, development, mutation, and genetic fine structure.

3–3.1   Analysis of Genetic Constitution and Behavior

In corn, efficient experimental tools are available to aid genetic analysis, including especially techniques associated with pollination and easy multiple testing of the genotype of single individuals. These are complemented by a broad foundation of specific biological and genetic information, and extensive knowledge of alterations in genetic transmission.

Testing for heritability of a new variant, its nuclear vs. cytoplasmic basis, the number of genes responsible, and interactions of the genes affecting the same process, while routine to the practicing geneticist, are essential to beginning any study and to documenting the information gained. For example, a proportion of 3/4 of one type to 1/4 of an alternative type in a progeny from self-fertilization, without other information, is strongly suggestive of a single-factor-pair segregation, but the rigor of Mendelian standards requires a few simple predictions to be tested: (i) the supposed recessive class should breed true to type in selfed progenies; (ii) the supposed dominant class should include approximately 1/3 that will breed true, and approximately 2/3 that will again segregate; (iii) crosses of the variant type both as male and as female parent with standard types should yield parallel types of progeny, in similar frequencies; (iv) crosses with several standard strains should display recovery of the variant in progeny (i.e., the variant should not "disappear"). Progeny size requirements in planning of experiments are given in Coe (1982). Given suitable results and interpretations, any variant should be checked for allelism with known variants having related effects, should be located to chromosome and should be mapped, and may be characterized in terms of its physiological interactions, its interrelationships with related factors, its biochemical basis, and its potential use in field production or in laboratory applications.

Procedures used in pollination (along with procedures used in plant culture, harvesting, and pedigree keeping) are given in Neuffer (1982a). While strains differ widely in ear habit and potential, self or cross-pollinations of one or more ears on a plant and multiple crosses with single or repeated collections of pollen can be chosen as convenient. Normally only one ear per plant is used, but two ears on one stalk can often be obtained if both ear shoots are well developed and both pollinations are completed on the same day; pollination of the lower ear a day ahead of the upper ear sometimes gives better results. Tillered plants may produce additional ears and pollen over a longer period of time. A single plant can be testcrossed as both pollen and ear parent, in an exactly reciprocal manner if desired.

Split pollination, a convenient manipulative technique, depends on the common practice of cutting back the end of the husks and silks to an even surface the day before pollination, allowing the silks to grow overnight into a convenient brush of receptive strands 1 to 2 cm long. Two or more pollen types can be applied to a single ear while separating the silk brush into segments with a card or other stiff object; ears with sharply defined sections usually result (see Sheridan and Clark, 1987).

Differential growth rates of pollen tubes are well documented, particularly in relation to silk length traversed before fertilization (e.g., Kempton, 1936; Mulcahy, 1971; Ottaviano et al., 1980, 1982, 1985). Pollen carrying wx is less sensitive than Wx to environmental exposure, resulting in ratios that are altered by differential survival (Kempton, 1936; Barnabas, 1985; Pfahler et al., 1986a). Differential selection or enrichment for specific pollen genotype has been employed (Schwartz and Osterman, 1976) to obtain alcohol dehydrogenase null mutants. Liquid media have been defined (Coe, 1966a) in which pollen can be suspended and exposed to selective agents or mutagenic agents before pollination (Neuffer and Coe, 1978). The silks can be pretreated with selected agents as well (Pfahler et al., 1986b). Pollen also can be separated according to size by sieving (e.g., Mangelsdorf, 1932). Information on genetically controlled constituents and gene functions in the male gametophyte is summarized in the section on gametogenesis.

Typically strains that are to be crossed are scheduled at planting so that they will be in flower at matched times. Silking is advanced by tassel removal. Pollen shedding can be delayed for some days if the plant can be moved into cool, low-light conditions or if the tassel is cut and kept with water under the same conditions. Shedding may be precocious or premature in unusually dry or hot conditions. Shed pollen typically remains viable for 10 to 30 min, and may be stored loose for 24 h or more at refrigeration temperatures. Pollen stored at liquid nitrogen temperatures after pretreatment by drying has retained viability for as long as a year (Barnabas and Rajki, 1976, 1981).

Testing of genetic constitution of single individuals can be very extensive and discriminating. Commonly, "tester" lines are planted solely for pollinations intended to identify the constitution of experimental plants. Emerson (1918) defined tester stocks singly recessive for each of the aleurone color factors, $a1$, $c1$, and r. For example, crosses with a "c tester" strain, which is homozygous recessive for $c1$ but dominant for $A1$, $A2$, $Bz1$, $Bz2$, $C2$, and R, will give colorless seeds only when crossed with an unknown carrying $c1$ or one of the color inhibitor factors.

The progeny from a typical crossed ear, up to several hundred kernels, can be expeditiously scored or observed for segregation ratios, recombinants, mutations, or variations in expression. On an ear with as many as 300 kernels, two proportions differing by as little as 10% can be distinguished with 95% confidence, and genotypes expected as infrequently as one in 64 will be included with 99% confidence (Hanson, 1959; see also Coe, 1982). The ease of making testcrosses and of scoring segregating ears makes feasible studies requiring the recognition and classification of ratio aberrancies, such as those caused by preferential segregation with the abnormal neocentric knob K-10 (Rhoades and Dempsey, 1966a), or by gametophyte factors (Emerson, 1934), as well as the detection of low-frequency mutational events such as the chromosome losses induced by B chromosomes (Rhoades and Dempsey, 1972, 1973a). Some types of experimental work are facilitated by carrying along recessive or otherwise concealed factors, traced entirely by test-crosses, in the strains under study. Tester-based analysis is particularly essential for the effective study of transposable element systems. Similarly, by repeated crosses to a series of uniform lines that amount to testers, exacting discriminations can be made among cytoplasm types affecting male fertility and among the nucleus types interacting with them (Beckett, 1966, 1971; Sisco et al., 1985).

Heterofertilization, the fertilization of the egg and the polar nuclei by sperm from different pollen tubes (Sprague, 1932), can lead to the embryo and endosperm being of differing genetic constitution (non-correspondence). In pollinations with artificially mixed pollen samples or with segregating pollen marked with endosperm and embryo markers it is possible to identify kernels derived from embryo sacs that have been penetrated by two pollen tubes and to analyze fertilizations or other events accordingly (e.g., Sarkar and Coe, 1971a). In recombination analyses involving an endosperm trait with an embryo or plant trait, however, segregating markers transmitted through the male must be verified by progeny tests whenever heterofertilization might confound the results. Heterofertilization frequencies of 1 to 2% are common, and Sprague (1932) reported up to 25% heterofertilization in some strains. In the presence of *ig*, heterofertilization frequencies as high as 7% are found (Kermicle, 1971). Another type of heterofertilization event, due to the regular non-disjunction of the centromere of B chromosomes in the male gameto-phyte, is recognizable by non-correspondence and deficiencies if a section of an A chromosome is translocated to the B centromere (Roman and Ullstrup, 1951). In spontaneous sectors trisomic for chromosome 3, te-traspory (all four products of meiosis contributing to the eight nuclei of the embryo sac) rather than monospory is found, causing noncorres-pondence and anomalous classes (Neuffer, 1964).

Gynogenesis or androgenesis (maternal or paternal haploidy or di-ploidy) can be recognized in the embryos of dry seeds by genetic marking (Coe and Sarkar, 1964; Greenblatt and Bock, 1967; Kermicle, 1969; Nanda and Chase, 1966). In crosses that involve a particular strain, Stock 6, the frequency of gynogenetic haploids is substantially increased over normal (Sarkar and Coe, 1966), while the frequency of androgenetic haploids is greatly increased in seed progeny from plants bearing *ig* (Kermicle, 1969). Androgenesis through culture of anthers in vitro, in which haploid mi-crospores at the binucleate stage are induced to proliferate and to form embryos, has recently been obtained in sufficient frequency and in suf-ficiently diverse materials to permit advancement of studies of the pro-cess. The method is being applied to derive inbred lines for commercial purposes (Barnabas et al., 1987; Dieu and Beckert, 1986; Pace et al., 1987; Petolino and Jones, 1986; Tsay et al., 1986).

Monosomy or trisomy may occur spontaneously or under the influ-ence of *r-x1* (Weber, 1986) and can cause noncorrespondence. Gynoge-netic diploids from crosses of 2n × 2n or 2n × 4n appear to be derived by the fusion of meiotic products to form diploid sporophytes rather than by the doubling of reduced products, and thus may not be homozygous (Sarkar and Coe, 1971b, c). Tetraploids arising from crosses of 2n × 4n, however, may be derived by doubling of reduced products to give diploid gametes through the ear parent, while tetraploids arising from 4n × 2n appear to be derived by fusion of meiotic products in the male (Sarkar and Coe, 1971b). Plants homozygous for *el* produce diploid eggs whose origin appears to be from incompletely reduced meiotic products (Rhoades and Dempsey, 1966b). The genetics of autotetraploids and trisomes, tak-ing into account all known phenomena that affect chromosome behavior and transmission, are detailed by Doyle (1973, 1979, 1982).

Polyembryony occurs at a considerable frequency (6%) with the in-determinate gametophyte factor, *ig*, in which twins are usually diploid and concordant for maternal contribution but nonconcordant for paternal contribution (Kermicle, 1969, 1971). Polyembryony is not strongly as-sociated with haploidy in *ig* or in normal material (Sarkar and Coe, 1966).

Several aspects of genetically controlled alterations in transmission are identified in the section on gametogenesis. Transmission can be af-fected by factors that result in lethality in the ovule (*lo2*) or pollen (*cms-S* with *rf3*; *lp*), including most chromosomal deficiencies; by factors that influence pollen grains or tubes differentially (*ga* group; *Sks* with *Ms21*; *wx*); by preferential assortment to functional megaspores (K-10 and knobs); by differential fertilization (B chromosomes); or by lethality of the zygote. More generally, pollen mixtures show differences in fertilization percentage among strains, depending on the pollen sources and ear parents (Pfahler, 1965, 1967a). Gamma irradiation, however, appears not to alter fertilization ability in competition but results in dominant lethality in the zygotes (Pfahler, 1967b). Mulcahy (1971) and Ottaviano et al. (1980, 1982, 1985) have demonstrated that competition in pollen mixtures is an effective selection screen for kernel and plant parameters of weight and growth rates. Murakami et al. (1972) have found that pollen of F1 hybrids succeeds in achieving higher fertilization percentages than the parent lines, in competition with a constant pollen type in mixtures.

Cytogenetically controlled transmission methods include duplication-deficiency products from reciprocal translocations (Phillips et al., 1971a; Patterson, 1978), tertiary trisomic products from B-A translocations (Beckett, 1987), and similar strategies. Each can be used to carry a particular gene on a duplicated segment that will transmit through the egg parent but not through the pollen. Examples include male sterility, in which a plant of *ms ms *Ms* constitution (the *Ms* chromosome carrying a segmental duplication) will be fertile but will transmit only *ms* gametes; and albinos or other lethals, e.g., *w w *W*.

3–3.2   Locating Factors to Chromosome and to Map Position

A factor pair that is not yet placed to chromosome can be located in one of the 10 linkage groups by the use of marker stocks for each chromosome. In addition to this conventional method, which can become tedious, a number of efficient special methods have been contrived, including the use of chromosomal aberrations as markers, aberrations associated with convenient gene markers, hemizygosity, transmission defects, and trisomy. Patterson (1982) discusses the use of markers and chromosomal aberrations for locating genes.

In conventional tests with marker stocks the unplaced factor is made heterozygous with each of a series of markers chosen to survey the linkage map and the F1 plants are testcrossed if possible, or self-fertilized. There is no standard set of markers; strains bearing contrasting markers of course are essential. The marker strains should carry two or more well-separated markers on the same chromosome or segment; usually it is not practical to include large numbers of closely linked markers with the intention of locating the factor and mapping it precisely in one cycle. Markers that affect the seed or young seedling are generally preferred because classifications may be conducted in the laboratory months ahead of field plantings and because expenditures of time and materials are substantially lower. Although dominant markers are efficient because coupling (cis) heterozygotes produce a mathematically more informative array in the F2 (Hanson, 1959), most are older-plant traits and many have low productivity combined with variable penetrance. Data can be tested for association in the assortment of two factor pairs with the 2×2 Chi-square test, which can be applied without concern for the linkage phase (cis vs. trans), the linkage ratios per se, or deviations in ratios. With codominant factors (e.g., isozymes, RFLPs), 2×3 or 3×3 tests are used. If necessary, agreement with the expected linkage phase and with expected individual ratios can be judged by inspection or by appropriate Chi-square tests. Any genetic interactions between a marker and the unplaced factor will confound the statistical test and can spuriously suggest linkage. Interactions should be reconciled by development of appropriate expected proportions and testing of observed values against these proportions. Data involving interactions are inefficient for the estimation of recombination percentages (Allard, 1956).

Chromosomal aberrations that have easily recognized phenotypic expression (e.g., semisterility of the pollen and eggs) are reliable markers for linkage tests with unplaced factors. Reciprocal translocations (interchanges) are often applied (see Burnham, 1966), because the semisterility that is characteristic of plants heterozygous for most interchanges is a clearly classifiable character. In pollen, semi-sterility (50% empty pollen grains) is recognized easily on a black, opaque surface with a 30X or higher pocket microscope in the field. On the ear, irregular seed set is observed, resulting from the abortion of half the ovules. Because homozygous interchanges have normal fertility that is indistinguishable from that of the standard chromosome constitution, the procedure normally followed is to testcross rather than to self-fertilize the F1 (translocation/mutant) and to analyze the data as a testcross. Because each interchange has breakpoints (semisterility points) in two chromosomes, sets of translocations are selected that will narrow the conclusion to a single chromosome; clues to map position are often detected with well-chosen sets, but recombination percentages are untrustworthy and cannot be matched with those for normal chromosome structure (in particular, it cannot be decided from one or two combinations whether a trait is in the same arm or the other arm of the chromosome, nor the approximate location relative to the standard linkage map). The common set of translocations maintained in the stocks of the Maize Genetics Cooperation Stock Center consists of a cycle of 20 translocations. The semi-sterility linkage method is so routine for simple factors that it is not often reported in print; for complex traits, references and a paradigm are given in the report by Scott et al. (1966).

Anderson (1956) and Burnham (1966) detail the use of the gene-marked translocation technique, in which a series of interchanges is selected to include a chromosome bearing a convenient gene marker associated by the translocation with each of the other chromosomes. The common set maintained in the Stock Center employs wx with 17 selected translocations. Crosses of the mutant strain are made with each of the *wx* translocation strains and the F1 plants are testcrossed or self-fertilized. Data are tested for association between the segregation for *wx* and the segregation of the mutant. This method is limited or inadequate if the mutant has an expression that is confounded with that of the gene marker. The method depends upon both the physical linkage of interchanged chromosome segments and the 'pseudolinkage' resulting from selective survival of complete chromosome segments. As with reciprocal translocations, recombination percentages cannot be matched with those for normal chromosomes.

Methods for locating a factor to a chromosome or to a segment that make use of hemizygosity (heterozygosity with a deficiency) are the most rapid and generally the most reliable. A recessive factor can be located through observations in the immediate generation if it is made hemizygous and is "uncovered" (i.e., shows recessive expression). Dosage-dependent factors and codominant factors also can be recognized in hemizygous progeny and can be located in the immediate generation. Dominant factors require a second-generation progeny test, which is usually definitive because of failure in transmission of the deficiency or inviability of the homozygote (i.e., in the critical test, when the dominant factor is hemizygous, no recessives will segregate from the hemizygote). Several procedures that make use of hemizygosity can be applied, including B-A translocations, monosomics, maintainable deficiencies, and induced deficiencies.

The most effective method by which to generate deficiencies of known location and extent is to apply B-A translocations (Roman and Ullstrup, 1951; see Beckett, 1978, 1988), in which the unique behavior of the supernumerary B chromosome results in transmissible sperm nuclei deficient for whatever portion of an arm of the A chromosome lies beyond the breakpoint of the translocation. A B-A translocation uncovering a substantial part of each arm is now available for 19 of the 20 arms of the A complement, with which at least 90% of the known map length can be made hypoploid (hemizygous) at will (J.B. Beckett, 1987, personal communication). Locations of each of these translocations are indicated on the accompanying linkage map (Fig. 3–1). The procedure is quite simple, in spite of the underlying intricacies on which it is based. Pollen from plants bearing the desired B-A translocation (homozygous or heterozygous) is crossed onto plants carrying the factor to be located (each pollen parent should also be crossed onto a known recessive tester that will validate the occurrence of deficient sperm). Hemizygotes in the kernel are recognized in the immediate endosperms or embryos. Hypoploid plants are usually distinct in morphology (Beckett, 1988) and range in frequency from about 10 to 45%. In the critical test (the one in which the factor of interest becomes hemizygous) a recessive factor will be revealed directly, as will a codominant or a dosage-dependent factor. A dominant factor can be located by progeny testing hypoploid plants, which will not segregate if the factor is in the segment. If needed, supposed hemizygotes can be progeny tested against errors, contamination, haploidy, or confounding of expressions. If a factor is in the centric region (between B-A translocations for the opposite arms), progeny tests of hypoploids will show deviant ratios in the critical case.

Plewa and Weber (1973) have demonstrated the use of monosomics to identify chromosomes carrying dosage-dependent factors affecting fatty-acid constitution. Monosomics are generated at high frequencies under the effects of the *r-xl* deficiency (Weber, 1973, 1986). Because each monosomic is morphologically distinctive and can be verified by root-tip cytology or meiotic analysis, it becomes possible through this system to locate any factor to chromosome by correlating the monosomy with the genetic results of hemizygosity. Viable recessives, dosage-dependent factors and codominants (e.g., RFLPs; Helentjaris et al., 1986b) will be placed by uncovering; others will be placed by failure of segregation from the critical monosomic.

A few small, maintainable deficiencies have been identified (Rhoades and Dempsey, 1973b), some as simple deletions and some as products derived from chromosomal aberrations. These can be used to localize factors very precisely in the chromosome, but they are very limited in extent and therefore are limited in usefulness. In addition to the simple deficiencies cited by Rhoades and Dempsey, which uncover *al*, *sh2*, *bm1*, *pyd*, *wd*, *yg2*, *cl*, *sh1*, *bz1*, *r*, and *sr2*, deficiencies derived from chromosomal aberrations include ones that uncover *fl* and *fl2* (Gopinath and Burnham, 1956), *po* and the organizer and satellite of chromosome 6 (Phillips et al., 1971b), and *ar* (Turcotte, 1956, MNL 30:164).

Locating of factors to chromosome and segment often has been done by inducing a series of losses of the dominant allele and determining cytologically, at the pachytene stage, the particular segments of chromosome that have been lost (Rhoades and McClintock, 1935). This approach was applied initially by McClintock (1931) to locate several factors affecting plant characters. The deficient chromosomes usually are not transmitted through either gametophyte and so are not maintained. The method may seem ineffective for endosperm traits, where the cytology cannot be conducted; however, it can be fully effective if the deficiency is induced in the pollen before the two sperm nuclei are separated, so that they correspond in carrying the deficiency to both the endosperm and the embryo. *Bz2*, *Dt2*, and *Dt3* were located in this fashion (Nuffer, 1955). Generally the other methods described in this section, especially the B-A translocations, are more easily applied because ad hoc cytology is not required.

Defective transmission, especially through the pollen, is characteristic of duplicated or deficient segments. Linkage of the defective transmission effect with factors in the same chromosome but outside the aberrant region permits tests for location of unplaced factors. Rhoades and Dempsey (1973b) point out that map distance from a simple deficiency to a gene determined in this way is as accurate as that obtained by gene-to-gene mapping. More complex deficiencies and duplications will provide less precise mapping data but greater efficiency in identifying linkage, inasmuch as recombination tends to be reduced when synapsis is complex. For example, when a series of tests with B-A translocations fails to uncover an unplaced recessive, the tests can be extended by applications of the defective transmission effect through self-fertilization or testcrossing of hypoploid F1 plants (Roman and Ullstrup, 1951). Factors located in the euploid segment of the chromosome will show sharply deviant ratios due to linkage with the deficient segment.

All of the 10 trisomes of maize are available and are identified rather easily, with the help of cytological verification, in uniform stocks. Trisomic inheritance for a factor, given information identifying which particular chromosome is trisomic, identifies the chromosome on which the factor is located. The trisomic method was used initially by McClintock and Hill (1931). Little application is made of trisomy for locating factors, because of the other tools now available, and relatively little use is made of equivalent techniques such as tertiary trisomes, or of telocentrics and isochromosomes, in locating factors to chromosome segment.

Mapping is relatively straightforward once a factor is located to chromosome, because the linkage groups are extensively established and many factors are identified approximately to cytological positions. Mapping, per se, is conventionally conducted by preparing a hybrid with three or more heterozygously marked points and testcrossing whenever possible, preferably with the homozygous tester as pollen parent in order to avoid problems arising from heterofertilization. Elementary genetics textbook examples of multiple-point testcross data analysis are typical of conventional mapping arithmetic and logic. When simple testcrosses are not available, procedures such as the product moment method (tables and formulas in Immer, 1930) or maximum likelihood (Allard, 1956) are applied to partial testcross, F2, F3, or other data sets. For systematic tabulation and reporting of data the concise but complete format used by Emerson et al. (1935), described by Coe (1982), should be followed, to provide the information necessary for mathematically combining sets of data toward comprehensive mapping. Analysis of F2 data for codominant factors with each other is highly efficient if multiple sites are available, as with RFLP loci. The mathematical treatment of data for mapping of multiple sites, including efficient algorithms for their calculation, is currently under development (Hoisington, 1987; Hoisington and Lander, manuscript in preparation). Annual updates of the working linkage maps for corn may be found in the Maize Genetics Cooperation News Letter, and biennially in Genetic Maps (Cold Spring Harbor Laboratory).

3–3.3 Developmental Analysis

In corn, as with any species in which diverse genetic materials are available, substantial leverage is available for the analysis of developmental processes through the use of genetic devices. Approaches may include morphological and physiological analysis of mutants, interactions of mutants, examination of chimeras, and clonal analysis.

Some examples of morphological-physiological analysis of mutants are cited in the section on plant form. The anatomical and morphological descriptions of development in the embryo and endosperm by Randolph (1936) and in the vegetative and reproductive parts by Kiesselbach (1949) form the foundations upon which experiments of these kinds can be based. The homologies of specific vegetative and reproductive structures have been deduced (Galinat and Andrew, 1953) from studies of the structural gradations in plants of *Cg1* genotype between extreme *corngrass* and normal or near-normal individuals induced by physiological conditions. Also in *Cg1*, changes in localized mitotic dynamics and the initiation of leaf primordia in the shoot apex have been recognized (Angeles, see Stebbins, 1967). Poethig (1985) has further described the homeotic effects of *Cg1*, *Tp1*, and *Tp2* in causing vegetative structures to be transformed from "adult" to "juvenile" form, and reproductive structures to leaves. Studies of defective-kernel mutants that have mutant endosperms but fail to germinate (Sheridan and Neuffer, 1982) have revealed loci that control development at different points in the morphogenesis of the embryo, and other loci that are essential for germination. Some (e.g., *dek23*) are blocked in formation of the shoot apex but not of the root primordium, while others (e.g., *dek22*) fail to go beyond the transition stage, or other specific points in development (Clark and Sheridan, 1986). Some mutants are conditional to the extent that, when cultured in vitro, they advance beyond the stage at which they stop in vivo, or when associated with a normal endosperm advance beyond the stage at which they stop when concordant with a mutant endosperm (Sheridan and Neuffer, 1986). The conditional nature of virescent mutants, dependent on developmental stage and in some cases on temperature, permits analysis of the sequence of events in formation of the cell types and the photosynthetic machinery of the leaf (e.g., Polacco et al., 1985). Similarly, responses of dwarf plants to gibberellic acid applied in a single "pulse" show the developmental-window consequences of supply of the hormone, recognizable only on the mutant backdrop, just as normal plants respond to gibberellic acid during early seedling growth by elongating internodes that will not ordinarily elongate (Johri and Coe, 1982).

Interactions of mutants that affect developmental processes are only beginning to be studied. Meiotic mutants (Golubovskaya and Khristolubova, 1985; Curtis, 1985) apparently show some combination-specific effects. A few other studies, on factors affecting reproductive structures in particular, are in progress in several laboratories (see also section 3–2.4 on Plant Form, page 180).

Chimeras of mutant and normal tissue in the aleurone, pericarp, leaf and other tissues in plants heterozygous for lethal mutants provide means to examine genes whose function is vital to the development of the plant.

Because most gene-controlled functions are cell autonomous, chimeras are well defined. Chimeras can be produced by a number of means: (i) radiation treatment of seeds or plants heterozygous for the target locus (Stadler, 1930; Coe and Neuffer, 1978; Johri and Coe, 1983, 1986; Hake and Freeling, 1986); (ii) ring chromosomes, somatically unstable, carrying the dominant allele of the target locus, with the normal chromosomes carrying recessives (Stadler and Roman, 1948); (iii) chromosome-breaking *Ds* elements on the arm carrying the dominant allele, heterozygous with the recessive allele of the target locus and with *Ac* present (Neuffer, MNL 60:55-56, 1986); (iv) tertiary trisomes, somatically unstable, carrying a B-A chromosome with the dominant allele and two normal chromosomes with the recessive (Birchler, 1983); (v) mutable alleles of the target locus. By any of these methods, cell lineages can be generated that carry the mutant phenotype in association with lineages that are normal. Chimeras for mutants conditioning lethal embryos or white, yellow, or necrotic seedlings can be evaluated during extended plant growth, and differences between general (housekeeping) factors and stage-specific ones can be recognized. Johri and Coe (1983) determined by chimeras that the effects of *ra*, for example, are cell-autonomous, expressing branching in the specific cell lineages that have become recessive by loss of the normal allele in heterozygous plants. In contrast, Hake and Freeling (1986) found by chimeras that *Kn* determines proliferation of epidermal cells by the mesophyll cells rather than in the epidermis per se; this is a "fate map" example for corn.

Cell lineages and their destinies can be diagnosed by production of marked chimeras (independently of mutant alterations in development), and a considerable body of knowledge has been derived from this approach. From seeds irradiated in nuclear bomb tests, Anderson et al. (1949) identified clonal sectors bearing chromosomal aberrations in the tassel by classifying for aborted pollen, branch by branch. The average sector included about two branches derived from one of seven or eight cells in the dormant meristem of the embryo destined to give rise to the tassel. Regiroli and Gavazzi (1975), by chemical mutagenesis on seeds, found ear sectors of 1/2 to 1/4 of the ear, indicating that 2 to 4 cell lineages in the dormant embryo are destined to the ear. Coe and Neuffer (1978) and Johri and Coe (1983) found evidence for about 2 cell lineages in the ear and 4 lineages in the tassel. The data from the study of Johri and Coe (1983) indicate that the tassel cells in the dormant seed are isolated from the rest of the plant body (although this may be strain- or condition-dependent). They demonstrate that the ear branches are formed from a subset of the cell lineages that form the plant body (reinforcing that no "germ line" exists), and they confirm that stem units consist of a leaf atop an internode with an ear primordium at its lower end, as proposed by Sharman (1942) on morphological grounds, rather than with the ear primordium above the leaf insertion. Different strains may very well differ in the number of cells with particular destinies, or in their concert of contributions to form, but likely not in the stem unit strategy.

X-ray induced sectors of loss of dominant *Yg2* in seeds heterozygous for this marker (Stein and Steffensen, 1959a,b) have permitted discrimination among the preformed vs. the predetermined vs. the undetermined leaves in the dormant embryo, and identification of differential lateral and horizontal divisions and growth depending upon cell positions in the leaf. Similar sectors induced in marked heterozygotes for *yg2* or for *wd* provide the data by which Steffensen (1968) developed a detailed reconstruction of the anatomy and elaboration of the shoot apex in defining leaves. Poethig (1984) has fully defined the development of the leaf, specifically by determining the anatomical stage at which sectors were induced, and has shown that the strategy of leaf development involves (i) contributions from a large group of cells in several tissue layers in the shoot apex, (ii) establishment of "founder" cells with a limited and characteristic destiny for the leaf lamina (rather than by "stem" cells), and (iii) a systematic program of spatial and temporal variation in the rate, directions, and duration of cell divisions that leads to the formed shapes of the leaf.

In the early divisions of the zygote, Steffensen (1968) gave evidence for occurrence of bilaterally symmetrical chimeras following induction at the 2d or 3d division. Poethig et al. (1986) determined further that other types of chimeras, offset from bilaterally symmetrical form, are also common, showing that these cell divisions are not regimented and, more particularly, that the shoot apex is defined in a group of cells whose body is not subdivided by clonal boundaries at that point in development.

Clonal sectors occurring during development of the ear can also be recognized from mutational changes of *P-vv* to red pericarp (Emerson, 1914). The striking potential of sister clones of cells developing in contiguity following reciprocal mutational events is shown in the study of twin mutations described and pictured by Brink and Nilan (1952; see Fig. 3–13) and Greenblatt and Brink (1962). Greenblatt (1985) describes the phenotypes and heritability, however, of two kinds of mutational events, from which it is apparent that the pericarp derives from two layers, one of which contributes to the gametogenetic tissue and the other not. Anderson (1923) extended the technical use of ear clonality to seedling traits, planting kernels according to their positions on the ear and generating "ear maps" of the sectorial distribution of a cytoplasmically varying chlorophyll trait, showing both the contiguity of lineages from which the kernels derive and the form of chimeral sectors, with a cytoplasmically inherited variant. In the developing plant, genetically determined chlorophyll sectoring generates clonal sectors suited for use in morphogenetic analysis.

During development of the endosperm, systematic cell divisions and enlargement (Coe, 1978; McClintock, 1978a) lead to conspicuous clonal events in the outer layer (aleurone tissue) following mutation of *al* to *Al* under the influence of *Dt* (as also in the anther wall, see Rhoades, 1938), and of *R-st* to *R-sc* (Fig. 3–6), among others. Striking figures show-

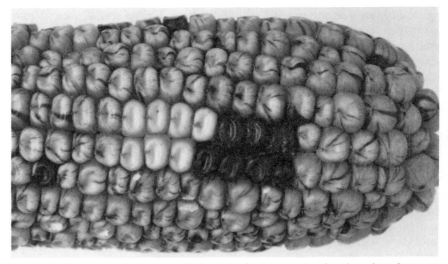

Fig. 3–13. Contiguous sister clones (twin spots) in the ear, showing the mirror-image relationship characteristic of the development of sister cells bearing the reciprocal products of a mutational event at *P-vv*. (From Brink and Nilan, 1952.)

ing the form of elaboration of the inner endosperm as marked by events occurring with mutable *wx* are pictured by McClintock (1965; see Fig. 3–14) and Peterson (1974).

3–3.4 Mutation Studies

Mutation can be defined in the broader sense as a change in some characteristic of a cell or organism that may be transmitted to succeeding generations. Included among mutational changes are effects ranging from changes in whole genomes to changes in a single nucleotide pair in the DNA molecule. This discussion is limited to methods of analysis that involve the gene itself and its relationships with its immediate neighbors on the chromosome. A given study may take any of several approaches, including analysis of spontaneous events or of events induced by mutagenic agents; of events at random loci or at selected loci; of the kind and nature of events or of mutational mechanisms. Methods that may be specific to a particular approach are discussed with that approach, while more general procedures and designs that facilitate identification, categorization, and quantitation of events are described in the latter part of this section.

Stadler (1946) pointed to the value of studies on spontaneous mutation in higher organisms as follows: "The study of spontaneous mutation is laborious at best, but it seems an indispensable preliminary to the interpretation of mutations induced experimentally, and it may be the only approach now open for the study of gene evolution." Much effort had already been and would continue to be spent on studying spontaneous

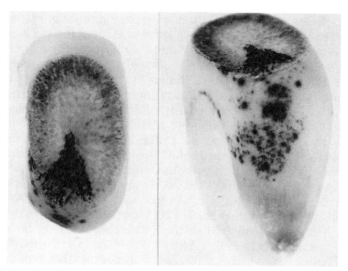

Fig. 3–14. Developmental patterns in the endosperm revealed by mutational changes proliferated into clones. The above kernel, shown in two views, began its growth with inactive
Ac plus *wx-m7* and *a1-m3* (both of which are mutable and can respond to active *Ac*).
During early development *Ac* became active in one cell, resulting in frequent reversions
to *Wx* (dark-staining areas in the inner endosperm) and to *A1* (pigmented spots in the
aleurone layer). The wedge-like clone characterizes the morphogenetic pattern in the
endosperm. (From McClintock, 1965.)

events at random loci, but a more productive approach has been to study
intensively the mutational behavior at a few selected loci. The special
technical suitability of maize for this approach, and deliberate experimental design, are discussed with unique explicitness by Stadler (1946).
The detasseled plot technique (described later) provided a method for
testing large numbers of female gametes in controlled matings with an
acceptable labor cost. Using multiple endosperm characters to provide
adequate tests against contamination, phenocopies, androgenesis, segmental deficiencies, and other sources of error, Stadler (1942) was able
to provide the first accurate measures of spontaneous mutation rates for
a number of genes in the same background. The rates established in this
early work range from 0 in 1.5×10^6 kernels for Wx to 273 in 0.55×10^6 kernels for R (a rate per embryo sac of 492×10^{-6}). Though later
research has identified considerable variation at these loci and has shown
that many events can be attributed to deficiency or to crossing over, these
frequencies did set the stage on which further investigations into mutation
and its causes have been conducted. In particular, the diagnosis of genetic
fine structure, which has revealed compoundness at some loci and intracistron recombination at others, has evolved out of these investigations, as has a substantial part of the remarkable work on transposable
elements; both are discussed in separate sections of this summary.

Artificially induced mutation was first identified through the studies of Stadler (1928) with x-rays. Losses of specific dominant markers were recognized as mosaic endosperms in kernels of recessive stocks that had been pollinated by dominant strains and x-rayed on the ear at or near the time of fertilization (this work, although some months earlier into print, was concurrent with other studies by Stadler demonstrating that heritable mutations were induced at random loci in barley). Irradiation at the fertilization stage is particularly difficult in that it requires either a portable x-ray unit with elaborate shielding, or growth of plants in containers that can be transported to the irradiation equipment. Consequently most irradiations are applied to either dormant seeds or pollen unless the specific purpose compels otherwise. For pollen, x-ray or gamma ray dosages in the range of 1000 to 2000 r are generally applied either to freshly shed pollen samples (e.g., Amano and Smith, 1965; Mottinger, 1970; Pfahler, 1971) or to flowering tassel branch segments, freshly picked, from which pollen is collected as the anthers open on the morning of treatment (e.g., Nuffer, 1957). Pfahler (1967b) has shown that gamma-irradiated pollen grains (up to 5000 r) are fully competitive with untreated ones in achieving fertilization, but that irradiation leads to increasing failure in kernel development (i.e., dominant lethality), with increasing dosages. For dormant dry seeds, dosages are generally applied in the range of 5000 to 30000 r (e.g., Pfahler, 1970); while for seeds soaked 24 h in water or for growing plants, dosages in the range of 1000 to 3000 r are typically suitable (e.g., Stein and Steffensen, 1959a). Although mutagenesis was not a part of the study, House and Nelson (1958) introduced ^{32}P into pollen by injecting a phosphate solution into a well bored in the stem just below the ear-bearing node at the time of first pollen shedding.

Ultraviolet light was demonstrated to be mutagenic by Stadler and Sprague (1936), who also found that shorter wavelengths were more effective, per unit of energy applied, than longer wavelengths. Stadler and Uber (1942) demonstrated that irradiation of pollen from two sides was substantially more effective than from one side, inasmuch as the constituents of the pollen absorb strongly. Because the sperm nuclei are eccentrically placed, more homogeneous treatment results from two-sided than from one-sided irradiation with the same total dose. Treatments accordingly are best done with a two-sided (e.g., Nuffer, 1957) or a tumbling system (e.g. Pfahler, 1973).

Early work with chemical mutagens was limited by the difficulties encountered in attempting to reach the germ cells and in trying to make reliable quantitative tests. Gibson et al. (1950) applied mustard gas vapor to pollen at saturation or diluted through a measuring and mixing apparatus. They found increasing effects with greater exposure times and concentrations. Kreizinger (1960) induced mutations by application of diepoxybutane to flowering tassels, either cut and held in solution to take up the mutagen through the cut ends or supplied with solution by means of a wick in a hole bored in the stalk of the tassel. Neuffer and Ficsor (1963) induced mutations with ethyl methane sulfonate (EMS) solutions introduced into cotton packed around the maturing tassel 3 to 5 d before flowering. Amano and Smith (1965) induced mutations with EMS by holding pre-soaked seeds in solutions or by immersing cut root ends of young seedlings. The problems of quantitation inherent in all of these early methods have been largely overcome through treatments applied to pollen in paraffin oil. Following the finding by Coe (1966a; MNL 40:108) that pollen could be suspended in paraffin oil for extended time periods before pollination, Neuffer (1968), Neuffer and Coe (1978) and Neuffer (1982b) perfected quantitative methods by which EMS or nitro-soguanidine (NG), or potentially any agent, can be applied to pollen. Fresh pollen is mixed with paraffin oil carrying the mutagen in suspension (freshly prepared and thoroughly dispersed by vigorous stirring), stirred intermittently for a measured period, and applied to receptive silks with a small brush. Treatment standards for concentration and exposure time can be established by in vitro germination tests of treated pollen on agar media (Neuffer, 1972; MNL 45:146). For material treated by this method the general mutation rate can be very high; for example, in one study with a control rate of 0.7%, 51% of surviving pollen grains treated with EMS underwent at least one mutation. The frequency with NG was even higher.

Stringent precautions must be taken to avoid contact with mutagens such as EMS and NG by the investigator, or inadvertent contact of others with treated materials or contaminated objects. Especially in oil, these potent mutagens-carcinogens can be particularly dangerous, penetrating, and difficult to sanitize.

Some of the pioneering studies on the nature of radiation-induced mutations have been conducted with corn. Heritable x-ray induced changes in both barley and corn (Stadler, 1930) were initially thought to be changes of the gene from one form to another (gene mutation), but continuing investigation by Stadler and his associates showed that, in corn, x-rays produce only chromosomal aberrations or losses of genetic material. Stadler and Sprague (1936) and Stadler (1939) identified significant differences in the types and frequencies of mutational events produced by ultraviolet light and x-rays. When mature pollen carrying dominant markers is treated and crossed onto a stock carrying recessive markers, x-ray treated material produces ears with many whole-kernel losses and smaller numbers of fractional losses, most of which are larger than 15/16 of the kernel surface. Ultraviolet light, on the other hand, produces a somewhat smaller number of whole-kernel losses and a larger number of fractionals, which distribute around a mean of one-half kernel in size. These differences were inter-preted by Stadler (1939) to indicate that x-rays cause chromosome-type changes while ultraviolet causes more discrete chromatid changes. The very large fractional losses produced by x-rays were suggested by Stadler to represent chromosome breakage events in which the fragment rejoins and regains mitotic distribution after a number of divisions, leading to "recovery spots" in limited portions of the endosperm. In addition, where x-rays produce high frequencies of endosperm and embryo losses, ultraviolet produces only 1/10 as many embryo losses per endosperm loss. This difference may result in part from the different morphogenetic patterns of the two structures, and perhaps in part from differential repair of x-ray and ultraviolet-induced changes in rapidly dividing young endosperm cells vs. the more slowly dividing embryo cells. Stadler and Roman (1948) obtained 415 cases of change of the *A* locus in material exposed to x-rays. Only two of these even approached the properties that would be required to classify them as changes of *A1* to *a1* (i.e., gene mutation), and each of these (*a1-X1* and *a1-X2*), like an obvious deficiency case (*a1-X3*) studied in comparison, involved more than one genetic trait, affected crossing over in the region, had altered transmission, and was inviable as a homozygote. To determine whether or not x-rays and ultraviolet light could change or remove a marker without affecting its close neighbors, Nuffer (1957) treated pollen carrying three closely linked markers (Alpha Beta *Sh2*, all within 0.3 map units) with these two mutagenic agents. Recognition of the critical cases (Alpha *Sh2*) was facilitated by the inclusion of *a-m* in the ear parent and *Dt* in the pollen parent. The absence of a single case of the critical type from x-ray treatment in a population of 8739 kernels, compared with 10 cases in 8888 from ultraviolet, indicates that x-rays do not often produce such discrete changes. With EMS, the limited results of a similar study by Neuffer and Ficsor (1963) indicate that this mutagen can cause discrete losses of Beta alone. Mottinger (1970) identified mutants of *Bz1* following x-ray treatment which, like the *a1-X* mutants of Stadler and Roman (1948), appear to be small deletions affecting more than the one locus. Seeking the equivalent of back mutations, which might be viewed as instances of discrete change, Stadler (1944) attempted to determine whether x-rays produce dominant mutation of *a1*, the recessive that reverts to *A1* in the presence of *Dt* but not in its absence. Stadler made crosses to produce kernels of *a1 a1 A1* and *a1 a1 a1* constitutions (both lacking *Dt*) on the same ears and treated the ears with x-rays 73 to 81 hours after pollination, a time selected to give loss sectors for *A1* of approximately the same size as the colored dots that occur on *a1 Dt* kernels. Treatment with 800 r of x-rays produced *A1 a1 a1* kernels with an average of 14 to 34 loss sectors, while the *a1 a1 a1* kernels from treatments with 800 and 1600 r had not a single colored dot in a population that would have had 900 000 losses of *A*. The same population would have produced 400 000 dots of *a1* to *A1* if *Dt* had been present in three doses. In a similar experiment using highly mutable alleles, *a1-m1* of the *Dt* system and *a1-m1* of the *Spm* system (see the section of transposable elements), Neuffer (1966) found that neither x-rays nor ultraviolet produces changes from *a1-m* to *A1* directly, but that both mutagens induce new *Dt* or *Spm* activity, which can produce in turn the reversions from *a1-m* to *A1*. The occurrence of new transpositional activity is known to result from chromosome breakage. All of the above evidence leads to the conclusion that, in corn, x-rays do not produce gene mutation at any appreciable frequency in comparison with chromosomal aberrations and gene losses. This is not in agreement with findings in other organisms, where the preponderance of evidence indicates that radiation-induced gene mutations are frequent. This difference has not yet been explained. Ultraviolet light, on the other hand, appears to produce discrete changes.

It is of historical interest to note that Stadler (1939) and Stadler and Uber (1942) reported the first genetic experiments that clearly pointed to nucleic acids as the basic genetic material. Pollen carrying dominant markers was subjected to a series of specific wavelengths of ultraviolet light and crossed onto recessive strains. Taking into account the differential absorption of each wavelength by the wall and contents of the pollen grain and the eccentric position of the nuclei, so as to estimate the effectiveness per unit of energy reaching the nucleus, they determined that the most effective wavelengths for producing mutations and losses were those around 254 to 265 nm. Since this action spectrum corresponds with the absorption spectrum for nucleic acids (Fig. 3–15), Stadler and Uber cautiously but correctly stated that "nucleic acid is intimately associated with the function of the genetic material."

Among the more convenient general procedures and methods for study of mutation at selected loci is the detasseled-plot technique developed as a genetically marked system by Stadler (1946). The method usually consists in planting two to four rows of ear stock carrying the dominant alleles of the loci to be studied alternately with one or two rows of pollen stock carrying the recessive alleles, ordinarily in an isolated field. The ear rows are detasseled and the ears are pollinated naturally by the pollen rows, as in the classical method of hybrid corn production. The ears so produced have kernels that are nominally heterozygous for the genes in question and may be examined for recessive mutants. This method has the advantage of producing large numbers of test kernels (populations of the order of 10^6 are feasible) with relatively modest effort.

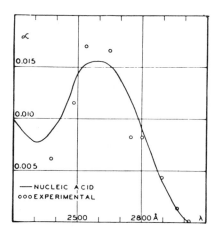

Fig. 3–15. Comparison of the mutagenic effectiveness of a series of wavelengths of ultraviolet light (open circles) with the absorption spectrum of DNA (smooth curve). (From Stadler and Uber, 1942)

Since the female gametes are held in place in regular kernel rows with fixed relationships, it is also possible to evaluate directly problems such as contamination and sectoring.

Quantitation of mutational events by the somatic-sector technique has been used by several investigators, including Steffensen (1968) and Ficsor (1965). It consists in preparing seeds heterozygous for genes expressed in the seedling or growing plant, treating the seeds with a mutagenic agent, growing them, and examining for mutant sectors. The size of a sector depends on the stage at which the treatment becomes effective and the extent of growth following mutation. The population tested depends on the number of primordial cells present at the time of treatment. The advantages of this method are that experiments are quickly and easily conducted once the seeds are produced, and that large populations of cells are tested in moderate-scale studies. One disadvantage is that progeny tests of the sectors are unobtainable except where they occur in the germ line; even then, a sector may include multiple copies of a single mutational event rather than independently arising mutations.

An extensively used method for studying mutation at random loci in species with perfect flowers involves seed treatment. It involves treating mature seeds with a mutagenic agent, growing an M1 (first generation from treatment), selfing or outcrossing the M1 plants, then planting and selfing an M2 to be classified in M3 for the segregation of recessive mutants. The advantage of this method is the ease of the initial treatment and the simplicity of subsequent operations. However, it has two major disadvantages for corn: first, it requires extensive testing of the M2 to save and identify individual mutants, and second, confusion arises about individual mutant identities and about frequencies because treatment gives rise to sectors that may transmit multiple copies of each mutational event. The relative efficiency of different procedures for the extraction of mutational events following seed treatment is considered in the latter part of this section.

Truly large and decisive populations can be obtained by use of pollen as the treated stage. By counting the pollen in individual anthers and multiplying by the number of anthers in a tassel, we have estimated that a modest-sized tassel will generate 15×10^6 pollen grains. With proper treatment and conservative distribution, the pollen from a few tassels can produce very large numbers of offspring. Pollen has additional advantages: (i) The gametophyte is a small, self-contained, and uniform but easily invaded structure; (ii) The three nuclei mutate independently, so that one sperm may be affected without impairing the function of the other or of the tube nucleus, thus permitting the transmission of quite deleterious mutants; (iii) Contaminations and spontaneous endosperm mutations that occur prior to the treatment time can be recognized because they will affect all three nuclei and will be transmitted as cases having a genetically corresponding endosperm and embryo, while mutations induced in mature pollen will appear in either the endosperm or the embryo, but not in both; (iv) Each kernel arising from treated pollen is potentially heterozygous for a unique induced mutant that can be expressed immediately (if dominant) or in the progeny of the M1 (if recessive). Thus when mature pollen carrying dominant endosperm markers is treated with a mutagenic agent and crossed on ears carrying recessive alleles for the same markers, losses or mutations will be expressed immediately in the endosperm; the embryo will carry similar but independent events that cannot be seen until the next generation. The initial endosperm events will include primarily events seen as whole kernel mutants having the recessive phenotype and secondary events expressed as sectors of recessive phenotype. The numbers, sizes, and characteristics of these sectors have been effectively used to analyze the actions of such treatments as x-rays and ultraviolet light (Stadler, 1939; Nuffer, 1957), chromosome breakage (McClintock, 1941), and chemical mutagens (Neuffer and Ficsor, 1963; Neuffer, 1978; Neuffer and Sheridan, 1980).

One important factor in the design of mutation experiments that is often overlooked or misinterpreted is the specific numerical efficiency of the method used. This can best be seen by comparing the consequences of different handling methods, including seed vs. pollen treatments, sample sizes, and selfing vs. crossing (Table 3–9).

In the mature seed there are two to four primordial cells that will develop into the male gametes and two to four that will develop into the female gametes, and different primordial cells are involved (Coe and Neuffer, 1978; Johri and Coe, 1983). Thus, mutations in the two types of gametes will not be concordant. Treatments applied at the seed stage may affect any one of the primordial cells independently and produce a sector generating half normal and half mutant gametes. If we assume four primordial cells and non-concordance, the population treated will be 16 genomes (4 × 2 for the ear and the same for the tassel) times the number of seeds treated. For those mutants having no selective effects, 1/16 of the gametes from an M1 plant undergoing a mutational event will carry the mutant (Neuffer, 1982b). If one treats 100 kernels, the resulting M1 plants will carry 1600 treated genomes, 800 that will be represented in eggs and 800 in pollen. If the treatment procedure produces mutants in 50% of the genomes (a frequency somewhat higher than is characteristically found for treatment at the seed stage, but used here in order to make equivalent comparisons with pollen treatment), then 800 mutants will have been produced. Crossing the M1 plants as female by a standard strain will produce 100 ears that will preserve half (400) of the mutants. The frequency with which the gametes and kernels will carry a particular mutant will be one in eight. For the recessive mutants, a self-fertilization will be required to express them. According to Hanson (1959), a sample of 23 individuals is required in order to have 95% certainty of obtaining one individual occurring at a frequency of one in eight. Therefore, to detect 95% (380) of the 400 mutants in the 100 ears, selfed progeny from 23 kernels from each ear will be required, a total of 2300 plants to be

Table 3–9. Comparison of the efficiency of different methods of treatment and handling for mutagenesis.

Treatment and handling	M1 Plants	Treated genomes	No. mutants at 50% effectiveness	M2 Selfed‡	Mutants detected	Plants grown M1 + M2	Efficiency (mutants per plant)
Seed							
M1 crossed							
Large M2	100	1600†	400	2300	380	2400	0.16
M1 selfed							
Large M2							
Concordance	100	800	400	2300	380	2400	0.16
Nonconcordance	100	1600	800	2300	760	2400	0.33
M1 selfed							
Minimal M2							
Concordance	1000	8000	4000	1000§	1000	2000	0.50
Nonconcordance	1000	16000	8000	1000¶	1000	2000	0.50
Pollen							
M1 selfed	2000	2000	1000	--	1000	2000	0.50

† Assuming four nonconcordant primordial cells each for the tassel and ear.
‡ Number required to detect 95% of mutants.
§ Samples 1000 genomes twice.
¶ Samples 2000 genomes once.

selfed. Thus an input of 2400 plants (100 M1 plus 2300 M2) will produce 380 mutants, an efficiency of 0.16 mutant/cultured plant.

Selfing the M1 plants is more efficient than crossing them by a standard strain. Assuming concordance (which is not the case for maize), again 23 M2 individuals from each progeny (2300 M2 plants), would be required to detect 380 mutants (efficiency 0.16). With nonconcordance (the true situation), a self will sample from each lineage of the four-celled primordial sets of the ear and the tassel for a total of 1600 treated genomes and 800 mutants. Because each kernel tests two genomes one in eight will carry the mutant and 2300 individuals will be required to detect 760 (95%) of the mutants, resulting in an efficiency of 0.33, which is double the value for concordance. The tendency to try to save all of the mutants by taking a very large sample from the M2 ears is counterproductive; for example, a sample of 35 kernels (total 3600 plants) would be required to save 99% (792) of the mutants (efficiency 0.22). An additional problem arises from maximal sampling, namely the duplication and confounding of mutants. A single mutant event in a primordial cell will be duplicated many times through the cell divisions before gamete formation, and many copies of the same mutant will be produced. For this reason, only one mutant of a particular type can be accepted in the progeny of each M1 plant as a unique mutant. This is of considerable consequence, inasmuch as recessive alleles at many loci have similar, confoundable phenotypes.

A more efficient sampling method, developed by Rédei (1974, 1984), is to treat large numbers of seeds and grow a large M1 and then take a minimal sample from each progeny for the M2 to be selfed. For corn the minimal sample would consist of a single seed from each M1 ear. Following previous assumptions (including non-correspondence), treatment of 1000 seeds will affect 16 000 genomes and produce 1000 plants that will carry 8000 mutants. Planting one seed from each M1 will test 2000 gametes and save 1000 of the mutants. In terms of total input, an investment of 2000 selfed plants (1000 M1 and 1000 M2) will yield 1000 mutants for an efficiency of 0.50. Furthermore, since only one sample of two gametes is taken from each M1 plant the problem of duplicate copies is eliminated. With nonconcordance there are two independent samples with no chance of homozygosity for the single event.

An equally efficient approach with some additional advantages over that just presented is to treat pollen; an investment of less than 100 plants for treatment plus a test by selfing of 2000 M1 plants will produce 1000 mutants for an efficiency of 0.48 (from 100 treated plus 2000 M1). Pollen treatment has several advantages: (i) Each mutant seen is an independent event, so that except for normal attrition all mutants produced are saved, allowing easy comparison of mutation rates and of relative frequencies of different mutant types; (ii) Variations among different lines or between the sexes in primordial cell number are not a concern in the estimation and comparison of mutation rates; (iii) Dominant mutants are easily recognized as such and are ready for immediate testing.

The potential for production of mutants on a large scale for biological and agronomic purposes has been very attractive. However, for maize there has been less need because of the great amount of natural variability in this naturally cross-fertilizing species. The following is a brief evaluation of mutagenic agents currently available. The agents showing some use are ionizing and non-ionizing radiation, somaclonal variations, transposable elements, and chemical mutagens.

Because ionizing radiations generally produce mostly chromosome breaks and deletions in maize their usefulness has been largely as a tool for chromosome restructuring. Much of the accumulated knowledge about the genetics of maize and other species has come from experiments using induced deficiencies and duplications, reciprocal translocations, B-A translocations, and other chromosome aberrations in genetic analysis. Non-ionizing radiation (mostly ultraviolet) has had little use, largely because of the difficulty of application, except for Stadler and Uber's (1942) identification of the genetic substance as nucleic acid through correlation of mutational action spectra and absorption spectra. Somaclonal variation (mutants arising in the progeny of plants regenerated from tissue culture) has only begun to be studied (Zehr et al., 1987). Much of the research in this area is being conducted in the private sector and has not yet appeared in the published literature. Transposable elements, described in another section, are capable of moving about in the genome and causing mutational changes, and have been employed in restructuring genetic information and producing recessive mutants. Dominant mutants, which are most useful for agronomic purposes, are not common from transposable element mutagenesis.

Several chemicals produce mutational changes when applied to the pollen or to kernels. The most effective mutagen, ethyl methane sulfonate (EMS), when used in paraffin oil to treat pollen, has been very effective in producing a wide spectrum of genetic changes in large numbers, including both recessive and dominant mutants and chromosome breaks (Neuffer, 1978; 1982b). In these experiments mutations of most conceivable loci for which workable screening methods were devised and attempted were found. The frequency of recessive mutants excluding chromosome breaks and deficiencies was 51% of treated gametes, and of dominants 0.25%. The average frequency of recessive mutants per locus was as high as 1 in 800. Mutants at known loci as well as many new loci were found. New loci included classes that provided access to new knowledge about the biology of maize. These included the *hcf* mutants involved in electron transport and related functions of photosynthesis (Miles et al., 1985); the *Les* mutants simulating disease symptoms (Neuffer and Calvert, 1975; Hoisington et al., 1982; Neuffer et al., 1986a); the *dek* mutants involved in kernel and embryo development (Neuffer et al., 1986a); and groups of mutants regulating meiosis (Nel and Neuffer, MNL 52:116-118, 1978), altering thylakoid differentiation (Polacco, et al., 1985), plastid differentiation (Hopkins et al., 1980a, b), auxotrophy (Neuffer and

Sheridan, 1980), and plant morphology (Freeling and Hake, 1985; Bird and Neuffer, 1985). Of special significance are the dominants, of which there are now 108. Thirty-six of these have been located to 9 of the 10 chromosomes. A comparison of this number with the 42 reported in *Mutants of Maize* (Neuffer et al., 1968) indicates the effectiveness of chemical mutagens.

Chemical mutagenesis is a useful tool for genetic and plant breeding research under the following considerations: (i) Production of desirable recessive mutants in an elite inbred line (e.g., *y1* or *o2* versions of existing lines). This can be accomplished by treatment to produce 3000 to 5000 M1 plants among which should appear three to five independent mutants for the desired trait. The new mutant in each case may be stabilized with one outcross to the original line followed by a self. Other mutants co-incidentally induced in the new inbred will be eliminated by standard stock multiplication practice. (ii) Removal of a dominant undesirable trait (e.g., *B* or *R*) from an elite inbred. This can be accomplished as in (i) above. (iii) Production of desirable dominant traits such as earliness, disease resistance, stress tolerance, etc. This can be accomplished by producing a large treated M1 and screening for the desired trait. These types will appear in the M1 as heterozygotes and may be stabilized free of coincident deleterious recessive mutants just as for recessive mutants. The chief difficulty with searching for dominant mutants is their relatively low frequency (averaging 0.5×10^{-5}, ranging from 1×10^{-3} to $< 1 \times 10^{-6}$). In the average case an M1 of 200 000 plants would be required for a 50% chance of getting one mutant. Producing 3000 selfed M1 ears and screening them for recessive mutants is a modest task. Producing 200 000-plus M1 seedlings and screening them for disease resistance or herbicide tolerance is a sizable task, and screening such an M1 for mature plant traits becomes a tremendous task.

3–3.5   Analysis of Genetic Fine Structure

The occurrence of high rates of "mutation" in homozygous plants engendered an early interest in detailed structural analysis at *A1* and *R*, which were soon found to be structurally compound; a few other loci have been explored at the level of genetic fine structure either in their own right genetically or out of morphological, evolutionary, or biochemical interest, and are simple in structure.

Although cytological proof is lacking and molecular data are just under development at this writing, the genetic evidence at both *A1* and *R* points overwhelmingly to the presence of varying numbers of segments (tandem repeats) that are related but distinguishable in function and are capable of synapsis and crossing over inter se. The primary observations supporting this compoundness are : (i) The occurrence of "mutational" changes in stages (inferring that two or more units are "mutating" independently); (ii) The association of events in homozygotes with recombination between flanking markers (inferring that synapsis and crossing over are occurring between differentiated components); and (iii) The demonstrable experimental reconstruction of compound forms. However, compound structure should not necessarily be assumed for a locus that has not been studied with the same thoroughness; several other loci that have been studied are composed of single functional units (cistrons), and undergo recombination between sites within the cistron. The operations and devices that have been employed thus far in studies of genetic fine structure include some that are common to any such study and some that are cunningly unique.

Laughnan (1949) pointed out that stepwise events at the *A1* locus, in which frequent changes occur from *A1-b* (strong color) to *A1-d* (dilute) and from *A1-d* to *a1* (colorless), but not from *A1-b* directly to *a1*, suggest that *A1-b* consists of two independently changing units differing in functional capacity. Similar patterns of events at the *R* locus (Stadler, 1951), changes from *R-r* to *R-g* or *r-r* but not directly to *r-g* (Fig. 3–8), bear the same implications. For *A1-b* Laughnan designated two components, *Alpha* and *Beta*; Stadler designated (P) and (S) components for *R-r*. Following development of a theoretical set of expectations, Emmerling (1958) was able to distinguish experimentally two classes of *R-g* derivatives from *R-r*, the first able to yield colorless (*r-g*) by crossing over in heterozygotes with *R-r* [inferring that synapsis could occur between an inactive plant color unit (p) in *R-g* and the (S) unit of *R-r*], and the second unable to yield such derivatives [inferring that no remnant plant color element synaptically homologous to (S) is present]. Laughnan (1961b) tested in a similar way for the presence of a synaptically effective but functionally inactive unit (*Beta-null*) in *A1-d* and found no evidence for it. Ashman (1965) found stepwise events involving *R-st*, for which the elements (Sc), (I-R), and (Nc) have been designated (Kermicle, 1974), and Sastry (1970) has postulated on similar grounds that *R-ch* alleles contain four or more independently mutating components.

Marking of the region under study to reveal association of "mutational" events with recombination of external markers has been a standard practice in each effective study of fine structure. Recombination occurring largely or entirely in a single direction is found for *A1-d* events from *A1-b/a1* (Laughnan, 1949) and *A1-b/A1-b:P* (Laughnan, 1955); for *r-r* events from *R-r/R-g* (Stadler and Nuffer, 1953); for *Wx* events from *wx-90/wx-C* (Nelson, 1962, 1968); for *r-g*, *r-nc* (near colorless) and compound events from *R-st/R-r* (Ashman, 1965); and for *Gl1* events from heteroallelic (*gl1-a/gl1-b*) hybrids (Salamini and Lorenzoni, 1970). Recombination in either direction is associated with *tu-d* and *tu-l* events from *Tu/tu* (Mangelsdorf and Galinat, 1964). As expected for a compound locus, recombination in either direction is associated with events arising in homozygotes of *R-r* (Stadler and Emmerling, 1956). From the proportion of *r-r* to *R-g* events arising by crossing over in *R-r/R-r*, Dooner and Kermicle (1971) have derived quantifications of the relative position of the sites differentiating (P) from (S) in their respective duplicated segments, of the frequency of oblique synapsis, and of the genetic length of the duplications. Recombination between insertion sites for *Ds* in the *R* locus (Kermicle, 1980) has suggested that the locus contains a tissue-specific component and a general, coding component. Evidence for displaced duplications of *R* components has been obtained for *Lc* (Dooner and Kermicle, 1976; Dooner, 1979b) and for *Mst* (Williams et al., 1984), based on deletions that arise from recombination. Dooner (1986) has carried out an extensive study of the *bz1* locus by recombinational analysis, including alleles with effects on stability and activity of the enzyme coded by this locus.

Nonrecombinant events from compound loci with tandem repeats are at least as informative as recombinant events, and can support the existence of a tandem repeat. Laughnan (1952, 1961a) determined not only that some *A1-d* events arise without crossing over from *A1-b/a1* but, further, that *A1-d* events arise from *A1-b* heterozygous with *a1* carried in an inversion, or even from hemizygous *A1-b*, in each case at a higher frequency than from *A1-b/a1*, which is unexpected. These observations among others have suggested (Laughnan, 1961b) the occurrence of auto-association (synapsis of tandem repeats within the same strand) and crossing over, to yield losses or gains in numbers of units, as the basis for "noncrossover" events at *A1*. The occurrence of a class of non-crossover *R-g* events, in which no synaptic unit homologous to (S) seems to be present,, may very well be due to the same mechanism (Emmerling, 1958). Kermicle (1970a) reports higher than normal frequencies of *R-sc* events from *R-st* hemizygotes. Bianchi and Tomassini (1965) studied the frequency of *Wx* events in plants hemizygous for *wx* and found a barely significant increase in events, which appear to include substantial numbers of premeiotic events that may spuriously infer auto-association.

Experimental construction or reconstruction of compounds by prediction is among the more impressive evidences supporting the existence of compoundness. Occurrence of a new compound with the properties of both the *Alpha* component and *a1* (with response to *Dt*) was found by Laughnan (1952) to be associated with crossing over in *A1-b/a1* hybrids. The reconstruction of a synthetic *A1-b* from *Alpha a1* by *Dt*-induced mutation of *a1* to *A1*, in which *A1* is the equivalent of *Beta*, produced a compound that once again yielded *Alpha* products in association with crossing over (Laughnan, 1961b). Mangelsdorf and Galinat (1964) reconstructed *Tu* from its products, *tu-d* and *tu-l*. Coe (1964) attempted unsuccessfully to construct compounds with *C1-I* and *C1*, and suggested that either compoundness or synaptic homology of compound parts was lacking. Reconstruction of *R-st* from its products was predicted and verified by Ashman (1970). A new compound in which the mutability element (I-R), originally in *R-st* in cis relationship with a seed color component, becomes associated with a plant color component and causes it to become mutable, has been shown to arise in association with crossing over (Kermicle, 1974). Construction through crossing over of a new compound, *R-nj:st*, that in turn yields predicted products by crossing over (Kermicle, 1970a, 1974) is a well-developed example of construction and reconstruction of a compound with differential repeated elements.

Comparative rates of events in themselves provide data by which the order of sites and the relative distances between them can be specified, a technique that has been applied especially to single-cistron loci, in which recombination frequency may be low but for which techniques can be specially derived to observe large numbers. At the *Wx* locus, Nelson (1959, 1962, 1968) mapped 24 alleles by determining whether *Wx* products arising from heteroallelic hybrids (*wx-a/wx-b*) exceed those arising from homoallelic constitutions; the data by which this mapping could be done were obtained by observations in large populations of pollen grains. Wessler and Varagona (1985) have characterized in molecular terms the deletions and insertions that have occurred at the *Wx* locus and have related them to the map of Nelson. Pollen data have also been used to map five alleles at the *ae* locus (Moore and Creech, 1972).

Association of events with the stage of meiosis is one of the major clues to recombinational rather than mutational causes. Laughnan (1952) has reasoned that the occurrence of noncrossover *A1-d* events singly rather than in clusters indicates a meiotic process rather than a mutational one. Emmerling (1958) reported one large sector of *r-r* on an ear of *R-r/R-r*, but the vast majority of events at the *R* locus are isolated (i.e., meiotic). In studies of the distributions of events in tassels of homozygous and hemizygous *wx* plants, Bianchi and Tomassini (1965) found clustering, indicating that the events in these constitutions frequently arise through mutation. To study the fine structure of the mutable allele *R-st*, Kermicle (1970a) concentrated on events influenced by crossing over by limiting consideration to events occurring in or near the meiotic phase.

ACKNOWLEDGMENT

This summary contains much material that depends on the sharing of information by "Cooperators" in the tradition of research workers in maize genetics, and we thank our colleagues for their continuing generosity. The manuscript was enhanced by critiques from Jack B. Beckett, Larry L. Darrah, and William F. Sheridan. Shirley Kowalewski skillfully refined and produced the copy. Timnit Ghebreyesus programmed and carried out the computer file processing that was needed. This work is a product of cooperative research between USDA-ARS and the Missouri Agricultural Experiment Station. Journal series No. 10437.

REFERENCES

Abbott, A. G., and C. M. R. Fauron. 1986. Structural alterations in a transcribed region of the T type cytoplasmic male sterile maize mitochondrial genome. Curr. Genet. 10:777–783.

Albertsen, M. C., and R. L. Phillips. 1981. Developmental cytology of 13 genetic male sterile loci in maize. Can. J. Genet. Cytol. 23:195–208.

Alexander, W. L., and H. Z. Cross. 1983. Grain-fill characteristics of early maize strains selected for variable *R-nj* expression. Euphytica 32:839–843.

Allard, R. W. 1956. Formulas and tables to facilitate the calculation of recombination values in heredity. Hilgardia 24:235–278.

Alleman, M., and M. Freeling. 1986. The *Mu* transposable elements of maize: evidence for transposition and copy number regulation during development. Genetics 112:107–119.

Amano, E., and H. H. Smith. 1965. Mutations induced by ethyl methanesulfonate in maize. Mutat. Res. 2:344–351.

Anderson, E. G. 1923. Maternal inheritance of chlorophyll in maize. Bot. Gaz. 76:411–418.

––––. 1924. Pericarp studies in maize. II. The allelomorphism of a series of factors for pericarp colors. Genetics 9:442–453.

––––. 1956. The application of chromosomal techniques to maize improvement. Brookhaven Symp. Biol. 9:23–36.

––––, A. E. Longley, C. H. Li, and K. L. Retherford. 1949. Hereditary effects produced in maize by radiations from the Bikini atomic bomb. I. Studies on seedlings and pollen of the exposed generation. Genetics 34:639–646.

Anderson, I. C., and D. S. Robertson. 1960. Role of carotenoids in protecting chlorophyll from photodestruction. Plant Physiol. 35:531–534.

Ashman, R. B. 1960. Stippled aleurone in maize. Genetics 45:19–34.

––––. 1965. Mutants from maize plants heterozygous R^r R^{st} and their association with crossing over. Genetics 51:305–312.

––––. 1970. The compound structure of the R^{st} allele in maize. Genetics 64:239–245.

Bachmann, M. D., D. S. Robertson, and C. C. Bowen. 1969. Thylakoid anomalies in relation to grana structure in pigment-deficient mutants of *Zea mays*. J. Ultrastruct. Res. 28:435–451.

––––, ––––, ––––, and I. C. Anderson. 1967. Chloroplast development in pigment deficient mutants of maize. I. Structural anomalies in plastids of allelic mutants at the w_3 locus. J. Ultrastruct. Res. 21:41–60.

––––, ––––, ––––, ––––. 1973. Chloroplast ultrastructure in pigment-deficient mutants of *Zea mays* under reduced light. J. Ultrastruct. Res. 45:384–406.

Barclay, P. C., and R. A. Brink. 1954. The relation between modulator and activator in maize. Proc. Natl. Acad. Sci. USA 40:1118–1126.

Barkan, A., D. Miles, and W. C. Taylor. 1986. Chloroplast gene expression in nuclear, photosynthetic mutants of maize. EMBO J. 5:1421–1427.

Barnabas, B. 1985. Effect of water loss on germination ability of maize (*Zea mays* L.) pollen. Ann. Bot. 55:201–204.

––––, P. F. Fransz, and J. H. N. Schel. 1987. Ultrastructural studies on pollen embryogenesis in maize (*Zea mays* L.). Plant Cell Rep. 6:212–215.

––––, and E. Rajki. 1976. Storage of maize (*Zea mays* L.) pollen at–196°C in liquid nitrogen. Euphytica 25:747–752.

––––, and ––––. 1981. Fertility of deep-frozen maize (*Zea mays* L.) pollen. Ann. Bot. 48:861–864.

Bazzaz, M. B. 1981. New chlorophyll chromophores isolated from a chlorophyll-deficient mutant of maize. Photobiochem. Photobiophys. 2:199–207.

Beadle, G. W. 1932. Genes in maize for pollen sterility. Genetics 17:413–431.

Beck, D. L., G. M. Dunn, D. G. Routley, and J. S. Bowman. 1983. Biochemical basis of resistance in corn to the corn leaf aphid. Crop Sci. 23:995–998.

Beckett, J. B. 1966. Inheritance of partial male fertility in maize in the presence of Texas sterile cytoplasm. Crop Sci. 6:183–184.

––––. 1971. Classification of male-sterile cytoplasms in maize (*Zea mays* L.). Crop Sci. 11:724–727.

––––. 1978. B-A translocations in maize. I. Use in locating genes by chromosome arms. J. Hered. 69:27–36.

––––. 1988. Cytogenetic, genetic and breeding applications of B-A translocations in maize. *In* T. Tsuchiya and P. K. Gupta (ed.) Chromosome engineering in plants. (In press).

Beckman, L., J. G. Scandalios, and J. L. Brewbaker. 1964. Catalase hybrid enzymes in maize. Science 146:1174–1175.

Bell, W. D., L. Bogorad, and W. J. McIlrath. 1958. Response of the yellow-stripe maize mutants (*ys₁*) to ferrous and ferric iron. Bot. Gaz. 120:36–39.

Bennetzen, J. L. 1985. The regulation of *Mutator* function and *Mu1* transposition. p. 343–353. *In* M. Freeling (ed.) (which see).

Bergquist, R. R. 1981. Transfer from *Tripsacum dactyloides* to corn of a major gene locus conditioning resistance to *Puccinia sorghi*. Phytopathology 71:518–520.

Bianchi, A., G. Bianchi, P. Avato, and F. Salamini. 1985. Biosynthetic pathways of epicuticular wax of maize ás assessed by mutation, light, plant age and inhibitor studies. Maydica 30:179–198.

————, and G. Marchesi. 1960. The surface of the leaf in normal and glossy maize seedlings. Z. Vererbungsl. 91:214–219.

————, M. R. Parlavecchio, and F. Restaino. 1969. Behaviour and linkage relationship of gametophyte factors in chromosome 9 of maize. Genet. Agrar. 22:345–361.

————, and C. Tomassini. 1965. Reversion frequency of *waxy* pollen type in normal and hypoploid maize plants. Mutat. Res. 2:352–365.

Birchler, J. A. 1979. A study of enzyme activities in a dosage series of the long arm of chromosome one in maize. Genetics 92:1211–1229.

————. 1981. The genetic basis of dosage compensation of alcohol dehydrogenase-1 in maize. Genetics 97:625–637.

————. 1983. Chromosome manipulation in maize. p. 380–403. *In* M. S. Swaminathan et al. (ed.) Cytogenetics of crop plants. Macmillan, New Delhi.

————, and K. J. Newton. 1981. Modulation of protein levels in chromosomal dosage series of maize: The biochemical basis of aneuploid syndromes. Genetics 99:247–266.

Bird, R. M., and M. G. Neuffer. 1985. Odd new dominant mutations affecting the development of the maize leaf. p. 818–822 *In* M. Freeling (ed.) (which see).

Boyer, C. D., and J. C. Shannon. 1983. The use of endosperm genes for sweet corn improvement. Plant Breeding Rev. 1:139–161.

Brakke, M. K. 1984. Mutations, the Aberrant Ratio phenomenon, and virus infection of maize. Annu. Rev. Phytopathol. 22:77–94.

————, R. G. Samson, and W. A. Compton. 1981. Recessive alleles found at *R* and *C* loci in maize stocks showing aberrant ratio at the *A* locus. Genetics 99:481–485.

Bray, R. A., and R. A. Brink. 1966. Mutation and paramutation at the *R* locus in maize. Genetics 54:137–149.

Brettell, R. I. S., and E. Thomas. 1980. Reversion of Texas male-sterile cytoplasm maize in culture to give fertile, T-toxin resistant plants. Theor. Appl. Genet. 58:55–58.

Brewbaker, J. L. 1974. Continuous genetic conversions and breeding of corn in a neutral environment. Proc. Corn Sorghum Res. Conf. 29:118–133.

————, and F. Aquilizan. 1965. Genetics of resistance in maize to a mosaic-stripe virus transmitted by *Peregrinus maidis*. Crop Sci. 5:412–415.

Brink, R. A. 1956. A genetic change associated with the *R* locus in maize which is directed and potentially reversible. Genetics 41:872–889.

————. 1958. Paramutation at the *R* locus in maize. Cold Spring Harbor Symp. Quant. Biol. 23:379–391.

————. 1973. Paramutation. Annu. Rev. Genet. 7:129–152.

————. 1984. Maize endosperm mutants affecting soluble carbohydrate content as potential additives in preparing silage from high protein forages. Maydica 29:265–286.

————, and I. M. Greenblatt. 1954. Diffuse, a pattern gene in *Zea mays*. J. Hered. 45:46–50.

————, and J. H. MacGillivray. 1924. Segregation for the waxy character in maize pollen and differential development of the male gametophyte. Am. J. Bot. 11:465–469.

————, and R. A. Nilan. 1952. The relation between light variegated and medium variegated pericarp in maize. Genetics 37:519–544.

Brown, A. H. D. 1971. Isozyme variation under selection in *Zea mays*. Nature 232:570–571.

Buchert, J. G. 1961. The stage of the genome-plasmon interaction in the restoration of fertility to cytoplasmically pollen-sterile maize. Proc. Natl. Acad. Sci. USA 47:1436–1440.

Burnette, D. C., and D. G. White. 1985. Inheritance of resistance to *Bipolaris maydis* Race O in crosses derived from nine resistant inbred lines of maize. Phytopathology 75:1195–1200.

Burnham, C. R. 1936. Differential fertilization in the *Bt-Pr* linkage group of maize. J. Am. Soc. Agron. 28:968–975.

————. 1966. Cytogenetics in plant improvement. p. 139–187 *In* K. J. Frey (ed.) Plant breeding. Iowa State Univ. Press, Ames.

Burr, B., and F. A. Burr. 1985. Toward a molecular characterization of multiple factor inheritance. p. 277–284. *In* M. Zaitlin, P. Day, A. Hollaender (ed.) Biotechnology in plant science, Academic Press, New York.

––––, S. V. Evola, F. A. Burr, and J. S. Beckman. 1983. The application of restriction fragment length polymorphism to plant breeding. p. 45–58. *In* J. K. Setlow and A. Hollaender (ed.) Genetic engineering principles and methods, Vol. 5. Plenum, New York.

Calub, A. G., B. J. Long, and G. M. Dunn. 1974. Production of inhibitory compounds in corn inbreds with monogenic and multigenic resistance to *Helminthosporium turcicum*. Crop Sci. 14:303–304.

Chandler, V. L., and V. Walbot. 1986. DNA modification of a maize transposable element correlates with loss of activity. Proc. Natl. Acad. Sci. USA 83:1767–1771.

Chen, Shu-Mei Hsu. 1973. Anthocyanins and their control by the *C* locus in maize. Ph.D. diss. Univ. Missouri, Columbia (Diss. Abstr. 35(2):883-B).

––––, and E. H. Coe, Jr. 1977. Control of anthocyanin synthesis by the *C* locus in maize. Biochem. Genet. 15:333–346.

Cheng, P. C., R. I. Greyson, and D. B. Walden. 1979. Comparison of anther development in genic male-sterile (*ms10*) and in male-fertile corn (*Zea mays*) from light microscopy and scanning electron microscopy. Can. J. Bot. 57:578–596.

Chollet, R., and W. L. Ogren. 1972. Greening in a virescent mutant of maize. II. Enzyme studies. Z. Pflanzenphysiol. 68:45–54.

––––, and D. J. Paolillo, Jr. 1972. Greening in a virescent mutant of maize. I. Pigment, ultrastructural, and gas exchange studies. Z. Pflanzenphysiol. 68:30–44.

Chourey, P. S. 1971. Interallelic complementation at the *Sh₁* locus in maize. Genetics 68:435–442.

––––. 1981. Genetic control of sucrose synthetase in maize endosperm. Mol. Gen. Genet. 184:372–376.

––––, M. D. Latham, and P. E. Still. 1986. Expression of two sucrose synthetase genes in endosperm and seedling cells of maize: evidence of tissue specific polymerization of protomers. Mol. Gen. Genet. 203:251–255.

––––, and O. E. Nelson. 1976. The enzymatic deficiency conditioned by the *shrunken-1* mutations in maize. Biochem. Genet. 14:1041–1055.

Clark, F. J. 1940. Cytogenetic studies of divergent meiotic spindle formation in *Zea mays*. Am. J. Bot. 27:547–559.

Clark, J. K., and W. F. Sheridan. 1986. Developmental profiles of the maize embryo-lethal mutants *dek22* and *dek23*. J. Hered. 77:83–92.

Clark, R. B., L. O. Tiffin, and J. C. Brown. 1973. Organic acids and iron translocation in maize genotypes. Plant Physiol. 52:147–150.

Coe, E. H., Jr. 1955. Anthocyanin synthesis in maize, the interaction of *A2* and *Pr* in leuco-anthocyanin accumulation. Genetics 40:568.

––––. 1957. Anthocyanin synthesis in maize—A gene sequence construction. Am. Nat. 91:381–385.

––––. 1959. A regular and continuing conversion-type phenomenon at the *B* locus in maize. Proc. Natl. Acad. Sci. USA 45:828–832.

––––. 1964. Compound versus bifunctional nature of the *C* locus in maize. Genetics 50:571–578.

––––. 1966a. Liquid media suitable for suspending maize pollen before pollination. Proc. Missouri Acad. Sci. 3:7–8.

––––. 1966b. The properties, origin, and mechanism of conversion-type inheritance at the *B* locus in maize. Genetics 53:1035–1063.

––––. 1978. The aleurone tissue of maize as a genetic tool. p. 447–459. *In* D. B. Walden (ed.) Maize breeding and genetics. John Wiley and Sons, New York.

––––. 1979. Specification of the anthocyanin biosynthetic function by *B* and *R* in maize. Maydica 24:49–58.

––––. 1982. Planning progeny sizes and estimating recombination percentages. p. 89–91. *In* W. F. Sheridan (ed.) Maize for biological research. Plant Molec. Biol. Assoc., Charlottesville, VA.

––––. 1983. Maternally inherited abnormal plant types in maize. Maydica 28:151–167.

––––. 1985. Phenotypes in corn: Control of pathways by alleles, time and place. p. 509–521. *In* M. Freeling (ed.) (which see).

––––, S. M. McCormick, and S. A. Modena. 1981. White pollen in maize. J. Hered. 72:318–320.

----, and M. G. Neuffer. 1977. The genetics of corn. *In* G. F. Sprague (ed.) Corn and corn improvement, 2d ed. Agronomy 18:111–223.

----, and M.G. Neuffer. 1978. Embryo cells and their destinies in the corn plant. p. 113–129. *In* S. Subtelny and I.M. Sussex (ed.) The clonal basis of development. Academic Press, New York.

----, and R. S. Poethig. 1982. Genetic factors affecting plant development. p. 295–300. *In* W. F. Sheridan (ed.) Maize for biological research. Plant Molec. Biol. Assoc., Charlottesville, VA.

----, and K. R. Sarkar. 1964. The detection of haploids in maize. J. Hered. 55:231–233.

----, D. L. Thompson, and V. Walbot. 1982. Nuclear genes and chloroplast modifications in maize. Stadler Genet. Symp. 14:29–46.

----, ----, and ----. 1988. The phenotypes mediated by the *iojap* genotype in maize. Am. J. Bot. 75:634–644.

Collins, G. N. 1917. Hybrids of *Zea ramosa* and *Zea tunicata*. J. Agric. Res. 9:383–395.

Conde, M. F., D. R. Pring, and C. S. Levings, III. 1979. Maternal inheritance of organelle DNA's in *Zea mays-Zea perennis* reciprocal crosses. J. Hered. 70:2–4.

Cone, K. C., F. A. Burr, and B. Burr. 1986. Molecular analysis of the maize anthocyanin regulatory locus *C1*. Proc. Natl. Acad. Sci. USA 83:9631–9635.

Correns, C. 1901. Bastarde zwischen Maisrassen, mit besonderer Berucksichtung der Xenien. Bibliotheca Botanica 53.

Couture, R. M., D. G. Routley, and G. M. Dunn. 1971. Role of cyclic hydroxamic acids in monogenic resistance of maize to *Helminthosporium turcicum*. Physiol. Plant Pathol. 1:515–521.

Cox, E. L., and D. B. Dickinson. 1971. Identification of maize seedling mutants lacking starch accumulation capacity. Biochem. Genet. 5:15–25.

Curtis, C. A. 1985. Meiotic mutants of maize. Ph.D. diss. Univ. Missouri, Columbia (Diss. Abstr. 47:914–B).

Dahlstrom, D. E., and J. H. Lonnquist. 1964. A new allele at the sugary-1 locus in maize. J. Hered. 55:242–246.

Darrah, L. L., and M. S. Zuber. 1986. 1985 United States farm maize germplasm base and commercial breeding strategies. Crop Sci. 26:1109–1113.

de la Roche, I. A., D. E. Alexander, and E. J. Weber. 1971. Inheritance of oleic and linoleic acids in *Zea mays* L. Crop Sci. 11:856–859.

Demerec, M. 1924a. A case of pollen dimorphism in maize. Am. J. Bot. 11:461–464.

----. 1924b. Genetic relations of five factor pairs for virescent seedlings in maize. Cornell Univ. Agric. Exp. Stn. Mem. 84.

Dempsey, E. 1985. Induction of activators of the *bz2-m* responding allele. p. 311–316. *In* M. Freeling (ed.) (which see).

Dicke, F. F. 1977. The most important corn insects. *In* G. F. Sprague (ed.) Corn and corn improvement, 2nd ed. Agronomy 18:501–590.

Dierks-Ventling, C., and C. Tonelli. 1982. Metabolism of proline, glutamate, and ornithine in proline mutant root tips of *Zea mays* L. Plant Physiol. 69:130–134.

Dieu, P., and M. Beckert. 1986. Further studies of androgenetic embryo production and plant regeneration from in vitro cultured anthers in maize (*Zea mays* L.). Maydica 31:245–259.

DiFonzo, N. D., L. Manzocchi, F. Salamini, and C. Soave. 1986. Purification and properties of an endospermic protein of maize associated with the *opaque-2* and *opaque-6* genes. Planta 167:587–594.

Doebley, J. F., M. M. Goodman, and C. W. Stuber. 1985. Isozyme variation in the races of maize from Mexico. Am. J. Bot. 72:629–639.

----, D. P. Ma, and W. T. Renfroe. 1987. Insertion/deletion mutations in the *Zea* chloroplast genome. Curr. Genet. 11:617–624.

Doerschug, E. B. 1973. Studies of dotted, a regulatory element in maize. I. Inductions of dotted by chromatid breaks. II. Phase variation of dotted. Theor. Appl. Genet. 43:182–189.

----. 1976. Studies of dotted, a regulatory element in maize. III. Transpositions of dotted and its stability at various locations. Theor. Appl. Genet. 48:119–130.

Dollinger, E. J. 1985. Effects of visible recessive alleles on vigor characteristics in a maize hybrid. Crop Sci. 25:819–821.

Dooner, H. K. 1979a. Flavonol glucosyltransferase activity in *bronze* embryos of *Zea mays*. Phytochemistry 18:749–751.

———. 1979b. Identification of an *R*-locus region that controls the tissue specificity of anthocyanin formation in maize. Genetics 93:703–710.

———. 1982. Gene-enzyme relationships in anthocyanin biosynthesis in maize. p. 123–128. *In* W. F. Sheridan (ed.) Maize for biological research. Plant Molec. Biol. Assoc., Charlottesville, VA.

———. 1983. Coordinate genetic regulation of flavonoid biosynthetic enzymes in maize. Mol. Gen. Genet. 189:136–141.

———. 1985. *Viviparous-1* mutation in maize conditions pleiotropic enzyme deficiencies in the aleurone. Plant Physiol. 77:486–488.

———. 1986. Genetic fine structure of the *bronze* locus in maize. Genetics 113:1021–1036.

———, and J. L. Kermicle. 1971. Structure of the R^r tandem duplication in maize. Genetics 67:427–436.

———, and ———. 1976. Displaced and tandem duplications in the long arm of chromosome 10 in maize. Genetics 82:309–322.

———, and O. E. Nelson. 1977a. Genetic control of UDPglucose:flavonol 3-0-glucosyltransferase in the endosperm of maize. Biochem. Genet. 15:509–519.

———, and ———. 1977b. Controlling element-induced alterations in UDPglucose:flavonoid glucosyltransferase, the enzyme specified by the bronze locus in maize. Proc. Natl. Acad. Sci. USA 74:5623–5627.

———, and ———. 1979. Interaction among *C*, *R* and *Vp* in the control of the *Bz* glucosyltransferase during endosperm development in maize. Genetics 91:309–315.

———, E. Weck, S. Adams, E. Ralston, M. Favreau, and J. English. 1985. A molecular genetic analysis of insertions in the bronze locus in maize. Mol. Gen. Genet. 200:240–246.

Doring, H.-P., R. Garber, B. Nelsen, and E. Tillmann. 1985. Transposable element *Ds* and chromosomal rearrangements. p. 355–367. *In* M. Freeling (ed.) (which see).

———, and P. Starlinger. 1984. Barbara McClintock's controlling elements: Now at the DNA level. Cell 39:253–259.

Doyle, G. G. 1973. Autotetraploid gene segregation. Theor. Appl. Genet. 43:139–146.

———. 1979. The allotetraploidization of maize. Part 2. The theoretical basis—the cytogenetics of segmental allotetraploids. Theor. Appl. Genet. 54:161–168.

———. 1982. The allotetraploidization of maize. Part 3: gene segregation in trisomic heterozygotes. Theor. Appl. Genet. 61:81–89.

Duvick, D. N. 1965. Cytoplasmic pollen sterility in corn. Adv. Genet. 13:1–56.

———. 1972. Potential usefulness of new cytoplasmic male steriles and sterility systems. Proc. Corn Sorghum Res. Conf. 27:192–201.

———, and S. W. Noble. 1978. Current and future use of cytoplasmic male sterility for hybrid seed production. p. 265–275. *In* D. B. Walden (ed.) Maize breeding and genetics. John Wiley and Sons, New York.

East, E. M., and H. K. Hayes. 1911. Inheritance in maize. Connecticut Agric. Exp. Stn. Bull. 167.

Emerson, R. A. 1914. The inheritance of a recurring somatic variation in variegated ears of maize. Am. Nat. 48:87–115.

———. 1917. Genetical studies of variegated pericarp in maize. Genetics 2:1–35.

———. 1918. A fifth pair of factors, *A a*, for aleurone color in maize, and its relation to the *C c* and *R r* pairs. Cornell Univ. Agric. Exp. Stn. Mem. 16.

———. 1921. The genetic relations of plant colors in maize. Cornell Univ. Agric. Exp. Stn. Mem. 39.

———. 1929. The frequency of somatic mutation in variegated pericarp of maize. Genetics 14:488–511.

———. 1934. Relation of the differential fertilization genes, *Ga ga*, to certain other genes of the *Su-Tu* linkage group of maize. Genetics 19:137–156.

———, G. W. Beadle, and A. C. Fraser. 1935. A summary of linkage studies in maize. Cornell Univ. Agric. Exp. Stn. Mem. 180.

Emmerling, M. H. 1958. An analysis of intragenic and extragenic mutations of the plant color component of the R^r gene complex in *Zea mays*. Cold Spring Harbor Symp. Quant. Biol. 23:393–407.

Escote, L. J., S. J. Gabay-Laughnan, and J. R. Laughnan. 1985. Cytoplasmic reversion to fertility in *cms-S* maize need not involve loss of linear mitochondrial plasmids. Plasmid 14:264–267.

Evola, S. V., F. A. Burr, and B. Burr. 1986. The suitability of restriction fragment length polymorphisms as genetic markers in maize. Theor. Appl. Genet. 71:765–771.

Eyster, W. H. 1933. Plastid studies in genetic types of maize: argentia chlorophyll. Plant Physiol. 8:105–121.

Faluyi, J. O., and O. Olorode. 1984. Inheritance of resistance to *Helminthosporium maydis* blight in maize (*Zea mays* L.). Theor. Appl. Genet. 67:341–344.

Fedoroff, N. V. 1983. Controlling elements in maize. p. 1–64. *In* J. A. Shapiro (ed.) Mobile genetic elements. Academic Press, New York.

––––, D. B. Furtek, and O. E. Nelson, Jr. 1984. Cloning of the *bronze* locus in maize by a simple and generalizable procedure using the transposable controlling element *Activator* (*Ac*). Proc. Natl. Acad. Sci. USA 81:3825–3829.

––––, S. Wessler, and M. Shure. 1983. Isolation of the transposable maize controlling elements *Ac* and *Ds*. Cell 35:235–242.

Felder, M. R., and J. G. Scandalios. 1971. Effects of homozygosity and heterozygosity on certain properties of genetically defined electrophoretic variants of alcohol dehydrogenase isozymes in maize. Mol. Gen. Genet. 111:317–326.

Ficsor, G. 1965. Chemical mutagenesis in *Zea mays*. Ph.D. diss. Univ. Missouri, Columbia (Diss. Abstr. 27(6B):1728).

Fischer, M., and D. Schwartz. 1973. Dissociation and reassociation of maize alcohol dehydrogenase: allelic differences in requirement for zinc. Mol. Gen. Genet. 127:33–38.

Fogel, S. 1946. The allelic variability and action of the gene *R* in maize. Ph.D. diss. Univ. Missouri, Columbia (Diss. Abstr. 9(2):94).

Fong, F., D. E. Koehler, and J. D. Smith. 1983. Fluridone induction of vivipary during maize seed development. p. 188–196. *In* J. E. Kruger and D. E. LaBerge (ed.) Third Intl. Symp. on Pre-Harvest Sprouting in Cereals. Westview Press, Boulder, CO.

Ford, R. E., and M. A. Mikel. 1984. Disease resistance in maize. p. 197–223. *In* S. P. Raychaudhuri and J. P. Verma (ed.) Review of tropical plant pathology, Vol. 1. Today and Tomorrows Printers and Publ., New Delhi.

Forde, B. G., and C. J. Leaver. 1979. Mitochondrial genome expression in maize: possible involvement of variant mitochondrial polypeptides in cytoplasmic male-sterility. p. 136–146. *In* D. R. Davies and D. A. Hopwood (ed.) The plant genome. John Innes Charity, Norwich, England.

Freeling, M. 1974. Dimerization of multiple maize ADHs studied *in vivo* and *in vitro*. Biochem. Genet. 12:407–417.

––––. 1976. Intragenic recombination in maize: pollen analysis methods and the effect of parental *Adh1*+ isoalleles. Genetics 83:701–717.

––––. 1984. Plant transposable elements and insertion sequences. Annu. Rev. Plant Physiol. 35:277–298.

––––. (ed.) 1985. Plant genetics. Alan R. Liss, Inc., New York.

––––, and S. Hake. 1985. Developmental genetics of mutants that specify knotted leaves in maize. Genetics 111:617–634.

Frei, O. M., C. W. Stuber, and M. M. Goodman. 1986a. Use of allozymes as genetic markers for predicting performance in maize single cross hybrids. Crop Sci. 26:37–42.

––––, ––––, and ––––. 1986b. Yield manipulation from selection on allozyme genotypes in a composite of elite corn lines. Crop Sci. 26:917–921.

Frova, C., G. Binelli, and E. Ottaviano. 1987. Isozyme and HSP gene expression during male gametophyte development in maize. p. 97–120. *In* M. C. Rattazzi et al. (ed.) Isozymes: Current topics in biological and medical research, Vol. 15. Alan R. Liss, New York.

––––, M. Sari Gorla, E. Ottaviano, and C. Pella. 1983. Haplo-diploid gene expression in maize and its detection. Biochem. Genet. 21:923–931.

Galinat, W. C. 1971a. The origin of maize. Annu. Rev. Genet. 5:447–478.

––––. 1971b. The evolution of sweet corn. Massachusetts Agric. Exp. Stn. Res. Bull. 591:1–20.

––––. 1975. The evolutionary emergence of maize. Bull. Torrey Bot. Club 102:313–324.

––––. 1978. The inheritance of some traits essential to maize and teosinte. p. 93–111. *In* D. B. Walden (ed.) Maize breeding and genetics. John Wiley and Sons, New York.

––––, and R. H. Andrew. 1953. Stolon-producing corn. Agron. J. 45:122–123.

––––, and A. W. Naylor. 1951. Relation of photoperiod to inflorescence proliferation in *Zea mays* L. Am. J. Bot. 38:38–47.

Gallais, A., L. Huguet, H. Berthet, G. Bertin, B. Broqua, A. Mourguet, and R. Traineau. 1980. Preliminary evaluation of brown midrib maize hybrids for their feeding and agronomic value in France. p. 319–339. *In* W. G. Pollmer and R. H. Phipps (ed.)

Improvement of quality traits of maize for grain and silage use. Martinus Nijhoff, Boston.

Garwood, D. L., and R. G. Creech. 1972. Kernel phenotypes of *Zea mays* L. genotypes possessing one to four mutated genes. Crop Sci. 12:119–121.

Gavazzi, G., M. Nava-Racchi, and C. Tonelli. 1975. A mutation causing proline requirement in *Zea mays*. Theor. Appl. Genet. 46:339–345.

Gee, M. S., O. E. Nelson, and J. Kuc. 1968. Abnormal lignins produced by the *brown-midrib* mutants of maize. II. Comparative studies on normal and *brown-midrib-1* dimethylformamide lignins. Arch. Biochem. Biophys. 123:403–408.

Gelinas, D. A., and S. N. Postlethwait. 1969. IAA oxidase inhibitors from normal and mutant maize plants. Plant Physiol. 44:1553–1559.

————, ————, and O. E. Nelson. 1969. Characterization of development in maize through the use of mutants. II. The abnormal growth conditioned by the knotted mutant. Am. J. Bot. 56:671–678.

Gengenbach, B. G., C. E. Green, and C. M. Donovan. 1977. Inheritance of selected pathotoxin resistance in maize plants regenerated from cell cultures. Proc. Natl. Acad. Sci. USA 74:5113–5117.

————, D. E. Koeppe, and R. J. Miller. 1973. A comparison of mitochondria isolated from male-sterile and nonsterile cytoplasm etiolated corn seedlings. Physiol. Plant. 29:103–107.

Gerats, A. G. M., J. Bussard, E. H. Coe, Jr., and R. Larson. 1984. Influence of *B* and *Pl* on UDPG:flavonoid-3-0-glucosyltransferase in *Zea mays* L. Biochem. Genet. 22:1161–1169.

Gibson, P. B., R. A. Brink, and M. A. Stahmann. 1950. The mutagenic action of mustard gas on *Zea mays*. J. Hered. 41:232–238.

Golubovskaya, I. N. 1979. Genetic control of meiosis. Intl. Rev. Cytol. 58:247–290.

————, and N. B. Khristolyubova. 1985. The cytogenetic evidence of the gene control of meiosis, maize meiosis, and mei-genes. p. 723–738. *In* M. Freeling (ed.) (which see).

Goodman, M. M., and C. W. Stuber. 1983. Maize. p. 1–33. *In* S. D. Tanksley and T. J. Orton (ed.) Isozymes in plant genetics and breeding, Part B. Elsevier Sci. Publ., Amsterdam.

————, ————, C.-N. Lee, and F. M. Johnson. 1980. Genetic control of malate dehydrogenase isozymes in maize. Genetics 94:153–168.

Gopinath, D. M., and C. R. Burnham. 1956. A cytogenetic study in maize of deficiency-duplication produced by crossing interchanges involving the same chromosomes. Genetics 41:382–395.

Grand, C., P. Parmentier, A. Boudet, and A. M. Boudet. 1985. Comparison of lignins and of enzymes involved in lignification in normal and brown midrib (*bm3*) mutant corn seedlings. Physiol. Veg. 23:905–911.

Greenblatt, I. M. 1974. Movement of modulator in maize: a test of an hypothesis. Genetics 77:671–678.

————. 1985. The pericarp of maize: A major tool to study transposable elements. p. 405–417. *In* M. Freeling (ed.) (which see).

————, and M. Bock. 1967. A commercially desirable procedure for detection of monoploids in maize. J. Hered. 58:9–13.

————, and R. A. Brink. 1962. Twin mutations in medium variegated pericarp maize. Genetics 47:489–501.

Greyson, R. I., and D. B. Walden. 1972. The Abphyl syndrome in *Zea mays*. I. Arrangement, number and size of leaves. Am. J. Bot. 59:466–472.

————, ————, and P. C. Cheng. 1980. LM, TEM and SEM observations of anther development in the genic male-sterile (*ms 9*) mutant of corn *Zea mays*. Can. J. Genet. Cytol. 22:153–166.

Guthrie, W. D., R. L. Wilson, J. R. Coats, J. C. Robbins, C. T. Tseng, J. L. Jarvis, and W. A. Russell. 1986. European corn borer (Lepidoptera: Pyralidae) leaf-feeding resistance and DIMBOA content in inbred lines of dent maize grown under field versus greenhouse conditions. J. Econ. Entomol. 79:1492–1496.

Hake, S., R. M. Bird, M. G. Neuffer, and M. Freeling. 1985. Development of the maize ligule and mutants that affect it. p. 61–71. *In* M. Freeling (ed.) (which see).

————, and M. Freeling. 1985. The *Knotted-1* locus of maize. p. 824–827. *In* M. Freeling (ed.) (which see).

————, and ————. 1986. Analysis of genetic mosaics shows that the extra epidermal cell divisions in Knotted mutant maize plants are induced by adjacent mesophyll cells. Nature 320:621–623.

Hamid, A. H., J. E. Ayers, and R. R. Hill, Jr. 1982. Host X isolate interactions in corn inbreds inoculated with *Cochliobolus carbonum* race 3. Phytopathology 72:1169–1173.

Hannah, L. C., D. M. Tuschall, and R. J. Mans. 1980. Multiple forms of maize endosperm ADP-glucose pyrophosphorylase and their control by Shrunken-2 and Brittle-2. Genetics 95:961–970.

Hanson, W. D. 1959. Minimum family sizes for the planning of genetic experiments. Agron. J. 51:711–715.

Harborne, J. B., and G. Gavazzi. 1969. Effect of *Pr* and *pr* alleles on anthocyanin biosynthesis in *Zea mays*. Phytochemistry 8:999–1001.

Harpster, M. H., S. P. Mayfield, and W. C. Taylor. 1984. Effects of pigment-deficient mutants on the accumulation of photosynthetic proteins in maize. Plant Mol. Biol. 3:59–71.

Hayes, H. K. 1932. Heritable characters in maize. XLIII. Zebra seedlings. J. Hered. 23:415–419.

––––, and H. E. Brewbaker. 1928. Glossy seedlings in maize. Am. Nat. 62:228–235.

Hedman, K. D., and C. D. Boyer. 1983. Allelic studies of the *Amylose-Extender* locus of *Zea mays* L.: Levels of the starch branching enzymes. Biochem. Genet. 21:1217–1222.

Helentjaris, T., G. King, M. Slocum, C. Siedenstrang, and S. Wegman. 1985. Restriction fragment polymorphisms as probes for plant diversity and their development as tools for applied plant breeding. Plant Mol. Biol. 5:109–118.

––––, M. Slocum, S. Wright, A. Schaefer, and J. Nienhuis. 1986a. Construction of genetic maps in maize and tomato using restriction fragment length polymorphisms. Theor. Appl. Genet. 72:761–769.

––––, D. F. Weber, and S. Wright. 1986b. Use of monosomics to map cloned DNA fragments in maize. Proc. Natl. Acad. Sci. 83:6035–6039.

––––, ––––, and ––––. 1988. Duplicate sequences in maize and identification of their genomic locations through restriction fragment length polymorphisms. Genetics 118:353–363.

Hertel, R., R. K. de la Fuente, and A. C. Leopold. 1969. Geotropism and the lateral transport of auxin in the corn mutant amylomaize. Planta 88:204–214.

Hoisington, D. A. 1987. Maize (*Zea mays* L.) RFLP clones and linkage map—A public set. Genetics 116:s27.

––––, M. G. Neuffer, and V. Walbot. 1982. Disease lesion mimics in maize. I. Effect of genetic background, temperature, developmental age, and wounding on necrotic spot formation with *Les1*. Dev. Biol. 93:381–388.

Hooker, A. L. 1978. Genetics of disease resistance in maize. p. 319–332. *In* D. B. Walden (ed.) Maize breeding and genetics. John Wiley and Sons, New York.

––––, and Y.-K. Tsung. 1980. Relationship of dominant genes in corn for chlorotic lesion resistance to *Helminthosporium turcicum*. Plant Dis. 64:387–388.

Hopkins, W. G. 1982. Formation of chloroplast pigments in a temperature-sensitive, virescent mutant of maize. Can. J. Bot. 60:737–740.

––––, and B. Elfman. 1984. Temperature-induced chloroplast ribosome deficiency in virescent maize. J. Hered. 75:207–211.

––––, J. B. German, and D. B. Hayden. 1980a. A light-sensitive mutant in maize (*Zea mays* L.). II. Photosynthetic properties. Z. Pflanzenphysiol. 100:15–24.

––––, D. B. Hayden, and M. G. Neuffer. 1980b. A light-sensitive mutant in maize (*Zea mays* L.). I. Chlorophyll, chlorophyll-protein and ultrastructural studies. Z. Pflanzenphysiol. 99:417–426.

––––, and D. B. Walden. 1977. Temperature sensitivity of virescent mutants of maize. J. Hered. 68:283–286.

Horovitz, S., and A. H. Marchioni. 1942. Herencia de la resistencia a la langosta en el maiz "Amargo." Anales Inst. Fitotecnico Santa Catalina 2(1940):27–52.

House, L. R., and O. E. Nelson, Jr. 1958. Tracer study of pollen-tube growth in cross-sterile maize. J. Hered. 49:18–21.

Hsu-Chen, S. M., and E. H. Coe, Jr. 1973. C_1 locus control of anthocyanin synthesis in maize. Genetics 74:s120–121.

Humaydan, H. S., and E. W. Scott. 1977. Methomyl insecticide selective phytotoxicity on sweet corn hybrids and inbreds having the Texas male sterile cytoplasm. Hortscience 12:312–313.

Hutchison, C. B. 1922. The linkage of certain aleurone and endosperm factors in maize, and their relation to other linkage groups. Cornell Univ. Agric. Exp. Stn. Mem. 60:1421–1473.

Ibrahim, M. A. 1954. Association tests between chromosomal interchanges in maize and resistance to the European corn borer. Agron. J. 46:293–298.

Immer, F. R. 1930. Formulae and tables for calculating linkage intensities. Genetics 15:81–98.

Isaac, P. G., V. P. Jones, and C. J. Leaver. 1985. The maize cytochrome c oxidase subunit I gene: Sequence, expression and rearrangement in cytoplasmic male sterile plants. EMBO J. 4:1617–1623.

Ishige, T., K. K. Storey, and B. G. Gengenbach. 1985. Cytoplasmic fertile revertants possessing S1 and S2 DNAs in S male-sterile maize. Jpn. J. Breed. 35:285–291.

Jellum, M. D., and N. W. Widstrom. 1983. Inheritance of stearic acid in germ oil of the maize kernel. J. Hered. 74:383–384.

Johri, M. M., and E. H. Coe, Jr. 1982. Genetic approaches to meristem organization. p. 301–310. In W. F. Sheridan (ed.) Maize for biological research. Plant Molec. Biol. Assoc., Charlottesville, VA.

----, and ----. 1983. Clonal analysis of corn plant development. I. The development of the tassel and the ear shoot. Dev. Biol. 97:154–172.

----, and ----. 1986. The development of corn plant. p. 175–180. In G. M. Reddy and E. H. Coe, Jr. (ed.) Gene structure and function in higher plants. Oxford & IBH Publ. Co., New Delhi.

Jones, R. J., J. Roessler, and S. Ouattar. 1985. Thermal environment during endosperm cell division in maize—effects on number of endosperm cells and starch granules. Crop Sci. 25:830–834.

Kahler, A. L., A. R. Hallauer, and C. O. Gardner. 1986. Allozyme polymorphisms within and among open-pollinated and adapted exotic populations of maize. Theor. Appl. Genet. 72:592–601.

----, and C. F. Wehrhahn. 1986. Associations between quantitative traits and enzyme loci in the F2 population of a maize hybrid. Theor. Appl. Genet. 72:15–26.

Kemble, R. J., R. E. Gunn, and R. B. Flavell. 1983. Mitochondrial DNA variation in races of maize indigenous to Mexico. Theor. Appl. Genet. 65:129–144.

Kempton, J. H. 1921. A brachytic variation in maize. USDA Bull. 925. U.S. Gov. Print. Office, Washington, DC.

----. 1936. Modification of a Mendelian ratio in maize by pollen treatments. J. Agric. Res. 52:81–121.

Kermicle, J. L. 1969. Androgenesis conditioned by a mutation in maize. Science 166:1422–1424.

----. 1970a. Somatic and meiotic instability of R-stippled, an aleurone spotting factor in maize. Genetics 64:247–258.

----. 1970b. Dependence of the R-mottled aleurone phenotype in maize on mode of sexual transmission. Genetics 66:69–85.

----. 1971. Pleiotropic effects on seed development of the indeterminate gametophyte gene in maize. Am. J. Bot. 58:1–7.

----. 1974. Organization of the paramutational components of the R locus in maize. Brookhaven Symp. Biol. 25:262–280.

----. 1978. Imprinting of gene action in maize endosperm. p. 357–371. In D. B. Walden (ed.) Maize breeding and genetics. John Wiley and Sons, New York.

----. 1980. Probing the component structure of a maize gene with transposable elements. Science 208:1457–1458.

----. 1985. Alternative tests of allelism. p. 491–507 In M. Freeling (ed.) (which see).

----, and J. D. Axtell. 1981. Modification of chlorophyll striping by the R region. Maydica 26:185–197.

Kiesselbach, T. A. 1949. The structure and reproduction of corn. Nebraska Agric. Exp. Stn. Res. Bull. 161.

Kindiger, B. 1986. Developmental abnormalities in hypoploid pollen grains of Zea mays L. Ph.D. diss., Univ. Missouri, Columbia.

Kirby, L. T., and E. D. Styles. 1970. Flavonoids associated with specific gene action in maize aleurone, and the role of light in substituting for the action of a gene. Can. J. Genet. Cytol. 12:934–940.

Klun, J. A., W. D. Guthrie, A. R. Hallauer, and W. A. Russell. 1970. Genetic nature of the concentration of 2,4-dihydroxy-7-methoxy 2H-1, 4-benzoxazin-3(4H)-one and resistance to the European corn borer in a diallel set of eleven maize inbreds. Crop Sci. 10:87–90.

Kreizinger, J. D. 1960. Diepoxybutane as a chemical mutagen in *Zea mays*. Genetics 45:143–154.

Kuc, J., and O. E. Nelson. 1964. The abnormal lignins produced by the *brown-midrib* mutants of maize. I. The *brown-midrib-1* mutant. Arch. Biochem. Biophys. 105:103–113.

––––, ––––, and P. Flanagan. 1968. Degradation of abnormal lignins in the *brown-midrib* mutants and double mutants of maize. Phytochemistry 7:1435–1436.

Kumar, D., and K. R. Sarkar. 1980. Correlation between pollen diameter and rate of pollen tube growth in maize (*Zea mays* L.). Indian J. Exp. Biol. 18:1242–1244.

––––, and ––––. 1985. Inheritance of maize (*Zea mays* L.) pollen tube growth in vitro. Indian J. Exp. Biol. 23:110–111.

Larque-Saavedra, A., and R. L. Wain. 1974. Abscisic acid levels in relation to drought tolerance in varieties of *Zea mays* L. Nature 251:716–717.

Larson, R. L., and J. B. Bussard. 1982. Flavonoid O-methylation in maize extracts. Plant Phys. Suppl. 69:710.

––––, ––––, and E. H. Coe, Jr. 1986. Gene-dependent flavonoid 3'-hydroxylation in maize. Biochem. Genet. 24:615–624.

––––, and E. H. Coe, Jr. 1968. Enzymatic action of the Bz_1 anthocyanin factor in maize. Proc. XII Int. Cong. Genet. 1:131.

––––, and ––––. 1977. Gene-dependent flavonoid glucosyltransferase in maize. Biochem. Genet. 15:153–156.

Laughnan, J. R. 1948. The action of allelic forms of the gene *A* in maize. I. Studies of variability, dosage and dominance relations. The divergent character of the series. Genetics 33:488–517.

––––. 1949. The action of allelic forms of the gene *A* in maize. II. The relation of crossing over to mutation of A^b. Proc. Natl. Acad. Sci. USA 35:167–178.

––––. 1950. The action of allelic forms of the gene *A* in maize. III. Studies on the occurrence of isoquercitrin in brown and purple plants and its lack of identity with the brown pigments. Proc. Natl. Acad. Sci. USA 36:312–318.

––––. 1951. Reaction sequence in anthocyanin synthesis in maize. Genetics 36:559–560.

––––. 1952. The action of allelic forms of the gene *A* in maize. IV. On the compound nature of A^b and the occurrence and action of its A^d derivatives. Genetics 37:375–395.

––––. 1953. The effect of the *sh2* factor on carbohydrate reserves in the mature endosperm of maize. Genetics 38:485–499.

––––. 1955. Structural and functional aspects of the A^b complexes in maize. I. Evidence for structural and functional variability among complexes of different geographic origin. Proc. Natl. Acad. Sci. USA 41:78–84.

––––. 1961a. An evaluation of the multiple crossover and sidechain hypotheses based on an analysis of alpha derivatives from the A^b-P complexes in maize. Genetics 46:1347–1372.

––––. 1961b. The nature of mutation in terms of gene and chromosome changes. p. 3-29. *In* Mutation and plant breeding. NAS-NRC Publ. 891.

––––, and S. J. Gabay. 1973a. Mutations leading to nuclear restoration of fertility in S male-sterile cytoplasm in maize. Theor. Appl. Genet. 43:109–116.

––––, and ––––. 1973b. Reaction of germinating maize pollen to *Helminthosporium maydis* pathotoxins. Crop Sci. 13:681–684.

––––, and S. Gabay-Laughnan. 1983. Cytoplasmic male sterility in maize. Annu. Rev. Genet. 17:27–48.

––––, ––––, and J. E. Carlson. 1981. Characteristics of *cms*-S reversion to male fertility in maize. Stadler Genet. Symp. 13:93–114.

Leaver, C. J., L. K. Dixon, E. Hack, T. D. Fox, and A. J. Dawson. 1983. Mitochondrial genes and their expression in higher plants. O. Ciferri and L. Dure (ed.) *In* Structure and function of plant genomes. Life Sci. 63:347–361.

Lemke, C. A., V. E. Gracen, and H. L. Everett. 1985. A new source of cytoplasmic male sterility in maize induced by the nuclear gene, iojap. Theor. Appl. Genet. 71:481–485.

Leng, E. R., and L. F. Bauman. 1955. Expression of the "Kys" type of male sterility in strains of corn with normal cytoplasm. Agron. J. 47:189–191.

Levings, C. S., III, B. D. Kim, D. R. Pring, M. F. Conde, R. J. Mans, J. R. Laughnan, and

S. J. Gabay-Laughnan. 1980. Cytoplasmic reversion of *cms-S* in maize: association with a transpositional event. Science 209:1021–1023.

————, and C. W. Stuber. 1971. A maize gene controlling silk browning in response to wounding. Genetics 69:491–498.

Lin, B. Y. 1975. Parental effects on gene expression in maize endosperm development. Ph.D. diss. Univ. Wisconsin, Madison (Diss. Abstr. 36:4850B).

————. 1982. Association of endosperm reduction with parental imprinting in maize. Genetics 100:475–486.

Longley, A. E. 1925. Segregation of carbohydrates in maize pollen. Science 61:542–543.

Lonsdale, D. M. 1985. Chloroplast DNA sequences in the mitochondrial genome of maize. p. 421–428. *In* L. van Vloten-Doting et al. (ed.) Molecular form and function of the plant genome. Plenum, New York.

————, C. L. Shardl, and D. R. Pring. 1984. The mitochondrial genome of the S-male sterile cytoplasm of maize: Organization and rearrangements associated with fertility reversion. Curr. Topics Plant Biochem. Physiol. 3:133–140.

Ma, Y., and O. E. Nelson. 1975. Amino acid composition and storage proteins in two high lysine mutants in maize. Cereal Chem. 52:412–419.

MacDonald, T., and J. L. Brewbaker. 1972. Isoenzyme polymorphism in flowering plants. VIII. Genetic control and dimeric nature of transaminase hybrid maize isoenzymes. J. Hered. 63:11–14.

————, and ————. 1974. Isoenzyme polymorphism in flowering plants. IX. The E_5-E_{10} esterase loci of maize. J. Hered. 65:37–42.

Madjolelo, S. D. P., C. O. Grogan, and P. A. Sarvella. 1966. Morphological expression of genetic male sterility in maize (*Zea mays* L.). Crop Sci. 6:379–380.

Mangelsdorf, P. C. 1932. Mechanical separation of gametes in maize. J. Hered. 23:288–295.

————, and G. S. Fraps. 1931. A direct quantitative relationship between vitamin A in corn and the number of genes for yellow pigmentation. Science 73:241–242.

————, and W. C. Galinat. 1964. The tunicate locus in maize dissected and reconstituted. Proc. Natl. Acad. Sci. USA 51:147–150.

————, and D. F. Jones. 1926. The expression of Mendelian factors in the gametophyte of maize. Genetics 11:423–455.

Manzocchi, L., C. Tonelli, G. Gavazzi, N. D. DiFonzo, and C. Soave. 1986. Genetic relationship between *o6* and *pro-1* mutants in maize. Theor. Appl. Genet. 778–781.

Marshall, D. R., P. Broue, and A. J. Pryor. 1973. Adaptive significance of alcohol dehydrogenase isozymes in maize. Nature (London) New Biol. 244:16–17.

Mascia, P. 1978. An analysis of precursors accumulated by several chlorophyll biosynthetic mutants of maize. Mol. Gen. Genet. 161:237–244.

————, and D. S. Robertson. 1978. Studies of chloroplast development in four maize mutants defective in chlorophyll biosynthesis. Planta 143:207–211.

————, and ————. 1980. Genetic studies of the chlorophyll biosynthetic mutants of maize. J. Hered. 71:19–24.

Mayfield, S. P., T. Nelson, W. C. Taylor, and R. Malkin. 1986. Carotenoid synthesis and pleiotropic effects in carotenoid-deficient seedlings of maize. Planta 169:23–32.

————, and W. C. Taylor. 1984. Carotenoid-deficient maize seedlings fail to accumulate light-harvesting chlorophyll *a/b* binding protein (LHCP) mRNA. Eur. J. Biochem. 144:79–84.

McCarty, D. R., J. R. Shaw, and L. C. Hannah. 1986. The cloning, genetic mapping, and expression of the constitutive sucrose synthase locus of maize. Proc. Natl. Acad. Sci. USA 83:9099–9103.

McClintock, B. 1931. Cytological observations of deficiencies involving known genes, translocations and an inversion in *Zea mays*. Missouri Agric. Exp. Stn. Res. Bull. 163.

————. 1938. The production of homozygous deficient tissues with mutant characteristics by means of the aberrant mitotic behavior of ring-shaped chromosomes. Genetics 23:315–376.

————. 1941. The association of mutants with homozygous deficiencies in *Zea mays*. Genetics 26:542–571.

————. 1944. The relation of homozygous deficiencies to mutations and allelic series in maize. Genetics 29:478–502.

————. 1947. Cytogenetic studies of maize and Neurospora. Carnegie Inst. Wash. Year Book 46:146–152.

————. 1950. The origin and behavior of mutable loci in maize. Proc. Natl. Acad. Sci. USA 36:344–355.

————. 1951. Chromosome organization and genic expression. Cold Spring Harbor Symp. Quant. Biol. 16:13–47.

————. 1952. Mutable loci in maize. Carnegie Inst. Wash. Year Book 51:212–219.

————. 1956. Controlling elements and the gene. Cold Spring Harbor Symp. Quant. Biol. 21:197–216.

————. 1965. The control of gene action in maize. Brookhaven Symp. Biol. 18:162–184.

————. 1968. Genetic systems regulating gene expression during development. Dev. Biol. Suppl. 1:84–112.

————. 1978a. Development of the maize endosperm as revealed by clones. Symp. Soc. Dev. Biol. 36:217–237.

————. 1978b. Mechanisms that rapidly reorganize the genome. Stadler Genet. Symp. 10:25–47.

————. 1984. The significance of responses of the genome to challenge. Science 226:792–801.

————, and H. E. Hill. 1931. The cytological identification of the chromosome associated with the R-G linkage group in Zea mays. Genetics 16:175–190.

McCormick, S. 1978. Pigment synthesis in maize aleurone from precursors fed to anthocyanin mutants. Biochem. Genet. 16:777–785.

McNay, J. W., D. R. Pring, and D. M. Lonsdale. 1983. Polymorphism of mitochondrial DNA 'S' regions among normal cytoplasms of maize. Plant Mol. Biol. 2:177–188.

McWhirter, K. S., and R. A. Brink. 1962. Continuous variation in level of paramutation at the R locus in maize. Genetics 47:1053–1074.

Mericle, L. W. 1950. The developmental genetics of the Rg mutant in maize. Am. J. Bot. 37:100–116.

Mertz, E. T., L. S. Bates, and O. E. Nelson. 1964. Mutant gene that changes protein composition and increases lysine content of maize endosperm. Science 145:279–280.

Mikula, B. C. 1961. Progressive conversion of R-locus expression in maize. Proc. Natl. Acad. Sci. USA 47:566–571.

Miles, C. D. 1982. The use of mutations to probe photosynthesis in higher plants. p. 75–107. In M. Edelman et al. (ed.) Methods in chloroplast molecular biology. Elsevier Biomedical Press, Amsterdam.

————, and D. J. Daniel. 1974. Chloroplast reactions of photosynthetic mutants in Zea mays. Plant Physiol. 53:589–595.

————, K. J. Leto, M. G. Neuffer, M. Polacco, J. F. Hanks, and M. A. Hunt. 1985. Chromosome arm location of photosynthesis mutants in Zea mays L. using B-A translocations. p. 361–365. In K. E. Steinbeck et al. (ed.) Molecular biology of the photosynthetic apparatus. Cold Spring Harbor Laboratory, Cold Spring Harbor, NY.

————, and J. G. Metz. 1985. The role of nuclear genes of maize in chloroplast development. p. 585–597. In M. Freeling (ed.) (which see).

Miller, R. J., and D. E. Koeppe. 1971. Southern corn leaf blight: susceptible and resistant mitochondria. Science 173:67–69.

Misra, P. S., R. Jambunathan, E. T. Mertz, D. V. Glover, H. M. Barbosa, and K. S. McWhirter. 1972. Endosperm protein synthesis in maize mutants with increased lysine content. Science 176:1425–1427.

Modena, S. A. 1985. Genetic variation affecting chloroplast thylakoid polypeptides in maize (Zea mays L.) and some teosintes. Ph.D. diss. Univ. Missouri, Columbia (Diss. Abstr. 46:3711-B).

Moore, C. W., and R. G. Creech. 1972. Genetic fine structure analysis of the amylose-extender locus in Zea mays L. Genetics 70:611–619.

Moore, R. 1986. Calcium movement, graviresponsiveness, and the structure of columella cells in primary roots of amylomaize mutants of Zea mays. Am. J. Bot. 73:417–426.

————, M. S. Davies, K. M. O'Connell, E. I. Harding, R. C. Wiegand, and D. C. Tiemeier. 1986. Cloning and expression of a cDNA encoding a maize glutathione-S-transferase in E. coli. Nucl. Acid. Res. 14:7227–7236.

————, and J. D. Smith. 1985. Graviresponsiveness and abscisic-acid content of roots of carotenoid-deficient mutants of Zea mays L. Planta 164:126–128.

Mottinger, J. P. 1970. The effects of X rays on the bronze and shrunken loci in maize. Genetics 64:259–271.

————. 1973. Unstable mutants of bronze induced by pre-meiotic X-ray treatment in maize. Theor. Appl. Genet. 43:190–195.

----, S. L. Dellaporta, and P. B. Keller. 1984a. Stable and unstable mutations in Aberrant Ratio stocks of maize. Genetics 106:751-767.

----, M. A. Johns, and M. Freeling. 1984b. Mutations of the *Adh1* gene in maize following infection with barley stripe mosaic virus. Mol. Gen. Genet. 195:367-369.

Mulcahy, D. L. 1971. A correlation between gametophytic and sporophytic characteristics in *Zea mays* L. Science 171:1155-1156.

Muller, L. D., R. F. Barnes, L. F. Bauman, and V. F. Colenbrander. 1971. Variations in lignin and other structural components of brown midrib mutants of maize. Crop Sci. 11:413-415.

Murakami, K. I., M. Yamada, and K. Takayangi. 1972. Selective fertilization in maize, *Zea mays* L. I. Advantage of pollen from F_1 plant in selective fertilization. Jpn. J. Breed. 22:203-208. (Japanese with English tables and summary).

Mustyatsa, S. I., and V. E. Miku. 1975. Phenotypic description of double homozygotes in terms of certain sex genes in maize. Genetika 11:10-14.

Nanda, D. K., and S. S. Chase. 1966. An embryo marker for detecting monoploids of maize (*Zea mays* L.). Crop Sci. 6:213-215.

National Research Council (U.S.). 1972. Genetic vulnerability of major crops. Nat. Acad. Sci., Washington, DC.

Neill, S. J., R. Horgan, and A. D. Parry. 1986. The carotenoid and abscisic acid content of viviparous kernels and seedlings of *Zea mays* L. Planta 169:87-96.

Nelson, O. E. 1959. Intracistron recombination in the *Wx/wx* region in maize. Science 130:794-795.

----. 1962. The waxy locus in maize. I. Intralocus recombination frequency estimates by pollen and by conventional analyses. Genetics 47:737-742.

----. 1967. Biochemical genetics of higher plants. Annu. Rev. Genet. 1:245-268.

----. 1968. The *waxy* locus in maize. II. The location of the controlling element alleles. Genetics 60:507-524.

----. 1981. A reexamination of the aberrant ratio phenomenon in maize. Maydica 26:119-131.

----. 1985. Aberrant ratio revisited. p. 1-12. *In* J. L. Key and T. Kosuge (ed.) Cellular and molecular biology of plant stress. Alan R. Liss, New York.

----, and B. Burr. 1973. Biochemical genetics of higher plants. Annu. Rev. Plant Physiol. 24:493-518.

----, and M. T. Chang. 1974. Effect of multiple aleurone layers on the protein and amino acid content of maize endosperm. Crop Sci. 14:374-376.

----, and G. B. Clary. 1952. Genic control of semi-sterility in maize. J. Hered. 43:205-210.

----, E. T. Mertz, and L. S. Bates. 1965. Second mutant gene affecting the amino acid pattern of maize endosperm proteins. Science 150:1469-1470.

----, and A. J. Ohlrogge. 1957. Differential responses to population pressures by normal and dwarf lines of maize. Science 125:1200.

----, and ----. 1961. Effect of heterosis on the response of *compact* strains of maize to population pressures. Agron. J. 53:208-209.

----, and A. J. Ullstrup. 1964. Resistance to leaf spot in maize. Genetic control of resistance to race I of *Helminthosporium carbonum* Ull. J. Hered. 55:194-199.

Neuffer, M. G. 1964. Tetrasporic embryo-sac formation in trisomic sectors of maize. Science 144:874-876.

----. 1966. Stability of the suppressor element in two mutator systems at the A_1 locus in maize. Genetics 53:541-549.

----. 1968. Chemical mutagens effective on maize pollen. Proc. XII Int. Cong. Genet. 1:118.

----. 1972. *In vitro* germination of pollen as a measure of effectiveness of chemical mutagens in maize. p. 26. *In* Agronomy abstracts. Am. Soc. Agron., Madison, WI.

----. 1978. Induction of genetic variability. p. 579-600. *In* D.B. Walden (ed.) Maize breeding and genetics. John Wiley and Sons, New York.

----. 1982a. Growing maize for genetic purposes. p. 19-30. *In* W.F. Sheridan (ed.) Maize for biological research. Plant Mol. Biol. Assoc., Charlottesville, VA.

----. 1982b. Mutant induction in maize. p. 61-64. *In* W.F. Sheridan (ed.) Maize for biological research. Plant Mol. Biol. Assoc., Charlottesville, VA.

----, and O. H. Calvert. 1975. Dominant disease lesion mimics in maize. J. Hered. 66:265-270.

----, M.-T. Chang, J. Clark, and W. F. Sheridan. 1986a. The genetic control of maize kernel development. p. 35–50. *In* J. C. Shannon et al. (ed.) Regulation of carbon and nitrogen reduction and utilization in maize. Am. Soc. Plant Physiol., Rockville, MD.

----, and E. H. Coe, Jr. 1978. Paraffin oil technique for treating mature corn pollen with chemical mutagens. Maydica 23:21–28.

----, and G. Ficsor. 1963. Mutagenic action of ethyl methanesulfonate in maize. Science 139:1296–1297.

----, D. A. Hoisington, V. Walbot, and S. E. Pawar. 1986b. Genetic control of disease symptoms. p. 123–134. *In* G. M. Reddy and E. H. Coe, Jr. (ed.) Gene structure and function in higher plants. Oxford and IBH Publ., New Delhi.

----, L. Jones, and M. S. Zuber. 1968. The mutants of maize. Crop Sci. Soc. Am., Madison, WI.

----, and W. F. Sheridan. 1980. Defective kernel mutants of maize. I. Genetic and lethality studies. Genetics 95:929–944.

Nevers, P., N. S. Shepherd, and H. Saedler. 1986. Plant transposable elements. Adv. Bot. Res. 12:103–203.

Newton, K. J., and E. H. Coe, Jr. 1986. Mitochondrial DNA changes in abnormal growth (nonchromosomal stripe) mutants of maize. Proc. Natl. Acad. Sci. USA 83:7363–7366.

Nickerson, N. H. 1960a. Studies involving sustained treatment of maize with gibberellic acid. II: Responses of plants carrying certain tassel-modifying genes. Ann. Mo. Bot. Gard. 47:243–261.

----. 1960b. Sustained treatment with gibberellic acid of maize plants carrying one of the dominant genes Teopod and Corn-grass. Am. J. Bot. 47:809–815.

----, and E. E. Dale. 1955. Tassel modifications in *Zea mays*. Ann. Mo. Bot. Gard. 42:195–212.

----, and W. M. Hewitson. 1963. Morphological and anatomical differences in maize induced by treatment with growth-regulating substances. Am. J. Bot. 50:622.

Nuffer, M. G. 1955. Dosage effect of multiple *Dt* loci on mutation of *a* in the maize endosperm. Science 121:399–400.

----. 1957. Additional evidence on the effect of X-ray and ultraviolet radiation on mutation in maize. Genetics 42:273–282.

----. 1961. Mutation studies at the A_1 locus in maize. I. A mutable allele controlled by *Dt*. Genetics 46:625–640.

O'Reilly, C., N. S. Shepherd, A. Pereira, Z. Schwarz-Sommer, I. Bertram, D. S. Robertson, P. A. Peterson, and H. Saedler. 1985. Molecular cloning of the *a1* locus of *Zea mays* using the transposable elements *En* and *Mu1*. EMBO J. 4:877–882.

Orr, A. R. 1969. Partial production of a normal morphological phenocopy in the *Zea mays* L. mutant, *Ramosa-1*. Iowa Acad. Sci. 76:82–89.

Ottaviano, E., M. Sari-Gorla, and D. L. Mulcahy. 1980. Pollen tube growth rates in *Zea mays*: implications for genetic improvement of crops. Science 210:437–438.

----, M. Sari-Gorla, and E. Pe. 1982. Male gametophytic selection in maize. Theor. Appl. Genet. 63:249–254.

----, E., P. Sidoti, and M. Villa. 1985. Pollen competitive ability in maize selection and single gene analysis. p. 21–26. *In* D.L. Mulcahy et al. (ed.) Biotechnology and ecology of pollen. Springer-Verlag, New York.

Ottoboni, L. M. M., and D. M. Steffensen. 1987. Localization of zein genes in maize. Biochem. Genet. 25:123–142.

Pace, G. M., J. N. Reed, L. C. Ho, and J. W. Fahey. 1987. Anther culture of maize and the visualization of embryogenic microspores by fluorescent microscopy. Theor. Appl. Genet. 73:863–869.

Pan, D., and O. E. Nelson, Jr. 1984. A debranching enzyme deficiency in endosperms of the *sugary-1* mutants of maize. Plant Physiol. 74:324–328.

Patterson, E. B. 1978. Properties and uses of duplicate-deficient chromosome complements in maize. p. 693–710. *In* D. B. Walden (ed.) Maize breeding and genetics. John Wiley and Sons, New York.

----. 1982. The mapping of genes by the use of chromosome aberrations and multiple gene marker stocks. p. 85–88. *In* W. F. Sheridan (ed.) Maize for biological research. Plant Molec. Biol. Assoc., Charlottesville, VA.

Pego, S. E., and A. R. Hallauer. 1984. Portuguese maize germplasm with abnormal ear shape. Maydica 29:39–53.

Penny, L. H., and F. F. Dicke. 1957. A single gene-pair controlling segregation for European corn borer resistance. Agron. J. 49:193–196.

Pereira, A., Z. Schwarz-Sommer, A. Gierl, I. Bertram, P. A. Peterson, and H. Saedler. 1985. Genetic and molecular analysis of the Enhancer (*En*) transposable element system of *Zea mays*. EMBO J. 4:17–23.

Peterson, P. A. 1953. A mutable pale green locus in maize. Genetics 38:682–683.

————. 1965. A relationship between the *Spm* and *En* control systems in maize. Am. Nat. 99:391–398.

————. 1974. Unstable genetic loci as a probe in morphogenesis. Brookhaven Symp. Biol. 25:244–261.

————. 1976. Gene repression and the evolution of unisexuality in the maize spikelet. Maydica 21:157–164.

————. 1985. The enhancer (*En*) system: A maize mobile-element system. p. 369–381. *In* M. Freeling (ed.) (which see).

Petolino, J. F., and A. M. Jones. 1986. Anther culture of elite genotypes of maize. Crop Sci. 26:1072–1074.

Pfahler, P. L. 1965. Fertilization ability of maize pollen grains. I. Pollen sources. Genetics 52:513–520.

————. 1967a. Fertilization ability of maize pollen grains. II. Pollen genotype, female sporophyte and pollen storage interactions. Genetics 57:513–521.

————. 1967b. Fertilization ability of maize pollen grains. III. Gamma irradiation of mature pollen. Genetics 57:523–530.

————. 1970. Reproductive characteristics of *Zea mays* L. plants produced from gamma-irradiated kernels. Radiat. Bot. 10:329–335.

————. 1971. *In vitro* germination and pollen tube growth of maize (*Zea mays* L.) pollen. V. Gamma irradiation effects. Radiat. Bot. 11:233–237.

————. 1973. *In vitro* germination and pollen tube growth of maize (*Zea mays* L.) pollen— VII. Effects of ultraviolet irradiation. Radiat. Bot. 13:13–18.

————, D. L. Mulcahy, and B. Barnabas. 1986a. The effect of forced shedding on pollen traits, seedsetting, and transmission at various maize (*Zea mays* L.) endosperm mutant loci. Acta Bot. Neer. 35:195–200.

————, ————, and ————. 1986b. The effect of pre-pollination stylar treatments on seedset and pollen transmission at various maize (*Zea mays* L.) endosperm mutant loci. Acta Bot. Neer. 35:201–207.

Phillips, R. L., C. R. Burnham, and E. B. Patterson. 1971a. Advantages of chromosomal interchanges that generate haplo-viable deficiency-duplications. Crop Sci. 11:525–528.

————, R. A. Kleese, and S. S. Wang. 1971b. The nucleolus organizer region of maize (*Zea mays* L.): chromosomal site of DNA complementary to ribosomal RNA. Chromosoma 36:79–88.

Phinney, B. O. 1956. Growth response of single-gene dwarf mutants in maize to gibberellic acid. Proc. Natl. Acad. Sci. USA 42:185–189.

————, and C. Spray. 1982. Chemical genetics and the gibberellin pathway in *Zea mays* L. p. 101–110. *In* P. F. Wareing (ed.) Plant growth substances, Academic Press, New York.

————, and ————. 1985. Gibberellins (GAs), gibberellin mutants and their future in molecular biology. Curr. Topics Plant Biochem. Physiol. 4:67–74.

————, and C. A. West. 1960. Gibberellins and the growth of flowering plants. Symp. Soc. Study Dev. Growth 18:71–92.

Pilet, P. E. 1983. Elongation and gravireactivity of roots from an agravitropic maize mutant: Implications of growth inhibitors. Plant Cell Physiol. 24:333–336.

Plewa, M. J., and D. F. Weber. 1973. The use of monosomics to detect genes conditioning lipid content in *Zea mays* L. embryos. Can. J. Genet. Cytol. 15:313–320.

————, and ————. 1975. Monosomic analysis of fatty acid composition in embryo lipids of *Zea mays* L. Genetics 81:277–286.

Poethig, R. S. 1984. Patterns and problems in angiosperm leaf morphogenesis. p. 413–432. *In* G. M. Malacinski and S. V. Bryant (ed.) Pattern formation: A primer in developmental biology. Macmillan, New York.

————. 1985. Homeotic mutations in maize. p. 33–43. *In* M. Freeling (ed.) (which see).

————, E. H. Coe, Jr., and M. M. Johri. 1986. Cell lineage patterns in maize embryogenesis: a clonal analysis. Dev. Biol. 117:392–404.

Polacco, M. L., M. T. Chang, and M. G. Neuffer. 1985. Nuclear, virescent mutants of *Zea mays* L. with high levels of chlorophyll (*a/b*) light-harvesting complex during thylakoid assembly. Plant Physiol. 77:795–800.

----, and D. B. Walden. 1987. Genetic, developmental, and environmental influences on *Oy-700* expression in maize. J. Hered. 78:81–86.

Poneleit, C. G., and D. E. Alexander. 1965. Inheritance of linoleic and oleic acids in maize. Science 147:1585–1586.

Postlethwait, S. N., and O. E. Nelson, Jr. 1957. A chronically wilted mutant of maize. Am. J. Bot. 44:628–633.

----, and ----. 1964. Characterization of development in maize through the use of mutants. I. The Polytypic (*Pt*) and ramosa-1 (*ra₁*) mutants. Am. J. Bot. 51:238–243.

Price, S. C., A. L. Kahler, A. R. Hallauer, P. Charmley, and D. A. Giegel. 1986. Relationships between performance and multilocus heterozygosity at enzyme loci in single-cross hybrids of maize. J. Hered. 77:341–344.

Pring, D. R., and C. S. Levings, III. 1978. Heterogeneity of maize cytoplasmic genomes among male-sterile cytoplasms. Genetics 89:121–136.

----, and D. M. Lonsdale. 1985. Molecular biology of higher plant mitochondrial DNA. Int. Rev. Cytol. 97:1–46.

----, ----, V. E. Gracen, and A. G. Smith. 1987. Mitochondrial DNA duplication/deletion events and polymorphism of the C group of male sterile maize cytoplasms. Theor. Appl. Genet. 73:646–653.

Pryor, A. J. 1974. Allelic glutamic dehydrogenase isozymes in maize—a single hybrid enzyme in heterozygotes? Heredity 32:397–401.

----. 1985. The '*Dotted*' controlling element system in maize. p. 419–431. *In* M. Freeling (ed.) (which see).

Racchi, M. L., G. Gavazzi, D. Monti, and P. Manitto. 1978. An analysis of the nutritional requirements of the *Pro* mutant in *Zea mays*. Plant Sci. Lett. 13:357–364.

Randolph, L. F. 1936. Developmental morphology of the caryopsis in maize. J. Agric. Res. 53:881–916.

Reddy, A. R., and P. A. Peterson. 1978. The action of the intensifier (*In*) gene in flavonoid production in aleurone tissue of maize. Can. J. Genet. Cytol. 20:337–347.

----, and G. M. Reddy. 1971. Chemico-genetic studies of leucoanthocyanidin in a maize mutant. Curr. Sci. 40:335–337.

Reddy, G. M. 1964. Genetic control of leucoanthocyanidin formation in maize. Genetics 50:485–489.

----, and E. H. Coe, Jr. 1962. Inter-tissue complementation: a simple technique for direct analysis of gene-action sequence. Science 138:149–150.

Rédei, G. P. 1974. Economy in mutation experiments. Z. Pflanzenzucht. 73:87–96.

----, G. N. Acedo, and S. S. Sandhu. 1984. Mutation induction and detection in *Arabidopsis*. p. 285–313. *In* E. H. Y. Chu and W. M. Generoso (ed.) Mutation, cancer, and malformation. Plenum Publ. Corp., New York.

Regiroli, G., and G. Gavazzi. 1975. Chemical mutagenesis at the *R* locus in maize. Maydica 20:57–66.

Renfro, B. L. 1984. Breeding methods and genetic control of disease resistance in tropical maize. Rev. Trop. Plant Path. 1:225–244.

Rhoades, M. M. 1931. Cytoplasmic inheritance of male sterility in *Zea mays*. Science 73:340–341.

----. 1933. The cytoplasmic inheritance of male sterility in *Zea mays*. J. Genet. 27:71–93.

----. 1936. The effect of varying gene dosage on aleurone colour in maize. J. Genet. 33:347–354.

----. 1938. Effect of the *Dt* gene on the mutability of the *a₁* allele in maize. Genetics 23:377–397.

----. 1941. The genetic control of mutability in maize. Cold Spring Harbor Symp. Quant. Biol. 9:138–144.

----. 1943. Genic induction of an inherited cytoplasmic difference. Proc. Natl. Acad. Sci. USA 29:327–329.

----. 1945. On the genetic control of mutability in maize. Proc. Natl. Acad. Sci. 31:91–95.

----. 1946. Plastid mutations. Cold Spring Harbor Symp. Quant. Biol. 11:202–207.

----. 1950. Gene induced mutation of a heritable cytoplasmic factor producing male sterility in maize. Proc. Natl. Acad. Sci. USA 36:634–635.

----. 1951. Duplicate genes in maize. Am. Nat. 85:105–110.

----. 1952. The effect of the bronze locus on anthocyanin formation in maize. Am. Nat. 86:105–108.

----. 1955. The cytogenetics of maize. p. 123–219 *In* G. F. Sprague (ed.) Corn and corn improvement. Academic Press, New York.

----, and E. Dempsey. 1966a. The effect of abnormal chromosome 10 on preferential segregation and crossing over in maize. Genetics 53:989–1020.

----, and ----. 1966b. Induction of chromosome doubling at meiosis by the elongate gene in maize. Genetics 54:505–522.

----, and ----. 1972. On the mechanism of chromatin loss induced by the B chromosome of maize. Genetics 71:73–96.

----, and ----. 1973a. Chromatin elimination induced by the B chromosome of maize. I. Mechanism of loss and the pattern of endosperm variegation. J. Hered. 64:12–18.

----, and ----. 1973b. Cytogenetic studies on a transmissible deficiency in chromosome 3 of maize. J. Hered. 64:125–128.

----, and B. McClintock. 1935. The cytogenetics of maize. Bot. Rev. 1:292–325.

Rhoades, V. H. 1935. The location of a gene for disease resistance in maize. Proc. Natl. Acad. Sci. USA 21:243–246.

Richardson, L. B., D. S. Robertson, and I. C. Anderson. 1962. Genetic and environmental variation: effect on pigments of selected maize mutants. Science 138:1333–1334.

Robertson, D. S. 1952. The genotype of the endosperm and embryo as it influences vivipary in maize. Proc. Natl. Acad. Sci. 38:580–583.

----. 1955. The genetics of vivipary in maize. Genetics 40:745–760.

----. 1961. Linkage studies of mutants in maize with pigment deficiencies in endosperm and seedling. Genetics 46:649–662.

----. 1975. Survey of the albino and white-endosperm mutants of maize: their phenotypes and gene symbols. J. Hered. 66:67–74.

----. 1978. Characterization of a mutator system in maize. Mutat. Res. 51:21–28.

----. 1982. Chlorophyll and carotenoid mutants. p. 313–315. *In* W. F. Sheridan (ed.) Maize for biological research. Plant Molec. Biol. Assoc., Charlottesville, VA.

----, and I. C. Anderson. 1961. Temperature-sensitive alleles of the Y_1 locus in maize. J. Hered. 52:53–60.

----, ----, and M. D. Bachmann. 1978. Pigment-deficient mutants: genetic, biochemical, and developmental studies. p. 461–494. *In* D. B. Walden (ed.) Maize breeding and genetics. John Wiley and Sons, New York.

----, M. D. Bachmann, and I. C. Anderson. 1966. Role of carotenoids in protecting chlorophyll from photodestruction—II. Studies on the effect of four modifiers of the albino cl_1 mutant of maize. Photochem. Photobiol. 5:797–805.

----, P. S. Stinard, J. G. W. Morris. 1985. Genetic and molecular studies on germinal and somatic instability in *mutator*-induced aleurone mutants of maize. p. 317–331. *In* M. Freeling (ed.) (which see).

Robichaud, C. S., J. Wong, and I. M. Sussex. 1980. Control of in vitro growth of viviparous embryo mutants of maize by abscisic acid. Dev. Genet. 1:325–330.

Roman, H., and A. J. Ullstrup. 1951. The use of A-B translocations to locate genes in maize. Agron. J. 43:450–454.

Rubenstein, I., and D. E. Geraghty. 1986. The genetic organization of zein. Adv. Cereal Sci. Technol. 8:297–315.

Saedler, H., Z. Schwarz-Sommer, and A. Gierl. 1985. The role of plant transposable elements in gene evolution. p. 271–281. *In* M. Freeling (ed.) (which see).

Salamini, F., N. DiFonzo, E. Fornasari, E. Gentinetta, R. Reggiani, and C. Soave. 1983. Mucronate, *Mc*, a dominant gene of maize which interacts with opaque-2 to suppress zein synthesis. Theor. Appl. Genet. 65:123–128.

----, and C. Lorenzoni. 1970. Genetical analysis of glossy mutants of maize. III. Intracistron recombination and high negative interference at the gl_1 locus. Mol. Gen. Genet. 108:225–232.

Sander, C., L. J. Laber, W. D. Bell, and R. H. Hamilton. 1968. Light sensitivity of plastids and plastid pigments present in the albescent maize mutant. Plant Physiol. 43:693–697.

Sando, C. E., R. T. Milner, and M. S. Sherman. 1935. Pigments of the mendelian color types in maize. Chrysanthemin from purple-husked maize. J. Biol. Chem. 109:203–211.

Saravitz, C. H., and C. D. Boyer. 1987. Starch characteristics in cultures of normal and mutant maize endosperm. Theor. Appl. Genet. 73:489–495.

Sarkar, K. R., and E. H. Coe, Jr. 1966. A genetic analysis of the origin of maternal haploids in maize. Genetics 54:453–464.

––––, and ––––. 1971a. Analysis of events leading to heterofertilization in maize. J. Hered. 62:118–120.

––––, and ––––. 1971b. Anomalous fertilization in diploid-tetraploid crosses in maize. Crop Sci. 11:539–542.

––––, and ––––. 1971c. Origin of parthenogenetic diploids in maize and its implications for production of homozygous lines. Crop Sci. 11:543–544.

Sastry, G. R. K. 1970. Paramutation and mutation of R^{ch} in maize. Theor. Appl. Genet. 40:185–190.

Sayed, G. S. 1956. Heterosis in corn; and the role of photosynthesis in the development of *Puccinia sorghi* Schw. Ph.D. diss. Cornell Univ. (Diss. Abstr. 16:216).

Scandalios, J. G. 1965. Subunit dissociation and recombination of catalase isozymes. Proc. Natl. Acad. Sci. USA 53:1035–1040.

––––, W-F. Tong, and D. G. Roupakias. 1980. *Cat3*, a third gene locus coding for a tissue-specific catalase in maize: genetics, intracellular location, and some biochemical properties. Mol. Gen. Genet. 179:33–41.

Schiefelbein, J. W., D. B. Furtek, V. Raboy, J. A. Banks, N. V. Fedoroff, and O. E. Nelson, Jr. 1985. Exploiting transposable elements to study the expression of a maize gene. p. 445–459. *In* M. Freeling (ed.) (which see).

Schwartz, D. 1950. The analysis of a case of cross-sterility in maize. Proc. Natl. Acad. Sci. USA 36:719–724.

––––. 1951. The interaction of nuclear and cytoplasmic factors in the inheritance of male sterility in maize. Genetics 36:676–696.

––––. 1960. Genetic studies on mutant enzymes in maize: synthesis of hybrid enzymes by heterozygotes. Proc. Natl. Acad. Sci. USA 46:1210–1215.

––––. Regulation of gene action in maize. Proc. XI Int. Cong. Genet. 2:131–135.

––––. 1969. An example of gene fixation resulting from selective advantage in suboptimal conditions. Am. Nat. 103:479–481.

––––. 1971a. Subunit interaction of a temperature-sensitive alcohol dehydrogenase mutant in maize. Genetics 67:515–519.

––––. 1971b. Dimerization mutants of alcohol dehydrogenase of maize. Proc. Natl. Acad. Sci. USA 68:145–146.

––––. 1971c. Genetic control of alcohol dehydrogenase—a competition model for regulation of gene action. Genetics 67:411–425.

––––. 1973. Comparisons of relative activities of maize Adh_1 alleles in heterozygotes—analyses at the protein (CRM) level. Genetics 74:615–617.

––––. 1979. Analysis of the size alleles of the *Pro* gene in maize—evidence for a mutant protein processor. Mol. Gen. Genet. 174:233–240.

––––. 1985. Differential activity of transposed *wx-m9Ac* derivatives on various *Ds* elements. p. 391–403. *In* M. Freeling (ed.) (which see).

––––, and W. J. Laughner. 1969. A molecular basis for heterosis. Science 166:626–627.

––––, and J. Osterman. 1976. A pollen selection system for alcohol-dehydrogenase-negative mutants in plants. Genetics 83:63–65.

Schwarz-Sommer, N. Shepherd, E. Tacke, A. Gierl, W. Rohde, L. Leclercq, M. Mattes, R. Berndtgen, P. A. Peterson, and H. Saedler. 1987. Influence of transposable elements on the structure and function of the *A1* gene of *Zea mays*. EMBO J. 6:287–294.

Scott, G. E., and C. M. Campbell. 1969. Internode length in normal and brachytic-2 maize inbreds and single crosses. Crop Sci. 9:293–295.

––––, F. F. Dicke, and G. R. Pesho. 1966. Location of genes conditioning resistance in corn to leaf feeding of the European corn borer. Crop Sci. 6:444–446.

––––, and C. O. Grogan. 1969. Location of a gene in maize conditioning susceptibility to atrazine. Crop Sci. 9:669–670.

––––, S. B. King, and J. W. Armour, Jr. 1984. Inheritance of resistance to Southern Corn Rust in maize populations. Crop Sci. 24:265–267.

Shadley, J. D., and D. F. Weber. 1980. Identification of a factor in maize that increases embryo fatty acid unsaturation by trisomic and B-A translocational analyses. Can. J. Genet. Cytol. 22:11–19.

----, and ----. 1986. Location of chromosomal regions controlling fatty acid composition of embryo oil in *Zea mays* L. Can. J. Genet. Cytol. 28:260–265.

Shah, D. M., C. M. Hironaka, R. C. Wiegand, E. I. Harding, G. G. Krivi, and D. C. Tiemeier. 1986. Structural analysis of a maize gene coding for glutathione-S-transferase involved in herbicide detoxification. Plant Mol. Biol. 6:203–212.

Sharman, B. C. 1942. Developmental anatomy of the shoot of *Zea mays* L. Ann. Bot. 6:245–282.

Shaver, D. L. 1967. Perennial maize. J. Hered. 58:270–273.

----. 1983. Genetics and breeding of maize with extra leaves above the ear. Proc. Annu. Corn Sorghum Res. Conf. 38:161–180.

Sheridan, W. F. (ed.) 1982. Maize for biological research. Plant Molec. Biol. Assoc., Charlottesville, VA.

----, and J. K. Clark. 1987. Allelism testing by double pollination of lethal maize *dek* mutants. J. Hered. 78:49–50.

----, and M. G. Neuffer. 1980. Defective kernel mutants of maize. II. Morphological and embryo culture studies. Genetics 95:945–960.

----, and ----. 1982. Maize developmental mutants: Embryos unable to form leaf primordia. J. Hered. 73:318–329.

----, and ----. 1986. Genetic control of embryo and endosperm development in maize. p. 105–122. *In* G. M. Reddy and E. H. Coe, Jr. (ed.) Gene structure and function in higher plants. Oxford and IBH Publ., New Delhi.

----, and Y. R. Thorstenson. 1986. Development profiles of three embryo-lethal maize mutants lacking leaf primordia: *ptd*-1130*, *cp*-1418*, and *bno*-747B*. Dev. Genet. 7:35–49.

Shih, K. L. 1969. Effects of pretreatment with X rays on paramutability or paramutagenicity of certain *R* alleles in maize. Genetics 61:179–189.

----, and R. A. Brink. 1969. Effects of X-irradiation on aleurone pigmenting potential of standard *R'* and a paramutant form of *R'* in maize. Genetics 61:167–177.

Shimabukuro, R. H., D. S. Frear, H. R. Swanson, and W. C. Walsh. 1971. Glutathione conjugation: an enzymatic basis for atrazine resistance in corn. Plant Physiol. 47:10–14.

Shumway, L. K., and T. E. Weier. 1967. The chloroplast structure of iojap maize. Am. J. Bot. 54:773–780.

Siemenroth, A., T. Borner, and U. Metzger. 1980. Biochemical studies on the iojap mutant of maize. Plant Physiol. 65:1108–1110.

Singh, A., and J. R. Laughnan. 1972. Instability of S male-sterile cytoplasm in maize. Genetics 71:607–620.

Singh, M., and J. M. Widholm. 1975. Study of a corn (*Zea mays* L.) mutant (*Blue Fluorescent-1*) which accumulates anthranilic acid and its beta-glucoside. Biochem. Genet. 13:357–367.

Singleton, W. R. 1946. Inheritance of indeterminate growth in maize. J. Hered. 37:61–64.

----. 1951. Inheritance of corn-grass, a macromutation in maize, and its possible significance as an ancestral type. Am. Nat. 85:81–96.

Sisco, P. H., V. E. Gracen, H. L. Everett, E. D. Earle, D. R. Pring, J. W. McNay, and C. S. Levings, III. 1985. Fertility restoration and mitochondrial nucleic acids distinguish at least five subgroups among *cms-S* cytoplasms of maize (*Zea mays* L.). Theor. Appl. Genet. 71:5–15.

Smith, D. R., A. L. Hooker, S. M. Lim, and J. B. Beckett. 1971. Disease reaction of thirty sources of cytoplasmic male-sterile corn to *Helminthosporium maydis* race T. Crop Sci. 11:772–773.

Smith, J. S. C. 1984. Genetic variability within United-States hybrid maize—Multivariate analysis of isozyme data. Crop Sci. 24:1041–1046.

----. 1986. Biochemical fingerprints of cultivars using reversed-phase high performance liquid chromatography and isozyme electrophoresis: A review. Seed Sci. Technol. 14:753–768.

----, M. M. Goodman, and C. W. Stuber. 1985a. Genetic variability within United States maize germplasm. 1. Historically important lines. Crop Sci. 25:550–555.

----, ----, and ----. 1985b. Genetic variability within United States maize germplasm. 2. Widely-used inbred lines 1970 to 1979. Crop Sci. 25:681–685.

----, ----, and ----. 1985c. Relationships between maize and teosinte of Mexico and Guatemala: Numerical analysis of allozyme data. Econ. Bot. 39:12–24.

Soave, C., and F. Salamini. 1984. Organization and regulation of zein genes in maize endosperm. Phil. Trans. R. Soc. London B 304:341–347.

Sorenson, J. C. 1982. Catalase: a system for studying the molecular basis of developmental gene regulation. p. 135–138. *In* W. F. Sheridan (ed.) Maize for biological research. Plant Molec. Biol. Assoc., Charlottesville, VA.

Spoehr, H. A. 1942. The culture of albino maize. Plant Physiol. 17:397–410.

Sprague, G. F. 1932. The nature and extent of hetero-fertilization in maize. Genetics 17:358–368.

————. 1933. Pollen tube establishment and the deficiency of waxy seeds in certain maize crosses. Proc. Natl. Acad. Sci. USA 19:838–841.

————, and H. H. McKinney. 1966. Aberrant ratio: an anomaly in maize associated with virus infection. Genetics 54:1287–1296.

————, and ————. 1971. Further evidence on the genetic behavior of AR in maize. Genetics 67:533–542.

————, ————, and L. Greeley. 1963. Virus as a mutagenic agent in maize. Science 141:1052–1053.

Springer, B., W. Werr, P. Starlinger, D. C. Bennett, M. Zokolica, and M. Freeling. 1986. The *Shrunken* gene on chromosome 9 of *Zea mays* L. is expressed in various plant tissues and encodes an anaerobic protein. Mol. Gen. Genet. 205:461–468.

Stadler, L. J. 1928. Genetic effects of x-rays in maize. Proc. Natl. Acad. Sci. USA 14:69–75.

————. 1930. Some genetic effects of x-rays in plants. J. Hered. 21:3–19.

————. 1933. On the genetic nature of induced mutations in plants. II. A haplo-viable deficiency in maize. Missouri Agric. Exp. Stn. Res. Bull. 204:1–29.

————. 1939. Genetic studies with ultraviolet radiation. Proc. VII Int. Cong. Genet. 269–276.

————. 1942. Some observations on gene variability and spontaneous mutation. Spragg memorial lectures on plant breeding (third series). Michigan State College, East Lansing.

————. 1944. The effect of X-rays upon dominant mutation in maize. Proc. Natl. Acad. Sci. USA 30:123–128.

————. 1946. Spontaneous mutation at the *R* locus in maize. I. The aleurone-color and plant-color effects. Genetics 31:377–394.

————. 1951. Spontaneous mutation in maize. Cold Spring Harbor Symp. Quant. Biol. 16:49–63.

————, and M. H. Emmerling. 1956. Relation of unequal crossing over to the interdependence of R^r elements (P) and (S). Genetics 41:124–137.

————, and M. G. Nuffer. 1953. Problems of gene structure. II. Separation of R^r elements (S) and (P) by unequal crossing over. Science 117:471–472.

————, and H. Roman. 1948. The effect of X-rays upon mutation of the gene *A* in maize. Genetics 33:273–303.

————, and G. F. Sprague. 1936. Genetic effects of ultra-violet radiation in maize. Proc. Natl. Acad. Sci. USA 22:572–591.

————, and F. M. Uber. 1942. Genetic effects of ultraviolet radiation in maize. IV. Comparison of monochromatic radiations. Genetics 27:84–118.

Starlinger, P., U. Courage, H.-P. Doring, W.-B. Frommer, R. Kunze, A. Laird, A. Merckelbach, M. Muller-Neumann, E. Tillmann, W. Werr, and J. Yoder. 1985. Plant transposable elements—Factors in the evolution of the maize genome? p. 251–270. *In* M. Freeling (ed.) (which see).

Stebbins, G. L. 1967. Gene action, mitotic frequency and morphogenesis in higher plants. Dev. Biol. Suppl. 1:113–135.

Steffensen, D. M. 1968. A reconstruction of cell development in the shoot apex of maize. Am. J. Bot. 55:354–369.

Stein, O. L. 1955. Rates of leaf initiation in two mutants of *Zea mays*, dwarf-1 and brachytic-2. Am. J. Bot. 42:885–892.

————, and D. M. Steffensen. 1959a. The activity of X-rayed apical meristems: a genetic and morphogenetic analysis in *Zea mays*. Z. Vererbungsl. 90:483–502.

————, and ————. 1959b. Radiation-induced genetic markers in the study of leaf growth in *Zea*. Am. J. Bot. 46:485–489.

Stern, D. B., and D. M. Lonsdale. 1982. Mitochondrial and chloroplast genomes of maize have a 12-kilobase DNA sequence in common. Nature 299:698–702.

Stinson, J., and J. P. Mascarenhas. 1985. Onset of alcohol dehydrogenase synthesis during microsporogenesis in maize. Plant Physiol. 77:222–224.

Stroup, D. 1970. Genic induction and maternal transmission of variegation in *Zea mays*. J. Hered. 61:139–141.

Stuber, C. W., and M. M. Goodman. 1983. Allozyme genotypes for popular and historically important inbred lines of corn, *Zea mays* L. Agric. Res. Serv. ARR S-16:1–29.

————, J. F. Wendel, M. M. Goodman, and J. S. C. Smith. 1988. Techniques and scoring procedures for starch gel electrophoresis of enzymes from maize (*Zea mays* L.). North Carolina State Agric. Exp. Stn. Res. Bull. 286.

Styles, E. D. 1970. Functionally duplicate genes conditioning anthocyanin formation in maize. Can. J. Genet. Cytol. 12:397.

————. 1986. Relating genotypes to phenotypes for genes controlling flavonoid pigments in maize. p. 135–145. *In* G. M. Reddy and E. H. Coe, Jr. (ed.) Gene structure and function in higher plants. Oxford & IBH Publ., New Delhi.

————, and R. A. Brink. 1966. The metastable nature of paramutable *R* alleles in maize. I. Heritable enhancement in level of standard *R*ʳ action. Genetics 54:433–439.

————, and ————. 1969. The metastable nature of paramutable *R* alleles in maize. IV. Parallel enhancement of *R* action in heterozygotes with *r* and in hemizygotes. Genetics 61:801–811.

————, and O. Ceska. 1972. Flavonoid pigments in genetic strains of maize. Phytochemistry 11:3019–3021.

————, and ————. 1975. Genetic control of 3-hydroxy- and 3-deoxy-flavonoids in *Zea mays*. Phytochemistry 14:413–415.

————, and ————. 1977. The genetic control of flavonoid synthesis in maize. Can. J. Genet. Cytol. 19:289–302.

————, and ————. 1981a. *P* and *R* control of flavonoids in bronze coleoptiles of maize. Can. J. Genet. Cytol. 23:691–704.

————, and ————. 1981b. Genotypes affecting the flavonoid constituents of maize pollen. Maydica 26:141–152.

————, ————, and K. T. Seah. 1973. Developmental differences in action of *R* and *B* alleles in maize. Can. J. Genet. Cytol. 15:59–72.

————, and E. H. Coe, Jr. 1986. Unstable expression of an *R* allele with *a3* in maize. J. Hered. 77:389–393.

Teas, H. J., and E. G. Anderson. 1951. Accumulation of anthranilic acid by a mutant of maize. Proc. Natl. Acad. Sci. USA 37:645–649.

Thompson, D. L., and R. R. Bergquist. 1984. Inheritance of mature plant resistance to *Helminthosporium maydis* Race O in maize. Crop Sci. 24:807–811.

Timothy, D. H., C. S. Levings, III, D. R. Pring, M. F. Conde, and J. L. Kermicle. 1979. Organelle DNA variation and systematic relationships in the genus *Zea*: teosinte. Proc. Natl. Acad. Sci. USA 76:4220–4224.

Tsai, C. Y. 1983. Genetics of storage protein in maize. Plant Breeding Rev. 1:103–138.

————, F. Salamini, and O. E. Nelson. 1970. Enzymes of carbohydrate metabolism in the developing endosperm of maize. Plant Physiol. 46:299–306.

Tsay, H. S., S. H. Miao, and J. M. Widholm. 1986. Factors affecting haploid plant regeneration from maize anther culture. J. Plant Physiol. 126:33–40.

Tseng, C. T., W. D. Guthrie, W. A. Russell, J. C. Robbins, J. R. Coats, and J. J. Tollefson. 1984. Evaluation of two procedures to select for resistance to the European corn borer in a synthetic cultivar of maize. Crop Sci. 24:1129–1133.

Ullstrup, A. J. 1965. Inheritance and linkage of a gene determining resistance in maize to an American race of *Puccinia polysora*. Phytopathology 55:425–428.

————. 1977. Diseases of corn. *In* G. F. Sprague (ed.) Corn and corn improvement, 2nd ed. Agronomy 18:391–500.

————. 1978. Evolution and dynamics of corn diseases and insect problems since the advent of hybrid corn. p. 283–297. *In* D. B. Walden (ed.) Maize breeding and genetics. John Wiley and Sons, New York.

van Overbeek, J. 1935. The growth hormone and the dwarf type of growth in corn. Proc. Natl. Acad. Sci. USA 21:292–299.

————. 1938. "Laziness" in maize due to abnormal distribution of growth hormone. J. Hered. 29:339–341.

Walbot, V., V. Chandler, and L. Taylor. 1985. Alterations in the mutator transposable element family of *Zea mays*. p. 333–342. *In* M. Freeling (ed.) (which see).

————, ————, L. P. Taylor, and P. McLaughlin. 1987. Regulation of transposable element activities during the development and evolution of *Zea mays* L. p. 265–284. *In* R. A. Raff and E. C. Raff (ed.) Development as an evolutionary process. Alan R. Liss, New York.

————, and E. H. Coe, Jr. 1979. Nuclear gene iojap conditions a programmed change to ribosome-less plastids in *Zea mays*. Proc. Natl. Acad. Sci. USA 76: 2760–2764.

————, D. A. Hoisington, and M. G. Neuffer. 1983. Disease lesion mimic mutations. p. 431–442. *In* T. Kosuge et al. (ed.) Genetic engineering of plants. Plenum Publishing Corp., New York.

Weatherwax, P. 1929. The morphological nature of Teopod corn. J. Hered. 20:325–330.

————. 1955. Structure and development of reproductive organs. p. 89–121. *In* G. F. Sprague (ed.) Corn and corn improvement, 1st ed. Academic Press, New York.

Weber, D. F. 1973. A test of distributive pairing in *Zea mays* utilizing doubly monosomic plants. Theor. Appl. Genet. 43:167–173.

————. 1986. The production and utilisation of monosomic *Zea mays* in cytogenetic studies. p. 191–204. *In* G. M. Reddy and E. H. Coe, Jr. (ed.) Gene structure and function in higher plants. Oxford and IBH Publ., New Delhi.

————, and D. E. Alexander. 1972. Redundant segments in *Zea mays* detected by translocations of monoploid origin. Chromosoma 39:27–42.

Weissinger, A. K., D. H. Timothy, C. S. Levings, III, and M. M. Goodman. 1983. Patterns of mitochondrial DNA variation in indigenous maize races of Latin America. Genetics 104:365–379.

Wendel, J. F., C. W. Stuber, M. D. Edwards, and M. M. Goodman. 1986. Duplicated chromosome segments in maize (*Zea mays* L.): further evidence from hexokinase isozymes. Theor. Appl. Genet. 72:178–185.

————, M. D. Edwards, and C. W. Stuber. 1987. Evidence for multilocus genetic control of preferential fertilisation in maize. Heredity 58:297–301.

Wessler, S. R., and M. J. Varagona. 1985. Molecular basis of mutations at the waxy locus of maize: Correlation with the fine structure genetic map. Proc. Natl. Acad. Sci. USA 82:4177–4181.

Weyers, W. H. 1961. Expression and stability of the marbled allele in maize. Genetics 46:1061–1067.

Wiegand, R. C., D. M. Shah, T. J. Mozer, E. I. Harding, J. Diaz-collier, C. Saunders, E. G. Jaworski, and D. C. Tiemeier. 1986. Messenger RNA encoding a glutathione-S-transferase responsible for herbicide tolerance in maize is induced in response to safener treatment. Plant Mol. Biol. 7:235–243.

Wienand, U., U. Weydemann, U. Niesbach-Klosgen, P. A. Peterson, and H. Saedler. 1986. Molecular cloning of the *c2* locus of *Zea mays*, the gene coding for chalcone synthase. Mol. Gen. Genet. 203:202–207.

Williams, W. M., K. V. Satyanarayana, and J. L. Kermicle. 1984. *R*-stippled maize as a transposable element system. Genetics 107:477–488.

Wilson, D. R., and B. A. Larkins. 1984. Zein gene organization in maize and related grasses. J. Mol. Evol. 20:330–340.

Wise, R. P., A. E. Fliss, D. R. Pring, and B. G. Gengenbach. 1987. *Urf13-T* of T cytoplasm maize mitochondria encodes a 13 kD polypeptide. Plant Mol. Biol. 9:121–126.

Wiseman, B. R., N. W. Widstrom, and W. W. McMillian. 1983. Influence of resistant and susceptible corn silks on selected developmental parameters of corn earworm (Lepidoptera: Noctuidae) larvae. J. Econ. Entomol. 76:1288–1290.

Wu, S.-M., and C. A. Rebeiz. 1985. Chloroplast biogenesis: Molecular structure of chlorophyll *b* (E489 F666). J. Biol. Chem. 260:3632–3634.

Zehr, B. E., M. E. Williams, D. R. Duncan, and J. M. Widholm. 1987. Somaclonal variation in the progeny of plants regenerated from callus cultures of seven inbred lines of maize. Can. J. Bot. 65(3):491–499.

4 The Cytogenetics of Corn[1]

WAYNE R. CARLSON

University of Iowa
Iowa City, Iowa

The history of corn (*Zea mays* L.) genetics includes a period of remarkable achievement in cytogenetics (Rhoades, 1984; Keller, 1983; Burr and Burr, 1983). Today, molecular biology is preeminent in corn genetics as it is in most areas of biology. However, cytogenetics remains an important research tool as well as a productive investigative area in its own right. In this chapter, the basic framework of corn cytogentics will be reviewed, with an emphasis on recent findings. Currently, significant areas of research include the development of several new chromosome-staining techniques, isolation of meiotic mutants, studies of the B chromosome, and continuing work on the process of synapsis and the expanding area of molecular cytogenetic research.

4–1 MEIOSIS

Meiosis in corn was described by Rhoades (1950, 1955) and his photographs are reproduced as Fig. 4–1 through 4–3. The only stage not represented is zygonema, which can be recognized by the extended state of its chromosomes and their tendency to clump together in a small region adjacent to the nucleolus. Observations of meiosis in corn have been made primarily with microsporocytes. However, limited studies of megasporogenesis show that meiosis is similar between the sexes (Sinha, 1960). The primary difference is degeneration in the female of three of the four meiotic products whereas all four produce functional gametophytes in the male.

The most significant event in meiosis is chromosomal pairing. Although pairing occurs during the first meiotic division, preparations for it may begin in the prior mitotic divisions. The prophase chromosomes of premeiotic cells are longer and thinner than those in somatic cells. Rhoades (1955) suggested that they are being made ready for the onset of meiosis. Maguire (1983a) studied the last premeiotic mitosis and pro-

---

[1]Occasional segments of the original chapter on cytogenetics by M.M. Rhoades have been retained intact.

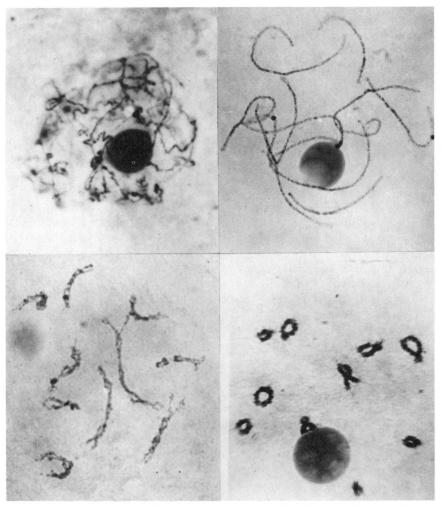

Fig. 4–1. Leptonema (*upper left*), pachynema (*upper right*), diplonema (*lower left*), and diakinesis (*lower right*). Photograph courtesy of M.M. Rhoades.

posed that some association or pairing of homologues occurs in this division.

Synapsis occurs during early substages of the first meiotic prophase. The chromosomes at this time are extremely long and attenuated compared to either somatic or premeiotic chromosomes (Palmer, 1971). The earliest substage of prophase is leptonema, during which the chromosomes are unpaired and appear extremely thin. The next substage, zygonema, is the time of chromosomal pairing. Synapsis is difficult to study in corn, since the zygotene chromosomes occupy a small area of the nucleus. However, serial section observations with the electron micro-

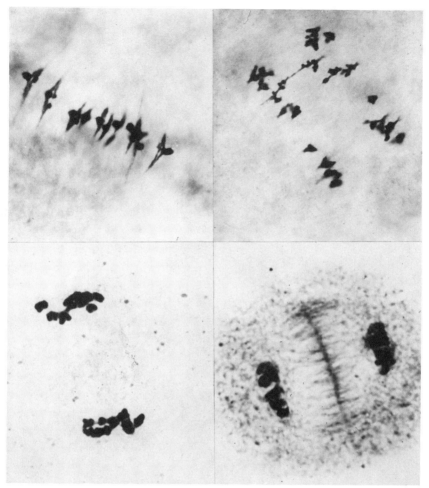

Fig. 4–2. Metaphase I (*upper left*), anaphase I (*upper right*), telophase I (*lower left*), and interphase II (*lower right*). Photograph courtesy of M.M. Rhoades.

scope have allowed analysis of zygonema (Gillies, 1975). Pachynema is defined as beginning when pairing has been completed. At this time, the paired chromosomes emerge from the zygotene knot and spread throughout the nucleus. Three kinds of chromosomal association are seen during pachynema. Most important is homologous pairing, which is usually complete along the length of each bivalent. A second form of chromosomal association, nonhomologous pairing, is found with chromosomes that lack pairing partners. A third type of "pairing" in pachynema is the formation of centromeric fusions and heterochromatic (knob) fusions. These involve associations between nonhomologous bivalents rather than pairs of chromosomes and are quite distinct from synapsis. Fusions are

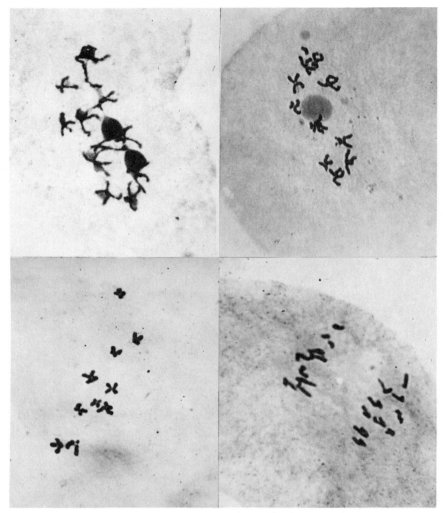

Fig. 4–3. Early and late prophase II (*upper left and right*), metaphase II (*lower left*), and anaphase II (*lower right*). Photograph courtesy of M.M. Rhoades.

transient contacts that are not mediated by synaptonemal complexes and do not result in chiasma formation (McClintock, 1933; Gillies, 1973; Weber and Alexander, 1972).

Properties of the remaining meiotic stages are well known and will not be described. For cytogenetic work, the most useful meiotic stage is pachynema. Due to the extended length of pachytene bivalents, their morphological detail is excellent. Studies of pachynema can be difficult due to overlapping and tangling of the attenuated chromosomes. However, the tendency for bivalents to be distributed around the nucleus at this time usually makes analysis possible. The stage is used for all studies that require precise characterization of chromosomal morphology. Pachynema is also the only stage in which the chromosomes are completely paired, allowing studies on the process of synapsis and the structure of chromosomal rearrangements. Other meiotic stages are also useful for certain purposes. The presence of a (heterozygous) translocation is most readily revealed at diakinesis when multivalent associations are obvious. Paracentric inversions can be detected at anaphase I by the tendency of inversion heterozygotes to produce bridge and fragment configurations (section 4–9.4). The quartet stage at the end of meiosis can be used to follow segregation of the nucleolus organizer region (NOR) of chromosome 6, as follows. When chromosome 6 is involved in a translocation, meiotic segregation of the T/N heterozygote may transmit 0, 1, or 2 NOR's to individual members of the quartet. Classification of the quartet for cells with 0, 1, or 2 nucleoli identifies the type of segregation from the translocation quadrivalent (Burnham, 1962).

4–2 MUTATIONS OF MEIOSIS

Mutations that affect meiosis are of considerable interest to the cytogeneticist, since they provide a method for identifying steps in the meiotic process. In addition, some meiotic mutants are sources of abnormal gametes (diploid, aneuploid, telotrisomic, and iso-trisomic) that can be exploited experimentally. Most of the corn mutations were identified by investigation of plants that displayed pollen sterility. Cytological studies of microsporogenesis allowed classification of sterility mutants into those that disrupt meiosis and those that act postmeiotically. At first, spontaneous mutations were collected as they appeared in populations. Recently, mutants have been induced by treating seeds with N-nitroso-N-methylurea (Golubovskaya and Mashnenkov, 1975, 1976, 1977; Golubovskaya, 1979; Golubovskaya and Sitnikova, 1980; Golubovskaya and Urbach, 1981; Golubovskaya and Khristolyubova, 1985). Specific cytological phenotypes for the meiotic mutants are listed below. (See also reviews by Golubovskaya and Khristolyubova, 1985 and Curtis, 1985.) The phenotypic groupings are broad and specific phenotypes may vary within groups.

Phenotype	Gene	Source
1. Absence of meiosis	*am 1 (ameiotic)*	Rhoades, 1956; Sinha, 1960; Palmer, 1971
	am 2	Doyle (as noted in Curtis, 1985)
2. Absence or disruption of synapsis	*as (asynaptic)*	Beadle and McClintock, 1928; Beadle, 1930, 1933; Miller, 1963; Baker and Morgan, 1969; Nel, 1979
	dy (desynaptic)	Nelson and Clary, 1952

(continued on next page)

Phenotype	Gene	Source
	dysl (*desynaptic*)	Golubovskaya and Mashnenkov, 1976
	dys2	Golubovskaya and Urbach, 1981
	afd (*absence of first division*)	Golubovskaya and Mashnenkov, 1975; Golubovskaya and Khristolyubova, 1985
3. Changes in structural organization of chromosomes	*el* (*elongate*)	Rhoades and Dempsey, 1966a; Nel, 1975
	st (*sticky*)	Beadle, 1932a, 1937; Schwartz, 1958
4. Improper meiotic segregation and/or defective meiotic spindle	*dv* (*divergent spindle*)	Clark, 1940
	ms 28	Golubovskaya and Sitnikova, 1980
	ms 43	Golubovskaya and Sitnikova, 1980
	Mei 025	Golubovskaya and Sitnikova, 1980
5. Failure of cytokinesis and/or irregularities of cell shape	*va1* (variable sterile)	Beadle, 1932b
	va2	Beadle, 1932c
	ms8	Albertsen and Phillips, 1981
	ms9	Albertsen and Phillips, 1981
6. Extra divisions following meiosis	*po* (*polymitotic*)	Beadle, 1929, 1931; West and Phillips, 1985; West, 1985
7. Mutants with several effects on meiosis	*pam1* (*plural abnormalities of meiosis*)	Golubovskaya and Mashnenkov, 1977
	pam2	Golubovskaya and Urbach, 1981
	ms17	Albertsen and Phillips, 1981

For the most part, cytological studies of megasporogenesis have not been performed. However, some of the mutants display female as well as male sterility, suggesting that meiosis is disrupted in both sexes. In addition, progeny tests with mutant females have shown that many of the mutants produce aneuploid eggs or diploid eggs or both (Beadle, 1930; Rhoades, 1956; Rhoades and Dempsey, 1966a; Curtis, 1985). In some cases (*val, va2*) progeny tests indicate a meiotic disruption in the female that was not obvious from calculations of female sterility (Curtis, 1985). Nevertheless, several mutants show no detectable disruption of female meiosis, indicating that the genes serve male specific functions.

Although meiotic mutants are the primary focus of this section, post-meiotic mutations that produce male sterility will be mentioned briefly.

Albertsen and Phillips (1981) analyzed a number of primarily postmeiotic male-sterile (*ms*) mutants. (By definition *ms* mutants are female fertile). For this purpose, they developed a classification system for identifying postmeiotic stages in the male. They then characterized 13 *ms* mutants for time of action and phenotypic effect. Three had a meiotic effect while the remaining 10 caused postmeiotic abnormalities. Each of the postmeiotic mutants behaves as a recessive in heterozygotes, even though the phenotype appears at haploid stages. Another class of postmeiotic mutants are the haploid-effective ones. They cause either pollen or egg lethality in gametophytes that carry the gene (Coe and Neuffer, 1977, p. 170).

4-3 CHROMOSOME MORPHOLOGY AND EVOLUTION

4-3.1 Meiotic Chromosomes

The 10 chromosomes of corn were first characterized by McClintock (1929a). She analyzed cells from the first pollen mitosis and classified the chromosomes primarily on the basis of overall length and centromere position. Later, McClintock (1930, 1931, 1933) found that much better morphological detail was available in the pachytene stage of meiosis. She demonstrated the considerable experimental value of pachynema in a series of pioneering cytogenetical studies. The original numbering of the chromosomes from mitotic studies is not entirely consistent with chromosome lengths found in pachynema. Consequently, the pachytene chromosome 5 is slightly longer than 4 and chromosome 8 is slightly longer than 7.

The pachytene chromosomes were described by Longley (1938, 1939) and Rhoades (1950, 1955). They are distinguished from each other on the basis of (i) overall length, (ii) centromere position (arm ratio), (iii) appearance of the centromeric heterochromatin, (iv) characteristic chromomeres, and (v) the possession of knobs at specific chromosomal sites. (Knobs are blocks of heterochromatin that are not associated with the centromere.) In addition, chromosome 6 is identified by the presence of its NOR.

Methods for analyzing pachynema will not be reviewed, except to note a few highlights. Cytological observation in certain genetic backgrounds is difficult because the pachytene chromosomes are tightly clumped and difficult to analyze. On the other hand, some inbred lines such as KyS give excellent spreading of the chromosomes so that pachynema is a magnificent stage. In most cases, experiments can be successfully performed without being concerned about genetic background. Another basic aspect of utilizing pachynema is the identification of centromeres for calculation of arm ratios. Centromeres in pachynema are light-staining and are sometimes confused with "gaps" on the chromosomes. Confusion can be avoided by realizing that centromeres (i) occur in the central regions of the chromosomes, except in the case of no. 6, (ii) are generally surrounded by dark-staining chromatin, and (iii) are translucent rather than transparent: they resemble ground glass in appearance. As noted in section 4–1, centromeres from different bivalents can fuse in pachynema to give the appearance of one large centromere with four arms radiating from it. Knobs also tend to fuse with each other to produce, apparently, one large knob. Fusions require a cytological discrimination of the figures into two bivalents. Finally, there are consistent hallmarks of certain chromosomes that allow rapid identification. The NOR on the short arm of chromosome 6 affixes the bivalent to the nucleolus, unlike any other bivalent. Chromosome 7 has a bulging, very dark region of centromeric heterochromatin in the long arm which is different from that on all the other chromosomes. Further details of chromosome identification were given by Rhoades (1955).

The basic features of pachytene chromosomes in corn are relatively constant throughout the species. Surveys of corn have shown little evidence for naturally occurring translocations (Cooper and Brink, 1937) or inversions (Rhoades and Dempsey, 1953). Variant centromere positions have been found for chromosomes 2 and 4 (McClintock, 1933). However, in a review of large-scale studies of corn in South America, McClintock (1978a) reported that chromosome lengths and centromere positions were constant among the races examined. In addition, chromomere-staining patterns seemed not to vary, although polymorphism for certain large chromomeres was found. The only rearrangement commonly observed was a small inversion on chromosome 8 that was first reported by McClintock in 1933.

Despite the relative uniformity of the corn karyotype, polymorphism is common for certain chromosomal features including heterochromatic knobs, an abnormal form of chromosome 10 and a supernumerary (B) chromosome (section 4–10). The common property of knobs, abnormal 10, and the B chromosome is their dispensable nature. The added chromatin they provide is not required for viability of the organism. As a consequence, variation for the presence or absence of these regions has been tolerated.

Knobs are polymorphic both in their presence or absence on a chromosome and in their size. In a study of Latin American corn, Longley and Kato (1965) found that some knob positions were represented more frequently than others. However, none of the knobs were universally present in all plants. In addition, knobs could be divided into five size classes. For many of the knob positions, all five classes were represented in the survey.

Cytological polymorphisms have been useful in analyzing the origin and evolution of corn. Extensive studies on the races of corn in the Americas were made by Longley and Kato (1965), Kato (1976) and McClintock et al. (1981). Kato (1984) recently reviewed the distribution patterns found for knobs, abnormal 10, and the B chromosome. He concluded that corn was derived from Mexican annual teosinte (*Z. mexicana*) populations and probably was originally domesticated at several different sites. Subsequently, corn was distributed from region to region by the migration of different people at different times.

4-3.2 Mitotic Chromosomes

The morphological detail available in mitotic chromosomes is considerably reduced from that found in pachynema. Mitotic prophase chromosomes show differential staining of heterochromatin and euchromatin just as is found in meiotic prophase. However, the condensed nature of chromosomes in mitosis makes the distinction between heterochromatin and euchromatin much more difficult to determine. Only large prominent heterochromatic regions are easily identified by conventional staining (Carlson, 1970a). In mitotic metaphase, the loss of morphological detail is even greater since the whole chromosome is densely stained. Also the reduced size of mitotic chromosomes makes accurate determinations of overall length or centromere position more difficult than with pachytene chromosomes. Nevertheless, Chen (1969) identified all the corn chromosomes in mitotic metaphase through the use of centromeric position, overall length and specific morphological features such as the secondary constriction on 6S (Fig. 4–4).

The main advantages of studying mitotic chromosomes are the ease with which the material can be obtained (root tips) and the simplicity of chromosome counting in well-spread cells. The disadvantages have been partially overcome by the application of newer techniques. C-banding of metaphase cells with Giemsa produces differential staining of metaphase chromosomes, with specific regions (bands) staining brightly. Ward (1980) used C-banding on different varieties of corn with known knob constitutions. He showed correspondence between the number of knobs and the number of C-bands. Similar results were reported by Aguiar-Perecin (1985). In addition, the staining patterns reported by Ward and Aguiar-Perecin showed that C-banding can be used to differentiate between classes of heterochromatin (section 4–4.3). Additional C-banding studies in corn were reported by Hadlaczky and Kalman, 1975; Chow and Larter, 1981; Mastenbroek and de Wet, 1983; Aguiar-Perecin and Vosa, 1985; and Rayburn et al., 1985. Another newer technique that has been applied to mitotic cells of corn is bromodeoxyuridine-mediated staining. The method produces differential staining of chromatids, as discussed in section 4–6.5. Chou (1985) used the procedure to study sister chromatid exchange in corn (Fig. 4–5).

Several additional techniques have been developed in recent years for improved staining of specific tissues or cell types. Lin (1977) developed a method for squashing and staining young corn endosperm. Kindiger and Beckett (1985) used chloral hydrate to clear starch from pollen grains, allowing staining of the second pollen mitosis. Phillips and Wang (1984) discussed methods of studying chromosomal variation in cultured cells and in plants regenerated from them.

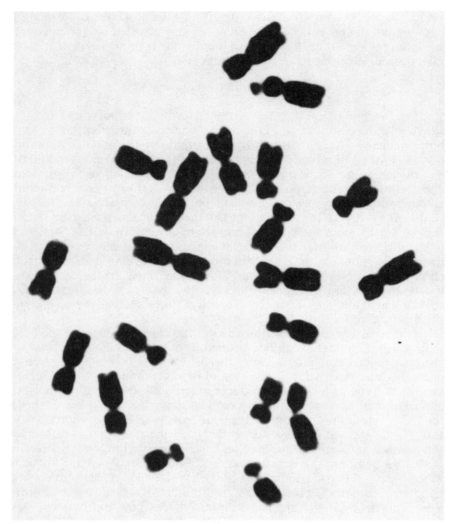

Fig. 4–4. Metaphase of mitosis. All chromosomes have a primary constriction (centromere). Chromosome 6 also has a secondary constriction (NOR). One member of the chromosome 6 pair can be identified in this photograph by its extra constriction. Photograph courtesy of J.D. Horn.

4–4 PROPERTIES OF INDIVIDUAL CHROMOSOMAL REGIONS

4–4.1 Centromeres and Telomeres

Proper division of eukaryotic chromosomes in mitosis depends on the presence of three types of elements: centromeres, telomeres, and replication initiation sites. This conclusion was elegantly proven in yeast

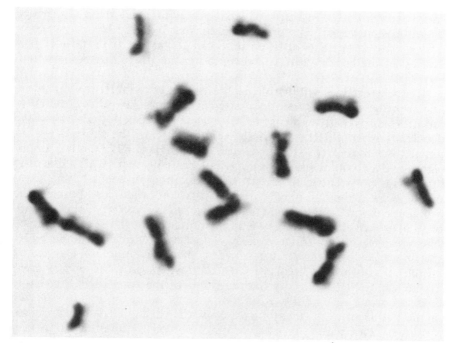

Fig. 4–5. Fluorescent plus Giemsa (FPG) staining of mitotic chromosomes. Some sister chromatid exchange is evident. Photograph courtesy of T.S. Chou.

through the cloning of each of these elements and the demonstration of their functioning in artificially constructed chromosomes (Blackburn, 1985).

The centromeres of corn are much larger than the 100 base pair CEN sequences which have been cloned in yeast. Corn centromeres are known to be duplicate structures (McClintock, 1932, 1938b), which may account for some or all of their increased size. However, the corn centromere may also be more complex than that of yeast. It is possible that studies of B-chromosome nondisjunction will help in identifying functional subdivisions of the centromere (section 4–10).

The consequences of deleting telomeres from chromosomes were first shown by McClintock's work in corn. She examined the fate of dicentric bridges produced by crossing over between inversion and normal chromosomes (McClintock, 1938a). The splitting of a dicentric bridge produces chromosomes which lack telomeric sequences in one arm. The chromosomes replicate improperly in the subsequent interphase and daughter chromatids are conjoined at the broken end. In the next anaphase, a bridge forms between dividing centromeres. Consequently, the formation of bridges in one division leads to re-formation of bridges in later divisions. With inversions, bridge formation in anaphase I is followed by bridge formation in the male and female gametophytic mitoses.

(Bridges do not occur in anaphase II, since second division is not preceded by DNA replication.) The process is referred to as the breakage-fusion-bridge cycle. It consists of (i) chromosome breakage, (ii) improper replication of the broken arm, (iii) formation of a bridge in anaphase, and (iv) repetition of step (i).

If gametophytes with broken chromatids are viable, the breakage-fusion-bridge cycle may continue after fertilization. However, the chromosomes derived from a dicentric are usually deficient and, unless the deficiency is small (Rhoades and Dempsey, 1953), the gametes are inviable. McClintock (1941a) developed two aberrations (a tandem duplication and a complex inversion) in which crossing over yields a dicentric bridge but no acentric fragment. Consequently, all genes of the chromosome are located on the dicentric. With appropriate positioning of the bridge breakpoint, functional gametophytes are produced. Using this approach, broken chromosomes were transmitted through the gametophyte. The breakage-fusion-bridge cycle was found to continue in the endosperm, producing a sectored loss of genes during development. Depending on the point-of-bridge breakage in the endosperm mitoses, one or more markers may be lost at any one division. In the sporophyte, the cycle does not occur. Apparently, a function present in the embryo but lacking in the endosperm or gametophyte causes a "healing" of broken chromosomes. The healing process is now assumed to entail addition of a new telomere to the chromosome end (McClintock, 1984).

One might expect the breakage-fusion-bridge cycle to produce complex deficient-duplicate chromosomes as a result of random bridge breakage, but this is not always true. McClintock (1941a) noted that the bridges involved in a cycle tend to break at the same place in successive divisions. The interpretation was that fusion of sister chromatids following breakage may be weak or incomplete. Similarly, a cytological study of corn endosperm by Schwartz and Murray (1957) showed that bridge formation does not always occur during a breakage-fusion-bridge cycle. They suggested that incomplete fusion of chromatids occurs frequently, leading to normal rather than dicentric anaphase configurations. In addition, Miles (1971) found that certain chromosomes derived from dicentric bridges always separated at the original breakage site during endosperm development. Specifically, breaks in heterochromatic regions sometimes showed a complete absence of the genetic losses associated with a breakage-fusion-bridge cycle.

The dicentric cycle described above is referred to as the chromatid breakage-fusion-bridge cycle. It involves fusion between daughter chromatids of the same chromosome. In addition to the chromatid cycle, McClintock (1942, 1978b) demonstrated the existence of a chromosome cycle. If two broken chromosomes are introduced into the zygote, one through the sperm and one through the egg, the broken ends frequently fuse with each other, forming a dicentric. The dicentric bridge now spans two different centromeres rather than connecting the chromatids of one centromere. In anaphase, *two* bridges are produced if the centromeres disjoin in opposite directions. (Bridges arise only when the two centromeres are rotated 180 ° with respect to each other, not in every anaphase.) Breakage of the bridges in anaphase sends two chromosomes with freshly broken ends to each pole. The broken chromosomes in each daughter cell fuse with each other to re-form a dicentric. Subsequent double bridge formation by the dicentric begins another cycle.

The chromosome cycle depends on the ability of freshly broken chromosome ends to fuse with each other, a property known as "stickiness." Apparently, this fusion occurs prior to DNA synthesis, since two broken chromosomes do not undergo separate chromatid cycles. Also, fusion occurs before sporophytic "healing" of broken ends, since the chromosome cycle is found in the sporpophyte as well as the endosperm. However, the cycle frequently ceases in later stages of sporophyte development, with production of two stable chromosomes from the dicentric (McClintock, 1942, 1978b).

The chromatid cycle and the chromosome cycle are distinct phenomena (McClintock, 1942, 1951). However, Schwartz and Murray (1957) found evidence that a chromatid cycle can convert spontaneously to a chromosome cycle. They made observations on the behavior of broken chromosomes in developing endosperm. In some sectors of the tissue, a single bridge (chromatid) pattern was changed into a two bridge (chromosome) cycle. The explanation given was that single bridges occasionally undergo nondisjunction rather than breakage in anaphase. Migration of both centromeres to one pole establishes a chromosome-type breakage-fusion-bridge cycle in successive divisions. (A method is described in section 4–10 by which B-type chromosomes can be used to convert a chromatid cycle to a chromosome cycle.)

Breakage-fusion-bridge cycles have a chaotic effect on the corn genome. Considerable evidence suggests that latent transposons can be activated in cells that are undergoing either a chromosome or a chromatid cycle. (McClintock, 1951, 1984; Doerschug, 1973; Rhoades and Dempsey, 1982, 1983). In addition, gross chromosomal rearrangements arise frequently in such cells and can include chromosomes not involved in the cycle (McClintock, 1951, 1978b). McClintock proposed that breakage-fusion-bridge cycles place genomes under severe stress, with genetic and chromosomal changes being a response to the stress. Other influences on the genome may have similar effects in activating transposons and rearranging chromosomes, as discussed by Freeling (1984).

4–4.2 Nucleolus Organizer Region

In mitotic metaphase cells, the chromosomes assume a densely staining appearance in which euchromatin and heterochromatin are indistinguishable. Each chromosome retains a band of light-staining material referred to as the primary constriction. It corresponds to the centromere.

In addition, some chromosomes may contain a secondary constriction that usually corresponds to a site for nucleolus formation. In corn, the NOR is located on chromosome 6 (6S) and is marked by a secondary constriction (Fig. 4–4). The NOR is responsible for reforming the nucleolus after all divisions.

In meiosis, the pachytene bivalent of chromosome 6 displays considerable detail of the NOR. The secondary constriction is a light-staining region, usually appressed to the nucleolus. It varies in length, apparently due to a stretching of the region during nucleolus formation (McClintock, 1934). Proximal to the constriction is a large, knob-like segment of heterochromatin. The "knob" is not always uniformly dark-stained as are conventional knobs. The heterochromatic region and the secondary constriction together constitute the NOR. Distal to the constriction is the short-terminus of 6S. It is referred to as the satellite, and contains four dark-staining chromomeres (McClintock, 1934). The satellite does not function in nucleolus formation.

McClintock (1934) studied the NOR by using a translocation with one breakpoint inside the NOR-knob (T6–9a). She found that both the 6^9 and 9^6 chromosomes formed nucleoli. Consequently, the NOR heterochromatin on 6^9 must be capable of forming a nucleolus in the absence of the secondary constriction. However, the 9^6 chromosome, which has less NOR heterochromatin than 6^9, forms a larger nucleolus. The latter finding suggests a role for the secondary constriction in nucleolus organization. Furthermore, Lima-de-Faria and Sarvella (1962) found that the secondary constriction is almost always closely attached to the nucleolus in pachytene cells. In their studies, the constriction plus the distal part of the NOR-knob were appressed to the nucleolus in 83.2% of cells. In 12.6% of cases, the constriction plus medial and distal segments of the NOR-knob were attached. An association of the heterochromatin but not the constriction to the nucleolus was found in only 2.5% of cells. The constriction by itself was bound to the nucleolus in the remaining 1.7% of cells. More conclusive evidence that the secondary constriction is important in nucleolus formation was provided by R.L. Phillips in studies of translocations involving the NOR. Phillips (1978, p. 727ff) determined the volumes of nucleoli formed by translocation chromosomes from 19 different rearrangements. Breakpoints of some translocations were within the NOR heterochromatin and in other cases within the secondary constriction. Breaks near the juncture of the heterochromatin and the constriction were most informative. The secondary constriction was found capable of forming large nucleoli in the absence of adjacent heterochromatin. However, the heterochromatin was relatively ineffective by itself in forming nucleoli. In general, chromosomes containing NOR heterochromatin but lacking the secondary constriction formed very small nucleoli. Certain translocation break positions in the knob seemed to have an enhancing effect on the size of nucleoli formed in the absence of a secondary constriction. Nevertheless, nucleoli formed by NOR-heterochromatin alone were always relatively small.

The experiments of Phillips indicate that the secondary constriction is the primary site of nucleolus organization. However, the NOR-knob can compensate for loss of the secondary constriction by forming a full-sized nucleolus (Phillips, 1978; Phillips et al., 1983; McClintock, 1934). Deletion of the secondary constriction can be accomplished by meiotic segregation in translocations that involve the NOR-knob (T6-X). For several translocation heterozygotes of this type, it was consistently found that 6^x + X microspores had normal-sized nucleoli (Phillips, 1978). Apparently, absence of the secondary constriction induces NOR activity by the heterochromatin.

It is perhaps surprising that two cytologically different regions such as the NOR knob and the constriction share a capacity for organizer activity. However, studies of their DNA composition have helped explain the relationship. It is now well established that the NOR of corn contains the genes for 18S and 28S ribosomal RNA (Phillips et al., 1971b; Phillips et al., 1974; Wimber et al., 1974; Ramirez and Sinclair, 1975; Doerschug, 1976). (Genes for 5S ribosomal RNA were placed on chromosome 2 by Wimber et al., 1974 and Mascia et al., 1981). The ribosomal RNA genes in 6S are repetitive, with thousands of copies per organizer. Givens and Phillips (1976) analyzed the distribution of these multiple copies in the NOR. They used a technique developed by Gopinath and Burnham (1956) to duplicate interstitial regions of chromosomes (section 4–9.3). In one type of duplication the NOR heterochromatin was made trisomic. In another case, the secondary constriction was made trisomic. Hybridization studies using ^{3}H ribosomal RNA showed that trisomy for the knob produced an approximate 50% increase in ribosomal RNA genes per genome. Similar tests on plants trisomic for the secondary constriction showed no elevation of ribosomal RNA genes from the control. The conclusion was that the majority of ribosomal RNA genes are located in the knob region, but statistical error allows for some to be present in the secondary constriction. Subsequent experiments used in situ hybridization of labeled RNA on pachytene chromosomes to identify sites of rRNA genes by autoradiography (Phillips et al., 1983). Label was found over both the NOR heterochromatin and the secondary constriction. In addition, quantitative studies of silver grain density indicated that 70 to 80% of the genes are located in the heterochromatin and the remainder in the euchromatic constriction. No hybridization was found in the satellite region. It can be concluded that cytological differences between the NOR-knob and the secondary constriction mask a basic similarity in DNA content.

It has been suggested (Givens and Phillips, 1976) that the NOR heterochromatin serves as an inactive reserve organizer. This conclusion was based partly on the tendency for the secondary constriction to control nucleolar organization. The knob serves as an active organizer only when the secondary constriction is deleted. It has also been shown that the number of copies of 18S and 28S genes is quite variable from one strain to the next. The variation may be tolerable if excess rRNA genes are sequestered in the NOR heterochromatin. This concept was considered and tested by Buescher et al. (1984). They analyzed the cellular rRNA content in 16 corn cultivars with gene copy numbers ranging from 5000 to 23 000. Increased numbers of genes did not produce an increase in rRNA. Some variation in ribosomal RNA content was found, but it bore no relationship to ribosomal gene copy number. The authors favored the explanation that heterochromatic inactivation of extra gene copies is used to determine the total number of active genes in the NOR.

4–4.3   Heterochromatin

Regions of the chromosome that are condensed and dark-staining throughout the meiotic and mitotic division cycles are referred to as *heterochromatin*. Additional properties usually associated with heterochromatin are late replication of the DNA in S phase and an absence of RNA synthesis. Two major classes of heterochromatin exist in nature: facultative and constitutive. Facultative heterochromatin is transitory: the chromatin has alternate euchromatic and heterochromatic states. Constitutive heterochromatin never assumes a euchromatic state. The role of facultative heterochromatin in the life cycle of an organism has been clearly defined. It exists as a mechanism for inactivating groups of genes (or whole chromosomes) for various purposes. However, despite considerable speculation for many years, no general role for constitutive heterochromatin has been demonstrated.

Heterochromatin in corn is all of the constitutive type. (In some respects, NOR heterochromatin may be considered facultative: see above.) Corn heterochromatin can be divided into several subgroups. The standard (A) chromosomes contain three classes of heterochromatin. One type is centric heterochromatin, which flanks the centromeres. A second category is NOR-heterochromatin, which has the unique ability to organize a nucleolus. Third are the knobs, which include all prominent heterochromatin (except NOR) that is located some distance away from the centromere. Two additional classes of heterochromatin are found on the B chromosome. These are centric B heterochromatin and distal B heterochromatin.

In total, five types of heterochromatin are present in corn. Each has distinctive features which set it apart from the other categories. In terms of cytological properties, the centric heterochromatin of A chromosomes is less darkly stained than other heterochromatin. It appears somewhat diffuse in standard aceto-carmine preparations (Rhoades, 1978). Also, knobs show distinctive staining properties when C-banding techniques are used. Ward (1980) and Aguiar-Perecin (1985) found that corn knobs stain prominently with C-banding methods whereas other heterochromatin stains less well or not at all. (Ward observed staining of the B centric heterochromatin with C-banding whereas Aguiar-Perecin did not.)

DNA constitution also varies between classes of heterochromatin. Knobs contain a highly repetitive 185 base pair sequence (Peacock et al., 1981; Viotti et al., 1985). The sequence is also present at reduced concentration in B chromosome centric heterochromatin, but not in other classes of heterochromatin. DNA of the NOR heterochromatin contains the ribosomal RNA genes. It also undergoes replication at the same time as euchromatin, whereas all other classes of heterochromatin are basically late-replicating (Pryor et al., 1980).

In addition to their distinctive cytological and biochemical properties, certain classes of corn heterochromatin have functional properties that serve to distinguish them. Nucleolus organizer region heterochromatin is capable of organizing a nucleolus. Knobs display centromeric activity during meiosis in the presence of abnormal chromosome 10 (Peacock et al., 1981 and section 4–10). Centromeric heterochromatin of the B controls division of the B centromere at the second pollen mitosis (section 4–10).

Much of the heterochromatin in corn is unnecessary to the organism. For example, knobs are highly polymorphic and their frequency in plants varies over a considerable range. Their presence or absence seems unimportant to the organism. Knobs are additions to the genome which increase the physical length of a chromosome when present (Rhoades, 1955, p. 127; Ward, 1980; Aguiar-Perecin, 1985; Aguiar-Perecin and Vosa, 1985). The association of some heterochromatic regions with accumulation mechanisms (section 4–10) suggests a possible parasitic relationship to the organism (Ostergren, 1945). However, some evidence suggests a useful role for heterochromatin. Centric heterochromatin is not polymorphic as are knobs, indicating that it may perform an important function (Rhoades, 1978). Also, some types of heterochromatin have effects on crossing over which may be significant to the organism (Rhoades, 1978). Understanding the role of heterochromatin in corn may involve separate studies on the five different classes that exist.

4–5 SYNAPSIS

Chromosome pairing during meiosis serves two basic functions. It sets the stage for a reduction in chromosome number and also allows for crossing over between homologues. As such, it has occupied the attention of cytologists for many years. Nevertheless, the basic mechanism of synapsis is not understood. Certainly the process is a complex one involving (i) DNA synthesis at zygonema and pachynema (Stern and Hotta, 1978, 1983, 1984; Bouchard and Stern, 1980; Friedman et al., 1982) (ii) formation of special structures (synaptonemal complexes) to mediate pairing, and (iii) organization of the chromosomes into thin, elongate forms. The complexity is not surprising, since the problem of matching homologous base sequences during pairing seems profound.

Theoretical explanations of the process of pairing have often foundered on the problem of preparing homologous chromosomes for synapsis. If chromosomes were randomly distributed in the leptotene nucleus, the association of homologues would have to occur over a distance of several microns, with the interference of nonhomologous contacts. Consequently, numerous proposals have been made by which homologues can be matched up prior to pairing. A common feature found in several proposals is that chromosomal migration in anaphase-telophase provides some alignment of chromosomes. The polar movement that occurs in anaphase places centromeres in one area of the cell and telomeres opposite. This distribution, referred to as the Rab1 orientation, persists from telophase through interphase and into the following prophase (Fussell, 1984). It is found in both mitotic and meiotic nuclei. The position of centromeres at one side of the nucleus and telomeres opposite is stabilized by the attachment of telomeres to a restricted area of the nuclear envelope (Gillies, 1975). During meiosis, the Rab1 orientation positions homologous sequences in the same orientation with respect to each other and at roughly the same distance from the nuclear envelope. In addition, other mechanisms may operate to produce chromosome alignment (see below).

Synapsis of the chromosomes begins in zygonema both at distal and intercalary sites on corn chromosomes. It proceeds to completion through formation of secondary contact sites and by extension (zipper synapsis) from regions already paired. Synapsis is initiated and completed during zygonema. Pachynema is the time during which the chromosomes are completely paired along their lengths. In diplonema, pairing ends except at the sites of chiasma formation.

Electron microscopy has revealed that synapsis is mediated by a thin, ribbon-like structure called the *synaptonemal complex* (Moses, 1968; Westergaard and von Wettstein, 1972; von Wettstein et al., 1984; Gillies, 1984). The complex can be subdivided cytologically into two lateral elements and one central element. In leptonema, each chromosome possesses a single lateral element (axial element), which probably is attached between sister chromatids. In zygonema, the lateral elements of homologues pair up and a central element forms between them to complete the synaptonemal complex. During pachynema, the complex is usually continuous throughout the length of each bivalent. When the chromosomes open out in diplonema the complex is lost, but remnants of it may remain at the chiasmata. By metaphase, the chromosomes are completely free of the synaptonemal complex and the brief existence of this structure is limited to the period of synapsis and crossing over.

Anderson et al. (1985) studied the relationship between the pachytene bivalent and its synaptonemal complex in 10 higher plants, including corn. They found that a constant amount of DNA is associated with a unit length of synaptonemal complex. The conclusion was that a similar chromosomal organization is present during pachynema in all species examined.

The synaptonemal complex probably does not play a role in prealignment of homologues. However, it does appear to be an integral part of the pairing process from initiation through completion and maintenance of synapsis. In addition, the synaptonemal complex is a prerequisite for crossing over. It may play a role in the organization of recombination nodules, which are sites of crossing over (von Wettstein et al., 1984). When the complex is missing from part of a bivalent or from a whole bivalent, the region affected lacks crossing over.

Having considered the basic elements of synapsis, we will now return to certain problems for a more detailed discussion. Pairing will be divided into three successive stages: alignment, synapsis, and maintenance of synapsis.

4–5.1 Chromosome Alignment in Somatic Nuclei

The idea that homologous chromosomes may be aligned prior to meiosis in preparation for pairing is not new (Smith, 1942). The presence of somatic pairing in an organism may indicate the presence of a system for aligning chromosomes at all cell divisions, including meiosis. Somatic association of homologues has been reported in corn (Horn and Walden, 1978) and many other plants (Avivi and Feldman, 1980; Comings, 1980). However, most studies have reported relatively loose associations between chromosomes. Part of the problem is the use of metaphase cells in making measurements. Most theories on alignment invoke the nuclear membrane as an element in holding homologues together. Consequently, metaphase chromosomes may only display a remnant of prior associations. Another problem is the method used in slide preparation (squashing) which converts a three-dimensional cell into a distorted two-dimensional form. In addition, some studies have used colchicine or other prefixatives to prepare metaphase cells. The treatments can disturb any preexisting chromosome relationships.

Ashley (1979) examined prophase rather than metaphase cells of *Ornithogalum virens* in search of a more direct indication of homologue alignment. She was aided in this study by low chromosome number (n = 3) and a distinctive C-banded pattern on each chromosome. Ashley found specific end-to-end associations of chromosomes in both haploid pollen grain and diploid root tip cells. The associations in haploid cells were necessarily between nonhomologous chromosomes rather than homologues. Nevertheless, they were specific associations that produced a chain of three chromosomes in specific order of chromosome number and chromosome arm. The same nonhomologous associations were found in diploid cells. In addition, diploid cells had two specific associations of homologous chromosome arms that linked together the haploid genomes into a ring of six chromosomes. Ashley and Pocock (1981) proposed a model for the organization of chromosomes in somatic and meiotic nuclei on the basis of these findings. They began with the assumption that interphase chromosomes are oriented in the Rabl configuration. They also assumed that the telomeres of all chromosomes are attached to the nuclear envelope, as has been widely reported for many organisms including corn (Gillies, 1975). They hypothesized that specific nonhomologous telomeres of a haploid set associate with each other at the nuclear envelope, probably during telophase. In a diploid, the two haploid chains link together to form a ring, as was found with *O. virens*. The ring is anchored and stabilized at the nuclear envelope from telophase through prophase. During metaphase/anaphase the chromosomes retain the same relative positions as in prophase. After division, specific telomeric associations are re-established at the nuclear envelope. The ring structure serves meiotic cells as a form of prealignment for homologues. The ring is believed to close on itself during pairing, bringing together homologues from opposite positions in the ring. The ring organization reduces nonhomologous contacts during the process of pairing.

Another approach to improving the study of somatic associations was taken by Bennett (1982, 1983). He studied somatic metaphase cells but used little or no pretreatment of chromosomes and avoided squash techniques. Instead, cells were embedded and sectioned for the electron microscope. Serial sections were used to reconstruct the three-dimensional arrangement of chromosomes in the cells. Individual chromosomes were identified by their volumes and arm ratios. In addition, C-bands and centromere volume were sometimes utilized for chromosome identification. (The size of centromeres was shown to be related to chromosome size: Bennett et al., 1981.) Bennett examined metaphases in several grass species and in their hybrids. He found in hybrid plants that genome separation is present at metaphase. The two genomes of hybrids show concentric separation, with one genome located near the center of the cell and the other at its periphery (Finch et al., 1981; Bennett, 1983). In nonhybrid cells, the genomes show a different form of separation. Frequently, a line can be drawn on the polar view of a cell which divides the two chromosome sets (Bennett, 1982). This is referred to as side-by-side separation. Due to genome separation, no association of homologues was found in these studies. However, based on centromere-to-centromere distances, Bennett found that chromosomes within a haploid set are arranged in a specific manner (Bennett, 1982; Heslop-Harrison and Bennett, 1983a, b; Bennett, 1983). The chromosome organization found for several species fits a model of somatic chromosome association developed by Bennett (1983). The model predicts that a haploid chromosome set is organized as a chain in which "pairing" is determined by the length of chromosome arms. Each long arm associates with another long arm and each short arm with another short arm, except at the ends of the chain. The chromosomes are organized so that arms of most similar length are paired. Unlike the model of Ashley and Pocock, there is no association between haploid sets to form a ring. However, the chains could become aligned prior to meiotic synapsis, thus reducing the interference in pairing from nonhomologous contacts.

Bennett's model has been tested with a computer-aided analysis for the best fit of centromere positions observed in a cell with the predicted order of the chain (Heslop-Harrison and Bennett, 1983a). The findings with several grasses strongly support the model. However, attempts to test the model on corn have been less successful (Bennett, 1983). No satisfactory prediction could be made for a single order of the 10 corn chromosomes. This was explained by proposing that corn has a tetraploid origin with four separate haploid sets. Putative homoeologues within the maize genome were identified and the existence of duplicate genes on the homoeologues predicted (section 4–9.5). An alternate interpretation of the analysis is that Bennett's model does not apply to corn. Chromosome size differences in corn may not be large enough to produce a specific pattern of chromosome associations (Maguire, 1983b; Fussell, 1984).

The relationship of Bennett's model to synapsis in corn was tested by Maguire (1983b). She studied pairing in diakinesis and metaphase I of two inversion heterozygotes. Pericentric inversions were used in order to alter the lengths of chromosome arms (*In 5a* and *In 7–3717*). Despite a considerable change in the arm ratios, no disruption of synapsis was found in either case, except for occasional asynapsis by one pair of homologues. Apparently, inversion heterozygosity only affected pairing in the bivalent carrying the inversion and did not disrupt any critical prealignment process.

Recently, Fussell (1984) proposed another model for somatic chromosome organization. She reviewed evidence for existence of the Rabl orientation during interphase and for attachment of telomeres to the nuclear envelope. She proposed that chromosome arms of similar length tend to pair at their telomeres. The association occurs during telophase of each division when the nuclear envelope is re-forming. At this time, chromosome arms of similar length have telomeres an equal distance from the pole, allowing attachments between them. The telomeric associations are stabilized by the nuclear envelope and remain through interphase and prophase. The proposal is referred to as the variable retricted model, because it allows a number of chromosome arrangements to occur. Telomeric associations are nonspecific and both homologous and nonhomologous pairing are allowed. Separation of haploid genomes is not predicted. Despite the flexibility of the model, Fussell believes it provides a system for prealignment that can aid pairing during meiosis.

The discussion thus far has centered on the organization of chromosomes in somatic nuclei. The evidence for nonrandom chromosome associations in these nuclei may or may not have relevance to the problem of meiotic synapsis. It is important, therefore, to look for specific associations of chromosomes during the period immediately prior to synapsis. Studies of the last premeiotic mitosis have been reported for several organisms with mixed results (Avivi and Feldman, 1980; Comings, 1980). In corn, Maguire (1983a) used light microscopy to examine the last premeiotic mitosis. She used both squash and sectioning techniques and found a rough alignment of some, apparently homologous, chromosomes. The alignment was more easily observed at some stages, especially late anaphase, than at other stages. In prophase, telomeres were attached to the nuclear envelope but usually there was no association between telomeres. The latter observation argues against a role in synapsis for several models of somatic association that have been proposed.

4–5.2 Chromosome Alignment in Meiosis

The most critical time for studying forces that align homologous chromosomes for synapsis is, of course, meiosis itself. The relevant stages are leptonema and early zygonema. Gillies (1975, 1984) analyzed serial sections of meiotic stages in corn with the electron microscope. He found that telomeres are attached to the nuclear envelope in leptonema and zygonema. Furthermore, the telomeres are restricted to a specialized area of the membrane next to the nucleolus. This restriction of telomeres to one area may result from a Rab1 orientation in the premeiotic telophase. Going from leptonoma to zygonema, lateral movements of telomeres occur along the nuclear envelope. These movements may control the initiation phase of synapsis by allowing contact between distal regions of homologous chromosomes.

Several lines of evidence suggest that distal regions are important for synaptic initiation. Gillies (1975, 1984) found both intercalary and distal pairing initiation sites in reconstructed corn zygotene nuclei. An average of four separate regions of pairing were seen per bivalent. However, a preference for initiation of pairing near the telomeres was found. (Studies with other organisms have sometimes shown a preference for distal initiation of synapsis and sometimes not: Rasmussen and Holm, 1980.) Independent evidence suggesting a tendency for distal synaptic initiation was provided by the studies of Burnham et al. (1972). They utilized 24 translocations between chromosome 1 and chromosome 5. In each experiment, two translocations involving 1 and 5 were combined in a single plant. The intercrosses between translocations were the "opposite-arms" type. If one translocation had breaks in 5L and 1L, the other translocation would have breaks in 5S and 1S. Combinations of 5L, 1S, and 5S, 1L were also made. Since two translocations are used in the experiments, two "crosses" may form during synapsis. Because the translocations involve the same chromosomes, the two crosses are found within a single, complex quadrivalent. In the absence of complete synapsis, which often happens in structural heterozygotes, bivalents sometimes form instead of quadrivalents. The bivalents are necessarily heteromorphic and, depending upon the type of synapsis, may be homologous in the region of the centromere and not at the telomeres or vice versa. If pairing regularly initiates in distal regions of the chromosome, bivalents with homologous ends are expected. Bivalents with nonhomologous ends are expected if synapsis begins at or near the centromeres. Most of the translocations examined have potential pairs in which one chromosome is noticeably longer than the other. Consequently, bivalents with homologous ends show "buckling" in the centromeric area, whereas pairs with proximal homology have overlapping chromosome ends. Using a wide variety of 1–5 translocation combinations with breakpoints in many different positions, Burnham et al. found that pairs with nonhomologous ends were virtually nonexistent. Further analysis led to an approximation of pairing initiation frequencies at different sites on the arms of corn chromosomes. The highest frequency of initiation is subterminal, while initiation in the proximal half of a chromosome arm occurs rarely, if at all. The results establish the existence of preferred sites of pairing initiation and are consistent with a nuclear membrane mediated alignment of homologous telomeres.

Further evidence for distal or telomeric control of synapsis was provided by the work of Doyle (1979a) on preferential pairing in corn. Preferential pairing is the tendency, when a choice of pairing partners is available, for bivalents to form between the most similar chromosomes. The phenomenon is important in nature since it is responsible for the bivalent pairing seen in allopolyploids. Preferential pairing can also exist, to a lesser extent, in autopolyploids or aneuploids if the chromosomes involved are genetically or structurally divergent. Doyle studied preferential pairing in trisomes for chromosome 3 using a genetic test, as follows. Assume that trisomy for chromosome 3 is available in an inbred line of corn. All three of the number 3 chromosomes are essentially identical. They are also marked with the recessive a (white endosperm). A trisomic plant is crossed as female to a normal plant (AA-colored endosperm) from a different genetic background. Progeny are selected which are trisomic (Aaa). The plants are crossed as male parents to a recessive tester. In this cross, only pollen with one chromosome 3 will survive. (Due to pollen competition, the n + 1 pollen will not transmit.) If gamete formation is random, the progeny should be one-third colored (A) and two-thirds white (a). However, if preferential pairing occurs, an excess of white kernels will be found. For instance, if preferential pairing is complete there will be no trivalents in meiosis. Only bivalent/univalent figures will form. In addition, the bivalents will always contain the two identical chromosomes with the a allele, whereas univalents will have A. Pollen produced by this arrangement will be haploid (a) and n + 1 (Aa). Only the haploid pollen will survive and the A allele will be eliminated from the cross. Less extreme forms of preferential pairing are usually found. They are identified by transmission rates for colored kernels (A) that are lower than the 33.3% value expected for random pairing.

Using a test of the sort described, Doyle found that inversions have a strong effect on pairing affinity. Trisomics containing $In/N/N$ chromosomes show preferential pairing of the normal chromosomes. A comparison was made between two different inversions of chromosome 3 for their effects on preferential pairing. Despite a similarity in length of the two inversions, the more distally located one was excluded from pairing more often than the proximal inversion. The finding suggests that distal regions control synaptic initiation. It should be noted, however, that rates of preferential pairing can be controlled in more than one way. For example, absence of crossing over between paired chromosomes leads to their dissociation in diplonema. The relationship between preferential pairing and synaptic initiation is, therefore, not clear-cut.

Despite the appealing simplicity of using telomere-nuclear envelope interactions to control synaptic initiation, problems exist with such hypotheses. Maguire (1984a) recently reviewed the subject. She concluded that models of homologue alignment which rely on telomeric associations cannot account for cases in which pairing between rearranged chromosomes must rely on the matching of intercalary regions (see also Maguire, 1984b, 1985). A model was proposed in which specific sites on each chromosome control long-range interactions between homologues. The sites bind filamentous proteins and the proteins connect homologous chromosomes. Alignment may be achieved through the action of contractile proteins which draw chromosomes together.

4-5.3 Synapsis

Following chromosome alignment, actual synapsis occurs. Gillies (1975, 1984) studied leptonema, zygonema, and pachynema in corn with the electron microscope. He reconstructed nuclei through observations of serial sections and provided a picture of synaptonemal complex formation. The synaptonemal complex (SC) first appears in zygonema. As noted earlier, initial SC formation seems to occur preferentially in distal regions near the nuclear envelope but also is found at several internal sites. Completion of synapsis may occur by a "zipping-up" process in which the synaptonemal complex is extended from initial contact sites. However, zipping-up probably occurs in tandem with the formation of secondary contact sites between homologues. By the end of zygonema, each bivalent contains a synaptonemal complex that is continuous from one end of the chromosome to the other. During pachynema, and at no other time, intimate pairing *via* the synaptonemal complex occurs throughout the bivalent.

Synapsis is usually a strictly homologous process. However, changes in ploidy or changes in chromosome structure can favor pairing between nonhomologous regions. Nonhomologous pairing does not result in crossing over, as indicated in section 4-6.1. Nevertheless, it is usually mediated by a synaptonemal complex. There are two different types of nonhomologous pairing. In one case, nonhomologous pairing is induced by heterozygosity for a chromosomal rearrangement such as an inversion or a translocation. Inversion heterozygotes may show completely nonhomologous ("straight") pairing rather than the inversion loop. Alternately, the loop may be reduced in size due to flanking regions of nonhomologous synapsis. Translocations often display variable positions of the "cross" in pachynema. The usual explanation for these findings is that the synaptonemal complex can extend from homologous regions into nonhomologous regions by "zipper" synapsis (Maguire, 1981, 1984a; Gillies, 1983).

An extreme effect of a rearrangement on pairing was discovered by Rhoades (1968). He studied a rearrangement between chromosomes 3 and 9 in which an internal segment of 3L was transposed to a site within 9S. Pairing between normal 9 and the modified (transposition) 9 was found to be quite irregular. Homologous pairing should produce a uniform buckle or loop in the region of insertion. Instead, Rhoades found that loop formation in 9S was highly variable in position and size and sometimes did not occur at all. The findings were confirmed by electron micrography of Gillies (1983) on spread synaptonemal complexes. Twenty-four pachytene nuclei were studied and the loops (seen as lateral elements) were extremely variable in size and position. In two cases, no loop was found. The results indicate that extensive nonhomologous pairing is the rule, rather than the exception, in *Tp9/N9* bivalents.

The second type of nonhomologous pairing results when chromosomes or chromosome regions have no opportunity for homologous pairing. In cases of haploidy, monosomy and partial monosomy, chromosome segments are present singly. These regions frequently engage in nonhomologous pairing. Single copy regions may synapse either with segments of the same chromosome (foldback pairing) or another chromosome (heterologous pairing). Gillies (1973) studied foldback pairing in the heteromorphic bivalents of partial monosomes. He found normal synaptonemal complexes were present in the region of nonhomologous pairing. Ting reported (1966, 1985) that pachytene chromosomes in haploids frequently engage in foldback pairing. He showed (Ting, 1973) that normal synaptonemal complexes form within the regions of foldback pairing. Heterologous pairing can also be observed in haploids at pachynema, but bivalents are usually classified in late meiotic prophase or metaphase I (Alexander, 1964; Snope, 1967). At these stages, the presence of a bivalent indicates that both synapsis and crossing over have occurred. Pairing detected in this manner most likely resulted from crossing over between homologous, duplicated segments of the genome, since true nonhomologous crossing over is rare or nonexistent (section 4–6.1).

Another aspect of the association of nonhomologues is the phenomenon of distributive pairing. Grell (1962) proposed that achiasmate pairing occurs between nonhomologues in *Drosophila* females when homologous pairing partners are not available. The pairing is maintained until anaphase, when the nonhomologues disjoin. The hypothesis accounts for the nonrandom distribution of univalents during meiosis in *Drosophila*. However, the absence of chiasmata suggests that the chromosomes are held together in first division of meiosis by a special mechanism. Whether distributive pairing is a unique property of *Drosophila* chromosomes was investigated by Weber (1973). He used the *r-x1* mutation to produce plants monosomic for two different chromosomes (section 4–8). Double monosomes have two univalents present in all meiotic cells and provide

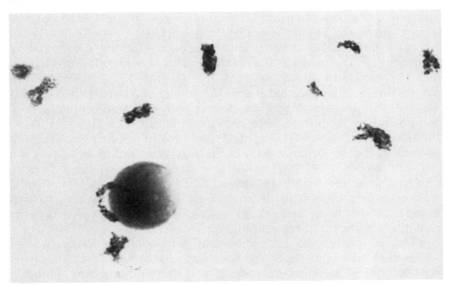

Fig. 4–6. Double monosomic cell in diakinesis. Photograph courtesy of D.F. Weber.

an ideal test of distributive pairing (Fig. 4–6). Weber found a uniformly low rate of pairing between nonhomologues at diakinesis (avg., 3.7% pairs) and metaphase I (avg., 2.2%) using five double monosome combinations. All associations (even atypical ones) were counted and the frequency of pairing may therefore be an overestimate. In addition, the possibility that monosomic pairs migrate to opposite poles was tested in anaphase I and prophase II with negative results. Thus, distributive pairing does not occur in corn.

4–5.4   Maintenance of Synapsis

Following synapsis in zygonema, the chromosomes remain paired through pachynema due to cohesiveness of the synaptonemal complex. During diplonema, the complex is usually lost and pairing is maintained subsequently by chiasmata. However, retention of the synaptonemal complex occurs until anaphase I in some cases of achiasmatic meiosis (*Bombyx* female; *Ectomylois* female; *Bolbe* male). In these insects, the complex apparently is needed to prevent dissociation of the bivalent prior to anaphase (reviewed by von Wettstein et al., 1984).

The pachytene stage may be viewed as a static period for the synaptonemal complex during which pairing is maintained. However, evidence from several organisms suggests that dramatic changes in pairing relationships happen at this time. A process referred to as *synaptic adjustment* has been postulated to explain modifications of pairing that occur in pachynema. The modifications tend to convert complex patterns of pairing, established in zygonema, into simpler forms. The process does not affect all complex associations, since the prior occurrence of crossing over in affected regions can block it.

One effect of synaptic adjustment is to remove the characteristic pairing patterns found in rearrangement heterozygotes. Loops formed by inversions are eliminated, giving bivalents with "straight" pairing. The quadrivalents of translocation heterozygotes are converted to pairs of bivalents. In both cases, bivalents are produced that contain regions of nonhomologous pairing. A similar phenomenon has been reported in polyploids. The tendency here is to convert multivalents, formed during zygonema, into bivalents. A third example of synaptic adjustment is the resolution of interlocking bivalents. Some observations with the electron microscope of late zygotene-early pachytene stages suggest that synapsis is initially less precise than was earlier believed. Considerable tangling and interlocking of bivalents has been found in some organisms. Resolution of the interlocking occurs during pachynema and may involve chromosome breakage (reviewed by von Wettstein, 1984; Gillies, 1984). This finding may make the need for prealignment mechanisms in synapsis less compelling.

The changes in pairing that are proposed to occur during pachynema could alter the interpretation of some cytological observations. Synaptic adjustment, rather than errors in synapsis, could produce some of the nonhomologous pairing seen in rearrangement heterozygotes. Also, preferential pairing in aneuploids and polyploids could depend on the conversion of multivalents to bivalents after synapsis has occurred. However, synaptic adjustment may not be a universal phenomenon. Studies of inversions with light microscopy (Maguire, 1981) and electron microscopy (Gillies, 1983, 1984) suggest that it does not occur in corn. In both studies, no tendency for resolution of abnormal pairing (loops) was found in the transition from early to late pachytene. Maguire suggested that reported cases of synaptic adjustment were found in organisms whose synaptic mechanisms are modified to meet unusual needs. However, one type of adjustment, the resolution of interlocking bivalents, may occur in corn (Gillies, 1983). Gillies suggested (1984) that the primary function of synaptic adjustment may be the resolution of tangled and interlocked bivalents.

4–6 CROSSING OVER

The basic rules of crossing over were established many years ago, with work in corn cytogenetics contributing a considerable amount of the needed information. The reader is referred to previous editions of this chapter for discussions of the early studies with corn (Rhoades, 1955; Carlson, 1977). Also, in light of considerable evidence, it will be assumed that crossing over is mediated by the synaptonemal complex (von Wettstein et al., 1984). The topics to be considered are ones of current interest in cytogenetics.

4–6.1   Nonhomologous Crossing Over

Synapsis in corn, as in other organisms, is usually completely homologous. However, nonhomologous synapsis can occur when a deviation from the normal chromosomal constitution is present. Nonhomologous pairing is mediated by an apparently normal synaptonemal complex
(section 4–5.3). This raises the question of whether crossing over is possible between nonhomologous sites. Most evidence suggests that it is not.
In structural heterozygotes, imprecise (nonhomologous) synapsis is associated with a reduction in crossing over (Burnham, 1934; Rhoades,
1968). Extensive attempts by Weber (1968) failed to select illegitimate
crossovers from a structural heterozygote with frequent nonhomologous
synapsis. Nevertheless, crossing over between nonhomologous chromosomes is occasionally found in haploids. Cytological observations from
diakinesis to anaphase I have shown that bivalents are present at low
frequency in haploids (McClintock, 1933; Snope, 1967). In addition, Alexander (1964) was able to recover a number of reciprocal translocations
from the progeny of haploid × diploid crosses. Translocations are the
expected products of crossing over between nonhomologues. Twenty-two
translocations recovered from haploids were examined cytologically by
Weber and Alexander (1972). Twelve were shown to be independent
isolations of the same aberration, with breakpoints on 6L and 7L at
approximately the same sites. Two other translocations appeared to be
isolations of the same rearrangement, between 2L and 6L. The remainder
were dissimilar. The repeated isolation of 6L-7L and 2L-6L translocations
is best explained by the existence of duplicated segments within the genome that engage in homologous rather than nonhomologous exchange.
The eight dissimilar translocations could represent exchange between short
or relatively divergent duplications. Alternatively, they could arise from
true nonhomologous crossing over. However, the results suggest that
nonhomologous crossing over is rare. Furthermore, the experiments failed
to identify any inversions in the gametes of haploids. Inversions are
expected if the foldback pairing frequently found in haploids is followed
by crossing over.

Another form of nonhomologous association, the fusion of centromeres and knobs, is frequently found in normal pachytene cells. Fusions
are not mediated by synaptonemal complexes and involve associations
between bivalents rather than pairs of chromosomes (section 4–1). They
do not lead to crossing over, since the expected translocations are absent
from gametes of normal diploids.

4–6.2   Comparisons of Crossing Over in Male and Female Flowers

It is of both practical and theoretical interest to know whether rates
of crossing over differ during micro- and megasporogenesis. The work of
many investigators was recently tabulated by Robertson (1984). The data
are often difficult to interpret, but a few general conclusions can be drawn:

1. Many chromosomal regions have similar rates of crossing over in male and female gametes.
2. When rates of crossing over differ between the sexes, it is usually higher in the male gametes.
3. Differences in rates of recombination between male and female flowers may appear in one genetic environment or chromosomal arrangement but not another.

Several proposals have been made to explain the origin of sex differences in crossing over. Rhoades (1941) proposed that one cause may be an effect of centromeric heterochromatin on proximal regions of corn chromosomes. He suggested that the heterochromatin may be more loosely coiled in microsporocytes than in megasporocytes and, therefore, subject to more crossing over. Although no experimental evidence exists for this theory, differences in male vs. female rates of crossing over are often found in proximal chromosomal regions. Rhoades (1978) also showed that another type of heterochromatin can induce differences in male vs. female crossover rates. He measured rates of crossing over in the short arm of chromosome 9 in the presence or absence of a large terminal knob. The frequency of crossing over with the homozygous knobless condition was similar for male and female gametes. However, presence of the knob in either homozygous or heterozygous condition produced a significant difference between the sexes in crossover frequency. Knob heterozygotes showed the greatest difference in crossover rates.

Mogensen (1977) used stocks from Rhoades to analyze the relationship between sex differences in crossing over and synaptonemal complex formation. He studied male and female meiocytes from one plant carrying the 9S knob (homozygosity vs. heterozygosity of the knob was not determined). Electron micrography, with serial sections, was used to reconstruct six male and five female nuclei in pachynema. Mogensen identified the chromosome 9 bivalent by its terminal knob. He determined the lengths of the synaptonemal complex in short and long arms of 9. The long arm SC was the same length in male and female nuclei (21.89 and 20.39 μm, respectively). However, the short arm SC was considerably longer in the male (14.55 μm) than the female (9.62 μm). The results were related to a hypothesis of Stern et al. (1975). In this hypothesis, certain regions of DNA are preselected during the early meiotic prophase for inclusion into the synaptonemal complex. Knobs may, therefore, affect participation of adjacent regions in the preselection process.

Recently, Robertson (1984) demonstrated that B-A translocations can induce sex differences in crossing over. He utilized B-A translocations to construct partial hemizygotes (hypoploids), containing one normal (A) chromosome and one translocation (A^B) chromosome. Absence of the complementary B^A chromosome in these plants means that the A^B cannot be transmitted in crosses (section 4–10). Genes on the A^B will only survive the gametophyte stage if they become attached to the A chromosome by crossing over. Consequently, transmission rates for A^B genes can be used as a measure of crossing over between the translocation breakpoint and the gene. Robertson constructed hypoploids for B-A translocations involving 4S, 5L, 9S, 9L, 10S, and 10L. In all cases tested, the rate of crossing over was considerably higher in the male parents. The differences between male and female crossing over were induced by the hypoploid condition, as was demonstrated by control crosses. Robertson considered a number of explanations for his data. One idea was that B heterochromatin, found at the end of A^B chromosomes, may influence crossing over in adjacent regions. It was also suggested that preferential recovery of noncrossovers may occur during female meiosis in hypoploids. Aneuploid effects of the hypoploid condition could also be the source of differences in male/female crossing over.

In summary, some cases of sex differences in crossing over seem traceable to effects of heterochromatin. However, only knob heterochromatin has been proven to induce such differences. It could be that several independent factors influence the phenomenon.

4–6.3 Intragenic Crossing Over

Recombination studies in corn and most eukaryotes have been largely confined to intergenic crossing over, since intragenic (allelic) crossing over requires large population sizes. However, Benzer's classic experiments on allelic crossing over in the virus T4 prompted Nelson (1957) to question whether genes in eukaryotes could also be subdivided by recombination. Nelson suggested use of the corn gametophyte (pollen) to obtain the large sample sizes needed. Since the *waxy* (*wx*) gene is expressed in the pollen and can be readily classified, this gene was proposed for testing. Nelson gathered different recessive alleles of *wx* and tested recombination between them. In heteroallelic plants, pollen was collected and classified by iodine staining into recessive (brown) and dominant (black) phenotypes. The pollen produced was mainly recessive, but an occasional dominant resulted from recombination. The dominant was seen as an isolated dark-staining pollen grain in a field of light-staining pollen. Rapid classification of large populations was possible and Nelson (1959, 1962, 1968) was able to measure distances between mutant sites within the *wx* locus.

Further studies have shown that *amylose extender* (*ae*) has a suitable pollen phenotype for studying intragenic crossing over (Creech and Kramer, 1961; Moore and Creech, 1972). Also, alleles of the widely studied *alcohol dehydrogenase-1* (*Adh1*) locus can be classified in the pollen by a staining procedure (Freeling, 1976, 1978; Freeling and Bennett, 1985). However, studies of intragenic crossing over have not been limited to genes with pollen phenotypes. Large-scale testcrosses have been used to detect intragenic crossing over at *glossy-1* (Salamini and Lorenzoni, 1970), *bronze* (Dooner, 1986) and the *R* locus (Dooner and Kermicle, 1986). The conventional approach has one advantage: genes flanking the site of intragenic crossing over can be classified. Flanking markers have proven useful in (i) establishing the map order of mutant sites within a gene and (ii) detecting the probable occurrence of gene conversion as a source of intragenic crossing over.

Studies of intragenic crossing over have often been performed to help understand the molecular mechanism of crossing over. Some information on the process has been obtained with corn. Dooner and Kermicle (1986) found that the pattern of intragenic crossing over at both the *bz* and *R* loci is greatly affected by the presence of an inserted transposon (*Ds*). When one gene of a heteroallelic cross is a *Ds*-induced mutation, intragenic recombination tends to be associated with conventional crossing over of flanking markers. However, when the *Ds* insertion is present in both genes (at different sites), flanking markers usually remain parental in the presence of intragenic crossing over. The findings may be due to an influence of *Ds* on the resolution of hybrid DNA complexes, as discussed by Dooner and Kermicle.

Most studies of intragenic crossing over in corn focus on the analysis of gene structure rather than the mechanism of crossing over. For example, Freeling (1978) found that the two most common *Adh-1* isoalleles, *Adh1-S* and *Adh1-F*, differ markedly in terms of intragenic crossing over. EMS-induced null mutations of the isoalleles were studied. Crossing over was found to occur at a much higher rate in heteroallelic crosses involving two *Adh1-S* mutations than when mutants of *Adh1-F* were tested. Also, intragenic crossing over did not occur in cases where one null allele was derived from *Adh1-F* and the other from *Adh1-S*. The results suggest that *Adh1-S* and *Adh1-F* are quite divergent. Sachs et al. (1986) used restriction endonuclease mapping and base-sequencing techniques to demonstrate that a conserved region is present in both alleles but is flanked (both 5′ and 3′) by highly polymorphic sequences.

4–6.4 Restriction Fragment Length Polymorphisms

When bulk DNA from an organism is digested with a restriction endonuclease, a specific complement of fragments is produced. The length of each fragment is determined by the location of enzyme cleavage sites within the genome. Polymorphisms exist in natural populations for the presence or absence of cleavage sites. These polymorphisms often do not affect the phenotype of an organism. They are detectable by population surveys for DNA variability. The procedure involves running DNA samples in a gel electrophoresis system. Radioactive cloned DNA is used as a probe on gel transfers to detect specific sequences. If no polymorphisms are present, a similar band pattern will be found for all individuals. Variation in the number or position of bands is an indicator of polymorphism.

Restriction fragment length polymorphisms (RFLP's) are a new source of allelic variation. They have several advantages over conventional markers, including (i) their codominant nature, (ii) their widespread occurrence in natural populations, and (iii) their phenotypic "expression" in all cells of an organism and at all stages of development. These advantages make RFLP's an especially important tool in human genetics, where studies are limited to natural populations. The major successes to date with RFLP mapping have been in the study of human genetic disease (Gusella et al., 1983; Phillips et al., 1980).

The value of using RFLP markers in plant breeding and genetics was discussed by Burr et al. (1983), Rivin et al. (1983), Beckman and Soller (1983), Soller and Beckman (1983), and Helentjaris et al. (1985). Among the uses proposed were (i) linkage of RFLP loci to quantitative traits for improved selection of agronomically valuable phenotypes, (ii) determination of RFLP profiles for plant varieties that need to be protected commercially, and (iii) the expansion of available genetic markers for general experimental usage. Studies with corn have indicated that the frequency of restriction site polymorphism is quite high. Consequently, corn is well suited for the identification and exploitation of RFLP's. Recently, Helentjaris et al. (1986) reported construction of a genetic linkage map in corn using RFLP loci. They assigned more than 100 loci to specific chromosomes and linkage relationships. Monosomic plants, generated with the *r-x1* system (section 4–8), were instrumental in the assignment of RFLP's to chromosomes. The work is an excellent example of the productive joining of molecular and cytogenetic methods.

4–6.5 Sister Chromatid Exchange

The phenomenon of sister chromatid exchange (SCE) is distinct from crossing over both in its time of occurrence (during meiosis and mitosis) and its biochemical properties (Latt, 1981; Wolff, 1982; Tice and Hollaender, 1984). Nevertheless, the topic is included here because it deals with exchanges between chromatids. Sister chromatid exchange is believed to arise during DNA replication in interphase. It usually has no effect cytologically and is therefore difficult to detect. However, sister exchange during mitosis in a ring chromosome produces a dicentric which is readily seen as a double bridge in anaphase (McClintock, 1938b). Ring chromosomes also form bridges following sister exchange in meiosis, but detection is more difficult due to the added effects of crossing over. Schwartz (1953a, b) studied the cytological consequences of meiotic sister exchange in plants heterozygous for a normal chromosome 6 and a ring chromosome 6. The ring was deficient for part of the satellite region in 6S and for a small distal segment of the long arm. Due to the shortness of 6S, only exchanges in the long arm between the ring and rod chromosomes were considered. Schwartz determined the anaphase configurations expected for single and double chiasmata in the absence of sister strand exchange. Conventional crossing over should produce dicentric bridges in AI and occasionally AII. The expected configurations were found plus an additional class of double bridges in AII (10%). The double bridges arose from sister strand exchange in the ring chromosome (plus no crossing over or a two strand double exchange between nonsister chromatids). Schwartz also found an excess of AII single bridges which can be explained by sister strand exchange. The findings were confirmed by Miles (1970), who analyzed crossing over in a ring-rod heterozygote of chromosome 10.

Sister chromatid exchange can be detected cytologically in normal (rod) chromosomes by using special staining methods. The techniques produce different staining intensities on the two chromatids of a metaphase chromosome. Tritiated thymidine was first used to label chromatids differentially. However, the autoradiographic image produced with tritium is not precise. A better picture of sister exchange is possible through use of the base analog, 5-bromodeoxyuridine. Chromatids which contain the analog stain less brightly than normal chromatids with the fluorescent dye, Hoechst 33258. Fluorescence decreases going from DNA that has no analog to DNA that has one substituted strand to DNA that has both strands containing the analog. The differences can be observed with a fluorescence microscope. Alternately, the fluorescent-stained chromosomes can be poststained with Giemsa. The same staining intensity differences will then be visible with light microscopy (Perry and Wolff, 1974; Latt, 1982). The latter technique, referred to as "fluorescent plus Giemsa" (FPG), is widely used. Chou (1985) applied the FPG method to mitotic cells of corn (Fig. 4–5). He showed that certain chemicals with mutagenic properties (atrazine and ethylmethanesulfonate) increase the rate of SCE formation.

One problem with interpreting studies of sister chromatid exchange is that the baseline (spontaneous) rate is not easily measured. Methods used to detect SCE's also contribute to their formation. Both ^{3}H thymidine and bromodeoxyuridine are known to induce sister chromatid exchange (Latt, 1981). Consequently, a persistent question is whether any of the sister chromatid exchanges detected in an organism arise naturally. In corn, the best evidence for spontaneous occurrence of sister exchange comes from the work on ring chromosomes discussed earlier.

4–7 THE EUPLOID SERIES

The euploid individual is defined as having a chromosome number that is a simple multiple of n. Normal diploid corn (2n) is part of a euploid series which also contains haploid plants (n) and polyploids (3n, 4n, etc.). Cell and nuclear size are smallest in haploids and become progressively larger as the degree of ploidy increases. Haploid sporophytes are smaller than their diploid sibs, but no striking morphological differences exist between members of the euploid series. Haploids will be discussed first, followed by polyploids.

By far, the majority of haploids that arise spontaneously are maternal in origin. The mechanism is not understood, but one sperm of the pollen grain affects fertilization of the polar nuclei while the other is, in some way, lost. Chase (1969) and Sarkar and Coe (1966) showed by gene dosage tests that fusion of both sperm from a pollen grain with the polar nuclei is *not* the source of maternal haploids. Androgenetic haploids are produced infrequently. In a population of 577 haploids studied by Chase (1963), seven were paternal in origin and the remainder maternal. Spontaneous loss of the maternal nucleus is obviously a rare event.

The frequency of haploids produced in most crosses is roughly 1/1000 kernels (Chase, 1969). However, the rate of haploid formation is under genetic control. The incidence of haploidy in a cross is affected by the genotypes of both male and female parents (Chase, 1949, 1951). Coe (1959) found a particular genetic stock (Coe's *stock 6*) which, when self-pollinated, produces maternal haploids at a rate in excess of 3%. Outcrosses of stock 6 as either male or female parent also give enhanced frequencies of haploids (Sarkar and Coe, 1966). Kermicle (1969) identified a mutant gene *ig* (*indeterminate gametophyte*) that has pleiotropic effects on embryo sac development. One consequence of the *ig* phenotype is a high frequency of haploid progeny (3%), of which the majority are *paternal* in origin. An interesting attribute of the *ig* system is the ability to combine the nucleus from a male parent with the cytoplasm from a female parent (Goodsell, 1961).

The production of haploids is greatly increased (from 0.1–3%) by the use of *stock 6* or the *ig* mutation. However, haploids can be identified in populations even when their frequency is quite low. Selective techniques have been developed to screen kernels for haploid embryos. The most successful of the methods employ endosperm and scutellum (embryo) color markers, in which selection can be applied prior to germination. The *C-I* marker (Coe and Sarkar, 1964) and the *R–nj/cudu* marker (Grenblatt and Bock, 1967; Nanda and Chase, 1966) have been successfully used in haploid selection. During screening, kernels are identified in which the endosperm has an expected dominant phenotype but the embryo does not. The systems work well as long as they are applied in genetic backgrounds that allow clear expression of the color phenotypes.

Recently, haploid production has been attempted through anther culture. Some successes have been reported and the reader is referred to the following articles for information on techniques and genotypes: Brettell et al., 1981; Ting et al., 1981; Sheridan, 1982; Pauk, 1985.

One problem in dealing with haploids is the recovery of progeny. As Chase (1969) has pointed out, the theoretical expectation for fertility in haploids is much too small in comparison to observed egg and pollen fertility. Random migration of 10 chromosomes to either pole should seldom give a single viable embryo sac on the ears of haploids. However, ears with 30 to 40 or more seeds have been found. According to Chase, the cells of haploids occasionally undergo chromosome doubling during development so that diploid sectors appear in the ear or tassel. Diploid sectors are relatively frequent in haploids, probably due to a competitive advantage over the haploid condition. They are observable as clusters of seeds on the ear or localized segments of pollen fertility on the tassel. Approximately 1 in 10 haploid plants has sufficient male and female fertility to be self-pollinated.

Several applications for haploids in plant breeding have been proposed (Nitzsche and Wenzel, 1977; Kasha and Seguin-Swartz, 1983). Among these are the suggestion that inbred lines, homozygous at all loci, can be produced instantly by self pollination of haploids. Also, since haploids express all their genes regardless of dominance or recessiveness, they may be useful in the screening of new mutations. In basic research, corn haploids have been used frequently in studies of nonhomologous pairing and crossing over (sections 4–5.3; 4–6.1).

Next to be discussed are the polyploids, among which triploids and tetraploids are most commonly encountered. Triploids which arise in normal populations usually come from the fertilization of a diploid (unreduced) egg by a haploid sperm. However, the combination of a haploid egg and a diploid sperm is also found occasionally (Rhoades, 1936). The spontaneous production of triploids in corn populations is an uncommon event. However, in lines with genically induced disturbances of meiosis diploid gametes may be produced at high frequency. Beadle (1930) reported many triploids in crosses of *asynaptic* plants as females with normal plants. Rhoades and Dempsey (1966a) found triploids in the progeny of plants homozygous for the *elongate* (*el*) gene. Triploids also occur regularly in the hybridization of diploid with tetraploid lines.

In triploids, homologous chromosomes are usually associated at metaphase I as trivalents and less frequently as bivalents and univalents. A great majority of the spores from triploid plants are aneuploid due to the difficulty of dividing three chromosome sets during meiosis. Many of the aneuploid spores are unable to develop into viable gametophytes, and triploids characteristically have a high percentage of aborted ovules and pollen grains. When triploids were used as the pollen parent in crosses with diploids, McClintock (1929b) found a marked selection in favor of pollen grains with 10, 11, or 12 chromosomes; those with higher numbers were unable to compete successfully in achieving fertilization. The competition found among the male gametophytes was not as evident in the reciprocal cross, where there was a wide range of chromosome numbers in the functional eggs. The different primary trisomes isolated by McClintock in the progenies of diploid by triploid crosses and their subsequent correlation with specific linkage groups marked the beginning of corn cytogenetics.

The low fertility of triploid corn is an unavoidable consequence of the segregation of three chromosome sets. Tetraploids, however, are potentially normal in fertility, since 2–2 disjunction of homologous chromosomes is possible. Consequently, tetraploid lines of corn have been developed and maintained. Randolph (1932) utilized heat treatment of young ears during early divisions of diploid embryos to produce tetraploid (as well as octoploid) plants. Alexander (1957) synthesized various tetraploid lines by crossing diploids homozygous for the *elongate* mutation as female to tetraploid males. Tetraploid corn resembles the diploid in height and growth habit but has broader leaves, sturdier stalks, larger tassels, and ears and kernels of increased size.

Randolph (1935) found that crosses between tetraploid plants produced some aneuploid progeny. The number of chromosomes he found ranged from 37 to 42, although 40 was the most frequent class. Apparently, the multivalent associations found in tetraploid meiosis are less reliable than bivalent pairing for producing proper chromosomal disjunction. Gilles and Randolph (1951) determined the relative frequencies of quadrivalent and bivalent associations in a tetraploid strain at the beginning and end of a 10-yr period. The tetraploid line was maintained during the period by selecting the more vigorous and fertile plants. There were fewer quadrivalents and more bivalents at the end of the 10-yr period than at the beginning. Consequently, selection for vigor and fertility also selected for a gene or genes influencing the type of chromosome association.

Doyle (1979a, 1979b, 1982, 1986) has studied the problem of chromosome pairing in tetraploids extensively. According to Doyle, it may be possible to construct an allotetraploid which contains only corn chromosomes. The basic idea is that a standard corn genome (Z) can be combined with a restructured genome (R) in a tetraploid (ZZRR). If the R genome is sufficiently rearranged and modified, preferential pairing should prevent quadrivalent formation in meiosis. Doyle (1986) has constructed one population of tetraploids from which Z genomes will be produced and another from which R genomes will be derived. The latter population has been repeatedly x-rayed (at the kernel stage) over a period of many generations. Cytological tests of bivalent vs. quadrivalent pairing were made on these populations and on a hybrid between them. Tests of preferential pairing were also made (section 4–5.2). The results indicate that some progress has been made in constructing two synaptically divergent genomes.

The tetraploid is the most frequently studied type of polyploid since it is by far the easiest one to maintain and utilize. Nevertheless, higher levels of polyploidy can be produced in corn, as demonstrated by Rhoades and Dempsey (1966a). They utilized the *elongate* mutation to construct a whole series of polyploids, including 3N, 4N, 5N, 6N, and 7N.

4–8   ANEUPLOIDY

In contrast to the euploid series, where each chromosome of the complement is present the same number of times, are the genically unbalanced aneuploid types. Any chromosome number that is not a simple multiple of *n* is aneuploid. However, discussion will be limited to the most common aneuploid types: 2n + 1 and 2n − 1.

Plants with a single extra chromosome are known as trisomes. There are several classes of trisomes, including primary, secondary, tertiary, and telo (telocentric) types. Primary trisomes are those in which one of the standard chromosomes is present in triplicate while the remainder are in duplicate. All of the 10 possible primary trisomes have been isolated in corn. These were originally derived from n + 1 gametes produced by triploids (McClintock, 1929b). However, they have also been selected as rare events in diploid populations (Ghidoni et al., 1982) and as products of r-x1-induced nondisjunction (see below). All of the primary trisomes are smaller and less vigorous than their disomic sibs. Some can be recognized by characteristic phenotype differences. This is especially true for trisomes 5, 7, and 8, whose phenotypes were described by Rhoades (1955). Burnham (1962) noted, however, that trisomic phenotypes can be difficult to classify in certain genetic or environmental backgrounds.

The primary trisomes have been extremely useful in cytogenetical studies. They first made it possible to assign genes to specific chromosomes. For example, McClintock and Hill (1931) placed the R locus on chromosome 10 with trisomic crosses. This method of gene placement depends on the aberrant genetic ratios found in trisomic crosses. Testcross ratios for the primary trisomes are subject to variation, depending on several factors, but are always strikingly different from 1:1 disomic ratios. If a trisomic plant of AAa constitution is testcrossed as female, a 5:1 ratio of $A{:}a$ is predicted, assuming 50% of the ovules are n + 1. Since less than half of the eggs are n + 1, owing to elimination of univalent chromosomes during meiosis (Einset, 1943), the ratio is somewhat less than 5:1. Not only does the observed trisomic ratio depend upon the frequency of n + 1 ovules, but it is also influenced by the amount and kinds of crossing over between the gene and the centromere. If the locus A is far enough removed from the centromere, assortment of the six chromatids approaches randomness. The result is a ratio of approximately 4:1 instead of 5:1, if equal numbers of n and n + 1 ovules are produced (Redei, 1982, Tables 11–9 and 11–11). Predictions are much simpler when using trisomics as pollen parents. In this case, n + 1 pollen does not survive and only the balanced gametes need be considered. The expected ratio for $aa ♀ × AAa ♂$ crosses is 2 dominant to 1 recessive. The ratio for $aa ♀ × Aaa ♂$ crosses is 2 recessive to 1 dominant. Doyle (1967, 1979a, 1982) employed the predicted genetic ratios for pollen-parent trisomic crosses to study preferential pairing in corn (section 4–5.2).

In a secondary trisome, an isochromosome consisting of two identical arms is present. If the order of loci in chromosome 5 is (a b c d e) centromere (f g h i j k), the isochromosome derived from one arm is (a b c d e) centromere (e d c b a) in constitution, and the other isochromosome is (k j i h g f) centromere (f g h i j k). Since each of the 10 chromosomes can give rise to two isochromosomes, a total of 20 secondary trisomes is possible. However, only a few have been recovered (Rhoades, 1933, 1940; Emmerling, 1958b; Maguire, 1962; Beckett, 1984).

Isochromosomes arise by breakage through the centromere and joining across of chromatids belonging to the same chromosome arm. The formation of an isochromosome may occur directly from a member of the chromosomal complement or indirectly from a telocentric chromosome. In both cases, the usual cause of centromeric breakage is "misdivision" of the centromere. Misdivision occurs when a centromere is under stress due to an inability to undergo polar migration in anaphase of mitosis or meiosis. Univalent chromosomes in meiosis are especially susceptible to misdivision because they lack the pairing partner needed for proper disjunction. The formation of isochromosomes can also be induced by irradiation (Morris, 1955; Maguire, 1962). However, isochromosomes produced by irradiation may arise from breakage adjacent to the centromere rather than within it. If so, a difference in proximal regions will exist between the arms of such a chromosome and it should be referred to as a pseudo-isochromosome.

In tertiary trisomes, the extra chromosome is composed of parts of two nonhomologous chromosomes. It is derived from one element of a reciprocal translocation. Whereas the number of primaries is 10 and that of secondaries is 20, there is no limit to the number of tertiary trisomes. Translocation heterozygotes give rise to tertiary trisomes through 3:1 disjunction of the ring of 4 in meiosis. Gametes are produced that contain 10 normal chromosomes and one translocation chromosome. Fertilization with a normal gamete produces the trisomic individual. Little cytogenetic work has been done with tertiary trisomes, but they have been used in the placement of genes within the cytological chromosome (Dempsey and Smirnov, 1964).

Telotrisomes contain an extra telocentric chromosome derived from 1 of the 20 chromosome arms in corn. As with isochromosomes, the usual source of telocentrics is centromeric misdivision. Thus far, only a few telocentrics have been recovered (Rhoades, 1940; Doyle, 1972a). Rhoades and Dempsey (1972) found a number of telocentrics in crosses involving a special genetic background. However, the telocentrics were present in hemizygous chromosome combinations such as 3, telo 3 rather than in trisomics and could not be recovered. Beckett (1984) discovered a promising method for identifying telotrisomes. He found that selection of small kernels on ears from the W23 genetic background yielded a high percentage of telotrisomes (as well as primary trisomes). It is known from other work that aneuploidy for several different chromosomal regions produces reduced endosperm size (Lin, 1982; Beckett, 1983). Consequently, selection of small kernels may allow recovery of a number of different telotrisomes.

In addition to the several trisomic classes, another basic type of aneuploid is the monosome. Monosomes have one of the standard chromosomes in single dose and the rest in duplicate. They are more difficult to utilize in corn than trisomes since the monosomic condition is not transmissible. The n − 1 gametophyte lacks genes necessary for survival and only balanced gametes are produced by 2n − 1 individuals. However, Kante Satyanarayama (in Weber, 1973) found that a particular mutation (r-x1) allows frequent production of monosomes. The r-x1 mutation is actually a minute deficiency on 10L which is only transmissible through the egg. It lacks a region required for normal chromosome division in the embryo sac. The result is frequent nondisjunction during postmeiotic divisions and the production of n − 1 and n + 1 eggs. The n − 1 eggs are viable because the embryo sac contains some nondeficient cells. The composition of the r-x1 embryo sac is determined by the timing of nondisjunction. Experiments of Lin and Coe (1986) indicate that nondisjunction occurs at the second embryo sac mitosis (see also Simcox et al., 1986).

Weber has utilized the r-x1 system to produce 9 of the 10 possible monosomes. The procedure is as follows (see also Weber, 1983). The visible phenotype of r-x1, produced by absence of the R locus, is colorless seed. A testcross of R/r-x1 ♀ X rr ♂ gives colored R and colorless (r-x1) progeny. Plants derived from colored seeds are all normal. However, colorless seeds contain 10 to 18% monosomes and 10 to 18% trisomes. A few multiple monosomes (Fig. 4–6) and trisomes are also produced, with the remainder being normal plants. A specific monosome can be selected by crossing plants containing r-x1 as female to pollen parents with a recessive plant marker on the relevant chromosome. The cross is R/r-x1 MM ♀ X rr mm ♂. Selection for white endosperm (r-x1) and mutant plant (m) almost invariably locates the monosome. Endosperm markers can also be used, but are less desirable. The endosperm does not show monosomic phenotypes, unlike the embryo, due to the timing of nondisjunction induced by r-x1. Consequently, the initial cross is followed by selection for small-sized plants. (Monosomes are generally small and some have distinctive morphologies: Weber, 1983.) Among the small plants, high levels of pollen sterility are selected as a further indicator of chromosome loss. Next, backcrosses to the endosperm marker are made. The correct monosome gives all recessive phenotypes in the backcross, since n − 1 gametes are lethal.

Monosomes have been used in a wide variety of applications, including locating genes to chromosomes, analyzing the cytological behavior of univalent chromosomes, and studying dosage variation of genes. Most recently, the r-x1 system has been used to help construct a map of restriction fragment length polymorphisms (section 4–6.4).

In addition to the basic aneuploid types discussed here, partial trisomes and partial monosomes are available through the use of B-A translocations (section 4–10). Also, a number of complex aneuploids have been found in other organisms, and these are discussed by Khush (1973). The mechanisms by which aneuploids arise in populations are considered in the book *Aneuploidy: Etiology and Mechanisms* (Dellarco et al., 1985).

4–9 CHROMOSOMAL REARRANGEMENTS

The breakage of chromosomes by chemical attack, irradiation, or other means allows the production of a wide range of chromosomal aberrations. Broken ends of chromosomes are said to be "sticky" since they have the capacity to join with other broken ends to form new chromosomal types. The number of chromosomal rearrangements that can be produced in this manner is large. However, only a few categories of commonly occurring rearrangements will be discussed.

4–9.1 Reciprocal Translocations

Reciprocal translocations (interchanges) are exchanges of segments between nonhomologous chromosomes. They arise when breaks occur in two different chromosomes producing two centric and two acentric chromosome fragments. Rejoining between appropriate fragments produces two new monocentric chromosomes, each carrying blocks of genes from both parental chromosomes. These interchanged chromosomes behave normally throughout the somatic mitoses and are completely stable. Major reviews of translocations were written by Burnham (1956) and Rickards (1983a).

The first translocations found in corn were of spontaneous origin. However, the great majority of those available were induced by ionizing radiation. Longley (1961) lists more than 1000 different translocations whose points of interchange have been cytologically determined. He concluded from his extensive work with translocations that breakpoints in the chromosomes were most frequent in heterochromatic regions, particularly in segments adjacent to the centromere. He suggested that heterochromatic regions are especially susceptible to chromosome breakage. Jancey and Walden (1972), Jancey (1975), and Walden and Jancey (1976) also examined the exchange points of corn translocations. They found a nonrandom distribution of breakpoints, with exchanges near the centromere being common. In addition, a preferred pattern of chromosome exchange between nonhomologues was found. For example, when the exchange point in one chromosome was a certain distance from the centromere, the breakpoint in the second chromosome was frequently at a similar distance from its centromere. The finding suggests that a specific organization exists within the interphase nucleus, as suggested by several workers (section 4–5).

Determination of the exchange points for a translocation can be made in pachynema. In plants heterozygous for a translocation, two normal and two interchanged chromosomes are present. A four-armed synaptic configuration is produced at pachynema by the pairing of homologous regions (Fig. 4–7). The center of the cross configuration marks the breakpoints, if strictly homologous pairing occurs. However, Burnham (1932a, 1934, 1981) and McClintock (1933) have shown that the position of the cross may vary in different cells. The nonhomologous associations responsible for shifting of the cross make it difficult to determine exact breakpoints unless the interchange occurred in regions of strikingly dissimilar chromomeric patterns.

In the pachytene cross produced by a translocation heterozygote, the presence or absence of chiasmata in specific regions will control the appearance of the chromosomes in diakinesis. For example, if all four arms are relatively long, one or more chiasmata will usually form in each arm, producing a ring configuration in diakinesis. However, in translocations where the break in one chromosome is near the end, one arm of the cross will be short. Failure of crossing over in the short region produces a chain of four chromosomes in diakinesis (Fig. 4–8). When the interchange points in both chromosomes are nearly terminal, two "pairs" rather than a quadrivalent are found in diakinesis due to pairing failure in two arms of the translocation complex (Clarke and Anderson, 1935). The relationship of chiasma formation to centromere position also affects the diakinesis figure. In the translocation cross, the interval from a centromere to the center of the cross is known as an interstitial region. If one or both centromeres are located some distance from the center of the cross, interstitial chiasmata can form. A ring of four chromosomes with an interstitial chiasma has a "figure 8" appearance in diakinesis.

Following diakinesis, translocation figures move onto the MI spindle. With a ring of four chromosomes (lacking interstitial chiasmata), the multivalent may assume either a zigzag (twisted ring) arrangement or an

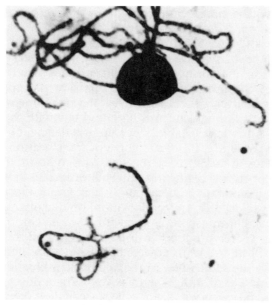

Fig. 4–7. Heterozygous translocation in pachynema. Photograph courtesy of M.M. Rhoades.

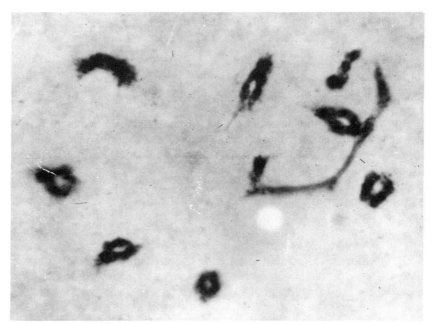

Fig. 4–8. Heterozygous translocation in diakinesis. Failure of exchange in one of the four arms of the "cross" gave this chain of 4 figure. Photograph courtesy of M.M. Rhoades.

open ring appearance. The zigzag orientation leads to alternate members of the ring passing to the same pole at anaphase (alternate disjunction). For example, with a translocation involving chromosomes 2 and 5 the ring of four will contain chromosomes 2, 5, 2^5, and 5^2 The normal pair of chromosomes (2 and 5) will be alternate (nonadjacent) members of the ring, as will the interchange pair (2^5 and 5^2). With alternate disjunction from a zigzag ring, the normal chromosomes 2 and 5 go to one pole and the interchange chromosomes 2^5 and 5^2 pass to the opposite pole at anaphase I. The quartet of spores formed at the end of meiosis will consist of two spores with normal chromosomes and two with the interchanged chromosomes. All four are viable, since none is deficient or duplicate for any genes. Consequently, the zigzag form of translocation ring produces all viable gametes. In addition to the zigzag orientation, the ring of four can assume an open ring configuration. This will result in adjacent members of the ring passing to the same pole. There are two forms of adjacent segregation. In adjacent-1 segregation, nonhomologous centromeres go to the same pole: chromosome 2 goes with 5^2 while chromosome 5 goes with 2^5. All the spores produced will be deficient and duplicate; consequently they will abort. With adjacent-2 disjunction, homologous centromeres pass to the same pole. In the above example, this would mean that chromosome 2 goes with 2^5 and 5 with 5^2. As in the case of adjacent-1 segregation, all products would abort because of their deficient-duplicate constitution.

If alternate, adjacent-1 and adjacent-2 forms of disjunction occurred with equal frequencies, two-thirds of the gametes from a translocation heterozygote would be abortive. However, pollen counts usually give 50% abortion rates, indicating that alternate orientation is more frequent than predicted. Ovule sterility is also about 50%, showing that orientation of the ring of four is essentially the same in megasporocytes as in microsporocytes. It now seems likely that two types of alternate orientation exist (Endrizzi, 1974; Rickards, 1983b; Kodura, 1984). They may be visualized as transformations of adjacent-1 and adjacent-2 rings into a zigzag arrangement by a twist of the rings. Both types of zigzag rings give alternate segregation and the two classes of rings are generally not distinguishable cytologically. However, in terms of orientation they are separate forms. If the four possible types of orientation (adjacent-1, adjacent-2, alternate 1, alternate 2) occur with equal frequencies, the 50% gametic sterility is explicable.

Three classes of disjunction—alternate, adjacent-1, and adjacent-2— can be identified cytologically by using translocations of chromosome 6. The total rate of adjacent segregation can be determined from the pollen abortion rate. In addition, the subclasses of adjacent segregation can be measured by classifying the NOR in microspores of meiotic quartets. When all cells of a quartet receive one nucleolus organizer, each cell develops one nucleolus. However, segregation from a translocation involving chromosome 6 gives some unbalanced spores in which cells with two nucleoli and zero nucleoli (diffuse nucleolar material) are found within a quartet. Burnham (1949, 1950, 1962) following the earlier work of McClintock (1934), made an extensive study of nucleolar segregation with chromosome 6 translocations. He reached the following conclusions:

1. In those translocations (discussed above) with no crossing over in the interstitial regions, adjacent-1 and adjacent-2 segregation occur with approximately the same frequency (about 25% each). Alternate segregation takes place in 50% of the microsporocytes.

2. In those translocations having long interstitial segments with frequent crossovers (figure 8 rings), there is little, if any, adjacent-2 disjunction. It is not possible to determine the ratio of alternate to adjacent-1 segregation when interstitial crossovers occur, since both segregation types produce cytologically identical quartets. The quartets have two viable and two abortive spores.

3. Chain-forming translocations have low frequencies of adjacent-2 segregation, irrespective of the amount of crossing over in the interstitial segments. Alternate and adjacent-1 segregation each occur with frequencies of approximately 50%. (This last rule applies to translocations in which the unpaired arm of the "cross" does not carry one of the centromeres. When a centromere-bearing arm of a translocation cross fails to associate, adjacent segregation is primarily type 2: Kodura, 1984. None of the chain-forming translocations in corn are of the latter type.)

The findings of Burnham and others with translocation heterozygotes can provide information on the mechanism of centromeric orientation. In rings without interstitial crossing over, adjacent-1 and adjacent-2 segregations occur with equal frequencies. Therefore, preferential disjunction of homologous centromeres seems unlikely as a mechanism of orientation. However, the major forms of segregation from a translocation quadrivalent all involve 2-2 separation of the chromosomes. Consequently, some regulation of chromosomal movement must operate on multivalent figures. In this regard, Nicklas and Koch (1969) found with grasshopper bivalents that stable centromeric orientation requires tension on the centromere. Tension is produced by the two centromeres of a bivalent pulling in opposite directions. In the absence of tension, spindle attachments are unstable and reorientation occurs. The usual 2/2 disjunction of translocation rings can be explained as the result of a requirement for centromeric tension. Each chromosome of a ring may need to disjoin from at least one adjacent chromosome to produce tension on its centromere. The absence of adjacent-2 segregation from chains of 4 may result from the same requirement. The effect of interstitial chiasmata on disjunction probably depends on a different property of centromeres. Nicklas (1967) has suggested that there is a tendency for centromeres to attach spindle fibers in a particular direction. When bivalents are detached by microsurgery from their spindle fiber attachments, the centromeres reattach in the direction in which they are approximately facing. Perhaps the inhibition of adjacent-2 segregation by interstitial chiasmata depends on the close association of homologous centromeres produced by flanking chiasmata. The centromeres are forced to face in opposite directions, as in a bivalent. (This form of centromeric orientation is now known to occur only rarely: Nicklas and Kubai, 1985. However, the concept may apply in the case of interstitial chiasmata).

The rules discussed for orientation of translocation quadrivalents apply to most situations in corn. However, orientation may follow somewhat different rules in other organisms, as discussed by Rickards (1983a). In particular, the general tendency for 50% alternate and 50% adjacent segregation in corn is not a universal phenomenon.

Although several different chromosomal combinations are produced by segregation from a translocation heterozygote, genetic recombination is influenced only by the classes of gametes which do not abort. Functional spores come only from the presence of two normal or two translocation chromosomes. Spores with one normal and one translocation chromosome are deficient-duplicate and abort. Consequently, the cross of a translocation heterozygote with a chromosomally normal plant gives two kinds of zygotes: those homozygous normal and those heterozygous for the translocation. The homozygous normal plants have no pollen or ovule sterility, whereas heterozygotes have 50% aborted pollen and ovules. As a result, inheritance of a translocation may be followed by classifying plants for either pollen or egg sterility.

The inheritance of a translocation can be treated in linkage tests as if semisterility were produced by a single gene. The translocation "gene" for semisterility (T) maps to the exchange point of the pachytene cross. Genes lying in the four arms of the cross will be linked with T and with each other. When only recombination values between T and the loci of a single arm are considered, the usual linear map is obtained with T located at one end of the map. However, when recombination values between genes in all four arms are determined, the combined linkage data form a cross-shaped map with T at the center of the cross.

Recombination values for regions near T in a translocation heterozygote are usually lower than for homologous regions in standard chromosomes. This reduction in crossing over is produced by imperfect synapsis in pachynema. Asynapsis at the center of the cross configuration accounts for some of the reduced crossing over. Also, nonhomologous pairing is frequent in this region for some translocation heterozyotes (Burnham, 1962, 1981). (Nonhomologous pairing is as effective as asynapsis in blocking crossing over: section 4–6.1.) In a few cases, translocation heterozygosity does not show any inhibitory effect on crossing over (Anderson et al., 1955; Maguire, 1968).

The T marker of translocation heterozygotes offers advantages over conventional genetic markers in studying the inheritance and linkage relations of genes determining agronomic characters. In particular, the presence of interchange chromosomes does not modify the plant phenotype or affect classification of traits being studied. Also, the frequent inhibition of recombination at the translocation point increases the distance over which linkage tests are effective. Traits such as ear length, days-to-silking, smut resistance, etc., have been linked to specific chromosomes with translocations by many workers.

Translocations have also proven useful in the placement of new gene mutations on chromosomes. Two general methods for testing the linking of new markers to translocations have been proposed (Burnham, 1966, 1982; Anderson, 1956). In one protocol, classification of semisterility (T) is utilized, as discussed earlier. A second method depends on classification of an endosperm marker which is closely linked to T. For the latter method, a series of chromosome-9 translocations has been developed in which each T site is linked to the *waxy* locus. The series is maintained by the Maize Genetics Stock Center at the Univ. of Illinois. It provides good coverage of the corn genome, and most of the chromosome arms are represented in combination with chromosome 9. With this series, classification of Wx vs. wx phenotypes in testcrosses is equivalent to classification of T vs. N pollen. If a trait shows linkage to the Wx locus in tests with all or many of the translocations, it must be located on chromosome 9. Otherwise, linkage to only one of the translocations places the gene on a specific chromosome other than 9.

4-9.2   Derivatives of Reciprocal Translocations

Segregation from a ring of 4 is not as regular as the segregation found with bivalents. Occasionally, 3:1 disjunction occurs. Various types of gametes result from this kind of segregation. One interesting product is the n + 1 gamete which has 10 standard chromosomes plus one translocation chromosome. It gives rise to a tertiary trisome when combined with a normal gamete, as discussed in section 4-8.

A second type of translocation derivative originates from the unbalanced gametes produced by adjacent segregation. The genetically deficient and duplicate nature of such gametes ordinarily results in spontaneous abortion. However, if the deficiency is small and genes essential for gametophyte development are not lost, the gametes can survive. Translocations with a near-terminal breakpoint on one of the chromosomes may produce a viable deficiency from adjacent-1 segregation (along with a second, inviable product). When the deficient-duplicate gamete is combined with a normal gamete, the zygote contains some deficient (single copy) and some duplicate (triple copy) regions. Segregation from a chain of four is expected to be 50% alternate and 50% adjacent-1. Therefore, if one product of adjacent-1 segregation is completely viable, gametic abortion rates will be 25% rather than 50% (Burnham 1932b, 1950). The increased fertility can be measured on the ear (75% of normal seed set) or in the tassel (75% normal pollen). However, the apparent viability of deficient-duplicate pollen in such cases is deceptive. The unbalanced chromosomal complement is rarely transmitted through the male, probably due to a pollen competition effect. Duplications, which may be sizable in deficient-duplicate gametes, are known to reduce or eliminate pollen transmission. Patterson (1978) has found instances of pollen transmission by some deficient-duplicate gametes, but they are rare. Consequently, the deficient-duplicate chromosome combination is usually maintained through female transmission (Patterson, 1978).

Phillips et al. (1971a) identified more than 50 translocations that are known or expected to produce viable deficient-duplicate gametes. One application for these translocations is in the placement of genes on chromosomes. When deficient-duplicate eggs are fertilized by recessive sperm, the recessive phenotype will be expressed if the locus lies within the deficient segment. Patterson (1952, 1959) demonstrated the validity of this approach by placing several loci on the cytological maps of chromosomes 2 and 9. The method is limited because only short terminal regions of the chromsomes can be analyzed. However, translocations with viable deficient-duplicate eggs can be used in a more widely applicable gene mapping system. The translocations give abnormal genetic ratios in testcrosses. Genes associated with the surviving adjacent-1 type of gamete are elevated in frequency with respect to alleles linked to the abortive chromosomal combination (Burnham, 1932b). Mutant genes may be tested for linkage to the viable adjacent-1 product by constructing a translocation/mutant heterozygote and testcrossing. In the absence of linkage, a 1:1 genetic ratio is expected, whereas complete linkage of mutant gene to the translocation exchange point gives a 2:1 ratio. The procedure does not rely on hemizygous expression of a recessive, and therefore requires an extra generation beyond the F_1. However, the technique is not limited to short, terminal chromosomal regions and can be used to mark the entire genome with an appropriate set of translocations (Phillips et al., 1971a). Further applications for deficient-duplicate chromosomal complements were suggested by Patterson (1978), including use in studies of synapsis, mutagenesis, and gene dosage effects.

4–9.3 Combinations of Two or More Translocations

The complexities of dealing with translocations are multiplied when two or more of the rearrangements are combined in a single plant. Depending on the chromosomes involved, the result in diakinesis may be production of a large ring or rings. It is important to remember in such situations that each ring, regardless of size, produces only two types of viable gametes. Any instance of adjacent segregation within a ring produces inviability. Consequently, as ring size increases the percent gametic abortion also increases. (The exception is in cases of directed segregation in which only alternate segregation occurs. The well-documented case of directed segregation in *Oenothera* translocations has been widely reviewed.)

The construction of large rings will be illustrated by considering formation of a circle of six chromosomes. Such a ring is produced by combining two translocations that have one chromosome in common. For example, a cross of homozygous T1–3 × homozygous T3–4 will give a circle of six. Alternate segregation from the circle of six gives two balanced genetic products containing T1–3 (1^3, 3^1, 4) and T3–4 (1, 3^4, 4^3). Thus, the plant yields two gametic classes that are identical to the ones used in its own production.

Another method for producing the circle of six is by constructing a multiple rearrangement. In this case, one chromosome is translocated twice. One way to accomplish this is by crossing over between two translocations. Using the same example as above, the multiple translocation would have one chromosome that is a combination of 3^1 and 3^4. The multiple translocation would contain 1^3, 4^3, $3^{1,4}$. If a homozygote for the multiple translocation were crossed to a normal plant, the progeny would contain a circle of six. The two viable gametes produced by the circle of six would have the multiple translocation (1^3, 4^3, $3^{1,4}$) and the normal chromosomes (1, 3, 4). Burnham (1962) has worked primarily with the latter system to produce large rings in corn (Fig. 4–9).

When bringing two translocations into a plant, it is possible to have the same chromosomes involved in both interchanges. For example, a cross of T3–4a × T3–4b could be made. A complex quadrivalent is expected, if all regions synapse accurately. Gopinath and Burnham (1956) identified several categories of "same chromosomes" translocation pairs (reviewed by Burnham, 1978). The classes differ in terms of chromosome arms involved and relative breakage positions. Studies of the same chromosomes pairs of tranlocations have been quite useful in two types of experiments. First, as described in section 4–5.2 the mode of pairing between certain translocation pairs provides a test for proximal vs. distal control of synapsis. Second, segregation of chromosomes from the type 2b class described by Gopinath and Burnham allows studies on gene

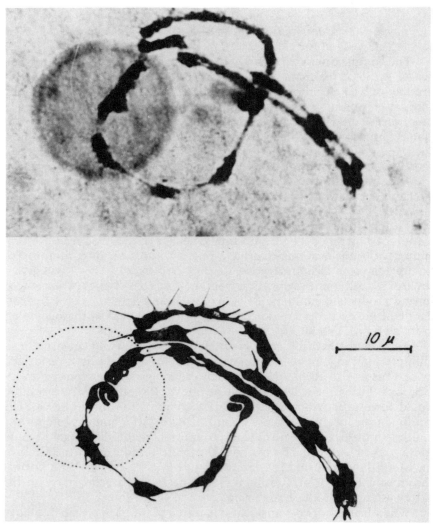

Fig. 4–9. Circle of 20 in diakinesis. A cross between two stocks, each carrying multiple translocations, produced this ring. Photograph by J.T. Stout; courtesy of C.R. Burnham.

duplication. One type of segregation produces two duplicated segments with no accompanying deficiency. In crosses to normal plants, the result is segmental trisomy for two short interstitial regions from different chromosomes. Birchler (1983a) has pointed out the experimental value of this technique. He noted that for the long arm of chromosome 1, 128 combinations of known translocations could be used to produce a series of duplications spanning 1L from 0.04 to 0.95.

4-9.4 Inversions

Compared with translocations, relatively little work has been done with inversions in corn, even though they constitute one of the more interesting types of aberrations. Convincing genetic evidence of inversions in *Drosophila* was found by Sturtevant (1931). The first cytogenetical studies of inversions were made by McClintock (1931, 1933) working with corn.

There are two kinds of simple inversions. In the paracentric type the affected segment lies within a single arm of the chromosome, whereas in the pericentric type the centromere is included within the inverted region. Paracentric inversions generally have no karyotypic effect in somatic cells, whereas pericentric inversions may produce marked changes in the position of the centromere. McClintock (1931, 1933) showed that in both types a loop-shaped configuration is produced at pachynema by homologous synapsis in normal/inversion heterozygotes (Fig. 4–10). However, the subsequent behavior of the two inversion types is strikingly different, since the dicentric bridges and acentric fragments produced by heterozygous paracentric inversions are not found with pericentric inversions.

The bridges found with paracentric inversions require chiasma formation in the loop. Bridges are absent when there is no exchange within

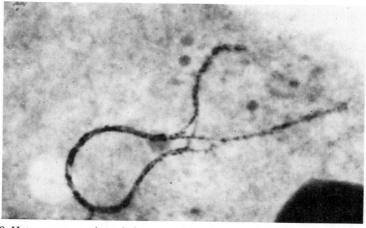

Fig. 4–10. Heterozygous pericentric inversion in pachynema. Photograph by D.T. Morgan Jr., courtesy of M.M. Rhoades.

the loop and also in the case of two strand doubles. A dicentric bridge is produced at anaphase I when either a single exchange or a three strand double are present in the loop. The bridge is accompanied by an acentric fragment which lags on the plate and is lost. Cells with two bridges and two fragments come from four strand double exchanges in the loop. Assuming that double chiasmata occur in a ratio of 1:2:1 for two strand/three strand/four strand events, the frequency of all doubles can be calculated from the two bridge, two fragment data.

Crossing over proximal to the inversion loop can affect the cytological behavior of paracentric inversions. A no bridge, one fragment configuration results from a three strand double exchange in which one chiasma is within the loop and one is between the centromere and the loop. In this case, bridge formation occurs in anaphase II rather than anaphase I and appears in only one of the two dividing cells (Rhoades and Dempsey, 1953).

Crossing over within paracentric loops produces gametes that are deficient for regions distal to the loop and, depending on bridge breakage, for part of the inverted region. The result expected is gametic abortion, with the rate of abortion being equal to the amount of crossing over. However, following meiosis in the female, three of the four products die and only the basal megaspore survives. If nondeficient chromatids are preferentially included in the basal megaspore, the effect of crossing over in inversion heterozygotes may be reduced in the female. The idea comes from findings with *Drosophila*. As in corn, only one of the meiotic products gives rise to an egg nucleus. Beadle and Sturtevant (1935) suggested that chromatids involved in a dicentric bridge are confined to the central nuclei of the *Drosophila* tetrad due to a failure of bridge breakage. Only noncrossover or double crossover balanced chromatids can migrate to the egg nucleus at second division. Support for the hypothesis was provided by Beadle and Sturtevant (1935) and Sturtevant and Beadle (1936). In corn, delayed breakage of the anaphase I bridge could potentially orient noncrossover chromatids to the outer poles for anaphase II (selective orientation). Since the surviving (basal) megaspore develops from one of the outer poles, the result would be a decrease in gametophytic lethality and a difference in the effects of inversion heterozygosity between the male and female. Indeed, Morgan (1950) with inversion 4a, and Russell and Burnham (1950), with inversion 2c, reported considerable pollen sterility, but low egg lethality in inversion heterozygotes. Rhoades and Dempsey (1953) did not find evidence of greater female than male fertility with inversion 3a. However, Rinehart (1970) studied inversion 3a and found a difference in male vs. female fertility.

Although selective orientation of chromatids may account for higher female fertility by inversion heterozygotes, an alternate explanation is possible. Perhaps rates of crossing over are lower in the female than in the male. Consequently, the female has a lower frequency of dicentric bridges and higher fertility. Supporting this idea are a considerable number of reports of lower female than male crossing over in specific chromosomal regions (section 4–6.2). Rhoades (1978) found evidence for sex-related differences in crossing over with inversion 3a. He showed that the presence of a homozygous knob in the inversion loop induces lower female than male rates of crossing over. No differences were found in the absence of the knob. The findings indicate that knob constitution is one variable that should be controlled in studies of selective orientation by inversion heterozygotes.

Crossing over in pericentric inversion loops gives deficient-duplicate chromatids, just as with paracentric inversions. However, no bridges are produced and selective orientation in the female is not possible. Both paracentric and pericentric inversions act as "suppressors" of crossing over through the production of lethal deficient-duplicate chromatids. A maximum frequency of 50% gametic abortion occurs with inversions and this value corresponds to the maximum rate of recombination.

Inversions of any kind are rare in corn populations for obvious reasons. However, the negative effect of an inversion is directly related to the crossover rate within its inversion loop. As a result, short inversions or inversions in regions with low recombination frequencies have occasionally been found. A paracentric inversion composed of the distal two-thirds of the short arm of chromosome 8 has been observed in certain races of corn (McClintock, 1959). A variant arm ratio for chromosome 4 was found by McClintock (1933) and attributed to a pericentric inversion. She also reported variability in the centromeric position of chromosome 2, which could have resulted from a small inversion.

Several experimental applications for inversions have been found. Most obvious is their widespread use as suppressors of crossing over. In addition, realization of the role of the centromere in the movement of chromosomes came from observations on the acentric fragments produced by inversion crossing over. Rhoades and Dempsey (1953) combined cytological and genetical data on crossing over in a paracentric inversion to provide evidence for random formation of the four double exchange classes in corn. Dobzhansky and Rhoades (1938) suggested that paracentric inversions can be utilized in the cytological placement of genes affecting agronomic characters. Sprague (1941) and Chao (1959) successfully employed the procedure in locating certain agronomic traits. McClintock (1938a, 1939, 1941a) studied the fate of dicentric bridges generated by crossing over in paracentric inversions and certain more complex rearrangements. This latter work led to the discovery of breakage-fusion-bridge cycles (section 4–4.1).

In recent years, most studies with inversions have dealt with the problems of synapsis or crossing over. Bellini and Bianchi (1963) and McKinley and Goldman (1979) studied interchromosomal effects of inversions on crossing over. They found that inversion heterozygosity causes some increased recombination in other chromosomes, but not of the magnitude that has been found in *Drosophila*. Maguire (1966, 1972) utilized inversion heterozygotes to study the relation between homologous pairing and chiasma formation. Inverted regions were classified as having homologous (loop) synapsis, nonhomologous (straight) pairing or asynapsis. A good correlation was found between homologous pairing and chiasma formation (as measured by anaphase bridge formation). She also used a paracentric inversion in studies of the "synaptic adjustment" phenomenon (Maguire, 1981 and section 4–5.4). Gillies (1981) used two paracentric inversions (and two translocations) to analyze the effectiveness of an electron microscopic technique. He adapted the Counce-Meyer method for spreading synaptonemal complexes to corn. The size and position of inversion loops was determined from SC arrangements that were found. For each inversion, good agreement was found between the EM technique and previous light microscopic measurements.

4–9.5 Duplications

The spontaneous duplication of base sequences, genes, chromosome segments, or whole chromosome sets has played an important, and, as yet, not fully documented role in evolution. Although the duplication and evolution of certain genes has been traced, the extent of gene duplication within any species is usually difficult to ascertain. Once duplication occurs, the functions of the duplicate loci may diverge with evolution until the relationships between them are no longer apparent.

Several adjacent duplications have been found in the corn genome. Compound loci that consist of tandem repeats have been found at the *R* locus (Stadler and Nuffer, 1953; Emmerling, 1958a; Dooner and Kermicle, 1971, 1974), the *A* locus (Laughnan, 1949, 1952a, b) and the *Tu* locus (Mangelsdorf and Galinat, 1964). The duplications were identified by their ability to produce new alleles through oblique synapsis and crossing over. The "mutants" produce by oblique synapsis are associated with recombination for flanking markers and thus can be distinguished from true mutations. The situation is similar to the classic case of oblique synapsis at the *Bar* locus in *Drosophila* except that in corn the duplications are naturally occurring.

The *A* and *R* loci have been studied extensively. Laughnan (1955, 1961) found evidence with the *A* locus that, in the absence of a pairing partner, the tandem repeat may pair on itself and undergo intrastrand crossing over. Evidence for intrachromosomal crossing over in *Drosophila* at the *Bar* duplication has also been found (Peterson and Laughnan, 1961, 1963; Gabay and Laughnan, 1973). Studies of the *R* locus have revealed a chromosomal region with a complex structure. The *R-r standard* form of the locus controls anthocyanin pigment production in the plant and the seed. It consists of a tandem duplication which has differentiated so that one element contains a plant color–determining gene (*P*) and the other a seed color–determining gene (*S*). In addition, each element has a gene for inhibition of chlorophyll striping (*Isr*) (Kermicle and Axtell,

1981). A plant pigmenting gene (*Lc*), is associated with the *R* locus in some isolates of chromosome 10. *Lc* is a displaced duplication of either the *P*-marked or *S*-marked element of *R-r standard*. It maps one unit distal to *R* (Dooner and Kermicle, 1976). Also, some *R* loci possess a unique capacity for mutation through a process referred to as paramutation (Brink, 1973). The complexity of the locus may have resulted in part from localized transposition events (Williams et al., 1984; Kermicle, 1984).

A number of nonadjacent duplications of genes or chromosome segments have also been found in the corn genome. The first evidence for this type of duplication came from the discovery of duplicate (15:1) genetic ratios (Rhoades, 1951). Subsequently, studies of occasional pairing and crossing over in haploids indicated redundancy within the genome (section 4–6.1). A new and promising approach to the identification of duplications is through gene cloning and analysis of restriction fragment length polymorphisms (Helentjaris et al., 1985, 1986).

The evolutionary source of duplications in the corn genome is unknown. They may have arisen entirely from individual duplications that formed and were incorporated into the species over a long period of time. Alternately, corn may have had a tetraploid origin (Rhoades, 1951). Khush (1973) listed several reasons for believing that corn is an amphidiploid. On the other hand, Weber (1983) noted that the chromosomes of corn seem distinct. For example, pairing in haploid corn is infrequent at diakinesis. Also, the loss of a chromosome is lethal to the gametophyte (and even the loss of a small chromosome segment is usually lethal). Bennett (1983) renewed the suggestion that corn is amphidiploid on the basis of his model of chromosome organization in somatic cells (section 4–5.1). Studies currently underway with RFLP analysis of the genome may eventually settle the question of polyploidy.

In addition to single-event kinds of duplications that have been considered, large-scale repetitions of base sequences have been found in corn, as in other organisms. These will not be considered here, but are discussed by Hake and Walbot (1980), Rivin et al. (1983, 1986), and Peacock et al. (1981).

Despite the presence of many naturally occurring duplications in the corn genome, it is often necessary to synthesize new duplications for experimental purposes. The value of inducing new duplication lies in comparisons that can be made between the standard and the duplicated situation. Duplication of whole chromosomes can be achieved through the use of primary trisomes or polyploids. Segmental duplications are produced by numerous methods, all involving some kind of chromosomal rearrangement as discussed below.

Doyle (1971, 1972b) developed a technique for inducing specific duplications by irradiation of chromosomes followed by phenotypic selection of the correct rearrangement. He irradiated kernels that were heterozygous (in repulsion) for the closely linked markers *a* and *sh2* of chromosome 3. The *A sh2/a Sh2* plants were grown and testcrossed, followed by selection of progeny with the *A Sh* phenotype. The selected phenotype may result from (i) crossing over, (ii) nondisjunction (trisomy) of chromosome 3 or (iii) some form of duplication. Doyle found that most *A Sh* cases arose from crossing over or trisome formation, but two duplications were identified. One was a tandem duplication whereas the other was a displaced duplication.

Most efforts at constructing segmental duplications have utilized existing chromosomal rearrangements in novel ways. Inversions have occasionally been used to generate duplications (Beadle and Sturtevant, 1935; Rhoades and Dempsey, 1956), but translocations are most commonly employed. Although complex chromosomal constitutions can be produced with translocations, the methods rest on a relatively small number of techniques. First is the construction of tertiary trisomes from 3:1 segregation by translocation heterozygotes (section 4–8). The trisomes carry an extra dose of genes from parts of two different chromosomes. Second is the method of Gopinath and Burnham (1956) in which two translocations involving the same chromosomes are combined in one plant. If translocation pairs are chosen with appropriate breakpoints, one product of meiotic segregation carries two interstitial duplicated regions and no deficiencies (section 4–9.3 and Birchler, 1983a). Third is utilization of the B chromosome to induce nondisjunction of A chromosome segments. B-A translocations attach A chromatin to the B centromere and subject it to both increases and decreases in dosage through nondisjunction (section 4–10.2). Fourth is manipulation of A chromosome segments through meiotic segregation of B-A translocations. Meiotic segregation in a B-A translocation heterozygote produces some viable duplication gametes that are products of adjacent segregation. Viability following adjacent segregation depends on the genetic inertness of B chromosomes (section 4–10.2).

The construction of duplications can be simplified through the use of appropriate genetic markers. Allozymes are especially suited for identifying duplications due to their codominant nature (Birchler, 1983b). Recent studies on manipulating gene dosage have been reported by Birchler (1983a), Carlson (1983), and Carlson and Curtis (1986a). The topic was recently reviewed (Birchler, 1988).

One experimental application for duplications is in studies of the relationship between gene dosage and gene activity. Work of B.-Y. Lin on the phenomenon of gene imprinting is discussed in section 4–10.2. In addition, Birchler (1979, 1981, 1985) and Birchler and Newton (1981) discovered a gene dosage effect in corn called the *inverse effect*. The phenomenon is defined as a negative correlation between the dosage of a chromosomal segment and the activity of a particular gene. Birchler looked at the effect of altering the dosage of 1L on a group of six enzymes. Four of the six were negatively affected, so that the monosomic had increased enzyme activity whereas the trisomic gave decreased enzyme activity.

Further studies led Birchler to conclude that most chromosomal segments will have an inverse effect on at least some of the proteins in a tissue. Also, any one protein can usually be negatively affected by several different chromosomal regions. Birchler has proposed that the inverse effect may account for at least some of the negative effects of aneuploidy. Studies with *alcohol dehydrogenase-1 (Adh)* provide an interesting perspective on the effect. *Adh* is located on 1L. Changes in dosage of the 1L arm have no effect in changing activity of the gene. However, when Birchler partitioned the chromosome arm with various duplications, he could separate two phenomena. Dosage changes of a small segment that included *Adh* showed a *positive* effect on gene activity. This resulted from changes in the copy number of *Adh*. However, manipulating the dosage of a region on 1L that lacks *Adh* gave an inverse effect on *Adh* activity. Consequently, when a dosage series for the whole arm was tested, the two effects cancelled each other out. Birchler refers to this as dosage compensation and believes that X chromosome dosage compensation in *Drosophila* may be controlled in a similar way.

4–9.6   Deficiencies

Deficient gametes arise in a number of ways, in addition to chromosomal breakage and loss of a segment. Adjacent segregation from translocation heterozygotes produces deficient (as well as duplicate) gametes. Crossing over in an inversion heterozygote results in the loss of chromosomal regions distal to the inversion loop. The breakage of dicentric bridges, generated in a number of ways, may result in chromatin loss. Chromosomal nondisjunction produces whole chromosome deficiencies.

Most deficiencies that arise are harmful to the organism and are selected against. Both the male and female gametophyte are highly sensitive to genetic loss so that even small deficiencies are often not transmissible. However, a number of viable deficiencies have been recovered in corn. In most cases, the deficiencies are only transmissible through the egg. The number of deficiencies found to be both egg and pollen viable is small (McClintock, 1944; Patterson, 1978; Rhoades and Dempsey, 1985).

Viable deficiencies are almost invariably small in size. For example, Rhoades and Dempsey (1953) isolated some egg-transmissible deficient chromosomes from inversion 3a heterozygotes. Deficiencies were generated by crossing over in the inversion loop and bridge formation. Surviving deficiencies arose by eccentric breakage of the bridge, with all genes from the inversion loop being incorporated into one chromatid. The only deficiency in these chromatids came from loss of the acentric fragment, carrying the terminal 5% of 3L. This region is not vital to development of the female gametophyte.

In other studies, Phillips et al. (1971a) listed a number of translocations which produce viable deficient-duplicate eggs from adjacent-1 segregation (section 4–9.2). Rhoades and Dempsey (1973a) identified a viable terminal deficiency that arose in an unknown manner. They also listed other cases of chromosomal regions whose absence is not lethal. Perhaps the best known viable deficiency is *r-x1*, which was induced by x-ray treatment (section 4–8).

Transmissible deficiencies are sometimes too small for cytological detection. This problem was encountered in experiments designed to elucidate the mutagenic properties of x-rays. The majority of mutations produced by x-rays result from gross chromosomal changes, including deletions, rather than intragenic changes. The work of Stadler and Roman (1948), Neuffer (1957) and Mottinger (1970) failed to demonstrate evidence of x-ray induced point mutations in corn. Among the "mutants" that were recovered from x-ray treatment, the most difficult to analyze were small chromosomal changes which were apparently short deficiencies rather than point mutations. In this work, several procedures for identifying short deficiencies were developed. When a putative intragenic mutation occurs at a locus not known to be vital to the organism, the association of pollen lethality or recessive sporophytic lethality with the mutation suggests the loss of vital loci adjacent to the gene being studied. Also, a reduction in crossing over in regions spanning the mutation is indicative of chromatin loss. The concomitant loss of adjacent markers when a locus mutates is strongly suggestive of a deficiency. In addition, an inability to select back mutations to wild type is characteristic of chromatin loss. However, no infallible test for short chromosomal deficiencies is available, and mutations that appear by one criterion to be deficiencies may not be confirmed by other criteria.

In addition to selection of nonlethal deficiencies, a second method for transmitting deficiencies is through the use of ring chromosomes (McClintock, 1938b, 1941b). This involves covering a deficient chromosome with a complementary ring. Plants can be constructed that carry a homozygous deficient chromosome plus a ring having the deleted segment. As the ring is spontaneously lost during development, the homozygous deficient phenotype can be seen and studied on the plant.

A third method for transmitting deficiencies is by inducing them in postmeiotic divisions. With this procedure, deficient gametes survive due to the presence of nondeficient cells in the gametophyte. The earliest method for producing deficiencies postmeiotically involved X-irradiation of pollen. McClintock (1931) used this method to induce deficiencies in sperm nuclei. She correlated cytologically observable deficiencies with the expression of recessive phenotypes in recessive ♀ × dominant ♂ crosses. Baker and Morgan (1969) used a similar approach to select deficiencies of chromosome 1. They pollinated chromosome 1 tester plants with irradiated pollen and selected recessive progeny. The purpose of the experiment was to produce plants that were hemizygous for the *asynaptic* locus. It was shown that two doses of the *As* gene are needed for normal meiotic synapsis. Hemizygous *As/–* plants showed varying degrees of asynapsis. Since *As/as* heterozygotes have normal chromosomal pairing, it was concluded that the *as* allele is not an amorphic but rather a hypomorphic allele. More recently, postmeiotic deficiencies have been produced through nondisjunction. The B-nondisjunctional system in the pollen and the *r-x1* system in the embryo sac are efficient methods for producing segmental or whole chromosome deficiencies. They are discussed in sections 4–8 and 4–10.2

4–9.7 Ring Chromosomes

The unusual properties of ring chromosomes were first investigated by McClintock. She studied two rings derived from the proximal region of the short arm of chromosome 5 (McClintock, 1932, 1938b, 1941b). Both of the rings were induced by x-rays and, in each case, one break occurred within the centromere and the second break in the short arm. Cytological observations revealed that the chromosomes did not replicate unaltered during development. In plants that inherited a 5S ring, some cells had large rings with certain segments in duplicate. Others had small rings deficient for portions present in the original ring. In still other cells, the ring chromosome had been completely eliminated.

The loss or modification of ring chromosomes occurs in the following way. In some mitotic prophases, as the probable result of sister strand exchange, the two chromatids of a ring chromsome form a single dicentric ring instead of two separate ring chromosomes. The result in anaphase is a double bridge. Stalling of the figure in the center of the spindle during anaphase can exclude the ring chromosome from daughter cells. Alternately, bridge breakage during anaphase and poleward migration produces, momentarily, rod chromosomes. However, fusion occurs between the broken ends of each rod chromosome, giving rise to ring chromosomes again. Ring chromosomes essentially participate in a chromosome type breakage-fusion-bridge cycle (section 4–4.1). The constitution of ring chromosomes newly derived from the splitting of a double bridge depends upon the position of bridge-breakage. Unequal breakage leads to one large ring and one small ring, with respect to the original chromosome.

In addition to producing dicentrics by sister exchange, ring chromosomes can also form interlocking rings. Stalling of interlocked rings on the metaphase plate can lead to loss of the chromosome. Breakage at anaphase produces, eventually, daughter ring chromosomes.

The somatic instability of ring chromosomes occurs in both the endosperm and the sporophyte, producing mosaic tissues. The mosaicism can be detected as a phenotypic effect if the ring carries dominant alleles while homologues have the recessives. Ring chromosome instability has provided experimenters with a useful cytogenetic tool. Homozygous deficiencies, which would normally be lethal, can be studied with the aid of rings which "cover" the deficiency in much of the plant and "uncover" it in sectors (section 4–9.6). Sister strand crossing over can be detected using ring chromosomes (section 4–6.5). A third application of rings is in the construction of deficiencies by crossing over between ring and rod chromosomes. Crossing over between a ring chromosome and the rod homologue produces a single bridge in anaphase I without the accompanying acentric fragment found with inversions. Breakage of the dicentric produces rod chromosomes which can stabilize (heal) in the sporophyte. The derivative chromosomes may have terminal deficiencies (or duplications) depending on the point of bridge-breakage. The procedure was used in studies of the terminal 10L segment of abnormal chromosome 10 (Emmerling, 1959; Miles, 1970).

Ring chromsomes are quite unstable. Sister chromatid exchanges occur in both mitotic and meiotic cells. In addition, crossing over in meiosis between a normal chromosome and a ring produces dicentric bridges. Consequently, maintenance of a ring chromosome in culture is difficult and the investigator is frequently faced with the necessity of producing a new one for a particular experiment. Ghidoni (1973) and Carlson (1973a) demonstrated a relatively simple technique for constructing ring chromosomes (reviewed by Carlson, 1986). They found that B^A chromosomes (from B-A translocations) form ring chromosomes with reasonable frequency in certain crosses. The rings are found when genetically marked A A B^A plants (segmental trisomes) are crossed as males to tester females. Variegated progeny usually contain the ring B^A. These ring chromosomes are relatively easy to maintain due to their small size compared to whole-chromosome rings. Reduced size means lesser susceptibility to both sister chromatid exchanges and crossing over.

4–10 SUPERNUMERARY ELEMENTS

Supernumerary elements are extra chromosomes or chromosomal segments that have no vital function and may be present or absent in different members of the species. Although heterochromatic knobs fall under this definition, we will limit the discussion to two unusual supernumerary elements identified in corn: the B chromosome and the extra segment of abnormal chromosome 10. There are a number of similarities between the B chromosome and the supernumerary region of abnormal 10. Both contain large heterochromatic regions as well as euchromatic segments. Both have specific and sometimes dramatic effects on the process of crossing over. In addition, they both possess systems, referred to as accumulation mechanisms, which act to maintain the supernumerary elements in populations. Despite these similiarities, Ting's (1958) suggestion of homology between the extra segment of abnormal 10 and the B chromosome seems unlikely. The accumulation mechanisms of the B chromosome and abnormal 10 are strikingly different (see below). There are also differences in their effects on crossing over (Nel 1973; Ward, 1975). Most telling is the lack of homology between prominent heterochromatic regions of the B and of abnormal 10. The large blocks of distal heterochromatin on the B chromosome lack a 185 base pair repeat sequence that is found in all other knobs, including the one in the supernumerary region of abnormal 10 (Peacock et al., 1981).

The origin of supernumerary elements is unknown, although hypotheses have often been proposed. Recently, Peeters et al. (1985) reported observations on the formation of new supernumerary chromosomes in corn. They found that fusions of meiotic cells occur spontaneously in a Himalayan popcorn. The fusions result in major karyotypic changes, including the production of small fragment chromosomes. It is possible, therefore, that the maize B chromosome resulted from a catastrophic genomic event. Other hypotheses concerning the origin of B chromosomes in various organisms are discussed by Jones and Rees (1982).

The role of supernumerary elements in the organism is uncertain. According to one idea, the evolution of a chromosomal region into a supernumerary element may be associated with inactivation of its genes. Consequently, the element becomes innocuous to the organism and cannot produce negative (aneuploid) or positive (selective) effects. On this hypothesis, supernumeraries are maintained in populations by their accumulation mechanisms, rather than selection (Ostergren, 1945). The alternate idea, that supernumeraries serve some useful genetic function, has been difficult to substantiate. In corn, neither the B chromosome nor abnormal 10 have any obvious phenotypic effects on the organism. They seem to possess few active genes, except those associated with their accumulation mechanisms. However, both supernumeraries change the distribution of chiasmata in the genome and may "unlock" genetic regions in which chiasmata seldom occur. Consequently, they tend to increase genetic variation, which may be beneficial to evolution of the population. Other possible beneficial effects of B chromosomes are discussed by Jones and Rees (1982).

Studies of the corn B chromosome and abnormal 10 have focussed primarily on identifying and exploiting their unique genetic traits. Both supernumeraries modify fundamental genetic processes, including chromosomal division, fertilization and crossing over, as discussed below.

4–10.1 Abnormal Chromosome 10

The chromosomes of corn are remarkably uniform in morphology throughout the species with the major variation being in the presence or absence of heterochromatic knobs. However, some strains of corn possess a modified chromosome 10 which differs from the norm in the distal region of 10L. The modified type of chromosome is referred to as abnormal chromosome 10. Several forms of the chromosome have been reported (Longley, 1937, 1938; Ting, 1958; Kikudome, 1961; Kato, 1984; Rhoades and Dempsey, 1985). We will be concerned here with the common form, referred to as type 1 by Kato (1984).

Type 1 abnormal 10 contains three large and distinct chromomeres in 10L that are not found in the corresponding section of normal 10. The most distal of these chromomeres lies near the position at which 10L terminates in the normal chromosome. The long arm of abnormal 10 is longer than that in normal 10, due to the presence of an added region of distal chromatin. Beginning just after the last prominent chromomere, there is a light-staining region comprising somewhat less than half of the extra length, at pachynema, of abnormal 10. Next a large heterochromatic knob is present, followed distally by a short euchromatic region with small and diffuse chromomeres (Fig. 4–11).

Three phenomena occur in plants carrying abnormal chromosome 10 in heterozygous or homozygous condition. These are: preferential segregation, neocentromere formation, and a recombinational effect. Rhoades and Dempsey (1966b) presented a comprehensive study of these phenomena and the subject was earlier reviewed by Rhoades (1952, 1955).

Preferential segregation is the accumulation mechanism of abnormal chromosome 10. It acts by increasing the frequency of chromosomal transmission through the egg parent. Rhoades (1942) found in abnormal 10/normal 10 heterozygotes that the abnormal chromosome is recovered through the female in about 70% of the progeny rather than 50%. Longley (1945) later found that abnormal 10 is able to induce preferential recovery

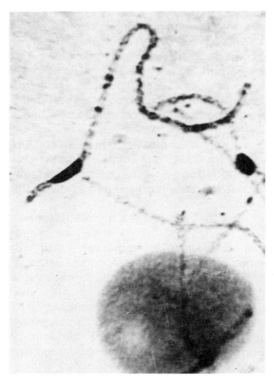

Fig. 4–11. Abnormal chromosome 10 in pachynema. Note the three chromomeres in 10L and the large heterochromatic knob. Photograph courtesy of M.M. Rhoades.

of other knobbed chromosomes, as long as they are paired in meiosis with a knobless chromosome. Genetic studies indicate that the preferential segregation effect is linked to knobs. Genes which are associated with knobs are recovered in frequencies above 50%. However, as the distance between a gene and a knob increases, preferential segregation of the gene declines due to crossing over. Kikudome (1959) also found that the frequency of preferential segregation by a knob depends on its size. Three chromosomes with small, medium, and large knobs at the distal end of 9S were each made heterozygous with a knobless 9. In the presence of abnormal 10, the knobbed chromosomes were recovered in 59, 65, and 69%, respectively, of the progeny. In addition, Kikudome found that pairwise combinations of chromosomes with knobs of different sizes resulted in preferential recovery of the chromosome with the larger knob.

The phenomenon of preferential segregation is an end product of neocentromere formation, according to the hypothesis of Rhoades (1952). Neocentromeres are regions that are separate from the normal centromeres but can, on certain occasions, attach spindle fibers. Rhoades and Vilkomerson (1942) found that abnormal 10 induces neocentromere formation on certain chromosomes at both meiotic divisions. The neocentromeres pull the chromosomes precociously to the poles, producing anaphase I dyads and anaphase II monads whose neocentric arms reach the poles in advance of the centromere (Fig. 4–12). The number of chromosomes which possess neocentromeres is the same as the number of knob-bearing chromosomes, and it is believed that knobs are sites of neocentromere formation. Rhoades' hypothesis, that neocentromeres account for preferential segregation, depends on the linear arrangement of the two meiotic spindles during megasporogenesis. Consider a bivalent consisting of one knobbed and one knobless chromosome. If a crossover occurs between the centromere and knob of the bivalent, dyads heteromorphic for the knob are produced. As the dyads separate in anaphase I, the knobbed chromatids take the lead and throughout anaphase are closer to the pole than are the knobless chromatids. Assuming that the relative orientation of chromatids is retained from anaphase I until metaphase II, the knobbed chromatids at second division will face the outer or terminal poles, while the knobless chromatids face inward. The knobbed chromatids would then pass to the outer megaspores, one of which, the basal megaspore, gives rise to the female gametophyte. On this scheme, only dyads with one knobbed and one knobless chromatid undergo preferential segregation. Support for the hypothesis came from the demonstration that crossing over proximal to a heterochromatic knob is essential for preferential segregation (Rhoades and Dempsey, 1966b). The lack of 100% preferential segregation in testcrosses could be attributed to an occasional lack of crossing over proximal to the knob or to multiple exchanges between the knob and centromere which do not yield heteromorphic dyads. Also, the extent to which orientation persists from one meiotic division to the next could influence the rate of preferential segregation.

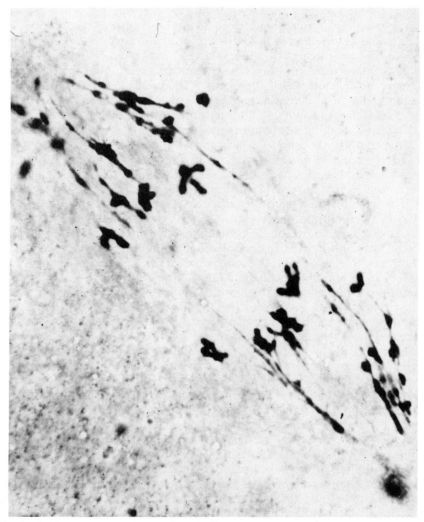

Fig. 4–12. Neocentromeres in anaphase I. Chromosome arms with neocentromeres are extended toward the poles in advance of the conventional centromere. Photograph courtesy of M. M. Rhoades.

In addition to its influence on centromeric activity, abnormal 10 has a striking effect on genetic recombination. Abnormal 10 appears to increase recombination in proximal regions of several chromosomes (Miles, 1970; Nel, 1971, 1973; Rhoades and Dempsey, 1966b; Rhoades, 1968) although the *Wx* to *G1–15* region of chromosome 9, which spans the centromere, is unaffected by it (Nel, 1973). Abnormal 10 also promotes crossing over in regions of structural heterozygosity and knob heterozygosity, possibly by reducing asynapsis in these regions (Rhoades and

Dempsey, 1966b; Kikudome, 1959; Rhoades, 1968; Gillies et al., 1973). Why abnormal 10 should enhance crossing over in the corn genome is not known. Possibly the phenomenon is another element of the abnormal 10 accumulation mechanism, since crossing over between a knob and its centromere is a prerequisite to preferential segregation. Alternatively, abnormal 10 may serve the function in corn populations of increasing genetic variability. Regardless, the chromosome provides a rare and useful tool in the study of recombination.

The genes which control abnormal 10 functions have not yet been located on the chromosome. At one time it seemed obvious that they would be found in the "extra" heterochromatin and euchromatin of abnormal 10 that extends beyond the end of normal 10L. In abnormal 10/ normal 10 heterozygotes, this region is unpaired in pachytene and seems superfluous. The subterminal 10L segment of abnormal 10, with its unique chromomeric pattern, pairs correctly with the end of normal 10L and was assumed to be homologous with it. Recent work of Rhoades and Dempsey (1985) has shown that this concept of abnormal 10 organization is incorrect. They constructed terminal deficiencies of abnormal 10 using a special system for inducing dicentric formation (Rhoades et al., 1967; Rhoades and Dempsey, 1972, 1973b). The system relies on the ability of B chromosomes (in a specific genetic background) to cause nondivision of heterochromatic knobs. Nondivision occurs only at the second pollen mitosis, and is an extension of the nondisjunctional system which is normally confined to B chromosomes. With application of this technique, abnormal 10 formed dicentric bridges at the second pollen mitosis. The bridges were fused at the knob position and subsequently broke at various sites. Rhoades and Dempsey selected cases of breakage that caused loss of the distal *Sr2* marker. In a cross of *g g sr2 sr2* ♀ × *G G Sr2 Sr2* (Abn 10/Abn 10) ♂, progeny were selected with the recessive *sr2* phenotype. Some of the selected plants were also recessive for the more proximal marker *g*, indicating transmission of a large 10L deficiency. Plants with the *sr2 G* phenotype were selected and five small deficiencies identified. Four of the deficient abnormal 10 chromosomes were longer than normal 10 and carried some of the extra chromatin. Nevertheless, they all lacked the *Sr2* gene found on normal 10. Therefore, some of the extra chromatin of abnormal 10 must be homologous to a region on normal 10. In addition, progeny tests showed that the *W2* gene was missing from one deficiency whereas both *W2* and *O7* were absent from another deficiency. This pattern of loss is unexpected, since *O7* is normally distal to *W2*. After studying the cytological and genetical patterns of loss, it was concluded that abnormal 10 has the organization depicted in Fig. 4–13. Sequences unique to abnormal 10 are located at two sites, separated by a segment that is homologous to the normal 10 terminus. The interposed segment is rearranged in gene order, with the *L13-W2* region being inverted. It is now clear that the subterminal region of abnormal 10 which usually pairs with the terminal region of normal 10 engages in nonhom-

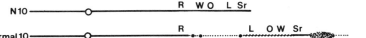

Fig. 4–13. Comparison of genetic organization between the normal chromosome 10 and abnormal 10. Dotted lines and the stippled knob are supernumerary regions. Wavy line is an inverted segment of 10. (Reprinted with permission from Rhoades and Dempsey, 1985.)

ologous pairing. This is consistent with previous findings that crossing over in normal 10/abnormal 10 heterozygotes is rare in distal regions of 10L (Rhoades, 1942; Kikudome, 1959).

The construction of terminal deficiencies by Rhoades and Dempsey (1985, 1986) provides a basis for mapping the chromosomal positions responsible for preferential segregation, neocentromere formation, and enhanced recombination. Earlier attempts by Emmerling (1959) and Miles (1970) to localize these functions were reviewed by Carlson (1977).

4–10.2 B Chromosome

A considerable number of organisms have supernumerary (B) chromosomes (Battaglia, 1964; Jones and Rees, 1982). The most heavily studied B chromosome is the one found in corn (reviewed by Beckett, 1978; Carlson, 1978b, 1986). It is a relatively small chromosome, being about 60% as long as chromosome 10 (Fig. 4–14). The corn B chromosome was described by McClintock (1933) and Ward (1973a). It has a subterminal centromere with a minute and often nonobservable short arm. Adjacent to the centromere in the long arm is a prominent segment of heterochromatin with a knob-like appearance. The heterochromatin contains DNA which is partly homologous to that found in knobs (section 4–4.3). Distal to the centric heterochromatin is a euchromatic region which makes up about one-third of the pachytene length of the chromosome. Next, a large block of heterochromatin is present which usually is divided into four parts (Ward, 1973a), although more segments can be seen occasionally (Pryor et al., 1980). This heterochromatin lacks DNA sequence homology with knobs (section 4–4.3). A short euchromatic region terminates the B chromosome.

Several unique properties are associated with the B chromosome. It divides normally during plant growth and during development of the female gametophyte. However, it is transmitted in excess numbers through the pollen. Roman (1947, 1948) analyzed pollen transmission of B chromosomes by using B-A translocations (see below). Two quite unusual phenomena were discovered. First, B chromosomes often undergo nondisjunction at the second pollen mitosis. If one B chromosome is present in the generative nucleus, dissimilar sperm containing zero, and two B chromosomes are frequently produced. Second, when sperm with zero Bs and two Bs are released into the embryo sac, the sperm with two Bs fertilizes the egg approximately twice as often as the zero B sperm. The latter phenomenon, referred to as preferential fertilization, increases the

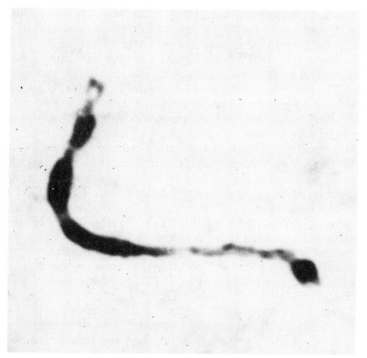

Fig. 4–14. The B chromosome in pachynema. Photograph courtesy of M.M. Rhoades.

frequency of Bs in the progeny above that present in the parent. Together, nondisjunction and preferential fertilization constitute an accumulation mechanism.

Roman's results were obtained with B-A translocations. The first translocation to be analyzed was between the B and chromosome 4 (TB-4Sa). In TB-4Sa, the point of interchange in chromosome 4 is in the short arm approximately 0.25 of the arm length away from the centromere. The breakpoint in the B is at or near the juncture of the proximal euchromatic region with the distal heterochromatin. The two new chromosomes formed by the translocation are A^B and B^A chromosomes, designated 4^B and B^4. The 4^B chromosomes contain the heavily heterochromatic portion of the B plus the terminal euchromatin. The B^4 chromosome has the B centromere with its adjacent heterochromatin plus the proximal euchromatic region of the B. A useful endosperm marker (*Su*) from 4S is located on the B^4. When plants homozygous for the translocation (4^B 4^B B^4-*Su* B^4-*Su*) were crossed as female to recessive *su* pollen parents, all of the resulting kernels were *Su* in phenotype. Plants germinated from the kernels contained one B^4, as expected. The reciprocal cross, however, gave ears with many kernels showing the *su* phenotype. These *su* kernels lacked the B^4 chromosome in the endosperm, but plants from such kernels carried two B^4 chromosomes. In addition, many of the

Su kernels had embryos lacking the B^4 chromosome. (Presumably, the endosperm contained two B^4s.) The dissimilarity in constitution between the embryo and endosperm was attributed to nondisjunction of the B^4 chromosome at the second pollen mitosis. Nondisjunction of the B^4 was not found 100% of the time, since some *Su* kernels gave rise to plants with one B^4. (Rates of nondisjunction are quite variable, but frequencies below 50% of pollen appear to be rare.) Other B-A translocations gave similar results. In all cases, the chromosome with the B centromere (B^A) engages in nondisjunction whereas the A^B does not.

Mitotic nondisjunction is an unusual event, seldom amenable to study. However, the frequent nondisjunction of B chromosomes and B^A chromosomes at the second pollen mitosis provides a powerful tool for examining the process. Roman (1949) showed with TB-4Sa that a distal region of the B, located on 4^B, is required for nondisjunction of the B^4. Roman's work was extended by Ward (1973b). He utilized TB-8La with a near terminal exchange point in the B to demonstrate that the distal euchromatic tip of the B (on 8^B) is required for nondisjunction.

Subsequent work identified additional regions on the B that are required for nondisjunction (Lin, 1978, 1979; Rhoades et al., 1967; Rhoades and Dempsey, 1972, 1973b; Carlson 1973b, 1978a, b; Carlson and Chou, 1981). These regions are separable from the centromere (Fig. 4–15) but control its behavior (reviewed by Carlson, 1986). Whether or not the regions shown in Fig. 4–15 contain single or multiple genetic loci controlling nondisjunction is not known. Also, the manner in which the regions control nondisjunction is not known. However, heterochromatin apparently plays a key role in preventing division of the centromere.

The role of heterochromatin in nondisjunction was first indicated by studies of Rhoades et al. (1967) and Rhoades and Dempsey (1972, 1973b). They found that a particular genetic background, referred to as "high loss," has a modifying effect on the B nondisjunctional system. It allows B chromosomes to induce nondivision of knobs on A chromosomes. In the presence of two or more B's and the "high loss" background, knobs fail to separate at the second pollen mitosis. Bridges form as a result, and breakage of the bridges frequently causes genetic markers to be lost. The "high loss" effect may result from reduced specificity in the B-nondisjunctional system. The idea is that B chromosomes produce a *trans*-active substance at the second pollen mitosis. The substance normally prevents

Fig. 4–15. Diagram of the B chromosome indicating the regions which are required for nondisjunction. Deletion of either region 1, 2, or 3 results in the complete elimination of nondisjunction. Deletion of region 4 (leaving a functional centromere) causes a reduction in the rate of nondisjunction. (Reprinted with permission from Carlson and Chou, 1981.)

division of a specific heterochromatic region on the B, resulting in non-disjunction. With the high-loss genetic background, the *trans*-active substance also affects division of knobs. The result, in this case, is bridge formation.

The nondividing heterochromatin of the B is believed to be the centric heterochromatin (region 3) rather than the distal blocks. The evidence is as follows. First, B chromosomes undergo nondisjunction rather than bridge formation and, therefore, require nondivision of a region near the centromere. Second, B^A chromosomes that completely lack the distal B heterochromatin are fully capable of nondisjunction. Third, A^B chromosomes that have large amounts of distal heterochromatin do not undergo nondisjunction. Fourth, region 3 heterochromatin shares some sequence homology with knob heterochromatin whereas distal B heterochromatin does not (Peacock et al., 1981).

The second component of the B chromosome accumulation mechanism is preferential fertilization. Rates of preferential fertilization are relatively constant, in contrast to rates of nondisjunction. Most workers using B-A translocations report fertilization of the egg by $A^B B^A B^A$ sperm in approximately two-thirds of pollinations while the A^B sperm succeeds one-third of the time. An exception to this rule was found when TB-9Sb plants were crossed as males to a particular inbred female. The female parent blocked preferential fertilization and the $9^B B^9 B^9$ sperm succeeded no more often than the 9^B sperm in fertilization of the egg (Carlson, 1969). The inbred line should be of value when studies on the nature of preferential fertilization are performed.

The mechanism by which preferential fertilization occurs is unknown. However, two general hypotheses have been tested. One idea is that B chromosomes confer an advantage on sperm in fertilization of the egg. An alternate proposal is that B chromosomes migrate to a particular pole during nondisjunction and sperm derived from that pole preferentially fertilize the egg. On the latter idea, B-type chromosomes should show specific patterns of migration at the second pollen mitosis. However, the B^4 and B^9 chromosomes of TB-4Sa and TB-9Sb segregate randomly with respect to each other during nondisjunction (Carlson, 1969). Also, if B's migrate to a specific pole, one might expect that preferential fertilization by a B^A chromosome will be unaffected by the addition of extra B chromosomes. However, when plants carrying TB-9Sb plus 6 to 8 B chromosomes were crossed as male parents to a tester, preferential fertilization by sperm carrying two B^9's was completely absent. It is assumed that B chromosomes entered both sperm of the pollen grains and nullified any advantage of the B^9-containing sperm (Carlson, 1969). The B chromosomes, therefore, actively influence the process of fertilization. They apparently do so by conferring a competitive advantage on sperm in fertilization of the egg (Carlson, 1970b).

Despite the evidence that B chromosomes influence fertilization of the egg, it is not known whether they carry genes for preferential fertilization. A difference in chromosome number or chromatin content between two sperm could trigger preferential fertilization in the absence of any specific genetic activity by the B chromosome. If sperm differing in the number of A chromosomes could be generated, the possible nonspecificity of preferential fertilization could be tested.

Nondisjunction and preferential fertilization act in concert to produce the B accumulation mechanism. The nondisjunctional system may also function separately in meiosis. Carlson and Curtis (1986b) provided evidence that univalent B chromosomes migrate to one pole in meiosis, rather than lagging on the plate, due to the nondisjunctional system. They noted that the movement of a univalent to one pole in meiosis is equivalent to nondisjunction of a chromosome during mitosis.

Beckett (1982) described a second accumulation mechanism for B chromosomes. He measured transmission of B-A translocations through the pollen in translocation heterozygotes. The rearrangements studied were TB-1La and TB-1Lc. It was expected that approximately 50% of the viable pollen would contain the balanced translocation. Instead, in repeated tests, Beckett found transmission to be well over 50%. He concluded that pollen containing the B chromosome can outcompete pollen lacking the B.

The properties described thus far are consistent with a parasitic role for the B chromosome. The B has a number of functions related to its survival in a population but has no genes required for viability of the plant. However, the B chromosome may provide a useful function to the organism by modifying crossover rates. Several studies have found small but significant effects of B chromosomes on crossing over (Rhoades, 1978; Carlson, 1978b). In addition, a specific and strong effect was reported by Rhoades in 1968. Rhoades studied a chromosomal rearrangement referred to as transposition 9 (see also section 4–5.3). In formation of the rearrangement, a segment of 3L was broken out of chromosome 3 and inserted into the short arm of chromosome 9 between C and Wx. As a result, the length of 9S was increased by 20%. Crossing over was tested between C and Wx for $Tp9/Tp9$ plants and compared to crossing over in the $N9/N9$ constitution. Surprisingly, the increased physical length of $Tp9$ did not increase the rate of crossing over. It was concluded that the transposed segment of chromosome 3 is refractory to chiasma formation. However, the presence of a single B chromosome caused a dramatic rise in crossing over. The rate of crossing over was approximately 18% in $Tp9/Tp9$ plants lacking the B but was 37% in the presence of one B. Increasing the number of B chromosomes gave a slight additional amount of C-Wx crossing over. The $Tp9$ effect was studied further by Ward (1973a, 1975). In one experiment, he attempted to localize the B chromosome site which increases crossing over in $Tp9$. However, all regions of the B seemed to contribute to crossing over rather than a single site. The findings with $Tp9$ suggest a potential value of the B chromosome to the organism. It may increase gametic diversity in corn, and therefore evolutionary potential, by allowing crossing over in regions that normally do not have chiasmata.

As noted above, the corn B chromosome has several unique properties. Experimentally, its most useful properties are those which allow manipulations of gene dosage among the standard (A) chromosomes. One method for changing gene dosage is by nondisjunction of B^A chromosomes at the second pollen mitosis. A second method is through adjacent segregation in meiosis by B-A translocation heterozygotes. (Some products of adjacent segregation are viable due to the genetic inertness of B chromosomes.) Crosses with a TB-4Sa heterozygote will be considered as an example of both methods. The cross between a normal plant and one heterozygous for the translocation can be denoted: 4 4 ♀ × 4 4 B^4 B^4 ♂. (The missing fourth member of the translocation group is the dispensable B chromosome.) The male parent will produce several microspore classes, including the balanced translocation ($4^B B^4$). Pollen formation by the 4^B B^4 class together with nondisjunction will give 4^B B^4 B^4 in one sperm and 4^B in the other sperm. (The tube nucleus retains the 4^B B^4 constitution.) Individuals derived from a normal egg and the nondisjunctional pollen grain will be either 4 4^B B^4 B^4 or 4 4^B, depending on the pattern of fertilization. The former constitution has three copies of a 4S segment. It is referred to as a partial trisome or a hyperploid individual. The 4 4^B plants are partial monosomes (hypoploids).

Nondisjunction produces both increases and decreases in gene dosage as noted above. Meiotic segregation produces hyperploidy for A chromosome segments, but not hypoploidy. The 4 4^B B^4 heterozygote produces the following meiotic products: 4; 4^B B^4; 4 B^4. The 4 B^4 class is disomic for part of 4S. Due to its duplication, pollen transmission of 4 B^4 is low and it is preferable to recover this chromosome combination through the female. (The fertilization of a 4 B^4 egg with a normal sperm produces a partial trisome: 4 4 B^4.) By reference to a standard translocation heterozygote, the 4 B^4 constitution results from adjacent-1 segregation. The gametophyte is viable, despite its origin by adjacent segregation, because its deficiency is for nonessential B chromatin. (The reciprocal 4^B class is inviable due to the deficiency of A chromatin.) Recently, Kindiger et al. (1984) found that A A^B gametes are produced by adjacent-2 segregation in some translocation heterozygotes. These gametes are also duplicate for A chromatin and deficient for B chromatin.

The systems for manipulating the dosage of A chromosome regions have been widely used experimentally. The nondisjunctional system has been applied to localization of genes to specific chromosomes (Roman and Ullstrup, 1951). For example, assume that a new recessive mutation (*m*) is crossed as follows: *mm* ♀ × *MM* ♂. Ordinarily, all the progeny will have the dominant phenotype. However, if *M* is carried on a B^A chromosome, some F_1 progeny will be recessive due to nondisjunction. With an endosperm phenotype, the recessive trait will be expressed when a hypoploid (B^A-deficient) sperm fertilizes the polar nuclei. If *M* controls a plant phenotype, the recessive will be found in cases of egg-fertilization by the hypoploid sperm. In either situation, a certain percentage of F_1 progeny will have the recessive phenotype uncovered. The gene will then be located to the chromosome arm which is carried on the B^A chromosome. In practice, gene placement tests employ a series of B-A translocations so that each chromosome arm in the corn genome can be checked. A gene being tested is uncovered by one member of the translocation series and not others (Beckett, 1978). The method has been frequently used, with an important example being localization of large numbers of induced mutations by Neuffer and Sheridan (1980).

A supplementary method for using nondisjunction to place genes on chromosomes has also been proposed (Roman and Ullstrup, 1951; Beckett, 1978). The technique applies to genes that are located proximal to available B-A translocations and cannot be uncovered by them. The procedure requires that crosses be made between a mutant and the B-A translocation series. Progeny are screened for A A^B plants and the hypoploids are backcrossed to the mutant. If the mutant allele is located on the A chromosome of an A A^B pair, selection will occur to increase its transmission above 50%. (The A^B gametic class is inviable due to deficiency.) Consequently, deviation from a 1:1 ratio in a testcross identifies linkage to a particular chromosome.

A second major use for B^A dosage changes has been in studying the relationship between gene number and phenotypic effect. The unusual phenomenon of "gene imprinting" has been demonstrated using B-A translocations. Gene imprinting is the preparation of a gene (in one generation) for its mode of activity in the next generation. The first well-documented case was found with the R locus (Kermicle, 1970, 1978). Transmission of a standard R allele through the female produces a solid-colored phenotype in the aleurone. However, transmission through the male gives a mottled phenotype. Thus, in reciprocal crosses of $RR \times rr$, the RR/r endosperm is solid-colored whereas the rr/R endosperm is mottled. (Genes to the left of the slash are of maternal origin; genes on the right are paternal.) The simplest conclusion is that dosage of the dominant allele determines the difference in phenotypes. However, further studies using TB-10La showed that parental origin of R controls its phenotype. Through manipulation of B^{10} dosage, it was possible to construct the complementary endosperm genotypes RR/rr and rr/RR. The former produced a solid-colored endosperm and the latter gave mottled kernels. Using other controls, Kermicle was able to demonstrate that gene imprinting, rather than gene dosage, controls the mottled vs. solid-colored phenotype. Lin (1982) identified another clear case of gene imprinting in corn. Previous work had shown that several chromosome arms contain genes that are required for normal endosperm development. Reduced dosage of these arms (produced by B^A nondisjunction) gives a small-kernel phenotype. Lin analyzed 10L for the small-kernel effect. He partitioned the chromosome arm by inducing 38 B-10L translocations with x-irradiation. The translocations provided a range of breakpoints in 10L and, consequently, a variety of B^{10} chromosomes. In general, hypoploidy for the B^{10} of these translocations produced reductions in kernel size. (The hyperploid class did not differ in phenotype from the normal dosage situation.) Four of the 38 translocations gave hypoploid kernels that were slightly less than 50% the normal size. These four translocations had the most proximal 10L breakpoints of the group. One translocation with a less proximal breakpoint gave a hypoploid class that was 74% of normal. Another translocation, slightly distal in breakpoint to the previous one, produced hypoploid kernels that were 85% of normal. The remaining 32 translocations had various breakpoints along 10L that were distal to the six mentioned. Hypoploidy for B^A dosage in the latter group had little effect on kernel size, but a reduction of about 5% was found. On the basis of these findings, Lin identified four *Ef* (*endosperm factor*) regions in 10L that affect endosperm development. When all four regions are hypoploid, as is true for translocations with the most proximal breakpoints, a drastic reduction in kernel size occurs. When only the most distal *Ef* is hypoploid, a minor and variable effect is seen.

The hypoploid effect of 10L was further analyzed to determine whether chromosomal dosage or gene imprinting control the small-kernel phenotype. One of the most proximal translocations, TB-10L (19), was used in a cross which produces various 10L constitutions: 10 10 $B^{10} \times 10^B$ $10^B B^{10} B^{10}$. It was possible to identify in progeny the maternal vs. paternal origin of 10L segments by using different alleles of the *R* locus on B^{10}. Lin found that one 10L arm of paternal origin is required for normal endosperm development. Absence of a paternal 10L could not be compensated for by the presence of a maternal 10L. For example, kernels that contained two maternal and two paternal doses of 10L developed normally. However, kernels with four maternal and zero paternal doses of 10L showed the small-kernel phenotype. Consequently, gene imprinting controls the phenotype, although in a different manner from that found for the *R* locus. With *Ef* loci, the paternal genes are active and control the phenotype whereas the opposite is true for *R*. Further studies on gene dosage effects and aneuploidy have been conducted by James Birchler, as discussed in section 4–9.5.

In addition to the procedures described above, a large number of experimental uses for B chromosomes and B-A translocations have been found. Carlson (1986) lists applications in (i) studies of heterochromatin, (ii) transfer of genes from one inbred line to another, (iii) production of ring chromosomes, (iv) studies of synapsis and crossing over, and (v) studies of centromeric misdivision. Applications continue to increase and one new experiment will be described.

As mentioned in section 4–4.1, there are two types of breakage-fusion-bridge cycles. The chromatid cycle produces single bridges, whereas the chromosome cycle gives double bridges. A chromatid cycle occasionally changes spontaneously into a chromosome cycle by nondisjunction of

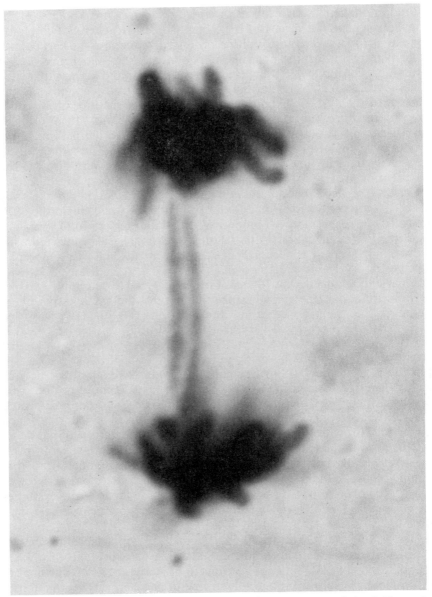

Fig. 4–16. Mitotic double bridge from a chromosome type breakage-fusion-bridge cycle. The dicentric chromosome was produced by crossing over within a B^9-Dp^9 chromosome followed by nondisjunction (see text).

the single bridge (Schwartz and Murray, 1957). The conversion from a chromatid to a chromosome cycle can be made to occur on a regular basis through the use of B chromosome nondisjunction. The procedure that was devised utilizes the B⁹ chromosome of TB-9Sb. The B⁹ was first modified through crossing over with a duplication-derivative of chromosome 9. The duplication consists of an extra short arm of 9 which is attached, in reverse order, to the end of 9S (McClintock, 1941a). Crossing over between the B⁹ and duplication 9 (*Dp9*) allowed transfer of the duplicated segment to the B⁹. Once the B⁹-*Dp9* chromosome was constructed, it was used to produce dicentrics. The two short arms of B⁹-*Dp9* frequently engage in foldback pairing and crossing over, with dicentric production. The result is initiation of chromatid breakage-fusion-bridge cycles during meiosis. Subsequently, the chromatid cycles are converted to chromosome cycles through nondisjunction at the second pollen mitosis. Among the progeny of crosses involving male transmission of B⁹-*Dp9*, many display the plant variegation associated with a chromosomal breakage-fusion-bridge cycle. The variegated plants also produce the expected double bridge configurations in mitotic anaphase (Fig. 4–16). The method may be useful in studying the properties of chromosomal cycles, which are usually difficult to initiate.

ACKNOWLEDGMENT

This material is based upon work supported by the Cooperative State Research Service, USDA under agreements 82–CRCR–1–1023 and 86–CRCR–1–2122.

REFERENCES

Aguiar-Perecin, M.L.R. de. 1985. C-banding in maize. I. Band patterns. Caryologia 38:23–30.

––––, and C.G. Vosa. 1985. C-banding in maize. II. Identification of somatic chromosomes. Heredity 54:37–42.

Albertsen, M.C., and R.L. Phillips. 1981. Developmental cytology of 13 genetic male sterile loci in maize. Can. J. Genet. Cytol. 23:195–208.

Alexander, D.E. 1957. The genetic induction of autotetraploidy: A proposal for its use in corn breeding. Agron. J. 49:40–43.

––––. 1964. Spontaneous reciprocal translocation during megasporogenesis of maize haploids. Nature (London) 201:737–738.

Anderson, E.G. 1956. The application of chromosomal techniques to maize improvement. p. 23–36. *In* Brookhaven symposium in biology: Genetics in plant breeding. No. 9. Brookhaven Natl. Lab, Upton, NY.

––––, H.H. Kramer, and A.E. Longley. 1955. Translocations in maize involving chromosome 4. Genetics 40:500–510.

Anderson, L.K., S.M. Stack, M.H. Fox, and Z. Chuanshan. 1985. The relationship between genome size and synaptonemal complex length in higher plants. Exp. Cell Res. 156:367–378.

Ashley, T. 1979. Specific end-to-end attachment of chromosomes in *Ornithogalum virens*. J. Cell Sci. 38:357–367.

––––, and N. Pocock. 1981. A proposed model of chromosomal organization in nuclei at fertilization. Genetica 55:161–169.

Avivi, L., and M. Feldman. 1980. Arrangement of chromosomes in the interphase nucleus of plants. Hum. Genet. 55:281–295.

Baker, R.L., and D.T. Morgan, Jr. 1969. Control of pairing in maize and meiotic inter-chromosomal effects of deficiencies in chromosome 1. Genetics 61:91–106.

Battaglia, E. 1964. Cytogenetics of B chromosomes. Caryologia 17:245–299.

Beadle, G.W. 1929. A gene for supernumerary mitoses during spore development in *Zea mays*. Science 70:406–407.

――――. 1930. Genetical and cytological studies of Mendelian asynapsis in *Zea mays*. p. 1–23. *In* Mem. Cornell Univ. Agric. Exp. Stn. 129.

――――. 1931. A gene in maize for supernumerary cell divisions following meiosis. p. 3–12. *In* Mem. Cornell Univ. Agric. Exp. Stn. 135.

――――. 1932a. A gene for sticky chromosomes in *Zea mays*. Z. Induk. Abstamm. Vererbungsl. 63:195–217.

――――. 1932b. A gene in *Zea mays* for the failure of cytokinesis during meiosis. Cytologia 3:142–155.

――――. 1932c. Genes in maize for pollen sterility. Genetics 17:413–431.

――――. 1933. Further studies for asynaptic maize. Cytologia 4:269–287.

――――. 1937. Chromosome aberration and gene mutation in *sticky* chromosome plants of *Zea mays*. Cytologia (Fujii Jubilee Vol.) 1937:43–56.

――――, and B. McClintock. 1928. A genic disturbance of meiosis in *Zea mays*. Science 68:433–434.

――――, and A.H. Sturtevant. 1935. X chromosome inversions and meiosis in *Drosophila melanogaster*. Proc. Natl. Acad. Sci. USA 21:384–390.

Beckett, J.B. 1978. B-A translocations in maize. J. Hered. 69:27–36.

――――. 1982. An additional mechanism by which B chromosomes are maintained in maize. J. Hered. 73:29–34.

――――. 1983. Kernel-weight effects and transmission of a partial trisome involving the long arm of chromosome 5 in maize. Can. J. Genet. Cytol. 25:346–353.

――――. 1984. An aneuploid-generating system in the maize inbred W23. Genetics 107:s9.

Beckman, J.S., and M. Soller. 1983. Restriction fragment length polymorphisms in genetic improvement: Methodologies, mapping and costs. Theor. Appl. Genet. 67:35–43.

Bellini, G., and A. Bianchi. 1963. Interchromsomal effects of inversions on crossover rate in maize. Z. Vererbungsl. 94:126–132.

Bennett, M.D. 1982. Nucleotypic basis of the spatial ordering of chromosomes in eukaryotes and the implications of the order for genome evolution and phenotypic variation. *In* G.A. Dover and R.B. Flavell (ed.) Genome evolution. Academic Press, London.

――――. 1983. The spatial distribution of chromosomes. *In* P. Brandham and M.D. Bennett (ed.) Proceedings of the second Kew chromosome conference. Allen and Unwin, London.

――――, J.B. Smith, J. Ward, and G. Jenkins. 1981. The relationship between nuclear DNA content and centromere volume in higher plants. J. Cell Sci. 47:91–115.

Birchler, J.A. 1979. A study of enzyme activities in a dosage series of the long arm of chromosome one in maize. Genetics 92:1211–1229.

――――. 1981. The genetic basis of dosage compensation of *alcohol dehydrogenase-1* in maize. Genetics 97:625–637.

――――. 1983a. Chromosomal manipulation in maize. *In* M.S. Swaminathan et al. (ed.) Cytogenetics of crop plants. Macmillan, New Delhi.

――――. 1983b. Allozymes in gene dosage studies. p. 85–108. *In* S.D. Tanksley and T.J. Orton (ed.) Isozymes in plant genetics and breeding, Part A. Elsevier Sci. Publ. B.V., Amsterdam.

――――. 1985. The inverse effect in maize and *Drosophila In* M. Freeling (ed.) Plant genetics. Alan R. Liss, New York.

――――. 1988. Chromosome manipulations in maize. *In* T. Tsuchiya and P.K. Gupta (ed.) Chromosome engineering in plants: Genetics, breeding and evolution. Elsevier Publ. B.V., Amsterdam.

――――, and K.J. Newton. 1981. Modulation of protein levels in chromsomal dosage series of maize: the biochemical basis of aneuploid syndromes. Genetics 99:247–266.

Blackburn, E.H. 1985. Artificial chromosomes in yeast. Trends in Genetics 1:8–12.

Bouchard, R.A., and H. Stern. 1980. DNA synthesized at pachytene in *Lilium*: a non-divergent subclass of moderately repetitive sequences. Chromosoma 81:349–363.

Brettell, R.I.S., E. Thomas, and W. Wernicke. 1981. Production of haploid maize plants by another culture. Maydica 26:101–111.

Brink, R.A. 1973. Paramutation. Ann. Rev. Genet. 7:129–152.

Buescher, P.J., R.L. Phillips, and R. Brambl. 1984. Ribosomal RNA contents of maize genotypes with different ribosomal RNA gene numbers. Biochemical Genet. 22:923–930.

Burnham, C.R. 1932a. The association of non-homologus parts in chromosomal interchange in maize. Proc. Int. Congr. Genet., 6th 2:19–20.

––––. 1932b. An interchange in maize giving low sterility and chain configurations. Proc. Natl. Acad. Sci. USA 18:434–440.

––––. 1934. Chromosomal interchanges in maize: Reduction of crossing over and the association of non-homologous parts. Am. Nat. 68:81–82.

––––. 1949. Chromosome segregation in maize translocations in relation to crossing over in interstitial segments. Proc. Natl. Acad. Sci. USA 35:349–356.

––––. 1950. Chromosome segregation in translocations involving chromosome 6 in maize. Genetics 35:446–481.

––––. 1956. Chromosomal interchanges in plants. Bot. Rev. 22:419–552.

––––. 1962. Discussions in cytogenetics. Burgess Publ., Minneapolis.

––––. 1966. Cytogenetics in plant improvement. In Plant breeding, a symposium held at Iowa State University. Iowa State Univ. Press, Ames.

––––. 1981. Chromosome pairing and recombination in the T5-9a interchange in maize. Maydica 26:153–174.

––––. 1982. The locating of genes to chromosomes by the use of chromosomal interchanges. In W.F. Sheridan (ed.) Maize for biological research. Univ. of North Dakota Press, Grand Forks.

––––, J.T. Stout, W.H. Weinheimer, R.V. Kowles, and R.L. Phillips. 1972. Chromosome pairing in maize. Genetics 71:111–126.

Burr, B., and F.A. Burr. 1983. Barbara McClintock: Nobel prize in physiology/medicine. Trends Biochem. Sci. 8:429–431.

––––, S.V. Evola, F.A. Burr, and J.S. Beckman. 1983. The application of restriction fragment length polymorphism to plant breeding. Genetics eng. 5:45–59.

Carlson, W.R. 1969. Factors affecting preferential fertilization in maize. Genetics 62:543–554.

–––– 1970a. Nondisjunction and isochromosome formation in the B chromosome of maize. Chromosoma 30:356–365.

––––. 1970b. A test for involvement of the polar nuclei in preferential fertilization. Maize Genet. Coop. News Lett. 44:91–92.

––––. 1973a. Instability of the maize B chromosome. Theor. Appl. Genet. 43:147–150.

––––. 1973b. A procedure for localizing genetic factors controlling mitotic nondisjunction in the B chromosome of maize. Chromosoma 42:127–136.

––––. 1977. The cytogenetics of corn. In G.F. Sprague (ed.) Corn and corn improvement. Agronomy 18:225–304.

––––. 1978a. Identification of genetic factors controlling centromeric function in maize. In D.B. Walden (ed.) Maize breeding and genetics. John Wiley and Sons, New York.

––––. 1978b. The B chromosome of corn. Ann. Rev. Genet. 12:5–23.

––––. 1983. Duplication of non-terminal A chromosome segments using B-A translocation. Maydica 28:317–326.

––––. 1986. The B chromosome of maize. CRC Crit. Rev. Plant Sci. 3:201–226.

––––, and T.S. Chou. 1981. B chromosome nondisjunction in corn: control by factors near the centromere. Genetics 97:379–389.

––––, and C. Curtis. 1986a. A new method for producing homozygous duplications in maize. Can. J. Genet. Cytol. 28:1034–1040.

––––, and ––––. 1986b. A meiotic function for the B chromosome nondisjunctional system. Maize Genet. Coop. News Lett. 60:67–68.

Chao, C.Y. 1959. Heterotic effects of a chromosomal segment in maize. Genetics 44:657–677.

Chase, S.S. 1949. Monoploid frequencies in a commercial double cross hybrid maize, and in its component single cross hybrids and inbred lines. Genetics 34:328–332.

––––. 1951. The monoploid method of developing inbred lines. Proc. 6th Annu. Hybrid Corn. Ind.—Res. Conf. 6:29–34.

––––. 1963. Androgenesis—its use for transfer of maize cytoplasm. J. Hered. 54:152–158.

————. 1969. Monoploids and monoploid derivatives of maize (*Zea mays* L.). Bot. Rev. 35:117–167.

Chen, Chi-Chang. 1969. The somatic chromosomes of maize. Can. J. Genet. Cytol. 11:752–754.

Chou, T.S. 1985. Sister chromatid exchanges in *Zea mays* L. Ph.D. diss. Illinois State Univ., Normal (Diss. Abstr. 46:1443-B).

Chow, C., and E. Lartner. 1981. Centromeric banding in maize. Can. J. Genet. Cytol. 23:255–258.

Clark, F.J. 1940. Cytogenetic studies of divergent meiotic spindle formation in *Zea mays*. Am. J. Bot. 27:547–559.

Clarke, A.E., and E.G. Anderson. 1935. A chromosomal interchange in maize without ring formation. Am. J. Bot. 22:711–716.

Coe, E.H. 1959. A line of maize with high haploid frequency. Am. Nat. 93:381–382.

————, and M.G. Neuffer. 1977. The genetics of corn. *In* G.F. Sprague (ed.) Corn and corn improvement. Agronomy 18:111–223.

————, and K.R. Sarkar. 1964. The detection of haploids in maize. J. Hered. 55:231-233.

Comings, D.E. 1980. Arrangement of chromatin in the nucleus. Hum. Genet. 53:131-143.

Cooper, D.C., and R.A. Brink. 1937. Chromosome homology in races of maize from different geographical regions. Am. Nat. 95:582-587.

Creech, R.G., and H.H. Kramer. 1961. A second region in maize for genetic fine structure studies. Am. Nat. 95:326-328.

Curtis, C. 1985. Meiotic mutants of maize. Ph.D. diss. Univ. of Missouri, Columbia (Diss. Abstr. 47:914-B).

Dellarco, V., P. Voytek, and A. Hollaender (ed.) 1985. Aneuploidy: etiology and mechanisms. Plenum Press, New York.

Dempsey, E., and V. Smirnov. 1964. Cytological location of *gl-15*. Maize Genet. Coop. News Lett. 38:71–73.

Dobzhansky, T., and M.M. Rhoades. 1938. A possible method for locating favorable genes in maize. J. Am. Soc. Agron. 30:668–675.

Doerschug, E.B. 1973. Studies of *dotted*, a regulatory element in maize. Theor. Appl. Genet. 43:182–189.

————. 1976. Placement of the genes for ribosomal RNA within the nucleolar organizing body of *Zea mays*. Chromosoma 55:43–56.

Dooner, H.K. 1986. Genetic fine structure of the *bronze* locus in maize. Genetics 113:1021–1036.

————, and J.L. Kermicle. 1971. Structure of the *R-r* tandem duplication in maize. Genetics 67:427–436.

————, and ————. 1974. Reconstitution of the *R*ʳ compound allele in maize. Genetics 78:691–701.

————, and ————. 1976. Displaced and tandem duplications in the long arm of chromosome 10 in maize. Genetics 82:309–322.

————, and ————. 1986. The transposable element *Ds* affects the pattern of intragenic recombination at the *bz* and *R* loci in maize. Genetics 113:135–143.

Doyle, G.G. 1967. Preferential pairing in trisomics of *Zea mays*. *In* Chromosomes today, Vol. 2. Plenum Press, New York.

————. 1971. Tandem duplications from translocations between homologous chromosomes in maize. Genetics 68:s16 (Abstr.).

————. 1972a. A telocentric trisome and its potential use in the production of commercial hybrid corn using genic male sterility. Maize Genet. Coop. News Lett. 46:142–146.

————. 1972b. A tandem duplication and an intrachromosomal displaced duplication induced by irradiation. Maize Genet. Coop. News Lett. 46:138–142.

————. 1979a. The allotetraploidization of maize. Part 1. The physical basis—Differential pairing affinity. Theor. Appl. Genet. 54:103–112.

————. 1979b. The allotetraploidization of maize. Part 2. The theoretical basis—The cytogenetics of segmental allotetraploids. Theor. Appl. Genet. 54:161–168.

————. 1982. The allotetraploidization of maize. Part 3. Gene segregation in trisomic heterozygotes. Theor. Appl. Genet. 61:81–89.

————. 1986. The allotetraploidization of maize. Part 4. Cytological and genetic evidence indicative of substantial progress. Theor. Appl. Genet. 71:585–594.

Einset, J. 1943. Chromosome length in relation to transmission frequency of maize trisomes. Genetics 28:349–364.

Emmerling, M.H. 1958a. An analysis of intragenic and extragenic mutations of the *R-r* gene complex in *Zea mays*. Cold Spring Harbor Symp. Quant. Biol. 23:393–407.

––––. 1958b. Evidence of non-disjunction of abnormal chromosome 10. J. Hered. 49:203–207.

––––. 1959. Preferential segregation of structurally modified chromosomes in maize. Genetics 44:625–645.

Endrizzi, J.E. 1974. Alternate-1 and alternate-2 disjunctions in heterozygous reciprocal translocations. Genetics 77:55–60.

Finch, R.A., J.B. Smith, and M.D. Bennett. 1981. *Hordeum* and *Secale* mitotic genomes lie apart in a hybrid. J. Cell Sci. 52:391–403.

Freeling, M. 1976. Intragenic recombination in maize: Pollen analysis methods and the effect of parental *Adh1*$^+$ isoalleles. Genetics 83:701–717.

––––. 1978. Allelic variation at the level of intragenic recombination. Genetics 89:211–224.

––––. 1984. Plant transposable elements and insertion sequences. Ann. Rev. Plant Physiol. 35:277–298.

––––, and D.C. Bennett. 1985. Maize *Adh1*. Ann. Rev. Genet. 19:297–323.

Friedman, B.E., R.A. Bouchard, and H. Stern. 1982. DNA sequences repaired at pachytene exhibit strong homology among distantly related higher plants. Chromosoma 87:409–424.

Fussell, C.P. 1984. Interphase chromosome order: A proposal. Genetica 62:193–201.

Gabay, S.J., and J.R. Laughnan. 1973. Recombination at the *Bar* locus in an inverted attached-X system in *Drosophila melanogaster*. Genetics 75:485–495.

Ghidoni, A. 1973. Changes in the structure of B^A chromosomes in maize. Theor. Appl. Genet. 43:151–161.

––––, N.E. Pogna, and N. Villa. 1982. Spontaneous aneuploids of maize (*Zea mays*) in a selected sample. Can. J. Genet. Cytol. 24:705–713.

Gilles, A., and L.F. Randolph. 1951. Reduction of quadrivalent frequency in autotetraploid maize during a period of 10 years. Am. J. Bot. 38:12–17.

Gillies, C.B. 1973. Ultrastructural analysis of maize pachytene karyotypes by three dimensional reconstruction of synaptonemal complexes. Chromosoma 43:145–176.

––––. 1975. An ultrastructural analysis of chromosomal pairing in maize. C. R. Trav. Lab. Carlsberg 40:135–161.

––––. 1981. Electron microscopy of spread maize pachytene synaptonemal complexes. Chromosoma 83:575–591.

––––. 1983. Ultrastructural studies of the association of homologous and non-homologous parts of chromosomes in the mid-prophase of meiosis in *Zea mays*. Maydica 28:265–287.

––––. 1984. The synaptonemal complex in higher plants. Crit. Rev. Plant Sci. 2:81–116.

––––, S.W. Rasmussen, and D. von Wettstein. 1973. The synaptinemal complex in homologous and nonhomologous pairing of chromosomes. Cold Spring Harbor Symp. Quant. Biol. 38:117–122.

Givens, J.F., and R.L. Phillips. 1976. The nucleolus organizer region of maize (*Zea mays* L.) Ribosomal RNA gene distribution and nucleolar interactions. Chromosoma 57:103–117.

Golubovskaya, I.N. 1979. Genetic control of meiosis. Int. Rev. Cytol. 58:247–290.

––––, and N.B. Khristolyubova. 1985. The cytogenetic evidence of the gene control of meiosis, maize meiosis, and *mei*-genes. p. 723–738. *In* M. Freeling (ed.) Plant genetics. Alan R. Liss, New York.

––––, and A.S. Mashnenkov. 1975. Genetic control of meiosis I. Meiotic mutation in corn (*Zea mays* L.) *afd*, causing the elimination of the first meiotic division. Genetika 11:11–17.

––––, and ––––. 1976. Genetic control of meiosis II. A desynaptic mutant of corn induced by N-nitroso-N-methylurea. Genetika 12:7–14.

––––, and ––––. 1977. Multiple disturbance of meiosis in corn caused by a single recessive mutation *pam A-A 344*. Genetika 13:1910–1921.

––––, and D.V. Sitnikova. 1980. Three meiotic mutations disturbing chromosome segregation at the first meiotic division in corn. Genetika 16:656–666.

––––, and V.G. Urbach. 1981. Allelic relationships between maize meiotic mutations with similar disturbances of meiosis. Genetika 17:1975–1982.

Goodsell, S.F. 1961. Male sterility in corn by androgenesis. Crop. Sci. 1:227–228.

Gopinath, D.M., and C.R. Burnham. 1956. A cytogenetic study in maize of deficiency-duplication produced by crossing interchanges involving the same chromosomes. Genetics 41:382–395.

Greenblatt, I.M., and M. Bock. 1967. A commercially desirable procedure for detection of monoploids in maize. J. Hered. 58:9–13.

Grell, R.F. 1962. A new hypothesis on the nature and sequence of meiotic events in the female of *Drosophila melanogaster*. Proc. Natl. Acad. Sci. USA 48:165–172.

Gusella, J., N. Wexler, P.M. Conneally, S. Naylor, M. Anderson, R. Tanzi, P. Watkins, K. Ottina, M. Wallace, A. Sakaguchi, A. Young, I. Shoulson, E. Bonilla, and J. Martin. 1983. A polymorphic DNA marker genetically linked to Huntington's disease. Nature (London) 306:234–238.

Hadlaczky, G.Y., and L. Kalman. 1975. Discrimination of homologous chromosomes of maize with Giemsa staining. Heredity 35:371–374.

Hake, S., and V. Walbot. 1980. The genome of *Zea mays*, its organization and homology to related grasses. Chromosoma 79:251–270.

Helentjaris, T., G. King, M. Slocum, C. Siedenstrang, and S. Wegman. 1985. Restriction fragment polymorphisms as probes for plant diversity and their development as tools for applied plant breeding. Plant Molec. Biol. 5:109–118.

————, D.F. Weber, and S. Wright. 1986. Use of monosomics to map cloned DNA fragments in maize. Proc. Natl. Acad. Sci. USA 83:6035–6039.

Heslop-Harrison, J.S., and M.D. Bennett. 1983a. Prediction and analysis of spatial order in haploid chromosome complements. Proc. R. Soc. London, B 218:211–223.

————, and ————. 1983b. The spatial order of chromosomes in root-tip metaphases of *Aegilops umbellulata*. Proc. R. Soc. London, B 218:225–239.

Horn, J.D., and D.B. Walden. 1978. Affinity distance values among somatic metaphase chromosomes in maize. Genetics 88:181–200.

Jancey, R.C. 1975. A new source of evidence for the polarized nucleus in maize. Can. J. Genet. Cytol. 17:245–252.

————, and D.B. Walden. 1972. Analysis of pattern in distribution of breakage points in the chromosomes of *Zea mays* L. and *D. melanogaster* meigen. Can. J. Genet. Cytol. 14:429–442.

Jones, R.N., and H. Rees. 1982. B Chromosomes. Academic Press, London.

Kasha, K.J., and G. Seguin-Swartz. 1983. Haploidy in crop improvement. *In* M.S. Swaminathan et al. (ed.) Cytogenetics of crop plants. Macmillan, New Delhi.

Kato, Y., T.A. 1976. Cytological studies of maize *Zea mays* L.) and teosinte (*Zea mexicana* Schrader Kuntze) in relation to their origin and evolution. Massachusetts Agric. Exp. Stn. Res. Bull. 635.

————. 1984. Chromosome morphology and the origin of maize and its races. Evol. Biol. 17:219–254.

Keller, E.F. 1983. A feeling for the organism. The life and work of Barbara McClintock. Freeman, Cooper and Co., San Francisco.

Kermicle, J.L. 1969. Androgenesis conditioned by a mutation in maize. Science 166:1422–1424.

————. 1970. Dependence of the *R*-mottled aleurone phenotype in maize on mode of sexual transmission. Genetics 66:69–85.

————. 1978. Imprinting of gene action in maize endosperm. p. 357–371. *In* D.B. Walden (ed.) Maize breeding and genetics. John Wiley and Sons, New York.

————. 1984. Recombination between components of a mutable gene system in maize. Genetics 107:489–500.

————, and J.D. Axtell. 1981. Modification of chlorophyll striping by the *R* region. Maydica 26:185–197.

Khush, G.S. 1973. Cytogenetics of aneuploids. Academic Press, New York.

Kikudome, G.Y. 1959. Studies on the phenomenon of preferential segregation in maize. Genetics 44:815–831.

————. 1961. Cytogenetic behavior of a knobbed chromosome 10 in maize. Science 134:1006–1007.

Kindiger, B., and J.B. Beckett. 1985. A hematoxylin staining procedure for maize pollen grain chromosomes. Stain Technol. 60:265–269.

————, ————, and C. Curtis. 1984. Evidence for frequent random disjunction of the A and A^B elements of certain B-A translocations. Maize Genet. Coop. News Lett. 58:66–67.

Kodura, P.R.K. 1984. Metaphase I orientation of chain-forming interchange quadrivalents: A theoretical consideration. Genetics 108:707–717.

Latt, S.A. 1981. Sister chromatid exchange formation. Ann. Rev. Genet. 15:11–55.

————. 1982. Sister chromatid exchange: New methods for detection. p. 17–40. *In* S. Wolff (ed.) Sister chromatid exchange. John Wiley and Sons, New York.

Laughnan, J.R. 1949. The action of allelic forms of the gene *A* in maize. II. The relation of crossing over to mutation of *A-b*. Proc. Natl. Acad. Sci. USA 35:167–178.

————. 1952a. The action of allelic forms of the gene *A* in maize. IV. On the compound nature of *A-b* and the occurrence and action of its *A-d* derivatives. Genetics 37:375–395.

————. 1952b. The *A-b* components as members of a duplication in maize. Genetics 37:598 (Abstr.).

————. 1955. Intrachromosomal association between members of an adjacent serial duplication as possible basis for the presumed gene mutations from *A-b* complexes. Genetics 40:580 (Abstr.)

————. 1961. The nature of mutations in terms of gene and chromosome changes. p. 3–29. *In* Mutations and plant breeding. Pub. 891. NAS-NRC, Washington, DC.

Lima-de-Faria, A., and P. Sarvella. 1962. Variation of the chromosome phenotype in *Zea, Solanum* and *Salvia*. Chromosoma 13:300–314.

Lin, B.Y. 1977. A squash technique for studying the cytology of maize endosperm and other tissues. Stain Technol. 52:197–201.

————. 1978. Regional control of nondisjunction of the B chromosome in maize. Genetics 90:613–627.

————. 1979. Two new B-10 translocations involved in the control of nondisjunction of the B chromosome in maize. Genetics 92:931–945.

————. 1982. Association of endosperm reduction with parental imprinting in maize. Genetics 100:475–486.

————, and E.H. Coe, Jr. 1986. Monosomy and trisomy induced by the *r-x1* deletion in maize, and associated effects on endosperm development. Can. J. Genet. Cytol. 28:831–834.

Longley, A.E. 1937. Morphological characters of teosinte chromosomes. J. Agric. Res. 54:835–862.

————. 1938. Chromosomes of maize from North American Indians. J. Agric. Res. 56:177–195.

————. 1939. Knob positions on corn chromosomes. J. Agric. Res. 59:475–490.

————. 1945. Abnormal segregation during megasporogenesis in maize. Genetics 30:100–113.

————. 1961. Breakage points for four corn translocation series and other corn chromosome aberrations maintained at the California Institute of Technology. Pampl. 34-16. USDA-ARS, Washington, DC.

————, and T.A. Kato Y. 1965. Chromosome morphology of certain races of maize in Latin America. Res. Bull. 1. CIMMYT, Chapingo, Mexico.

Maguire, M.P. 1962. Pachytene and diakinesis behavior of the isochromosomes 6 of maize. Science 138:445–446.

————. 1966. The relationship of crossing over to chromosome synapsis in a short paracentric inversion. Genetics 53:1071–1077.

————. 1968. The effect of synaptic partner change on crossover frequency in adjacent regions of a trivalent. Genetics 59:381–390.

————. 1972. The temporal sequence of synaptic initiation, crossing-over and synaptic completion. Genetics 70:353–370.

————. 1981. A search for the synaptic adjustment phenomenon in maize. Chromosoma 81:717–725.

————. 1983a. Chromosome behavior at premeiotic mitosis in maize. J. Hered. 74:93–96.

————. 1983b. Homologous chromosome pairing remains an unsolved problem: A test of a popular hypothesis utilizing maize meiosis. Genetics 104:173–179.

————. 1984a. The mechanism of meiotic homologue pairing. J. Theor. Biol. 106:605–615.

————. 1984b. The pattern of pairing that is effective for crossing over in complex B-A chromosome rearrangements in maize. Chromosoma 89:18–23.

————. 1985. The pattern of pairing that is effective for crossing over in complex B-A chromosome rearrangements in maize. II. Chromosoma 91:101–107.

Mangelsdorf, P.C., and W.C. Galinat. 1964. The *tunicate* locus in maize dissected and reconstituted. Proc. Natl. Acad. Sci. USA 51:147–150.

Mascia, P.N., I. Rubenstein, R.L. Phillips, A.S. Wang, and L.Z. Xiang. 1981. Localization of the 5S rRNA genes and evidence for diversity in the 5S rDNA region of maize. Gene 15:7–20.

Mastenbroek, I., and J.M. de Wet. 1983. Chromosome C-banding of *Zea mays* and its closest relatives. Can. J. Genet. Cytol. 25:203–209.

McClintock, B. 1929a. Chromosome morphology in *Zea mays*. Science 69:629.

————. 1929b. A cytological and genetical study of triploid maize. Genetics 14:180–222.

————. 1930. A cytological demonstration of the location of an interchange between two non-homologous chromosomes of *Zea mays*. Proc. Natl. Acad. Sci. USA 16:791–796.

————. 1931. Cytological observations of deficiencies involving known genes, translocations and an inversion in *Zea mays*. Res. Bull. Mo. Agric. Exp. Stn. 163.

————. 1932. A correlation of ring-shaped chromosomes with variegation in *Zea mays*. Proc. Natl. Acad. Sci. USA 18:677–681.

————. 1933. The association of non-homologous parts of chromosomes in the mid-prophase of meiosis in *Zea mays*. Z. Zellforsch. Mikroskop. Anat. 19:191–237.

————. 1934. The relation of a particular chromosomal element to the development of the nucleoli in *Zea mays*. Z. Zellforsch. Mikroskop. Anat. 21:294–328.

————. 1938a. The fusion of broken ends of sister half-chromatids following chromatid breakage at meiotic anaphases. Res. Bull. Mo. Agric. Exp. Stn. 290:1–48.

————. 1938b. The production of homozygous deficient tissues with mutant characteristics by means of aberrant mitotic behavior of ring-shaped chromosomes. Genetics 23:315–376.

————. 1939. The behavior in successive nuclear divisions of a chromosome broken at meiosis. Proc. Natl. Acad. Sci. USA 26:405–416.

————. 1941a. The stability of broken ends of chromosomes in *Zea mays*. Genetics 26:234–282.

————. 1941b. The association of mutants with homozygous deficiencies in *Zea mays*. Genetics 26:542–571.

————. 1942. The fusion of broken ends of chromosomes following nuclear fusion. Proc. Natl. Acad. Sci. USA 18:458–463.

————. 1944. The relation of homozygous deficiencies to mutations and allelic series in maize. Genetics 29:478–502.

————. 1951. Chromosome organization and genic expression. Cold Spring Harbor Symp. Quant. Biol. 16:13–47.

————. 1959. Chromosome constitutions of Mexican and Guatemalan races of maize. Carnegie Inst. Washington Year Book 59:461–472.

————. 1978a. Significance of chromosome constitutions in tracing the origin and migration of races of maize in the Americas. *In* D.B. Walden (ed.) Maize breeding and genetics. John Wiley and Sons, New York.

————. 1978b. Mechanisms that rapidly reorganize the genome. Stadler Genet. Symp. 10:25–47.

————. 1984. The significance of responses of the genome to challenge. Science 226:792–801.

————, and H.E. Hill. 1931. The cytological identification of the chromosome associated with the *R-G* linkage group in *Zea mays*. Genetics 16:175–190.

————, T.A. Kato Y., and A. Blumenschein. 1981. Chromosome constitution of races of maize. Its significance in the interpretation of relationships between races and varieties in the Americas. Colegio de Postgraduados, Chapingo, Mexico.

McKinley, C.M., and S.L. Goldman. 1979. The interchromosomal effect of inversions in maize. Molec. Gen. Genet. 172:119–125.

Miles, J.H. 1970. Influence of modified K10 chromosomes on preferential segregation and crossing over in *Zea mays*. Ph.D. diss. Indiana Univ., Bloomington (Diss. Abstr. 71–17 450).

————. 1971. Probable weak fusion of chromatids during a breakage-fusion-bridge cycle. Maize Genet. Coop. News Let 45:136–139.

Miller, O.L. 1963. Cytological studies in *asynaptic* maize. Genetics 48:1445–1466.

Mogensen, H.L. 1977. Ultrastructural analysis of female pachynema and the relationship between synaptonemal complex length and crossing-over in *Zea mays*. Carlsberg Res. Commun. 42:475–497.

Moore, C.W., and R.G. Creech. 1972. Genetic fine structure analysis of the *amylose-extender* locus in *Zea mays* L. Genetics 70:611–619.

Morgan, D.T., Jr. 1950. A cytogenetic study of inversions in *Zea mays*. Genetics 35:153–174.

Morris, R. 1955. Induced reciprocal translocation involving homologous chromosomes in maize. Am. J. Bot. 42:546–550.

Moses, M. 1968. Synaptinemal complex. Ann. Rev. Genet. 2:363–412.

Mottinger, J.P. 1970. The effect of x-rays on the *bronze* and *shrunken* loci in maize. Genetics 64:259–271.

Nanda, D.K., and S.S. Chase. 1966. An embryo marker for detecting monoploids of maize (*Zea mays* L.). Crop Sci. 6:213–215.

Nel, P.M. 1971. Studies on the genetic control of recombination in *Zea mays*. Ph.D. diss. Indiana Univ., Bloomington (Diss. Abstr. 31:759–B).

————. 1973. The modification of crossing over in maize by extraneous chromosomal elements. Theor. Appl. Genet. 43:196–202.

————. 1975. Crossing over and diploid egg formation in the *elongate* mutant of maize. Genetics 79:435–450.

————. 1979. Effects of the *asynaptic* factor on recombination in maize. J. Hered. 70:401–406.

Nelson, O.E. 1957. The feasibility of investigating genetic fine structure in higher plants. Am. Nat. 91:331–332.

————. 1959. Intracistron recombination in the *Wx/wx* region in maize. Science 130:794–795.

————. 1962. The *waxy* locus in maize. I. Intralocus recombination frequency estimates by pollen and by conventional analysis. Genetics 47:737-742.

————. 1968. The *waxy* locus in maize. II. The location of the controlling element alleles. Genetics 60:507–524.

————, and G.B. Clary. 1952. Genic control of semi-sterility in maize. J. Hered. 43:205–210.

Neuffer, M.G. 1957. Additional evidence on the effect of x-ray and ultraviolet radiation on mutation in maize. Genetics 42:273–282.

————, and W.F. Sheridan. 1980. Defective kernel mutants of maize. I. Genetic and lethality studies. Genetics 95:929–944.

Nicklas, R.B. 1967. Chromosome micromanipulation II. Induced reorientation and the experimental control of segregation in meiosis. Chromosoma 21:17–50.

————, and C.A. Koch. 1969. Chromosome micromanipulation III. Spindle fiber tension and the reorientation of maloriented chromosomes. J. Cell Biol. 43:40–50.

————, and D.F. Kubai. 1985. Microtubules, chromosome movement, and reorientation after chromosomes are detached from the spindle by micromanipulation. Chromosoma 92:313–324.

Nitzsche, W., and G. Wenzel. 1977. Haploids in plant breeding. *In* W. Horn and G. Robbelen (ed.) Advances in plant breeding. (Suppl. 8 to J. of Plant Breed.) Verlag Paul Parey, Berlin.

Ostergren, G. 1945. Parasitic nature of extra fragment chromosomes. Bot. Notiser 2:157–163.

Palmer, R. 1971. Cytological studies of *ameiotic* and normal maize with reference to premeiotic pairing. Chromosoma 35:233–246.

Patterson, E.B. 1952. The use of functional duplicate-deficient gametes in locating genes in maize. Genetics 37:612–613 (Abstr.).

————. 1959. Report on maize cooperative. Maize Genet. Coop. News Lett. 33:131.

————. 1978. Properties and uses of duplicate-deficient chromosome complements in maize. *In* D.B. Walden (ed.) Maize breeding and genetics. John Wiley and Sons, New York.

Pauk, J. 1985. Production of haploid plants of maize (*Zea mays* L.) through androgenesis. Cereal Res. Commun. 13:47–53.

Peacock, W.J., E.S. Dennis, M.M. Rhoades, and A.J. Pryor. 1981. Highly repeated DNA sequence limited to knob heterochromatin in maize. Proc. Natl. Acad. Sci. USA 78:4490–4494.

Peeters, J.P., A.J.F. Griffiths, and G. Wilkes. 1985. *In vivo* karyotypic modifications following spontaneous cell fusion in maize (*Zea mays* L.). Can. J. Genet. Cytol. 27:580–585.

Perry, P., and S. Wolff. 1974. New Giemsa method for the differential staining of sister chromatids. Nature (London) 251:156–158.

Peterson, H.M., and J.R. Laughnan. 1961. Nonrecombinant derivatives at the *Bar* locus in *Drosophila melanogaster*. Genetics 46:889 (Abstr.).

————, and ————. 1963. Intrachromosomal exchange at the *Bar* locus in *Drosophila*. Proc. Natl. Acad. Sci. USA 50:126–133.

Phillips, J., S. Panny, H. Kazazian, C. Boehm, A. Scott, and K. Smith. 1980. Prenatal diagnosis of sickle cell anemia by restriction endonuclease analysis: *Hind*III polymorphisms in γ-globin genes extend test applicability. Proc. Natl. Acad. Sci. USA 77:2853–2856.

Phillips, R.L. 1978. Molecular cytogenetics of the nucleolus organizer region. p. 711–741. *In* D.B. Walden (ed.) Maize breeding and genetics. John Wiley and Sons, New York.

————, C.R. Burnham, and E.B. Patterson. 1971a. Advantages of chromosomal interchanges that generate haplo-viable deficiency-duplications. Crop Sci. 11:525–528.

————, R.A. Kleese, and S.S. Wang. 1971b. The nucleolus organizer region of maize (*Zea mays* L.): chromosomal site of DNA complementary to ribosomal RNA. Chromosoma 36:79–88.

————, and A.S. Wang. 1984. Chromosome analysis. p. 712–727. *In* Cell culture and somatic cell genetics of plants, Vol. 1. Academic Press, New York.

————, ————, and R.V. Kowles. 1983. Molecular and developmental cytogenetics of gene multiplicity in maize. Stadler Genet. Symp. 15:105–118.

————, D.F. Weber, R.A. Kleese, and S.S. Wang. 1974. The nucleolus organizer region of maize (*Zea mays* L.): Tests for ribosomal gene compensation or magnification. Genetics 77:285–297.

Pryor, A.J., K. Faulkner, M.M. Rhoades, and W.J. Peacock. 1980. Asynchronous replication of heterochromatin in maize. Proc. Natl. Acad. Sci. USA 77:6705–6709.

Ramirez, S.A., and J.H. Sinclair. 1975. Ribosomal gene localization and distribution (arrangement) within the nucleolar organizer region of *Zea mays*. Genetics 80:505–518.

Randolph, L.F. 1932. Some effects of high temperature on polyploidy and other variations in maize. Proc. Natl. Acad. Sci. USA 18:222–229.

————. 1935. Cytogenetics of tetraploid maize. J. Agric. Res. 50:591–605.

Rasmussen, S.W., and P.B. Holm. 1980. Mechanics of meiosis. Hereditas 93:187–216.

Rayburn, A.L., H.J. Price, J.D. Smith, and J.R. Gold. 1985. C-band heterochromatin and DNA content in *Zea mays*. Am. J. Bot. 72:1610–1617.

Redei, G.P. 1982. Genetics. Macmillan Pub., New York.

Rhoades, M.M. 1933. A secondary trisome in maize. Proc. Natl. Acad. Sci. USA 19:1031–1038.

————. 1936. Note on the origin of triploidy in maize. J. Genet. 33:355–357.

————. 1940. Studies of a telocentric chromosome in maize with reference to the stability of its centromere. Genetics 25:483–520.

————. 1941. Different rates of crossing over in male and female gametes of maize. J. Am. Soc. Agron. 33:603–615.

————. 1942. Preferential segregation in maize. Genetics 27:395–407.

———— 1950. Meiosis in maize. J. Hered. 41:58–67.

————. 1951. Duplicate genes in maize. Am. Naturalist 85:105–110.

————. 1952. Preferential segregation in maize. p. 66–80. *In* J.W. Gowen (ed.) Heterosis. Iowa State College Press, Ames.

————. 1955. The cytogenetics of maize. *In* G.F. Sprague (ed.) Corn and corn improvement. Agronomy 5:123–219.

————. 1956. Genic control of chromosomal behavior. Maize Genet. Coop. News Lett. 30:38–42.

————. 1968. Studies on the cytological basis of crossing over. p. 229–241. *In* W.J. Peacock and R.D. Brock (ed.) Replication and recombination of genetic material. Australian Acad. of Sci., Canberra, Australia.

————. 1978. Genetic effects of heterochromatin in maize. p. 641–671. *In* D.B. Walden (ed.) Maize breeding and genetics. John Wiley and Sons, New York.

————. 1984. The early years of maize genetics. Ann. Rev. Genet. 18:1–29.

————, and E. Dempsey. 1953. Cytogenetic studies of deficient-duplicate chromosomes derived from inversion heterozygotes in maize. Am. J. Bot. 40:405–424.

————, and ————. 1956. Studies with overlapping inversions. Maize Genet. Coop. News Lett. 30:42–47.

————, and ————. 1966a. Induction of chromosome doubling at meiosis by the *elongate* gene in maize. Genetics 54:505–522.

————, and ————. 1966b. The effect of abnormal chromosome 10 on preferential segregation and crossing over in maize. Genetics 53:989–1020.

————, and ————. 1972. On the mechanism of chromatin loss induced by the B chromosome of maize. Genetics 71:73–96.

————, and ————. 1973a. Cytogenetic studies on a transmissible deficiency in chromosome 3 of maize. J. Hered. 64:125–128.

————, and ————. 1973b. Chromatin elimination induced by the B chromosome of maize. J. Hered. 64:13–18.

————, and ————. 1982. The induction of mutable systems in plants with the high-loss mechanism. Maize Genet. Coop. News Lett. 56:21–26.

————, and ————. 1983. Further studies on two-unit mutable systems found in our high-loss studies and on the specificity of interaction of responding and controlling elements. Maize Genet. Coop. News Lett. 57:14–17.

————, and ————. 1985. Structural heterogeneity of chromosome 10 in races of maize and teosinte. *In* M. Freeling (ed.) Plant genetics. Alan R. Liss, New York.

————, and ————. 1986. Evidence that the K10 knob is not responsible for preferential segregation and neocentric activity. Maize Genet. Coop News Lett. 60:26–27.

————, ————, and A. Ghidoni. 1967. Chromosome elimination in maize induced by supernumerary B chromosomes. Proc. Natl. Acad. Sci. USA 57:1626–1632.

————, and H. Vilkomerson. 1942. On the anaphase movement of chromosomes. Proc. Natl. Acad. Sci. USA 28:433–436.

Rickards, G.K. 1983a. Orientation behavior of chromosome multiples of interchange (reciprocal translocation) heterozygotes. Ann. Rev. Genet. 17:443–498.

————. 1983b. Alternate-1 and alternate-2 orientations in interchange (reciprocal translocation) quadrivalents. Genetics 104:211–213.

Rinehart, K.V. 1970. A study of selective orientation in heterozygous paracentric inversions of maize. Ph.D. diss. Indiana Univ., Bloomington (Diss. Abstr. 322:103-B).

Rivin, C.J., C.A. Cullis, and V. Walbot. 1986. Evaluating quantitative variation in the genome of *Zea mays*. Genetics 113:1009–1019.

————, E.A. Zimmer, C.A. Cullis, V. Walbot, T. Huynh, and R.W. Davis. 1983. Evaluation of genomic variability at the nucleic acid level. Plant Molec. Biol. Rep. 1:9–16.

Robertson, D.S. 1984. Different frequency in the recovery of crossover products from male and female gametes of plants hypoploid for B-A translocations in maize. Genetics 107:117–130.

Roman, H. 1947. Mitotic nondisjunction in the case of interchanges involving the B-type chromosome in maize. Genetics 32:391–409.

————. 1948. Directed fertilization in maize. Proc. Natl. Acad. Sci. USA 34:36–42.

————. 1949. Factors affecting mitotic nondisjunction in maize. Rec. Genet. Soc. Am. 18:112.

————, and A.J. Ullstrup. 1951. The use of A-B translocations to locate genes in maize. Agron. J. 43:450–454.

Russell, W.A., and C.R. Burnham. 1950. Cytogenetic studies of an inversion in maize. Sci. Agric. 30:93–111.

Sachs, M.M., E.S. Dennis, W.L. Gerlach, and W.J. Peacock. 1986. Two alleles of maize *alcohol dehydrogenase 1* have 3′ structural and poly(A) addition polymorphisms. Genetics 113:449–467.

Salamini, F., and C. Lorenzoni. 1970. Genetical analysis of *glossy* mutants of maize. III. Intracistron recombination and high negative interference at the *g1* locus. Molec. Gen. Genet. 108:225–232.

Sarkar, K.R., and E.H. Coe. 1966. A genetic analysis of the origin of maternal haploids in maize. Genetics 54:453–464.

Schwartz, D. 1953a. The behavior of an x-ray induced ring chromosome in maize. Am. Nat. 87:19–28.

————. 1953b. Evidence for sister-strand crossing over in maize. Genetics 38:251–260.

————. 1958. A new temperature sensitive allele at the *sticky* locus in maize. J. Hered. 49:149–152.

————, and C. Murray. 1957. A cytological study of breakage-fusion-bridge cycles in maize endosperm. Proc. Int. Genet. Symp. 1956:277–279.

Sheridan, W.F. 1982. Anther culture of maize. *In* W.F. Sheridan (ed.) Maize for biological research. Univ. of North Dakota Press, Grand Forks.

Simcox, K.D., J.D. Shadley, and D.F. Weber. 1986. Detection of the time of occurrence of nondisjunction induced by the *r-X1* deficiency in *Zea mays*. Genetics 113:s20.

Sinha, S.K. 1960. Cytogenetic and biochemical studies of the action of a gene controlling meiosis in maize. Ph.D. diss. Indiana Univ., Bloomington (Diss. Abstr. Mic 60–6327).

Smith, S.G. 1942. Polarization and progression in pairing. II. Premeiotic orientation and the initiation of pairing. Can. J. Res. 20:221–229.

Snope, A.J. 1967. The relationship of abnormal chromosome 10 to B-chromosomes in maize. Chromosoma 21:243–249.

Soller, M., and J.S. Beckman. 1983. Genetic polymorphism in varietal identification and genetic improvement. Theor. Appl. Genet. 67:25–33.

Sprague, G.F. 1941. The location of dominant favorable genes in maize by means of an inversion. Genetics 26:170 (Abstr.).

Stadler, L.J., and M.G. Nuffer. 1953. Problems of gene structure II. Separation of R-r elements (S) and (P) by unequal crossing over. Science 117:471–472.

----, and H. Roman. 1948. The effect of X-rays upon mutation of the gene A in maize. Genetics 33:273–303.

Stern, H., and Y. Hotta. 1978. Regulatory mechanisms in meiotic crossing-over. Ann. Rev. Plant Physiol. 29:415–436.

----, and ----. 1983. Meiotic aspects of chromosome organization. Stadler Genet. Symp. 15:25–41.

----, and ----. 1984. Chromosome organization in the regulation of meiotic prophase. Symp. Soc. Exp. Biol. 38:161–175.

Stern, H., M. Westergaard, and D. von Wettstein. 1975. Presynaptic events in meiocytes of *Lilium longiflorum* and their relation to crossing over: A preselection hypothesis. Proc. Natl. Acad. Sci. USA 72:961–965.

Sturtevant, A.H. 1931. Known and probably inverted sections of the autosomes of *Drosophila melanogaster*. Carnegie Inst. Wash. Pub. 421:1–27.

----, and G.W. Beadle. 1936. The relations of inversions in the X chromosome of *Drosophila melanogaster* to crossing over and disjunction. Genetics 21:554–604.

Tice, R., and A. Hollaender. (ed.) 1984. Sister chromatid exchanges: 25 Years of experimental research. Part A, The nature of SCEs. Plenum Press, New York.

Ting, Y.C. 1958. On the origin of abnormal chromosome 10 in maize. (*Zea mays* L.). Chromosoma 9:286–291.

----. 1966. Duplications and meiotic behavior of the chromosomes in haploid maize (*Zea mays* L.). Cytologia 31:324–329.

----. 1973. Synaptonemal complex of haploid maize. Cytologia 38:497–500.

----. 1985. Meiosis and fertility of anther culture-derived maize plants. Maydica 30:161–169.

----, M. Yu, and W.-Z. Zheng. 1981. Improved anther culture of maize (*Zea mays* L.). Plant Sci. Lett. 23:139–145.

Viotti, A., E. Privitera, E. Sala, and N. Pogna. 1985. Distribution and clustering of two highly repeated sequences in the A and B chromosomes of maize. Theor. Appl. Genet. 70:234–239.

Von Wettstein, D., S.W. Rasmussen, and P.B. Holm. 1984. The synaptonemal complex in genetic segregation. Ann. Rev. Genet. 18:331–413.

Walden, D.B., and R.C. Jancey. 1976. Reassociation patterns among segmental interchanges in maize. Heredity 36:293–304.

Ward, E.J. 1973a. The heterochromatic B chromosome of maize: The segments affecting recombination. Chromosoma 43:177–186.

----. 1973b. Nondisjunction: Localization of the controlling site in the maize B chromosome. Genetics 73:387–391.

----. 1975. Further studies on the effects of accessory chromatin in maize. Can. J. Genet. Cytol. 17:124–126.

----. 1980. Banding patterns in maize mitotic chromosomes. Can. J. Genet. Cytol. 22:61–67.

Weber, D.F. 1968. A test for nonhomolgous recombination in *Zea mays*. Genetics 60:235 (Abstr.).

----. 1973. A test for distributive pairing in *Zea mays* utilizing doubly monosomic plants. Theor. Appl. Genet. 43:167–173.

----. 1983. Monosomic analysis in diploid crop plants. *In* M.S. Swaminathan et al. (ed.) Cytogenetics of crop plants. Macmillan, New Delhi.

----, and D.E. Alexander. 1972. Redundant segments in *Zea mays* detected by translocations of monoploid origin. Chromosoma 39:27–42.

West, D.P. 1985. *Polymitotic*, canalization and probability. Maize Genet. Coop. News Lett. 59:107.

----, and R.L. Phillips. 1985. *Polymitotic*: Supernumerary repetitions of meiosis II. Maize Genet. Coop. News Lett. 59:106–107.

Westergaard, M., and D. von Wettstein. 1972. The synaptinemal complex. Ann. Rev. Genet. 6:71–110.

Williams, W.M., K.V. Satyanarayana, and J.L. Kermicle. 1984. *R-stippled* maize as a transposable element system. Genetics 107:477–488.

Wimber, D.E., P.A. Duffey, D.M. Steffensen, and W. Prensky. 1974. Localizaition of the 5S RNA genes in *Zea mays* by RNA-DNA hybridization *in situ*. Chromosoma 47:353–359.

Wolff, S. (ed.) 1982. Sister chromatid exchange. John Wiley and Sons, New York.

5

Cell/Tissue Culture and In Vitro Manipulation

R.L. PHILLIPS

University of Minnesota
St. Paul, Minnesota

D.A. SOMERS

University of Minnesota
St. Paul, Minnesota

K.A. HIBBERD

Molecular Genetics, Inc.
Minnetonka, Minnesota

Cell and tissue culture techniques for corn (*Zea mays* L.) are rapidly approaching the full spectrum of culture systems possible in plants. Haploid, diploid, triploid, and aneuploid tissue cultures can be initiated from a variety of tissue explants. Plant regeneration takes place via organogenesis and/or somatic embryogenesis from haploid, diploid, and aneuploid tissue cultures. Triploid endosperm cultures fail to regenerate plants. Protoplasts of most graminaceous monocots have been recalcitrant to culture; however, recent successes with cereal species indicate that in the near future corn protoplast cultures will be available for routine plant genetic manipulations. Corn cell and tissue culture initiation, maintenance, and plant regeneration are dependent on the choice of tissue explant, its genotype and developmental stage, and the culture media and environment used for each stage of the tissue culture process. Cell and tissue culture per se generates genetic variation detected in the progeny of regenerated plants. Understanding the mechanism of tissue culture-induced variation is essential in learning how to control the occurrence of polyploidization, chromosomal breakage, aneuploidy, activation of transposable elements and point mutations so that corn tissue culture may be used to produce clonal regenerated plants or to produce variants. Tissue culture selection of corn mutants has likely been successful due to mutations generated during tissue culture. Success in the selection of mutants resistant to pathotoxins, amino acids and their analogs, and herbicides demonstrates the usefulness of tissue culture selection of biochemical mutants for crop improvement and biochemical genetics studies focused on elucidating gene-enzyme relationships controlling metabolic pathways of corn.

5–1 CELL, TISSUE, AND ORGAN CULTURE SYSTEMS

5–1.1 Triploid Tissue Cultures

Triploid endosperm cultures were the first examples of proliferating corn tissue cultures (LaRue, 1949). The first endosperm cultures described by LaRue (1949) were most successfully initiated from sugary endosperm genotypes. Endosperm cultures were later initiated from inbreds and hybrids with starchy endosperms; endosperm starch composition was of lesser importance for culture initiation than the explant genotype (Tabata and Motoyoshi, 1965). Specific corn genotypes from which endosperm cultures have been initiated are listed in Table 5–1. Endosperm traits have been investigated in endosperm culture by backcrossing the genes encoding the traits into corn genotypes that readily initiated cultures (Reddy and Peterson, 1977).

Endosperm culture initiation is dependent on the stage of development of the endosperm and is subject to environmental variation (Sun and Ullstrup, 1971). Isolating immature endosperm 6 to 18 d after pollination for successful culture initiation appears advisable. Endosperm culture medium originally contained tomato juice which was later replaced by yeast extract (Straus and LaRue, 1954). Yeast extract served as a N source and has been replaced by asparagine (Straus, 1960). The complete definition of a synthetic endosperm culture medium and the ability to culture endosperm tissues in liquid suspension cultures make these cultures ideal material for studies on endosperm development and metabolism (Graebe and Novelli, 1966; Shannon and Liu, 1977; Shannon, 1982). Endosperm cultures consist of uniform populations of unorganized cells that carry out specific endosperm functions such as starch and pigment synthesis. Endosperm cultures also have been used to study

Table 5–1. Corn genotypes from which endosperm cultures have been initiated.

Genotype	Reference
Black Mexican Sweet	Straus and LaRue, 1954
Surprise Sweet	Straus and LaRue, 1954
Marcross 6.13 (Our choice)	Sternheimer, 1954
Yellow Sugary†	Tamaoki and Ullstrup, 1958
Starchy L317	Tamaoki and Ullstrup, 1958
Waxy L317	Tamaoki and Ullstrup, 1958
Country Gentleman	Tamaoki and Ullstrup, 1958
S41 × S42	Tabata and Motoyoshi, 1965
S42	Tabata and Motoyoshi, 1965
P14	Sun and Ullstrup, 1971
A636	Shannon and Batey, 1973
R168	Shannon and Batey, 1973
P3369A	Shannon and Batey, 1973
Px610	Shannon and Batey, 1973
R168 (wx m-8)	Reddy and Peterson, 1977

† Hybrids were also reported (Tamaoki and Ullstrup, 1958).

the action of transposable elements (Gorman and Peterson, 1978; Bartkowiak and Peterson, 1984; Culley, 1986). Plant regeneration has not been achieved from corn endosperm cultures, although LaRue (1947) observed limited morphogenesis in initial studies of endosperm culture initiation.

5-1.2 Nonregenerable Diploid Tissue Cultures

Initiation of nonregenerable diploid corn tissue cultures was first reported by Mascarenhas et al. (1965). These cultures were initiated from root and stem sections of Golden Bantam sweet corn seedlings. Diploid tissue cultures have since been initiated from a number of explants and genotypes (Table 5-2). Some of these tissue cultures, and liquid suspensions established from them, consist of relatively uniform populations of dedifferentiated cells and therefore represent true callus tissues (Green, 1977; Meadows, 1982/83). Organ formation such as root regeneration has been induced in some cultures (Mascarenhas et al., 1965; Linsmaier-Bednar and Bednar, 1972; Chourey and Zurawski, 1981). The diversity of explants that proliferate to form callus indicates that immature tissues that continue cell division during plant development will likely respond to exogenous auxin and produce callus. Callus growth rate is significantly influenced by the explant genotype; general and specific combining ability differences for callus growth rate have been observed (Nesticky et al., 1983).

5-1.3 Regenerable Diploid Cultures—Type I and Type II Callus

Plant regeneration from corn tissue cultures was first reported by Green and Phillips (1975) demonstrating that specific corn tissues were totipotent (Table 5-3). A major contributing factor in initiating regenerable cultures was identification of the immature embryo as a totipotent explant and placement of this organ with the shoot-root axis in contact with modified MS (Murashige and Skoog, 1962) culture medium containing 2,4-D [(2,4-dichlorophenoxy) acetic acid] as an auxin source. This orientation retards embryo germination and induces proliferation of scutellar cells to produce the tissue culture (Green and Phillips, 1975). The term "Type I" callus has been used to describe these compact callus cultures (Armstrong and Green, 1985). The cultures described by Green and Phillips (1975) are proliferating mixtures of tissues exhibiting shoot meristems and scutellar-like structures (Springer et al., 1979). Type I tissue cultures have been described as sustainable cultures of repressed shoot primordia that proliferate adventitiously (King et al., 1978). Meristematic regions in the callus give rise to shoot apices, which are suppressed at the two-leaf stage, and which are not structurally associated with root meristems indicating that organogenesis is the primary mode of regenerable structure formation in this form of Type I callus (Springer et al., 1979; Freeling et al., 1976). Somatic shoot apices are structurally

Table 5-2. Corn genotypes and explants used for initiation of nonregenerable diploid callus and suspension cultures.

Genotype	Explant	Donor plant age, d	Reference
Golden Bantam	Stem and root sections	7–8	Mascarenhas et al., 1965
A632 and others	Mesocotyl	Mature embryos	Burr and Nelson, 1972
B-48	Macerated	Mature embryos	Gresshoff and Doy, 1973
Minnhybrid 5301	Seedling shoot	30	Green et al., 1974
P39	Seedling shoot	30	Green et al., 1974
Ia 5125	Seedling shoot	30	Green et al., 1974
Oh51A × Os420	Seedling shoot	30	Green et al., 1974
A493 × Ms1334	Seedling shoot	30	Green et al., 1974
Oh51A × A286	Seedling shoot	30	Green et al., 1974
B9A × A619	Seedling shoot	30	Green et al., 1974
Ill 186 × P39	Seedling shoot	30	Green et al., 1974
A545	Seedling shoot	30	Green et al., 1974
B9A	Seedling shoot	30	Green et al., 1974
Black Mexican Sweet	Stem section		Sheridan, 1975a
W23 × M24 (Advanced generation)	Stem section	21	Sheridan, 1975b
A619	Coleoptile node		Gengenbach and Green, 1975
Alhexo	Immature embryo	18	Freeling et al., 1976
Wf9	Immature embryo	18	Freeling et al., 1976
Oh43	Immature embryo	18	Freeling et al., 1976
Hull-less Pop	Immature embryo	18	Freeling et al., 1976
Parker Flint	Immature embryo	18	Freeling et al., 1976
Black Mexican Sweet	Stem sections	7	Green, 1977
C103 × W155	Stem internodes	30–40	Polikarpochkina et al., 1979
Coe's (K55 × W23)	Stem section	21	Sheridan, 1977
Longfellow Flint	Stem section	21	Sheridan, 1977
Ohio Yellow Pop	Stem section	21	Sheridan, 1977
Neuffer's stock 1 × Coe's	Stem section	21	Sheridan, 1977
Mo 17Ht	Stem section	21	Sheridan, 1977
Coe's (M14 × W23)	Stem section	21	Sheridan, 1977
Large kernel, Guat.	Stem section	21	Sheridan, 1977
Doyle's (W23 × genetic stocks)	Stem section	21	Sheridan, 1977
Neuffer's Stock 1	Stem section	21	Sheridan, 1977
Ibadan B composite	Stem section	21	Sheridan, 1977
Va 26Ht	Stem section	21	Sheridan, 1977
SI104	Mesocotyl		Balzan, 1978
2717	Stem protoplasts	56	Potrykus et al., 1979
P14	Seedlings	4	Oswald et al., 1977
P39-5	Seedlings	4	Oswald et al., 1977
W64A	Seedlings	4	Oswald et al., 1977
Mo17	Seedlings	4	Oswald et al., 1977
Black Mexican Sweet	Mesocotyl (seedling)		Chourey and Zurawski, 1981
F71	Subnodal		Bartkowiak, 1981
RB420	Mature embryo		Nesticky et al., 1983
RC109	Mature embryo		Nesticky et al., 1983
Tva10870	Mature embryo		Nesticky et al., 1983

(continued on next page)

Table 5-2. Continued.

Genotype	Explant	Donor plant age, d	Reference
RC150	Mature embryo		Nesticky et al., 1983
F115	Mature embryo		Nesticky et al., 1983
F7	Mature embryo		Nesticky et al., 1983
Seneca 60	Leaf	14–28	Wenzler and Meins, 1986
White Giant Horsetooth	Mesocotyl	9	Abou-Mandour and Hartung, 1986

similar to the apical meristem (Lowe et al., 1985). Plant regeneration occurs via elongation of meristems when the tissue culture is transferred to a medium with reduced auxin (Green and Phillips, 1975; Freeling et al., 1976). Regenerated shoots must be rooted after removal from the culture. Scutellar-like structures form prior to shoot emergence from Type I cultures. The scutellum is an embryonic organ and its presence in Type I callus indicates that limited embryogenic development takes place in Type I organogenic cultures (Freeling et al., 1976). Somatic embryogenesis has been observed in Type I callus supporting this view (Lu et al., 1982). The formation of shoot apices and/or somatic embryos in Type I callus raises the possibility that shoot apices, which lack structural relation to root apices, arise by precocious germination of somatic proembryos (Tomes, 1985b).

Somatic embryogenesis in corn Type I cultures initiated from immature embryos was first reported by Lu et al. (1982). Immature embryos isolated from 11 open-pollinated hybrid corn cultivars produced compact, opaque embryogenic callus when plated on culture medium containing 2,4-D and up to 12% sucrose (Lu et al., 1982, 1983; Table 5–3). The scutella of immature embryos proliferated to form somatic embryoids (Vasil et al., 1984, 1985). Somatic embryoids were similar in structure to zygotic embryos consisting of well-defined root-shoot axes supported by broad-based suspensor-like structures on the callus surface (Vasil et al., 1984, 1985). The compact, embryogenic callus is difficult to maintain for more than a few subcultures because of increasing organization of tissues within the callus resulting in decreasing callus growth rates (Lu et al., 1982; Vasil and Vasil, 1986). Furthermore, suspension culture initiation has been difficult from Type I tissue cultures of corn presumably due to complex composition and slow growth rate of the cultures (Green, 1977; Vasil and Vasil, 1986).

Immature embryos have been the most widely used explant for initiation of regenerable diploid tissue cultures. During culture initiation, the zygotic embryo per se is not recovered, which is a major limitation when using ears segregating for the trait of interest, such as in the case of establishing cultures from genetically produced aneuploids (Rhodes et al., 1986b). Type I tissue cultures with plant regeneration capacity also have been initiated from the mesocotyl of seedlings (Harms et al., 1976),

Table 5-3. Corn inbreds, hybrids, and populations from which immature embryos initiate regenerable callus.

Genotype	Callus Type†	Reference
A188	I	Green and Phillips, 1975
A188 × W22 R-nj R-nj	I	Green and Phillips, 1975
A619	I	Green and Phillips, 1975
B9A	I	Green and Phillips, 1975
W64A	I	Green and Phillips, 1975
Alhexo single kernel, cycle IV	I	Freeling et al., 1976
S65	I	Edallo et al., 1981
R168	I	Bartkowiak, 1982
F2	I	Bartkowiak, 1982
S72	I	Bartkowiak, 1982
PR37	I	Bartkowiak, 1982
Edo	I	Bartkowiak, 1982
Sm 378	I	Bartkowiak, 1982
WF9	I	Green and Rhodes, 1982
ND 203	I	Green and Rhodes, 1982
BMS	I	Sach et al., 1982
A188	II	Green, 1982
Asgrow R × 112	I	Lu et al., 1982, 1983‡
Coker 16	I	Lu et al., 1982, 1983‡
Coker 22	I	Lu et al., 1982, 1983‡
DeKalb XL80	I	Lu et al., 1982, 1983‡
DeKalb XL82	I	Lu et al., 1982, 1983‡
Funks G4864	I	Lu et al., 1982, 1983‡
Funks G4507A	I	Lu et al., 1982, 1983‡
Jac 247	I	Lu et al., 1982, 1983‡
McCurdy 8190	I	Lu et al., 1982, 1983‡
Pioneer 1360	I	Lu et al., 1982, 1983‡
Pioneer 3320	I	Lu et al., 1982, 1983‡
Silver Queen	I	Lu et al., 1982, 1983‡
Chi-31	I	Novak et al., 1983
B73	II	Tomes and Smith, 1985
B76	I	Tomes and Smith, 1985
Mo17	I	Tomes, 1985b
B73	I + II	Lowe et al., 1985
Florida Stay Sweet	I	Vasil et al., 1985
Cudu	I	Radojevic, 1985
A641		Bruneau, 1985
F19		Bruneau, 1985
CO1048		Bruneau, 1985
F1048		Bruneau, 1985
A631		Bruneau, 1985
F1412		Bruneau, 1985
A634	I	Hodges et al., 1985
W64A	I	Hodges et al., 1985
W117	I	Hodges et al., 1985
H95	I	Hodges et al., 1985
MS71	I	Hodges et al., 1985
W153R	I	Hodges et al., 1985
H99	I	Hodges et al., 1985
WF9	I	Hodges et al., 1985
H49	I	Hodges et al., 1985
CM105	I	Hodges et al., 1985
83-0323 (fl-a)	I	Rapela, 1985
83-0324 (fl-a)	I	Rapela, 1985
83-0326 (RF)	I	Rapela, 1985

(continued on next page)

Table 5-3. Continued.

Genotype	Callus Type†	Reference
84-3306 (fl-a)	I	Rapela, 1985
84-3321 (RF)	I	Rapela, 1985
84-3349 (RF)	I	Rapela, 1985
84-3354 (RF)	I	Rapela, 1985
84-3356 (D)	I	Rapela, 1985
83-0323 (fl-a) × 83-0333 (RF)	I	Rapela, 1985
83-0330 (RF) × 83-0310 (fl-a)	I	Rapela, 1985
83-0331 (RF) × 83-0324 (fl-a)	I	Rapela, 1985
83-0345 (RF) × 83-0337 (RF)	I	Rapela, 1985
84-3356 (D) × 84-3308 (fl-a)	I	Rapela, 1985
84-3306 (fl-a) × 84-3356 (D)	I	Rapela, 1985
B73		Fahey et al., 1986
Mo17		Fahey et al., 1986
LH38		Fahey et al., 1986
H99		Chalmers and Thompson, 1986
DeKalb XL82	II	Vasil and Vasil, 1986
W64A	I	Lupotto, 1986
W64A × BMS	I + II	Lupotto, 1986

† Type I callus refers to compact organogenic and/or embryogenic callus. Type II callus refers to friable, embryogenic callus. Blank indicates that culture type was not specified.
‡ Open pollinated.

mature embryos (Torne et al., 1980), immature tassels (Rhodes et al., 1986a), nodal shoot tissues (Lowe et al., 1985), immature glumes (Suprasanna et al., 1986), and seedling meristems (Ahoowalia, 1986). Somatic embryogenesis also has been initiated from the leaf base of young seedlings (Chang, 1983; Gupta and Nanda, 1986) and immature inflorescences (Reddy, 1986). Explant isolation and culture techniques have been reviewed by King and Shimamoto (1984).

Friable, embryogenic tissue cultures (Type II callus) were initially isolated from spontaneous sectors observed in A188 Type I tissue cultures in the laboratory of B.G. Gengenbach, Univ. of Minnesota. This friable, embryogenic callus consists of somatic proembryoids and embryoids borne on suspensor structures which in some cases are narrow at the base suggesting a potential single cell origin (Green, 1982, 1983; Fig. 5-1). The isolation of Type I callus consisting of meristems and embryoids and Type II callus from the scutella of immature embryos suggests that the different callus types may originate from the same initial cells within the scutella. If so, the differences in callus type appear to be due to effects of embryo genotype, stage of embryo development, and culture media in controlling the development of the precursor meristematic regions within the explant into meristems and/or embryos and in suppressing the development of somatic embryos. The number of initial cells involved in the organization of meristematic centers during culture initiation, how these meristems organize and proliferate in culture to give rise to shoot primordia and/or somatic embryos, and how the suspensor-borne somatic embryos arise from the Type II callus are questions that merit further investigation.

Fig. 5–1. Friable, embryogenic callus (Type II) of A188. Photograph courtesy of C.L. Armstrong.

Armstrong and Green (1985) demonstrated that the addition of L-proline to N6 medium (Chu et al., 1975) induced the formation of embryogenic Type II callus from immature embryos of A188. The metabolic role of proline in the induction of friable, embryogenic callus is not understood. D-proline had no effect on initiation of somatic embryogenesis, whereas betaine, a quaternary amine compound that accumulates to high levels with proline in leaves of some drought-stressed monocots, also increased somatic embryogenesis (Armstrong, 1984). Initiation of friable, embryogenic callus from A188 was optimal from embryos about 1.5 mm in length which are normally isolated 10 to 12 d after pollination indicating that there are precise periods during embryo development when scutellar cells exhibit competence to proliferate totipotent cell cultures (Green and Phillips, 1975; Armstrong and Green, 1985). Embryo length appears to be a more reliable indicator of critical initiation stage than embryo age after pollination. Plant regeneration procedures for friable, embryogenic callus were first described by Armstrong and Green (1985) and later by Kamo et al. (1985).

Initiation of regenerable Types I and II callus in corn is affected by genotype of the immature embryo. Corn genotypes that have been used for culture initiation are listed in Table 5–3. A significant heritability for organogenic callus initiation and plant regeneration was determined from a diallel trial involving eight corn inbreds (Beckert and Qing, 1984).

Furthermore, plant regeneration capacity of Type I cultures was improved through breeding and selection. Regenerable structure formation was observed from A188 and hybrids of A619 or B73 with A188 (Armstrong et al., 1985). Additive genetic effects were highly significant for A188 × A619 and A188 × B73 crosses indicating that selection for regenerable structures should be effective. An inheritance study of Type I callus initiation from A188 and Mo17 indicated that possibly two genes controlled callus initiation in this cross (Hodges et al., 1985). The effect of inbred genotype on initiation of somatic embryogenic callus (Types I and II) was determined for B73, B76, and proprietary inbreds (Tomes and Smith, 1985; Tomes, 1985b). B73 is a poor responder compared with A188 (Armstrong et al., 1985). Tomes and Smith (1985) observed a low frequency of initiation of Type II callus from B73. Significant genetic differences in callus initiation were observed among the inbreds tested by Tomes and Smith (1985). Diallel analyses of Type II callus initiation showed that significant genotypic variation was due to specific combining ability, indicating that inbred sampling did not reveal the genetic potential of a genotype to produce Type II callus in specific crosses (Tomes and Smith, 1985; Tomes, 1985a, b). Genotype effects on plant regeneration frequency from embryogenic callus have been reported (Bruneau, 1985; Hodges et al., 1985).

The high heritability of culture response indicates that callus initiation may be improved by crossing recalcitrant genotypes with highly responsive genotypes and culturing the hybrid embryos or selecting for callus initiation among segregating progeny from the cross (Tomes and Smith, 1985; Tomes, 1985a, b; Tomes et al., 1986; Hodges et al., 1985). This approach has been used to develop B73 backcross lines from A188 × B73 crosses that form friable, embryogenic callus at high frequency (C.L. Armstrong, 1985, personal communication). Friable, embryogenic callus of B73 and B73 crosses with other elite inbreds have retained plant regeneration capacity for more than 1 yr (Tomes and Smith, 1985). Friable, embryogenic callus initiated from A188 × B73 F_1 embryos and the F_2 of reciprocal crosses of A188 and B73 also exhibited increased culture stability compared with A188 friable, embryogenic callus (Donovan and Somers, 1986). Embryogenic callus initiation was similar for B73 normal and C and S male-sterile cytoplasms indicating that these mitochondrial genomes have little effect on culture initiation and that, for the most part, nuclear genes are involved for the inbreds studied (Tomes, 1985b). Culture initiation was obtained from B73 embryos about 2 mm in length, indicating that interactions between embryo development and genotype are also important in Type II callus initiation. Type II friable, embryogenic callus initiation occurs at lower frequency than Type I embryogenic callus for a particular genotype and is more subject to environmental variation affecting the donor plant and culture conditions (Tomes, 1985 a, b).

Regenerable tissue cultures of elite corn inbreds are required for the rapid incorporation of traits modified by in vitro genetic manipulations into breeding lines. Extending the range of genotypes that give rise to plant regenerating tissue cultures has been largely achieved by a media modification so that regenerable cultures can be initiated from most corn inbreds. The modified N6 medium containing proline promotes high-frequency initiation of Type II callus of A188 (Armstrong and Green, 1985). Other genotypes produce embryogenic callus at higher frequencies when plated on the MS medium containing 1 mM of asparagine described by Green and Phillips (1975) than when plated on N6 medium containing 6 mM of proline (Tomes and Smith, 1985). A medium formulation described by Duncan et al. (1985) using dicamba (3,6-dichloro-o-anisic acid) as an auxin has dramatically increased the number of inbreds that may be cultured. The cultures were Type I embryonic callus as Lu et al. (1982) described. Of 218 selfed inbred lines and germplasm stocks, 199 produced callus with plant regeneration capacity (Duncan et al., 1985). The effectiveness of Duncan's medium for regenerable callus initiation has been corroborated by Wilkinson and Thompson 1986. Other conjugated and derivatized auxins also induce regenerable tissue cultures of corn (McCormick, 1980; Hodges et al., 1985; Close and Ludeman, 1986). Other media manipulations such as modification of the ratio of reduced to oxidized N and the inclusion of osmoticum have been successful in improving embryogenic callus initiation of specific inbreds (Fahey et al., 1986). Preliminary studies indicated that 5-azacytidine, a DNA methylation inhibitor, increased the frequency of embryogenic callus initiation (Swedlund and Locy, 1986).

5–1.4 Liquid Suspension Cultures

Nonregenerable callus from Black Mexican Sweet (BMS) (Green, 1977; Chourey and Zurawski, 1981), B73 (Potrykus et al., 1979), C 103 × W155 (Polikarpochkina et al., 1979) and a few other genotypes initiate rapidly growing liquid suspension cultures. The suspension cultures do not exhibit plant regeneration. These cultures have proven useful as model systems to study the requirement of nurse cultures to support low density culture of corn cell colonies (Smith et al., 1984; Kuang et al., 1984) and for protoplast studies (see section 5–1.5).

Totipotent suspension cultures can be initiated from friable, embryogenic (Type II) callus cultures. A188 callus cultures were inoculated into liquid medium containing low levels of abscisic acid to suppress somatic embryoid development (Green et al., 1983). Replating the suspension onto callus maintenance medium resulted in proliferation of somatic embryogenic callus from which plant regeneration was effected. Suspension cultures have since been initiated from friable, embryogenic callus of B73 (Tomes and Smith, 1985; Lowe et al., 1985; Paterson et al., 1986), F_1 and F_2 embryos from crosses of A188 and B73 (Kamo and Hodges, 1986; Donovan and Somers, 1986); DeKalb XL82 (Vasil and Vasil, 1986) and other inbreds (Cheng et al., 1986).

5–1.5   Protoplast Cultures

Initial attempts to culture protoplasts of corn and many other cereal species concentrated on using plant tissues, mostly the mesophyll, as a source of protoplasts (for review see Vasil, 1983a). Only limited evidence of rare cell divisions in cultured mesophyll protoplasts were reported for corn. Potrykus et al. (1977) reported callus formation from protoplasts isolated from young stem sections of B73. However, sustained cell divisions in protoplasts isolated from plant tissues have yet to be reproducibly induced (Vasil, 1983a). Lack of reproducibility seems related to the inability to induce callus formation from the same tissues indicating that cells within these explants are incapable of resuming cell division once tissue-specific cell differentiation occurs. Resumption of cell division of corn mesophyll protoplasts has been induced by fusion with sorghum (*Sorghum bicolor* L. Moench) protoplasts that were capable of division (Brar et al., 1980). Fusion products formed colonies of 8 to 10 cells. Totipotent corn cells occur in immature embryos, tassels, glumes, meristems, and anthers; these organs give rise to regenerable callus. Dividing protoplast cultures isolated from these complex tissues have not been reported.

Corn callus and suspension cultures are logically the most promising source tissues for protoplast isolation and culture because they are fairly uniform populations of rapidly dividing, dedifferentiated cells which in some cases are totipotent. The culture of corn protoplasts to form callus has been achieved with protoplasts isolated from nonregenerable suspension cultures of BMS (Chourey and Zurawski, 1981), C105 × W155 (Kuang et al., 1984), B73 (Potrykus et al., 1979), and other genotypes (Morocz et al., 1986). Root-like structures have been regenerated from protoplast-derived callus (Chourey and Zuwarski, 1981; Morocz et al., 1986); however, plant regeneration has not been achieved.

Protoplast-to-callus culture systems from nonregenerable suspension cultures have been used as model systems for genetic manipulations (see chapter 6 in this book) and for investigation of culture conditions and medium modifications for optimal colony formation from protoplasts. Nurse cultures of BMS suspension cultures support colony formation from isolated BMS cell colonies (Smith et al., 1984) and protoplasts (Ludwig et al., 1985) plated at suboptimal densities indicating that BMS cell cultures produce culture metabolites that support corn cell division (Birnberg and Somers, 1986). Callus colonies isolated from BMS protoplast cultures have been shown to grow without exogenous auxin, indicating that the suspension culture was habituated (Hawes et al., 1985). Further knowledge of media requirements and plating techniques that provide optimal colony formation from BMS protoplasts will serve as a guide for optimizing totipotent corn protoplast culture.

Embryogenic suspensions can be manipulated during subculture to yield dedifferentiated embryogenic colonies of small starch-filled cells that are totipotent (Vasil and Vasil, 1986). Recently, protoplasts isolated from these suspensions have been cultured to form embryogenic callus; however, plant regeneration has not been achieved (Vasil et al., 1986). Isolation procedures, media, and culture conditions have been extensively investigated for protoplasts isolated from Types I and II regenerable callus (Swanson et al., 1985; Imbrie-Milligan and Hodges, 1986). Microcallus formation was observed from these protoplasts; however, sustained callus formation was not observed (Imbrie-Milligan and Hodges, 1986).

Further studies of conditions required for corn protoplast division and sustained callus formation will likely enable researchers to culture corn protoplasts to form plant regenerating callus. If so, protoplast fusion-mediated wide hybridization and transformation by direct DNA uptake into protoplasts will become feasible in vitro genetic manipulations in corn.

5–1.6 Haploid Tissue Cultures

Anther culture of corn was first reported in 1975 by 401 Research Group, Laboratory of Plant Cell and Tissue Culture, Academica Sinica, People's Republic of China (Ku et al., 1978). Subsequent progress in establishing routine anther culture protocols has been hampered because of the extremely limited number of genotypes that respond in culture (Petolino and Jones, 1986b). Initial success with hybrids derived in the People's Republic of China such as "Ching-Huang 13" were confirmed by Genovesi and Collins (1982). These authors also observed that selection 1522 of Coker's Armstrong landrace responded under the medium conditions that they developed. Genotypes that have been used for the successful regeneration of haploid plants are shown in Table 5–4. Although certain inbreds and hybrids respond to anther culture, cold pretreatment and orientation of the anther on culture medium did not improve culture callus initiation (Genovesi and Yingling, 1986). Haploid callus has been maintained over several years and continues to regenerate plants via embryogenesis (Cao et al., 1981; Gu et al., 1983). Haploid, diploid, and haploid-diploid chimeric plants have been regenerated from corn anther cultures (Genovesi and Collins, 1982; Ting, 1985a, b; Ting et al., 1981).

Unfertilized ovary cultures offer the potential of regenerating haploid plants. Haploid plants derived in this manner have been reported (Ao et al., 1982; Truong-Andre and Demarly, 1984).

5–1.7 Organ Cultures

Conditions for culturing immature corn organs have been developed, including those for kernels, tassels, and roots. Kernel development and maturation in culture has been reported by Gengenbach (1977). Corn ovaries were removed from the plant with a portion of the cob and cultured on solid medium. Pollinations could be accomplished in vitro

Table 5-4. Corn genotypes that give rise to regenerable anther cultures.

Genotype	Reference
Ching-Huang 13	Ku et al., 1978
Lai-pin pai	Ku et al., 1978
Hsu-kochuang	Ku et al., 1978
Hsaio-pa-tang × Shui-pai	Miao et al., 1978
Ba-Tang-pai	Cao et al., 1981
Seneca 60	Brettell et al., 1981
Dan San 91	Ting et al., 1981
Ching Huang 13	Genovesi and Collins, 1982
1522 Coker's Armstrong	Genovesi and Collins, 1982
Hsi-Ba-Tang × Shui Bai	Nitsch et al., 1982
Lai-Pin Pai	Nitsch et al., 1982
Illinois High Oil (IHO) × BMS	Nitsch et al., 1982
W23 × BMS	Nitsch et al., 1982
IHO/BMS × W23/BMS	Nitsch et al., 1982
BMS × LPP/Golden 113	Nitsch et al., 1982
Alexander's High Oil × LIP/Golden	Nitsch et al., 1982
H99†	Petolino and Jones, 1986a, b
FR16	Petolino and Jones, 1986a, b
Pa91	Petolino and Jones, 1986a, b

† Best responders in this study. Several other genotypes exhibited response frequencies of 1.0% or greater.

or on the plant prior to excision. Development of the kernel was completed in 40 d postpollination with approximately 4% normal seed produced. A number of researchers have used this method for metabolic studies, e.g., Misra and Oaks (1985).

Tassel cultures have been reported by Polowick and Greyson (1982). Immature tassels (1 cm) increased 1000-fold in fresh weight with 4% normal floral development after 14 d in culture. Later improvements in culturing conditions increased normal spikelet formation frequencies to greater than 50% (Pareddy and Greyson, 1985). Pollen from cultured tassels can be germinated on agar medium or silks (Pareddy et al., 1986). This culturing system should be of value in metabolic and developmental studies, in the analysis of male-sterile mutants, and in testing potential gametocides.

Corn root cultures have been reported since the 1920s. Growth rates and root diameters decreased with each subculturing and after four to six 10-d subcultures growth ceased altogether (Robbins, 1922; Robbins and Maneval, 1924). Corn roots like those of most monocotyledonous species were generally found to be recalcitrant to long-term culturing. McClary (1940) was able to maintain vigorous corn root cultures for more than 100 d. Later attempts to repeat this result have not been successful, which may indicate that a specific genotype or media contaminant was important. Continuous culture of rye (*Secale cereale* L.) roots was shown to be dependent on the presence of an auxin or auxin precursor in the medium (Roberts and Street, 1955). Addition of synthetic or natural growth regulators could lead to a reproducible continuous corn root culturing method. Short-term corn root cultures have been useful for detecting resistance to amino acid analogues in progeny of tissue culture selected plants (Diedrick, 1984).

Shoot tip culture methods for corn have been described (Raman et al., 1980). Stem segments of 20-d-old seedlings were dissected to remove leaves except for the youngest primordia from the intercalary meristem to expose five to six axillary bud primordia. Inclusion of kinetin and auxin in MS basal medium stimulated axillary bud formation. Shoots were rooted on a separate medium.

5-2 TISSUE CULTURE-INDUCED CHROMOSOMAL VARIATION

Variation, both genetic and cytogenetic, is a common feature of plant cell and tissue cultures. The likelihood appears to be quite low that a corn plant regenerated from culture is identical in genotype to the donor tissue or that two regenerated plants are identical to each other. Passage of cells through a callus- or suspension-culture phase clearly does not produce clonally identical genotypes. The resultant variation poses many opportunities, especially for recovering new and interesting genetic and cytogenetic variants.

Spontaneous variation usually is found among the first- or second-generation progeny of regenerated plants and provides the basis for several major screening programs in the public and private sectors. The variation can be the result of single gene nuclear mutations, organellar DNA changes, alterations in chromosome number and structure, or other less defined, but nevertheless obvious, changes in expression of quantitative traits. Selection schemes for various traits have been employed to further increase the efficiency of recovering special types. The apparent multicellular origin of plantlets regenerated from culture leads to complexities within the plant itself, to unexpected segregation ratios in progeny, and to the appearance of new segregating phenotypes in second generation progeny.

5-2.1 Chromosomal Variation in Cultured Cells

The mitotic index of callus cultures or cell suspensions is normally low. Black Mexican Sweet corn suspension cultures, for example, display a mitotic index of about 4% unless special methods are employed to increase the accumulation of mitotic figures (Wang et al., 1986). Because of the low mitotic index, relatively little is known about chromosomal variation in the cultures themselves.

Black Mexican Sweet corn suspension cultures may be maintained for a long period of time. The cultures, although initiated from presumably normal diploid tissues, contain both aneuploid and euploid cells with tetraploidy being the most common ploidy level (Brar et al., 1979;

Wang et al., 1986). Euploid levels from 1x (10 chromosomes) to 8x (80 chromosomes) have been reported for BMS suspension cultures (Wang et al., 1986). About 21% of the cells were reported to be aneuploid. A B73 cell suspension culture was shown to be comprised of only about 50% diploid cells; chromosome numbers ranged from 16 to 32 (Meadows, 1982/83).

Studies of callus cultures usually also indicate the presence of cells with chromosome number alterations. Edallo et al. (1981) reported that among 15 embryo-derived cultures only two appeared to possess solely 20-chromosome cells. Analysis at the third or fourth subculture revealed 163 2n cells for one of the two immature embryo-derived callus cultures and 80 2n cells for the other. Certain callus cultures derived from other embryos of the same inbred lines had as high as 47% non-2n cells. Some cultures probably are more stable than others even though derived from the same inbred line.

Callus cultures of A188 × W22 *R-nj R-nj* derived from immature embryos were shown to contain 5% or fewer dividing cells with other than the diploid chromosome number (McCoy and Phillips, 1982). Callus derived from reciprocal crosses gave similar results. Nondiploid cell counts included one cell with 22 chormosomes, 13 with 21, 13 with 19, 5 with 18, 3 with 17, and 1 with 15. A total of 837 cells were counted.

Balzan (1978) utilized a nonregenerable callus culture derived from mesocotyl tissue of inbred SI104. A high frequency of cells was observed with abnormal chromosome numbers (79% tetraploid cells). Dicentrics, fragments, and anaphase bridges also were observed. Edallo et al. (1981) studied callus cells of two genotypes, W64A and S65, and reported 8 and 15.5% nondiploid cells, respectively, including 4 to 7% that were tetraploid. Aneuploid cells with 31 to 39 chromosomes were observed less frequently, indicating the possiblity of loss of chromosomes after tetraploidization. In contrast, Gresshoff and Doy (1973) reported that a diploid corn culture maintained chromosomal stability for 1 yr.

Endosperm cultures also are unstable in chromosome number although most cells are triploid. Chromosome numbers have been reported to range from 21 to 200 (Boyer and Shannon, 1974). Straus (1954) observed anaphase bridges and other abnormalities.

An interesting feature of haploid cultures is that they have a strong tendency to diploidize over time (Bock and Greenblatt, 1965); this diploidization may be genotype dependent (Dhaliwal and King, 1979c). Anther-derived haploid cultures of corn may be more stable. Gu et al. (1983) reported 90% haploid and 10% diploid cells in 1-yr-old cultures; only a few aneuploid cells were observed. A study of long-term anther cultures indicated that cultures became nearly all diploid or haploid depending on which ploidy level predominated in the first 20 to 60 weeks of culture (Gu and Ting, 1985).

Changes in chromosome structure, as opposed to changes in chromosome number, have only been reported occasionally in corn callus or cell suspension cultures. Based on the numerous structural changes reported among regenerated plants, such cytogenetic events no doubt also occur in at least the regenerable callus cultures but have gone undetected to date due to the limitations of mitotic analysis.

5-2.2 Chromosomal Variation Among Regenerated Plants

Early cytogenetic analyses of regenerated corn plants indicated that alterations could occur in chromosome number and structure. Cytology of 43 plants regenerated from A188 × W22 *R-nj R-nj* revealed that only two were abnormal, both being sectored (Green et al., 1977). The tassel of one was sectored for normal and monosomic chromosome 5 tissue and the other had a tetraploid tassel sector. Three plants regenerated from a 3-yr-old culture all possessed an apparent terminal deficiency for part of the long arm of chromosome 6 (Green et al., 1977). McCoy and Phillips (1982) subsequently reported only five cytologically altered plants among 119 regenerants; three of the five were sectored based on pollen sterility. Only one of the sectored plants was observed to possess a cytologically altered karyotype—monosomy for an unidentified chromosome. One of the nonsectored plants carried a deficient chromosome 10 missing most of the short arm. Edallo et al. (1981) found one tetraploid and one trisomic plant among 110 regenerants of immature-embryo derived callus cultures of inbreds W64A and S65. Pollen sterility determinations, however, indicated the presence of chromosome rearrangements in certain regenerants.

Focusing on meiotic analysis has revealed higher levels of chromosomal variation. Many more structural chromosome alterations have been detected by meiotic analysis because chromosome pairing allows the ready detection of heterozygosity for aberrations such as translocations or duplications and deficiencies. For example, Rhodes et al. (1986b) reported that 40% of the 257 plants regenerated from cultures initiated from immature tassels of W22 *R r-x1* × A188 were cytologically abnormal, based on meiotic analysis. Certain cultures were initiated from aneuploid plants, but aneuploidy per se did not seem to contribute to the instability. The cultures all carried the *r-x1* allele which is known to cause nondisjunction and perhaps some chromosome fragmentation in embryo sacs. Whether this mutation caused instability in culture is not known. About 26% of the regenerants were heterozygous for a structural chromosome change and about 19% possessed a change in chromosome number. Overall, 12% of the regenerants possessed translocations, 14% heteromorphic pairs (heterozygous deficiencies and/or duplications), 14% genomic doublings, and 5% additions or losses of chromosomes. The high percentage of plants with genomic doubling is misleading because most arose from one cell line.

An extensive study of chromosomal instability of organogenic cultures initiated from immature embryos of Oh43 male-sterile (*ms*) isoline

× A188 crosses revealed quite different frequencies of regenerants with abnormal chromosomes after 12 weeks to 16 weeks compared to 32 to 36 weeks of culture (Lee and Phillips, 1987b). Meiotic analysis revealed no abnormalities in 78 plants regenerated 12 to 16 weeks after culture initiation. After 32 to 36 weeks, 91 of 189 regenerants were karyotypically altered. Most of the 108 aberrations detected were the result of changes in chromosome structure (96%); translocations (42%) and deficiencies and duplications (54%) were about equally frequent. Breakpoints usually involved chromosome arms possessing a heterochromatic knob.

Benzion (1984) performed meiotic analyses on 370 regenerated plants initiated from cell lines of 22 immature embryos of nine corn genotypes. About 11% of the 370 regenerants possessed cytological aberrations. Most aberrations were the result of chromosome breakage (65% translocations and 35% deficiencies) and usually involved a chromosome arm possessing a heterochromatic knob. Genomic doubling had occurred in 2% of the plants examined.

Later consideration of the problem of instability led to the idea that plants regenerated from embryogenic cultures would be less likely to possess aberrations (Vasil, 1983b). This prediction was based on the expectation that the formation of a somatic embryo is such a precise morphogenetic process that it would tend to screen out genetically abnormal cells from participating in embryogenesis. Armstrong (1986) analyzed meiosis in corn plants from cultures initiated from immature embryos of A188, six-backcross recoveries of A188 containing various genetic markers, and segregating progenies with an A188/B73 genetic background. Cytological abnormalities were detected in 12% (2 out of 17 plants) and 15% (9 out of 59) of the plants regenerated at 16 and 32 weeks culture age, respectively. The abnormal types included four independent translocations, one trisomic, one tetraploid, and one desynaptic plant. Pollen sterility was scored to provide another indication of cytological aberrations. Armstrong showed that 37% (10/27) and 42% (37/89) of the plants regenerated at 16 and 32 weeks culture age, respectively, possessed higher than background levels of pollen sterility. Thus, regeneration by somatic embryogenesis in corn apparently does not preclude the participation of cytologically abnormal cells in the regeneration process. Armstrong also analyzed organogenic cultures and observed no cytological aberrations after 16 weeks of culture but 6% (2/35) after 32 weeks. Pollen sterility was detected in 24% (10/41) and 26% (15/58) of the regenerants after 16 and 32 weeks in culture, respectively.

5–2.3 Genotype Effects

Several genotypes have been employed in assessing the frequency of chromosomal variation among regenerated plants. These include the use of a number of inbred lines such as A188 (Armstrong, 1986; Benzion, 1984; Rice, 1982), S65 and W64A (Edallo et al., 1981) PG6 (Rice, 1982);

and hybrids such as A188 × W22 *R-nj R-nj* (McCoy and Phillips, 1982; Green et al., 1977), W22 *R rx-1* × A188 with various genetic markers (Rhodes et al., 1986b), B73/A188 derivatives (Armstrong, 1986), and (Oh43 *ms* isolines × A188) F_2's (Lee and Phillips, 1987b). These genetic materials all appear to be unstable in culture as judged by chromosome number and structure alterations in regenerated plants. No genetic line has been documented to produce populations of regenerants from tissue culture that are free of chromosomal changes. Whether there is a genotype (genetic background) effect is difficult to assess, although the possiblity certainly exists. The unusually high frequency of chromosomal alterations observed in some studies, such as the one by Rhodes et al. (1986b), could be explained by differences other than genetic background. In the Rhodes et al. (1986b) study, the *r-x1* gene was present and the cultures were initiated from immature tassels, making it impossible to know if the *r-x1* gene was responsible for the greater instability. Carefully controlled experiments are needed to further test the question of genotype effect. One also needs to be cognizant that even the best cytogenetic methods available today detect only a fraction of the induced rearrangements. The actual frequency may be much higher than reported. Thus, the available evidence indicates that chromosomal alterations probably are to be expected in all genotypes. In section 5–2.9, we present evidence implicating heterochromatin in the breakage events. Because heterochromatin amount and distribution vary among lines, a genotype effect would be expected on this basis alone.

5–2.4   Sectoring (Chromosomal Mosaics or Chimeras)

Organogenic tissue cultures appear to form meristems of multicellular origin from which plantlets arise; Springer et al. (1979) presented histological evidence for corn. The expectation follows that a culture heterogeneous for cells of different karyotypes would at least occasionally produce mosaic plantlets comprised of cells with differing karyotypes. This expectation has been confirmed by analyzing meiotic cells of different tassel portions. Several studies with corn have reported tassels sectored for a particular chromosomal alteration (Green et al., 1977; McCoy and Phillips, 1982; Benzion, 1984; Rhodes et al., 1986b; Armstrong, 1986; Lee and Phillips, 1987b). Although such sectoring is indicative of cell heterogeneity in culture, similar results could occur if chromosomal alterations were induced during the ontogeny of the regenerated plant. Rhodes et al. (1986b) found that sectoring occurred in 20% of the plants from aneuploid cultures and 33% of the plants from euploid cultures, based on cytology and/or pollen sterility assessments. Certain tassel sectoring patterns, such as differences between the upper and lower portions of the central rachis, would indicate that the alteration occurred during plant development. At least three such cases occurred in the study by Rhodes et al. (1986b). But repeated occurrences of an aberration from a single tissue culture line, however, would indicate the aberration occurred prior to regeneration, and a regenerant sectored for such an alteration would likely be the result of the multicellular origin of regenerated plants. Such cases were reported by Benzion (1984).

Sectoring among regenerated corn plants was summarized by Benzion et al. (1986). Out of a total of 264 regenerated plants that were meiotically determined to possess a chromosomal alteration, 84 (32%) were sectored for normal and altered cells in different parts of the tassel. Armstrong (1986) recently reported 11-sectored regenerants among 57 (19%) with alterations. The combined frequency of sectoring over the various studies is 30% (95/321). Clearly this value could be an underestimate because cytological analysis would normally involve microsporocytes from only a small proportion of the tassel. Based on these results, one probably should not be surprised if every regenerated plant from organogenic cultures were sectored. Of course, the occurrence of sectoring would depend upon the frequency and distribution of chromosomally altered cells in the culture. The possible advantages of deriving regenerants from embryogenic cultures are discussed in section 5–2.8. Lee (1984) and Armstrong (1986) both observed approximately 50% less sectoring in older cultures (32 vs. 16 weeks). Perhaps early occurrences of an alteration lead to a proliferation of tissue that is more likely to be homogeneous in older cultures.

The occurrence of sectoring also has important implications relative to recovering the karyotypic alteration in subsequent progeny. Lack of transmission of an alteration via the male or female inflorescence may simply reflect its absence in that tissue. Johri and Coe (1983) showed that cells for the two inflorescences are already set apart in the embryo of a mature kernel. By analogy, a regenerated plant's tassel and ear may trace back to different cells in the meristem formed by cultured cells. Sectoring within either of the two inflorescences also would result in complex genetic ratios (see section 5–3.2)

5–2.5   Callus Age and Cytological Abnormalities

The effect of length of time in vitro on chromosomal instability is not straightforward. Edallo et al. (1981) showed that the frequencies of cellular chromosome number changes are not consistent from transfer to transfer, and the relationship with culture age is not obvious. The frequencies of regenerants with altered karyotypes were reported by Rhodes et al. (1986b) to be relatively constant from 12 weeks to as many as 68 weeks of culture age. McCoy and Phillips (1982) also observed little difference in chromosomal alteration frequencies for 16- vs. 32-week-old cultures; however, the overall frequency of instability was low in the study.

On the other hand, more recent studies have indicated an increase in instability with increasing time in vitro. Lee and Phillips (1987b) observed that at 12 to 16 weeks after culture initiation, none of the 78 plants regenerated from 49 cultures possessed a detectable abnormal karyotype. In contrast, 48% of the plants regenerated from 32- to 36-week-old cultures were cytologically abnormal. Armstrong (1986) also showed that 32-week cultures produced higher frequencies of cytologically abnormal plants than 16-week cultures. Benzion (1984) noted an increased frequency of cytologically abnormal plants over time in culture. However, a pedigree cell lineage analysis by Benzion (1984) indicated that many of the aberrations occurred early in the culture phase. Mutation rate could be constant throughout but mutations would tend to accumulate with time.

5-2.6   Haploids and Aneuploids

Haploid cell and tissue cultures have definite advantages in allowing the expression of newly induced, recessive mutations. Maternal or paternal haploids can be readily obtained in corn by utilizing genetic markers in crosses; appropriately marked haploid individuals can be placed in culture. One of the problems with such cultures is that, although initially haploid, the cultures will ultimately possess low to high numbers of diploid cells. An early report by Bock and Greenblatt (1965) indicated that the percentage of diploid cells increased over time in haploid root tissue cultures. Dhaliwal and King (1979b) counted chromocenters (dark-staining heterochromatic areas) in interphase cells of haploid corn cultures to estimate the frequency of haploid vs. diploid cells. Two genotypes were evaluated; one possessed 54% and the other 70% diploid cells in haploid cultures. Alternatively, anther culture is possible with certain genotypes and provides a source of haploid cells. Haploid cultures from anthers might be more stable, based on the work of Gu et al. (1983) and Gu (1986); only about 10% of the cells were diploid. Ting (1985a) found that 95% of the anther culture regenerants were haploid, 12 were doubled haploids ($2n = 20$) and one was aneuploid ($2n = 18$).

Because of the occurrence of diploid cells in haploid cultures, monosomic cultures were initiated and their stability assessed. Monosomics have certain advantages over haploids. Recessive mutations detected in such cultures theoretically would be located on the monosomic chromosome. Monosomic plants obtained by regeneration would shed pollen in most cases and could be self-pollinated. Because only n mature pollen grains and ovules would be produced, the progeny would be uniformly diploid and homozygous for the recessive mutation. Dhaliwal and King (1979b) used the *r-x1* gene to generate monosomic (and trisomic) seedlings which were used to initiate cultures. Cultures monosomic for chromosomes 2, 6, 7, 9, and 10 were established. A small proportion of tetraploid cells was found in these cultures. Later Rhodes et al. (1986b) also used the *r-x1* gene to generate aneuploid cultures. About 40% of the 144 regenerated plants had an altered karyotype. Although the most common alterations involved chromosome breakage producing translocations or heteromorphic pairs, genomic doubling to 38 chromosomes or the loss or addition of a chromosome also occurred. It was interesting that diploid regenerants with 20 chromosomes occurred at a frequency of about 6% from 19-chromosome monosomic cultures. Apparently, nondisjunction had occurred for the monosomic chromosome. Because the karyotypic alteration infrequently involved the monosomic chromosome, it was concluded that monosomic cultures should be useful for selecting recessive mutants. Also, 60% did not have a detectably altered karyotype.

Cultures of trisomic 1, 3, and 4 have been established (Dhaliwal and King, 1979b). Unidentified telocentric chromosomes were eventually present in these cultures. B chromosome-containing cultures (0–5 B's) also have been developed (Das and Widholm, 1982) and the B chromosomes appeared to be stable in number.

5–2.7   Explant Source

Different tissues of a plant may vary in chromosome constitution and almost certainly in physiology. On this basis, explant source may well be expected to influence the level of variation found in tissue cultures. The first regeneration of whole corn plants that could be grown to maturity was from tissue cultures initiated from the scutellar tissue of immature embryos (Green and Phillips, 1975) and this explant source is still used most frequently. Most studies on tissue culture-induced variation, therefore, have utilized immature embryo-initiated callus tissue. Variability from immature embryo-, as well as immature tassel-, and anther-initiated cultures is discussed in other sections of this chapter. In addition, variability has been assessed in cultures initiated from mesocotyl and endosperm tissues. Balzan (1978) found that mesocotyl-initiated tissue cultures became predominantly tetraploid over a 32-week period. Three-yr-old cultures initiated from triploid endosperm tissue maintained mostly triploid (or hexaploid) cells, although cells with 21 to 200 chromosomes also existed (Boyer and Shannon, 1974). The various studies involving different tissues report different arrays of changes. The possibility exists that explant source could be an important variable in determining the frequency of variation. The proper comparisons have not been made, however, to adequately evaluate the effects of explant source relative to tissue culture-induced variability.

5–2.8   Type I vs. Type II Cultures

Two types of cultures can be initiated from immature embryos of corn as discussed earlier in this chapter; these are termed Types I and II cultures (Armstrong and Green, 1985). Type I refers to the organogenic/ embryogenic cultures described by Green and Phillips (1975) that are compact with most plantlets forming from organized meristems. Type II

Table 5-5. Stability of organogenic vs. embryogenic corn tissue cultures based on plants regenerated after 16 and 32 weeks (Armstrong, 1986).

Abnormality	16 weeks		32 weeks	
	Organogenic	Embryogenic	Organogenic	Embryogenic
		%		
Cytological aberrations	0 (0/31)	12 (2/17)	6 (2/35)	15 (9/59)
Pollen sterility	24 (10/41)	37 (10/27)	26 (15/58)	42 (37/89)
Variant segregation	22 (5/23)	19 (4/21)	38 (6/16)	42 (19/45)
(Combined)†	21 (15/72)	33 (15/45)	24 (22/91)	37 (55/148)
Sectoring				
Cytological ab.	44 (4/9)	40 (2/5)	18 (2/11)	9 (3/32)
Variant seg.	60 (3/5)	50 (2/4)	33 (2/6)	21 (4/19)

† Numbers are not additive because some plants were aberrant in more than one category.

cultures are friable in growth habit and plantlets originate from somatic embryos (Green, 1982, 1983; Armstrong, 1986).

Because somatic embryogenesis is a precise morphogenetic process leading to somatic embryos with a bipolar axis, Vasil (1983b) hypothesized that cells with genetic/cytogenetic abnormalities may be less likely to form somatic embryos than normal cells. The exciting possibility was advanced that plants regenerated from Type II cultures might possess fewer genetic and cytological alterations; early estimates of chromosomal variability indicated considerable stability (Vasil et al., 1984; Benzion, 1984).

Compact, organogenic (Type I) and friable, embryogenic (Type II) corn cultures both were initiated from a common callus line of A188 (or its derivatives with various genetic markers) or segregating progenies of A188 × B73 by Armstrong (1986). Pollen sterility and cytological abnormalities were assessed in plants regenerated from both culture types 16 and 32 weeks after culture initiation. Surprisingly, the embryogenic cultures, based on analysis of regenerated plants, were found to be more unstable chromosomally than organogenic cultures at both 16 and 32 weeks (Table 5-5). Freeling et al. (1976) reported a higher frequency of tetraploid and octoploid cells in friable callus than in compact callus. The greater variability associated with Type II corn cultures may have more to do with the rapid growing, friable nature of the cultures than regeneration by embryogenesis.

5-2.9 Types of Aberrations and Breakpoint Positions

Most common types of chromosomal alterations have been observed in corn tissue cultures or regenerated plants. Recent meiotic analyses, however, indicate that changes in chromosome structure due to chromosome breakage are much more common than changes in chromosome number (Table 5-6).

Translocations and deletions appear to occur in about equal fre-

Table 5-6. Chromosomal variations among plants regenerated from corn tissue cultures. Modified from Benzion et al. (1986).

Chromosomal alterations	Aberration frequency (no., %)			
	Benzion, 1984	Lee and Phillips, 1987b	Rhodes et al., 1986b	Armstrong, 1986
Polyploidy	6 (2)	2 (0.7)	37 (14)†	1 (0.7)
Aneuploidy	0	1 (0.4)	14 (5)	1 (0.7)
Structural alterations				
Interchanges	23 (6)	45 (17)	32 (13)	7 (5)
Inversions	1 (0.3)	1 (0.4)	0	0
Deletions/duplications	13 (4)	59 (22)	36 (14)	0
Total plants scored	370	267	257	142

† Mostly from one embryo-derived callus line.

quencies among corn regenerants. In addition, one regenerated plant heterozygous for a paracentric inversion was recovered in studies by both Benzion (1984) and Lee and Phillips (1987b). Seven plants with translocations involving three chromosomes to give a ring-of-six or a chain-of-six at diakinesis were reported by Lee and Phillips (1987b). Regenerated plants also may possess more than one aberration. In the study by Lee and Phillips (1987b), 9% of the plants regenerated 32 to 36 weeks after culture initiation possessed two or three chromosome aberrations.

The positions of the breakpoints appear to be nonrandom. The breaks tend to occur between the knob and the centromere in chromsome arms with heterochromatic knobs (Fig. 5–2). Table 5–7 summarizes the pachytene breakpoints reported in four studies.

All of these studies included A188, which has knobs on chromosome arms 5L, 7L, 8L, and 9S (terminal). The study by Lee (1984) mostly involved F_2's of Oh43/A188. The inbred Oh43 possesses a small knob on 6L as well as on 4L, 7L, and 9S (terminal). Further tests are needed to establish whether more breaks occur in an arm if a knob is present, as the current evidence indicates.

5–2.10 Unusual Cytological Abnormalities Among Regenerated Plants

Rhodes et al. (1986b) reported regenerated plants from monosomic and other chromosomally deficient cultures with coenocytic microsporocytes possessing 2 to 60 nuclei. Metaphase I plates with 80 or more chromosomes were observed. In certain cases, lack of cell wall formation during meiosis I and II resulted in four microspore nuclei in one ctyoplasm. Cases of microspores with two nuclei, each with two nucleoli, in a common cytoplasm and quartet-stage microspores completely without nuclei were reported. Extra large pollen sometimes occurred indicating the production of 2n pollen. Irregular quartets also were observed by Lee (1984). He reported unusual anaphase I cells with elongated chromosomes.

Table 5-7. Summary of chromosomes and breakpoints involved in cytological aberrations recovered in plants regenerated from corn tissue cultures. Each aberration represents an independently occurring event (Armstrong, 1986).

Interchange		Deletions		Other
1S.24/6L.36	Benzion, 1984	5S (0.3–0.4)	Benzion, 1984	Monosomic 5
5S.71/7L.16	Benzion, 1984			Green et al.,
6L.80/7L.52	Benzion, 1984	2L (0.1–0.3)	Lee, 1984	1977
7L.59/8L.70	Benzion, 1984	4L (0.3–0.5)	Lee, 1984	
7L.61/8L.72	Benzion, 1984	5L (0.1–0.3)	Lee, 1984	
7L.63/8L.76	Benzion, 1984	8L (0.3–0.5)	Lee, 1984	
		10L (0.4–0.6)	Lee, 1984	
6L.85/ ?	Lee, 1984			
6L / ?	Lee, 1984	6L	Green et al., 1977	
6L / ?	Lee, 1984			
6L / ?	Lee, 1984	10S	McCoy and Phillips, 1982	
6L / ?	Lee, 1984			
6S (sat.)/ ?	Lee, 1984			
6S (sat.)/ ?	Lee, 1984			

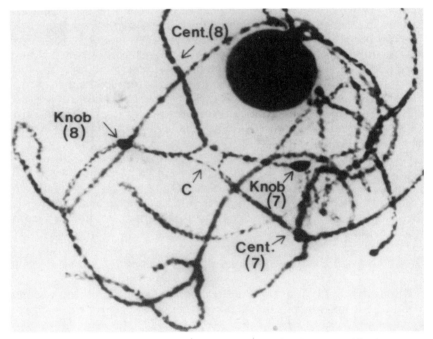

Fig. 5–2. Interchange heterozygosity in a R_0 plant. Note that breaks occurred in chromosome arms with heterochromatic knobs. Photograph courtesy of G. Benzion.

5–3 TISSUE CULTURE-INDUCED GENETIC VARIATION

In addition to cytological alterations, the spontaneous mutation rate among tissue culture cells is sufficiently high to generate extensive genetic variation among regenerated plants and their first or second generation progeny. A possible mechanism accounting for at least a portion of observed tissue-culture induced variation is proposed in section 5–3.6. Variants recovered from tissue culture may segregate in a Mendelian fashion or a quantitative fashion. Both cytoplasmic and nuclear genetic variation occur.

5–3.1 Traits

More than 50 single-gene mutant phenotypes have been recovered among progeny of corn regenerants (Table 5–8 and Fig. 5–3). Defective-kernel and albino variants are the ones most commonly found segregating among progeny of regenerated plants; these traits also are commonly observed segregating after mutagenic treatments in vivo. Allelism tests

Table 5–8. Variant phenotypes controlled by a single recessive gene segregating in first or second self-generation families (Lee, 1984; Armstrong, 1986).

Trait	No. independent occurrences	Trait	No. independent occurrences
Defective kernels	17	Necrotic-3†	1
Albino	16	Necrotic patches	1
Striate	11	Yellow stripe	1
Light green lethal	8	Narrow leaf-thin stalk	1
Virescent-4†	8	Male-sterility	1
Dwarf	6	Tassel seed	1
Zebra chlorotic	6	Light green (late)	1
Narrow leaf	5	Lineate (younger leaves)	1
Virescent	5	Striate-crinkled	1
Chlorotic patches	4	Multiple flag leaves	1
Luteus	4	Albino (unstable)	1
Necrotic leaf margins	4	Yellow	1
Adherent	3	Necrotic lethal	1
Disease lesion mimic	3	Branched silkless	1
Lower leaf necrosis	3	Lazy	1
Pale green	3	Barren stalk	1
Ragged leaf	3	Virescent-like lethal	1
Striped lethal	3	Early lethal	1
Wilted	3	Yellow green lethal	1
Yellow green stunted	3	Stunted	1
Yellow striate	3	Necrotic spots	1
Coleoptile lethal	2		
Interveinal necrosis	2		
Light green stunted	2		
Meristem lethal	2		
Necrotic leaf lethal	2		
Necrotic streaks	2		
Pale green lethal	2		
Ragged-stiff stalk	2		
Viviparous	2		
White leaf tips	2		
Zebra necrotic	2		

† These variants resemble known mutants *virescent-4* and *necrotic-3*, but allelism tests have not been performed.

Fig. 5-3. Tissue culture-induced single gene variants. Ear segregating for a defective kernel mutant (*upper left*); diurnal chlorotic striping mutant (*lower left*); two dwarf seedlings flanking a normal sibling (*upper right*); and a japonica-like stripe variant (*lower right*). Photographs courtesy of C.A. Armstrong, G. Benzion, and V.M. Peschke.

have not been performed in most instances, so the number of loci represented is unknown at this time. The phenotypes scored in most studies, including the ones summarized in Table 5-8, were only those that were readily visible on the ear or as seedlings or in developing plants. For example, Edallo et al. (1981) described endosperm mutants—opaque, etched, white cap, and germless; and seedling mutants—lethal plant, abnormal growth, yellow, yellow green, pale green, albino, fine stripe, yellow stripe, virescent, reduced plant, dwarf, and viviparous. Woodman and Kramer (1986) discovered knotted leaf and white-cob variants. Williams and Widholm (1986) reported single gene mutants such as albino, yellow green, ragged leaves, dwarf, white endosperm, vivipary, and male sterility. Nonvisible traits, such as isozymes or variations at the DNA level, have not been extensively tested. The array illustrated in Table 5-8, therefore, represents only a small sampling of the variants that no doubt occur.

Quantitative traits also are modified as a result of passage through tissue culture, although the number of studies with corn is limited. Traits evaluated have included vigor, grain yield, moisture, pollen shed and silking dates, lodging, plant height, ear length, kernel rows, and kernel weight (Beckert et al., 1983; Earle and Gracen, 1985; Williams and Widholm, 1986; Lee, 1986). The most extensive study involved 305 tissue culture-derived and 48 control lines from (Oh43/A188) F_2 populations evaluated as S_2 lines per se and in a testcross at three locations (Lee, 1986). Although grain yield was reduced on average in the tissue culture-derived lines, the highest-yielding line per se in three of six trials and the top-ranked line (based on rank summation index using grain yield and moisture) in five of six trials for yield were tissue culture-derived lines. A general trend toward earlier maturity also existed. The results indicated that earlier maturing lines with yields at least equivalent to the control may be obtained via tissue culture. Further tests are needed, however, as the data were gathered in a year that apparently favored earliness in the controls as well.

Cytoplasmic variation also occurs among corn plants regenerated from tissue culture. A high level of variation in mitochondrial DNA has been shown by several investigators (Gengenbach et al., 1981; Brettell et al., 1982; Kemble et al., 1982; McNay et al., 1984; Chourey et al., 1986). Changes in a specific region of the corn mitochondrial DNA (mt DNA) have been associated with conversions of Texas cytoplasmic male sterile (*cms*-T), southern corn leaf blight (caused by *Helminthosporium maydis* race T) susceptible callus types to types which produce fertile, resistant regenerants (Gengenbach et al., 1981; Brettell et al., 1982; Gengenbach and Umbeck, 1982; Wise et al., 1985, 1987). Such phenotypic changes were shown by Brettell et al. (1982) not to depend on the presence of the phytotoxin. Tissue cultures from immature embryos of corn inbred W182BN with *cms*-S were established and plants subsequently regenerated (Earle and Gracen, 1986). Fertile plants were identified among regenerants from 13 out of 14 cultures. More fertiles occurred among regenerants from older cultures. All fertile plants recovered lacked the S-1 and S-2 plasmid-like elements. Mitochondrial changes have been shown in cultured cells. Callus derived from *cms*-S was not stable for the presence of the S1 and S2 sequences, and loss of these sequences was correlated with altered callus morphology (Chourey and Kemble, 1982).

The stoichiometry of several mt DNA restriction fragments were altered in BMS corn suspension cultures compared to seedlings (McNay et al., 1984). A high level of mitochondrial DNA variability has been detected among BMS corn protoclone cultures (Chourey et al., 1986). A certain portion of the mitochondrial genome appears to be quite variable and these portions represent repeated DNA regions. Chourey and co-workers noted that protoplast isolation delays the cell division process and may, in some fashion, lead to the observed DNA variation.

The high variability for mitochondrial DNA indicates that tissue or cell culture might also be used to induce new and interesting cytoplasmic variants. None have been reported to date. Lee and Phillips (1987a) attempted to recover a cytoplasmic variant that would restore fertility in a homozygous recessive nuclear male-sterile genotype but were not successful.

5–3.2 Genetic Nonconcordance

Corn is a monoecious plant. Cells for the tassel and the ear are already set apart in the embryo of mature kernels (Johri and Coe, 1983). Because meristems in organogenic corn tissue cultures appear to be of multicellular origin (Springer et al., 1979), there is a certain likelihood, depending on the culture's stability, that the meristem would be composed of cells with different genotypes. In that case, those cells that ultimately populate the tassel may not derive from the same meristematic cells that comprise the ear. Even the male or female inflorescence may not originate from a single primordial meristem cell. Genetic nonconcordance would therefore be an expected outcome in certain cases. A recessive mutation induced in a diploid tissue culture may be present in heterozygous condition in one inflorescence and not the other. Self-pollination of such a plant would produce either homozygous wild-type or heterozygous genotypes; the homozygous recessive genotype would be absent. Upon selfing the first generation progeny (R_1), those that are heterozygous would produce segregating progenies in the R_2. The frequency of segregating R_2 families should depend on the proportion of heterozygotes among the R_1 plants, which would be a reflection of the nature of the sectoring. Thus, segregation of a recessive phenotype in the R_2 and not in the R_1 is taken to indicate genetic nonconcordance in the original regenerant (R_0). Nonconcordance could also result from mutation during the ontogeny of the regenerated plant; however, the occurrence of a specific mutant in progenies of more than one regenerant from a specific cell line implies nonconcordance due to a multicellular origin of regenerated plants.

Apparent genetic nonconcordance is detected in about 50% of the regenerated plants that segregate for one or more new mutants (Table 5–9). Such a high frequency of detectable nonconcordance implies that every regenerant could be genotypically mosaic. Testing for additional mutant types presumably would allow the detection of nonconcordance in many additional plants. The potentially high frequency of genetic nonconcordance is consistent with the frequent sectoring observed for chromosomal alterations cited in section 5–2.4. Edallo et al. (1981) scored for mutant phenotypes only in the R_2 generation but recognized the implications of chimerism. A lack of concordance between male and female inflorescences also was discussed by McCoy and Phillips (1982). They predicted genetic nonconcordance based on selfing of 51 cytologically normal regenerants of which eight segregated for defective kernels in the R_1 and an

Table 5-9. Genetic nonconcordance in regenerated plants based on mutant segregation in the R_2 but not in the R_1 generation.

Reference	No. sectored/total segregating	Percentage
Type I cultures		
Benzion, 1984	29/45	64
Lee, 1984	43/81	53
Armstrong, 1986	5/11	46
Total	77/137	56
Type II cultures		
Armstrong, 1986	6/23	26

additional eight only segregated in the R_2 generation. Rice (1982) also noted genetic nonconcordance.

Regeneration via somatic embryogenesis would be expected to eliminate most genetic nonconcordance if the embryos are of a single cell origin. Armstrong (1986) found that the frequency of sectoring was statistically significantly lower in plants regenerated from friable, embryogenic cultures than from organogenic cultures. The frequency of R_0 plants from embryogenic cultures that segregated for mutants in the R_2 but not the R_1 generation was 26% (6/23), compared to 46% (5/11) from organogenic cultures. Of the chromosomally aberrant plants, only 14% (5/37) from embryogenic cultures were sectored for cytological aberrations compared to 30% (6/20) from organogenic cultures (Table 5–5). The cases of nonconcordance for embryogenically derived regenerants could be due to the plants arising from somatic embryos with a multicellular origin. Vasil et al. (1985) and Armstrong (1986) have reported that some somatic embryos arise from groups of cells. Of course, another possibility is that the mutations occurred during the ontogeny of the regenerated plant. For whatever reason, regenerants from embryogenic corn cultures appear less likely to be chimeric, both genetically and cytogenetically.

5–3.3 Variant Frequencies

Because mutation rate is difficult to estimate due to the many unknown parameters, Edallo et al. (1981) presented the first estimate of mutability in terms of the "number of variants per regenerated plant." Table 5–10 presents the various estimates that have been published.

More than one single-gene, recessive variant can occur in a regenerated plant. Lee (1984) reports up to five variants per regenerated plant. He showed that the frequency of regenerants possessing more than one new mutation increases with culture age (10% at 16 weeks vs. 36% at 32 weeks).

Generally, the newly induced genetic variants have not been asso-

Table 5–10. Frequency of variants per regenerated plant.

Source	Genotype	Variants/R_0
Edallo et al., 1981	W64A	1.2
	S65	0.8
Lee, 1984	(Oh43 ms isolines/A188)F_2	
16-week cultures		0.52
32-week cultures		1.32
McCoy and Phillips, 1982	A188 × W22 *R-nj R-nj*	0.3
Rice, 1982	A188	0.15
	PG6	0.20
Woodman and Kramer, 1986	B73	0.35
Armstrong, 1986†	A188 and A188/B73	0.41

† Armstrong (1986) found that the frequency of genetic variants was nearly the same regardless of whether the regenerants arose from Type I or II cultures.

ciated with a particular chromosomal aberration. One notable exception appears to be the abphyll syndrome (opposite leaf orientation). The abphyll plants found by Green et al. (1977) were deficiency heterozygotes for part of chromosome 6L. Abphylly also occurred in an average of 33% (range 20–80%) of the plants regenerated from monosomic chromosome 6 cultures (Rhodes et al., 1986b). Hemizygosity for part of chromosome 6L apparently leads to the abphyll phenotype.

5–3.4 Transposable Elements

Chromosome breakage in corn can lead to the occurrence of transposable elements (McClintock, 1950, 1951; Neuffer, 1966; Bianchi et al., 1969; Doerschug, 1973). Because chromosome breakage appears to be a common occurrence, if not the principal cytogenetic event in corn tissue culture cells, transposable elements among regenerants or their progenies perhaps should be expected. Burr and Burr (1981) and McClintock (1984) had predicted transposable elements in corn regenerants based on the thought that tissue culture represented a genomic shock.

Evola and co-workers (1984; 1984, personal communication) have noted activation of both *Activator* (*Ac*) and *Suppressor-mutator* (*Spm*) in a small population of regenerated plants. Tests of 1200 R_o, R_1, and R_2 plants for the presence of *Ac* were made by Peschke (1986); 54 tests were positive. The 1200 tests represented 301 R_o plants from 94 immature embryo-initiated callus lines; the frequency estimate was 3%. At least two and perhaps three independent occurrences of *Ac* are represented among the genetic materials tested. Since there is no reason to believe that one or more of the other corn transposable element systems are not also activated, the 3% estimate probably is a gross underestimate of the occurrence of transposable elements among corn regenerants.

Endosperm cultures with *c-m2* homozygous (*Ds* present) and cultures with the standard *c* (no *Ds*) were observed for the production of anthocyanin, indicative of *C* expression (Culley, 1986). A high frequency of sectoring was noticed in all *c-m2* cultures but in none of the *c* cultures. Preliminary molecular evidence indicates the presence of *Ac*-like sequences in the DNA from *c-m2* cultures (D.E. Culley, 1986, personal communication). Gorman and Peterson (1978) and Bartkowiak and Peterson (1984) had previously shown that a transposable element, in that case *Enhancer* (*En*), can be active in corn endosperm tissue cultures. Lupotto et al. (1985) initiated immature embryo callus lines with and without *Ac*. Molecular analysis of 31 regenerants with *Ac* revealed a significant instability of *Ac*-hybridizing restriction fragments.

The discovery of transposable element activation via tissue culture leads to the idea that at least a portion of the induced variants are due to insertional events. Although some unstable phenotypes have arisen from tissue culture, such as an unstable albino (Armstrong, 1986) and an unstable white cob mutant (Woodman and Kramer, 1986), most appear quite stable. Thus, a better test may be to analyze at the molecular level some of the mutants of known loci for which probes are available. This has been accomplished for one *Adh1* variant; a single base pair change was found to be the basis for the mutation (Brettell et al., 1986). Evola et al. (1984) analyzed several *sh* mutants probably produced during plant regeneration for insertions or deletions of 50 base pairs or more, but none were found. Future molecular analyses of several such mutations induced during tissue culture should indicate whether some of the induced mutants are due to insertional events.

5-3.5 DNA Methylation

The numerous qualitative and quantitative genetic changes noticed in regenerated plants and their progenies conceivably could be related to DNA methylation. Brown and Lorz (1986) restricted DNA from A188 regenerants with methylation-sensitive enzymes and hybridized it with various gene sequences. Significantly increased methylation was found. In an earlier study by Benzion (1984), DNAs from 25 A188 regenerated plants and one seed-grown plant were restricted with EcoR1, Bam H1, and Sst1, and hybridized with a labelled 9 kb ribosomal DNA probe. No large DNA deletions, insertions, or sequence modifications were detected. The materials used by Brown and Lorz were reported by Gobel and Lorz (1986) to be extremely variable showing a wide range of phenotypes including early necrosis, albinos, leaf striping, reduced vigor, dwarfs, sterility, and vivipary. Perhaps these cultures were unusually variable and accounted for Brown and Lorz's ability to detect changes in methylation. Further tests clearly will be interesting.

5-3.6 A Possible Mechanism

Several genetic and cytogenetic points seem to be evident from the foregoing discussion of tissue culture-induced variation.

1. The principal cytogenetic event occurring in culture appears to be chromosome breakage—manifested by regenerants heterozygous for translocations and deficiencies/duplications in about equal frequencies.
2. Heterochromatin is implicated in these breakage events—manifested by breaks often involving chromosome arms with a heterochromatic knob and commonly between the knob and the centromere.
3. In addition to a high frequency of breakage, the occurrence of new mutations is elevated in frequency—manifested by the appearance of 0.15 to 1.32 variants per regenerated plant.
4. The elevated frequencies of both chromosomal alterations and single gene mutations could occur because newly activated (or generated) transposable elements presumably produced by chromosome breakage would have the potential of inserting into any locus and

result in a new mutant, but not necessarily on the same chromosome in which the original break occurred.

Based on the above observations, the initial event could be one that leads to chromosome breakage. Since heterochromatic knobs are implicated and they replicate last in the S (DNA synthetic) period (Pryor et al., 1980), the improper or delayed replication of that DNA may be the underlying cause of tissue culture-induced variation, both cytogenetic and genetic. The tissue culture environment might cause a problem in duplicating the late-replicating DNA at the proper time. If it is delayed in replication, one would expect chromosome bridges involving knobbed chromosomes and subsequent breakage. In diploid cells, such events involving the knobbed chromosomes could generate at least the principal classes of aberrations observed among corn regenerants.

The precedence in corn for the above hypothesis relates to the mechanism of chromatin loss induced by the B chromosome. Rhoades and Dempsey (1972, 1973) showed that if two or more B chromosomes are present in the proper genetic strains, then knobbed chromosomes break at the second postmeiotic mitosis in the microspore. This apparently leads to the generation of progeny carrying deficient or translocated (nonreciprocal) chromosomes. Similar events occurring in diploid tissue culture cells, as opposed to haploid microspores, would be expected to give deficiencies, duplications, and reciprocal translocations (though probably not exact reciprocals). These types of aberrations are the principal ones detected among regenerated corn plants. Transposable elements would then be an expected result of chromosome breakage and might be one source of the genetic variation.

5–4   SELECTIONS IN CELL CULTURE

5–4.1   Traits Selected

Over the past 12 yr, a variety of cellular level selections have been conducted including selections for disease, herbicide, and antibiotic tolerances and for altered levels of free amino acids. These selections were conducted with a variety of cultured cell types including cell suspensions, compact regenerable callus and friable, embryogenic callus. Mutagenic agents were utilized in approximately one-half of the studies.

Selections for resistance to southern corn leaf blight were conducted using the host-specific phytotoxin isolated from the causal organism *Helminthosporium maydis* (*Drechslera maydis*) Race T. The initial selections were made in nonregenerable T-cytoplasm cultures (Gengenbach and Green, 1975). The resistant lines were at least 40-fold less sensitive to the toxin than were controls. In later selections, plantlets were obtained that showed both phytotoxin and disease resistance (Gengenbach et al., 1977). Most regenerated plants and progeny that were toxin insensitive were also shown to be male fertile in contrast to the male-sterile toxin-sensitive line initially placed in culture. Characterization of selected progeny at the molecular level has indicated significant changes in the restriction pattern of the mitochondrial DNA. A 6.7-kb *Xbo* I fragment found in T cytoplasm mtDNA is absent in toxin insensitive progeny and specifically within this fragment an alteration in or deletion of a 365 bp open reading frame correlates with the change from t-toxin sensitivity to insensitivity (Wise et al., 1987).

Corn cultures have been selected for tolerance to the herbicides in the imidazolinone (1,3-diaza-2,4-cyclopentadiene) family and to paraquat (1,1,dimethyl-4,4'-bipyridinium). Friable cultures have been obtained with greater than 100-fold increased tolerance to the imadazolinone, imazaquin (Anderson et al., 1984; Anderson and Georgeson, 1986). Tolerance to this herbicide is associated with an alteration in the enzyme acetohydroxyacid synthase. This enzyme is the first enzyme unique to the biosynthesis of the branch chained amino acids, leucine, valine, and isoleucine. In selected callus lines the enzyme is no longer significantly inhibited by the herbicide. Progeny of regenerated plants are also tolerant to imazaquin at sufficiently high levels to give useful field tolerance. Bowman and Duvick (1986) have recently reported selecting corn cultures with increased tolerance to the herbicide, paraquat. Several selected cell lines could tolerate 3- to 10-fold higher levels of the herbicide than nonselected tissues. Cross-resistance to the fungal toxin cercosporin was also noted.

Antibiotic-tolerant corn cultures have been selected using the dihydrofolate analog aminopterin and the chloroplast inhibitor, streptomycin. Shimamoto and Nelson (1981) selected BMS cell cultures that showed 10- to 40-fold more resistance to aminopterin. In the four lines characterized, two were found to have four- to sixfold increased dihydrofolate reductase (DHFR) activity, and two lines showed decreased sensitivity of their DHFR to aminopterin. One of the latter two lines also showed decreased uptake of aminopterin. The four lines were also 10- to 30-fold less sensitive to methotrexate {N-[4-[[(2,4-diamino-6-pteridin-yl)methyl] methyl amino] benzoyl]-L-glutamic acid}. Tuberosa and Phillips (1986) obtained several methotrexate resistant cell lines in a regenerable background. Total DHFR activity and sensitivity of DHFR to methotrexate did not appear to be altered, but in five of six of the selected lines the ploidy levels were increased. Plants and seed have been obtained from the diploid resistant line but have yet to be characterized. Streptomycin-tolerant corn cultures have been reported by Umbeck and Gengenbach (1983). Cultures resistant to 100 μmol were noted but with a concurrent reduction in growth rates. Regenerated plants did not survive beyond the four leaf stage.

Selections in corn cultures have been made for increased levels of free amino acids for the aspartate-derived amino acids (lysine, threonine, isoleucine, and methionine) and for tryptophan. Increased free threonine was obtained in selections for growth of corn callus in the presence of lysine plus threonine (LT) (Hibberd et al., 1980; Hibberd and Green, 1982; Diedrick, 1984; Miao et al., 1986). Free threonine in the selected callus ranged from 8- to 20-fold higher than in control tissues. Increases in free methionine (4x) and to a lesser extent free lysine and isoleucine (2x) were also noted. In one LT-resistant cell culture line, the lysine sensitivity of the enzyme aspartate kinase was significantly reduced (Hibberd et al., 1980). Progeny of regenerated plants from other selected cultures express LT resistance as would be expected for a single dominant nuclear trait. An allelism test between two LT resistant lines, LT19 and LT20, indicates that variants of at least two loci can result in increased free threonine (Frisch and Gengenbach, 1986). Threonine overproduction is greatest in plants homozygous for the LT-resistance trait. Free threonine accumulation in the seed can be sufficiently high to increase total threonine by 50% (Hibberd and Green, 1982). Selections for resistance to the lysine analog aminoethylcysteine have been conducted in several laboratories; however, none have yet reported selected callus lines with increases in free lysine greater than two- to fourfold (B.G. Gengenbach, 1986, personal communication; K.A. Hibberd, 1986, unpublished data).

Selections for increased tryptophan in corn cultures have proven successful. Hibberd and co-workers (1986a, b) and Miao and co-workers (1986) have obtained callus lines with 10- to 50-fold increased tolerance to the tryptophan analog 5-methyltryptophan (5MT). Free tryptophan levels in the callus are reported to increase from 2- to 171-fold. Increased free phenylalanine was also noted in some lines (Miao et al., 1986). Anthranilate synthase, the branch point enzyme for tryptophan biosynthesis, was similar in total activity but reduced in sensitivity to feedback inhibition by tryptophan (Hibberd et al., 1986b). Progeny of regenerated plants segregate for expression of resistance to 5MT as expected for a single dominant nuclear trait. Increases in free tryptophan in seed ranged from 2- to >100-fold with total tryptophan increasing as much as threefold.

5–4.2 Selection Approaches

Early selections with corn cultures were conducted with firm organized callus. These included selections for *H. maydis* toxin, lysine plus threonine, and streptomycin resistance. Nonregenerable friable callus and suspensions were used in the selections for aminopterin tolerance. More recent selections have utilized friable, embryogenic cultures. Recent LT selections as well as those for imazaquin and methotrexate tolerance have been with this type of culture.

Mutagens have been utilized in several corn cell culture selections including treatments with ethylmethane sulfonate (EMS), N-methyl-N'-nitrosoguanidine (MNNG) and sodium azide. Their value in increasing mutation frequencies in cultured corn cells has been examined in only two studies. The MNNG increased the recovery of desired variants about 100-fold from BMS cultures while EMS was ineffective (Shimamoto and Nelson, 1981). Recovery frequency of LT variants was not improved following treatment of callus with sodium azide (S.B. Dotson and D.A. Somers, 1986, unpublished data). No mutagens were used in many of the reported selections, indicating that sufficient variation exists in corn cell cultures for the recovery of desired variants.

Selection approaches with corn cultures have involved one of two basic methods. Single inhibitor concentration selections have been conducted using a level of the selection agent just above that which completely inhibits growth. A second and more common approach has been to initially select with a sublethal concentration of the inhibitor, then to step-up the selection levels in subsequent transfer of the cultures. With nonregenerable BMS cultures, either method gave similar results in aminopterin selections (Shimamoto and Nelson, 1981). With regenerable cultures the step-up procedure can offer advantages. Most importantly, the capacity of cultures to regenerate plants may be more sensitive to the selection agent than is overall growth.

5–5   FUTURE PERSPECTIVES

The efficacy of cell and tissue culture technology relates to the cell being the unit of selection instead of the whole plant as it is in conventional corn genetic and breeding procedures. Improvements in manipulating single cells will be an important part of advancing the field. These improvements will involve the ability to effectively regenerate plants from protoplast cultures or single cell suspensions derived from various explant tissues and genotypes. Further development of highly efficient selection schemes also will be essential in making cell and tissue culture technology a routine part of corn breeding programs. Past successes using selective agents in cell and tissue cultures and obtaining plants or even grain on these plants with the desired qualities, such as disease resistance, improved protein quality, and herbicide resistance, clearly demonstrate the power of the approach. Recovery of transformed cells by techniques such as electroporation or microinjection also will likely depend on appropriate selection techniques.

The genetic stability of different culture systems must be understood in the future in order to have a defined and predictable technology. Although instability may be desirable for purposes of creating variability, the investigator must know what to expect to properly design experiments. Development of a somatic cell genetic approach for corn depends on a genetically predictable cellular system.

Progress in corn cell and tissue culture since the regeneration of corn plants from culture in 1975 indeed has been impressive. The increased interest by private industry as well as public institutions and agencies will continue to expand the scope of applications of these cellular techniques to corn genetics and breeding.

REFERENCES

Abou-Mandour, A.A., and W. Hartung. 1986. The effect of abscisic acid and increased osmotic potential of the media on growth and root regeneration of Zea mays callus. J. Plant Physiol. 122:139–145.

Ahoowalia, B.S. 1986. Plant regeneration from meristem culture of corn, Zea mays L. p. 445. In D.A. Somers (ed.) Abstr. 6 Int. Congr. Plant Tissue Cell Cult., Minneapolis, MN. 4–8 August. Univ. of Minnesota, Minneapolis.

Anderson, P.C., and M.A. Georgeson. 1986. Selection of imidazolinone tolerant mutant of corn. p. 437. In D.A. Somers (ed.) Abstr. 6 Int. Congr. Plant Tissue Cell Cult., Minneapolis. 4–8 August. Univ. of Minnesota, Minneapolis.

----, ----, and K.A. Hibberd. 1984. Cell culture selection of herbicide resistant corn. p. 56. In Agronomy abstract. ASA, Madison, WI.

Ao, G., S. Zhao, and G. Li. 1982. In vitro induction of haploid plantlets from unpollinated varieties of Zea mays. Acta Genet. Sin. 9:281–283.

Armstrong, C.L. 1984. Genetic and environmental factors affecting the initiation of friable maize callus capable of somatic embryogenesis. M.S. thesis. Univ. of Minnesota, Minneapolis.

----. 1986. Genetic and cytogenetic stability of maize tissue cultures: A comparative study of organogenic and embryogenic cultures. Ph.D. diss. Univ. of Minnesota, Minneapolis (Diss. Abstr. 86–20179).

----, and C.E. Green. 1985. Establishment and maintenance of friable, embryogenic maize callus and the involvement of L-proline. Planta 164:207–214.

----, C.E. Green, R.L. Phillips, and R.E. Stucker. 1985. Genetic control of plant regeneration from maize tissue cultures. Maize Genet. Coop. News Lett. 59:92–93.

Balzan, R. 1978. Karyotype instability in tissue cultures derived from the mesocotyl of Zea mays seedlings. Caryologia 31:75–87.

Bartkowiak, E. 1981. Tissue culture of maize: Selection of friable callus lines. Plant Cell Rep. 1:52–55.

----. 1982. Tissue cultures of maize. III. Plantlet regeneration from scutellar callus. Genet. Pol. 23:93–101.

----, and P.A. Peterson. 1984. Expression of controlling element mutability in solid and liquid cultures of the maize endosperm in vitro. Bull. Pol. Acad. Sci. Biol. 32:371–377.

Beckert, M., M. Pollacsek, and M. Caenen. 1983. Etude de la variabilite genetique obtenue chez le maiz apres callogenese et regeneration de planter in vitro. Agronomie 3:9–18.

----, and C.M. Qing. 1984. Results of a diallel trial and a breeding experiment for in vitro aptitude in maize. Theor. Appl. Genet. 68:247–251.

Benzion, G. 1984. Genetic and cytogenetic analysis of maize tissue cultures: a cell line pedigree analysis. Ph.D. diss. Univ. of Minnesota, Minneapolis (Diss. Abstr. 84–27597).

----, R.L. Phillips, and H.W. Rines. 1986. Case histories of genetic variability in vitro: Oats and maize. p. 435–448. In I.K. Vasil (ed.) Cell culture and somatic cell genetics of plants, Vol. 3. Academic Press, New York.

Bianchi, A., F. Salamini, and R. Parlavecchio. 1969. On the origin of controlling elements in maize. Genet. Agrar. 22:335–344.

Birnberg, P.R., and D.A. Somers. 1986. Purification of culture metabolites that increase colony formation from "Black Mexican Sweet" corn protoplasts. p. 298. In Abstr. 6 Int. Congr. Plant Tissue Cell Cult., Minneapolis. 4–8 August. Univ. of Minnesota, Minneapolis.

Bock, M., and I. Greenblatt. 1965. Karyotype stability of haploid and diploid maize root tissue cultures. Maize Genet. Coop. News Lett. 39:121–125.

Bowman, T.R., and J. Duvick. 1986. Selection for resistance to paraquat in maize. p. 73. In D.A. Somers (ed.) Abstr. 6 Int. Congr. Plant Tissue Cell Cult., Minneapolis. 4–8 August. Univ. of Minnesota, Minneapolis.

Boyer, C.D., and J.C. Shannon. 1974. Chromosome constitution and cell division in in vitro cultures of Zea mays endosperm. In Vitro 9:458–462.

Brar, D.S., S. Rambold, F. Constabel, and O.L. Gamborg. 1980. Isolation, fusion and culture of sorghum and corn protoplasts. Z. Pflanzenphysiol. 96:269–275.

----, ----, O. Gamborg, and F. Constabel. 1979. Tissue culture of corn and sorghum. Z. Pflanzenphysiol. 95:377–388.

Brettell, R.I.S., M.F. Conde, and D.R. Pring. 1982. Analysis of mitochondrial DNA from four different maize lines obtained from a tissue culture carrying Texas cytoplasm. Maize Genet. Coop. News Lett. 56:13–14.

----, E.S. Dennis, W.R. Scowcroft, and W.J. Peacock. 1986. Molecular analysis of a somaclonal mutant of maize alcohol dehydrogenase. Mol. Gen. Genet. 202:235–239.

----, B.V.D. Goddard, and D.S. Ingram. 1979. Selections of Tms-cytoplasm maize tissue cultures resistant to Drechslera maydis T-toxin. Maydica 24:203–213.

----, E. Thomas, and W. Wernicke. 1981. Production of haploid maize plants by anther culture. Maydica 26:101–111.

Brown, P.T.H., and H. Lorz. 1986. Methylation changes in progeny of tissue culture derived maize plants. p. 261. In D.A. Somers (ed.) Abstr. 6 Int. Congr. Plant Tissue Cell Cult., Minneapolis. 4–8 August. Univ. of Minnesota, Minneapolis.

Bruneau, R. 1985. Regeneration in vitro a partir de cals d'embryons immatures de mais. Aspects quantitatifs et transmission hereditaire. Agronomie 5:591–596.

Burr, B., and F. Burr. 1981. Transposable elements and genetic instabilities in crop plants. p. 115–128. In Stadler symposium, Vol. 13. Missouri Agric. Exp. Stn., Columbia.

----, and O. Nelson. 1972. Induction and maintenance of maize callus tissue. Maize Genet. Coop. News Lett. 46:202–203.

Cao, Z., C. Ono, and J. Hao. 1981. A study of embryogenesis in pollen callus of maize (Zea mays L.). Acta Genet. Sin. 8:269–273.

Chalmers, N.L., and S.A. Thompson. 1986. Screening twelve elite inbreds of maize for embryogenic callus formation and plant regeneration. p. 44. In D.A. Somers (ed.) Abstr. 6 Int. Congr. Plant Tissue Cell Cult., Minneapolis. 4–8 August. Univ. of Minnesota, Minneapolis.

Chang, Y.F. 1983. Plant regeneration in vitro from leaf tissues derived from cultured immature embryos of Zea mays L. Plant Cell Rep. 2:183–185.

Cheng, D.S., A.S. Wang, K. Close, M. Hollingsworth, L. Ludeman, and J. Milcic. 1986. Developmental characteristics of elite corn inbred lines cultured in vitro. p. 332. In D.A. Somers (ed.) Abstr. 6 Int. Congr. Plant Tissue Cell Cult., Minneapolis. 4–8 August. Univ. of Minnesota, Minneapolis.

Chourey, P.S., and R.J. Kemble. 1982. Transposition event in tissue cultured cells of maize. p. 425–426. In Abstr. 5 Int. Congr. Plant Tissue Cell Cult., Tokyo, Japan. 11–16 July. Japanese Assoc. for Plant Tissue Culture, Tokyo.

----, R.E. Lloyd, D.Z. Sharpe, and N.R. Isola. 1986. Molecular analysis of hypervariability in the mitochondrial genome of tissue cultured cells of maize and sorghum. p. 177–191. In S. Mantell et al. (ed.) The chondriome—Second Wye Int. symposium. Longman Group, England.

----, and D.B. Zurawski. 1981. Callus formation from protoplasts of a maize cell culture. Theor. Appl. Genet. 59:341–344.

Chu, C.C., C.C. Wang, C.S. Sun, C. Hsu, K.C. Yin, C.Y. Chu, and F.Y. Bi. 1975. Establishment of an efficient medium for anther culture of rice through comparative experiments on the nitrogen sources. Sci. Sin. (Chin. Ed.) 18:658–659.

Close, K., and L. Ludeman. 1986. Induction of somatic embryogenesis from elite maize inbreds. Structure/activity relationships of auxin-like plant growth regulators (PGRs) and genetic considerations. p. 342. In D.A. Somers (ed.) Abstr. 6 Int. Congr. Plant Tissue Cell Cult., Minneapolis. 4–8 August. Univ. of Minnesota, Minneapolis.

Culley, D.E. 1986. Evidence for the activation of a cryptic transposable element Ac in maize endosperm cultures. p. 220. In D.A. Somers (ed.) Abstr. 6 Int. Congr. Plant Tissue Cell Cult., Minneapolis. 4–8 August. Univ. of Minnesota, Minneapolis.

Das, P.K., and J.M. Widholm. 1982. Tissue culture of Zea mays seedlings with B chromosomes. p. 189. In Abstr. 5 Int. Congr. Plant Tissue Cell Cult., Tokyo, Japan. 11–16 July. Japanese Assoc. for Plant Tissue Culture, Tokyo.

Dhaliwal, H.S., and P.J. King. 1979a. Biochemical selection of immature haploid embryos of Zea mays L. Theor. Appl. Genet. 55:252–257.

----, and ----. 1979b. Haploid and aneuploid corn cultures. Maize Genet. Coop. News Lett. 53:13–14.

----, and ----. 1979c. Ploidy analysis of haploid-derived tissue cultures of Zea mays by chromocentre counting. Maydica 24:103–112.

Diedrick, T.J. 1984. Amino acid and field evaluations of two amino acid overproducing mutants in corn (*Zea mays* L.). Ph.D. diss., Univ. of Minnesota, Minneapolis (Diss. Abstr. 85–08140).

Doerschug, E.G. 1973. Studies of *Dotted*, a regulatory element in maize. I. Induction of *Dotted* by chromosome breaks. II. Phase variation of *Dotted*. Theor. Appl. Genet. 43:182–189.

Donovan, C.M., and D.A. Somers. 1986. Genotype effects on stability of friable, embryogenic callus and suspension cultures of *Zea mays*. p. 183. *In* D.A. Somers (ed.) Abstr. 6 Int. Congr. Plant Tissue Cell Cult., Minneapolis. 4–8 August. Univ. of Minnesota, Minneapolis.

Duncan, D.R., M.E. Williams, B.E. Zehr, and J.M. Widholm. 1985. The production of callus capable of plant regeneration from immature embryos of numerous *Zea mays* genotypes. Planta 165:322–332.

Earle, E.D., and V.E. Gracen. 1985. Somaclonal variation in progeny of plants from corn tissue cultures. *In* R. Henke et al. (ed.) Propagation of higher plants through tissue culture. Plenum Press, New York.

————, and ————. 1986. Reversion from S-cytoplasmic male sterility to fertility in plants from maize tissue cultures. Plant Physiol. 80:132.

Edallo, S., C. Zucchinali, M. Perenzin, and F. Salamini. 1981. Chromosomal variation and frequency of spontaneous mutation associated with *in vitro* culture and plant regeneration in maize. Maydica 26:39–56.

Evola, S.V., F.A. Burr, and B. Burr. 1984. The nature of tissue culture induced mutations in maize. *In* Eleventh Annu. Aharon Katzir-Katchalsky Conf., Jerusalem, Israel. 8–13 January.

Fahey, J.W., J.N. Reed, T.L. Readdy, and G.M. Page. 1986. Somatic embryogenesis from three commercially important inbreds of *Zea mays*. Plant Cell Rep. 5:35–38.

Freeling, M., J.C. Woodman, and D.S.K. Cheng. 1976. Developmental potentials of maize tissue cultures. Maydica 21:97–112.

Frisch, D.A., and B.G. Gengenbach. 1986. Allelism test for two threonine over-producer mutants. Maize Genet. Coop. News Lett. 60:115.

Gengenbach, B.G. 1977. Development of maize caryopses resulting from *in vitro* pollination. Planta 134:91–93.

————, J.A. Connelly, D.R. Pring, and M.F. Conde. 1981. Mitochondrial DNA variation in maize plants regenerated during tissue culture selection. Theor. Appl. Genet. 59:161–167.

————, and C.E. Green. 1975. Selection of T-cytoplasm maize callus cultures resistant to *Helminthosporium maydis* race T pathotoxin. Crop Sci. 15:645–649.

————, ————, and C.M. Donovan. 1977. Inheritance of selected pathotoxin resistance in maize plants regenerated from cell cultures. Proc. Natl. Acad. Sci. USA 74:5113–5117.

————, and P. Umbeck. 1982. Characteristics of T cytoplasm revertants from tissue culture. Maize Genet. Coop. News Lett. 56:140–142.

Genovesi, A.D., and G.B. Collins. 1982. In vitro production of haploid plants of corn via anther culture. Crop. Sci. 22:1137–1144.

————, and R.A. Yingling. 1986. Preliminary results from three corn anther culture experiments. p. 99. *In* D.A. Somers (ed.) Abstr. 6 Int. Congr. Plant Tissue Cell Cult., Minneapolis. 4–8 Aug. Univ. of Minnesota, Minneapolis.

Gobel, E., and H. Lorz. 1986. Somaclonal variation in tissue culture derived maize plants and their selfed progeny. p. 284. *In* D.A. Somers (ed.) Abstr. 6 Int. Congr. Plant Tissue Cell Cult., Minneapolis. 4–8 August. Univ. of Minnesota, Minneapolis.

Gorman, M.B., and P.A. Peterson. 1978. The interaction of controlling element components in a tissue culture system. Maydica 23:173–186.

Graebe, J.E., and G.D. Novelli. 1966. A practical method for large scale plant tissue culture. Exp. Cell Res. 41:509–520.

Green, C.E. 1977. Prospects for crop improvement in the field of cell culture. HortScience 12:7–10.

————. 1982. Somatic embryogenesis and plant regeneration from the friable callus of *Zea mays*. p. 107–108. *In* A. Fujiwara (ed.) Plant tissue culture. Maruzen Co., Tokyo, Japan.

————. 1983. New developments in plant tissue culture and plant regeneration. p. 195–209. *In* J. Hollaender et al. (ed.) Basic biology of new developments in biotechnology. Plenum Press, New York.

————, C.L. Armstrong, and P.A. Anderson. 1983. Somatic cell genetic systems in corn. p.

147–157. *In* K. Downey et al. (ed.) Molecular genetics of plants and animals, Vol. 20. Academic Press, New York.

----, and R.L. Phillips. 1975. Plant regeneration from tissue cultures of maize. Crop Sci. 15:417–421.

----, ----, and R.A. Kleese. 1974. Tissue cultures of maize (*Zea mays* L.): initiation, maintenance and organic growth factors. Crop Sci. 14:54–58.

----, ----, and A.S. Wang. 1977. Cytological analysis of plants regenerated from maize tissue cultures. Maize Genet. Coop. News Lett. 51:53–54.

----, and C.A. Rhodes. 1982. Plant regeneration in tissue cultures of maize. p. 367–372. *In* W.F. Sheridan (ed.) Maize for biological research. Plant Molecular Biological Assoc., Charlottesville, VA.

Gresshoff, P.M., and C.H. Doy. 1973. *Zea mays*: Methods of diploid callus culture and the subsequent differentiation of various plant structures. Aust. J. Biol. Sci. 26:505–508.

Gu, M.G. 1986. Cytogenetic stability and variability of calli and cell clones originated from maize pollen and their regenerated plants. p. 79–90. *In* Haploids of higher plants *in vitro*. Springer Verlag New York, New York.

----, and Y.C. Ting. 1985. Ploidy stability of maize callus lines. Maize Genet Coop. News Lett. 59:29.

----, X.Q. Zhang, Z.Y. Cao, and C.Y. Guo. 1983. Totipotency and cytogenetic stability in subcultures of maize (*Zea mays* L.) pollen callus. p. 105–116. *In* Cell and tissue culture technique for cereal crop improvement. Science Press, Beijing, People's Republic of China.

Gupta, S.L., and K. Nanda. 1986. Plant regeneration from seedling leaf tissues of *Zea mays* L. p. 444. *In* D.A. Somers (ed.) Abstr. 6 Int. Congr. Plant Tissue Cell Cult., Minneapolis. 4–8 August. Univ. of Minnesota, Minneapolis.

Harms, C.T., H. Lorz, and I. Potrykus. 1976. Regeneration of plants from callus cultures of *Zea mays* L. Z. Pflanzenzuecht. 77:347–351.

Hawes, M.C., D.Z. Sharpe, M. Plata, S.G. Pueppke, and P.S. Chourey. 1985. Auxin independent growth of maize tissue culture cells. Plant Sci. 40:197–202.

Hibberd, K.A., P.C. Anderson, and M. Barker. 1986a. Tryptophan overproducer mutants of cereal crops. U.S. Patent 4 581 847. Date issued: 15 April.

----, M. Barker, P.C. Anderson, and L. Linder. 1986b. Selection for high tryptophan maize. p. 440. *In* D.A. Somers (ed.) Abstr. 6 Int. Congr. Plant Tissue Cell Cult., Minneapolis. 4–8 August. Univ. of Minnesota, Minneapolis.

----, and C.E. Green. 1982. Inheritance and expression of lysine plus threonine resistance selected in maize tissue culture. Proc. Natl. Acad. Sci. USA 79:559–563.

----, T. Walter, C.E. Green, and B.G. Gengenbach. 1980. Selection and characterization of a feedback-insensitive tissue culture of maize. Planta 148:183–187.

Hodges, T.K., K.K. Kamo, M.R. Becwar, and S. Schroll. 1985. Regeneration of maize. p. 15–33. *In* M. Zaitlin et al. (ed.) Biotechnology in plant science. Academic Press, New York.

Imbrie-Milligan, S.W., and T.K. Hodges. 1986. Microcalli formation from maize protoplasts prepared from embryogenic callus. Planta 168:395–401.

Johri, M.M., and E.H. Coe, Jr. 1983. Clonal analysis of corn plant development. I. The development of the tassel and ear shoot. Dev. Biol. 97:154–172.

Kamo, K.K., M.R. Becwar, and T.K. Hodges. 1985. Regeneration of *Zea mays* L. from embryogenic callus. Bot. Gaz. 146:327–334.

----, and T.K. Hodges. 1986. Establishment and characterization of long-term embryogenic maize calli and cell suspension cultures. Plant Sci. 45:111–117.

Kemble, R.J., R.D. Flavell, and R.I.S. Brettell. 1982. Mitochondrial DNA analysis of fertile and sterile maize plants derived from tissue culture with the Texas male sterile cytoplasm. Theor. Appl. Genet. 62:213–217.

King, P.J., I. Potrykus, and E. Thomas. 1978. *In vitro* genetics of cereals: Problems and perspectives. Physiol. Veg. 16:381–399.

----, and K. Shimamoto. 1984. Maize. p. 69–91. *In* W.R. Sharp et al. (ed.) Handbook of plant cell culture, Vol. 2. Macmillan Publ. Co., New York.

Ku, M., W. Cheng, L. Kuo, Y. Kuan, H. An, and C. Huang. 1978. Induction factors and morphocytological characteristics of pollen-derived plants in maize (*Zea mays*). p. 35–42. *In* Proceedings of a symposium on plant tissue culture. Beijing, People's Republic of China.

Kuang, V.D., Z.B. Shamina, and R.G. Butenko. 1984. Use of nurse tissue culture to obtain clones from cultured cells and protoplasts of corn. Fiziol. Rast. 30:803–812.

LaRue, C.D. 1947. Growth and regeneration of the endosperm of maize in culture. Am. J. Bot. 34:585–586.

————. 1949. Cultures of the endosperm of maize. Am. J. Bot. 36:798.

Lee, M. 1984. Cytogenetic analysis and progeny evaluation of maize (*Zea mays* L.) plants regenerated from organogenic callus cultures. M.S. thesis. Univ. of Minnesota, Minneapolis.

————. 1986. Agronomic evaluation of inbred lines derived from tissue cultures of maize. Ph. D. diss. Univ. of Minnesota, Minneapolis (Diss. Abstr. 86–27025).

————, and R.L. Phillips. 1987a. A search for cytoplasmic restoration of genetic male sterility among regenerated plants and their progeny. Maize Genet. Coop. News Lett. 61:87.

————, and ————. 1987b. Genomic rearrangements in maize induced by tissue culture. Genome 29:122–128.

Linsmaier-Bednar, E.M., and T.W. Bednar. 1972. Light and hormonal control of root formation in *Zea mays* callus cultures. Dev. Growth Diff. 14:165–174.

Lowe, K., D.B. Taylor, P. Ryan, and K.E. Paterson. 1985. Plant regeneration via organogenesis and embryogenesis in the maize inbred line B73. Plant Sci. 41:125–132.

Lu, C., I.K. Vasil, and P. Ozias-Akins. 1982. Somatic embryogenesis in *Zea mays* L. Theor. Appl. Genet. 62:109–112.

————, V. Vasil, and I.K. Vasil. 1983. Improved efficiency of somatic embryogenesis in tissue cultures of maize (*Zea mays* L.) Theor. Appl. Genet. 66:285–289.

Ludwig, S.R., D.A. Somers, W.L. Petersen, R.F. Pohlman, M.A. Zarowitz, B.G. Gengenbach, and J. Messing. 1985. High frequency callus formation from maize protoplasts. Theor. Appl. Genet. 71:344–350.

Lupotto, E. 1986. In vitro culture of isolated somatic embryos of maize (*Zea mays* L.). Maydica 31:193–201.

————, A. Spada, and R. Marotta. 1985. Instability of transposable elements in the genome of maize (*Zea mays* L.) plants regenerated from *in vitro* cultures. Preliminary results. Genet. Agrar. 39:327.

Mascarenhas, A.F., B.M. Sayagaver, and V. Jagannathan. 1965. Studies on the growth of callus cultures of *Zea mays* L. p. 283–291. *In* C.V. Rame Akrishna (ed.) Tissue culture. Junk Publ., The Hague.

McClary, J.E. 1940. Synthesis of thiamin by excised roots of maize. Proc. Natl. Acad. Sci. USA 26:581–587.

McClintock, B. 1950. The origin and behavior of mutable loci in maize. Proc. Natl. Acad. Sci. USA 36:344–355.

————. 1951. Chromosome organization and genic expression. p. 13–47. *In* Cold Spring Harbor Symp. Quant. Biol., Vol. 16. Cold Spring Harbor, New York.

————. 1984. The significance of responses of the genome to challenge. Science 226:792–801.

McCormick, S. 1980. Friable maize callus and suspension cultures using IAA amino acid conjugates. Maize Genet. Coop. News Lett. 54:45–46.

McCoy, T.J., and R.L. Phillips. 1982. Chromosome stability in maize (*Zea mays*) tissue cultures and sectoring in some regenerated plants. Can. J. Genet. Cytol. 24:559–565.

McNay, J.W., P.S. Chourey, and D.R. Pring. 1984. Molecular analysis of genomic stability of mitochondrial DNA in tissue cultured cells of maize. Theor. Appl. Genet. 67:433–437.

Meadows, M.G. 1982/83. Characterization of cells and protoplasts of the B73 maize cell line. Plant Sci. Lett. 28:337–348.

Miao, S.H., D.R. Duncan, and J.M. Widholm. 1986. Selection of lysine plus threonine and 5-methyltryptophan resistance in maize tissue culture. p. 380. *In* D.A. Somers (ed.) Abstr. 6 Int. Congr. Plant Tissue Cell Cult., Minneapolis. 4–8 August. Univ. of Minnesota, Minneapolis.

————, C. Kuo, Y. Kwie, A. Sun, S. Ku, W. Lu, and Y. Wang. 1978. Induction of pollen plants of maize and observations on their progeny. p. 23–34. *In* Proceedings of a symposium on plant tissue culture. Beijing, People's Republic of China.

Misra, S., and A. Oaks. 1985. Glutamine metabolism in corn kernels cultured *in vitro*. Plant Physiol. 77:520–523.

Morocz, S., D. Dudits, and J. Neimeth. 1986. Two approaches to rendering *Zea mays* applicable to tissue culture manipulations. p. 190. *In* D.A. Somers (ed.) Abstr. 6 Int. Congr. Plant Tissue Cell Cult., Minneapolis. 4–8 August. Univ. of Minnesota, Minneapolis.

Murashige, T., and J. Skoog. 1962. A revised medium for rapid growth and bioassays with tobacco tissue cultures. Physiol. Plant. 15:473–497.

Nesticky, M., F.J. Novak, A. Piovarci, and M. Dolezelova. 1983. Genetic analysis of callus growth of maize (*Zea mays* L.) *in vitro*. Z. Pflanzenzuecht. 91:322–328.

Neuffer, M.G. 1966. Stability of the suppressor element in two mutator systems of the *A-1* locus in maize. Genetics 53:541–549.

Nitsch, C., S. Andersen, M. Godard, M.G. Neuffer, and W.F Sheridan. 1982. Production of haploid plants of *Zea mays* and *Pennisetum* through androgenesis. p. 69–91. *In* E. Earle and Y. Demarly (ed.) Variability in plants regenerated from tissue culture. Praegar Press, New York.

Novak, F.J., M. Dolezelova, M. Nesticky, and A. Piovarci. 1983. Somatic embryogenesis and plant regeneration in *Zea mays* L. Maydica 28:381–390.

Oswald, T.H., R.L. Nicholson, and L.F. Bauman. 1977. Cell suspension and callus culture from somatic tissue of maize. Physiol. Plant. 41:45–50.

Pareddy, D.R., and R.I. Greyson. 1985. *In vitro* culture of immature tassels of an inbred field variety of *Zea mays* cv Oh43. Plant Cell Tissue Organ Cult. 5:119–128.

----, ----, and D.B. Walden. 1986. Production of germinable and viable pollen from *in vitro* cultured maize tassels. p. 178. *In* D.A. Somers (ed.) Abstr. 6 Int. Congr. Plant Tissue Cult., Minneapolis. 4–8 August. Univ. of Minnesota, Minneapolis.

Paterson, K.E., K.S. Lowe, K.L. Ruby, P.L. Ryan, and D.B. Taylor. 1986. Embryogenesis in maize suspension cultures. p. 342. *In* Abstr. 6 Int. Congr. Plant Tissue Cell Cult., Minneapolis. 4–8 August. Univ. of Minnesota, Minneapolis.

Peschke, V.M. 1986. Discovery of *Ac* activity among progeny of regenerated maize plants. M.S. thesis. Univ. of Minnesota, Minneapolis.

Petolino, J.F., and A.M. Jones. 1986a. Anther culture in commercial germplasm of *Zea mays* L. p. 414. *In* D.A. Somers (ed.) Abstr. 6 Int. Congr. Plant Tissue Cell Cult., Minneapolis. 4–8 August. Univ. of Minnesota, Minneapolis.

----, and ----. 1986b. Anther culture of elite genotypes of maize. Crop Sci. 26:1072–1074.

Polikarpochkina, R.T., K.Z. Gamburg, and E.E. Khavin. 1979. Cell suspension culture in maize (*Zea mays* L.). Z. Pflanzenphysiol. 95:57–67.

Polowick, P.L., and R.I. Greyson. 1982. Anther development, meiosis and pollen formation in *Zea* tassels cultured in defined liquid medium. Plant Sci. Lett. 26:139–145.

Potrykus, I., C.T. Harms, H. Lorz, and E. Thomas. 1977. Callus formation from stem protoplasts of corn (*Zea mays* L.). Molec. Gen. Genet. 156:347–350.

----, ----, and ----. 1979. Callus formation from cell culture protoplasts of corn (*Zea mays* L.). Theor. Appl. Genet. 54:209–214.

Pryor, A., K. Faulkner, M.M. Rhoades, and W.J. Peacock. 1980. Asynchronous replication of heterochromatin in maize. Proc. Natl. Acad. Sci. USA 77:6705–6709.

Radojevic, L. 1985. Tissue culture of maize *Zea mays* Cudu I. somatic embryogenesis in the callus tissue. J. Plant Physiol. 119:435–441.

Raman, K., D.B. Walden, and R.I. Greyson. 1980. Propagation of *Zea mays* L. by shoot tip culture: A feasibility study. Ann. Bot. 45:183–189.

Rapela, M.A. 1985. Organogenesis and somatic embryogenesis in tissue cultures of Argentine maize (*Zea mays* L.). J. Plant Physiol. 121:119–122.

Reddy, A.R., and P.A. Peterson. 1977. Callus initiation from waxy endosperm of various genotypes of maize. Maydica 22:125–130.

Reddy, G.M. 1986. Callus induction, somatic embryogenesis and plantlet regeneration from young inflorescences of rice and maize. p. 444. *In* D.A. Somers (ed.) Abstr. 6 Int. Congr. Plant Tissue Cell Cult., Minneapolis. 4–8 August. Univ. of Minnesota, Minneapolis.

Rhoades, M.M., and E. Dempsey. 1972. On the mechanism of chromatin loss induced by the B chromosome of maize. Genetics 71:73–96.

----, and ----. 1973. Chromatin elimination induced by the B chromosome of maize. J. Hered. 64:12–18.

Rhodes, C.A., C.E. Green, and R.L. Phillips. 1986a. Factors affecting tissue culture initiation from maize tassels. Plant Sci. 46:225–232.

----, R.L. Phillips, and C.E. Green. 1986b. Cytogenetic stability of aneuploid maize tissue cultures. Can. J. Genet. Cytol. 28:374–384.

Rice, T.B. 1982. Tissue culture induced genetic variation in regenerated maize inbreds. p. 148–162. *In* Proc. 37 Annu. Corn. Sorghum Ind. Res. Conf., Chicago. 8–9 December. ASTA, Washington, DC.

Robbins, W.J. 1922. Effect of autolysed yeast and peptone on the growth of excised corn root tips in the dark. Bot. Gaz. 74:59–79.

————, and W.E. Maneval. 1924. Effect of light on growth of excised roots tips under sterile conditions. Bot. Gaz. 78:424–432.

Roberts, E.H., and H.E. Street. 1955. The continuous culture of excised rye roots. Physiol. Plant. 8:238–262.

Sach, M.M., H. Lorz, E.S. Dennis, A. Elizur, R.J. Ferl, W.L. Gerlach, A.J. Pryor, and W.J. Peacock. 1982. Molecular genetic analysis of the maize anaerobic response. p. 139–144. In W.F. Sheridan (ed.) Maize for biological research. Plant Molecular Biol. Assoc., Charlottesville, VA.

Shannon, J.C. 1982. Maize endosperm cultures. p. 397–403. In W.F. Sheridan (ed.) Maize for biological research. Plant Molecular Biol. Assoc., Charlottesville, VA.

————, and J.W. Batey. 1973. Inbred and hybrid effects on establishment of in vitro cultures of Zea mays L. endosperm. Crop Sci. 13:491–493.

————, and J.W. Liu. 1977. A simplified method for the growth of maize (Zea mays) endosperm tissue in suspension culture. Physiol. Plant. 40:285–291.

Sheridan, W.F. 1975a. Growth of corn cells in culture. J. Cell. Biol. 67:396a.

————. 1975b. Tissue cultures of maize. I. Callus induction and growth. Physiol. Plant. 33:151–156.

————. 1977. Tissue culture of maize. II. Effect of glutamate, aspartate and aromatic amino acid families on callus growth of several maize strains. Physiol. Plant. 41:172–174.

Shimamoto, K., and O.E. Nelson. 1981. Isolation and characterization of aminopterin-resistant cell lines in maize. Planta 153:436–442.

Smith, J.A., C.E. Green, and B.G. Gengenbach. 1984. Feeder layer support of low density populations of Zea mays L. suspension cells. Plant Sci. Lett. 36:67–72.

Springer, W.D., C.E. Green, and K.A. Kohn. 1979. A histological examination of tissue culture initiation from immature embryos of maize. Protoplasma 101:269–281.

Sternheimer, E.P. 1954. Method of culture and growth of maize endosperm in vitro. Bull. Torrey Bot. Club 81:111–113.

Straus, J. 1954. Maize endosperm tissue grown in vitro. II. Morphology and cytology. Am. J. Bot. 41:833–839.

————. 1960. Maize endosperm tissue grown in vitro. III. Development of a synthetic medium. Am. J. Bot. 47:641–647.

————, and C.D. LaRue. 1954. Maize endosperm tissue grown in vitro. I. Culture requirements. Am. J. Bot. 41:687–694.

Sun, M.H., and A.J. Ullstrup. 1971. In vitro growth of corn endosperm. Bull. Torrey Bot. Club 98:251–258.

Suprasanna, P., K.V. Rao, and G.M. Reddy. 1986. Plantlet regeneration from glume calli of maize (Zea mays L.). Theor. Appl. Genet. 72:120–122.

Swanson, E.B., R.S.C. Wang, and R.J. Kemble. 1985. A novel method for the isolation and purification of protoplasts from friable, embryogenic corn (Zea mays L.) callus. Plant Sci. 40:137–144.

Swedlund, B., and R.D. Locy. 1986. The effect of 5 azacytidine on initiation of embryogenic cultures of Zea mays. p. 443. In D.A. Somers (ed.) Abstr. 6 Int. Congr. Plant Tissue Cell Cult., Minneapolis. 4–8 August. Univ. of Minnesota, Minneapolis.

Tabata, M., and F. Motoyoshi. 1965. Hereditary control of callus formation in maize endosperm cultured in vitro. Jpn. J. Genet. 40:343–355.

Tamaoki, T., and A.J. Ullstrup. 1958. Cultivation in vitro of excised endosperm and meristem tissues of corn. Bull. Torrey. Bot. Club 85:260–272.

Ting, Y.C. 1985a. Genes and chromosomes of maize anther culture-derived microspore plants. Genetics 110:S22.

————. 1985b. Meiosis and fertility of anther culture-derived maize plants. Maydica 30:161–169.

————, M. Yu, and W.C. Zheng. 1981. Improved anther culture of maize (Zea mays). Plant Sci. Lett. 23:139–145.

Tomes, D.T. 1985a. Cell culture, somatic embryogenesis and plant regeneration in maize, rice, sorghum and millets. p. 175–203. In S.W.J. Bright and M.G.K. Jones (ed.) Advances in agricultural biotechnology: Cereal tissue and cell culture. Nijhoff/Junk, Boston.

————. 1985b. Opportunities and limitations of the genotypic influences on establishment and plant regeneration from callus and cell cultures of crop species. p. 3–14. *In* M. Zaitlin et al. (ed.) Biotechnology in plant science. Academic Press, New York.

––––, and O.S. Smith. 1985. The effect of parental genotype on initiation of embryogenic callus from elite maize (*Zea mays* L.) germplasm. Theor. Appl. Genet. 70:505–509.

––––, S. Sulc, M. Welter, and S. Reege-Denny. 1986. Inheritance of Type II embryogenic response from cultured immature embryos of maize breeding lines. p. 191. *In* D.A. Somers (ed.) Abstr. 6 Int. Congr. Plant Tissue Cell Cult., Minneapolis. 4–8 August. Univ. of Minnesota, Minneapolis.

Torne, J.M., M.A. Santos, A. Pons, and M. Blanco. 1980. Regeneration of plants from mesocotyl tissue cultures of immature embryos of *Zea mays* L. Plant Sci. Lett. 17:339–344.

Truong-Andre, I., and Y. Demarly. 1984. Obtaining plants by *in vitro* culture of unfertilized maize ovaries (*Zea mays* L.) and preliminary studies on the progeny of a gynogenetic plant. Z. Pflanzenzuecht. 92:309–320.

Tuberosa, R., and R.L. Phillips. 1986. Isolation of methotrexate-tolerant cell lines of corn. Maydica 31:215–225.

Umbeck, P.F., and B.G. Gengenbach. 1983. Streptomycin and other inhibitors as selection agents in corn tissue cultues. Crop Sci. 23:717–719.

Vasil, I.K. 1983a. Isolation and culture of protoplasts of grasses. Int. Rev. Cytol. Suppl. 16:79–87.

––––. 1983b. Regeneration of plants from single cells of cereals and grasses. p. 233–252. *In* P.F. Lurquin and A. Kleinhofs (ed.) Genetic engineering in eukaryotes. Plenum Press, New York.

––––, C. Srinivason, and V. Vasil. 1986. Culture of protoplasts isolated from embryogenic cell suspension cultures of sugarcane and maize. p. 443. *In* D.A. Somers (ed.) Abstr. 6 Int. Congr. Plant Tissue Cell Cult., Minneapolis. 4–8 August. Univ. of Minnesota, Minneapolis.

Vasil, V., C. Lu, and I.K. Vasil. 1985. Histology of somatic embryogenesis in cultured immature embryos of maize (*Zea mays* L.). Protoplasma 127:1–8.

––––, and I.K. Vasil. 1986. Plant regeneration from friable embryogenic callus and suspension cultures of *Zea mays* L. J. Plant Physiol. 124:399–408.

––––, ––––, and C. Lu. 1984. Somatic embryogenesis in long-term callus cultures of *Zea mays* L. (Gramineae). Am. J. Bot. 71:158–161.

Wang, A.S., R.L. Phillips, and C.C. Mi. 1986. Cell cycle parameters and accumulation of metaphase cells in maize suspension cultures. Plant Sci. 46:53–61.

Wenzler, H., and F. Meins, Jr. 1986. Mapping regions of maize leaf capable of proliferation in culture. Protoplasma 131:103–105.

Wilkinson, T.C., and S.A. Thompson. 1986. Genotype and medium effects on the establishment of regenerable maize callus. p. 43. *In* D.A. Somers (ed.) Abstr. 6 Int. Congr. Plant Tissue Cell Cult., Minneapolis. 4–8 August. Univ. of Minnesota, Minneapolis.

Williams, M.E., and J.M. Widholm. 1986. Somaclonal variation in progeny of plants regenerated from *Zea mays* L. tissue cultures and the possible involvement of transposable elements. p. 285. *In* D.A. Somers (ed.) Abstr. 6 Int. Congr. Plant Tissue Cell Cult., Minneapolis. 4–8 August. Univ. of Minnesota, Minneapolis.

Wise, R.P., D.R. Pring, and B.G. Gengenbach. 1985. Mitochondrial DNA rearrangements associated with reversion of T cytoplasm to male fertility and disease resistance. Maize Genet. Coop. News Lett. 59:50.

––––, ––––, and ––––. 1987. Mutation to male fertility and toxin insensitivity in T-cytoplasm maize is associated with a frameshift in a mitochondrial open reading frame. Proc. Natl. Acad. Sci. USA 84:2858–2862.

Woodman, J.C., and D.A. Kramer. 1986. The recovery of somaclonal variants from tissue cultures of B73, an elite inbred line of maize. p. 215. *In* D.A. Somers (ed.) Abstr. 6 Int. Congr. Plant Tissue Cell Cult., Minneapolis. 4–8 August. Univ. of Minnesota, Minneapolis.

6 Molecular Genetics of Corn

VIRGINIA WALBOT

Stanford University
Stanford, California

JOACHIM MESSING

Waksman Institute
Rutgers, The State University of New Jersey
Piscataway, New Jersey

This third edition of *Corn and Corn Improvement* is the first to include a chapter devoted to the molecular genetics of corn (*Zea mays* L.). In 1977, the application of recombinant DNA technology to corn had hardly begun, but today the first genes have been cloned and sequenced, complete physical maps exist for both the mitochondrial and plastid genomes, and methods have been developed to reintroduce genetic material into corn cells to study the regulation of gene expression. Thus, in a single decade we have learned much about the structure and function of corn genes, but, of course, a great deal more remains to be discovered. In that sense, this chapter is a first glimpse of corn molecular biology. Because the pace of molecular research on corn is rapidly accelerating, the data and models presented here will soon be supplemented by much more detailed information. Thus, to make the chapter as useful as possible, our goal has been to outline the historical context of current research, describe briefly what is known about the structure of corn genes, summarize some important findings particularly as they relate to establishing genetic maps, and highlight the current, major lines of investigation. The literature survey is not comprehensive; instead, we will direct the reader to recent in-depth reviews of specific topics.

6-1 OVERVIEW OF GENOME ORGANIZATION

Corn contains three genomes: nuclear, mitochondrial, and plastid. The nuclear genome is of medium size in comparison to other higher plants, with estimates ranging from 2.5 to 3.0 pg/haploid genome based on recent microspectrophotometric measurements (Rayburn et al., 1985) to 5.5 to 6.0 pg/haploid genome based on the reassociation kinetics of corn single copy DNA (Hake and Walbot, 1980). From the viewpoint of molecular biologists, the genome is of enormous size, about twice the size of mammalian genomes. In general, molecular biologists use units of base pairs rather than weight measurements for DNA sizes, and the corn genome is usually assumed to contain about 5×10^6 kilobase (kb) pairs. Genome size determines how many different recombinant clones must be obtained to have a reasonable chance of recovering an individual gene (Maniatis et al., 1982). For example, in a recombinant DNA library containing 20 kb fragments, more than 10^6 different phage must be obtained to have a 99% probability that any particular 20 kb corn segment is represented in the library.

The smaller organellar genomes were originally distinguished from the nuclear genome on the basis of their buoyant density in neutral CsCl, a physical parameter related to the base composition of the genome. The nuclear genome has an apparent G + C content of 43% based on its buoyant density (Shah and Levings, 1974); after correction for the effect of methylated cytosine residues on buoyant density, the G + C content is calculated to be 49% (Hake and Walbot, 1980). The plastid DNA has a buoyant density similar to nuclear DNA but contains few, if any, modified bases; the plastid DNA has a base composition of 41% G+ C. Corn mitochondrial DNA also contains few, if any modified bases, but has a higher G + C content of 47% (Shah and Levings, 1974).

6–1.1   Organization of the Corn Plastid Genome

A physical map has been constructed for the corn plastid genome by detailed analysis of the restriction sites on multiple, overlapping plasmid clones; the most recent map is illustrated in Fig. 6–1. Based on this map,

---

►

Fig. 6–1. Genetic map of corn plastid DNA. The 139 kbp circular corn plastid chromosome has been physically mapped by Bedbrook and Bogorad (1976) and Larrinua et al. (1983). The genetic map of the chromosome is presented, and includes genes sequenced through about December 1987. The coordinate system of Larrinua et al. (1983) is shown on the innermost circle (inward pointing slashes); the "0/139" kbp coordinate begins with BamHI fragment 1 in the small single copy region of the chromosome (1200 h). The outward pointing slashes on the innermost circle delimit the 26 largest BamHI restriction fragments of the chromosome (designated by arabic numerals). The next two circles show the location of sequenced genes. Those genes on the middle circle are transcribed clockwise, while those on the outer circle are transcribed counterclockwise. The brackets outside the outer circle indicate the extent of the two large (22.5 kbp) inverted repeats (from coordinates 5.5 – 28.0, and 111.0 –133.5) which divide the chromosome into two single copy (unique) DNA segments— a small single copy region (11 kbp) and a large single copy region (83 kbp). Stippled boxes represent those regions of the chromosome containing strongly photoregulated genes— i.e., genes whose transcripts increase appreciably in abundance during light-induced plastid development (Bedbrook et al., 1978; Rodermel and Bogorad, 1985). Unidentified open reading frames are designated by "ORF" followed by the number of amino acids in the putative polypeptide product encoded by that particular gene. Those genes containing introns are followed by a star (*). The nomenclature for corn plastid genes follows the conventions of Hallick and Bottomley (1983). However, due to confusion in the literature arising largely from the discovery of new plastid-encoded components, a separate table has been provided containing a description of the gene product encoded by each maize locus (See Table 6–1). (This figure was kindly provided by S. Rodermel and L. Bogorad).

the genome is 139 kb, similar to that of other higher plants (Larrinua et al., 1983). More than 50 genes including many tRNA genes (Selden et al., 1983) have been placed on the corn plastid map. Now that the complete sequence of a tobacco (*Nicotiana tabacum* L.) plastid DNA has been reported (Shinozaki et al., 1986), many additional plastid-encoded genes have been discovered that are likely to be found in corn as well. Thus far, about 20% of the corn plastid genome has been sequenced (see review by Crouse et al., 1985; keep up-to-date through DNA sequence data bases), and it is possible that the entire sequence will be available within the next decade.

The most striking feature of corn plastid genome organization is the presence of a 22.5 kb inverted repetitive sequence. Genes such as the rDNA located within the inverted repeat sequence are present twice in

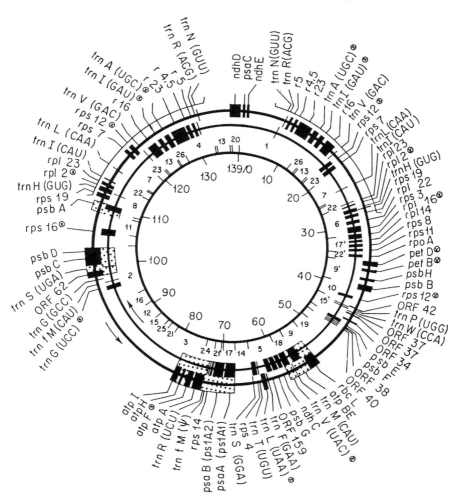

Table 6-1. Plastid genes and gene products of corn.

Gene product	Gene	Reference
Ribosomal RNAs:		
4.5S rRNA	r4.5	Edwards et al., 1981; Strittmatter and Kossel, 1984
5S rRNA	r5	Strittmatter and Kossel, 1984
16S rRNA	r16	Schwarz and Kossel, 1979, 1980;
23S rRNA	r23	Edwards and Kossel, 1981
Transfer RNAs:		
Alanine	trnA (UGC)	Koch et al., 1981
Arginine	trnR (UCU)	Rodermel et al., 1987
	trnR (ACG)	Dormann-Przybyl et al., 1986
Asparagine	trnN (GUU)	Dormann-Przybyl et al., 1986
Glycine	trnG (GCC)	S. Rodermel and L. Bogorad, 1987, unpublished data
	trn (UCC)	S. Rodermel and L. Bogorad, 1987, unpublished data
Histidien	trnH (GUG)	Schwarz et al., 1981; Larrinua and McLaughlin, 1987
Isoleucine	trnI (GAU)	Koch et al., 1981
	trnI (CAU)	I. Larrinua, 1987, unpublished data
Leucine	trnL (CAA)	Steinmetz et al., 1983
	trnL (UAA)	Steinmetz et al., 1982
Methionine-initiator	trnfM (CAU)	S. Rodermel and L. Bogorad, 1987, unpublished data
Methionine-interior (pseudogene)	trnfM (U)	Rodermel et al., 1987
Methionine-elongator	trnM (CAU)	Steinmetz et al., 1983
Phenylalanine	trnF (GAA)	Steinmetz et al., 1983
Proline	trnP (UGG)	J. Lukens and L. Bogorad, 1987, unpublished data
Serine	trnS (GCA)	Steinmetz et al., 1983
	trnS (UGA)	Krebbers et al., 1984
Threonine	trnT (UGU)	Steinmetz et al., 1983
Tryptophan	trnW (CGA)	J. Lukens and L. Bogorad, 1987, unpublished data
Valine	trnV (UAC)	Krebbers et al., 1984
	trnV (GAC)	Schwarz et al., 1981
Photosystem I Components:		
P700 chlorophyll a apoprotein A1	psaA (pslA2)	Fish et al., 1985; Fish and Bogorad, 1986
P700 chlorophyll a apoprotein A2	psaB (pslA2)	Fish et al., 1985; Fish and Bogorad, 1986
Apoprotein of Fe-S centers A and B	psaC	R. Schantz and L. Bogorad, 1987, unpublished data
Photosystem II Components:		
32 kDa herbicide-binding polypeptide ("D-1" protein)	psbA	L. McIntosh and L. Bogorad, 1980, unpublished data
51 kDa P680 chlorophyll a apoprotein	psbB	Rock et al., 1987
44 kDa chlorophyll a apoprotein	psbC	E.T. Krebbers, K. Muskavitch, H. Roy, D. Russell, and L. Bogorad, 1987, unpublished data
"D-2" protein	psbD	E.T. Krebbers, K. Muskavitch, H. Roy, D. Russell, and L. Bogorad, 1987, unpublished data
Apocytochrome b-559, 9 kDa subunit	psbE	J. Lukens and L. Bogorad, 1987, unpublished data
Apocytochrome b-559, 4 kDa subunit	psbF	J. Lukens and L. Bogorad, 1987, unpublished data

(continued on next page)

Table 6-1. Continued.

Gene product	Gene	Reference
24 kDa membrane-associated protein	*psb* G	Steinmetz et al., 1986
10 kDa phosphorprotein	*psb* H	Rock et al., 1987
Cytochrome b6/f Components:		
Apocytochrome b6	*pet* B	Rock et al., 1987
Subunit IV	*pet* D	Rock et al., 1987
ATP Synthetase Components:		
CF$_1$: alpha subunit	*atp* A	Rodermel and Bogorad, 1987
beta and epsilon subunits	(fused gene)	Krebbers et al., 1982
DF$_0$: subunit I	*atp* F	S. Rodermel and L. Bogorad, 1987, unpublished data
subunit III (proteolipid)	*atp* H	Rodermel and Bogorad, 1987
subunit IV	*atp* I	S. Rodermel and L. Bogorad, 1987, unpublished data
70S Ribosomal Proteins:		
Proteins homologous to *E. coli*		
30S ribosomal subunit proteins:		
S3	*rps* 3	McLaughlin and Larrinua, 1987c
S4	*rps* 4	Subramanian et al., 1983
S7	*rps* 7	A. Subramanian, 1987, unpublished data
S8	*rps* 8	U. Markmann-Mulisch and A. Subramanian, 1988,
S11	*rps* 11	A. Subramanian, 1987, unpublished data
S12	*rps* 12	A Subramanian, 1987, unpublished data
S14	*rps* 14	Rodermel et al., 1987
S16	*rps* 16	A. Subramanian, 1987, unpublished data
S19	*rps* 19	McLaughlin and Larrinua, 1987a
Proteins homologous to *E. coli*		
50 S ribosomal subunit proteins:		
L2	*rpl* 2	Larrinua and McLaughlin, 1987
L14	*rpl* 14	U. Markmann-Mulisch and A. Aubramanian, 1987,
L16	*rpl* 16	Gold et al., 1987; McLaughlin and Larrinua, 1987d
L22	*rpl* 22	McLaughlin and Larrinua, 1987b
L23	*rpl* 23	Larrinua and McLaughlin, 1987
Other stromal proteins:		
Large subunit of ribulose bisphosphate carboxylase	*rbc* L	McIntosh et al., 1980; Poulsen, 1981
Protein homologous to alpha subunit of *E. coli* RNA polymerase	*rpo* A	D. Russell, D. Zaitlin, and L. Bogorad, 1987, unpublished data
Other membrane proteins:		
Proteins homologous to human and bovine mitochondrial NADH dehydrogenase complex proteins:		
ND3	*ndh* C	A. Steinmetz and L. Bogorad, 1987, unpublished data
ND4	*ndh* D	R. Schantz and L. Bogorad, 1987, unpublished data
ND4l	*ndh* E	R. Schantz and L. Bogorad, 1987, unpublished data

the genome. The inverted repeat sequences also divide the genome into two parts—a small 11.0-kb single copy region and a large 83.0-kb single copy region—and recombination within the inverted repetitive sequences flips the orientation of one single copy region relative to the other (Palmer, 1983).

The genes analyzed thus far on the corn plastid genome encode functions required for plastid maintenance (ribosomal RNAs, tRNAs, ribosomal proteins) and for photosynthesis (Table 6–1). Because these genes are essential for growth of a green plant, few viable mutations are expected to map to the plastid genome. Natural and selected mutations in plastid DNA are known, however, that confer resistance to killing agents. The best studied of these is the atrazine-resistance trait; this phenotype results from an amino acid substitution in the plastid gene $psbA$ (Hirschberg and McIntosh, 1983). The natural variation of corn plastid genomic organization with respect to either restriction site polymorphism or as variation in DNA sequences has not yet been adequately assessed. Based on the high conservation of sequence information between corn and distantly related species such as barley (Zurawski et al., 1984), the plastid genome is assumed to evolve only slowly (see discussion in Palmer, 1985).

An area of active investigation is the pattern of plastid gene transcription during the development and subsequent greening of corn leaves. For a C4 plant such as corn, this requires analysis of both mesophyll and bundle sheath plastid differentiation and differential gene expression. Development of these cell types is likely to involve complex interactions between the nuclear and plastid compartments (Taylor et al., 1984). Light induction of specific plastid transcripts has been demonstrated in several studies (Fish et al., 1985), and regulation through the phytochrome system has also been established for some plastid genes. Transcription has been studied in some detail from the viewpoint of the nature of the plastid DNA template (Stirdivant et al., 1985) and the nucleotide sequences of promoters and sites of transcript initiation (Mullet et al., 1985). Multiple transcript initiation sites have been documented for corn plastid genes; differential use of promoters could offer a means of differential gene regulation during development or physiological responses. In vitro transcription of plastid DNA offers a new, powerful approach for studying the biochemistry of the transcription progress and elucidating the physical properties and regulation of the corn plastid RNA polymerase(s) (Hanley-Bowdoin et al., 1985). A combination of in vivo and in vitro studies will be required to determine the signals that regulate gene expression during development of the mesophyll and bundle sheath plastids.

6–1.2 Corn Mitochondrial Genome

In contrast to the relative stability of the corn plastid genome, the mitochondrial genome of corn is dynamic. Historically, interest in corn mitochondrial genome organization was sparked by the observation in

1976 that the T-type cytoplasmic male-sterility (*cms*) trait was correlated with alteration in the restriction digestion patterns of mitochondrial but not plastid DNA (Levings and Pring, 1976). Subsequent work showed that *cms*-T, C, and S each had unique restriction digestion patterns (Pring and Levings, 1978), and that there was diversity among the normal cytoplasms (Levings and Pring, 1977) and among the *cms*-C cytoplasm (Pring et al., 1980). The restriction digestion surveys indicated that the corn mitochondrial genome was considerably larger than the plastid genome; in addition, multiple circular molecules were observed in mitochondrial DNA preparations in contrast to the single circular size class typical of plastid DNA (Levings et al., 1979). Variation in the stoichiometry of restriction fragments and the plethora of molecular forms of mitochondrial DNA led to the hypothesis that the genome is organized on a number of discrete chromosomes differing in their representation in the organelle population.

Using overlapping cosmid clones, Lonsdale et al. (1984) have assembled a physical map of the corn mitochondrial genome (Fig. 6–2). In the course of this work, six pairs of repetitive sequences >2 kb were detected. As with the plastid genome, recombination between pairs of inverted repetitive sequences flips the orientation of flanking regions relative to each other. However, recombination between homologous pairs found in a direct orientation on the genome would produce subgenomic circular molecules (Lonsdale et al., 1984). The subgenomic circular molecules can also recombine at sites of homology recreating larger molecules.

The observation of numerous size classes of circular molecules in mitochondrial DNA preparations supports this model. In addition, the expected recombination products predicted from the organization of repeated DNA flanking sites of S plasmid homology in the *cms*-S genome have been cloned and studied in detail. This resulted in the discovery that recombination between the main genome and the plasmids linearizes the main mitochondrial genome in the *cms*-S sterile plants (Schardl et al., 1984). Numerous short repetitive sequences, <2kb, also exist in the corn mitochondrial genome, and recombination involving these sequences might be expected to create dozens of different forms. Consequently, although a single map of 570 kb is presented as the "master" corn mitochondrial chromosome, the mitochondrial genome most likely exists in vivo as numerous subgenomic molecules.

In addition to the complexities of the main mitochondrial genome, numerous small linear and circular DNA episomes and double stranded RNAs are found in corn mitochondria (reviewed in Pring and Lonsdale, 1985). Of particular interest are two linear molecules found in mitochondrial DNA prepared from the *cms*-S genotype; these related episomes, termed S-1 and S-2, were originally postulated to play a role in determining male sterility, because they integrated into the main mitochondrial genome in cytoplasmic revertants to fertility (Levings et al., 1980). Subsequent studies have demonstrated that after cytoplasmic re-

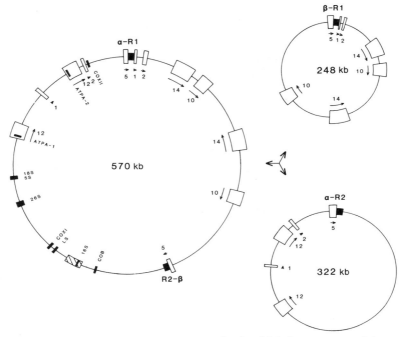

Fig. 6–2. Physical map of the 570 kb master mitochondrial chromosome and two recombination products of 322 and 248 kb. Repetitive sequences in the genome are denoted by open boxes; the number below each box gives the approximate length of that repetitive sequence. In this example, recombination between the 5 kb repeats results in fractionation of the genome into two subgenomic circular molecules; note that sequences flanking the repeat (R1 and R2 at the arrowhead end of each repeat and alpha and beta at the opposite end of the 5 kb sequence) are different in the recombination products than in the master circular chromosome. The locations of most known genes are indicated on the 570 kb chromosome; for definition of terms consult Table 6–2. The hatched box shows the location of the 12-kb piece of plastid DNA translocated to the mitochondrial genome. (Provided by D.M. Lonsdale and reprinted with permission from IRL Press, Oxford.)

version to fertility in some lines, the S-1 and S-2 episomes integrate at sites of homology (Braun et al., 1986) in the main genome; these events result in loss of one end of the integrated episome forms (Schardl et al., 1985). However, not all *cms*-S cytoplasmic revertants to fertility lose the S episomes (Escote et al., 1985), breaking the correlation between the episomes and the sterility phenotype. At present it appears that the nuclear genome plays a role in determining both the relative stoichiometry of restriction fragments of the main mitochondrial genome (Borck and Walbot, 1982) as well as the maintenance and ratio of S-1 to S-2 (Escote et al., 1985).

Another curious feature of corn mitochondrial DNA is that it contains numerous pieces of the plastid genome; this "promiscuous DNA" was discovered by Stern and Lonsdale (1982). Segments of plastid DNA transferred to the main mitochondrial genome include the *rbc*L, plastid rDNA genes, and other sequences (Stern and Palmer, 1984). The S-1 plasmid also contains a region of homology to a portion of the *psb*A gene (Sederoff et al., 1986), and the 2.3 kb linear plasmid contains two plastid tRNAs (Leon et al., 1988). The only plastid sequence postulated to contribute an essential function to corn mitochondria is a tRNA$^{\text{trp}}_{\text{UGG}}$ gene contained on the 2.3-kb plasmid. This is apparently the only tRNA$^{\text{trp}}_{\text{UGG}}$ in the corn mitochondrial genome; this gene is found in the main mitochondrial genome of a corn relative (*Z. diploperennis*) and in dicots. In addition, corn mitochondrial and plastid DNA sequences are found in corn nuclear DNA (Bedinger et al., 1986 and references therein).

About 20 genes of known function have been sequenced from the corn mitochondrial genome (Table 6–2). These were usually identified by homology to mitochondrial genes of yeast or mammals. In addition, there are four open reading frames on the S-1 and S-2 plasmids (Levings and Sederoff, 1983; Paillard et al., 1985) and one on the 2.3-kb plasmid (Leon et al., 1988). Using polyclonal antibodies raised to a translational fusion containing part of open reading frame 1 of the S-2 plasmid, this gene has been shown to encode a 130 kDa protein found in mitochondria of sterile *cms*-S lines (Manson et al., 1986) as well as lines restored to fertility by the nuclear gene *Rf3* (Zabala et al., 1987). The *cms*-T plants synthesize a 13 kDa protein encoded by a highly rearranged gene sequence unique to this cytoplasm (Dewey et al., 1986).

As more is learned about the molecular changes associated with each type of *cms*, elucidation of the role of the dominant nuclear genes restoring pollen fertility may be possible. For example, do the restorers suppress expression of the novel gene products associated with *cms*? If so, by what mechanism?

Thus far, the number of genes identified on the corn mitochondrial genome is small relative to the size of the genome. The genes identified by heterologous nucleic acid hybridization encode products required for organelle maintenance and respiration, in parallel with what was found in the more complete analysis of plastid DNA coding capacity. Additional mitochondrially encoded proteins may be identified by producing the translation product of each mitochondrial open reading frame, raising an antibody to this product, and then using the antibody to identify a particular protein synthesized by mitochondria. This approach should allow detection of genes not found in the much smaller animal and fungal mitochondrial genomes.

Another interesting aspect of the linear and circular episomes in corn mitochondria is certainly their potential as molecular probes for mitochondrial DNA replication. Some of the circular extrachromosomal DNA found in mitochondria occur only in their free form and do not integrate into the mitochondrial genome; one would expect that they carry all the cis-acting sequences necessary for replication. One of these circles has been sequenced recently and contains three tandem copies of the consensus sequences for autonomous replicating sequences (ARS) in yeast. Probing these structures for their potential to promote replication in corn mitochondria may also open an avenue for developing a mitochondrial vector system (Ludwig et al., 1985).

Table 6-2. Genes of the corn mitochondrial genome.†

Gene‡	Map coordinates§	References
rRNA		
26S	398.42–401.97	Dale et al., 1984
18S	418.07–420.04	Chao et al., 1984
5S	417.83–417.96	Chao et al., 1983
tRNA		
trn M-1	37.52–38.30	Parks et al., 1984
trn D-1	38.30–39.26	Parks et al., 1985
trn Y	92.73–103.05	Marechal et al., 1985a
trn M-3	105.4–108.6	Marechal et al., 1986
trn D-2	127.72–126.68	Parks et al., 1985
trn M-2	125.68–266.5	Parks et al., 1984
trn C	258.4–266.5	J.-M. Grienenberger, 1986, unpub. data¶
trn F	258.4–266.5	Marechal et al., 1985b
trn S	258.4–266.5	J.-M. Grienenberger¶
trn fM	308.9–320.7	Parks et al., 1984
cox 1	353.60–355.20	Isaac et al., 1985#
cox 2	537.70–539.32	Fox and Leaver, 1981
cox 3	427.89–450.69	McCarty et al., 1987, unpub. data¶
cob	311.60–312.80	Dawson et al., 1984
atp 6	556.74–561.04	Dewey et al., 1985a
atp 8		Not reported, although present in yeast
atp 9	298.84–301.49	Dewey et al., 1985b
atp 1	454.21–452.68	Braun and Levings, 1985
		Isaac et al., 1985b
atp 2	521.11–519.58	Braun and Levings, 1985
var 1		Not reported, although present in yeast
nd-1	320.75–327.75	Bland et al., 1986††
S13	320.75–327.75	Bland et al., 1986

† An annual update of the corn mitochondrial gene list, map, and other pertinent information can be found in the *Maize Genetics Cooperators News Letter*. Appropriate nomenclature for corn mitochondrial genes is still under discussion. A three-letter code will probably be adopted for all genes.

‡ *cox* = subunit of cytochrome oxidase; *cob* = apocytochrome b; *atp* = subunit of ATPase; *var* 1 and *S13* = ribosomal protein based on homology to genes in other organisms; *nd* = NADH:Q oxidoreductase based on homology to genes in other organisms. *atp* 1 is present in two copies in the normal cytoplasm of corn within an approximately 12 kb repetitive sequence.

§ Map coordinates are based on position zero being within the α-R1 repeat (5 kb repeat at the 1200 h position on the 570 kb map).

¶ Reported at the 1986 Airlie Plant Mitochondrial Genome Meeting.

A single copy of *cox* 1 exists in the normal corn genome, but this gene exists in multiple genomic linkages in the *cms*-S genome, because it is closely linked to the 186 bp site of recombination between the S plasmids and the main genome. *atp* alpha is a single copy in the *cms*-S genome, but two copies are present in the normal mtDNA because in that genome the gene is found on a direct repeat sequence.

†† *nd*-1 has been cloned and sequenced from watermelon mtDNA, and antibodies raised against a fusion protein containing a portion of this URF-1 (name of gene in *Neurospora*) crossreact with a plant mitochondrial protein (D.B. Stern and G. Zabala, 1987, personal communication). Part of a corn *nd-1* gene sequence was reported by Bland et al. (1986).

6-1.3   Prospects for Future Research on Organellar Genomic Organization

It is highly likely that sequencing and structural studies of organelle genes will continue over the next decade. In vitro transcription has already been developed for plastids, and a method is likely to be developed for corn mitochondria as well. Possible also is the development of protocols for transient gene expression in organelles and even organelle transformation for the detailed study of mutations in organelle genes and regulatory sequences. The major emphasis in plastid research is likely to remain light-regulation of gene expression and for mitochondria, elucidating the link between genomic rearrangements and *cms*.

The other aspect of organelle genome structure likely to receive considerable attention is the role of "promiscuous DNA" sequences. As will be discussed in more detail below, a number of transposable elements of corn nuclear DNA have now been characterized, and a role for them in generating allelic diversity during evolution has been postulated (Schwarz-Sommer et al., 1985b). The transfer of sequences between the organelle genomes and between the organelles and the nuclear genome in corn suggests that transfer of complete genes can also occur. Are such transfers directed or accidental? Do transfers rely on homologous recombination or involve transposable elements? When first transferred, these new genes will most likely lack appropriate signals for transcription and termination. If they are functional in their new location, how do the transferred genes acquire appropriate regulatory signals? The plastid $tRNA_{UGG}^{trp}$ gene in the mitochondrial 2.3 kb plasmid is transcribed and processed to an appropriate size, suggesting that regulatory signals can be shared or are selected after transfer. In the complete tobacco plastid DNA sequence, the entire set of mitochondrial NADH:Q oxidoreductase genes was unexpectedly discovered (Shinozaki et al., 1986), raising the possibility that corn plastid DNA is a recipient as well as a donor of sequences. Does the plastid contain heretofore undetected oxidoreductase activity?

6–2 CORN NUCLEAR GENES

Most corn genes listed in Chapter 3 of this book were recognized by the novel phenotypes present in mutants defining each locus. A few of these genes have now been cloned (*waxy, shrunken*, genes of the anthocyanin biosynthetic pathway: *c1, c2, a1, bz1, bz2, R*) as well as a number of genes not otherwise defined by mutational analysis (i.e., zeins and histones). It is the purpose of this chapter to discuss how these cloned genes and other cloned sequences are being used to construct a physical map of the corn genome and to discuss the preliminary conclusions regarding the regulation of expression of corn genes. It is beyond the scope of this chapter to review all of the methodology utilized in the cloning and subsequent sequencing of isolated corn genes or to discuss the structure of each gene. Instead, a few results will be presented to highlight recent progress in gene cloning, and several phenomena specific to corn will be discussed. For a general introduction to recombinant DNA methods readers should consult Hackett et al. (1988) and/or Watson et al.

(1983). Complete lists of all published nucleotide sequences can be found in the Bionet, EMBL, and Genebank data bases.

6–2.1 Gene Cloning

Genomic and cDNA clones for a number of corn genes have been obtained (Table 6–3 is a partial listing). Three methods have been used to clone these gene sequences:

1. Recovery of genes by virtue of homology to genes cloned from other organisms.
2. Construction of cDNA libraries screened with RNAs derived from different developmental stages or mutants or use of cDNAs to cause hybrid-arrest translation of mRNA from different developmental stages.

Table 6–3. Partial list of cloned corn nuclear genes.

Gene/Location†	Function of product	Reference
a1/3L	Required for anthocyanin	O'Reilly et al., 1985
Ac/-	Controlling element	Fedoroff et al., 1983
Act1/-	Actin	Shah et al., 1983
Adh1/1L	Alcohol dehydrogenase	Dennis et al., 1984
Adh2/4S	Alcohol dehydrogenase	Dennis et al., 1985
bz1/9S	Required for anthocyanin (a glucosyl transferase)	Fedoroff et al., 1984
bz2/1L	Required for anthocyanin	Theres et al., 1987, McLaughlin and Walbot, 1987
c1/9S	Required for anthocyanin	Pas-Ares et al., 1986
c2/4L	Required for anthocyanin	Wienand et al., 1986
*Cab/-†	Chlorophyll a/b binding protein	Nelson et al., 1984
Css2/9L	Sucrose synthetase	McCarty et al., 1986
Glu/-	Glutamine-synthetase	Snustad et al., 1988
*Gst/-	Gluthathione-S-transferase	Shah et al., 1986
*His3/-	Histone H3	Chaubet et al., 1986
*His4/	Histone H4	Chaubet et al., 1986k
*Hsp70/-	70 kDa heat shock protein	Rochester et al., 1986
P/1S	Required for anthocyanin	J. Chen et al., 1987, personal communication
*Pep/-	PEP carboxylase	Nelson et al., 1984
R/10L	Required for anthocyanin	S. Dellaporta et al., 1986, personal communication
*rbc*S/2,4L	Ribulose bisphosphate carboxylase (*sms1* and *sms2* in Fig. 6–3)	Nelson et al., 1984
sh/9S	Sucrose synthetase	Sheldon et al., 1983
Spm/-	Controlling element	Pereira et al., 1986
*Tpi/-	Triose phosphate isomerase	Marchionni and Gilbert, 1986
wx/9S	Starch debranching enzyme	Shure et al., 1983
*Zp/4L 7S 10L	Zein storage protein genes	Heidecker and Messing, 1986 Pedersen et al., 1982

† Three letter gene symbols are suggested for genes not yet assigned a name; these genes are starred in the table. For example, the zein genes (*Zp*) could be given the three letter name of *Zen*. In Fig. 6–3 various abbreviations are used for heterologous probes used to map the locations of homologous sequences in the corn genome. When the corn gene is obtained, a name conforming to standard nomenclature should be used.

3. Transposon tagging.

Cloning or confirming corn genes using a heterologous probe has been successful for several well-conserved genes such as actin (Shaw et al., 1984), histones 3 and 4 (Chaubet et al., 1986), *rbc*S (small subunit of ribulose bisphosphate carboxylase, Nelson et al., 1984), triose phosphate isomerase (Marchionni and Gilbert, 1986) and *c2* (chalcone synthase, Wienand et al., 1986). As more genes are cloned from additional higher plant species, this method should allow ready access to a number of corn genes. Among the earliest genes cloned were those involved in maturation of endosperm tissue, isolated by virtue of the abundance of the mRNAs encoding them (*waxy*: Shure et al., 1983; *shrunken-1*: Sheldon et al., 1983; zein alleles, Wienand et al., 1979, and review of Heidecker and Messing, 1986 and references cited therein). Similarly, the relative abundance of mRNA for alcohol dehydrogenase in hypoxic corn roots paved the way for cloning alleles of both *Adh1* and *2* (Dennis et al., 1984, 1985; Bennetzen et al., 1984; Freeling and Bennett, 1985).

A method applicable to corn and just a few other higher plants with characterized transposable element systems is the use of transposon insertion mutants for gene cloning. The basic strategy was outlined by Wienand et al. (1982) and successfully applied in the published reports of the cloning of *bz1* (Fedoroff et al., 1984) and *a1* (O'Reilly et al., 1985) as well as a number of more recent cases (*R, P, bz2*, see Table 6–3). Using cloned copies of individual transposable elements as the probe and a library containing a mutant allele with an insertion of a homologous element, the target gene can be recovered. This strategy works best if low copy number transposable elements are utilized (i.e., *Ac*), because, as will be discussed in a subsequent section, many transposable element families are present in 20 to 100 copies per genome. To overcome this difficulty, mutable alleles caused by two different transposable elements can be analyzed, a strategy that aided the identification of *a1* (O'Reilly et al., 1985).

A fourth method of gene cloning that should find widespread application to corn in the future is the use of antibodies to screen expression libraries (Helfman et al., 1983; Young and Davis, 1983). Antibodies have already been used to match some mitochondrial proteins to open reading frames (Manson et al., 1986; Zabala et al., 1987), and similar strategies should be useful in analyzing the protein products of cDNAs from specific cytoplasmic mRNA populations. The antibody method can be used to generate both nucleic acid and probes to differentially expressed genes prior to their functional identification.

Confirmation of the tissue specificity of expression of individual cDNA or genomic clones will be greatly aided by the application of in situ hybridization to analyze the distribution of transcripts in tissues. This method can provide information on the tissue or even cell-type specificity of expression of genes. It can be used to analyze the regulation of cloned sequences of unknown biochemical function that show discrete patterns of expression in tissue or even cell types at specific stages of development.

Although there may be other methods evolving than the ones mentioned above, one last one has quite some potential. Recently, P. Snustad et al. (1988, unpublished data) have used the *Escherichia coli* K12 *gln*A mutant as a recipient of a corn cDNA library from mRNA of a BMS tissue culture that was cloned in the pUC expression vector (Vieira and Messing, 1982). When the transformed cells were grown under appropriate plating conditions, a strain was recovered that contained a cDNA clone of the corn glutamine synthetase under the control of the lac regulatory region of the vector. Although the *E. coli* enzyme and the corn enzyme differ in their structure, it appears that they can complement in their function. Although this is not proven for other basic metabolic enzymes, it may be quite possible that such an approach would be suitable for the cloning of other corn cDNAs.

6–2.2 Restriction Fragment Length Polymorphism Map of the Corn Nuclear Genome

For genes identified by classical genetic techniques, the map position is already known before the gene is cloned. For genes cloned in the absence of a mutational definition of the locus, establishing the map position can be accomplished using the cloned gene and appropriate hybridization tests. There is high sequence polymorphism near the corn *Adh1* gene (Johns et al., 1983), the *Waxy* gene (Wessler and Varagona, 1985), and other single copy sequences (Helentjaris et al., 1985, and references therein); in fact, the polymorphism among corn inbred lines is much higher than in the commercial tomato (*Lycopersicon esculentum*: Helentjaris et al., 1985) or other higher organisms for which restriction fragment length ploymorphism (RFLP) (pronounced riflip) maps are being assembled.

To identify restriction polymorphisms, cloned DNA sequences isolated from genomic or cDNA libraries that represent single or low copy sequences are hybridized to genomic DNA blots of restricted samples from several corn lines. Those probes that identify novel fragments in one or more lines are then used to analyze the segregation of the novel fragments. The RFLPs provide convenient, usually unselected genetic markers apparently randomly distributed throughout the genome. Linkage between individual RFLPs and difficult to score traits (disease resistance, quantitative genetic traits, etc.) will likely be useful in the future as a method for following such traits through crosses.

Translocation stocks, particularly those involving the B chromosomes, can be used to speed RFLP mapping in the same way they aid standard genetic mapping (Evola et al., 1986). The nondisjunction of B chromosomes during the second mitosis of microspore development can simplify the analysis of RFLPs in a way that is thus far unique for corn. Linkage between an RFLP marker and translocation breakpoints and known genetic traits will be used to order these arbitrary markers along the known chromosomal maps.

In addition to providing a physical map, the RFLP information can be used for the following:

1. Test whether individual corn lines have colinear maps.
2. Compare the order of markers in corn and close relatives in evolutionary studies.
3. Search for duplicated segments in the corn genome.
4. Identify the positions of duplicate or pseudogenes corresponding to known genetic loci.
5. Aid in the analysis of cytogenetic phenomena by pinpointing the position of translocation breakpoints and sites of recombination during linkage analysis.

For these reasons and others that will emerge as the maps become more detailed, RFLP maps of the corn genome promise to become essential tools for future research.

An updated version of the first RFLP map of corn (Helentjaris et al., 1986a, b) is shown in Fig. 6–3. The use of monosomic stocks has been a powerful method for placing sequences on the map (Helentjaris et al., 1986b), and for testing the interesting initial observation that regions of chromosomes 2 and 7 share great similarity in the order of probe sequences (Fig. 6–4). Evidence of such similarity suggests that modern corn could be a tetraploid species. The identification of many loci of duplicate function by classical corn genetics also suggests this hypothesis.

To date, maps encompassing more than 200 markers are available, and as additional laboratories participate in this project, maps with more than 1000 markers should become available. As the corn linkage map encompasses approximately 1200 map units, physical maps with 1000 markers should bracket any known locus within a few map units. However, note in Fig. 6–3 that the RFLP markers are not randomly distributed; a dense map with 1 marker per map unit might require mapping several thousand sequences. Dooner et al. (1985) in studies involving the *bz1* locus have demonstrated a poor correspondence between recombination units and physical length as measured either by pachytene chromosome length or kilobase pairs. Assuming that the corn genome is about 5×10^6 kb and that each map unit includes the same amount of DNA, there would be approximately 4×10^3 kb per map unit. This enormous length and the presence of substantial repetitive DNA in the corn nuclear genome suggest that simple "walking" from the site of an RFLP sequence to a known gene one map unit away would prove difficult with current cloning technology. This problem can be addressed in part by the recovery of more and more RFLP information for a given region. However, as with traditional markers, recovery of recombinants necessary for the accurate placement of markers is increasingly difficult as the distance between the markers decreases.

6–2.3 Repetitive Elements in the Corn Nuclear Genome

Solution hybridization analysis has been used to construct a C_0t curve to determine the fraction of repeated and unique sequences in the corn

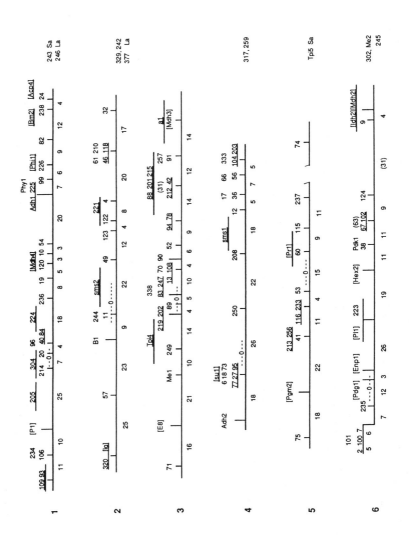

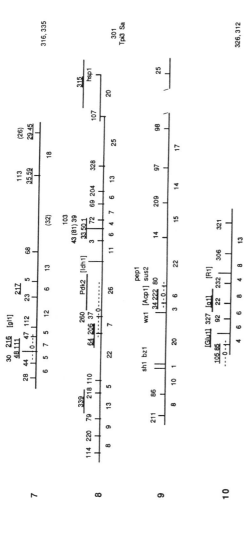

Fig. 6–3. Physical map of the corn nuclear genome based on hybridization of DNA probes and RFLPs. Horizontal bars denote the chromosomes and RFLP loci are represented above those lines by numerical designations. Numbers below the lines represent interloci distances in map units. Loci along the right side of the figure have been assigned to chromosomes, and in some cases to arms, but accurate linkage data is not available for these markers. Loci in brackets were identified by either morphological or isozyme markers. All other loci were determined solely by RFLP analysis. The approximate location of the centromeres is denoted by ---0---. (Map provided by Tim Helentjaris and his colleagues.)

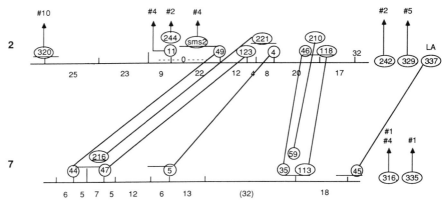

Fig. 6-4. Comparison of the physical linkage of DNA sequences on chromosomes 2 and 7. Only duplicate loci from the map in Fig. 6-3 are shown here. Loci circled and connected by a line represent loci detected by the same clone on both chromosomes. Loci duplicated on other chromosomes are indicated by small numbers next to the clone number. (Diagram provided by Tim Helentjaris and his colleagues.)

genome (Hake and Walbot, 1980). Highly repeated sequences (more than 50 000 copies in the family) constitute about 20% of the genome; these sequences are present in about 10 superabundant sequence types. There are more than 1000 different moderately repetitive sequence families (10–10 000 copies) collectively representing 40% of the genome. This leaves approximately 40% single copy sequences, or more than 10^6 approximately gene size pieces. A fraction of the sequence measured as single copy is likely to be highly divergent repeated sequences (sequence families whose members share <75% sequence homology). Because of this, a more accurate method should be used to assess the gene number in corn. For example, mRNA hybridized to total DNA could be used to estimate what fraction of the genome is transcribed; an analysis of the diversity of transcripts in various organs could provide further refinement of this approach.

Knobs are a prominent cytogenetic feature of corn, found in characteristic locations on each chromosome (see Chapter 4 of this book). A 185 bp sequence present in more than 100 000 copies per genome has been localized to the knobs by in situ hybridization (Peacock et al., 1981). This sequence is present in long, tandem arrays within the knobs; however, knobs may contain other sequences, perhaps even individual knob-specific sequences.

A second prominent cytogenetic feature of corn chromosomes is the nucleolus organizer (NOR) located on chromosome 6 (McClintock, 1934). This region contains the ribosomal DNA (rDNA), which is organized in 9 kb repeats of the 28S and 18S rDNA genes and spacer regions. Interestingly, there can be considerable variation among corn lines in the number of rDNA cistrons from about 5000 to 15 000 copies per haploid genome (Rivin et al., 1986 and references cited therein). The functional significance, if any, of this variation is unknown. Restriction site polymorphism, primarily in the spacer regions of the rDNA cistrons, could be used as a marker to follow the inheritance of individual NORs and for taxonomic studies.

Variation in copy number in repetitive families among corn inbred lines appears to be a common occurrence (Rivin et al., 1986). Both tandemly arranged and dispersed repeats, ranging in number from 10s to 100s of thousands of copies, may vary over a two- to fivefold range of copy number. Such variation may explain the 30% difference in corn genome size (Rayburn et al., 1985). Much further research will be required to understand the basis of copy number regulation of repeated sequences in corn. Unequal crossing over is hypothesized to contribute greatly to copy number variation in tandem arrays, but it is more mysterious how dispersed repetitive sequences evolve in copy number and position in the genome. One dispersed repeat sequence family (ARS1) appears to have a reasonably fixed copy number in diverse corn lines (Rivin et al., 1986). This 600 bp sequence is present about 10 000 times in the nine different inbred lines examined. This sequence was recovered via a functional assay for origins of replication in transformed yeast cells, but its function in corn is entirely unknown.

For *Drosophila*, Rubin (1983) has hypothesized that all dispersed repeats are former transposable elements now frozen in place; this possibility has been raised for the dispersed repeats in the corn genome as well (Freeling, 1984), although sequence analysis of a variety of repeated elements will be required to evaluate this hypothesis. The dispersed, repetitive *Cin* elements of the corn genome (Shepherd et al., 1982, 1984) have the structure of transposable elements but do not transpose. Perhaps many additional similar sequences await discovery.

The organization of repeated sequences near protein-coding genes has not been investigated to any great extent. For those studying gene organization, repetitive elements create some technical problems, so that such sequences have been identified but not yet sequenced in many instances. For example, there are short (about 100 bp) blocks of repeated sequences within the zein gene clusters (Kriz et al., 1988). Repetitive sequences may be indirectly (through an impact on chromosome folding) or directly (by containing specific sequences) involved in the regulation of gene expression. Consequently, additional study of the repetitive sequence families of corn could be worthwhile.

Some genes are repeated sequences: 5S rDNA (Mascia et al., 1981), the larger rDNA genes, histones (Chaubet et al., 1986), and zeins (see review by Heidecker and Messing, 1986) with more likely to be discovered. Thus far, pseudogenes—genes that would produce no or aberrant products but are homologous to functional genes—have not been encountered frequently on sequencing genomic or cDNA clones except for the zeins, so that multicopy (5–50 copies), protein-coding genes may nearly all be functional. With a large number of loci great diversity could exist in the patterns of expression of individual genes in terms of tissue specificity, amount of expression, or timing during development. Clearly, much further research will be required to describe the patterns of expression for some of the complex multigene families. Duplicate loci are also prevalent for some known functions such as chalcone synthase (*c2* and *whp*), alcohol dehydrogenase (*Adh1* and *2*), etc. Alleles of both loci encoding ADH have already been sequenced (Dennis et al., 1984, 1985). In addition, molecular cloning has demonstrated duplicate loci that were unsuspected from classical genetics; for example, when the oat phytochrome gene is hybridized to corn DNA, two distinct RFLP markers are identified (see Fig. 6–3; P. Quail, 1987, personal communication).

6–2.4 Transposable Elements of Corn

One of the most exciting advances in the molecular biology of corn has been the elucidation of the physical structure of transposable elements (TE). Progress on this subject has been extensively reviewed (Freeling, 1984; Döring and Starlinger, 1984; Saedler and Nevers, 1985; Nevers et al., 1986) and an excellent historical perspective is provided in Fedoroff (1983). Using proof of transposition in a stock under observation (as opposed to polymorphism in distribution in various lines) as the criterion for classification as a TE, four corn TE families have been analyzed at the molecular level: *Ac/Ds*, *Spm/Rs* (also known as *En-I*), *Mu*, and *Bs1*. Now that the *A1* locus has been cloned, probes exist for the recovery of the receptor of *Dotted* in *a1-m1*; a molecular description of this element is likely soon. Other element systems have been described at the genetic level (see Chapter 3 in this book) and await description at the molecular level. It is likely that these elements will be cloned by virtue of their insertion into genes for which probes already exist.

The principal findings about corn TEs include:

1. Most corn TEs contain inverted repetitive sequences at their termini, except for *Bs1* (Johns et al., 1985) which has 304 bp direct repeats at its ends.
2. Several examples of the *Spm(En)*, *Ac/Ds*, and *Mu* element family members have been sequenced, and analyses of the sequences demonstrated that each element family creates host sequence duplications of characteristic length at the site of TE insertion: 3 bp for the *Spm(En)* family (Periera et al., 1986 and references cited therein), 8 bp for the *Ac/Ds* family (Sutton et al., 1984; Pohlman et al., 1984; Müller-Neumann et al., 1984), 9 bp for the *Mu* family (Barker et al., 1984), and 6 bp for *Bs1* (Johns et al., 1985).
3. Autonomous elements are generally larger than nonautonomous members of the same family, many of which appear to be deletion derivatives of the autonomous element (c.f. Fedoroff et al., 1983).
4. Minimally family members share sequence homology at their termini; the shared sequence can be as short as 10 to 11 bp in the case of some *Ds* elements.

5. Elements are present in multiple copies in corn, both in lines exhibiting the active TE family and in those lines lacking the phenotypic or genotypic manifestations of TE activity (Chandler et al., 1986).

6. Insertion does not require homology with the host sequence.

7. Excision rarely restores the original gene sequence. Pooling data from several studies of element excision (*Ac/Ds*, Pohlman et al., 1984; Sutton et al., 1984; Dennis et al., 1986) and *Rs* (the nonautonomous derivative of the *Spm* or *En-I* family (Schwarz-Sommer et al., 1985b), the following conclusions can be drawn:

   a. Approximately half of the excision products retain the host sequence duplication; this will create a one amino acid addition in *Rs* revertants and a frameshift mutation for *Ds* revertants if the elements are in coding exons.

   b. The second most common event is base alteration and/or partial deletion of the host duplication.

   c. More rarely, the host sequence duplication is precisely removed restoring the exact progenitor gene sequence.

   d. Deletions larger than the host sequence duplication do occur as do chromosomal rearrangements.

8. Deletion of host DNA contiguous to a TE without element excision has also been observed (Taylor and Walbot, 1985).

9. Changes of state, usually irreversible alterations in the pattern of excision of a nonautonomous element, are correlated with internal deletions in the element (Schwarz-Sommer et al., 1985a; Schiefelbein et al., 1985).

10. Changes of phase, reversible changes in the TE family's activities, can be correlated with altered levels of DNA modification. This is best documented for the *Ac/Ds* and *Mu* element families, in which masking of restriction sites in the elements is correlated with suppression of TE activities (Chandler and Walbot, 1986; Schwartz and Dennis, 1986; Chomet et al., 1987). For example, the cycling of *Ac* activity has been studied in the *wx-m7* allele; when active, *Ac* in *wx-m7* restricts with *Pvu*II whereas inactive *Ac* at the same locus does not (Chomet et al., 1987).

The genetic analysis of TEs in corn, initiated by Barbara McClintock and later pursued by other corn geneticists, provided conclusive evidence for element autonomy, transposition, and various aspects of regulatory behavior in the *Spm/Rs* and *Ac/Ds* element families. This genetic underpinning has greatly facilitated the interpretation of recent molecular data. For *Mu*, however, definition of the autonomous elements based on molecular analysis alone has thus far proven impossible. The inheritance of the copy number of the elements (Alleman and Freeling, 1986) and the Mutator phenomenon itself (Robertson, 1978) suggest that multiple copies of an autonomous element exist in all Mutator stocks; the failure of an autonomous element to segregate has precluded a genetic definition of the autonomous element type. Thus, although the sequences for several types of *Mu* elements are available, none can be unambiguously assigned as the autonomous element.

The protein product encoded by an autonomous TE is predicted to be a transposase, the enzyme(s) required for the specific excision of members of the TE family. Elucidation of the transcripts and protein products of corn TE is just beginning, and much remains to be learned about the regulation of the autonomous TE. How is transcription of the TE activated? Do the elements respond to other cellular factors, in part accounting for the diversity of activity—pattern, timing, frequency of excision—during development? One promising approach is to study the elements in another species. Baker et al. (1986) recently reported that *Ac* will transpose in transgenic tobacco. Thus, tobacco cells must contain all of the cellular factors for *Ac* movement even though tobacco contains no *Ac* elements; these results suggest that no corn-specific activities are required. Further studies with mutant forms of *Ac* will now be possible to define the *cis* and *trans*-acting features of this autonomous element. As will be described in a subsequent section, transformation of corn cells is also possible, so that parallel studies of TE activities in the normal host may also be feasible.

6–3   STRUCTURE OF CORN GENES

6–3.1   Cloning of Corn Genes

In higher eukaryotes gene products are frequently encoded by multigene families. This is certainly true for corn as well. However, there are a number of gene products that are encoded by single genes per haploid genome. Both types are important for the study of gene structure and function. While complex multigene families are an interesting model for gene amplification, single genes are more suitable for studying the regulation of gene expression on the transcriptional or posttranscriptional level.

The storage protein genes in corn are among the first plant genes that have been studied on the molecular level. As we discussed above, the corn genome is too complex to isolate genomic clones directly without a cDNA or heterologous probe. Therefore, it is important to prepare cDNA libraries and screen for the particular cDNA clone first. Because zein mRNA was one of the first plant nuclear mRNAs that was translated in a cell free in vitro system (Larkins et al., 1976; Burr et al., 1978), it is not surprising that it was also the first one to be cloned (Wienand et al., 1979).

In the meantime, a large number of zein cDNAs have been cloned mostly using hybrid selected mRNA in an in vitro cell free translation system or by sequence homology (Burr et al., 1982; Heidecker and Messing, 1983; Hu et al., 1982; Marks and Larkins, 1982; Marks et al., 1985;

Pedersen et al., 1982; Prat et al., 1985; Viotti et al., 1982; Wang and Esen, 1986). More recently, a zein cDNA has been cloned by a different technique that is more common for cloning mammalian mRNAs. The zein protein in question is a minor component that is high in methionine. The protein was purified and partially sequenced. The amino acid sequence was used to design an oligonucleotide and the corresponding cDNA was identified with the designed probe (Kirihara et al., 1988).

In general, however, it has proven difficult to sequence zein proteins because they represent a complex protein family. Use of recombinant DNA techniques has helped to circumvent this problem. In fact, the first complete amino acid sequence of a plant storage protein was derived from a cDNA clone (Geraghty et al., 1981). Furthermore, with development of techniques of cloning complete copies of mRNAs (Heidecker and Messing, 1983, 1985), more has been learned about 5' leader sequences, AUG initiator codons, and 3' ends of zein mRNAs.

6–3.2   The Structure of Corn mRNAs

There are about 30 cDNA sequences known from corn that include the AUG initiator codon (Fig. 6–5). Most of them are derived from zein mRNAs and the others include *shrunken, waxy, Adh,* and actin mRNA. The 5' leader sequence varies in length between 63 (zein ZG124) and 194 (*waxy*) nucleotides. Although the second codon varies for different zein mRNAs, the capping sequence is invariant so far and consists of the AUC trinucleotide. However, some of the other mRNAs that are also expressed in corn endosperm, have a different sequence in this position, i.e., *shrunken* (AAA) and *waxy* (GUC). It will be interesting to see what specificity the AUC trinucleotide sequence might have in the expression of storage protein messages.

6-3.3   The Initiator Codon

One could envision the 5' end of the mRNA as an anchoring position for the 40S ribosome subunit. The subunit scans along the mRNA to search for the first AUG triplet before the large subunit complex is formed and then proper initiation occurs. Consequently, the scanning mechanism and ·the complex formation are rate-limiting steps in the initiation of translation and a number of elegant experiments have been carried out to test this concept (Kozak, 1980, 1981, 1984). Because most of these studies are done in a cell-free in vitro translation system from wheat germ, one should expect to find that a number of conclusions drawn apply to plant mRNAs as well.

From these studies it appears that the first AUG is preferentially used, and the fourth base is usually a purine often a guanosine (Kozak, 1986). This is exactly what we find for corn mRNAs so far. The first AUG is always used—there are exceptions in other plant systems (Hoffman et al., 1982); the 5' leader sequence of corn actin mRNA has not been determined yet (Shah et al., 1983). The second codon is usually an alanine or GCN codon with two exceptions that have the alternate purine in the fourth position. It has been speculated that the specificity of the second codon could play an important role in the rate of initiation of translation and thereby exercise a control in gene expression (Heidecker and Messing, 1986), however, no further experimental data to support such a concept are yet available.

Alternatively, in prokaryotes, the efficiency of initiation of translationhas been correlated with the efficiency of base pairing between the 3' end of the small subunit ribosomal RNA and the sequence preceding the AUG codon of the mRNA (Shine and Dalgarno, 1974). No such base pairing can be derived from the sequence of the corn 18S ribosomal RNA and corn mRNAs (Messing et al., 1984).

6–3.4 Potential RNA Processing Signals

From the analysis of complete cDNA sequences it has been found that more than one poly-A addition signal is recognized and that the consensus sequence is less conserved than in nonplant systems (Messing et al., 1983; Heidecker and Messing, 1986). The corn cDNAs are still consistent with this observation and a consensus sequence for the poly-A addition signal is presented in Fig. 6–6.

If we search for a poly-A signal consensus sequence, AAUAAA, similar to other eukaryotic mRNAs near the 3' end (Benoist et al., 1980), we simply do not find it in plant mRNAs. Actually only 3 out of 25 samples show the canonical AAUAAA in the correct position. The others are all variants, and only the first two AA residues seem to be invariant. In one case the U is replaced by the other pyrimidine and frequently, the other A's by the other purine. The last purine is usually a G rather than an A. The distance from the central pyrimidine varies between 16 and 37 nucleotides. However, in most cases another poly-A type addition signal sequence occurs between the stop codon and the described signal. Because of the comparison of very similar cDNAs that differ in the length of their 3' ends, we know that more than one signal sequence may be utilized. Therefore, many plant genes may have more than one signal sequence for the addition of poly-A. The signal sequence can deviate

➡

Fig. 6–5. Alignment of 5' untranslated leader sequences of corn mRNAs (*ZMAUG*). The University of Wisconsin program *lineup* has been used to align the 5' untranslated leader sequences of known corn mRNAs and the *pretty* command to produced the printout (Devereux et al., 1984). All sequences include the first two codons. The EMBL databank and GenBank differ in their entry of nucleotide sequences by converting the T to U. Since both data libraries have been used to retrieve the data, our printout uses both the DNA and the RNA form. Gaps were introduced to allow greater degree of homology. The N at the beginning of the sequence indicates a longer 5' end, and the lack of a nucleotide at the beginning either indicates an incomplete cDNA clone or a shorter 5' untranslated leader sequence. The line designated zmaug was derived by using the consensus command of the program.

```
              LINEUP of: ZMAUGa from: 1 to: 85    16-NOV-1986 14:33

              1                                                    50
   adhaug    NTTTCGTAAC TGGTGAAGGA CTGAGGGTCT CGGAGTGGAT CGATTTGGGA
   actaug    .......... .......... .......... .........A CTGAACGCTG
  waxyaug    NGTGTACTGC TCCGTCGACC AGTGCGCGCA CCGCCCGGCA GGGCTGCTCA
    shaug    NAACCCTCCC TCCCTCCTCC ATTGGACTGC TTGCTCCCTG TTGACCATTG
  10kzaug    .......... .......... .......... .......... ..........
  15kzaug    ATC....... .......AT CATCCAATCC AGATCAGCAA AGCGGCAGTG
  27bkzaug   ATC....... ..ACCACCAC TGGGTCTTCA GACCATTAGC TTTATCTACT
    gl2aug   .......... .......... .......... .......... ..........
  27akzaug   ATC....... ..ACCACCAC TGGGTCTTCA GACCATTAGC TTTATCTACT
  z19dlaug   .......... .......... .......... .......... ....ACATAG
   z22caug   .......... .......... .......... .......... ..........
   z22aaug   .......... ..UCUCCCAU AAUAUUUCA GCAUUCAAAA ACACACCAAG
   pcmlaug   .......... ..........AATATTTTGA GCATTCAGAA ACACACCAAG
   pmllaug   ATCGTGTATC CATCACCTAT AATATTTTGA GCATTCAGAA ACACACCTAG
    zalaug   .......ATC CATCACCCAT AATATTTTGA GCATTCAGAA ACACACCAAG
    zmaug    a.c....... .....cccat attattgaga ccaactagca acatagaaag
    z7aug    ATC....... ....GCCCAT AATATTTTGA GCATTCAGAA ACACACAAAG
   a30aug    .......... .......... .......... .......... ..........
  z19blaug   ATC....... ....GCACAT ATTATTGAGA CCAACTAGCA ACATAGAAAG
  zg124aug   ATC....... ....ACACAT ATTAGTGAGA CCAACTAGCA ACATAGAAAG
   zg7aug    ATC....... ....GCACAT ATTATTGAGA CCAACTAGCA ACATAGAAAG
  z19aaug    AUC....... ....GCACAU AUUAUUGAGA CCAACUAGCA AUAUAGAAAG
 z19ablaug   ATC....... ....GCACAT ATTATTGAGA CCAACTAGCA ATATAGAAAG
  zg99aug    ATC....... ....GCACAT ATTATTGAGA CCAACTAGCA ATATAGAAAG
    z4aug    ATC....... ....GCACAT ATTATTGAGA CCAACTAGCA ACATAGAAAG
  z19c2aug   .......... .......... .......... ...ACAAGCA ACAUAGAAAG
  z19claug   .......... .......... .......... ........CA ACAUAGAAAG
  zg15aug    .......... ....AACCAT ATTATTGAGA CCAACAAGCA ACATAGAAAG
  zg14aug    ATC....... ....AACGAT ATTATTGAGA CCAACAAACA ACATAGAAAG
   zm6aug    .......... ....AACCAU AUUAUUGAGA CCAACAAGCA ACAUAGAAAG
   a20aug    AUC....... ....AACCAU AUUAUUGAGA CCAACAAGCA ACAUAGAAAG

              51                                           85
   adhaug    TTCTGTTCGA AGATTTGCGG AGGGGGGCAA TGGCG
   actaug    AACTTTGGTC TGTTACAGAA TAGTTGAGAA TGGCT
  waxyaug    TCTCGTCGAC GACCAGTGGA TTAATCGGCA TGGCG
    shaug    ........GG TATTCTGAAC CATCGAGCCA TGGCT
  10kzaug    ........GG AAGCAAGGAC ACCACCGCCA TGGCA
  15kzaug    CGTAGAGAGG ATCGTCGAAC CAGAACAGCA TGAAG
  27bkzaug   CCAGAGCGCA GAAGAACCCG ATCGACACCA TGAGG
    gl2aug   .......... ........CCG ATCGACACCA TGAGG
  27akzaug   CCAGAGCGCA GAAGAACCCG ATCGACACCA TGAGG
  z19dlaug   TGAAGTACAC TAGCAACATC TTAGCACCAA TGGCA
   z22caug   .......... .......AAC CUAACAACAA UGGCU
   z22aaug   CGAAGCGCAC UAGCAACGAC CUAACACCAA UGGCU
   pcmlaug   CGAAGCTACC TAGCAACGAC TTAACAACAA TGGCT
   pmllaug   GGAAGCGCAC TAGCAACGAC CTAACAACAA TGGCT
    zalaug   CGAAGCTCAC TAGCAACGAC CTAACAACAA TGGCT
    zmaug    cgcaat.cag tagcaacaac atagcaacaA tGgcg
    z7aug    GGAAGTGCAC TAGCAACTTC CTAACAACAA TGGCT
   a30aug    .......... .......... ........CAA UGGCA
  z19blaug   CAC....... TAGCAATAGT GTACCAACAA TGGCA
  zg124aug   CACAATAGTG TAC....... ....CAACAA TGGCA
   zg7aug    CACAATAGTG TAC....... ....CAACAA TGGCA
  z19aaug    CACAAUAUUG UAC....... ....CAAUAA UGGCA
 z19ablaug   CACAATATTG TAC....... ....CAATAA TGGCA
  zg99aug    CACAATATTG TAC....... ....CAATAA TGGCA
    z4aug    CACAATATTG TAC....... ....CAATAA TGGCA
  z19c2aug   UGGAAUCCAG UAGCAACAAU AGAGCAACAA UGGCG
  z19claug   UGGAAUCCAG UAGCAACAAC AGAGCAACAA UGGCG
  zg15aug    TGGAATACAT TAGCAACAAT AGAGCAACAA TGGCG
  zg14aug    TGGAATCCAG TAGCAACAAT ACAGGAACAA TGGCG
   zm6aug    UGGAAUCCAG UAGCAACAAU AGAGCAACAA UGGCG
   a20aug    UGGAAUCCAG UAGCAACAAC AGAGCAACAA UGGCG
```

from the consensus sequence of animal mRNAs and in many cases the variant is preferred over the canonical consensus sequence.

In contrast to the poly-A addition signal sequence, the splice concensus sequences are conserved and the GT-AG rule is followed (Breathnach and Chambon, 1981). In most cases plant gene introns are smaller than those in animal genes. This information is still limited because the genes that we know most about, the zein genes, do not have introns at all. This interesting finding and its relationship to gene amplification and gene conversion are discussed elsewhere (Heidecker and Messing, 1986).

6–3.5   The CCAAT/AGGA and TATA Boxes

An analysis of the flanking sequences of the sequenced corn genes is still preliminary. First, the number of corn genes that have been sequenced is a far smaller number than the cDNAs; second, the regeneration of transgenic corn plants allowing a functional analysis is still ahead of us. Therefore, our analysis can only be descriptive. The sequence that one would look for first is the TATA box (Proudfoot, 1979). We could only do this with genomic sequences where the position of the 5' end of the message was known. The position of the start of the coding region does not provide sufficient information. Therefore, only nine TATA boxes have been aligned that are positioned between 29 to 34 nucleotides from the transcriptional start site; this is in good agreement with all known data from animal genes.

Although we can draw a consensus sequence from the TATA box that is similar to other eukaryotic genes, it is noteworthy that the two genes in carbohydrate synthesis, the *waxy* and the *shrunken-1* gene are quite variant from the consensus sequence (Klösgen et al., 1986; Werr et al., 1985). The *waxy* gene has hardly any TATA box: only the TA is common; the *shrunken* has only a TAT left. Although it appears that quite a few sequences upstream and downstream have enhancing capabilities and tissue specificity, the TATA box seems to be essential for the correct start of transcription in plants, too (An et al., 1986). Both the *shrunken* and the *waxy* messages are abundant in corn endosperm, thus the variation to the TATA consensus sequences does not limit their expression. Site-directed oligonucleotide mutagenesis will be useful here to determine what variation is tolerated in the TATA box in corn or plant genes in general.

While the TATA box has been shown to be essential for defining the start site of transcription by RNA polymerase II (Breathnach and Chambon, 1981), both in vivo (Grosveld et al., 1982) and in vitro (Grosveld et al., 1981), other 5' upstream sequences have been shown to be involved in the stimulation of transcription. One of those sequences is the so-called CAAT box consensus sequence GGC/TCAATCT in position −80 of the transcriptional start site (Breathnach and Chambon, 1981). However, while the TATA box seems to be quite conserved through many

LINEUP of: ZMPA^a from: 1 to: 100   1-DEC-1986 17:31

```
          1                                                          50
waxypa    .TACCGATCG GTAATTTTAT ATTGCGAGTA AATAAATGGA CCTGTAGTGG
susypa    .GGCCAGCGC TGGCCTGGTT CCTAGTATGG TGGGAATTGG CTGCACCTTT
adhpa     .TTGTTTGCT TATGTGTTTG TTTGCTTGTA TTTGCTGGTG TCTGTATCGC
10kzpa    .AAATATTTG TGTTGTTACC GAAAATGAGG ACATGCCATC GCGTGTGACT
15kzpa    .TGCAGTAAG ACGACACACA TTATCATGTG TGGTATGACC AATAATATAT
27dkzpa   .GTAATAATG TGTCACGCAT CACCATGGGT GGCAGTGTCA GTGTGAGCAA
27ckzpa   .AATAATGTG TCACGCATCA CCATGGGTGG CAGTGTCAGT GTGTGAGCAA
z19d1pa   .TTATGCTTT ATACTGTAAT AATAAAGTTC TCATACTGAT ATGTGCAACT
zmpa      .ttat.agt. ataattcaat aataaaggt. tttggatgat gtttgtggct
za1pa     .TTACATATG AAATGTACTT GATAATGGTG CCCTCATACC GGCATGTGTT
z22c2pa   .ACAATATAT TGATTGAGAT TTATCTCGAT ATATTGTTGA ACTATGTTCA
z22b1pa   .UUACAUAUG AGAUGUACUC GAUAAUGGUG CCCUCAUACC GCCAUGUGUU
pcm1pa    .TTACATATG AGATGTACTC GATAATGGTG CCCTCATACC GGCATGTGTT
b49pa     .UUACAUAUG AGAUGUACUC GAUAAUGGUG CCCUCAUAGC GGCAUGUGUU
zg124pa   .TTATGAGTT ATAGTTCAAT AATAAAGTTT TTTGTCTGAT GTTTGTGGCT
zg7pa     .......... .......... .......... ...ATTGCTT ATGAGTTATA
z19a2pa   .TTATGAGTT ATAGTTCAAT AATGAAGTTT TTTGGATGAT GTTTGTGGCT
z19b1pa   .TTATGAGTT ATAGTTCAAT AATAAAGTTT TTTATCTGAT GTTTGTGGCT
z19c2pa   .TTATTAGTT GTAATTCAAT AATAAAGTTT TTTGGATGAT GTATGTGGCC
a30pa     .UUAUGAGUU AUAGUUCAAU AAUAAAGUUU UUUGUCUGAU GUUUGUGGCU
zg15pa    .TTATTAGTT GTAATTCAAT AATGAAGTTT TTTGGCTGAT GTATGTGGCC
zg14pa    .TTATTAGTT GTAATTTAAT AATAAAGGTT TTTGGATGAT GTATGTGGCC
zm6pa     .UUAUUAGUU GUAAUUCAAU AAUAAAGUUU UUUGGAUGAU GUAUGUGGCC
a20pa     .UUAUUAGUU GUAAUUCAAU AAUAAAGUUU UUUGGAUGAU GUAUGUGGCC

          51                                                        100
waxypa    TGGAGTAAAT AATCCCTGCT GTTCGGTGT. .......... ..........
susypa    TGCTTCGAAT AAAAATGCCT GCTCGTTCAC CTGCTC.... ..........
adhpa     GGGATGCAAT GAGTTGTTGT TTGGTTGTGT CAACCAGGCT CAAAT.....
10kzpa    CATTATTAAC AAAAAACAAG TTCCTCTTAT TATCTTTTT. ..........
15kzpa    GCATCATAAT AAAGTTTTGG TCATACCACA CATGATAATG TGTG......
27dkzpa   TGACCTGAAT GAACAATTGA AATGAAAAGA AAAAG.... ..........
27ckzpa   TGACCTGAAT GAACAATTGA AATGAAAAGA AAAAG.... ..........
z19d1pa   TCTCAGTAAT AAAAGATTAG AGATCTATAT TTTATT.... ..........
zmpa      tcccagaAAt aAgaaattac atttcta.a. ..t....... ..........
za1pa     TCCTAGAAAT AATCAATATA TTGATTGAGA TTT....... ..........
z22c2pa   TCATATAAAT AATTGAAAAC ATCAAATCGT AATTATAAAC T.........
z22b1pa   UCCUAGAAAU AAUCAAUAUA UUGGUUG... .......... ..........
pcm1pa    TCCTAGAAAT AAACAATATA TTGATTGAGA TTT....... ..........
b49pa     UCCUAGAAAU AAUCAAUAUA UUGAUUGAGA UUUAUCUCGG UAUAUUU...
zg124pa   TCCCAGAAAT AAGAAAGTAC ATTTCT.... .......... ..........
zg7pa     GTTCAATAAT AAAGTTTTTT TTGCAG.... .......... ..........
z19a2pa   TCCCAGAAAT AAGAAAGTAC ATTTCT.... .......... ..........
z19b1pa   TCCCAGAAAT AAGAAAGTAC ATTTCTAGAT TCT....... ..........
z19c2pa   AACCAGAAAT AAGAAGTTAC ATTTCC.... .......... ..........
a30pa     UCCCAGAAAU AAGAAAGUAC AUUUCUAGAU UCU....... ..........
zg15pa    TCCTAGAAAT AAGAAGTTAC ATTTCC.... .......... ..........
zg14pa    AACCAGAAAT AACAACTTAC ATTTGCAGAT TCT....... ..........
zm6pa     AACCAGAAAU AAGAAGUUAC AUUUCCAGAU UCUA...... ..........
a20pa     AACCAGAAAU AAGAAGUUAC AUUUCCAGAU UUU....... ..........
```

Fig. 6–6. Alignment of 3′ untranslated sequences of corn mRNAs (*ZMPA*). The data has been retrieved and used as described in Fig. 6–5. Sequences have been aligned to allow maximal homology for the poly-A addition signal sequence prior to the 3′ end. The line zmpa was derived by using the consensus command. The last nucleotides are followed by the poly-A.

eukaryotic genes, the CAAT sequence is not as conserved and in many cases it is difficult to find a similar consensus sequence in the −80 position of a growing number of genes. On the other hand, investigators have proposed other types of consensus sequences that could substitute for the CAAT box like the AGGA box (Messing et al., 1983) in many of the zein genes (Fib. 6–7). Recently, Shaw et al. (1984) have shown in deletion studies of the nopaline synthetase promotor that elimination of the −80 position significantly reduces gene activity. Therefore, one would expect that despite the sequence heterogeneity found in this region for the corn genes described, CCAAT, AGGA, or other consensus sequences in the −80 position are required for maximal gene expression.

6–3.6 Enhancer Sequences

In addition to the CCAAT/AGGA and TATA boxes, sequences similar to the SV40 core enhancer have been found to stimulate RNA polymerase II transcription when placed near other genes (Khoury and Gruss, 1983; Haslinger and Karin, 1985; Zenke et al., 1986). This consensus sequence of GTGGA/TA/TA/TG is not present in all corn genes sequenced so far. The zein genes and the *waxy* gene, do not have a sequence like this close to the 5' start site. However, the *shrunken* gene has such a sequence in position −600, where it is part of a 16 bp direct repeat (Werr et al., 1985). This is quite a distance from the TATA box and many of the published sequences do not include sequence information extending that far. Therefore, it cannot be excluded that such a sequence is present in most genes but in different positions in the 5' region. However, recently, Chen et al. (1986) have shown in deletion

```
        LINEUP of: ZMPRO^a from: 1 to: 91    15-NOV-1986 20:48 ‐

          1                                                      50
adhpro    AACCGCACCC TCCTTCCCGT CGTTTCCCAT CTCTTCCTCC TTTAGAGCTA
waxypro   GCGCGGCCGG GTCACGCAAC GCGCCCCACG TACTGCCCTC CCCCTCCGCG
shpro     CACCAGCTCG GCACCTCACG CTCGCAGCGC ATGGAGCCTA GGAGCAGCTG
27akzpro  CTCGGTGGCA TAAGAACACA A....GAAAT TGTGTTAATT .AA..TC...
za1pro    TATTGTTTGG AAAAAATACA AAATCCAAAA AAAA.TATTT GAGA.CCTCA
z7pro     TATTGTTTGG CAAAAAGACA AAATCCAAAT ATATATATAT GAGA.TCTCA
zg99pro   TATTCTTTTT GCAAAATCGA AAATTAATCT TGCACAAGCA CAAGGACTGA
z4pro     TATTCTTTTT GCAAAATCGA AAATTAATCT TGCACAAGCA CAAGGACTGA
pml1pro   TGTTGTTTGG AAAAAAGACA AAATCCAAAA AAATATATAT GAG..TCTCC
zmpro     tattgtttgg g.aaaacaca aaatccaaat ..ctatattt gaa..actca

          51                                                     91
adhpro    CCACTATATA AAT.CAG.GG CTCATTTTCT CGCTCCTCAC
waxypro   CGCGC.TAGA AATACCGAGG CCTGGACCGG GGGGGGCCC
shpro     CCCGTCTATT TAT.T.GGTC CCTCTCCCGT ...CCCAGAG
27akzpro  AAAGC.TATA AATAACGCTC GCATGCCTGT GCACTTCTCC
za1pro    CC..TATATA AATAG..CTC CCATATCAG. TAGTTAATCC
z7pro     CA..TGTATG AATAT..CTC CCAAATCAG. TAGTTAATTC
zg99pro   GATGTGTATA AATAT..CTC TTAGATTAGC TAGCTAATAT
z4pro     GATGTGTATA AATAT..CTC TTAGATTAG. TAGATAATAT
pml1pro   ....TGTATA AGCACACAAA TTTTGGTA.. TGTATGTCCA
zmpro     ca.gtgTAta aatat..ctc cca.atcag. tag.taat.c
```

Fig. 6–7. Alignment of corn TATA boxes (*ZMPRO*). The data has been retrieved and manipulated as described in Fig. 6–5. Gaps were introduced to allow homology for the TATA and CAAT/AGGA boxes. The last nucleotide is the one that precedes the presumptive start site of transcription. The line zmpro was derived by using the consensus command.

studies in transgenic plants that a core enhancer-like sequence of GTGGATAG at −560 of the soybean conglycinin storage protein gene does not show any influence on gene expression. More functional studies will be necessary to determine the importance of such consensus core enhancer sequences.

The same type of studies described above yield a different picture for the so-called GC box, a sequence recognized by transcription factor SP1 in animal cells (Dynan and Tijan, 1985; Kandonaga et al., 1986; Myers et al., 1986). In the case of the conglycinin gene from soybean [*Glycine max* (L.) Merr.] an essential region that stimulates transcription 20-fold contains four repeats of the 6 bp GC-rich sequence (AA(CGA)CCGA) between −159 and −257. Similar sequences are also found in corn genes, and because of the functional studies in soybean may well be a constant part of the 5′ regulatory signal sequence context.

In summary, several types of regulatory sequences can be expected to be established as important from future studies. Besides the −30 and −80 positions for the TATA and CCAAT/AGGA boxes, a number of specific enhancers that differ in their position relative to the transcriptional start site will be identified. These may include sequences like the GC repeats or other sequences that are recognized by specific nuclear factors. In this respect, it is interesting to note that Maier et al. (1987) have preliminary data using footprinting methods that such a factor from corn endosperm binds to the 15-bp sequence 5′ CACATGTGTAAAGGT that is upstream of the GC repeats in most zein genomic clones. A more detailed analysis of the *Adh1* gene using footprinting methods is described below.

6–3.7   DNase I Hypersensitive Sites

Another important feature of the regulation of RNA polymerase II activity comes from investigations that study the chromatin structure of active and inactive genes. Endonuclease DNase-I has been used to test changes in the nucleosomal organization of genes that become active (Weintraub and Groudine, 1976). These changes are often associated with the opening of regions of the chromosomes that become accessible to nonhistone proteins and transcription factors. These type of studies are just beginning for plant genes.

When corn nuclei are isolated and the corn gene for alcohol dehydrogenase (*Adh1*) is probed for DNase-I hypersensitivity, two such regions are found (Paul et al., 1987). There are three major sites in the first region between −170 to −700. The second region from −35 to −150 is hypersensitive when the *Adh1* gene is induced by anaerobic conditions. It is interesting that the second region includes the CCAAT/AGGA and TATA boxes. Similar investigations with the *Adh2* gene from corn, however, do not show such qualitative differences (Ashraf et al., 1987). Here three such sites are found at −40 to −70, at −150 to −180, and at

−250 to −285. Under induced conditions, however, no additional sites become apparent, but quantitative differences can be detected in the degree of DNA accessibility.

While the studies with the *Adh1* gene are in agreement with the importance of the −80 and −30 positions, some recent studies by Ferl (1987) also show that some other upstream sequences of this gene are protected by nuclear factors under induced conditions. He describes mainly three regions, A at −100 to −108, B1 and B2 at −120 and −140, and C at −187 to −190. While A and C are only protected under induced conditions, region B1-B2 is protected both under noninduced and induced conditions. However, B1 and B2 are close together so that any factors that bind under noninduced or induced conditions may overlap. The binding to B2 changes during induction indicating that the factor bound to B2 undergoes a conformational change upon anaerobiosis. These protected regions that potentially bind nuclear factors specific for activating the gene do not have any similarities with the GC box mentioned above (Dynan and Tijan, 1985). However, the sequences protected in the A and C positions are also conserved in the *Adh* gene from *Arabidopsis* (Chang and Meyerowitz, 1986). Therefore, upstream consensus sequences may be more specific for a particular gene family and the variation we observe may reflect simply different affinities of these nuclear factors to their corresponding binding sites in the 5′ region.

6–4   GENE EXPRESSION IN CORN

The availability of mutants in corn has been an attraction for molecular biologists studying plant gene expression. More is known about the genes of corn than any other higher plant species. For example, in *Adh1*, gene sequencing demonstrated that a single base pair change within the coding region was the basis for the difference between the fast- and slow-migrating forms of the enzyme. Mutable alleles of this gene have been analyzed to learn how insertions disrupt gene expression (see review by Freeling and Bennett, 1985). Similarly, as discussed above, the existence of the *cms* traits spurred research on the mitochondrial genomes of corn.

Sequencing of mutant alleles of genes important in physiological processes, such as responses to hypoxia (Freeling and Bennett, 1985) can provide insight into the physical basis for the mutation. However, with the advent of site-directed mutagenesis of cloned sequences, a detailed analysis of the DNA sequences important in gene expression need not rely solely on recovery of natural variants or induced mutations. Provided that DNA can be re-introduced into the organism, insertion, deletion, rearrangement, and base substitution mutations can be created in vitro and tested for function in vivo.

Agrobacterium-mediated transformation is efficient for many dicot species and there is now also a published report of DNA transfer from this bacterium to cereal crops. Production of opines, a chemical marker for transformation, has been reported in corn seedlings infected with the bacteria (Graves and Goldman, 1986), but transfer of DNA remains the primary criterion for transformation (Grimsley et al., 1987). Thus far, published studies of the expression of introduced genes in corn have relied on the technique of electroporation (Fromm et al., 1985) in which an electric field reversibly creates holes in the plasma membrane of protoplasts through which DNA can enter. Most of the genes transferred by this route are expressed only transiently after passage to the nucleus (by an unknown mechanism). In about 1% of the protoplasts that reform cell walls and begin to divide, at least one functional copy of the introduced gene is stably integrated in the corn chromosomes (Fromm, et al., 1986). Electroporation can also be used to introduce mRNA into cells resulting in a rapid assay from translation of a particular type of RNA (J. Callis and V. Walbot, 1987, unpublished data). Because mRNA need only enter the cytoplasm to be translated, protein products can be detected in 1 h or less; in contrast, detection of products after electroporation of DNA generally requires 12 to 24 h.

The protoplasts prepared from BMS cell lines used in electroporation-mediated DNA uptake studies are not competent to regenerate whole plants under any of the conditions tried; consequently, stable callus lines are the transformed product. Although the inability to regenerate plants severely limits the exploration of the regulation of gene expression in various cell types and during development, much can be learned about gene expression in calli. Callus tissue can respond to heat shock (J. Callis and V. Walbot, 1987, unpublished data) and perhaps other environmental parameters in a manner mimicking intact plants, allowing identification of the DNA sequences required to make a heterologous reporter gene responsive to heat. Promoter strength can be compared by linking individual promoters to the same reporter gene. Reporter genes in use include those making cells resistant to antibiotics such as kanamycin or hygromycin, those giving cells a novel isozyme (fast and slow electromorphs of *Adh1*), and those giving corn cells an entirely novel phenotype (light emission via luciferase). Because the techniques for the transient gene expression assay and for the stable transformation of corn cells have only recently been developed, there is little to summarize at present; however, it is likely that many studies of gene expression will rely on transformation assays in the future.

An alternative to introducing of corn genes into corn cells is to transfer these constructs into dicots via *Agrobacterium* in an attempt to study gene regulation during plant development. Studies of this type have demonstrated some profound differences between monocot and dicot regulatory sequences. As already mentioned above, Kevin and Chua (1986) recently demonstrated that the sixth intron of corn *Adh1* is poorly spliced from constructs in transgenic tobacco (*Nicotiana tabacum* L.). Similarly, transcription termination signals used in the corn *Adh1* gene are not used in transformed dicots (J. Callis et al., 1985, unpublished data). Major differences in the absolute amounts of gene activity programmed by various monocot and dicot promoters are also found when identical constructs are electroporated into different species of protoplasts. For example, in one study the 35S promoter of Cauliflower mosaic virus, corn *Adh1*, and the nopaline synthase gene of the Ti-DNA of *Agrobacterium tumefaciens* were compared in directing the expression of chloramphenicol acetyl transferase gene as a reporter gene in monocot and dicot cells (M. Fromm et al., 1985, unpublished data). The *Adh1* promoter was much more efficiently used in corn than in the dicots tested. From this scanty data it appears that although monocots and dicots may have diverged only within the last 100 to 200 million yr, gene regulatory signals may be sufficiently diverged such that there are major differences in the efficiency of recognition of corn promoters, termination sequences, and perhaps intron/exon boundaries in dicot cells.

There are, however, some cases of successful expression of corn genes in dicots. As mentioned previously, *Ac* transposes in tobacco, suggesting that it can be adequately expressed in a heterologous system. Also, two different zein genes have been introduced into sunflower via *Agrobacterium*-mediated transfer (Matzke et al., 1984; Goldsborough et al., 1986) where they show low, constitutive expression in the callus tissue rather than high expression exclusively in the endosperm (or seed). Importantly, the sites of both transcription initiation and termination of the zein genes introduced into sunflower (*Helianthus annuus* L.) were identical to those found in corn endosperm tissue. Anatomical and developmental differences, i.e., in the role and size of the endosperm in corn compared to tobacco, may make it difficult to analyze zein expression, or that of other corn genes, in homologous organs of dicots.

6-5 PROSPECTS

Progress in the molecular analysis of corn genome organization, gene structure, and expression has accelerated in the past 10 yr and promises to continue into the next decade. The major limitations to progress, particularly in linking the existing genetic description of this organism to modern molecular analysis, include (i) the lack of a transformation protocol yielding whole, fertile plants and (ii) the difficulty in cloning genes responsible for interesting developmental phenotypes (floral morphology, restoration of pollen fertility, etc.). This latter problem can, in part, be addressed by the recovery of transposable element-mediated mutations in the genes of interest or by analysis of stage-specific gene expression at the cDNA level, comparing mutant to wild type in hopes of identifying a missing function in the mutant. The former problem awaits a breakthrough either in the techniques for coaxing protoplasts to regenerate into whole plants or in the procedures for introducing DNA into intact cells or embryos capable of regeneration. Now that the expression of scorable as well as selectable markers has been documented in corn (Fromm et al., 1985, 1986), the gene constructions exist for exploring novel methods of DNA introduction in corn cells and tissues.

ACKNOWLEDGMENT

We thank many corn workers and our colleagues for permission to quote unpublished studies as cited in the text. Ms. Alexandra Bloom deserves our praise for maintaining order during the hectic final stages of preparing the manuscript. We also thank John Fernandez, Sally Otto, Ernest Quirones, and John Wu for proofreading the text. Primary literature review completed in 1986.

REFERENCES

Alleman, M., and M. Freeling. 1986. The *Mu* transposable elements of maize: Evidence for transposition and copy number regulation during development. Genetics 112:107–119.

An, G., P.R. Ebert, B. -Y. Yi, and C. -H. Choi. 1986. Both TATA box and upstream regions are required for the nopaline synthase promoter activity in transformed tobacco cells. Mol. Gen. Genet. 203:245–250.

Ashraf, M., V. Vasil, I. Vasil, and R.J. Ferl. 1987. Chromatin structure at the 5′ promoter region of the maize *Adh2* gene and its role in gene regulation. Mol. Gen. Genet. 208:185–190.

Baker, B., J. Schell, H. Lörz, and N.V. Fedoroff. 1986. Transposition of the maize controlling element "Activator" in tobacco. Proc. Natl. Acad. Sci. USA 83:4844–4848.

Barker, R.F., D.V. Thompson, D.R. Talbot, J. Swanson, and J.L. Bennetzen. 1984. Nucleotide sequence of the maize transposable element *Mu1*. Nucl. Acids Res. 12:5955–5967.

Bedbrook, J.R., and L. Bogorad. 1976. Endonuclease recognition sites mapped on *Zea mays* chloroplast DNA. Proc. Natl. Acad. Sci. USA 73:4309–4313.

————, G. Link, D.M. Coen, L. Bogorad, and A. Rich. 1978. Maize plastid gene expressed during photoregulated development. Proc. Natl. Acad. Sci. USA 75:3060–3064.

Bedinger, P., E.L. de Hostos, P. Leon, and V. Walbot. 1986. Cloning and characterization of a linear 2.3 kb mitochondrial plasmid of maize. Mol. Gen. Genet. 205:206–212.

Benoist, C., K. O'Hare, R. Breathnach, and P. Chambon. 1980. The ovalbumin gene-sequence of putative control regions. Nucl. Acids Res. 8:127–142.

Bennetzen, J.L., J. Swanson, W.C. Taylor, and M. Freeling. 1984. DNA insertion in the first intron of maize *Adh1* affects message levels: Cloning of progenitor and mutant *Adh1* alleles. Proc. Natl. Acad. Sci. USA 81:4125–4128.

Bland, M.M., C.S. Levings III, and D.F. Matzinger. 1986. The tobacco mitochondrial ATPase subunit 9 gene is closely linked to an open reading frame for a ribosomal protein. Mol. Gen. Genet. 204:8–16.

Borck, K.S., and V. Walbot. 1982. Comparison of the restriction endonuclease digestion patterns of mitochondrial DNA from normal and male sterile cytoplasms of *Zea mays* L. Genetics 102:109–128.

Braun, C.J., and C.S. Levings III. 1985. Nucleotide sequence of the F_1-ATPase alpha subunit gene from maize mitochondria. Plant Physiol. 79:571–577.

————, P.H. Sisco, R.R. Sederoff, and C.S. Levings III. 1986. Characterization of inverted repeats from plasmid-like DNAs and the maize mitochondrial genome. Curr. Genet. 10:625–630.

Breathnach, R., and P. Chambon. 1981. Organization and expression of eukaryotic split genes coding for proteins. Annu. Rev. Biochem. 50:349–383.

Burr, B., F.A. Burr, I. Rubenstein, and M.N. Simon. 1978. Purification and translation of zein messenger RNA from maize endosperm protein bodies. Proc. Natl. Acad. Sci. USA 75:696–700.

————, ————, T.P. St. John, M. Thomas, and R.D. Davis. 1982. Zein storage protein gene family of maize. J. Mol. Biol. 154:33–49.

Chandler, V., C.J. Rivin, and V. Walbot. 1986. Stable non-mutator stocks of maize have sequences homologous to the *Mu1* transposable element. Genetics 106:1007–1021.

————, and V. Walbot. 1986. DNA modification of a transposable element of maize correlates with loss of activity. Proc. Natl. Acad. Sci. USA 83:1767–1771.

Chang, C., and E.M. Meyerowitz. 1986. Molecular cloning and DNA sequence of the *Arabidopsis thaliana* alcohol dehydrogenase gene. Proc. Natl. Acad. Sci. USA 83:1408–1412.

Chao, S., R.R. Sederoff, and C.S. Levings III. 1983. Partial sequence analysis of the 5S to 18S rRNA gene region of the maize mitochondrial genome. Plant Physiol. 71:190–193.

————, ————, and ————. 1984. Nucleotide sequence and evolution of the 18S ribosomal RNA gene in maize mitochondria. Nucl. Acids Res. 12:6629–6644.

Chaubet, N., G. Philipps, M. -E. Chaboute, M. Ehling, and C. Gigot. 1986. Nucleotide sequences of two corn histone H3 genes. Genomic organization of the corn histone H3 and H4 genes. Plant Mol. Biol. 6:253–263.

Chen, Z. -L., M.A. Schuler, and R.N. Beachy. 1986. Functional analysis of regulatory elements in a plant embryo-specific gene. Proc. Natl. Acad. Sci. USA 83:8560–8564.

Chomet, P.S., S. Wessler, and S.L. Dellaporta. 1987. Inactivation of the maize transposable element *Activator* (Ac) is associated with its DNA modification. EMBO J. 6:295–302.

Crouse, E.J., J.M. Schmitt, and H. -J. Bohnert. 1985. Chloroplast and cyanobacterial genomes, genes and RNAs: A compilation. Plant Mol. Biol. Rep. 3:43–89.

Dale, R.M.K., N. Mendu, H. Ginsburg, and J.C. Kridl. 1984. Sequence analysis of the maize mitochondrial 26S rRNA gene and flanking regions. Plasmid 11:141–150.

Dawson, A.J., V.P. Jones, and C.J. Leaver. 1984. The apocytochrome b gene in maize mitocondria does not contain introns and is preceded by a potential ribosome binding site. EMBO J. 3:2107–2113.

Dennis, E.S., W.L. Gerlach, and W.J. Peacock. 1986. Excision of the *Ds* controlling element from the *Adh1* gene of maize. Maydica 31:47–57.

————, ————, A.J. Pryor. J.L. Bennetzen, A. Inglis, D. Llewellyn, M.M. Sachs, R.J. Ferl, and W.J. Peacock. 1984. Molecular analysis of the alcohol dehydrogenase (*Adh1*) gene of maize. Nucleic Acids Res. 12:3983–4000.

————, M.M. Sachs, W.L. Gerlach, E.J. Finnegan, and W.J. Peacock. 1985. Molecular analysis of the alcohol dehydrogenase-2 (*Adh2*) gene of maize. Nucl. Acids Res. 13:727–743.

Devereux, J., P. Haeberli, and O. Smithies. 1984. A comprehensive set of sequence analysis programs for the VAX. Nucl. Acids Res. 12:387–395.

Dewey, R.E., C.S. Levings III, and D.H. Timothy. 1985a. Nucleotide sequence of ATPase subunit 6 gene of maize mitochondria. Plant Physiol. 79:914–919.

————, ————, and ————. 1986. Novel recombinations in the maize mitochondrial genome produce a unique transcriptional unit in the Texas male-sterile cytoplasm. Cell 44:439–449.

————, A. M. Schuster, C.S. Levings III, and D.H. Timothy. 1985b. Nucleotide sequence of F_0-ATPase proteolipid (subunit 9) gene of maize mitochondria. Proc. Natl. Acad. Sci. USA 82:1015–1019.

Dooner, H.K., E. Weck, S. Adams, E. Ralston, M. Favreau, and J. English. 1985. A molecular genetic analysis of insertions in the bronze locus in maize. Mol. Gen. Genet. 200(2):240–246.

Döring, H.-P., and P. Starlinger. 1984. McClintock's controlling elements now at the DNA level. Cell 39:253–259.

Dormann-Przybyl, D., G. Strittmatter, and H. Kossel. 1986. The region distal to the rRNA operon from chloroplasts of maize contains genes coding for tRNA^{Arg} (ACG) and tRNA^{Asn} (GUU). Plant Mol. Biol. 7:419–431.

Dynan, W.S., and R. Tijan. 1985. Control of eukaryotic messenger RNA synthesis by sequence-specific DNA binding proteins. Nature (London) 316:774–778.

Edwards, K., J. Bedbrook, T. Dyer, and H. Kossel. 1981. 4.5S rRNA from *Zea mays* chloroplasts shows structural homology with the 3′ end of procaryotic 23S rRNA. Biochem. Int. 2:533–538.

————, and H. Kossel. 1981. The rRNA operon from *Zea mays* chloroplasts: nucleotide sequence of 23S rDNA and its homology with *E. coli* 23S rDNA. Nucleic Acids Res. 9:2853–2869.

Escote, L.J., S.J. Gabay-Laughnan, and J.R. Laughnan. 1985. Cytoplasmic reversion to fertility in *cms-S* maize need not involve loss of linear mitochondrial plasmids. Plasmid 14:264–267.

Evola, S.V., F.A. Burr, and B. Burr. 1986. The suitability of restriction fragment length polymorphisms as genetic markers in maize. Theor. Appl. Genet. 71:765–771.

Fedoroff, N.V. 1983. Controlling elements in maize. p. 1–63. *In* J.A. Shapiro (ed.) Mobile genetic elements. Academic Press, New York.

––––, D.B. Furtek, and O.E. Nelson, Jr. 1984. Cloning of the *bronze* locus in maize by a simple and generalizable procedure using the transposable controlling element *Activator* (*Ac*). Proc. Natl. Acad. Sci. USA 81:3825–3829.

––––, S. Wessler, and M. Shure. 1983. Isolation of the transposable maize controlling elements *Ac* and *Ds*. Cell 35:235–242.

Fish, L.E., and L. Bogorad. 1986. Identification and analysis of the maize P700 chlorophyll a apoproteins PSI-A1 and PSI-S2 by high pressure liquid chromatography analysis and partial sequence determination. J. Biol. Chem. 261:8134–8139.

––––, U. Kuck, and L. Bogorad. 1985. Two partially homologous adjacent light-inducible maize chloroplast genes encoding polypeptides of the P700 chlorophyll a-protein complex of photosystem I. J. Biol. Chem. 260:1413–1421.

Ferl, R.J., and H.S. Nick. 1987. In vivo detection of regulatory factor binding sites in the 5′ flanking region of maize *Adh1* before and during induction of gene activity. J. Biol. Chem. 262:7947–7950.

Fox, T.D., and C.J. Leaver. 1981. The *Zea mays* mitochondrial gene coding cytochrome oxidase subunit II has an intervening sequence and does not contain TGA codons. Cell 26:315–323.

Freeling, M. 1984. Plant transposable elements and insertion sequences. Ann. Rev. Plant Physiol. 35:277–298.

––––, and D.C. Bennett. 1985. Maize *Adh1*. Ann. Rev. Genet. 19:297–323.

Fromm, M., L.P. Taylor, and V. Walbot. 1985. Expression of genes transferred into monocot and dicot plant cells by electroporation. Proc. Natl. Acad. Sci. USA 82:5824–5828.

––––, ––––, and ––––. 1986. Stable transformation of maize after gene transfer by electroporation. Nature (London) 319:791–793.

Geraghty, D., M.A. Peifer, I. Rubenstein, and J. Messing. 1981. The primary structure of a plant storage protein: Zein. Nucl. Acids Res. 9:5163–5174.

Gold, B.N. Carrillo, K.K. Tewari and L. Bogorad. 1987. Nucleotide sequence of a preferred maize chloroplast genome template for *in vitro* DNA synthesis. Proc. Natl. Acad. Sci. USA 84:194–198.

Goldsbrough, P.B., S.B. Gelvin, and B.A. Larkins. 1986. Expression of maize zein genes in transformed sunflower cells. Mol. Gen. Genet. 202:374–381.

Graves, A.C.F., and S.L. Goldman. 1986. The transformation of *Zea mays* seedlings with *Agrobacterium tumefaciens*: Detection of T-DNA specific enzyme activities. Plant Mol. Biol. 7:43–50.

Grimsley, N., T. Hohn, J.W. Davies, and B. Hohn. 1987. *Agrobacterium,*-mediated delivery of infectious maize streak virus into maize plants. Nature (London) 325:177–179.

Grosveld, G.C., C.K. Shewmaker, P. Jat, and R.A. Flavell. 1981. Localization of DNA sequences necessary for transcription of the rabbit beta-globin gene in vitro. Cell 25:215–226.

––––, E. de Boer, C.K. Shewmaker, and R.A. Flavell. 1982. DNA sequences necessary for transcription of the rabbit beta-globin gene in vivo. Nature (London) 295:120–126.

Hackett, P.B., J.A. Fuchs, and J.W. Messing. 1988. An introduction to recombinant DNA techniques. 2nd ed. Benjamin/Cummings Publ., Menlo Park, CA.

Hake, S., and V. Walbot. 1980. The genome of *Zea mays*, its organization and homology to related grasses. Chromosoma 79:251–270.

Hallick, R.B. and W. Bottomley. 1983. Proposals for the naming of chloroplast genes. Plant Mol. Biol. Rep. 1:38–43.

Hanley-Bowdoin, L., E.M. Orozco Jr., and N. -H. Chua. 1985. In vitro synthesis and processing of a maize chloroplast transcript encoded by the ribulose 1,5-bisphosphate carboxylase large subunit gene. Mol. Cell Biol. 5:2733–2745.

Haslinger, A., and M. Karin. 1985. Upstream promoter element of the human metallothionein-II$_A$ gene can act like an enhancer element. Proc. Natl. Acad. Sci. USA 82:8572–8576.

Hawley, D.K., and W.R. McClure. 1983. Compilation and analysis of *Escherichia coli* promoter DNA sequences. Nucl. Acids Res. 11:2237–2255.

Heidecker, G., and J. Messing. 1983. Sequence analysis of zein cDNAs obtained by an efficient mRNA cloning method. Nucl. Acids Res. 11:4891–4906.

——, and ——. 1986. Structural analysis of plant genes. Annu. Rev. Plant Physiol. 37:439–466.

——, and ——. 1987. A method for cloning full-length cDNA in plasmid vectors. Methods Enzymol. 154:28–41.

Helentjaris, T., G. King, M. Slocum, C. Siedenstrang, and S. Wegman. 1985. Restriction fragment polymorphisms as probes for plant diversity and their development as tools for applied plant breeding. Plant Mol. Biol. 5:109–118.

——, M. Slocum, S. Wright, A. Schaefer, and J. Nienhuis. 1986a. Construction of genetic linkage maps in maize and tomato using restriction fragment length polymorphisms. Theor. Appl. Genet. 72:761–769.

——, D.F. Weber, and S. Wright. 1986b. Use of monosomics to map cloned DNA fragments in maize. Proc. Natl. Acad. Sci. USA 83:6035–6039.

Helfman, D.M., J.R. Feramisco, J.C. Fiddes, G.P. Thomas, and S.H. Hughes. 1983. Identification of clones that encode chicken tropomyosin by direct immunological screening of a cDNA expression library. Proc. Natl. Acad. Sci. USA 80:31–35.

Hirschberg, J., and L. McIntosh. 1983. Molecular basis of herbicide resistance in *Amaranthus hybridus*. Science 222:1346–1348.

Hoffman, L.M., Y. Ma, and R.F. Barker. 1982. Molecular cloning of *Phaseolus vulgaris* lectin mRNA and use of cDNA as a probe to estimate lectin transcript levels in various tissues. Nucl. Acids Res. 10:7819–7828.

Hu, N-T, M.A. Peifer, G. Heidecker, J. Messing, and I. Rubenstein. 1982. Primary structure of a zein genomic clone. EMBO J. 1:1337–1342.

Isaac, P.G., A. Brennicke, S.M. Dunbar, and C.J. Leaver. 1985. The mitochondrial genome of fertile maize (*Zea mays* L.) contains two copies of the gene encoding the α-subunit of the F_1-ATPase. Curr. Genet. 10:321–328.

——, V.P. Jones, and C.J. Leaver. 1985. The maize cytochrome oxidase subunit I gene: Sequence, expression and a rearrangement in cytoplasmic male sterile plants. EMBO J. 4:1617–1623.

Johns, M.W., J.P. Mottinger, and M. Freeling. 1985. A low copy number, *copia*-like transposon in maize. EMBO J. 4:1093–1102.

——, J.N. Strommer, and M. Freeling. 1983. Exceptionally high levels of restriction site polymorphism in DNA near the maize *Adh1* gene. Genetics 105:733–743.

Kandonaga, J.T., Jones, and R. Tijan. 1986. Promoter-specific activation of RNA polymerase II transcription by Spl. Trends Biochem. Sci. 11:20–23.

Kevin, B., and N.-H Chua. 1986. Monocot and dicot pre-mRNAs are processed with different efficiency in transgenic tobacco. EMBO J. 5:2419–2425.

Khoury, G., and P. Gruss. 1983. Enhancer elements. Cell 33:313–314.

Kirihara, J.A., J.P. Hunsperger, W.C. Mahoney, and J.W. Messing. 1988. Differential expression of a gene for a methionine-rich storage protein in maize. Mol. Gen. Genet. 211:477–484.

Klösgen, R.B., A. Gierl, Z. Schwarz-Sommer, and H. Saedler. 1986. Molecular analysis of the *waxy* locus of *Zea mays*. Mol. Gen. Genet. 203:237–244.

Koch, W., K. Edwards and H. Kossel. 1981. Sequencing of the 16S-23S spacer in a ribosomal RNA operon of *Zea mays* chloroplast DNA reveals two split tRNA genes. Cell 25:203–213.

Kozak, M. 1980. Role of ATP in binding and migration of 40S ribosomal subunits. Cell 22:459–467.

——. 1981. Possible role of flanking nucleotides in recognition of the AUG initiator codon by eukaryotic ribosomes. Nucl. Acids Res. 9:5233–5252.

——. 1984. Selection of initiation sites by eukaryotic ribosomes: Effect of inserting AUG triplets upstream from the coding sequence for preproinsulin. Nucl. Acids. Res. 12:3873–3893.

——. 1986. Regulation of protein synthesis in virus-infected animal cells. Adv. Virus Res. 31:229–292.

Krebbers, E.T., I.M. Larrinua, L. McIntosh, and L. Bogorad. 1982. The maize chloroplast genes for the beta and epsilon subunits of the photosynthetic coupling factor CF_1 are fused. Nucleic Acids Res. 10:4985–5002.

——, A. Steinmetz, and L. Bogorad. 1984. DNA sequences for the *Zea mays* tRNA genes tV-UAC and tS-UGA: tV-UAC contains a large intron. Plant Mol. Biol. 3:13–20.

Kriz, A.L., R.S. Boston, and B.A. Larkins. 1988. Structural and transcriptional analysis of genes that encode M$_r$ 19,000 zeins. Mol. Gen. Genet. (In press.)

Larkins, B.A., R.A. Jones, and C.Y. Tsai. 1976. Isolation and in vitro translation of zein messenger ribonucleic acid. Biochemistry 15:5506–5511.

Larrinau, I.M., and W.E. McLaughlin. 1987. A gene cluster in the Z. *mays* plastid genome is homologous to part of the S10 operon of *E. coli. In*, J. Biggens (ed.) Progress in photosynthesis research, Vol. IV. Martinus Nijhoff Publ., Dordrecht, Netherlands.

————, K.M.T. Muskavitch, E.J. Gubbins, and L. Bogorad. 1983. A detailed restriction endonuclease site map of the *Zea mays* plastid genome. Plant Mol. Biol. 2:129–140.

Leon, P., P. Bedinger, and V. Walbot. 1988. The linear 2.3 kbp plasmid of maize mitochondria: Apparent capture of tRNA genes from the main mitochondrial genome. (Submitted for publication.)

Levings, C.S.III, B.D. Kim, D.R. Pring, M.F. Conde, R.J. Mans, J.R. Laughnan, and S.J. Gabay-Laughnan. 1980. Cytoplasmic reversion of cms-S in maize: association with a transpositional event. Science 209:1021–1023.

————, and D.R. Pring. 1976. Restriction endonuclease analysis of mitochondrial DNA from normal and Texas cytoplasmic male sterile maize. Science 193:158–160.

————, and ————. 1977. Diversity of mitochondrial genomes among normal cytoplasms of maize. J. Hered. 68:350–354.

————, D.M. Shah, W.W.L. Hu, D.R. Pring, and D.H. Timothy. 1979. Molecular heterogeneity among mitochondrial DNAs from different maize cytoplasms. p. 63–89. *In* D.J. Cummings et al. (ed.) Extrachromosomal inheritance. Academic Press, New York.

————, and R.R. Sederoff. 1983. Nucleotide sequences of the S-2 mitochondrial DNA from the S cytoplasm of maize. Proc. Natl. Acad. Sci. USA 80:4055–4059.

Lonsdale, D.M., T.P. Hodge, and C.M.-R. Fauron. 1984. The physical map and organization of the mitochondrial genome from the fertile cytoplasm of maize. Nucl. Acids Res. 12:9249–9261.

Ludwig, S.R., R.F. Pohlman, J. Vieira, A.G. Smith, and J. Messing. 1985. The nucleotide sequence of a mitochondrial replicon from maize. Gene 38:131–138.

Maier, V.-G, J.W.S. Brown, C. Toloczyki, and G. Feix. 1987. Binding of a nuclear factor to a consensus sequence in the 5′ flanking region of zein genes from maize. EMBO J. 6:17–22.

Maniatis, T., E.F. Fritsch, and J. Sambrook. 1982. Molecular cloning. Cold Spring Harbor Lab., Cold Spring Harbor, NY.

Manson, J.C., A.D. Liddell, C.J. Leaver, and K. Murray. 1986. A protein specific to mitochondria from S-type male-sterile cytoplasm of maize is encoded by an episomal DNA. EMBO J. 5:2775–2780.

Marchionni, M., and W. Gilbert. 1986. The triose phosphate isomerase gene from maize: Introns antedate the plant-animal divergence. Cell 46:133–141.

Markmann-Mulisch, U., and A.R. Subramanian. 1988. Nucleotide sequence and linkage map position of the genes for ribosomal proteins L14 and S8 in the maize chloroplast genome. (Submitted for publication.)

Marechal, L., P. Guillemaut, J.M. Greinenberger, G. Jeannin, and J.H. Weil. 1985. Sequence and codon recognition of bean mitochondria and chloroplast tRNAs^{trp}: Evidence for a high degree of homology. Nucl. Acids Res. 13:4411–4416.

————, ————, ————, ————, and ————. 1986. Sequences of initiator and elongator methionine tRNAs in bean mitochondria. Plant Mol. Biol. 7:245–253.

Marks, M.D., and B.A. Larkins. 1982. Analysis of sequence microheterogeneity among zein messenger RNAs. J. Biol. Chem. 257:9976–9983.

————, J.S. Lindell, and B.A. Larkins. 1985. Nucleotide sequence analysis of zein mRNAs from maize endosperm. J. Biol. Chem. 260:16451–16459.

Mascia, P.N., I. Rubenstein, R.L. Phillips, A.S. Wang, and L.Z. Xiang. 1981. Localization of the 5S rDNA genes and evidence for diversity in the 5S rDNA region of maize. Gene 15:7–20.

Matzke, M.A., M. Susani, A.N. Binns, E.D. Lewis, I. Rubenstein, and A.J.M. Matzke. 1984. Transcription of a zein gene introduced into sunflower using a Ti plasmid vector. EMBO J. 3:1525–1531.

McCarty, D.R., J.R. Shaw, and L.C. Hannah. 1986. The cloning, genetic mapping and expression of the constitutive sucrose synthetase locus of maize. Proc. Natl. Acad. Sci. USA 83:9099–9103.

McClintock, B. 1934. The relation of a particular chromosomal element to the development of the nucleoli in *Zea mays*. Z. Zellforsch. Mikrosk, Anat. 21:294–328.

McIntosh, L., C. Poulsen, and L. Bogorad. 1980. Chloroplast gene sequence for the large subunit of ribulose bisphosphate carboxylase of maize. Nature (London) 288:556–560.

McLaughlin, W.E. and I.M. Larrinua. 1987a. The sequence of the maize *rps*19 locus and of the inverted repeat/unique region junctions. Nucleic Acids Res. 15:3932.

————, and ————. 1987b. The sequence of the maize plastid encoded *rpl*22 locus. Nucleic Acids Res. 15:4356.

————, and ————. 1987c. The sequence of the maize plastid encoded *rps*3 locus. Nucleic Acids Res. 15:4689.

————, and ————. 1987d. The sequence of the first exon and part of the intron of the maize plastid encoded *rpl*16 locus. Nucleic Acids Res. 15:5896.

Messing, J., J. Carlson, G. Hagen, I. Rubenstein, and A. Oleson. 1984. Cloning and sequencing of the ribosomal RNA genes in maize: The 17S region. DNA 3:31–40.

————, D. Geraghty, G. Heidecker, N-T. Hu, J. Kridl, and I. Rubenstein. 1983. Plant gene structure. p. 211–227. *In* T. Kosuge et al. (ed.) Genetic engineering of plants. Plenum Press, New York.

Müller-Neumann, M., J.I. Yoder, and P. Starlinger. 1984. The DNA sequence of the transposable element *Ac* of *Zea mays* L. Mol. Gen. Genet. 198:19–24.

Mullet, J.E., E.M. Orozco Jr., and N. -H Chua. 1985. Multiple transcripts for higher plant *rbc* and *atp*B genes and localization of the transcription initiation site of the *rbc*L gene. Plant Mol. Biol. 4:39–54.

Myers, R.M., K. Tilly, and T. Maniatis. 1986. Fine structure genetic analysis of a beta-globin promoter. Science 232:613–618.

Nelson, T., M.H. Harpster, S.P. Mayfield, and W.C. Taylor. 1984. Light-regulated gene expression during maize leaf development. J. Cell Biol. 98:558–564.

Nevers, P., N.S. Shepherd, and H. Saedler. 1986. Plant transposable elements. Adv. Bot. Res. 12:103–203.

O'Reilly, C., N.S. Shepherd, A. Pereira, Z. Schwarz-Sommer, I. Bertram, D.S. Robertson, P.A. Peterson, and H. Saedler. 1985. Molecular cloning of the *al* locus of *Zea mays* using the transposable elements *En* and *Mul*. EMBO J. 4:877–882.

Paillard, M., R.R. Sederoff, and C.S. Levings III. 1985. Nucleotide sequences of the S-1 mitochondrial DNA from the S cytoplasm of maize. EMBO J. 4:1125–1128.

Palmer, J.D. 1983. Chloroplast DNA exists in two orientations. Nature (London) 301:92–93.

————. 1985. Evolution of chloroplast and mitochondrial DNA in plants and algae. p. 131–240. *In* R.J. MacIntyre (ed.) Monographs in evolutionary biology: Molecular evolutionary genetics. Plenum Publ. Corp., New York.

Parks, T.D., W.G. Dougherty, C.S. Levings III, and D.H. Timothy. 1984. Identification of two methionine transfer RNA genes in the maize mitochondrial genome. Plant Physiol. 76:1079–1082.

————, ————, ————, and ————. 1985. Identification of an aspartate transfer RNA gene in maize mitochondrial DNA. Curr. Genet. 9:517–519.

Pas-Ares, J., U. Wienand, P.A. Peterson, and H. Saedler. 1986. Molecular cloning of the *c* locus of *Zea mays*: A locus regulating the anthocyanin pathway. EMBO J. 5:829–833.

Paul, A. -L., V. Vasil, I. Vasil, and R.J. Ferl. 1987. Constitutive and anaerobically induced DNase-I hypersensitive sites in the 5′ region of the maize *Adh1* gene. Proc. Natl. Acad. Sci. USA 84:799–803.

Peacock, W.J., E.S. Dennis, M.M. Rhoades, and A.J. Pryor. 1981. Highly repeated DNA sequence limited to knob heterochromatin in maize. Proc. Natl. Acad. Sci. USA 78:4490–4494.

Pedersen, K., P. Argos, S.V.L. Nayavana, and B.A. Larkins. 1986. Sequence analysis and characterization of a maize gene encoding a high sulfur zein protein of M_r 15,000. J. Biol. Chem. 261:6279–6284.

————, J. Devereux, D.R. Wilson, E. Sheldon, and B.A. Larkins. 1982. Cloning and sequence analysis reveal structural variation among related zein genes in maize. Cell 29:1015–1026.

Pereira, A., H. Cuypers, A. Gierl, Z. Schwarz-Sommer, and H. Saedler. 1986. Molecular analysis of the En/Spm transposable element system of *Zea mays*. EMBO J. 5:835–841.

Pohlman, R.F., N.V. Fedoroff, and J. Messing. 1984. The nucleotide sequence of maize controlling element *Activator*. Cell 37:635–643; correction in Cell 39:417.

Poulsen, C. 1981. Comments on the structure and function of the large subunit of the enzyme ribulose bisphosphate carboxylase-oxygenase. Carlsberg Res. Commun. 46:259–278.

Prat, S., J. Cortadas, P. Puigdomenech, and J. Palau. 1985. Nucleic acid (cDNA) and amino acid sequence of the maize endosperm protein glutelin-1. Nucl. Acids Res. 13:1493–1509.

Pring, D.R., M.F. Conde, and C.S. Levings III. 1980. DNA heterogeneity within the C group of maize male-sterile cytoplasms. Crop Sci. 20:159–162.

----, and C.S. Levings III. 1978. Heterogeneity of maize cytoplasmic genomes among male-sterile cytoplasms. Genetics 89:121–136.

----, and D.M. Lonsdale. 1985. Molecular biology of higher plant mitochondrial DNA. Int. Rev. Cytol. 97:1–46.

Proundfoot, N.J. 1979. Eukaryotic promoters? Nature (London) 279:376.

Rayburn, A.L., H.J. Price, J.D. Smith, and J.R. Gold. 1985. C-band heterochromatin and DNA content in Zea mays. Am. J. Bot. 72:1610–1617.

Rivin, C.J., C.A. Cullis, and V. Walbot. 1986. Evaluating quantitative variation in the genome of Zea mays. Genetics 113:1009–1019.

Robertson, D.S. 1978. Characterization of a mutator system in maize. Mutat. Res. 51:21–28.

Rochester, D.E., J.A. Winters, and D.M. Shah. 1986. The structure and expression of maize genes encoding the major heat shock protein hsp70. EMBO J. 5:451–458.

Rock, C.D., A. Barkan, and W.C. Taylor. 1987. The maize plastid psbB - psbF -petB - petD gene cluster: Spliced and unspliced petB and petD RNAs encode alternative products. Curr. Genet. 12:69–77.

Rodermel, S.R. and L. Bogorad. 1985. Maize plastid photogenes: mapping and photoregulation of transcript levels during light-induced development. J. Cell Biol. 100:463–476.

----, and L. Bogorad. 1987. Molecular evolution and nucleotide sequences of the maize plastid genes for the alpha subunit of CF_1 (atpA) and the proteolipid subunit of CF_0 (atpH). Genetics 116:127–139.

----, P. Orlin, and L. Bogorad. 1987. The transcription termination region between two convergently-transcribed photoregulated operons in the maize plastid chromosome contains rps14, trnR (UCU) and a putative trnfM pseudogene. Nucleic Acids Res. 15:5493.

Rubin, G.M. 1983. Dispersed repetitive DNAs in Drosophila. p. 329–361. In J.A. Shapiro (ed.) Mobile genetics elements. Academic Press, New York.

Saedler, H., and P. Nevers. 1985. Transposition in plants: A molecular model. EMBO J. 4:585–590.

Schardl, C.L., D.M. Lonsdale, D.R. Pring, and K.R. Rose. 1984. Linearization of maize mitochondrial chromosomes by recombination with linear episomes. Nature (London) 310:292–296.

----, D.R. Pring, and D.M. Lonsdale. 1985. Mitochondrial DNA rearrangements associated with fertile revertants of S-type male-sterile maize. Cell 43:361–368.

Schiefelbein, J.W., V. Raboy, N.V. Fedoroff, and O.E. Nelson, Jr. 1985. Deletions within a defective supressor-mutator element in maize affect the frequency and developmental timing of its excision from the bronze locus. Proc. Natl. Acad. Sci. USA 82:4783–4787.

Schwartz, D., and E. Dennis. 1986. Transposase activity of the Ac controlling element in maize is regulated by its degree of methylation. Mol. Gen. Genet. 203:476–482.

Schwarz, Zs., S.O. Jolly, A.A. Steinmetz, and L. Bogorad. 1981. Overlapping divergent genes encoding the maize chloroplast chromosome and in vitro transcription of the gene for tRNA[His]. Proc. Natl. Acad. Sci. USA 78:3423–3427.

----, and H. Kossel. 1979. Sequencing of the 3'-terminal region of a 16S rRNA gene from Zea mays chloroplast reveals homology with E. coli 16S rRNA. Nature (London) 279:520–522.

---- and ----. 1980. The primary structure of 16S rDNA from Zea mays chloroplast is homologous to E. coli 16S rRNA. Nature (London) 283:739–742.

----, ----, E. Schwarz and L. Bogorad. 1981. A gene coding for tRNA[Val] is located near 5' terminus of 16S rRNA gene in Zea mays chloroplast genome. Proc. Natl. Acad. Sci. USA 78:4748–4752.

Schwarz-Sommer, Z., A. Gierl, R. Berndtgen, and H. Saedler. 1985a. Sequence comparison of 'states' of al-ml suggests a model of Spm (En) action. EMBO J. 4:2439–2443.

----, ----, H. Cuypers, P.A. Peterson, and H. Saedler. 1985b. Plant transposable elements generate the DNA sequence diversity needed in evolution. EMBO J. 4:591–597.

Sederoff, R.R., P. Ronald, P. Bedinger, C. Rivin, V. Walbot, M. Bland, and C.S. Levings III. 1986. Maize mitochondrial plasmid S-1 sequences share homology with chloroplast gene psbA. Genetics 113:469–482.

Selden, R.F., A. Steinmetz, L. McIntosh, L. Bogorad, G. Burkard, M. Mubumbila, M. Kuntz, E.J. Crouse, and J.H. Weil. 1983. Transfer RNA genes of Zea mays chloroplast DNA. Plant Mol. Biol. 2:141–153.

Shah, D.M., R.C. Hightower, and R.B. Meagher. 1983. Genes encoding actin in higher plants: Intron positions are highly conserved but the coding sequences are not. J. Mol. Appl. Genet. 2:111–116.

————, and C.S. Levings III. 1974. Mitochondrial DNA from maize hybrids with normal and Texas cytoplasms. Crop Sci. 14:852–853.

————, C.M. Hironaka, R.C. Wiegand, E.I. Harding, G.G. Kirvi, and D.C. Tiemeier. 1986. Structural analysis of a maize gene coding for glutathione-S-transferase involved in herbicide detoxification. Plant Mol. Biol. 6:203–211.

Shaw, C.H., G.H. Carter, M.D. Watson, and C.H. Shaw. 1984. A functional map of the nopaline synthase promoter. Nucl. Acids Res. 12:7831–7846.

Sheldon, E., R. Ferl, N. Fedoroff, and L.C. Hannah. 1983. Isolation and analysis of a genomic clone encoding sucrose synthetase in maize—evidence for 2 introns in Sh. Mol. Gen. Genet. 190:421–426.

Shepherd, N.S., Z. Schwarz-Sommer, U. Wienand, H. Sommer, B. Duemling, P.A. Peterson, and H. Saedler. 1982. Cloning of a genomic fragment carrying the insertion element Cin 1 of Zea mays. Mol. Gen. Genet. 188:266–271.

————, ————, J. Blumberg vel Spaive, M. Gupta, U. Wienand, and H. Saedler. 1984. Similarity of the Cin1, repetitive family of Zea mays to eukaryotic transposable elements. Nature (London) 307:185–187.

Shine, J., and L. Dalgarno. 1974. The 3′-terminal sequence of Escherichia coli 16S ribosomal RNA: Complementarity to nonsense triplets and ribosome binding sites. Proc. Natl. Acad. Sci. USA 71:1342–1346.

Shinozaki, K., et al. 1986. The complete nucleotide sequence of the tobacco chloroplast genome: Its gene organization and expression. EMBO J. 5:2043–2049.

Shure, M., S. Wessler, and N.V. Fedoroff. 1983. Molecular identification and isolation of the waxy locus in maize. Cell 35:225–233.

Steinmetz, A.A., M. Castroviejo, R.T. Sayre, and L. Bogorad. 1986. Protein PSII-G. An additional component of photosystem II identified through its plastid gene in maize. J. Biol. Chem. 261:2485–2488.

————, E.J. Gubbins, and L. Bogorad. 1982. The anticodon of the maize chloroplast gene for tRNA^{Leu} (UAA) is split by a large intron. Nucleic Acids Res. 10:3027–3037.

————, E.T. Krebbers, Zs. Schwarz, E.J. Gubbins, and L. Bogorad. 1983. Nucleotide sequences of five maize chloroplast transfer RNA genes and their flanking regions. J. Biol. Chem. 258:5503–5511.

Stern, D.B., and D.M. Lonsdale. 1982. Mitochondrial and chloroplast genomes of maize have a 12 kb sequence in common. Nature (London) 299:696–702.

————, and J.D. Palmer. 1984. Extensive and widespread homologies between mitochondrial DNA and chloroplast DNA in plants. Proc. Natl. Acad. Sci. USA 81:1946–1950.

Stirdivant, S.M., L.D. Crossland, and L. Bogorad. 1985. DNA supercoiling affects in vitro transcription of two maize chloroplast genes differently. Proc. Natl. Acad. Sci. USA 82:4886–4890.

Strittmatter, G., and H. Kossel. 1984. Cotranscription and processing of 23S, 4.5S and 5S rRNA in chloroplasts from Zea mays. Nucleic Acids Res. 12:7633–7647.

Subramanian, A.R., A. Steinmetz, and L. Bogorad. 1983. Maize chloroplast DNA encodes a protein sequence homologous to the bacterial ribosome assembly protein S4. Nucleic Acids Res. 11:5277–5286.

Sutton, W.D., W.L. Gerlach, D. Schwartz, and W.J. Peacock. 1984. Molecular analysis of Ds controlling element mutations at the Adh1 locus of maize. Science 223:1265–1268.

Taylor, L., and V. Walbot. 1985. A deletion adjacent to a maize transposable element accompanies loss of gene expression. EMBO J. 4:869–876.

Taylor, W.C., S.P. Mayfield, and B. Martineau. 1984. The role of chloroplast development in nuclear gene expression. p. 601–610. In E.H. Davidson and R.A. Firtel (ed.) UCLA symposia on molecular and cellular biology, Vol. 19. Alan R Liss, New York.

Vieira, J., and J. Messing. 1982. The pUC plasmids, and M13mp7 derived system for insertional mutagenesis and sequencing with univeral primers. Gene 19:259–268.

Viotti, A., D. Abildstein, N. Pogna, E. Sala, and V. Pirrotta. 1982. Multiplicity and diversity of cloned zein cDNA sequences and their chromosomal localization. EMBO J. 1:53–58.

Wang, S. -Z., and A. Esen. 1986. Primary structure of a proline-rich zein and its cDNA. Plant Physiol. 81:70–74.

Watson, J.D., J. Tooze, and D.T. Kurtz. 1983. Recombinant DNA: A short course. W.H. Freeman Co., New York.

Weintraub, H., and M. Groudine. 1976. Chromosome subunits in active genes have altered conformation. Science 193:848–856.

Werr, W., W.B. Frommer, C. Maas, and P. Starlinger. 1985. Structure of the sucrose synthase gene on chromosome 9 of *Zea mays* L. EMBO J. 4:1373–1380.

Wessler, S.R., and M.J. Varagona. 1985. Molecular basis of mutations at the waxy locus of maize: Correlation with the fine structure genetic map. Proc. Natl. Acad. Sci. USA 82:4177–4181.

Wienand, U., C. Brusch, and G. Feix. 1979. Cloning of double-stranded DNAs derived from polysomal mRNA of maize endosperm: Isolation and characterization of zein clones. Nucl. Acids Res. 6:2707–2715.

————, H. Sommer, Zs. Schwarz, N. Shepherd, H. Saedler, F. Kreuzaler, H. Ragg, E. Fautz, K. Hahlbrock, B. Harrison, and P.A. Peterson. 1982. A general method to identify plant structural genes among genomic DNA clones using transposable element induced mutations. Mol. Gen. Genet. 187:195–201.

————, U. Weydemann, U. Niesback-Klösgen, P.A. Peterson, and H. Saedler. 1986. Molecular cloning of the *c2* locus of *Zea mays*, the gene coding for chalcone synthetase. Mol. Gen. Genet. 203:202–207.

Young, R.A., and R.W. Davis. 1983. Yeast RNA polymerase II genes: isolation with antibody probes. Science 222:778–782.

Zabala, G., C. O'Brien-Vedder, and V. Walbot. 1987. S-2 plasmid of maize mitochondria encodes a 130 kilodalton protein found in both male sterile and fertile plants. Proc. Natl. Acad. Sci. USA 84:7861–7865.

Zenke, M., T. Grundstrom, H. Matthes, M. Winzerith, C. Schatz, A. Wintzerith, C. Schatz, A. Wildeman, and P. Chambon. 1986. Multiple sequence motifs are involved in SV40 enhancer function. EMBO J. 5:387–397.

Zurawski, G., M.T. Clegg, and A.H.D. Brown. 1984. The nature of nucleotide sequence divergence between barley and maize chloroplast DNA. Genetics 106:735–749.

7 The Use of Physiological Traits for Corn Improvement

R. H. HAGEMAN and R. J. LAMBERT

Department of Agronomy
University of Illinois
Urbana, Illinois

Consistent increases in yields have been observed for the major crops grown in the USA during the past 40 yr. Most of the improvement in the corn (*Zea mays* L.) hybrids currently used has been achieved by the use of conventional plant breeding methods. Selections in corn and other crops have been made, primarily, on the basis of visual morphological traits (vigor, stalk quality, green score, and disease resistance) and other readily counted or measured traits (ear number, yield components, and especially grain weight). Diverse production factors such as higher levels of fertility, especially N, and improved equipment that greatly shortens time required for planting and harvesting have also contributed to the steady increases in crop yields. However, the contribution of the genetic gains to the steady increase in crop yields has been estimated to be: for corn (Duvick, 1984) 92 kg ha^{-1} yr^{-1} (1930–1980); wheat (*Triticum aestivum* L.) (Schmidt, 1984) 0.74% yr^{-1} (1958–1980); soybean [*Glycine max* (L.) Merr.] (Specht and Williams, 1984) 21 kg ha^{-1} yr^{-1} (1924–1980); sorghum [*Sorghum bicolor* (L.) Moench] (Miller and Kebede, 1984) 7.0% yr^{-1} (1950–1980); and cotton (*Gossypium hirsutum* L.) (Meredith and Bridge, 1984) 9.5 kg ha^{-1} yr^{-1} (1936–1980). Relative to other factors associated with increased productivity, improved genotypes have been estimated to account for 57 to 63% of the increased yield for corn; 35 to 50% for wheat; and 9 to 31% for oat (*Avena sativa* L.) (Rodgers et al., 1983). While changes in physiological traits such as photosynthesis, partitioning of assimilates, etc. can be associated with increased yields of the currently used cultivars, these changes have been achieved indirectly by conventional breeding methods rather than by direct selection for the trait.

The concept of and need to identify physiological traits, useful for crop improvement, is not new. In 1907, Robertson (1923) noted the similarity between plant growth curves and curves of product produced by a monomolecular autocatalytic reaction. He proposed that growth was controlled by a rate-limiting (enzymic) step of processes that affected growth. Engledow and Wadham (1923) initiated work with cereals, with the objectives of identifying plant characters that control yield and development of a systematic system of hybridization that would incorporate these desired traits into a single genotype. They also stated "To plant physiology we must look for a final solution to the 'yield problem' but meantime for plant breeding the only practical course is to seek an advance by investigation of the statistical characters which are more amenable to observation than those terms of which physiology has to proceed."

Stephens (1942) reiterated the possibility raised for other cereals that his oat cultivars already possessed the optimum genetic compositions for maximum yield under the environments used for their culture. The same idea was proposed by Stringfield (1964) for corn. Wittwer (1978) expressed this same view, i.e., that restrictions in genetic diversity, breeding techniques, and management practices were now or soon would be limiting yields.

There is evidence that genetic diversity still exists in the available breeding stocks. Selection progress is still being made in corn for variation in: percentage composition in oil and protein of the grain (Dudley, 1977), nitrate reductase activity (NRA) (Sherrard et al., 1986), photosynthetic activity (Crosbie et al., 1981; Musgrave, 1971; Nubel, 1986), and grain yield (Duvick, 1977). For example, average corn yields for the USA were 2650, 4670, 5430, and 7430 kg ha^{-1} in 1955, 1965, 1975, and 1985, respectively. Segmented regressional analysis of the data over the 1955 to 1978 period revealed a linear increase with no indication of a leveling off of yields (W. M. Walker, 1980, personal communication).

The consistent grain yield gains in commercial corn hybrids for the period 1930 to 1980 were accompanied by large and consistent genetic gains in resistance to stalk and root lodging, a reduction in premature plant death, reduced barrenness, greater tolerance to higher plant densities and greater responsiveness to higher soil fertility levels (Duvick, 1984). The newer developed hybrids also had consistently superior performance in low yield environments. These genetic changes in the commercial hybrids over this period were also associated with an increase in upright leaves and stover dry weight plant^{-1}, heavier and fewer kernels plant^{-1}, and a decrease in kernel row ear^{-1}. Analysis of several inbred diallel sets indicated that general combining ability effects for yield, standability, and stress resistance have improved during this period. Specific combining effects may have been important in the genetic gains observed for yield in recent years. Also midparent heterosis for yield increased at a linear rate of 40 kg ha^{-1} yr^{-1} (Duvick, 1984).

Based on these results and related studies future genetic gains in corn breeding should continue at about this same rate. The future rate of genetic gain may also be increased because of an increase in the total number of corn breeders that should enhance the total corn breeding effort. Application of knowledge gained from physiological measurements (photosynthesis, respiration, and N metabolism) and genetic engineering techniques (DNA characterization, herbicide resistance, and drought stress) to and in conjunction with improved corn breeding methods should ensure continued increases in productivity.

In addition to advances in design of farm machinery, increased application of fertilizers and improved soil management practices have also increased yields. For example, over a period of years an Illinois farmer, Herman Warsaw, has incorporated large amounts of fertilizer, crop residue and manure, and used deep chisel plowing to establish a deep rooting zone rich in nutrient elements and organic matter with high capacity for retention of water (Nelson and Reetz, 1986; Warsaw, 1985). With the corn hybrid, Farm Service brand 854, yields of 21 300, 19 700, 20 800, 18 900 and 23 300 kg ha^{-1} were obtained (without irrigation) from 0.5 ha plots (selected on different fields) in 1975, 1979, 1981, 1982, and 1985, respectively. Several hybrids, with FS854 being predominant, grown on one 12-ha field produced an average yield of 16 800 kg ha^{-1} over a 14-yr period. The FS854 hybrid is a relatively old hybrid (year of release 1970). FS854 does not have the canopy ideotype specified by Mock and Pearce (1975) or good stalk quality.

These observations would indicate that neither genetic diversity of the existing germ plasm nor management practices have been optimized for corn yields. In view of the evidence of ample genetic diversity, "why has there been as little progress in achieving the objectives or responding to the plea for useful physiological traits raised in 1923 (Engledow and Wadham, 1923)?"

In this article we propose to: (i) classify and list the requirements of a physiological selection trait; (ii) briefly outline the early development and use of physiological selection criteria; (iii) discuss attempts to use physiological traits, and where appropriate compare the usefulness of physiological traits with conventional traits used to develop improved cultivars; (iv) discuss problems with physiological traits; (v) outline future approaches for the use of physiological traits; and (vi) present a brief summary.

7–1 REQUIREMENT FOR PHYSIOLOGICAL SELECTION TRAIT

7–1.1 Classes

According to the basic concept that all aspects of growth and yield are the end product of all enzyme catalyzed processes under a specified environment, all traits could be classed as biochemical. However, use and tradition has established several classes of traits, namely, vegetative, morphological, yield components, growth rate, physiological, and biochemical. The classes are not distinct and most traits can be listed in more than one class. Enzyme activity is logically a biochemical trait; however for plant breeding procedures, activity values are commonly used as an estimate of product formation by a metabolic system. For this reason, the adjective "physiological" will be used to designate enzyme or metabolic activity that is under consideration as a selection trait (Sprague, 1969).

7-1.2 Requirements

Selection criteria should have the following requirements (Hageman et al., 1976; Mahon, 1983; Sherrard et al., 1986): (i) genetic variability for the trait must be present in the breeding materials; (ii) the trait should have high heritability; (iii) procedures for measurement of the trait should be accurate, rapid, and simple; large number of assays are needed for conventional breeding programs; (iv) the trait should have a high genetic correlation with grain yield; (v) the trait should be critical to metabolism. For example, if an enzyme is the trait, it should be the rate-limiting step in the pathway, preceding a branch point or be critical in some manner.

For corn, genetic variability and heritability have been reported for numerous traits such as: metabolite composition (Dudley, 1977); mineral constituents (Gorsline et al., 1964); morphology (Mock and Pearce, 1975); enzyme activity (Sherrard et al., 1986); and photosynthetic rates (Heichel and Musgrave, 1969; Musgrave, 1971). For these and other traits, adequate, but not ideal, methods of measurement were developed. Morphological and metabolic traits have been used extensively in the development of the corn cultivars in current use. Many of these traits were assessed visually or measured on the final product, which represents the integration of genetic and environmental interactions. Unfortunately, the association between traits that measure metabolic activity and yield of the selected cultivar under field conditions have not been consistent or dramatic enough to prompt use of these traits per se for development of commercial cultivars. Two factors limit the successful use of physiological traits (e.g., activity of one enzyme): (i) the lack of knowledge of how alterations of activity of one enzyme affect and interact with the entire metabolic system over time and with environmental changes; (ii) the inability to accurately relate enzyme activity (or the product of the enzyme or enzymic system) with yield which results from the interaction of the entire metabolic system (genotype) with the environment throughout the growing season.

7-2 EARLY WORK AND GROWTH RATE ANALYSIS

In his review of the physiological basis of crop yields, Watson 1952) states that one of the first attempts to analyze yield in relation to characters and plant growth that precedes yield was in 1917. In these early studies, measurements were made of the daily rates of: (i) elongation of the main stem; (ii) flower opening; and (iii) fruit ripening. A possible explanation for the lack of success of these studies is the traits are not independent expressions of plant growth and do not closely reflect the underlying physiological processes that affect yield (Watson, 1952). These changes were used to interpret variations in yield in response to planting dates and rates, and water supply. Although numerous investigators continued and expanded these types of studies to include tillering, yield components, and other morphological traits, traits per se useful for breeding programs were not identified (Watson, 1952). However, current evidence shows selection based only on some morphological traits might have been successful for some crop plants. The stem diameter and upper leaf canopy of modern sugarcane (*Saccharum officinarum* L.) cultivars are 20-fold greater than for *S. spontaneum*, their progenitor (Gifford and Evans, 1981). Assuming the increased leaf area is always proportional to photosynthate production and the increased stalk diameter is always proportional to sucrose storage volume, then concurrent selection for both traits would be a prerequisite for a successful breeding program based on these morphological parameters.

The development of "growth analysis" that relates rates of change in plant weight and/or leaf area was considered an advance over the measurements of morphological traits because weight and area changes presumably were more directly related to physiological processes. Blackman (1919) compared plant growth to the process of continuous compound interest and developed the following equation to describe relative growth rate (RGR). The RGR $= (1/W)(dW/dt)$ where W is the dry weight of the plant and dW is the change in W over the time interval represented by dt. Because not all of the dry weight is metabolically active (capital), a rate of increase in plant dry weight, net assimilation rate (NAR) was computed. The NAR $= (1/L)(dW/dt)$ where L is the total leaf area per plant and dW and dt are as previously noted. The NAR and L are estimates of the efficiency and capacity, respectively, of the photosynthetic system. The product of NAR by L represents the absolute growth rate. The two traits more directly reflect the contributions of two major metabolic processes (photosynthesis and respiration) than the previously cited traits.

Although small variations in NAR were recorded among and within species and with environment (water, nutrients, especially N, and temperature) the limited variability in NAR under normal production fields indicated NAR would be of little use in plant-breeding programs (Heath and Gregory, 1938; Watson, 1952). The validity for this view has been sustained in part by most carbon exchange rate (CER) measurements. Duncan and Hesketh (1968) compared the response of corn races adapted to high altitudes with races from low altitudes to different growing temperatures (controlled environments). There was no difference among the races for CER. However, the high-altitude races produced more leaves with greater relative leaf growth rates at the cooler temperatures than the low-altitude races. Currently, other workers are utilizing this approach to select corn inbreds, compatible with the cooler New Zealand temperatures, from populations heterozygous for U.S. Corn Belt and Mexican high-altitude germ plasm. (Hardacre et al., 1984). Selections are based on chlorophyll content and rate of emergence and growth in conjunction with agronomic performance. These workers established that traits per se without yield and related data were inadequate for producing acceptable genotypes.

In contrast to NAR, leaf area per plant varied within species and in general was positively associated with dry matter accumulation (Watson, 1952). Other leaf area parameters, leaf area duration (LAD), and leaf area index (LAI) were also associated with yield. For irrigated corn, nonlinear increases in yields were obtained as LAI values increased from 1.5 to 4.7; however, at a LAI of 8 yields were 16% lower than at a LAI of 4.7 (Duncan, 1975). For wheat, the conclusion that yields were proportional to LAI during grain-fill is probably only valid at LAI values under 8 (Thorne et al., 1979). However, for wheat grown over a wide range of environments, LAD accounted for about half of the variation in grain yield (Evans et al., 1975). Relative to NAR, these leaf traits (number, area, and duration) were more useful to plant-breeding programs even though they were not as closely associated with the underlying physiological processes (photosynthesis and respiration) as NAR. A major advantage of the leaf traits was that they could be estimated visually by plant vigor, leaf number, and green score.

The relationship of stand, tillering, and leaf area noted in growth analysis and related studies lead to further examination of the canopy and canopy architecture (Duncan, 1971) and served as a basis for modeling (Duncan et al., 1967; Loomis et al., 1979; Watson, 1952; Wit and Brouwer, 1968). These studies and their own observations led Mock and Pearce (1975) to propose a corn plant "ideotype". There is little evidence that desirable leaf traits of the ideotype were ever used as the sole selection criterion in the development of U.S. Corn Belt hybrids. However, prior to the identification of these desirable canopy traits in the ideotype (Mock and Pearce, 1975), such traits were present in the available inbreds and hybrids as a result of conventional breeding methods. In addition, studies with two diallel sets, one with five erect-leaf and another with five horizontal-leaf inbreds revealed that overall the horizontal-leaf hybrids outyielded the erect-leaf hybrid (Russell, 1972). In both diallel groups, Russell (1972) noted that some of the best-yielding hybrids were of the erect-leaf type (near 65° from horizontal), but cautioned the corn breeder not to restrict his germplasm base to the erect-leaf type. In other words, the ability of the plant to absorb and utilize the maximum amount of light energy for photosynthate production must be accompanied by a high, efficient conversion of photosynthate to grain. This second requirement was also specified for the ideotype plant (Mock and Pearce, 1975). It appears the ideotype approach to corn breeding also has shortcomings.

From these observations two points can be made. First, NAR and absolute growth rate were never used as the sole selection criteria in the development of superior inbreds of corn hybrids. Second, the morphological traits (leaf area and duration) in conjunction with conventional methods have been more useful to breeding programs than the physiological trait, NAR, which more closely reflects photosynthetic and respiratory activities.

7-3 PHYSIOLOGICAL SELECTION TRAITS

7-3.1 Metabolite Composition

7-3.1.1 Starch

Although much is known about the enzymes and pathway involved in the conversion of sugars to starch (Bear et al., 1958; Goodwin and Mercer, 1985; Nelson, 1980; Pridham, 1974; Shannon, 1978; Vineyard and Bear, 1952), the use of this knowledge in producing the modified starch hybrids (waxy and amylose-extender) was limited. Some associations between mutant endosperm types that differ in starch composition and related enzyme activity have been observed (Alexander and Creech, 1977; Nelson, 1980; Whistler et al., 1984).

The major pathway of amylose synthesis is by the transfer of glucose from adensine diphosphate glucose (ADPG) to the nonreducing end of a preexisting primer molecule (short-chain glucose polymer with α-1-4 bonds). With appropriate enzymes, uridine diphosphate glucose (UDPG) and glucose-1-phosphate can also act as glucose donors for amylose synthesis. Amylose is considered to be the precursor of amylopectin. Branching enzymes (transferases) cleave (breaks an α-1,4 glucosidic bond) segments from an amylose molecule and transfer (makes an α-1,6 glucosidic bond) it to another starch molecule making a branch chain. For amylose synthesis, four ADPG-type enzymes have been identified. Two are bound to the starch granule and two are soluble. For amylopectin synthesis, three branching enzymes have been identified.

Corn kernels homozygous for the waxy gene were shown to be devoid or deficient in amylose synthesizing enzymes bound to the starch granules (Nelson, 1980; Whistler et al., 1984). These observations indicate a major role for this bound activity in the accumulation of amylose (Nelson, 1980). If amylose is the precursor of amylopectin, amylose must be synthesized in these amylose mutants. The distinction between bound and soluble enzymes is based on in vitro manipulations. In situ the soluble enzymes may also be bound to the starch granule; however, their rate of reaction, orientation or "compartment effect" on the starch granule may permit complete conversion of amylose to amylopectin.

Corn kernels homozygous for sugary and amylose-extender genes lacked one of the three branching enzymes found in the nonmutant (Boyer and Preiss, 1978).

Based on the level of metabolites in starch granules isolated by nonaqueous techniques, Shannon (1978) suggested the enzyme that interconverts glucose-1-phosphate and glucose-6-phosphate may limit starch synthesis.

Selection procedures used to achieve the near linear increases (92 kg ha^{-1} yr^{-1}) in corn grain yields have also increased the total amount of starch production (Russell, 1986). There has been little alteration in the percentage of starch (about 72% of the kernel dry weight) of the commercial corn processed by Corn Products, Argo, IL (H. T. McNary, 1980, personal communication) during this same time period.

Production of the specialized starch types was facilitated by the identification of 117 natural corn mutants that produced kernels with varying concentrations and contents of sucrose, water soluble polysaccharides, and starch (amylose plus amylopectin) (Collins, 1909, Senti, 1967; Sprague et al., 1943; Vineyard and Bear, 1952; Zuber, 1965). Many of these mutants were characterized by visual differences in texture and endosperm structure of their kernels. After these visual traits were associated with type and level of metabolites, assessed by appropriate chemical assays, they became useful in breeding programs.

The mutant, waxy, was used to develop commercial corn hybrids having only amylopectin in their kernels (Hixon and Sprague, 1942). The mutants sugary, dull, and amylose extender were used in appropriate combinations to produce hybrids with kernels having half of their starch as amylose (Bear et al., 1958). The importance of the kernel phenotype in the development of these specialized hybrids is illustrated by the fact that 300 000 ears of corn were evaluated visually to select the initial 12 mutants for development of the first high-amylose corn hybrids (Bear et al., 1958).

The development of corn hybrids, high in amylopectin for commercial purposes, used kernel phenotype (including iodine staining) in conjunction with other desirable vegetative traits and yield. In general, waxy hybrids produce lower grain yields than their normal counterparts. If commercial hybrids with amylose content higher than 50% are desired, screening of parental lines for mutant types lacking the branching enzymes is suggested as a reasonable approach.

7–3.1.2 Lipids

Much is known about the metabolic pathways and biosynthesis of lipids and related compounds (Stump and Conn, 1980), and loci associated with some of the fatty acids have been located on specific chromosomes (Weber, 1987). In contrast, little is known about the enzymes produced by these genes and how these enzymes affect the concentrations, contents, and partitioning of the major components of the kernel (i.e., composition and percentage of oil, protein, and carbohydrates). With the knowledge now available, it is still difficult to identify an enzyme useful as a selection criterion when the objective is to increase oil concentration or quality. There is evidence, based primarily on metabolite assay, of genetic diversity in corn for: (i) amount and percentage of oil in the kernel; (ii) composition of fatty acids and possibly phospholipid; and (iii) orientation of the fatty acids within the triglyceride (Weber, 1980). Genetic variation also exists for composition of fatty acids, phospholipids, and related compounds (Jellum, 1970; Weber, 1980, 1987).

Divergent mass selection for percentage of grain oil in the open-pollinated corn cv., Burr's White, has resulted in the production of high and low oil strains (Alexander and Creech, 1977; Dudley, 1977; Dudley et al., 1974). Bulked samples of grain were extracted and assayed for oil in this work. Subsequently, phenotypic recurrent selection in the corn synthetic, Alexho, was made using the extraction assay only for the first cycles of selection and a single kernel nondestructive nuclear magnetic resonance (NMR) assay thereafter (Alexander et al., 1967; Bauman et al., 1963). Selection progress was accelerated with the NMR procedure as similar increases in oil concentrations were achieved in Alexho with fewer (26 vs. 85) cycles of selection than in Burr's White (Alexander, 1967; Alexander and Creech, 1977). Visual evaluation for "high oil" strains based on embryo size (Curtis et al., 1968; Leng, 1961) in conjunction with grain yield as selection traits in the Burr's White strains did not lead to the development of acceptable high oil commercial hybrids. The poor parental material and the marked improvements of the commercial (control) hybrids, rather than the use of the visual selection trait was the cause of failure. Selections based on metabolite assay, other desirable traits and grain yield have resulted in the development, from the Alexho synthetic, of high oil (8–10%) hybrids with yields only slightly lower than the best available "normal" hybrids (Alexander and Creech, 1977; Miller et al., 1981).

Given that high grain yield and high oil are the breeder's objectives, metabolite assay and conventional breeding procedures including selection for grain yield seem to be the best selection traits. Visual traits indicative of the metabolite level are "time savers" but not a requirement for a successful program. If the objective is to develop corn oil with a composition similar to olive or linseed oil, it is possible that assays for stearic and oleic desaturases might be beneficial but not obligatory criteria. However, little knowledge about the underlying and causal metabolism is acquired by the use of metabolite assay as the selection technique.

7–3.1.3 Nitrogen-whole Plant

Although NRA of whole seedlings for a given cultivar was highly correlated with the total amount or organic nitrogen accumulated (Brunetti and Hageman, 1976), correlations between activity and plant or grain N were low and variable for diverse field grown cultivars (Hageman, 1986; Hageman et al., 1976). Further, measurements of N in plant parts or in the whole plant, at intervals or at maturity, are less laborious and give a better estimate of the rate and amount of NR than does NRA. Consequently, assays of N content and concentrations in plant parts of whole plants have been used to investigate N metabolism and develop selection traits.

Muruli and Paulsen (1981) selected N-efficient and N-inefficient strains using half-sib families from the cv. Mex-Mix. Plants were grown on soil fertilized with 0 and 200 kg of N ha^{-1}. Strains developed from the highest-yielding families grown at 0 N (N efficient) and at 200 kg of N ha^{-1} (N inefficient) were tested for grain yield when fertilized with 0, 50, 100, and 200 kg of N ha^{-1}). Only at the low levels of N fertilization did the efficient strains out-yield the original population and the N-inefficient strains. The N-inefficient strain yielded most (4722 kg ha^{-1}) at the high level of N fertility. The grain yield of the inefficient strain at 200 kg of N ha^{-1} was greater (908 kg ha^{-1}) than the yield of the efficient strain at 50 kg of N ha^{-1}. Assuming the price of corn is $2.50 per 25.4 kg and N is $0.15 per 454 g, and other costs were identical, it would be economically advantageous to grow the inefficient strain fertilized with 200 kg of N ha^{-1}. It is highly probable the grain yield of the efficient strain can be improved with further selection. However, assuming the concentration of grain N is to be maintained, the question can be raised "What will be the source of the extra N" required, when no fertilizer N is supplied?

Moll et al. (Jackson et al., 1986; Moll et al., 1982, 1983) developed methods for estimating N-use efficiency by measuring N-utilization efficiency and N-uptake efficiency. These estimates came from the total N and dry weight for all of the aboveground plant parts, assuming the fertilizer N applied represents the total N supply of the plant. This work has been summarized by Jackson et al. (1986). They define: (i) N-uptake efficiency as the amount of N in the plant per unit of fertilizer N supplied; (ii) N-utilization efficiency as the amount of grain produced per unit of N in the plant; and (iii) N-use efficiency as the amount of grain per unit of fertilizer N supplied. The product of the ratios of the N-uptake and utilization efficiencies is equal to the N-use efficiency. These workers have shown genetic diversity exists in corn genotypes for each of the traits involved in N acquisition. The authors (Jackson et al., 1986) conclude such traits will permit the development of strategies for selection and development of superior hybrids.

Measurement of N content in the plant (all aboveground parts) at silking and maturity shows most corn hybrids accumulate from 70 to 75% of their total N by silking (Crafts-Brandner et al., 1984a; Swank et al., 1982). Swank et al. (1982) found the hybrid, Farm Service brand 854 differed by accumulating about 50% of its N by silking. This work was repeatable (unpublished) and subsequently confirmed with ^{15}N (Sheppers et al., 1985). Relative to other hybrids (e.g., B73 $\times$ Mo17), the increased accumulation of N during grain development of FS854 has been associated with delayed leaf senescence, prolonged photosynthetic activity, and negligible acceleration of leaf senescence in response to ear removal (Connell et al., 1988; Crafts-Brandner et al., 1984a, b; Swank et al., 1982).

7–3.1.4 Nitrogen-leaf

The use of NRA in leaves as a selection trait for increased grain yield will be discussed in a later section. However, as for the whole plant, the assays for concentration and content of organic nitrogen (a metabolite) in leaves can be used as a selection trait. Although genetic diversity for content and concentration of organic nitrogen exists among corn genotypes and these traits are heritable (Below, 1981), the use of these traits for selection in corn has been limited. Some reasons why leaf N could affect yield are: (i) increases in N supply, within limits, are associated with increases in leaf area and weight, carboxylases, and chlorophyll (Hageman, 1986; Wong et al., 1985); (ii) leaf N concentrations and photosynthetic activity have been positively correlated (Hageman, 1986); (iii) concentration of leaf N (2.9% of ear leaf at silking) was correlated with grain yield (Tyner, 1946); (iv) supplemental N fertilization is often based on leaf assay for N; and (v) remobilization of leaf N (associated with genetically controlled leaf senescence) provides N required for normal growth and development of the kernel (Hageman, 1986). Knowledge of the interaction of variable levels of leaf N and other metabolic activities at various stages of plant development is lacking.

With half-sib family procedures, Castleberry et al. (1978) found heritabilities of 15 and 16% for concentration of N of the ear leaf at silking and 28 and 14% for yield of two corn populations, based on Lancaster and Reid types, respectively. For both populations, four generations of selfing with divergent selection for ear leaf N concentration at silking resulted in limited progress in selection for low leaf N (%). Selection for high leaf N was effective (25% gain in mean values over four generations). Some lines had leaf N concentrations of 4%. Yield trials with hybrids made by crossing selected strains were not completed.

Half-sib family selection for various N traits, including content and concentration of N of all leaves at anthesis, and grain yield was made in the RSSSC corn synthetic (Sherrard et al., 1986). Half-sib family means were used to estimate heritabilities. The estimates were: 44 and 47% for leaf N content, 35 and 27% for leaf N concentration and 31 and 69% for grain yield in 1980 and 1981, respectively. The only significant correlation between the N traits and yield was for leaf reduced N content in 1980. Two strains were selected in cycle 0, one for grain yield only and the other for grain yield + leaf reduced-N content at anthesis. Half-sib family selection was used for three cycles with a 20% selection intensity in both strains. Field trials, averaged over 3 yr, showed cycle 3 of selection for the grain yield only produced 1% (85 kg ha^{-1}) more grain than cycle 0. However, cycle 3 of grain yield + leaf reduced-N strain produced 8% (503 kg ha^{-1}) more grain than cycle 0. These results indicate that combining selection for a physiological trait with grain yield in RSSSC resulted in greater yield gains than selection for grain yield per se.

7–3.1.5   Nitrogen-grain

Physiological selection traits were not used in the development of commercial corn hybrids that produce grain differing in amount of protein or in the development of strains having grain with improved protein quality. For quantity, assays of protein content of the final product provided the best and simplest approach. Although knowledge of the metabolic reactions involved in protein synthesis are extensive (Alexander and Creech, 1977; Below, 1981; Nelson, 1980; Weber, 1980), the identification of protein mutants, with visible differences in kernel phenotype, provided a simpler and more useful selection approach. However, modification of certain physiological traits (zein synthesis) may provide additional modifications in protein quality.

Genetic diversity for percentage grain N exists among corn genotypes in the long-term divergent mass selection for grain N, and oil concentration (Dudley, 1977; Leng, 1961). Although percentage grain protein was the only trait used in the long-term selection program for the Illinois Low Protein (ILP) and Illinois High Protein (IHP) strains (Dudley, 1977; Leng, 1961), traits other than percentage protein and kernel morphology were also altered (Below, 1981; Wyss, 1986). Illinois Low Protein plants produce more (100%) grain of lower protein content than the IHP plants. By anthesis both strains accumulated similar amounts of dry matter and nonstructural carbohydrates in the stover; however by time of grain maturity the stover of ILP weighed more (25%) and had more (50%) carbohydrates than the stover of IHP. This indicates that after anthesis, ILP maintained photosynthetic activity at higher rates or for a longer time or both than IHP. At anthesis, the stover of ILP had less (35%) organic nitrogen content than IHP while at physiological maturity IHP had less (11%) organic nitrogen than ILP. Illinois Low Protein fails to remobilize as much organic nitrogen from the leaves in support of grain development as IHP. Leaves of ILP plants retain moisture and green color 20 d longer than IHP (ILP leaves senesce slower). At anthesis leaves of ILP have higher (20%) levels of NRA than IHP. Illinois High Protein retains negligible levels of NRA during the last 2 to 3 weeks of grain development. In contrast, ILP retains much more (30% than at anthesis) of its NRA throughout grain-fill.

Many of the traits of the Illinois protein strains are expressed (midparent means) in hybrid combinations. The IHP strain (cycle 75) crossed with B73 produced less grain (27%) but more protein (15%) than B73 × Mo17. Grain yields and protein of Illinois Reverse Low Protein × B73 and B73 × Mo17 were found to be identical in a 1979 study (Below, 1981). The expression of various traits of IHP and ILP in F_1 hybrid combinations indicate the Illinois protein strains might be used to alter the time and extent of partitioning of metabolites, photosynthate, N metabolism, and leaf senescence as well as grain yield and grain protein. Because of traits acquired, indirectly, via selection for grain protein and of the nature of the parental material (Burr's White), the strains may not be well adapted for commercial hybrid production. However, detailed physiological studies of the strain and hybrid progeny should provide information about the inheritance of physiological traits. For example, more complete understanding of the relationship (often negative between grain yield and protein) (J. W. Dudley, 1987, personal communication) could provide leads that would speed up the selection response. Singletary and Below (1986) have initiated in vitro studies with developing corn kernels which could lead to a better understanding of the negative association of grain yield and protein in corn.

Breeding for improved grain protein quality (primarily higher lysine) was initiated with the finding the corn mutant opaque-2 produces kernels low in zein and with higher concentrations, but not necessarily content, of lysine (Mertz et al., 1964). Relative to wild type, the opaque-2 kernel differs in structure (phenotype), metabolism, and metabolite level. The mutation at the opaque-2 locus may act in a regulatory manner to depress zein synthesis. Additional alterations in metabolism have been noted (Nelson, 1969, 1980) for the mutant kernels. These studies have not identified any key or regulatory enzyme that would be useful as a selection tool.

In the development of corn hybrids with high lysine several problems were encountered: (i) grain yield was lower than normal hybrids; (ii) grain was susceptible to cracking and to insect and microbial attack; and (iii) food made from the grain was not well accepted (Nelson, 1980). Some, but not all, of these problems have been solved by conventional breeding methods that included visual examination of the kernel and rapid staining as a way to determine normal or high-lysine phenotypes (Sung and Lambert, 1982). In the U.S. Corn Belt, the use of "high-lysine" hybrids is negligible. Physiological procedures may be developed that would produce plants with a higher concentration of lysine in their grain. A successful system, analogous to the tryptophan system (Brotherton et al., 1986; Carlson and Widholm, 1978; Hibberd et al., 1986), for screening cells or protoplasts for mutants that have an isozyme capable of overproducing lysine in the regenerated plants, is being sought. Although the development of plants that over-produce lysine would be exciting and potentially useful, the effect of the higher concentration of lysine on metabolism, yield, quantity, and quality of protein in commercial corn hybrids cannot be predicted.

7–3.1.6 Mineral Nutrients

The uptake of mineral nutrients by the corn plant from the soil is under genetic control (Baker et al., 1964, 1967, 1970, 1971; Barber et al., 1967; Bradford et al., 1966; Bruetsch and Estes, 1976; Gorsline et al., 1961, 1964). The genetic control can be direct or indirect by controlling root size, shape, growth rate (Baligar and Barber, 1979; Nielsen and Barber, 1978), and root mass. Genetic control of nutrient uptake can be greatly affected by the soil environment. Because of the essential nature of minerals for normal growth and development of the corn plant, increasing the mineral content of the vegetation would appear to be a possible way to improve grain yields. However, there is little evidence in the literature to support this concept (Baker et al., 1967, 1970; Baligar and Barber, 1979; Castleberry et al., 1978). Certain levels of mineral elements must be necessary to mediate the numerous biochemical reactions essential for growth and development of the corn plant.

Sayre (1955) found a wide variation in nutrient concentration of the ear leaf at anthesis among 13 corn inbreds for N, P, K, Ca, Mg, and Fe and suggested the concentration of these elements was under genetic control. A number of studies with corn inbreds and hybrids all demonstrate that nutrient concentration in the leaves is under genetic control (Baker et al., 1964, 1967; Baligar and Barber, 1979; Barber et al., 1967; Gorsline et al., 1961, 1964; Nielsen and Barber, 1978). Genetic variation for ear leaf N, P, and K concentrations at anthesis was estimated in two corn synthetics by Castleberry et al. (1978). Heritability estimates for ear leaf concentration at anthesis of P and K in a Reid Yellow Dent and a Lancaster-type synthetic ranged from 16 to 47%. Selection for high and low leaf concentration at anthesis for P and K was done during four generations of selfing. Individual lines were selected that ranged in ear leaf concentration from 0.23% to 0.66% for P, and 0.74 to 4.0% for K in the two populations. Lines from the two populations were crossed to produce three groups of hybrids of high × high, high × low, and low × low leaf concentrations, for P and K, respectively. Limited performance tests showed the mean of the high × high groups for P produced more grain (9.7 vs. 8.2 kg ha^{-1}) than the low × low group, but were not superior to the check hybrid DeKalb brand XL43 (10.7 kg ha^{-1}). For K the high × high group produced more grain (8.9 vs. 8.0 kg ha^{-1}) than the low × low groups and less than the check hybrid XL43 (9.6 kg ha^{-1}). Because the high × high groups had higher P and K than the check hybrid, it is difficult to draw definitive conclusions. It may be inferred that selection for mineral nutrient concentration in corn must be used with other important agronomic traits or some other measure of nutrient composition used to affect grain yield increases in corn.

A more realistic approach to using mineral elements as selection criteria in breeding programs would be to measure efficiency of ion uptake or utilization. Barber and co-workers (Baligar and Barber, 1979; Nielsen and Barber, 1978) have measured several root parameters simultaneously to determine the efficiency of P uptake. The results show that corn inbreds and hybrids differ in uptake in the several parameters evaluated. Differences among genotypes were found both in solution culture and field experiments. Heterosis (increases over the high parent) was observed for several P uptake parameters. It would be difficult to utilize these procedures in a breeding program because of the large number of samples required during growth and development before ion-uptake efficiency can be determined.

7–4 ENZYMES

The concepts of "one gene-one enzyme" arising from the work of Beadle and Tatum (1941) and limiting factors resulting from bottle-neck genes, as described by Manglesdorf (1952) provided the basis for examining the level of enzyme activity as a critical factor in growth and productivity of crop plants.

7–4.1 Enzymes-heterotrophic Seedlings

One of the first attempts to establish a relationship between the amount of enzyme activity and heterosis of corn was initiated in 1955 (Hageman et al., 1967). Three enzymes were selected for study. Two of these enzymes, triosephosphate dehydrogenase (TDP) and glucose-6-phosphate dehydrogenase, (G-6-P) were associated with energy generation while the third enzyme, aldolase (ALD) provides the substrate for TPD during heterotrophic seedling growth. Two single cross corn hybrids and their respective inbred parents (selected without prescreening) were grown in the dark. Weights of endosperm and embryo and enzyme activities were determined daily. This work led to the following conclusion: (i) seedling growth and endosperm loss were heterotic; (ii) No genetic diversity was found for ALD and TPD, as activity levels in inbreds and progeny were similar; (iii) for one hybrid set, but not the other, G-6-P activity was higher in one inbred than the other and activity in the hybrid was equal to the midpoint parental value; and (iv) when seedlings were grown under semiaerobic conditions, activities were altered, showing the interaction of enzymic activities and environment. This system also provided some of the information that led to the concept of balanced metabolism or the need to coordinate all reactions and systems for efficient growth under a given environment (Hageman et al., 1967). Selection based on these enzyme activities was never attempted.

7–4.2 Enzymes-autotrophic Plants

With the development in 1958 of a procedure that permitted extraction of numerous active enzymes from the green leaves of crop plants (Hageman and Waygood, 1959), work was extended to field-grown corn. The marked effect on corn yields from the increased use of fertilizer N (Hageman, 1979), and the critical role of N in increasing plant growth (Hageman, 1986), prompted the examination of NR as a bottle-neck enzyme. At that time, additional reasons for the selection of NR were: (i) it was considered to be the rate-limiting enzyme step between nitrate (NO_3^-) and protein [subsequently verified (Hewitt and Cutting, 1979)]; (ii) it was heritable (Warner et al., 1969); and (iii) the level of NR was proportional to the NO_3^- supply because NR was induced by its substrate and was labile in the absence of NO_3^- [not fully supported by subsequent work, especially among diverse genotypes (Hageman, et al., 1976)]. Under certain conditions and with a given genotype, NRA was shown to closely parallel accumulation of organic nitrogen by the whole plant. However, the correlation values between NRA and grain yield or grain protein among genotypes grown under field conditions were low even when significant (Deckard et al., 1973; Hageman et al., 1976; Sherrard et al., 1986).

To minimize the genotype effect, divergent selection for leaf NRA at 10 and 20 d after anthesis, in the Super-Stiff Synthetic (SSS) corn cultivar was initiated in 1974. Other details are published (Sherrard et al. 1986). A summary of preliminary results obtained from growing cycles 0, 2, 4, and 6 under field conditions in 1982 were: (i) selection for NRA was significant and continuous; cycle 6 high had 59% more and cycle 6 low had 38% less NRA than cycle 0; (ii) there was no effect of selection on the stover or organic nitrogen content of the stover or grain with the exception that grain yield and grain organic nitrogen content of cycle 6 low was significantly lower than cycle 0 or cycle 6 high; (iii) selection for high NRA was associated with a more rapid loss of chlorophyll from the leaves (increased rate of senescence); and (iv) selection for high NRA was associated with an increase in specific leaf weight relative to the low selection or cycle 0.

Ultimately, eight cycles of the divergently selected strains were concurrently evaluated for high and low postanthesis leaf NRA. The plants were grown at three N fertility rates, although the selections were made only on the lowest rate 112 kg of N ha^{-1}. These data showed the high strain had an average increase in NRA of 43% and the low strain had an average decrease of 50% compared to cycle 0 at the 112 kg of N rate (Eichelberger, 1986). At the 224 kg of N rate the high strain had an average increase in NRA of 42% and the low strain an average decrease of 52% compared to cycle 0. At the 336 kg of N rate the high strain had an average increase in NRA of 33% and the low strain an average decrease of only 31% compared to cycle 0. The results demonstrate the N environment used during selection has an effect on selection response for postanthesis NRA. The first six cycles of selection for high NRA showed small but consistent decreases in yield at all N fertilizer rates in the high strain. These yield decreases could be accounted for by inbreeding effects in the high strain. The low NRA strain had large correlated yield decreases that could not be accounted for by inbreeding effects. The yield decreases were a function of N rates, as yields were 66% lower at 112 than at 336 kg of N ha^{-1} (Eichelberger, 1986). The increase in yield of the low NRA strain with increasing N rates was the result of an increase in kernel number plant^{-1}. Little change was observed in either the high or the low NRA strain in dry weight and reduced N content of stover at anthesis, regardless of N rates. A decrease in grain N content of the low NRA strain was observed which may indicate plants of the low NRA strain are unable to supply the developing ear with adequate supplies of reduced N so that kernel initiates and development can proceed in a normal manner. These results indicate that selecting for low postanthesis leaf

NRA was associated with decreased N metabolism after anthesis as indicated by the marked decrease of N content in the grain but not the stover.

The increased NRA and grain production of the low NRA strains in response to increased N fertility implies that NO_3^- uptake and transport are associated components. More specifically, these observations may indicate that the indirectly identified NO_3^- permease(s) (Jackson et al., 1973) could be another of the rate limiting steps in the accumulation of organic N by the plant. Jackson et al. (1986) have found both influx and efflux of NO_3^- from roots. The efflux complicates the measurement of a NO_3^- influx permease as the rate-limiting step in acquisition and accumulation of organic nitrogen by the plant.

From these studies of divergent selections for NRA, it is obvious that high levels of NRA do not reflect the input of reduced N to the plant. Other factors (uptake and transport of NO_3^-, metabolic regulation, availability of energy) must influence the in vivo reduction process. Nevertheless, these strains with their different levels of NRA may be of use in studying factors that affect uptake, transport, and regulation of nitrate reduction. They may also be crossed to inbreds to increase or decrease the measurable level of leaf NRA. In this vein, Deckard et al. (1985) found that leaf NRA decreased and grain yields increased as a function of the date of release of wheat cultivars.

Schrader and students (Chevalier and Schrader, 1977; Schrader, 1974, 1985; Schrader et al., 1974) determined the seasonal average activities for seven enzymes extracted from the leaves of field-grown plants of four corn inbreds and their F_1 hybrids. These enzymes were selected on the basis of perceived importance to metabolism and growth. They also determined cumulative NO_3^- uptake from nutrient media for the inbreds and hybrids. From these studies they concluded:

1. Enzyme activity of the F_1 hybrid could be predicted from the mean of the parental activities.

2. Significant genotypic differences in level of activity for each of the seven enzymes was found when the four inbreds were assayed. Even greater differences in genetic variability of enzyme activities were found when the number of genotypes screened was increased.

3. Depending on the inbreds selected for crossing the additive genetic effect for each enzyme permits the hybrid to achieve a median level of activity of each enzyme relative to the parents. This is consistent with earlier data and the "balanced input" concept of heterosis (Hageman et al., 1967). What is not known is whether these changes in level of activities affect the rate of metabolism and growth.

4. Nitrate uptake (multigene control) of the hybrids was not predictable from the NO_3^- uptake of the inbred.

Schrader et al. (1974) made improvements in the enzyme extraction procedures that demonstrated the heterotic level of NR reported for one corn hybrid (Warner et al., 1969) was an artifact. In the absence of an inert protective protein in the extraction medium, NR of one of the parental inbreds was extremely unstable. No attempt was ever made to use these enzyme activities as selection traits in breeding programs.

7-4.3 Isozymes

Schwartz (1960) and Schwartz et al. (1965) used electrophoretic techniques to separate esterase isozymes from corn seedlings. They found that a new "hybrid" enzyme as well as the enzymes exhibited by the parents was detected in extracts from the single cross hybrid. The hybrid enzyme did not appear to be an association of the parental types. Beckman et al. (1964a, b) using similar techniques also found the hybrid seedling contained additional electrophoretic bands (isozymes) of leucine aminopeptidase and catalase. The leucine aminopeptidase variants were controlled by two alleles with co-dominance. It was proposed that catalase could exist as a tetramer and the hybrid isozyme may have resulted from the random association, in different combinations, of two different monomers.

In his review Scandalios (1974) discussed the need to define isozyme, that is, polypeptide bands appearing on the chromotagraphic media may or may not be products arising from different alleles. He reviewed work that showed allozyme bands have been found for 28 different enzymes. Isozymes have been found in numerous plant species, some are tissue specific and others vary in level of activity with plant development.

The presence of an isozyme that possesses superior kinetic properties or resistance to adverse environmental stress could confer a degree of biological flexibility, at least to one reaction, if not to the whole metabolic system. The possibility also exists that increased amounts of one metabolite could be detrimental as well as beneficial to the growth of the organism. Because so little is known about the kinetic and related properties of the large number of known isozymes (Scandalios, 1974), it is difficult to interpret the possible effects, if any, on the flow of metabolites and resultant changes in growth and productivity of the plant.

However, the induction of a specific isozyme has been shown to affect viability and metabolite production in plants. This is based on initial work with bacteria that demonstrated 5-methyl-tryptophan (5MT) would inhibit anthranilate synthase (AS), the first step in the biosynthesis of tryptophan, and growth of the wild type cells (Moyed, 1960). Mutant cells of potato (*Solanum tuberosum* L.) (Carlson and Widholm, 1978), tobacco (*Nicotiana tabacum* L.) (Brotherton et al., 1986), and corn (Hibberd et al., 1986) were selected in a medium containing 5MT. Data obtained indicated the mutant cells contained a second form of AS. The two forms of AS could be separated by gel filtration techniques and differed in sensitivity to 5MT and tryptophan and in molecular weights. Selection against 5MT permitted the expression of one isozyme independent of the other. The two isozymes existed in different compartments of the cell. Brotherton et al. 1986) concluded the two isozymes were products of separate genes. Other work has shown the 5MT isozyme was expressed in corn as well as for the other two plant species. Free tryptophan in the seed was higher (2–100-fold) than controls in some variant lines. The stability of this system, the effect on grain composition and yield of commercial hybrids, and the economic advantage of the higher level of free tryptophan are still to be determined.

Stuber et al. have published several studies on the use of allozyme loci as genetic markers for use in selecting for possible linked loci of quantitative traits of agronomic importance (Frei et al., 1986; Stuber et al., 1980, 1982, 1987; Stuber and Moll, 1972). Stuber et al. (1982) evaluated the effectiveness of selection for allozyme loci in corn to improve grain yield in the cv. Jarvis. A strain from unselected Jarvis (cycle 0) was developed by selecting for certain allozyme allele frequencies at seven loci that were identical to allozyme allele frequencies of cycle 10 of the classical full-sib selection program in Jarvis for increased yield. Field evaluation of this selected Jarvis strain produced yields 6% higher than cycle 0 of Jarvis. The yield progress from one cycle of selection for alleles at seven allozyme loci in corn produce yield increases that were equal to 1.5 cycles of conventional full-sib selection.

Frei et al. (1986) developed a 30 inbred corn synthetic that had 23 allozyme loci with contrasting alleles. The synthetic had a high degree of linkage disequilibrium so that the allozyme loci could be used in a selection program to improve yield. One cycle of topcross tests of S_2 lines was used to establish divergent strains for eight yield associated allozyme loci that had high and low multi-allele frequencies. When the divergent strains were tested as topcrosses over seven locations the magnitude of the effects of allozyme alleles on yield were positive but small in this specific population.

The use of allozyme loci as selection criteria for linked desirable agronomic traits for corn breeding using population improvement methods is complicated by the highly heterogenous genetic nature of populations. The use of allozyme loci in the pedigree method of corn breeding may be more successful because less genetic variation is encountered with this procedure.

Stuber et al. (1987) evaluated the F_2 generation from two different single cross corn hybrids to identify and locate quantitative loci associated with grain yield and 24 yield-related component traits. One F_2 population had 20 isozyme marker loci segregating and the other 17 marker loci. These isozyme marker loci were located on 8 of the 10 maize chromosomes in each population. About two-thirds of the possible associations between isozyme markers and yield-related traits were statistically significant. However, in more than one-half of these associations, the isozyme loci could only account for <2% of the observed variation in grain yield. A few isozyme marker loci did account for about 10% of the variation in yield-related traits. These results indicate the successful use of this technique in a corn-breeding program are possible, if more markers can be found that are randomly distributed throughout the corn genome. The use of restriction fragment length polymorphisms should allow for a more complete coverage of the corn genome than isozyme marker loci. These newer techniques could be used to follow major loci controlling certain physiological traits in corn breeding programs.

7-5 ENZYME SYSTEMS

7-5.1 Mitochondria

Much excitement was generated by the mitochondrial complementation studies of the 1960s (McDaniel and Sarkissian, 1966, 1968; Sarkissian and Skrivaslava, 1967). These workers reported that mixing equal amounts of mitochondria extracted from etiolated seedlings of two corn inbreds resulted in heterotic activities (O_2 consumption and energy generation) similar to the activities exhibited by equal amounts of mitochondria extracted from the hybrid seedling. Mitochondrial heterosis was found only when the inbreds were of diverse origin and their hybrid exhibited heterotic growth. In subsequent studies, mitochondrial heterosis was significantly correlated with grain yield of wheat and barley (McDaniel, 1972). However, Ellis et al. (1973) failed in their attempts to repeat these findings. They stated the complementation procedure was not a useful selection procedure for breeding cereals.

Hind-sight indicates a modification and expansion of the work initiated by Hageman et al. (1967) and by Sarkissian's group (McDaniel and Sarkissian, 1966) could have provided a better understanding of the relationship between metabolism and heterosis of the heterotic growth of dark grown corn seedlings. Specific points of modification would be: (i) initial screening of inbreds to establish genetic diversity for critical enzymes; (ii) measurement of respiration and establishment of the correlation with mitochondrial activity; (iii) assaying of the numerous metabolites between starch and CO_2 as a means of identifying possible rate limiting enzymes (Shannon, 1978); and (iv) measuring rates of protein synthesis both in vitro and in vivo (e.g., rates of induction of NR). This study would need to be conducted with numerous hybrid sets because it is quite possible the cause of heterotic growth is different for each set. The possibility of multiple genetic causes of heterotic growth and yield, that change with the stage of growth and environment, is inherent in the concept of "proper balance" of inputs from the gamut of metabolic pathways (Hageman et al., 1967).

A major problem in using physiological traits, for selection to improve cultivars, is that only a limited amount of information is available on how enzymes and metabolite levels affect growth. Extensive studies of such a heterotic system should supply information relating metabolism to early seedling growth.

7–5.2 Respiration

A negative association between dark respiration rate of roots and fully grown leaves has been reported for various crops (Fernandez, 1977; Heichel, 1971; Penning De Vries, 1974; Wilson, 1981). Other workers have suggested the desirability of elimination of at least part of the dark respiration component (McCree, 1974; Wilson and Jones, 1982). In 1975, Wilson (1975) found that of the following traits, apparent photorespiration, dark respiration, net photosynthesis, and leaf starch accumulation, only dark respiration negatively correlated with dry matter yield and rate of shoot regrowth of perennial rye grass (*Lolium perenne* L). Successful selection for strains with fast or slow rates of dark respiration in the mature leaves were completed (Wilson, 1982). From this material, fast or slow respiring parents were selected and crossed to provide 15 F_1 families with fast and 15 with slow respiration. The slow respiration F_1 families produced significantly more (30%) growth or regrowth during the summer months (May–November). During the winter months or during the initial canopy development period there was no difference in growth of the divergent families. Under field conditions, progeny, derived from the selected families with slow respiration rates, consistently outyielded (6–13%) the parental (unselected) cultivar (Wilson, 1982). Little additional progress was made in obtaining lower respiration rates by additional selection from the F_1 generation. This result was predicted from the earlier work (Wilson, 1981), because part of dark respiration is probably essential for growth.

Similar to Schrader's (1974) results with individual enzymes from corn, the dark respiration rates of the F_1 ryegrass crosses were similar to the midparent value of the parental material (Wilson, 1982).

An alternate energy-inefficient pathway of electron transport characterized by the lack of inhibition of cyanide but inhibited by salicylhydroxamic acid, has been observed in many higher plant species including corn (Lambers, 1985; Lambers and Day, 1987; Laties, 1982; Rich et al., 1978). It was suggested (Lambers and Steingrover, 1978) this cyanide resistant respiration functions as an "energy overflow" system and may operate in situ only when carbohydrates are accumulated in excess of needs for growth and maintenance (Lambers et al., 1981).

An investigation of the rye grass strains having fast and slow rates of respiration, surprisingly found the alternate pathway did not contribute to the respiration in mature leaves or meristems in either strain (Day et al., 1985). The fast respiring strains had a greater respiratory capacity and higher turn-over of ATP than the slow respiring strains. The dark respiration rate of a mature leaf was limited by adenylate control of glycolysis. This contrasts with the results from wheat where respiration was controlled by the concentration of sugar in the leaf. The possibility of investigating the effect of the alternate pathway on corn grain yield has been facilitated by finding corn genotypes with and without the alternate pathway (Musgrave et al., 1986).

7–5.3   Photosynthesis

The high concentration of C (40–45% C, dry weight basis) dictates a major role for the photosynthetic reduction of CO_2 in corn production. Genetic variability in photosynthetic rates per unit of leaf area has been reported for corn and other plant species (Crosbie et al., 1977; Heichel and Musgrave, 1969; Moss and Musgrave, 1971; Wilson, 1981). Heritability of light-saturated photosynthetic rates have also been estimated for corn (Crosbie et al., 1978; Moss and Musgrave, 1971). However, the key criterion of a useful trait, the relationship between the photosynthetic rates and grain yield was not found.

Christy et al. (1986) measured canopy net photosynthesis of field-grown corn at intervals throughout the growing season. Measurements were made with a modification of a field photosynthetic system developed by Peters et al. (1974). Seasonal photosynthetic activity was calculated in arbitrary units that represented the total amount of C fixed. Data obtained showed two corn hybrids, with similar seasonal photosynthetic activities, differed in grain yield by 30%. Variations in plant stands (17 000 to 112 000 plants ha^{-1}) did not alter the seasonal photosynthetic activities (most of the measurements were made after LAI reached 4) while grain yields increased from 1.55 to 2.40 kg plot^{-1}. Christy et al. (1986) concluded that grain yield did not appear to be limited by photosynthesis. When artificial shading was applied at different stages of plant development, evidence was obtained that indicated photosynthetic activity was associated with grain yield. Accordingly, they (Christy et al., 1986) modified their conclusion by indicating that under certain conditions of shading or high yields photosynthesis could limit grain yield.

Because of the residual carbohydrate content of the stover at maturity, other investigators (Hageman, 1986; Tollenaar, 1977) have concluded that the source was not limiting corn production in the U.S. Corn Belt.

Measurements of canopy net photosynthesis of field-grown single cross hybrids selected as representative of the decade of their release (1930–1970) revealed the following: (i) the earlier released, lower yielding, hybrids exhibited a faster rate of loss of photosynthetic activity between anthesis and grain maturity than the higher yielding later released hybrids. There was little difference in photosynthetic activity among the hybrids during vegetative development; (ii) during the grain-fill period the hybrids also responded differently to environmental conditions. The hybrids with the higher photosynthetic activity showed greater increases in activity with high light intensities and favorable conditions while hybrids with lower activity were depressed more by adverse environments (D. B. Peters, 1987, personal communication). These results could be due to later released hybrids having greater leaf disease resistance or slower senescing leaves.

In 1982, half-sib family selection for differences in field canopy photosynthesis (FCP) was initiated in the RSSSC corn synthetic (Nubel, 1986). General patterns of FCP were similar for all families during a 30-d measurement period that usually started just prior to or at half-silk. Because greatest differences were noted in the 10-d period following half-silking, selections were made on measurements at that time. Through four cycles of selection, changes in the trait, FCP, were significant and progressive. For each year, the correlation between FCP of all half-sib families under test and their grain yields were positive and significant. However, for the families selected for high FCP, grain yields were not associated with activity, and yields for the last three cycles were lower than the first cycle. In 1987, all four cycles of high FCP will be grown concurrently for evaluation of FCP and grain yield for a conclusive evaluation of the correlated response with grain yield.

A comparison of two "stay green" corn hybrids, Pioneer brand 3382 and Farm Service brand 854 revealed that FS854 had higher net photosynthesis, based on dry matter accumulation, and CER of a selected leaf during the last 2 to 3 weeks of grain-fill (Connell et al., 1988; Crafts-Brandner et al., 1984a, b). Their data are in agreement with the greater rate of loss of FCP of the older, lower yielding "era" hybrids noted by Peters (see preceding). Collectively, these observations raise the possibility that photosynthate production during the reproductive phase could be increased by selection for greater photosynthetic capacity (Nubel, 1986) or by the duration of the photoactivity during grain-fill (Connell et al., 1988; Crafts-Brandner et al., 1984a, b). Whether there are any metabolic factors (end-product inhibition, cyanide-resistant respiration, transport, rate and capacity of storage) of the plant or grain that prevent the effective use of the additional photosynthate remains elusive.

Some of the data (Crafts-Brandner et al., 1984a, b) indicate "green score" is not a reliable measure of photosynthate production which is consistent with the dogma that there is little relationship between photosynthetic activity and chlorophyll. Attempts are underway to confirm preliminary data that show a relationship between the absence of accelerated leaf senescence following ear removal (Crafts-Brandner et al., 1984a, b) and extended duration of leaf photosynthesis.

7–6 PHYSIOLOGICAL TRAITS–PROBLEMS

There are numerous problems associated with the use of physiological traits for corn improvement. First, no single trait has been identified that exhibits a high, positive correlation with grain yield among genotypes over years. Second, for enzymes used as selection traits, the activity measured in vitro may not accurately reflect the activity in situ, among genotypes over time. This is true even for NR where the activity is labile and induced by and dependent on substrate level. Nitrate reductase is also the rate limiting step in the assimilation system. Consequently, activity measured for one enzyme of a metabolic process need not reflect the amount of product provided by the process. A possible exception would be the deletion of an enzyme involved in production of a final product. Third, the genotype by environment interaction involved in grain yield is so complicated that the effects of a single enzyme or enzyme process is obscured. This complexity arises from the internal regulation of each enzyme and enzyme process and the interactions of all the metabolic processes throughout the life cycle of the plant. All these complexities contribute to the genotype $\times$ environment interaction. Knowledge of the regulatory factors and interactions is inadequate. Fourth, measurement of physiological traits are usually laborious and expensive. Consequently, when available, visual estimates of the traits are used in selection programs in preference to the physiological measurement (assay).

In 1987, as in 1923, there is still a need for detailed and extensive studies of physiological and metabolic processes involved in corn productivity. As indicated by the preceding sections, knowledge of how enzymes and enzyme systems interact to produce the vegetation and grain is too fragmentary to permit their use in breeding programs to improve grain yields. There is need for the breeders, physiologists, and molecular biologists to work together to acquire more knowledge about these processes. Work is underway in an attempt to associate DNA fragments (restriction fragment length polymorphism) with quantitative traits in corn. Such a project could be expanded to include physiological traits that could be associated with yield. An initial list of these traits could include the rate and duration of net photosynthesis, NR and assimilation, partitioning of dry matter and N among leaves and stalks, and grain harvest indices for dry weight, and N, and respiration. There is a need to expand physiological and molecular studies so that this basic information is applicable to breeding programs.

7–7 SUMMARY

A review of the importance of physiological processes, i.e., starch, lipid, N, and nutrient metabolism along with the importance of enzymes, photosynthesis, and respiration in determining plant productivity is presented. In addition, attempts to use physiological traits in crop breeding programs are discussed. While each physiological process affects plant productivity, to some extent, a process does not act alone to ensure maximum yield. Each process must be integrated with the whole system and in turn the system responds to the environment throughout the life cycle of the plant. A genotype that provides the proper amounts of the metabolites at the right time and place should produce the most yield. Because grain yield reflects the integration of all the genetically controlled physiological processes with the environment, the corn breeder uses yield as the best estimate of superior physiological processes. It is not surprising that selection based on yield and pest resistance has indirectly selected genotypes with superior physiological traits. This statement is supported by the observation that newer released corn hybrids stay green longer (delayed leaf senescence), produce greater dry weight per plant and have greater photosynthetic activity during grain-fill than older released hybrids. While successful from a production standpoint, the breeders approach provides little knowledge about the complex nature of the system. For example, "what is the role and interaction of N metabolism in determining size of the plant and in extending the duration of color and activity of the leaves?"

Physiological studies have provided much information concerning plant growth and development, responses to stress, and grain yield that may be used, directly or indirectly, by the corn breeder. Although nonvisual physiological traits are not used extensively for corn improvement, some visual traits reflect physiological processes. For example, green score and vigor reflect chlorophyll and RGR. In addition physiological studies have revealed: (i) the complex nature of the processes involved in grain production; (ii) some of the effects of environmental stresses; (iii) that alteration of activity of a specified enzyme by a change in environment is a function of the genotype; (iv) the need for a "balance of metabolic processes" for maximum productivity; (v) some of the physiological factors that are associated with the rate of development of leaf senescence, among genotypes; (vi) there are regulatory factors that often operate in situ to modify enzyme activity, thereby nullifying the use of in vitro activity as a measure of product formation; (vii) the importance of stage of development of the plant relative to the requirements for supply of assimilates (C, N, etc.); and (viii) mid-parent enzyme activity values of two inbreds approximates the activity value of the F_1 progeny.

Results show that grain yield improvement in corn-breeding programs is not likely to occur if only one physiological trait is used as the selection criterion. This is especially valid if the enzyme or trait is concerned with an intermediate metabolic step. Because the concurrent use of several physiological traits is expensive and laborious, such studies are rarely undertaken. However, the overall effort expended in the use of physiological traits as selection criteria for corn improvement is less than the effort expended by conventional breeding programs. The more extensive and successful use of physiological traits in corn-breeding programs will occur when selection for physiological traits can be integrated with selection for grain yield, pest resistance, and other important agronomic traits. In the future it is possible that an "integrated effort" by corn breeders, plant physiologists, and molecular geneticists using physiological traits in corn-breeding programs will lead to an enhancement in the rate of genetic gain in future corn yields.

REFERENCES

Alexander, D.E. 1988. Maize. *In* G. Robbelon (ed.) Oil crops of the world. Macmillan Publ. Co., New York. (In press.)

----, and R.G. Creech. 1977. Breeding special industrial and nutritional types. *In* G.F. Sprague (ed.) Corn and corn improvement. Agronomy 18:363–390.

----, L. Silvela, F.I. Collins, and R.C. Rodgers. 1967. Analysis of oil content of maize by wide-line NMR. J. Am. Oil. Chem. Soc. 44:555–558.

Baker, D.E., R.R. Bradford, and W.I. Thomas. 1967. Accumulation of Ca, S, Mg, P, and Zn by genotypes of corn (*Zea mays* L.) under different soil fertility levels. p. 465–477. *In* Isotopes in plant nutrition and physiology. IAEA, Vienna.

----, A.E. Jarrel, L.E. Marshall, and W.I. Thomas. 1970. Phosphorus uptake from soils by corn hybrids selected for high and low phosphorus accumulation. Agron. J. 62:103–106.

----, W.I. Thomas, and G.W. Gorsline. 1964. Differential accumulation of strontium, calcium, and other elements by corn (*Zea mays* L.) under greenhouse and field conditions. Agron. J. 56:352–355.

----, F.J. Wooding, and M.W. Johnson. 1971. Chemical element accumulation by populations of corn (*Zea mays* L.) selected for high and low accumulation of P. Agron. J. 63:404–406.

Baligar, V.C., and S.A. Barber. 1979. Genotypic differences of corn for ion uptake. Agron. J. 71:870–873.

Barber, W.D., W.I. Thomas, and D.E. Baker. 1967. Inheritance of relative phosphorus accumulation in corn (*Zea mays* L.). Crop Sci. 7:104–107.

Bauman, L.F., T.F. Conway, and S.A. Watson. 1963. Heritability of variations in oil content of individual corn kernels. Science 139:498–499.

Beadle, G.W., and E.L. Tatum. 1941. Genetic control of biochemical reactions in *Neurospora crassa*. Proc. Natl. Acad. Sci. USA 27:499–506.

Bear, R.P., M.L. Vineyard, M.M. MacMasters, and W.L. Deatherage. 1958. Development of high "amylomaize"—corn hybrids. II. Results of breeding efforts. Agron. J. 50:598–602.

Beckman, L., J.G. Scandalios, and J.L. Brewbaker. 1964a. Genetics of leucine aminopeptidases isozymes in maize. Genetics 50:899–904.

----, ----, and ----. 1964b. Catalase hybrid enzymes in maize. Science 146:1174–1175.

Below, F.E. 1981. Nitrogen metabolism as related to productivity in 10 maize genotypes. M.S. thesis. Univ. of Illinois, Urbana.

Blackman, V.H. 1919. The compound interest law and plant growth. Ann. Bot. 33:353–360.

Boyer, C.D., and J. Preiss. 1978. Multiple forms of starch branching enzyme of maize: Evidence for independent genetic control. Biochem Biophys. Res. Commun. 80:169–175.

Bradford, R.R., D.E. Baker, and W.I. Thomas. 1966. Effect of soil treatments on chemical element accumulation of four corn hybrids. Agron. J. 58:614–617.

Brotherton, J.E., R.M. Hauptmann, and J.M. Widholm. 1986. Anthranilate synthase forms in plant and cultured cells of *Nicotiana tabacum* L. Planta 168:214–221.

Bruetsch, T.F., and G.O. Estes. 1976. Genotype variation in nutrient uptake efficiency in corn. Agron. J. 68:521–523.

Brunetti, N., and R.H. Hageman. 1976. Comparison of *in vivo* and *in vitro* assays of nitrate reductase in wheat (*Triticum aestivum* L.) seedlings. Plant Physiol. 58:583–587.

Carlson, J.E., and J.M. Widholm. 1978. Separation of two forms of anthranilate synthatase from 5-methyltryptophan-susceptible and -resistant cultured *Solanum tuberosum* cells. Physiol. Plant 44:251–255.

Castleberry, R.M., C.W. Crum, and B. Tsotis. 1978. Stratification of corn germplasm for physiological traits. p. 88–119. *In* Fourteenth Annu. Illinois Corn Breeders School. Univ. of Illinois, Urbana.

Chevalier, P., and L.E. Schrader. 1977. Genotypic differences in nitrate absorption and partitioning of N among plant parts in maize. Crop Sci. 17:897–901.

Christy, A.L., D.R. Williamson, and A.S. Wideman. 1986. Maize source development and activity. p. 11–12. *In* Regulation of carbon and nitrogen reduction and utilization. J.C. Shannon et al. (ed.) Am. Soc. Plant Physiologists, Rockville, MD.

Collins, G.N. 1909. A new type of Indian corn from China. U.S. Bureau Plant Inds. 161:31.

Connell, T.R., F.E. Below, R.H. Hageman, and M.R. Willman. 1987. Photosynthetic components associated with differential senescence in maize hybrids following ear removal. Field Crops Res. 17:55–61.

Crafts-Brandner, S.J., F.E. Below, J.E. Harper, and R.H. Hageman. 1984a. Differential senescence of maize hybrids following ear removal. I. Whole plant. Plant Physiol. 74:360–367.

----, ----, V.A Wittenbach, J.E. Harper, and R.H. Hageman. 1984b. Differential senescence of maize hybrids following ear removal. II. Selected leaves. Plant Physiol. 74:368–373.

Crosbie, T.M., J.J. Mock, and R.B. Pearce. 1977. Variability and selection advance for photosynthesis in Iowa Stiff Stalk Synthetic maize population. Crop Sci. 17:511–514.

----, ----, ----. 1978. Inheritance of photosynthesis in a diallel among eight maize inbred lines from Iowa Stiff Stalk Synthetic. Euphytica 27:657–664.

----, R.B. Pearce, and J.J. Mock. 1981. Selection for high CO_2 exchange rate among inbred lines of maize. Crop Sci. 21:629–631.

Curtis, P.E., E.R. Leng, and R.H. Hageman. 1968. Developmental changes in oil and fatty acid content of maize strains varying in oil content. Crop Sci. 8:689–693.

Day, D.A., O.C. DeVos, D. Wilson, and H. Lambers. 1985. Regulation of respiration in the leaves and roots of two *Lolium perenne* L. populations with contrasting mature leaf respiration rates and yields. Plant Physiol. 78:678–683.

Deckard, E.L., R.H. Busch, and K.D. Kofoid. 1985. Physiological aspects of spring wheat improvements. p. 46–54. *In* J.E. Harper et al. (ed.) Exploitation of physiological and genetic variability to enhance crop production. Am. Soc. Plant Physiologists, Rockville, MD.

----, R.J. Lambert, and R.H. Hageman. 1973. Nitrate reductase activity in corn leaves as related to yield of grain and grain protein. Crop Sci. 13:343–356.

Dudley, J.W. 1977. Seventy-six generations of selection for oil and protein in maize. p. 459–489. *In* E. Pollack et al. (ed.) Proceedings international conference on quantitative genetics. Iowa State Univ. Press, Ames.

----, R.J Lambert, and D.E. Alexander. 1974. Seventy generations of selection for oil and protein concentration in the maize kernel. p. 181–211. *In* J.W. Dudley (ed.) Seventy generations of selection for oil and protein in maize. CSSA, Madison, WI.

Duncan, W.G. 1971. Leaf angles, leaf area and canopy photosynthesis. Crop Sci. 11:482–485.

----. 1975. Corn. p. 23–50. *In* L.T. Evans (ed.) Crop physiology, some case histories. Cambridge Univ. Press, Cambridge.

----, and J.D. Hesketh. 1968. Net photosynthesis rates, relative leaf growth rates and leaf numbers of 22 races of maize grown at eight temperatures. Crop Sci. 8:670–674.

----, R.S. Loomis, W.A. Williams, and R. Hanau. 1967. A model for simulating photosynthesis in plant communities. Hilgardia 38:181–205.

Duvick, D.N. 1977. Genetic rates of gain in hybrid maize yields during the past 40 years. Maydica 22:187–196.

----. 1984. Genetic contributions to yield gains of U.S. Maize Hybrids, 1930 to 1980. p. 15–47. *In* W.R. Fehr (ed.) Genetic contributions to yield gains of five major crop plants. CSSA, Madison, WI.

Eichelberger, K.D. 1986. Response of eight cycles of divergent phenotypic recurrent selection for nitrate reductase activity and correlated responses in maize (*Zea mays* L.). M.S. thesis. Univ. of Illinois, Urbana.

Ellis, J.R.S., C.I. Brunton, and J.M. Palmer. 1973. Can mitochondrial complementation be used as a tool in breeding hybrid cereals? Nature (London) 241:45–47.

Engledow, F.L., and S.M. Wadham. 1923. Investigations on yield in the cereals. J. Agric. Sci. 13:390–439.

Evans, L.T., J.F. Wardlaw, and R.A. Fischer. 1975. Wheat. p. 101–105. *In* L.T. Evans (ed.) Crop physiology, some case histories. Cambridge Univ. Press, Cambridge.

Fernandez, C.J. 1977. Differences in carbon economy among five grain sorghum cultivars. M.S. thesis. Texas A&M Univ., College Station.

Frei, O.M., C.W. Stuber, and M.M. Goodman. 1986. Yield manipulation from selection on allozyme genotypes in a composite of elite corn lines. Crop Sci. 26:917–921.

Gifford, R.M., and L.T. Evans. 1981. Photosynthesis, carbon partitioning and yield. Annu. Rev. Plant Physiol. 32:485–509.

Goodwin, T.W., and E. Mercer. 1985. Introduction to plant biochemistry. 2nd ed. Pergamon Press, New York.

Gorsline, G.W., J.L. Ragland, and W.I. Thomas. 1961. Evidence for inheritance of differential accumulation of calcium, magnesium, and potassium by maize. Crop Sci. 1:155–156.

----, W.I. Thomas, and D.E. Baker. 1964. Inheritance of P, K, Cu, B, Zn, Mn, Al and Fe concentrations by corn (*Zea mays* L.) leaves and grain. Crop Sci. 4:207–210.

Hageman, R.H. 1979. Integration of nitrogen assimilation in relation to yield. p. 591–611. *In* E.I. Hewitt and C.V. Cutting (ed.) Nitrogen assimilation of plants. Academic Press, New York.

----. 1986. Role of nitrogen metabolism in crop productivity. p. 105–116. *In* J.C. Shannon et al. (ed.) Regulation of carbon and nitrogen reduction and utilization in maize. Am. Soc. Plant Physiologists, Rockville, MD.

----, R.J. Lambert, D. Loussaert, M. Dalling, and L.R. Klepper. 1976. Nitrate and nitrite reductase as factors limiting protein synthesis. p. 103–133. *In* Genetic improvements in seed protein. Workshop Proc. NAS, Washington, DC.

----, E.R. Leng, and J.W. Dudley. 1967. A biochemical approach to corn breeding. Adv. Agron. 19:45–86.

----, and E.R. Waygood. 1959. Methods for the extraction of enzymes with special reference to the triosephosphate dehydrogenases. Plant Physiol. 34:396–400.

Hardacre, A.K., H.A. Eagles, and H.L. Turnbull. 1984. Physiology of inbreds in the cool-tolerant maize breeding programme. Biennial Rep. 38. Plant Physiol. Div., DSIR Palmerston North, NZ.

Heath, O.V.S., and F.S. Gregory. 1938. The constancy of the mean net assimilation rate and its ecological importance. Ann. Bot. N.S. 2:811–818.

Heichel, G.H. 1971. Confirming measurements of respiration and photosynthesis with dry matter accumulation. Photosynthetica 5:95–98.

----, and R.B. Musgrave. 1969. Varietal differences in net photosynthesis of *Zea mays* L. Crop Sci. 9:483–486.

Hewitt, E.J., and C.V. Cutting. 1979. Nitrogen assimilation of plants. Academic Press, New York.

Hibberd, K.A., M. Barker, P.C. Anderson, and L. Linder. 1986. Selection for high tryptophan maize. p. 440. *In* D.A. Somers (ed.) Abstr. 6 Int. Congr. of Plant Tissue Cell Cult., Minneapolis. 4–8 August. Univ. of Minnesota, Minneapolis.

Hixon, R.M., and G.F. Sprague. 1942. Waxy starch of maize and other cereals. Ind. Eng. Chem. 34:959–962.

Jackson, W.A., D. Flesher, and R.H. Hageman. 1973. Nitrate uptake by dark-grown corn seedlings. Plant Physiol. 51:120–127.

----, W.L. Pan, R.H. Moll, and E.J. Kamprath. 1986. Uptake, translocation and reduction of nitrate. p. 73–108. *In* C.A. Neyra (ed.) Biochemical basis of plant breeding. CRC Press, Boca Raton, FL.

Jellum, M.D. 1970. Plant introductions of maize as a source of oil with unusual fatty acid composition. J. Agric. Food Chem. 18:365–367.

Lambers, H. 1985. Respiration in intact plants and tissues: Its regulation and dependence on environmental factors, metabolism and invaded organisms. p. 418–473. *In* R. Douce and D.A. Dag (ed.) Encyclopedia of plant physiology-higher plant cell respiration. Springer-Verlag, Berlin.

----, T. Blacquiere, and B. Stuiver. 1981. Interactions between osmoregulation and the alternative respiratory pathway in *Plantago coronopus* as affected by salinity. Physiol. Plant. 51:63–68.

----, and D.A. Day. 1987. Respiration in intact tissues: Problems and perspectives. *In* A.L. Moore and R.B. Beechy (ed.) Plant mitochondria: structural functional and physiological aspects. Plenum Press, New York.

----, and E. Steingrover. 1978. Growth respiration of a flood-tolerant and a flood-intolerant Senecio species: Correlation between calculated and experimental values. Physiol. Plant 43:219–224.

Leng, E.R. 1961. Predicted and actual responses during long-term selection for chemical composition in maize. Euphytica 10:368–378.

Loomis, R.S., R. Rabbinge, and E. Ng. 1979. Explanatory models in crop physiology. Annu. Rev. Plant. Physiol. 30:339–367.

Laties, G.G. 1982. The cyanide-resistant, alternative path in higher plant respiration. Annu. Rev. Plant Physiol. 33:519–555.

Mahon, J.D. 1983. Limitations to the use of physiological variability in plant breeding. Can. J. Plant Sci. 63:11–25.

Manglesdorf, P.C. 1952. Hybridization in the evolution of maize. p. 175–198. *In* J.W. Gowen (ed.) Heterosis. Iowa State College Press, Ames.

McCree, K.J. 1974. Equations for the rate of dark respiration of white clover and grain sorghum, as functions of dry weight, photosynthetic rate and temperature. Crop Sci. 14:509–514.

McDaniel, R.G. 1972. Mitochondrial heterosis and complementation as biochemical measures of yield. Nature New Biol. 236:190–191.

----, and I.V. Sarkissian. 1966. Heterosis: complementation by mitochondria. Science 152:1640–1642.

----, and ----. 1968. Mitochondrial heterosis in maize. Genetics 59:465–475.

Meredith, W.R., and R.R. Bridge. 1984. Genetic contributions to yield changes in upland cotton p. 75–86. In W.R. Fehr (ed.) Contributions to yield gains of five major crop plants. CSSA, Madison, WI.

Mertz, E.T., L.S. Bates, and O.E. Nelson. 1964. Mutant gene that changes protein composition and increases lysine content of maize endosperm. Science 145:279–280.

Miller, F.R., and Y. Kebede. 1984. Genetic contributions to yield gains in sorghum, 1950 to 1980. p. 1–12. In W.R. Fehr (ed.) Genetic contributions to yield gains of five major crop plants. CSSA, Madison, WI.

Miller, R.L., J.W. Dudley, and D.E. Alexander. 1981. High intensity selection for percent oil in corn. Crop Sci. 21:433–437.

Mock, J.J., and R.B. Pearce. 1975. An ideotype of maize. Euphytica 24:613–623.

Moll, R.H., E.J. Kamprath, and W.A. Jackson. 1982. Analysis and interpretation of factors which contribute to efficiency of nitrogen utilization. Agron. J. 74:562–568.

----, ----, and ----. 1983. The potential for genetic improvement in nitrogen use in maize. p. 48–68. In D. Wilkinson and R. Brown (ed.) Proc. 38 Annu. Corn and Sorghum Indus. Res. Conf., Chicago. 7–8 December. ASTA, Washington, DC.

Moss, D.N., and R.B. Musgrave. 1971. Photosynthesis and crop production. Adv. Agron. 23:317–338.

Moyed, H.S. 1960. False feedback inhibition: Inhibition of tryptophan biosynthesis by 5-methyltryptophan. J. Biol. Chem. 235:1098–1102.

Muruli, B.I., and G.M. Paulsen. 1981. Improvement of nitrogen use efficiency and its relationship to other traits in maize. Maydica 26:63–73.

Musgrave, R.B. 1971. Photosynthetic efficiency in corn. p. 186–192. In Proc. 26 Ann. Corn Sorghum Ind. Res. Conf., Chicago. 14–16 December. ASTA, Washington, DC.

Musgrave, M.E., J. Antonovics, and J.N. Siedow. 1986. Is male-sterility in plants related to lack of cyanide-respiration in tissue? Plant Sci. 44:7–11.

Nelson, O.E. 1969. Genetic modification of protein quality in plants. Adv. Agron. 21:171–174.

----. 1980. Genetic control of polysaccharide and storage protein synthesis in the endosperms of barley, maize and sorghum. p. 41–71. In Y. Pomeranz (ed.) Advances in cereal science and technology, Vol. 2. Am. Assoc. Cereal Chemists, St. Paul.

Nelson, W.L., and H.F. Reetz, Jr. 1986. Herman Warsaw's high corn yields. Crops Soils 38:5–6.

Nielsen, N.E., and S.A. Barber. 1978. Difference among genotypes of corn in the kinetics of P uptake. Agron. J. 70:695–698.

Nubel, D.S. 1986. Selection in maize for field photosynthesis. M.S. thesis. Univ. of Illinois, Urbana.

Penning De Vries, F.W.T. 1974. Substrate utilization and respiration in relations to growth and maintenance in higher plants. Netherlands J. Agric. Sci. 22:40–44.

Peters, D.B., B.F. Clough, R.A. Graves, and G.R. Stahl. 1974. Measurement of dark respiration, evaporation and photosynthesis in field plots. Agron. J. 66:460–462.

Pridham, T.B. 1974. Plant carbohydrate biochemistry. ch. 3,6,8,9,12. In Proceedings of the Phytochemistry Society symposium no. 10. Academic Press, New York.

Rich, P.R., N.K. Wiegand, H. Blum, A.L. Moore, and W.D. Bonner. 1978. Studies on the mechanism of inhibition of redox enzymes by substituted hydroxamic acids. Biochem. Biophys. Acta. 525:325–337.

Robertson, T.B. 1923. The chemical basis of growth and senescence. J.B. Lippincott Co., Philadelphia.

Rodgers, D.M., J.P. Murphy, and K.S. Frey. 1983. Impact of plant breeding on the grain yield and genetic diversity of spring oats. Crop. Sci. 23:737–740.

Russell, W.A. 1972. Effect of leaf angle on hybrid performance in maize (Zea mays L.). Crop Sci. 12:90–92.

――――. 1986. Contribution of breeding to maize improvement in the United States. 1920s–1980s. Iowa State J. Res. 61:5–34.

Sarkissian, I.V., and H.K. Skrivaslava. 1967. Mitochondrial polymorphism in maize. II. Further evidence of correlation of mitochondrial complementation and heterosis. Genetics 57:843–850.

Sayre, J.D. 1955. Mineral nutrition of corn. *In* G.F. Sprague (ed.) Corn and corn improvement. Agronomy 18:192–222.

Scandalios, J.G. 1974. Isozymes in development and differentiation. Annu. Rev. Plant Physiol. 25:225–258.

Schmidt, J.W. 1984. Genetic contribution to yield gain in wheat. p. 89–101. *In* W.R. Fehr (ed.) Genetic contributions to yield gains of five major crop plants. CSSA, Madison, WI.

Schrader, L.E. 1974. Seasonal patterns and genotypic differences in glucose-6-phosphate dehydrogenase activity in a diallel cross of corn. Crop Sci. 14:201–205.

――――. 1985. Selection for a metabolic balance in maize. p. 79–89. *In* J.E. Harper et al. (ed.) Exploitation of physiological and genetic variability to enhance crop productivity. Am. Soc. Plant Physiologists, Rockville, MD.

――――, D.A. Cataldo, D.M. Peterson, and R.D. Vogelzang. 1974. Nitrate reductase and glucose-6-phosphate dehydrogenase activities as influenced by leaf age and addition of protein to extraction media. Physiol. Plant. 32:337–341.

Schwartz, D. 1960. Genetic studies on mutant enzymes in maize: Synthesis of hybrid enzymes by heterozygotes. Proc. Natl. Acad. Sci. USA 46:1210–1216.

――――, L. Fuchsman, and K.M. McGrath. 1965. Allelic isozymes of the pH 7.5 esterase in maize. Genetics 52:1265–1268.

Senti, F.R. 1967. High amylose corn starch: Its production, properties and uses. p. 499–522. *In* R.L. Whistler and E.F. Paschall (ed.) Starch: Chemistry and technology, Vol. 2. Industrial aspects. Academic Press, New York.

Shannon, J.C. 1978. Physiological factors affecting starch accumulation in corn kernels. *In* Proc. 33 Annu. Corn Sorghum Ind. Res. Conf., Chicago. 12–14 December. ASTA, Washington, DC.

Sheppers, J.S., F.E. Below, and R.H. Hageman. 1985. Genotypic variation for postanthesis nitrogen uptake and distribution in maize. Plant Physiol. 77:32.

Sherrard, J.H., R.J. Lambert, F.E. Below, R.T. Dunand, M.J. Messmer, M.R. Willman, C.S. Winkels, and R.H. Hageman. 1986. Use of physiological traits especially those of nitrogen metabolism for selection in maize. p. 109–130. *In* C.A. Neyra (ed.) Biochemical basis of plant breeding. CRC Press, Boca Raton, FL.

Singletary, G.N., and F.E. Below. 1986. Effect of C/N nutrition on starch and protein biosynthesis in developing maize kernels. p. 330. *In* J.C. Shannon et al. (ed.) Regulation of carbon and nitrogen reduction and utilization in maize. Am. Soc. Plant Physiology, Rockville, MD.

Specht, J.E., and J.H. Williams. 1984. Contribution of genetic technology to soybean productivity. p. 49–73. *In* W.R. Fehr (ed.) Genetic contributions to yield gains of five major crop plants. CSSA, Madison, WI.

Sprague, G.F., B. Brimhall, and R.H. Hixon. 1943. Some effects of the waxy gene in corn on properties of the endosperm starch. J. Am. Soc. Agron. 35:817–822.

――――. 1969. Germplasm manipulations of the future. p. 375–387. *In* J.D. Eastin et al. (ed.) Physiological aspects of crop yields. ASA, Madison, WI.

Stephens, S.G. 1942. Yield characters of selected oat varieties in relation to cereal breeding. J. Agric. Sci. 32:217–254.

Stringfield, G.H. 1964. Objectives in corn improvement. Adv. Agron. 16:101–137.

Stuber, C.W., M.D. Edwards, and J.F. Wendel. 1987. Molecular marker-facilitated investigations in maize: II. Factors influencing yield and its component traits. Crop Sci. 27:639–648.

――――, M.M. Goodman, and R.H. Moll. 1982. Improvement of yield and ear number resulting from selection at allozyme loci in a maize population. Crop Sci. 22:737–740.

――――, ――――, H. Schaffer, and B.S. Weir. 1980. Allozyme frequency changes associated with selection for increased gain yield in maize. Genetics 95:236–275.

――――, and R.H. Moll. 1972. Frequency changes of isozyme alleles in a selection experiment for grain yield in maize. Crop Sci. 12:337–340.

Stump, P.R., and E.E. Conn. 1980. The biochemistry of plants. p. 498. *In* A comprehensive treatise. Lipids: Structure and function, Vol. 4. Academic Press, New York.

Sung, T.M., and R.J. Lambert. 1982. Ninhydrin color test for screening modified endosperm opaque-2 maize. Cereal Chem. 60:84–85.

Swank, J.C., F.E. Below, R.J. Lambert, and R.H. Hageman. 1982. Interaction of carbon and nitrogen metabolism in the productivity of maize. Plant Physiol. 70:1185–1190.

Thorne, G.N., S.T. Thomas, and I. Pearman. 1979. Effects of nitrogen nutrition on physiological factors that control the yield of carbohydrate in the grain. p. 90–101. In J.H.J. Spiertz and T. Kramer (ed.) Crop physiology and cereal breeding. Center for Agric. Publ. and Documentation, Wageningen, Netherlands.

Tollenaar. 1977. Sink-source relationships during reproductive development in maize. A review. Maydica 22:49–75.

Tyner, E.H. 1946. The relation of corn yields to leaf nitrogen, phosphorus and potassium content. Soil Sci. Soc. Am. Proc. 11:317–323.

Vineyard, M.L., and R.P. Bear. 1952. Amylose content. Maize Genet. Coop. News Lett. 26:5.

Warner, R.L., R.H. Hageman, J.W. Dudley, and R.J. Lambert. 1969. Inheritance of nitrate reductase activity in Zea mays L. Proc. Natl. Acad. Sci. USA 62:788–792.

Warsaw, H. 1985. High yield corn production—Farmers perspective. p. 20. In Agronomy abstracts. ASA, Madison, WI.

Watson, D.J. 1952. The physiological basis of variations in yield. Adv. Agron. 10:101–145.

Weber, E.J. 1980. Corn kernel modification. p. 97–137. In T. Swain and R. Keiman (ed.) The resource potential in phytochemistry, Vol. 14. Plenum Press, New York.

-----. 1987. Lipids of the kernel. p. 84–99. In S. Watson and P. Ramstad (ed.) Corn (Zea mays L.). Chemistry and technology. Assoc. Cereal Chemists, St. Paul.

Whistler, R.L., J.N.B. Miller, and E.F. Paschall. 1984. Starch chemistry and technology, 2nd ed. Academic Press, New York.

Wilson, D. 1975. Variation in leaf respiration in relation to growth and photosynthesis of Lolium. Ann. Appl. Biol. 80:323–328.

-----. 1981. Breeding for morphological and physiological traits. p. 27–42. In K.I. Frey (ed.) Plant breeding II. Iowa State Univ. Press, Ames.

Wilson, D. 1982. Response to selection for dark respiration rate of mature leaves in Lolium perenne L. and its effects on growth of young plants and simulated swards. Ann. Bot. 49:303–312.

-----, and J.G. Jones. 1982. Effect of selection for dark respiration rate of mature leaves on crop yields of Lolium perenne L. cv. 523. Ann. Bot. 49:313–320.

Wit, C.T. de, and R. Brouwer. 1968. Über ein dynamisches Modell des vegetativen Wachstums von Pflanzenbestanden. Zeitschr. Angew. Bot. 42:1–12.

Wittwer, S.H. 1978. The next generation of agricultural research. Science 199:375–382.

Wong, S., I.A. Cowan, and G.O. Farquhar. 1985. Leaf conductance in relation to rate of CO_2 assimilation. I. Influence of nitrogen nutrition, phosphorus nutrition, proton flux density and ambient partial pressure of CO_2 during ontogeny. Plant Physiol. 78:821–825.

Wyss, C.W. 1986. Characteristics of chemical composition and interacting in the grain and stover of the Illinois protein strains of maize. M.S. thesis. Univ. of Illinois, Urbana.

Zuber, M.S. 1965. Genetic control of starch development. p. 43–63. In R.L. Whistler and E.F. Poschall (ed.) Starch chemistry and technology, Vol. 1. Fundamental aspects. Academic Paschall Press, New York.

8   Corn Breeding[1]

A. R. HALLAUER

USDA-ARS
Ames, Iowa

WILBERT A. RUSSELL

Iowa State University
Ames, Iowa

K. R. LAMKEY

USDA-ARS
Ames, Iowa

Corn (*Zea mays* L.) breeding for hybrid development was begun in the early 1900s with the work of Shull (1909), East (1908), and others, but a primitive type of breeding was conducted for thousands of years by the American Indians before the European colonists began settlement in the New World. The U.S. Corn Belt dents were derived from crosses that included germ plasm of the northeastern flint and southern dent or gourd-seed types, beginning about 1850, with subsequent selection that developed the U.S. Corn Belt dents. Open-pollinated cultivars, such as Reid Yellow Dent, Krug, Leaming, and Lancaster Sure Crop were developed by a type of mass selection that was based on plant, ear, and grain type. This early work, which was done primarily by farmers and seedsmen, provided the germplasm sources from which were developed the inbred parental lines that were used to produce the first double-cross hybrids used in the USA. Even to the present time, relatively little germ plasm from other countries has been used in corn breeding programs in the USA (Brown, 1975).

Breeding procedures were used to improve and develop new strains of the open-pollinated cultivars in the late 1800s and early 1900s before the development of inbred lines for hybrid seed production was begun. These breeding procedures included varietal hybridization, mass selection, and ear-to-row selection. Descriptions of the procedures have been published in earlier years, and results from a few studies were summarized by Sprague and Eberhart (1977). These procedures were not successful to effect yield improvements. In some instances, varietal hybridization

[1]Joint contribution of the USDA-ARS, and Journal Paper no. J-12562 of the Iowa Agric. and Home Econ. Exp. Stn., Ames, IA 50011. Project no. 2778.

gave crosses that produced better than the higher-yielding parent, but the procedure was not accepted widely for commercial use. Selection programs were successful in producing numerous strains that varied for maturity, plant type, ear and grain type, and pest resistance. Corn shows conducted at the start of the 20th century also caused selection for a distinct ear and grain appearance. Close selection to type, however, may have caused some inbreeding, which may have been the primary reason that yield improvements were not realized. Mass selection and ear-to-row breeding were gradually discontinued as inbred development for hybrid use became the accepted method. Modifications to mass selection (Gardner, 1961) and ear-to-row selection (Lonnquist, 1964) recently have been used to enhance the effectiveness of these selection methods for improving yield in breeding populations.

Results of breeding studies by Shull, East, and Jones in the early 1900s led to the establishment of programs at many U.S. agricultural experiment stations and by the USDA for the development and evaluation of inbred lines and hybrids during the period of 1915 to 1925. Corn breeding as a private commercial enterprise came a few years later. It was the 1930s before farmer use of hybrid seed became an acceptable practice; hybrid corn occupied approximately 100% of the corn area in Iowa by 1943, 90% of the corn area in the U.S. Corn Belt, but only 60% of the corn area for the entire USA (Fig. 8–1). Double-cross hybrids were the predominant type in the USA until about 1960 when the use of single crosses began to increase. Single crosses became the predominant type in a few years, with considerably fewer hectares being planted to related-line single crosses, three-way crosses, and double crosses.

Corn breeding for the development of inbred lines and hybrids in other parts of the world expanded rapidly after World War II. Corn has proved to be a flexible species amenable to selection such that progress

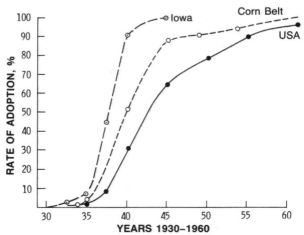

Fig. 8–1. Rate of acceptance of double-cross hybrids in Iowa, the U.S. Corn Belt, and the USA.

has been achieved to develop types adapted to many areas where it was not grown or was relatively unimportant in earlier years. An excellent example has been the tremendous expansion in some European countries, made possible by the selection of earlier maturity, better adapted cultivars that can be grown successfully in areas where such was not feasible 40 years ago (Trifunovic, 1978). Some inbred development and evaluation were done in a few European countries before 1940, and such programs were expanded greatly after 1945. In the first period of this expansion, materials from the USA were evaluated and some U.S. hybrids were used. Subsequently, European and U.S. lines in hybrid combinations were developed and these helped to expand the corn-growing area and to give higher yields. The European lines introduced greater cold tolerance and adaptation for earlier maturity and the U.S. lines added improved yield and standability. These combinations permitted the expansion of hybrid corn into central Europe. In France, for example, the hectarage has increased more than five times from pre-World War II to the present time, and France is now a leading corn producer in Europe. Corn has become the most important feed crop in southern and central Europe.

Corn ranks second to wheat in total production among the world's cereal crops (CIMMYT, 1984). World corn production now normally exceeds 400 million t. During the period 1970–72 to 1981–83, world corn production increased about 120 million t, which represents a 42% increase in the world supplies at a rate of 3.1% yr^{-1}. More than 50% of the total world area planted with corn is in Latin America, Africa, and south and southwest Asia, but probably <25% of the total grain production is in this area (Wellhausen, 1978). Hybrids are the primary type grown in Argentina, South Africa, and parts of Brazil, but the remainder of the area uses open-pollinated cultivars, improved synthetics, variety crosses, and hybrids. In some areas where corn grain is used primarily for human consumption, considerable work has been done to improve protein quality through the use of *opaque-2*. As the technology is improved, it seems likely that hybrid types will become more important in most of the tropical and subtropical areas.

Corn grain yields in the USA have increased from approximately 1.3 Mg ha^{-1} in 1930 to 7.5 Mg ha^{-1} in 1985 (Fig. 8–2). Before 1930, average yields were static because no yield gains were realized from breeding and essentially no improvement occurred because of changes in cultural practices. The mass and ear-to-row selection methods that breeders and seedsmen used before 1930 were not effective in yield improvement. Yield increases have occurred since mid-1930s because of the use of hybrids, increased use of fertilizers, better weed control, higher plant densities, and improved management. The rate of yield gain increased beginning about 1960 when single-cross hybrids gradually replaced double crosses. Also, there was a rapid increase in the use of N fertilizer during 1960 to 1970 (Thompson, 1986). Mean yields plotted in Fig. 8–2 show a greater variability among years for average yields in the 1970s, but there is no

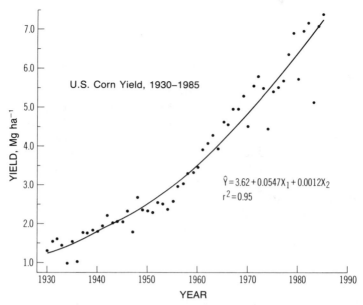

Fig. 8-2. National average of corn yields in the USA for the period including 1930–1986.

evidence of a plateau effect. Thompson (1975), by using a regression equation derived from corn yields and weather data in Illinois, predicted yields in that state would level off at 7.5 Mg ha^{-1} by 1985.

Evidence for the contribution of breeding to corn yield increases has been obtained in several experiments (Russell, 1974, 1984, 1985a, 1986; Duvick, 1977, 1984; Crosbie, 1982; Tapper, 1983; Castleberry et al., 1984; Meghji et al., 1984). Most of these experiments included hybrids that were representative of materials grown from 1930s to 1970 or 1980; in a few studies open-pollinated cultivars from prehybrid times were included. Frey (1971) and Darrah (unpublished data reported by Hallauer, 1973) obtained estimates by using data from the Iowa Corn Yield Tests; all other data were obtained in experiments designed purposely to obtain information to assess genetic gains. A summary that includes total and genetic gains is given in Table 8-1. Total gains ranged from 0.078 to 0.110 Mg ha^{-1}yr^{-1} and genetic gains were 0.033 to 0.092 Mg ha^{-1}yr^{-1}. The estimates, using open-pollinated cultivars as the basis for the proportion of total gain that was caused by genetic improvement, ranged from 56 to 89% for the planned experiments; some may be considered actual genetic gains whereas other estimates were biased because of harvest method. For example, the estimates of machine-harvested plots (see footnotes, Table 8-1) are likely biased in favor of newer hybrids because greater stalk lodging of the older hybrids would be expected to have caused greater harvest losses. The combined effects of improved cultural practices and better hybrids were confounded in these experiments. The hybrids have increased in yield because of their continued improvement in genetic potential to take advantage of improved cultural practices.

Table 8-1. Summary of 13 estimates of total grain yield gain and the genetic total yield gain of corn hybrids. (Table 3 from Russell, 1986). Adapted from Duvick (1984).†

Author	Year reported	Time span	Experiment yr	Total gain	Genetic gain	
				— Mg ha⁻¹ yr⁻¹ —		%
Frey	1971	1926–1968	1926–1968	--	--	56
Darrah	1973	1930–1970	1930–1970	0.099	0.033	33
Russell	1974	1930–1970	1971–1973	0.078	0.063	79
Russell‡	1974	1930–1970	1971–1973	0.078	0.049	63
Duvick	1977	1935–1971	1972–1973	0.088	0.050	57
Duvick	1977	1935–1972	1972–1973	0.088	0.053	60
Tapper§	1983	1930–1970	1980–1981	--	--	42
Tapper§	1983	1930–1970	1980–1981	--	--	67
Castleberry et al.	1984	1930–1980	1980–1981	0.110	0.082	75
Duvick	1984	1930–1980	1978–1980	0.103	0.092	89
Duvick	1984	1930–1980	1977–1979	0.103	0.073	71
Russell	1984	1930–1980	1981–1982	0.090	0.071	79
Russell‡	1984	1930–1980	1981–1982	0.090	0.050	56

† Gains calculated basis U.S. corn yields by Castleberry et al. (1984); basis Iowa state yields for all other estimates.
‡ Adjustments made to estimate gains because of difference between experiment and Iowa state average yields.
§ Gains calculated relative to 1930-era hybrids; first estimate—total yields, second estimate—machine harvest yields.

The newer hybrids, 1970 or 1980, compared with hybrids of the 1930s had higher yields at all plant densities, and the differences generally were greater at higher plant densities. The newer hybrids had the genetic potential to take advantage of the higher number of plants per unit field area and, thus, to produce much higher yields than the older hybrids. The older hybrids generally had more barrenness at the higher plant densities than did the newer hybrids. Also, differences between the older and newer hybrids for lodging increased with higher plant densities, with the newer hybrids showing considerable superiority.

Castleberry et al. (1984) compared cultivars from six decades, 1930 to 1980, in low- and high-fertility conditions at one location for 2 yr. The high-fertility area had received normal fertilizer applications for 20 yr, whereas the low-fertility area had been in continuous corn and unfertilized since 1958. The higher fertility area received approximately 200 kg of N ha⁻¹, 90 kg of P_2O_5 ha⁻¹, and 150 kg of K_2O ha⁻¹ in 2 yr of test; the low-fertility area received no fertilizer. The yield response relative to decades of cultivars was 0.087 Mg ha⁻¹yr⁻¹ in the high-fertility condition and 0.051 Mg ha⁻¹yr⁻¹ in the low-fertility condition. The newer hybrids were superior to the older cultivars in both fertility levels, and the superiority was greater for the high-fertility area than for the low-fertility area.

Duvick (1984) evaluated four single crosses representative of four decades, 1940 to 1970, at low, intermediate, and high N levels. His newer hybrids outyielded the older hybrids at all N levels, but the hybrid × N level interaction was not significant. Carlone and Russell (1987) included four cultivars from each of seven eras (pre-1930–1980) and evaluated them in 12 treatment combinations of three plant densities and four N levels. Grain yields showed that the treatments (plant densities and N levels) were interdependent, and the interaction of the two treatments varied among cultivars; i.e., the densities $\times$ N levels $\times$ cultivars interaction was statistically significant. The newer cultivars, 1970 and 1980 eras, were the highest yielding at all N levels, and each cultivar seemed to have a unique plant density-N level combination at which it produced a maximum yield. Differences among eras for N response showed no distinct patterns relative to the eras.

Improvement for resistance to root and stalk lodging, which was necessary to permit machine harvesting and the use of higher plant densities, was achieved. Selection for disease resistance has been an integral part of corn breeding for many years, yet there are little data that reflect directly on the effect of greater resistance to grain yield. Improvement for stay-green, which is primarily a visual rating for plant health, has been well documented (Duvick, 1984; Tapper, 1983; Meghji et al., 1984; Russell, 1985a), and stalk quality is dependent upon total plant health. Stay-green may also reflect improvement for resistance or tolerance to second-generation European corn borer [*Ostrinia nubilalis* (Hübner)]. Duvick (1984) showed a continuous improvement in the resistance to second-generation European corn borer from the 1930 to the 1980 hybrids, which would be conducive to greater stalk quality and reduced harvest losses.

The commercial use of single-cross hybrids has been made feasible by improvement of parental inbred lines. Agronomic improvements include cold tolerance such that germination and emergence are better, resistance to plant diseases and insects, resistance to barrenness, resistance to lodging, better pollen production, higher seed yield, and better seed quality. Duvick (1984) found that 1970 inbreds compared with 1930 inbreds had a yield gain of 0.05 Mg ha^{-1}yr^{-1}, or a total predicted gain of 2.0 Mg ha^{-1}. Meghji et al. (1984) obtained no yield increase for 1950- compared with 1930-era inbreds, but the 1970-era inbreds had an average yield increase of 14.5% over the 1950 lines. Furthermore, the 1950- and 1970-era inbreds were improved for plant health and resistance to lodging compared with the 1930 inbreds. Whereas in earlier years breeders selected lines primarily on the basis of hybrid performance, now more emphasis is given to the development of lines that have greater vigor and, thus, higher seed yields.

Yield increases in other corn-growing countries began later than in the USA partly because improved cultivars, including hybrids, were not generally used until after World War II. For Europe, the estimated yield increase per hectare was 2.4-fold for 1969 to 1973 over 1934 to 1938 (Trifunovic, 1978). In France, the yield increase per hectare was 3.2-fold for the same period. These increases occurred because of both improved cultivars and better field husbandry. Wellhausen (1978) reported that a double-cross hybrid released in Brazil in 1958 yielded approximately 50 and 58% better than 'Paulista' and 'Cateto', respectively, the two most common races grown in Brazil in earlier years. Kuhn and Gevers (1980) found for 2 yr, in South Africa 1977/78 and 1978/79, that the best hybrids yielded 41.2% above the mean for the first hybrids released. Most of the increase in world corn production was achieved by yield improvement. In developing countries, yields increased 2.6% yr^{-1} while the area planted increased 1% yr^{-1} (CIMMYT, 1984).

Further increases in corn yields are expected primarily because of the combined effects of two factors: (i) improved cultural practices and management and (ii) increased genetic potential of the hybrids. The rate of genetic gain for grain yield could become even greater than shown previously because there are now more breeders and companies with breeding programs. It seems likely further gains will be achieved by the development and evaluation of parental materials at higher plant densities. Stalk lodging will be a problem and must be corrected if higher plant densities are to be used. Recurrent selection can be used effectively to improve stalk quality in breeding populations, but must be done with yield evaluation to avoid yield declines (Devey and Russell, 1983; Martin and Russell, 1984a, b). Genetic engineering techniques have not yet had an impact on corn improvement, but effects for some aspects of corn improvement may be realized in the near future. Also, we have only just begun to explore in greater depth the possible utilization of germ plasm from other areas.

8–1 BREEDING METHODS

8–1.1 Methods for Line Development

The essential features of the inbred-hybrid concept used in corn breeding were eloquently described by Shull (1908, 1909, 1910). The major focus of corn breeding programs is the same as that stated by Shull (1909) ". . . the object of the corn breeder should not be to find the best pure line, but to find and maintain the best hybrid combination." Shull's suggestion was not immediately accepted because of the practical concerns of producing adequate quantities of hybrid seed at an acceptable cost. These concerns were alleviated with Jones' (1918) suggestion that single crosses be used as parents to produce double crosses rather than inbred lines used to produce single crosses, as suggested by Shull (1909). Hence, the basis for producing and growing hybrid corn was in place by 1920. During the 1920s, the USDA, state agriculture experiment stations, and individuals initiated corn breeding programs to develop and test inbred lines and hybrids. Agencies and individuals responded to Shull's

(1910) plea that, "My anxiety is not for success of the pure-line methods outlined by myself, but that serious experimentation shall be undertaken by every station within the corn-growing region for the purpose of discovering what is the best method."

8–1.1.1 Pedigree Selection

Pedigree selection is the most widely used breeding method to develop inbred lines for use as parents of hybrids. The types of populations sampled, methods of selection used, and the emphasis given to traits during selection have changed, but the basic principles of pure-line development are used. Initially, pedigree selection was practiced in the open-pollinated landrace cultivars that were adapted to the areas in which the breeding programs were located. Useful inbred lines (e.g., L317, L289, I205, Os420, WF9, etc.) were developed from the landrace cultivars, but it soon became obvious that repeated samplings of the same landrace cultivars were not productive. A logical sequel was to cross pairs of elite inbred lines that complemented one another, produce the F_2 generation, and practice pedigree selection by sampling the F_2 population. F_2 populations of single crosses are the most frequently (37%) used source populations for line development (Bauman, 1981). Other populations frequently used by U.S. breeders to initiate pedigree selection include genetically broad- (15%) and narrow-base (16%) populations improved by selection for specific traits, and populations (14%) formed by intermating elite inbreds that may be either related or unrelated (Bauman, 1981). The choice of germ plasm depends on the breeding objectives, stage of development of breeding program, and germ plasm available.

The scheme of the pedigree selection program depends on the skills of the individual breeder, primary breeding goals, the resources available for advancing the progenies, intensity of selection, and scope of testing. Different breeders emphasize selection for different traits because of locally important pests at different stages of inbreeding. The intensity of selection will vary, depending on the effective screens available for pests, environments available, and types of material under selection. One common feature, however, is that records are kept for each progeny for the traits selected for each generation of inbreeding.

Adequate sample sizes of the source breeding populations are necessary to include the range of possible segregants. In most instances, however, it is not possible to have a sample size that includes the theoretical number of possible genotypes for the segregating loci. If, for example, the cross between two parents differed for five allelic pairs, the smallest theoretical F_2 population would require 1024 individuals; if the parents differed for 10 allelic pairs, the theoretical F_2 populations would include 1 048 576 individuals. Most of the traits emphasized in selection of lines are controlled by more than five genetic factors, and, therefore, compromises are made for sample sizes because the breeder usually is sampling more than one population. Generally, the decision on sample size depends on the heritability of the trait to be improved and(or) the experience of the breeder making the selections among progenies. Bauman (1981) reported there was great variation among the initial sample sizes, with sample size of 500 being the more common. After the initial sampling, the number of progenies surviving in subsequent generations of inbreeding (without testcross evaluation) was quickly reduced. The idealized number of surviving progenies after sampling 500 plants (S_1 progenies) was reported by Bauman (1981) to be 180 in the S_2 generation, 80 in the S_3 generation, and 40 in the S_4 generation. Average selection intensities were 63, 56, and 50% in the S_1, S_2, and S_3 generations, respectively, for visually selected traits. The breeders preferred use of smaller sample size in a greater number of populations rather than greater sample size in one or two populations.

The general procedure with use of F_2 populations is to initiate selection and selfing without any genetic recombination. The breeder usually has a mental image of the ideotype desired, and, depending on the skill of the breeder, desirable ideotypes of the favorable parent can be recovered with slight modifications. Favorable linkages would be desirable in these instances. The effects of random mating within F_2 populations before sampling are not conclusive. Pederson (1974) and Bos (1977) have presented theoretical arguments against random mating in F_2 populations of self-pollinating species. Altman and Busch (1984) reported there was insufficient useful recombination to justify random mating single-cross populations of wheat (*Triticum aestivum* L.) before initiating selection. Humphrey et al. (1969) in tobacco (*Nicotiana tobacum* L.) and Nordquist et al. (1973) in sorghum [*Sorghum bicolor* (L.) Moench] reported random mating increased genetic recombination which provided desirable recombinants.

Empirical data for random mating single crosses of corn before conducting pedigree selection are limited. Covarrubias-Prieto (1987) estimated the variability among 100 S_1 progenies in F_2 populations of B73 × Mo17 (cross of unrelated lines) and B73 × B84 (cross of related lines) and after five generations of random mating 250 plants in each F_2 population. Objectives of the study were to determine if random mating was effective for increasing genetic variability in populations formed from single crosses and if the relatedness of the inbred lines used to make the cross was an important consideration for random mating. Preliminary evidence suggests that random mating did not increase genetic variability in either F_2 population. Estimates of the S_1 components of variance were similar for the F_2 and F_2 random mated six times. Indirect evidence suggests that selection and intermating are effective via use of recurrent selection procedures (e.g., B14, B37, B73, and B84 derived by pedigree selection from cycles of selection in BS13).

Pedigree selection will always be an important component of modern corn-breeding programs. Based on surveys by Hallauer (1979) and Bauman (1981), it seems pedigree selection will be emphasized in populations with a restricted genetic base. Because of the availability of elite lines and competition among private companies to provide high-performance hybrids, germplasm sources that include favorable linkages will be used to increase the odds of recovering elite lines and hybrids. The skills of the breeder in selection and the precision of testing have been found effective for developing improved lines and hybrids by pedigree selection (Duvick, 1977; Bauman, 1977). Except for germplasm sources, the methods of selection and hybrids currently produced and grown are those described by Shull (1909, 1910).

8–1.1.2 Backcrossing

Backcross method of breeding is a modification of the pedigree method and is an important component of most breeding programs. Bauman (1981) reported that 17% of the total effort for inbred line development was allocated to backcross sources. The main difference between backcross and pedigree selection is in the objective of the crosses and the level of recovery of the recurrent parental genotype. The complexity of the backcross method depends on type of trait being transferred (single gene vs. several genes), level of expressivity, whether cytoplasmic or nuclear inheritance, and the types of parents included in the crosses. For single gene traits that are relatively easy to classify, the backcross method is effective and relatively easy to manage. For traits that have a more complex inheritance, the backcross method requires greater selection pressure for the desired trait, but it has been successfully used to transfer traits in which the effects of individual genes were not known (e.g., Duvick, 1974).

Modifications of the backcross method have been suggested. Convergent improvement was a concept developed by Richey (1927) for the parallel improvement of two inbred lines by the reciprocal addition of dominant favorable genes present in one line but lacking in the other line. Richey and Sprague (1931) and Murphy (1942) presented experimental evidence that convergent improvement was effective for yield improvements of the recovered lines and their respective single crosses. However, convergent improvement is apparently not an important component of current breeding programs.

For traits that have a more complex inheritance, usually some modifications are needed to transfer the trait effectively. Bailey (1977) and Johnson (1980) presented formulae and examples of the probabilities of recovering more than "n" loci with "x" favorable alleles. Their theoretical calculations, based on F_2 populations where $p = q = 0.5$ for segregating loci, support the experiences in breeding. If the trait being transferred has a high heritability (nearly 100%) for a trait, such as *Ht* conditioning resistance to *Helminthosporium turcicum* Pass. (Hooker, 1961), the chances of recovering the favorable alleles of the recurrent parent are good with successive backcrosses. Tight linkages of unfavorable alleles with the gene being transferred from the donor parent would, of course, affect the outcome in an obvious manner (Bailey and Comstock, 1976).

If the trait is conditioned by 20 genes, has a heritability of 0.50, and a 10% selection intensity is used, Bailey (1977) showed that the probability of obtaining a recovery with 80% of the favorable alleles was 0.271 in the second backcross. The greater the number of loci, the lower the probabilities in recovering all of the favorable alleles. Johnson (1980) concluded that, the more divergent the parents in making the crosses, several backcrosses to the better parent will be required to enhance the probability of obtaining a recovery superior to the better parent.

8–1.1.3 Gamete Selection

Gamete selection is a scheme devised by Stadler (1944) for sampling elite gametes from a population. Stadler's premise was that, if superior zygotes occur with a frequency of p^2, the superior gametes would occur with a frequency of p. The procedure involves crossing an elite line with a random sample of pollen of plants from a source population; each of the F_1 plants and the elite line are testcrossed to a common tester and the F_1 plants are also selfed; testcrosses are evaluated in replicated trials; and the testcrosses of F_1 plants that exceed the elite line by tester are presumed to have obtained a superior gamete from the source population. Experiments testing the effectiveness of gamete selection reported by Pinnell et al. (1952), Lonnquist and McGill (1954), El-Hifny et al. (1969), and Burton (1982) suggested superior lines could be recovered from the use of gamete selection. But Giesbrecht (1964) reported the method was not effective. It should be emphasized, however, that it is not possible to recover the superior gamete itself because the F_1 plants were self-fertilized; this has been the primary criticism of the purported advantage of the gamete selection scheme (Richey, 1947). The disadvantage of the original concept of gamete selection can be alleviated if individual plants from the source population are crossed to the elite line and also self-fertilized, in which case superior genotypes rather than superior gametes are selected (Hallauer, 1970). Though gamete selection is not used as extensively as pedigree and backcross methods, it does have some intrinsic features that interest breeders, and, consequently, gamete selection is included in some breeding programs.

8–1.1.4 Special Techniques

Several suggestions have been made for the instantaneous derivation of homozygous inbred lines. These techniques have involved the doubling of haploids derived from either maternal or paternal gametes (Chase, 1952; Goodsell, 1961; Kermicle, 1969). Genetic markers were used to identify haploids, and the haploids were doubled to form homozygous diploid inbred lines. The disadvantages of the methods were the low frequency of the occurrence of haploids and doubling of haploids to the diploid state. Kermicle (1969) reported on a spontaneous mutant (*ig*) that increased the frequency of occurrence of haploids (about 3%). Advantages of the use of haploids were the rapid production of new inbred lines and use in the conversion of inbred lines from normal to sterile cytoplasms. Each of the methods has been used and tested, but it does not seem they are important components of most breeding programs. Although the methods are capable of rapid development of homozygous inbred lines, they would represent a random sample of genotypes that would require the standard methods of evaluation (Thompson, 1954).

Somaclonal variation within inbred lines submitted to tissue culture has been reported (Edallo et al., 1981; McCoy and Phillips, 1982; Earle and Gracen, 1985; Lee et al., 1988). Hence, it seems genetic variation can be derived within inbred lines for selection without making crosses between lines to create genetic variability. Most of the variation observed phenotypically is due to single genes; e.g., albinos. If, however, genetic variation for traits conditioned by 20 or more genes approaches a normal density distribution, tissue culture may permit the recovery of second-cycle lines that include the original genome that also include a gene(s) for other traits; e.g., resistance to a specific herbicide. Tissue culture would have the advantage over other breeding methods for creating variation within an inbred line. The disadvantages, however, would be the same as for the other standard breeding methods: restriction of germ plasm and the probabilities of recovering all the favorable genes of the original line may be low. The genetic changes seem to occur randomly, and, consequently, it would be necessary to evaluate the derived materials similar to other breeding methods (Lee et al., 1988). Somaclonal variation is a recent source of genetic variability that may have an important role in breeding programs. But pedigree and(or) backcross breeding methods will be used to determine its future use.

8–1.1.5 General

After the initial sampling of the landrace cultivars, breeding methods that emphasized inbred line modification have been widely used. A few inbred lines (e.g., B14, B37, C103, and Oh43) possessed traits considered important as lines themselves and in crosses with other elite lines. The lines were included in pedigree and backcrossing breeding programs to modify certain traits (e.g., earlier flowering strains of A632 and CM105 with B14 background and of A619 with Oh43 background), improved pest resistance (e.g., improved first-generation European corn borer resistant strains of B64 and B68 with B14 background and of B76 with B37 background), and improved ear shoot emergence (e.g., Mo17 with C103 background and B76 with B37 background). Because of the nature of the traits under selection, combinations of pedigree and backcross methods sometimes were used to attain the level of expression needed for effective selection. Development of lines B64 and B68 is an example. Both lines were derived from an initial cross of B14 and Amargo 41.2504B made in 1950. B14 was susceptible to first-generation European corn borer leaf feeding, whereas Amargo 41.2504B, an introduction from Argentina, had first-generation, leaf-feeding resistance. The objective of the cross was to increase the level of resistance to first-generation European corn borer leaf feeding in B14. Two backcrosses were made to B14 to recover the B14 genotype, but with selection for leaf-feeding resistance under artificial infestation. B64 was developed from the second backcross generation (Amargo 41.2504B × B14^3) with the use of standard pedigree selection methods and released in 1964. The level of resistance relative to Amargo 41.2504B, however, decreased with backcrosses to B14. Selfed progenies from the second backcross were artificially infested with corn borer egg masses. Progenies that exhibited higher levels of resistance to leaf feeding were intermated. Selected progenies from the first intermated generation also were infested, rated, and intermated to form the second generation of intermating. Pedigree selection was initiated in the second intermated generation and B68 was released in 1966. Although B64 and B68 were derived from the same backcross generation, the differences in breeding methods used (standard pedigree selection for B64 and intermating, selfing, intermating, and seven generations of selfing for B68) isolated lines with differences large enough to justify release. In addition to the breeding methods used for developing B64 and B68, the source of germplasm also has been a contributing factor in their use (Zuber and Darrah, 1980). Because B64 and B68 also possessed tolerance to corn lethal necrosis, which is caused by a combination of maize dwarf mosaic virus (strain B) and maize chlorotic mottle virus (Doupnik et al., 1981), Amargo 41.2504B also seems to have contributed genes for tolerance to corn lethal necrosis.

The conversion of late-maturity lines to earlier derivatives is another illustration of the effective combination of breeding methods to develop second-cycle lines that have earlier maturity. The methods used to develop earlier maturity derivatives depend on the inbred line being converted and the source of earlier maturity. B14 has acceptable stalk strength, good pest tolerance, rapid grain dry-down, and good combining ability for the central U.S. Corn Belt. Because of these favorable traits, it was considered desirable to obtain earlier maturity second-cycle recoveries of B14 for use at higher latitudes. Earlier maturity recoveries have been obtained, but the breeding methods used have varied. In most instances, early-by-late crosses are produced with subsequent selection for the late phenotype that has earlier maturity. Rinke and Sentz (1961) outlined the breeding methods used in Minnesota. Their program was successful for developing earlier maturity recoveries of genotypes that have been widely used in commercial hybrids (Table 8–2). A632 and A634 were obtained from a cross of Mt42 × B14. A632 was extracted by pedigree selection after the third backcross to B14. A634 also included three backcrosses to B14, but there was one generation of selfing after the first backcross; there were two additional backcrosses made to B14 after one generation of selfing. A635, A640, and A641 were selected from a cross of ND203 × B14; A635 was selected after two backcrosses to B14, whereas A640 and

Table 8-2. Breeding methods used in the development of earlier maturity lines from early
× late crosses. Adapted from Rinke and Sentz (1961).

Breeding method after cross No. of generations		Frequency of late parent	Example of method
Backcrosses to late parent	Self-fertilization		
	no.		
4	3	5	A671
3	4	4	A632, A634
2	5	3	A635
1	6	2	A619, CM105†
0	7	1	A640, A641

† CM105 developed by John Giesbrecht (1974, personal communication).

A641 were pedigree selected directly from the F_2 generation. Although Mt42 and ND203 have similar flowering dates (about 85 d), selection for earlier flowering progenies with genotypes similar to B14 must have been easier in crosses to ND203 than to Mt42. In a separate program, CM105 was developed by pedigree selection in the first backcross generation of the cross, CMV3 × B14 (J. Giesbrecht, 1974, personal communication). Hence, earlier derivatives of B14 were obtained after three (A632 and A632), two (A635), one (CM105), or zero (A640 and A641) backcrosses followed by pedigree selection. The combination of breeding methods depends on the heritability of the trait, expressivity of the trait from the nonrecurrent parent in the cross, and the extent one wishes to recover the phenotype of the recurrent parent. Table 8-3 illustrates briefly some of the methods suggested for managing late × early crosses. Similar methods could be used for other traits.

The traditional pedigree selection methods of corn breeding obviously have been effective (Duvick, 1977; Russell, 1974, 1984, 1986). But there has been concern that the genetic base of the germ plasm included in breeding programs has become restricted to a few elite genotypes (Anonymous, 1972, p. 97–118). Jenkins (1978) emphasized that the intercrossing of elite lines and reselection to develop second-cycle lines gradually limits the genetic base of the breeding germ plasm. Second-cycle lines have become the main component of present-day breeding programs, at least for lines released by public agencies. Jenkins (1936) listed 350 lines released by public agencies of which only eight (2%) were second-cycle lines. The trend has increased in subsequent decades, and it is estimated that by 1976 76% of the lines released by public agencies were second-cycle lines. The same trends seem to have occurred in the private sector (Smith, 1988).

Some of the limitations of the pedigree method of breeding were suggested by Bailey and Comstock (1976) and Bailey (1977) in simulation studies. They studied intra-line selection within an F_2 population developed from a pair of inbred lines followed by selection among pure lines.

Table 8-3. Breeding selection methods suggested and used for developing early lines from early by late crosses.

Season	Rinke and Sentz (1961)	Baker†	Troyer†
1	Early × late cross	Early × late cross	Balanced set early × late crosses
2	Produce F_2 500 plants	Produce F_2	Yield test for GCA and SCA Produce F_2
3	Backcross (BC) earliest F_2 to late parent	Self earliest F_2 plants	Self earliest 5 to 10% F_2 plants
4	Grow 15 BC ear-to-row with 100 plants per progeny. Self or BC 10 early plants in 3 early progeny rows	Self earliest plants in early progenies with late parent phenotype	Sib or BC earliest plants to late parent
5	BC or self BC. Select earliest plants in early progeny rows in each generation.	Self earliest plants in early progenies with late parent phenotype	Grow 800 plants and self or BC to late parent the earliest 5 to 10%
6	BC or self BC. Select earliest plants in early progeny rows in each generation.	Self earliest plants in early progenies with late parent phenotype	Grow 800 plants and self or BC to late parent the earliest 5 to 10%
7	BC or self BC. Select earliest plants in early progeny rows in each generation.	Yield test for GCA	Repeat BC or begin pedigree selection
8	Yield test topcrosses	Backcross best to late parent	Repeat BC or begin pedigree selection
9	Make selections	Backcross best to late parent	Repeat BC or being pedigree selection
10	Make selections	Backcross best to late parent	Repeat BC or being pedigree selection

† Raymond Baker and A.F. Troyer (1982, personal communication).

The objective of their studies was to determine the relative probabilities of accumulating in one derived progeny all of the favorable alleles present in either one of inbred lines used to produce the cross. Chances of success, of course, depended on the parents included in the cross. If one parent of a cross is decidedly better than the other parent, as in the case of B14 compared with Amargo 41.2504B, the chances of obtaining a derivative line superior to the better parent are remote. If the two inbred lines included in the cross differ in alleles for a moderate number of loci (e.g., 25 or more), it is unlikely that all of the favorable alleles would be assembled in one line. The other situation examined included two inbred lines that had equal numbers of loci with favorable alleles; e.g., each line included 15 favorable alleles of the 30 loci heterozygous in the F_1. The probability of obtaining a derivative line from this cross that is homozygous for 16 or more favorable alleles is 0.825, and the probability that a derived line is homozygous for 20 or more favorable alleles is 0.292. Johnson (1980) also concluded from a theoretical study that little or no progress could be expected from pedigree selection unless the parents were nearly equal in value. The theoretical simulation studies support the general observation that selection is more productive within populations developed from crosses of good lines × good lines than from crosses of good lines × poor lines. The latter situation is reserved primarily for transferring specific traits that are not available from crosses of good lines.

Although Jenkins (1978) suggested more attention should be devoted to broadening the genetic base of new breeding germ plasm, practical considerations often limit a breeder's choice of germ plasm. New alleles can be introduced from other sources, but new sources usually do not meet the performance standards of the elite germ plasm currently available. The chances of obtaining lines that exceed the currently available well-evaluated inbred lines are not good. Hence, the tendency is to continue to recycle elite inbred lines that have demonstrated performance in hybrids. Other sources of germ plasm will not be used until they have been developed to be competitive with current germplasm sources.

8–1.2 Developing Inbred Lines

The development of inbred lines by self pollination and the evaluation for hybrid performance is the basic procedure in corn breeding programs of the U.S. Corn Belt and in many other areas where corn breeding is done. Information from research and experience has increased effectiveness of breeding procedures compared to earlier years. Breeders continue to search for better methods that will be more effective in the development and identification of inbred lines that have the genetic potential to contribute superior agronomic performance to hybrids. The breeder seeks the procedure that permits the greatest genetic gain per unit of resource input.

Most applied breeders seem to use similar procedures, with minor variations such as plant densities, number of plants per progeny row, number of self pollinations per row, generation at which to start hybrid testing, etc. Probably there is considerable similarity of germplasm sources used by breeders in different programs. Most breeders use an ear-to-row system with inbreeding and selection for several generations until a line is highly homozygous and homogeneous. Some breeders may use only two or three generations of self pollination with subsequent reproduction by sibmating within progenies. This latter procedure will produce somewhat more vigorous lines that yield more seed and produce more pollen than highly inbred lines, but genetic stability may be a problem. Although the single-seed descent procedure used by breeders of self-pollinated crops is used by few corn breeders, there may be a use for it (Brim, 1966). For example, in winter nurseries where the cost per unit land area is high, single-seed descent may be useful to advance a generation for a large number of lines at the S_1 or S_2 level of inbreeding.

One system of inbred-line development relies on phenotypic selection among and within ear-to-row progenies for several selfing generations before evaluation for hybrid performance. Selection is performed to isolate lines with resistance to important pests, maturity for certain areas of adaptation, plant canopy type, ear size, and grain quality. These traits have reasonably high heritability estimates and are deemed necessary for hybrid performance. For the first progenies of self pollination, S_1 lines, the additive genetic variance among lines is σ_A^2, and this becomes $2\sigma_A^2$ when $F = 1$. The within-line genetic variance is maximum in the S_1 generation, but decreases rapidly with self pollination and is zero when $F = 1$. Consequently, phenotypic differences among lines increase with continued self pollination in ear-to-row progenies, but success of selection within a line becomes reduced usually by the S_3 and later generations. Therefore, selection effort should be directed primarily to among progenies and less within progenies as inbreeding continues. Testing for hybrid performance may be delayed to about the fifth generation of selfing when the number of selections should be greatly reduced. This breeding system assumes favorable relationships of plant, grain, and ear traits of inbred lines with combining ability for grain yield; thus, the selected lines should be better for hybrid performance than would a random set of lines from the same source (Jenkins, 1935; Sprague, 1946).

A second system of inbred development is based on an evaluation for hybrid performance in the early generations of self pollination; e.g., testcrosses of the S_0 plants or S_1 lines. Genotypes that are identified for above-average hybrid performance in these tests are continued in the selfing and selection nursery. The procedure has been called "early testing," and the assumption is that the combining ability of a line is determined early in its development and will change relatively little in subsequent generations of inbreeding and selection. By early testing, the breeder is able to discard some portion of lines that are inadequate in hybrid performance, thus expending resources on materials that have more promise. Jenkins (1935) proposed the early testing procedure; Sprague (1946), Lonnquist (1950), Russell and Teich (1967), Hallauer and Lopez-Perez (1979), Johnson (1980), and Landi et al. (1983) presented data that support it. Russell and Teich (1967) also found that visual selection of inbred lines in a high plant density was just as effective as the early testing procedure in the identification of lines with above-average hybrid yield performance. The original objective of early testing seems valid because the only purpose is to identify those lines that are relatively good or poor and to emphasize selection for those that have above-average combining ability. Proponents do not claim that one should expect an exact ranking at two different stages of inbreeding.

Probably most breeders use a method that is intermediate between the two systems just described, i.e., first hybrid evaluations are of S_2 or S_3 lines. Bauman (1981) found in his survey that breeders begin evaluations as follows: S_2, 18%; S_3, 33%, S_4, 27%. Consequently, testing for hybrid performance and selfing and selection are being done simultaneously. Regardless of the system used, a selected line must be one that can be used profitably in commercial hybrid seed production either as a male or female parent.

Self pollination of individual plants within single-plant progenies grown ear-to-row is the most common procedure used to develop inbred lines. This breeding procedure has two important problems: (i) Vigor of the lines is decreased with inbreeding because of loss of favorable dominant alleles and any heterozygous loci that have overdominant effects. Many lines are so poor in seed yield, pollen production, or some other desired agronomic attribute that they cannot be used in a program to produce single-cross hybrid seed. (ii) Effective selection within the row for plants that have desired agronomic traits becomes minimal in generations beyond S_3; frequently, phenotypic uniformity is evident by the S_2 generation. Once the locus becomes homozygous in a line no further selection for segregating types is possible.

A second system that may be used to develop inbred lines involves some method of sibmating rather than self pollination. Stringfield (1974) has called this a conservative procedure, and he has given a theoretical discussion of the advantages of such a method compared with the development of lines by self pollination. Sib-mating permits the recombination and segregation for loci that have more than one allele in the progeny, thus giving the breeder more opportunity to select for desirable attributes. If sib-mating per progeny involves enough plants, inbreeding will be at a slower rate so that the plants are more vigorous than in a highly inbred line. Such lines would be better for seed yield and pollen production and, therefore, fewer such lines would have to be discarded because they couldn't be used in single-cross hybrid seed production. Sib-mated lines would have some level of genetic heterogeneity; thus, crosses of such lines would have less aesthetic value in hybrid appearance, which seems important to many producers. Greater heterogeneity, however, may give greater stability of field performance. Stangland and Russell (1981) reported that the variability within hybrids of $S_2 \times S_2$ lines was similar to hybrids that have related-line crosses for parents, but less variable than double crosses. Such lines may have gene frequency changes over a period of several generations of maintenance. Because of the heterogeneity of loci it may be more difficult to insert some single genes, as for disease resistance, or to convert to male-sterile cytoplasm by a backcross procedure. Also, it will be more difficult to identify contaminants in lines that are not highly inbred.

An important problem in a conservative program as outlined by Stringfield (1974) is the number of lines that one could develop for evaluation. Considerable time is required to select plants for sib mating at pollination and again at harvest, which means that it is more time-consuming than the standard practice of self pollination. Also, the success is dependent upon the ability of a person to select those plants that have the desired attributes (Mock and Pearce, 1975). Consequently, it is not a procedure to be used by untrained personnel who do much of the pollination in corn-breeding nurseries.

8–1.3   Correlation of Inbred Traits with Hybrid Performance

Breeders assume favorable correlations between plant, ear, and grain traits of the parental lines and performance in hybrid combination. Several studies have shown that correlation of an inbred trait with the same trait in the hybrid is relatively high, except for yield. Although many r values of inbred traits, including yield, with hybrid yield have been positive and significant, in most instances they have been too low to be of predictive value. Consequently, extensive evaluation in hybrid progenies is required to determine the true value of an inbred.

The earlier correlation studies (Jenkins, 1929; Hayes and Johnson, 1939) were done in field husbandry conditions that were at a much lower productivity index than those now used in corn production. The relationship between inbred traits and hybrid performance, however, may be greater in a higher productivity environment with the improved cultivars.

Results from two breeding methods studies (Russell and Teich, 1967; El-Lakany and Russell, 1971) suggested that greater relationships may occur when materials are grown in stress environments, such as high plant densities. Data were presented by Russell and Machado (1978) on inbred lines and correlations of inbred-line traits with hybrid yields when materials were grown at different densities. The source population was BS1 synthetic, which is genetically diverse and adapted to the U.S. Corn Belt. After four generations of phenotypic selection and self pollination, S_1 to S_4, they had 76 S_5 lines. The lines were evaluated in relatively low and high plant densities and testcrosses of the lines (double-cross hybrid tester) were evaluated in low, intermediate, and high plant densities. Although the lines had been selected rigorously for several agronomic traits, there were highly significant differences among the lines for 13 agronomic traits. Also, there were highly significant differences among the lines for testcross yield performance. None of the plant traits in either density of the inbreds had correlations with hybrid yields that were high enough to be of predictive value. Only leaf area showed an important relationship, and it was greater for the lower density than for the higher density of the inbreds, and increased from the highest to the lowest density of the testcrosses. For ear and grain traits, except grain yield, r values were slightly greater at the higher inbred density, but changed little from the lowest to the highest density of the testcrosses. For inbred grain yield, r values were greater at the higher inbred density, but changed little from the lowest to the highest density of the testcrosses. For example, inbred yields at the low density correlated with testcross yields at low, intermediate, and high densities had r values of 0.33, 0.28, and 0.33; for inbreds at the high density and testcross yields at low, intermediate, and

Table 8-4. Multiple correlation coefficients between traits of inbred parents at two densities and hybrid yields at three densities. Adapted from Russell and Machado (1978).

Traits correlated	Hybrid densities			
	Low	Medium	High	Avg.
Hybrid yield vs.	Inbred low density			
all inbred traits	0.54	0.52	0.54	0.56
inbred plant traits	0.43	0.38	0.30	0.38
inbred ear and grain traits	0.42	0.42	0.51	0.49
Hybrid yield vs.	Inbred high density			
all inbred traits	0.61	0.60	0.64	0.65
inbred plant traits	0.46	0.35	0.36	0.40
inbred ear and grain traits	0.53	0.53	0.60	0.60

high densities the r values were 0.42, 0.40, and 0.43, respectively. The r values for the inbreds at high densitiy with testcross yields were higher than obtained in most earlier studies. Selection for high-yielding inbreds would tend to select lines that are above average for hybrid yields. Lamkey and Hallauer's (1986) data support this conclusion.

Actually, the corn breeder selects for total phenotype, or an ideotype, of the inbred line; consequently, it seems more appropriate to consider multiple correlation coefficients (Table 8-4). The R values were greater for the higher density of the inbred lines than for the lower density; plant traits showed decreases from the highest to the lowest density of the testcrosses, whereas ear and grain traits showed increases from the lowest to the highest density of the testcrosses. The R values suggest that visual selection for inbred development in a higher plant density should be more effective for hybrid yield performance. For the higher density of the inbreds and highest density of the testcrosses, $R^2 = 0.41$, which indicates that 41% of the variability of the testcrosses for yield was accounted for by the variability among inbred lines for 13 plant, ear, and grain traits. Furthermore, the selected lines would be much better than a random set from the same source for traits such as maturity, height, pest resistance, grain quality, and seed yield.

The r values obtained by Russell and Machado (1978) may have been confounded by the inbred selection that would have reduced genetic variability. Gama and Hallauer (1977), however, used random lines from 'Iowa Stiff Stalk Synthetic' (BSSS) and obtained R values for inbred traits with hybrid yields of only 0.23 and 0.21 for two methods of calculation. They concluded that phenotypic appearance of a line does not seem a good indicator of its worth in single-cross hybrids.

Some evidence for a stronger relation of inbred yield and yield components with hybrid yields is evident in Tables 8-5 and 8-6 (Russell and Machado, 1978). Data in Table 8-5 are for the five highest and five lowest yielding testcrosses in the highest density. The high group had only an average decrease of 0.11 Mg ha^{-1} across densities, whereas the low group

Table 8-5. Grain yields and percentage of barren plants for the five highest- and five lowest-yielding testcrosses, averaged for eight environments. Adapted from Russell and Machado (1978).

| Selection no. | Plants ha⁻¹ (× 1000) | | | Avg. | Barren plants† |
	39.0	54.0	69.0		
	——— Mg ha⁻¹ ———				%
4	6.86	6.42	6.77	6.69	18.6
34	7.17	6.74	6.92	6.94	10.4
53	7.53	6.94	6.76	7.08	6.8
54	6.56	6.91	6.80	6.76	11.4
55	6.76	7.36	7.06	7.06	9.8
$\bar{x}$	6.97	6.87	6.86	6.91	11.4
18	6.10	5.67	5.04	5.60	20.3
27	5.70	5.66	4.97	5.44	30.6
39	6.02	5.59	4.94	5.52	15.6
63	6.21	5.48	5.24	5.60	34.6
65	5.68	5.50	5.08	5.42	28.0
$\bar{x}$	5.94	5.58	5.05	5.52	25.8

† At 69 000 plants ha⁻¹.

Table 8-6. Ear and grain data in the high density for the inbreds per se that were the five highest and five lowest in testcross yield performance. Adapted from Russell and Machado (1978).

Selection no.	Ear length	Wt. 300 kernels⁻¹	Yield
	cm	g	Mg ha⁻¹
4	12.8	73.5	4.58
34	17.2	71.2	6.02
53	13.2	56.0	3.40
54	12.6	76.5	3.62
55	15.4	79.4	6.60
$\bar{x}$	14.2	71.3	4.84
18	12.0	68.6	3.21
27	6.8	55.0	1.98
39	11.4	56.2	3.12
63	8.8	71.4	2.23
65	11.6	71.8	2.98
$\bar{x}$	10.1	64.6	2.70

had a decrease of 0.89 Mg ha^{-1}. The low group had a significantly higher frequency of barren plants. For the parental lines at the high density, the average yield for the high group was 2.14 Mg ha^{-1} more than for the low group (Table 8–6). Ear length and weight per 300 kernels were important components in the yield differences.

A stress environment may be caused by a low availability of N. Balko and Russell (1980b) evaluated 40 inbred lines from BSSS and 20 single crosses of these at five N levels: 0, 60, 120, 180, and 240 kg of N ha^{-1} in four location-year environments. Inbred line plant, ear, and grain traits had little relationship with single-cross yield at any N level; only two significant r values were obtained. Gama and Hallauer (1977) also found

Table 8-7. Multiple correlations coefficients between the traits of 40 inbred parents and the yield of 20 single crosses, calculated at each N level and combined over all N levels. Adapted from Balko and Russell (1980).

Traits correlated	Nitrogen applied, kg ha^{-1}					Combined
	0	60	120	180	240	
Hybrid yield vs.						
all inbred traits	0.94	0.80	0.72	0.70	0.88	0.76
inbred plant traits	0.87	0.71	0.57	0.41	0.51	0.73
inbred ear and grain traits	0.42	0.28	0.40	0.47	0.69	0.52

low *r* values when using inbred lines from this source. Multiple R values between 13 inbred traits and single-cross yields are presented in Table 8-7. With all inbred traits, the highest R values were from N levels of 0 and 240 kg ha^{-1}. For plant traits, R increased from the 180 kg of N level to the zero level, but for ear and grain traits R increased from the 60 kg of N level to the 240 kg of N level. Yield response to N levels (Balko and Russell, 1980a) suggested that the most efficient single crosses for N use may be identified best when grown in a soil environment where available N is equivalent to 120 kg of N ha^{-1}.

8-1.4 Testers and Testing

Usually it is relatively simple to develop a large number of inbred lines that are agronomically satisfactory as lines per se. The primary problem is to have adequate testing of the lines to determine performance in hybrid combination. The most complete information for hybrid performance is obtained in a single-cross diallel because this procedure gives information of general and specific combining ability (Sprague and Tatum, 1942). The single-cross diallel is not practical, however, because of the large number of crosses required for only a few lines. Generally, for preliminary hybrid evaluation the breeder needs to determine the relative general combining ability for new lines.

Davis (1927) and Jenkins and Brunson (1932) suggested use of a common tester to evaluate lines for general combining ability. In earlier years, breeders used an open-pollinated cultivar as the common tester, and it would be highly heterogeneous. Matzinger (1953) showed that a heterogeneous tester contributes less to line × tester interaction than does a narrow genetic-base tester. It was suggested that a double-double cross tester that included the eight most commonly used lines within a given maturity group would be a good tester for general combining ability.

The choice of a tester is an important decision. Hull (1945) concluded, on a theoretical basis, that the most efficient tester would be one that is homozygous recessive at all loci. Rawlings and Thompson (1962) stated two requisites for a good tester to evaluate inbred lines: (i) the entries under test must be classified correctly; and (ii) the tester must discriminate effectively among the materials under test. Hallauer (1975) suggested that

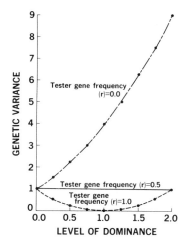

Fig. 8-3. Relation of total genetic variation to tester gene frequency and level of dominance. Adapted from Rawlings and Thompson (1962).

a tester should include simplicity in use, provide information that correctly classifies merit of lines, and maximizes genetic gain. Rawlings and Thompson (1962) showed that, for a given set of testcrosses, the genetic variation among the testcross progenies was directly proportional to the square of $[1 + (1 - 2r_i)a_i]$, where r_i is the allele frequency at the ith locus for the tester and a_i is a measure of dominance at the ith locus. Thus, genetic theory indicates that the best tester is one that has low allele frequencies for the favorable alleles that condition agronomic traits in the materials being evaluated (Fig. 8-3; Hallauer, 1975). All testers will give an equal measure of genetic variance if there is no dominance. As the level of dominance increases, however, the advantage of a tester with low allele frequency is obvious.

Rawlings and Thompson (1962) examined the tester theory by an evaluation of crosses in which the parental materials had been classified for level of performance in previous studies. Their results supported the theory that low-performing testers, which they assumed to have a low frequency of favorable alleles at the important loci, were the most effective testers. Further information comparing types of testers was obtained in a detailed study by Hallauer and Lopez-Perez (1979). They used an unselected sample of 50 S_1 and 50 S_8 inbred lines whose source was BSSS. The 50 S_8 lines were direct descendants of the 50 S_1 lines. The lines were crossed to five testers: (i) BSSS, the parental source population; (ii) BS13(S)C1, which is a BSSS population after eight cycles of recurrent selection, primarily for grain yield; (iii) BSSS-222, a low-yielding S_8 line derived from BSSS; (iv) B73, a high-performance inbred line derived from BS13(HT)C5 after five cycles half-sib recurrent selection; and (v) Mo17, an unrelated high performance line. Frequencies for favorable alleles in the four testers related to the tested lines would be expected to be highest for B73, followed in descending order by BS13(S)C1, BSSS, and BSSS-

222. Inbred Mo17 is unrelated to the other testers and, therefore, would be expected to differ in frequencies of favorable alleles from the other testers. The relative magnitudes among testers for the estimated components of variance when S_1 lines were evaluated are as expected on the basis of gene frequencies (Table 8–8). For the S_8 lines, the estimated components of variance are greater than for the S_1 lines, as would be expected, and the relative magnitudes for the related testers are similar to the S_1 lines, except for B73 which is larger.

The testers used by breeders will be dictated by the stage of development of breeding programs, availability of testers, type of material under test, and type of hybrids for which the lines are to be used. Probably in established corn-breeding programs, the first use of any new inbred lines will be with one or more lines that are already established as parental lines. Thus, it seems logical that, for the first or preliminary evaluations of new lines for hybrid performance, one or more of the established lines should be used as testers, either individually or in some type of cross. If specific combining ability is an important factor, the breeder will be taking advantage of it when the testers are individual lines. For lines that are identified as worthy of advanced testing, additional proven lines in the maturity group can be used as testers. The philosophy for choice of tester in earlier years was that a heterogeneous cultivar (i.e., open-pollinated cultivar) was needed if the purpose was to obtain a measure of general combining ability. The use of a narrow genetic-base tester, such as an inbred line or a single-cross hybrid, would emphasize specific combining ability. Results from more recent studies (Horner et al., 1973, 1976; Russell et al., 1973; Hoegemeyer and Hallauer, 1976; Russell and Eberhart, 1975; Walejko and Russell, 1977) show that an inbred line tester gives relatively more information for general than for specific combining ability. Bauman's (1981) survey of corn breeders in the USA found that 89% use an inbred line and 11% use a single cross.

Table 8–8. Estimates of components of variance and standard errors for yield (Mg ha^{-1}) for S_1 and S_8 testcrosses. Adapted from Hallauer and Lopez-Perez (1979).

Tester†	S_1	S_8
BSSSCO	0.184 ± 0.065	0.417 ± 0.120
BS13(S)C1	0.106 ± 0.045	0.341 ± 0.102
BSSS-222	0.217 ± 0.064	0.387 ± 0.111
B73	0.038 ± 0.035	0.264 ± 0.080
Mo17	0.259 ± 0.085	0.298 ± 0.095
Avg.	0.161 ± 0.059	0.341 ± 0.102

† BSSSCO is the original Stiff Stalk Synthetic population from which the lines under test were developed by single-seed descent. BS13(S)C1 is an improved strain of BSSSCO after seven cycles of half-sib selection with double-cross Ia13 as tester and one cycle of S_1-S_2 selection. BSSS-222 is an inbred line derived from BSSSCO and identified as one of the lowest-yielding lines. B73 was derived from BS13(HT)C5, which is a strain of BSSSCO after five cycles of half-sib selection. Mo17 was obtained by pedigree selection from the cross of (187-2 × C103) and was considered unrelated to the other materials included for test.

Single-cross hybrids have become the predominant type in the USA and in many other areas of corn production. Because vigorous parental lines are required, greater attention is given to seed yield and pollen production than was necessary when double crosses were used. Consequently, yield testing of the lines per se along with hybrid evaluation may be justified. It probably should not be necessary to test the lines as extensively as testcrosses. A single observation row in the breeding nursery with open pollination can give a good indication of potential seed production and, if grown for 2 to 3 yr while the line is being evaluated for hybrid performance, may be adequate to determine if the line can be used in seed production. Testing of the lines per se may give information that can be used to predict hybrid performance, except for grain yield. Hallauer and Lopez-Perez (1979) obtained no significant r values for yield between the lines per se and their testcrosses. Jensen et al. (1983) found for yield that topcrosses of S_2 lines (S_2TC) were a much better predictor of topcrosses of S_5 line (S_5TC) performance than were S_2's per se. Only two of six experiments showed r values significant ($P \leq 0.05$) for S_2 vs. S_5TC, compared with six of six experiments for S_2TC vs. S_5TC. Smith (1986) used a computer simulation procedure to calculate correlations between lines per se and testcross performance, and testers were of three types: average, above average, and unrelated. The r values between lines per se and the three testers were 0.34, 0.22, and 0.28, respectively. These simulation results support actual data that yields of lines per se are not good predictors for the lines in hybrids.

The generation of inbreeding in which breeders begin evaluation for hybrid performance seems to depend on personal choice. A philosophy of early testing is that selection for two to three generations before hybrid testing is not effective in enhancing combining ability, whereas breeders who delay hybrid testing until the S_4 or a later generation believe selection will obtain lines that are better than average. The source population may also be a decisive factor. If the source population is elite material because of considerable earlier improvement, further selection during generations of self pollination may not achieve further gains, and hybrid testing can be started in early generations. Conversely, if the source population is relatively unselected material, visual selection during two or three selfing generations is useful to select for certain agronomic traits, and hybrid evaluation may be delayed to about S_4. Opponents of the early testing procedure believe the system does not justify the additional cost and cite low r values between early and late generation tests to support their argument.

8–1.5 Breeding Sources

Planned crosses of inbred lines are the most frequently used sources in which to begin the isolation of inbred lines (Bauman, 1981). Single-cross hybrids are used more frequently. Most backcross sources will have only one backcross to the recurrent parent, except in instances where the purpose is to transfer one or two genes that control a specific trait. Dudley (1982) showed that, in most instances, it would not be desirable to use more than one backcross. Strict attention should be given to maintaining known heterotic patterns when planned crosses are used. Breeders also use competitive private company hybrids as source material, but, in such instances, usually it will not be known where derived lines fit in a heterotic pattern.

The selection of the breeding source material is an item of prime importance. Pedigree selection in planned crosses permits the use of high-combining lines, but has some limitations such as decreasing genetic diversity and, perhaps, the failure to introduce new, favorable alleles into the program. Frequently, the breeder's goal is to improve one or both parent lines of an elite single cross. Dudley (1984a, b) has presented a method, along with the theory and some supporting data, that should be helpful to assist a breeder in the selection of donor lines.

Limited use is being made of synthetic cultivars (Bauman, 1981). The selection of a synthetic may be based on the pedigree of the synthetic and on information from previous evaluations. The diallel analysis and evaluation of synthetics per se are useful to identify superior sources (Hallauer, 1972; Hallauer and Eberhart, 1966; Hallauer and Sears, 1968; Hallauer and Malithano, 1976; Lamkey and Hallauer, 1984). Improved versions of a synthetic are expected to be better sources than the original synthetic (Russell, 1985b). Dudley (1984c; 1988) has presented a method for identifying populations of exotic germ plasm that contain useful new alleles.

A part of sampling in inbred development is the number of sister lines to grow from each S_1 line or from individual lines in later generations. Greater gain is expected from sampling among S_0-derived lines rather than within lines at the S_1 and later selfed generations. Proliferation of sister lines from individual S_1 lines, or from individual lines in later generations, should be avoided because it is not an efficient use of resources.

8–1.6 Types of Hybrids

Basically, three types of crosses have been used commercially: double crosses, three-way crosses, and single crosses. Delay in the widespread use of single crosses probably occurred because published data indicated greater genotype $\times$ environment interaction, or less performance stability, for single crosses than for double crosses. Data published by Sprague and Federer (1951) indicated an average situation, but it did not mean there were no single crosses equal to the best double crosses for stability of performance. The three-way cross has a single cross as female parent and an inbred line as male parent. Thus, the seed is produced on a high-yielding parent, but the male parent is an inbred line that may not always be a reliable pollen producer, which has probably been a restriction for the use of three-way crosses. The related-line single cross is another hybrid type that has been widely used. In this instance one or both parents are crosses of related lines, thus the parents are more vigorous than pure-line inbreds. There is no standard definition for related lines and, in some instances, the term has been used loosely; e.g., designating two lines from the same source synthetic as related lines. More generally, for two lines to be designated as related, the genetic commonality would be 50% or greater. Single-crosses became more widely used in the 1960s in some areas, whereas double-cross hybrids are still the predominant type in some areas where seed production for single crosses is a risky adventure because of unfavorable climatic conditions.

Each of the three basic hybrid types has advantages and disadvantages. Theoretically, double crosses are expected to be more stable than single crosses over a series of environments because they are genetically heterogeneous. This has been designated as genetic homeostasis by Lerner (1958) or population buffering by Allard and Bradshaw (1964). Several studies have confirmed this comparison, but some individual single crosses may be as stable as the most stable double cross (Eberhart and Russell, 1966). Such single crosses may have developmental homeostasis (Lerner, 1958) or individual buffering (Allard and Bradshaw, 1964).

On the basis of simple gene action (i.e., additive and dominance but no epistasis), single crosses are expected to be superior to double crosses. Eberhart and Russell (1969) compared 45 single crosses among 10 elite inbred lines with a balanced set of 45 double crosses for the same lines in 22 environments in the U.S. Corn Belt. Averaged over all hybrids, the single crosses yielded 1.9% more than the double crosses, but the highest-yielding single cross yielded 8.0% more than the highest-yielding double cross. For yield, the double crosses had less genotype $\times$ environment interaction than the single crosses; however, 2 of the 10 highest-yielding single crosses were as stable as the most stable double crosses. Because the single cross has only two parental inbred lines, one should expect to identify certain single crosses that are superior to double crosses for other agronomic traits such as root and stalk strength, pest resistance, and grain quality.

The expected relative performance of single crosses $>$ three-way crosses $>$ double crosses may be changed by some types of epistatic gene action. Epistatic gene action has been observed in several studies (Bauman, 1959; Gorsline, 1961; Sprague et al., 1962; Sprague and Thomas, 1967; Weatherspoon, 1970; Stuber et al., 1973; Schnell and Singh, 1978; Melchinger et al., 1986). The effects of epistasis may be negative or positive, i.e., the yield of a three-way cross hybrid may be either greater or lesser than predicted from the mean of the two nonparental single crosses. In 60 comparisons for yields of the three-way crosses with predictions from component single crosses, Sprague et al. (1962) obtained significant epistasis and for all, except one, the three-way cross yielded less than predicted. Schnell and Singh (1978) reported that 9 of 36 comparisons were significant, and in all instances the single-cross prediction was greater than observed for the three-way crosses. Stuber et al. (1973) also found evidence for epistasis, but they concluded that the effects of genotype $\times$ environment interaction were of greater importance than epistasis.

8-1.7 Maintenance of Inbred Lines

A primary purpose for developing lines that are highly inbred is to obtain genotypes whose genetic integrity will be maintained without change during generations of reproduction. At least two assumptions are involved: (i) the inbred line is homozygous and, therefore, no further changes can occur because of heterozygous loci that have persisted from the S_0 plant; and (ii) there are no mutations that give rise to genetic changes. Several studies have shown that neither of these assumptions is valid. Sprague et al. (1960) studied the genetic stability of 11 inbred lines, in which each line evolved from a doubled monoploid plant. Such lines would be truly homozygous in the first diploid generation. They found, however, that these lines became genetically variable with successive generations of reproduction by self pollination, and calculated that there were 4.5 mutations per attribute per 100 gametes tested. A similar study that used inbred lines developed by the conventional system of self pollination in ear-to-row progenies found a mutation rate of 2.8 per attribute per 100 gametes tested (Russell et al., 1963). Busch and Russell (1964) found 38% of the changes in two lines were expressed in hybrid progenies.

Relic heterozygosity either from the original S_0 plant or from a mutation in some later generation may also be the cause for measurable changes over generations of reproduction. This has been shown to occur in lines after they have been interchanged among experiment stations and then reproduced in different environments for several generations. Fleming et al. (1964) observed significant variation among stocks in all but one of six inbred lines that had been maintained at five to seven experiment stations, and concluded that, because of selection, variants were isolated that had become adapted to their particular environment. Subsequently, Fleming (1971) found that more than 50% of the significant variations among strains were detected as significant in testcrosses. Grogan and Francis (1972) found significant variation for one or more traits in four of six inbred lines obtained from six experiment stations. They also observed an unexpected amount of heterosis among source $\times$ source crosses of the same line.

The genetic stability of an inbred line that is maintained for a number of years at one location is important to breeders and seedsmen. Russell and Vega (1973) reported a study in which 11 long-time inbred lines were maintained for 11 successive generations with self pollination in ear-to-row progenies. They measured 10 quantitatively inherited plant, ear, and grain traits and found for 106 tests of differences among generations that

42 were significant. The evidence indicates that changes occurred because of both mutations and segregation from residual heterozygosity. In a similar study, Bogenschutz and Russell (1986) evaluated genetic stability in 10 long-time inbred lines that were maintained for 11 successive generations by both self pollination and sib mating. There were 93 possible comparisons to check for genetic stability in each method of maintenance, and 28 in the sib mating and 52 in the self pollination showed significance among generations. Also, over all generations, means of the two methods were different for 51% of the comparisons, and the selfed lines were less vigorous for 79% of the significant comparisons. They concluded that sib mating lessens the observed effects of genetic instability. In both these previous studies, some lines seemed inherently stable and others seemed inherently unstable. Fleming and Kozelnicky (1965) also compared sib mating with self pollination and reported a yield trend in favor of sib mating.

Breeders and seedsmen will use a system of line maintenance that seems most logical for a given situation. A system of self pollination with progenies grown ear-to-row for breeders' seed offers the best opportunity to observe changes for plant, ear, and grain traits. A large number of ear-row progenies per line is probably unnecessary because genetic changes usually are not found unless measurements are made in several replications. Reproduction by either sib mating or self pollination will gradually increase genetic variability. Changes that occur usually are small in effect and probably not of practical importance in most instances. If, however, a line is reproduced over a period of years—some lines may remain in a program for up to 20 yr—accumulation of changes may gradually give rise to a line that is considerably different from the line as it was in the S_6 generation. A stock culture of a line should be placed in cold storage, with reproduction only as needed to maintain seed viability, so that the breeder or seedsmen can return to this culture at any time. The time at which the culture is placed in storage will vary among stations, but a logical time seems to be when the line is released from an experiment station or when it is first used for commercial seed production.

8–2 IMPROVEMENT OF GERM PLASM

8–2.1 Introduction

The pure-line concept suggested by Shull (1909, 1910) was extensively applied and proved useful for the development of inbred lines and hybrids. It became evident, however, that other germplasm sources were needed to develop new, improved lines. The first logical sequel was the recycling of the superior lines via use of pedigree and backcross breeding methods. Because of the nature of the traits under selection and the need to develop improved sources of germ plasm, it was realized different selection methods were needed to supplement the classical pedigree and backcross breeding methods.

Many of the traits considered important in corn breeding have a complex inheritance and, consequently, are not easily amenable to visual selection among a limited number of individual plants. These types of traits are designated as quantitative traits; i.e., the traits are controlled by a relatively large, unknown number of genetic factors with each factor having a small effect on the expression of the trait. Additionally, the effects of the individual factors are affected by the environments in which they are measured. The distribution of the phenotypes, based on the genetic and environmental effects, is usually assumed to approximate a normal density distribution (Fig. 8–4). Because of the complexity of the inheritance of many of the traits considered important in corn breeding, it was not possible to accurately measure the genetic merit of individuals based on visual selection. Hence, the original suggestions of mass selection and ear-to-row selection were not effective for the improvement of yield (Fig. 8–2). It was acknowledged, however, that the genetic factors involved in the inheritance of quantitative traits behaved in a Mendelian manner, but it was not possible to correctly classify individuals into discrete classes. The problems related to the improvement of traits inherited in a quantitative manner included the genetic basis of quantitative traits, methods of measuring differences among individuals, and methods of selection to improve the traits of interest. These problems were being addressed during the 1930s and 1940s to further exploit Shull's inbred-hybrid concept.

Three factors had a significant impact in the rationale used for the improvement of corn germ plasm: development of quantitative genetic theory and its application to plant populations; further developments in experimental and mating designs and data analysis; and development of selection procedures to increase the frequency of favorable alleles of com-

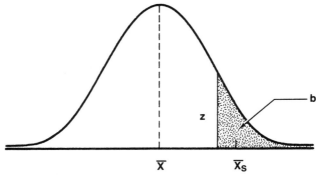

Fig. 8–4. Phenotypic distribution of a quantitative trait in a hypothetical population showing the population mean ($\bar{x}$), portion (b) selected for recombination, height or ordinate (Z) at point of tuncation selection, and the mean ($\bar{x}_S$) of the selected progenies used in recombination.

plex traits. Each of the three factors supported the others. It was realized that information on the nature of the inheritance of quantitative traits was necessary for selection to be effective. Proper experimental designs (both field and mating) were needed to obtain valid estimates and to permit the interpretation of the data (Dudley and Moll, 1969). Empirical studies suggested genetic variability within corn populations, particularly the portion due to additive genetic effects, was adequate and should not be a serious constraint in the improvement of corn populations (Hallauer and Miranda, 1981). Selection methods were developed to capitalize on the information obtained from the quantitative genetic studies. A valid basis, therefore, was established to improve germ plasm to meet specified objectives.

The newer techniques and information were accepted and applied in corn breeding. Because of corn morphology and mode of reproduction, most of the suggestions were applicable and could be tested for the improvement of corn populations (Hallauer and Miranda, 1981). Based on the information reported and their interpretations, selection schemes were developed for the improvement of quantitative traits to generate improved sources of germ plasm. These selection schemes are generally referred to as recurrent selection.

8–2.2 Recurrent Selection—Methods

As the name implies, recurrent selection includes selection methods that are conducted in a repetitive manner (Fig. 8–5). Regardless of the trait under selection, the objectives of recurrent selection are twofold: (i) increase the frequency of the favorable alleles, which is to change the mean of the population in a favorable direction; and (ii) maintain genetic variability for continued selection by intermating superior progenies for

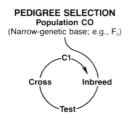

PEDIGREE SELECTION
Population CO
(Narrow-genetic base; e.g., F₂)

C1
Cross Inbreed
Test

RECURRENT SELECTION
Population CO
(Broad-genetic base; e.g., variety)

C1
Recombine Develop Progenies
Test

Fig. 8–5. Cyclical nature of pedigree and recurrent selection for the systematic improvement of corn germ plasm.

each cycle of selection. In its broadest context, the pedigree breeding methods that include crossing of elite lines to select second-cycle lines are a form of recurrent selection (Fig. 8–5); i.e., elite lines are crossed to initiate pedigree selection in either F_2 or backcross populations. Usually, recurrent selection is reserved for selection conducted repetitively for quantitative traits in genetically broad based populations.

To realize the objectives of recurrent selection, three distinctive phases are common for all except phenotypic mass selection: (i) development of progenies from the selected source populations; (ii) evaluation of progenies in replicated trials that may be conducted in different environments; and (iii) recombination of selected progenies, based on the evaluation trials, to form a population for continued selection (Fig. 8–5). The three phases complete one cycle of recurrent selection. The types of progenies developed and evaluated, the extent of evaluation, the methods of recombination, and the number of growing seasons or years required to complete one cycle of recurrent selection varies among recurrent selection methods. Thus, careful consideration must be given to each of these variables to maximize genetic gain on either a per cycle or a per year basis (Eberhart, 1970; Hallauer, 1985).

Decisions that are critical to the ultimate success and usefulness of germ plasm improved via recurrent selection need to be considered (Eberhart, 1970; Hallauer and Miranda, 1981; Hallauer, 1985). Decisions are required for choice of population(s) in which to initiate selection, types of progenies evaluated, extent of evaluation, effective population size, method of recombination of selected progenies, and efficient use of growing seasons for each phase of the program. For some items, information and data are available to provide guidelines in making choices. For others, only limited data are available to support a particular choice of alternatives. Choice of germ plasm for use in selection is important to meet the objectives of selection, but critical information to base the decision on choice of germ plasm is often limited. If proper choices were made for all other aspects of the recurrent selection program, the ultimate success of selection may be disappointing because the favorable alleles either were not present or were at low frequencies.

Relative progress within a chosen source of germ plasm also will be influenced with the use of an "effective screen" to measure genetic differences among progenies. Depending on the trait under selection, determination of the genetic differences among progenies will depend on the screening techniques and resources available. Effective screens, for example, have been developed for the artificial infestation and infection for many of the common pests of corn, analyses for the chemical composition of the plant and grain, and measures for determining maturity. Selection, therefore, is effective where the genetic differences can be measured accurately. Penny et al. (1967) reported that three cycles of selection for leaf-feeding resistance to the first-generation European corn borer were adequate to develop germplasm sources with acceptable levels of resistance. Manual application of laboratory reared egg masses on S_1 progenies was effective in determining the genetic resistance of S_1 progenies to leaf feeding and minimizing escapes. Williams and Davis (1983) infested individual corn plants with southwestern corn borer [*Diatraea grandiosella* (Dyar)] egg masses and were not successful to increase the level of resistance after two cycles of individual plant selection. Although artificial means of infestation were used, Williams and Davis (1983) concluded that some type of progeny evaluation rather than individual plant selection was needed for selection to be effective.

Grain yield is the most important economic trait in corn breeding. Hence, response, whether direct or indirect, of yield to selection is usually of prime importance. Yield is a complex trait whose expression is dependent on the environmental effects experienced during the life of the individual plants and progenies. Effective screens for determining genetic differences for yield among genotypes have been limited because of the sporadic and unpredictable environmental effects. Also, the measures of genetic differences will depend on the types of progenies evaluated (Lamkey and Hallauer, 1987). The heritabilities of grain yield can vary from < 10% for individual plants in one environment to >80% for S_2 progenies evaluted in two replications at three environments (Table 8–9). Thus, types of progenies used can have an effect on the relative ability for determining differences among genotypes, and, therefore, effectiveness of selection. Replicated trials in a series of environments (location-year) are routinely conducted to separate the environmental and genetic effects. But the effectiveness of selection also is dependent on the types of progenies evaluated.

Recurrent selection methods are not new. Sprague and Brimhall (1950) credit Hayes and Garber (1919) with the first use of the objectives of recurrent selection to develop cultivars with greater protein content. Only one cycle of selection and recombination, however, was completed. It

Table 8–9. Pooled estimates of six parameters of grain yield for seven recurrent selection methods. Adapted from Lamkey and Hallauer (1987).

Method of selection	Parameters†					
	σ^2	σ^2_{GE}	σ^2_G	σ^2_P	h^2	GCV
	Mg ha^{-1} × 10^2					
Half-sib	78.1 ± 3.3	9.2 ± 3.0	22.7 ± 2.9	38.8 ± 2.8	58.5	7.5
Broad-base tester	55.1 ± 0.6	9.9 ± 0.6	21.0 ± 0.7	33.5 ± 0.7	62.7	6.9
Inbred tester	79.1 ± 1.3	9.6 ± 1.1	19.0 ± 1.0	35.4 ± 0.9	53.8	5.9
Full-sib	90.0 ± 2.7	18.1 ± 2.8	44.3 ± 3.2	65.1 ± 3.1	68.0	11.0
S_1	53.3 ± 1.0	14.2 ± 1.0	54.0 ± 1.9	67.6 ± 1.9	79.8	18.4
S_2	54.5 ± 1.0	24.1 ± 1.3	58.5 ± 2.2	75.6 ± 2.2	77.3	24.3
Reciprocal full-sib	107.2 ± 2.4	13.8 ± 2.2	27.3 ± 1.9	49.8 ± 1.8	54.9	7.7

† σ^2, σ^2_{GE}, σ^2_G, and σ^2_P = estimates of experimental error, genotype × environment interaction, genotypic, and phenotypic components of variance, respectively. h^2 = estimate of heritability on a progeny mean basis. GCV = genetic coefficient of variation.

seems Jenkins (1940) was the first to appreciate the long-term effects and the application of recurrent selection principles in corn breeding. Jenkins (1940) provided a detailed description of a method that included development of S_1 progenies; early testing of lines for general combining ability, using the source population as the tester; intermating remnant S_1 seed of the progenies that had superior performance in the testcross trials; and repeating the procedures for continued selection. Jenkins' (1940) suggestion was based on half-sib family selection that emphasized selection for additive genetic effects. Hull (1945), however, was of the belief that overdominance was of greater importance, and he suggested a recurrent selection scheme that emphasized selection for specific combining ability. The primary difference between the suggestions of Jenkins (1940) and Hull (1945) was the type of testers used to evaluate lines. Because of the conflict between the opposing views on the relative importance of general and specific combining abilities, Comstock et al. (1949) suggested reciprocal recurrent selection, also based on half-sib families, to capitalize on both effects.

Numerous suggestions have been made for conducting recurrent selection in corn (Table 8–10). The first method used by humans for the improvement of corn was simple mass selection based on visual selection for phenotypic differences among individual ears and plants. Except for traits with greater heritabilities (e.g., ear height), simple mass selection generally was not effective (Sprague, 1955). Because of the confounding effects of environment and pollen control, Gardner (1961) suggested modifications to increase the efficiency of mass selection. Ear-to-row selection was designed to base selection on progenies rather than individual plants (Hopkins, 1899). But experimental technique and pollen control also limited its effectiveness. It was not until Lonnquist (1964) and Compton and Comstock (1976) suggested methods of improved experimental techniques and pollen control that ear-to-row selection became an acceptable method for germplasm improvement. Both mass selection and ear-to-row selection have received greater attention in recent years because of improvements to increase the efficiency of selection for determining genetic differences among individuals and progenies.

Most of the other suggested methods of recurrent selection are modifications of the original suggestions of Jenkins (1940), Hull (1945), and Comstock et al. (1949). In most instances, the modifications were made to increase efficiency of selection, based on quantitative genetic theory and data from empirical studies, and to adapt for specific situations. Except for inbred progeny selection, selection is based on either half-sib or full-sib families. Selection based on inbred (S_1, S_1 ... S_n) progenies has received greater emphasis during the past 10 to 15 yr for the following reasons. Quantitative genetic studies indicated that additive genetic effects with partial to complete dominance were of greater importance than nonadditive effects in corn populations. Hence, selection methods that emphasized selection for additive effects would be appropriate. The coef-

Table 8-10. Recurrent selection methods suggested for the improvement of corn populations.

Method of selection	Progenies evaluated	Progenies used for recombination	Pollen control (c) of progenies recombined	Reference
Intrapopulation				
Mass				
Modified	Individual plants	Individual plants	Population (c = 0 − 0.5)	Original method
Unselected males	Individual plants	Individual plants	Population (c = 0.5)	Gardner, 1961
Selected males	Individual plants	Individual plants	Selected plants (c = 1.0)	Eberhart, 1970
Half-sib				
Ear-to-row	Half-sibs	Half-sibs	Population (c = 0 − 0.5)	Hopkins, 1899
Modified	Half-sibs	Half-sibs	Population (c = 0.5)	Lonnquist, 1964
Modified-modified	Half-sibs	Half-sibs	Selected half-sibs (c = 1.0)	Compton and Comstock, 1976
General combining ability	Half-sibs	Half-sibs	Selected half-sibs (c = 1.0)	Jenkins, 1940
	Half-sibs	S_1's	S_1's of selected half-sibs (c = 2.0)	
Specific combining ability	Half-sibs	Half-sibs	Selected half-sibs (c = 1.0)	Hull, 1945
	Half-sibs	S_1's	S_1's of selected half-sibs (c = 2.0)	
Full-sib	Full-sibs	Full-sibs	Selected full-sibs (c = 1.0)	Moll and Robinson, 1966
	Full-sibs	S_1's	S_1's of selected full-sibs (c = 2.0)	Sprague and Eberhart, 1977
Inbred				
S_1	S_1	S_1	Selected S_1's (c = 1.0)	Eberhart, 1970
S_2	S_2	S_1 or S_2	Selected (c = 1.0)	
S_n	S_n	S_n	Selected (c = 1.0)	
Single-seed descent	S_n	S_n	Selected (c = 1.0)	Brim, 1966
Interpopulation				
Reciprocal half-sib				
Remnant half-sib	Half-sibs	Half-sibs	Selected half-sibs (c = 1.0)	Comstock et al., 1949
S_1	Half-sibs	S_1's	S_1's of selected half-sibs (c = 2.0)	
Remnant half-sib	Half-sibs	Half-sibs	Selected half-sibs (c = 1.0)	Paterniani and Vencovsky, 1977
Remnant half-sib	Half-sibs	Half-sibs	Selected half-sibs (c = 0.5)	Paterniani, 1978
Inbred testers	Half-sibs	S_1's	S_1's of selected half-sibs (c = 2.0)	Russell and Eberhart, 1975
				Comstock, 1979
Reciprocal full-sib				
Full-sib	Full-sibs	S_1's	S_1's of selected full-sibs (c = 2.0)	Hallauer and Eberhart, 1970
Full-sib	Full-sibs	Varies	Selected progenies (c = 0.5 − 2.0)	Marquez-Sanchez, 1982

ficients for the additive genetic component of variance among progenies are 1.0 for S_1 progenies, 1.5 for S_2 progenies, and nearly 2.0 for S_n progenies, but only 0.25 among half-sib and 0.5 among full-sib families. Therefore, the expected genetic variation, assuming only additive genetic effects, among S_1 progenies is expected to be four times greater than among half-sib families and twice that among full-sib families. These expected differences for efficiency of selection also are reflected in the empirical estimates of heritability (Table 8–9). The other reasons for the use of inbred progeny selection are of a practical nature, primarily, for integrating recurrent selection methods with the requirements for applied breeding programs. Inbred recurrent selection usually is restricted to S_1 and S_2 progenies. Inbred progeny selection is effective for exposing deleterious recessive alleles and, consequently, reducing the genetic load of the populations under selection. S_1 progeny selection also is effective for increasing the level of pest resistance. Combinations of S_1 and S_2 progeny selection can be effectively used to screen large (500 to 1000) numbers of S_1 progenies for maturity and pest resistance in one environment and evaluating S_2 progenies, derived from acceptable S_1 progenies, in replicated trials for traits that have lower heritabilities (e.g., yield and lodging resistance). Because single crosses have become of greater importance, greater attention has been given to the vigor and productivity of inbred lines per se to permit their use in the production of hybrid seed. Inbred progeny evaluation, therefore, imposes selection for vigor, standability, and yield. The other important feature of inbred progeny recurrent selection is that it is amenable to applied breeding programs and can be easily integrated with the other aspects of pedigree selection.

The choice of recurrent selection method will be dictated by the objectives for improving populations. Each of the methods, if properly conducted, is effective (Sprague and Eberhart, 1977; Hallauer, 1981; Hallauer and Miranda, 1981; Hallauer, 1985). The choice of selection method probably is not as critical as the choice of population chosen for selection. Mass selection, for example, has been effective in some populations and environments for yield (Johnson, 1963; Gardner, 1977), but it was not effective in other populations and environments (Hallauer and Sears, 1969; Mulamba et al., 1983). Mass selection was effective in modifying plant height (Acosta and Crane, 1972), maturity (Troyer and Brown, 1972; Compton et al., 1979), ear length (Salazar and Hallauer, 1986), and prolificacy (Lonnquist, 1967), but it was not effective for increasing the level of resistance to southwestern corn borer (Williams and Davis, 1983). Similar results can be expected for the other recurrent selection methods. If selection is not effective, the lack of response may be due to either the choice of selection method or the choice of population used. However, a change in selection methods can be made with less disruption in genetic progress than a change in populations. A change in selection methods can be made to increase the efficiency of selection, and the progress made from previous selection is not lost. If, however, one changes populations included for selection, the genetic gain realized by previous selection will be lost even though the selection method was seemingly ineffective. An unfortunate choice of populations can occur, and it may become evident that the population will not contribute to the breeding program. The only recourse is to discard and start over. Unfortunately, the loss in time and resources can be costly. Choice of germ plasm, therefore, seems more important that choice of recurrent selection method because changes in methods and testers cause little loss in accumulated improvement.

8–2.3 Recurrent Selection—Results

Recurrent selection studies have been conducted in corn since 1939. Data monitoring the response to selection are more extensive for some methods than for others. In several instances, selection was conducted for two or three cycles of selection and discontinued either because the objectives of the program were attained or because of a change in emphasis in the breeding program. For some traits that have a relatively high heritability because of an effective screen, two or three cycles are adequate to achieve the objectives. Some programs were not continued to determine the long-term effects of selection due to the trait under selection, effective population sizes used, effectiveness of different types of testers, and types of genetic effects affected by the selection method. Sprague and Eberhart (1977) and Hallauer and Miranda (1981) presented summaries of the response to selection for different selection methods, primarily for grain yield. Response to selection averaged 2 to 4% per cycle of selection for most recurrent selection methods, emphasizing that recurrent selection, if properly conducted, can effectively increase the frequency of favorable alleles for grain yield. Hence, the choice of method of selection should be dictated by how the method of selection and population under selection contribute to the overall breeding goals.

Some specific examples will be reviewed and summarized to illustrate the types of results obtained by different methods of recurrent selection for different traits. The direct and correlated responses to selection will be included to demonstrate some of the anomalies of selection for specific traits. The differences among the studies are related to the emphasis given to traits under selection, use of effective screens to reduce the confounding effects of genetic and environmental factors, and the correlations between the primary trait of selection and other traits that are important in applied breeding programs.

8–2.3.1 Intrapopulation Selection

Recurrent selection studies conducted within corn populations have been more commonly used because of simplicity, and their applicability for a greater number of traits. They have been particularly effective for improving pest resistance, adapting germ plasm for specific environments, and changing the chemical composition of the grain. Mass, half-sib family, and S_1 progeny selection are the more commonly used methods with half-sib family selection primarily used for grain yield improvement.

8–2.3.1.1 Mass Selection. The classic mass selection study was conducted in 'Hays Golden'. Gardner (1961) suggested modifications to reduce the effects of environment on selection and to increase parental control with use of adequate isolation. Gardner (1977, 1978) reported a realized gain in grain yield of 3.00% per cycle as a linear response over the first 15 cycles of selection. The realized gain was in excellent agreement with the expected response of 3.08% per cycle. Response to mass selection, however, tended to plateau at cycle 13 and started decreasing at cycle 17. This disturbing trend was discussed relative to possible changes in the original population of Hays Golden, environmental effects experienced because of change in selection sites, changes in genetic variance of the population, and relative importance of nonadditive effects. Although there was some decline in the additive genetic variance with selection, the more plausible explanation was the series of stress environments experienced during the latter cycles of selection (Mareck and Gardner, 1979). Experiments conducted to evaluate selection indicated that the selected cycles did not perform as well in stress environments as the original Hays Golden population. Correlated responses with mass selection for yield included a delay in maturity, an increase in number of ears per plant, and increases in ear and plant height, all of which are often associated with selection that emphasizes increased yield.

Salazar and Hallauer (1986) summarized the direct and correlated responses after 15 cycles of divergent mass selection for ear length, a component of yield. Mass selection for ear length was effective for increased and decreased ear length (Fig. 8–6). Because of the initial composition of the population ('Iowa Long-ear Synthetic'), selection was more

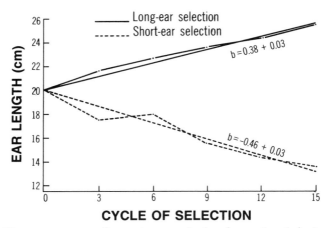

Fig. 8–6. Direct response to divergent mass selection for ear length in Iowa Long Ear Synthetic. Adapted from Salazar and Hallauer (1986).

effective for decreased (-0.46 ± 0.03 cm cycle^{-1}) ear length than for increased (0.38 ± 0.03 cm cycle^{-1}) ear length. Grain yield, as a correlated trait, however, decreased for both selection programs. The decreased yield (-0.044 ± 0.011 Mg ha^{-1}cycle^{-1}) with selection for increased ear length occurred because kernel depth and number of kernel rows significantly decreased over cycles of selection. Yield decreased because the negative effects of kernel depth and kernel row number negated the effects of increased ear length. Yield decreased (-0.104 ± 0.011 Mg ha^{-1} cycle^{-1}) at a greater rate with selection for decreased ear length even though there was a significant increase in kernel depth and number of kernel rows. Other correlated effects included later flowering, greater plant height, and greater stalk lodging with mass selection for increased ear length; opposite effects occurred with mass selection for decreased ear length.

Mass selection is effective for a broad range of plant and ear traits (Hallauer and Miranda, 1981). In most instances, single-trait selection was emphasized. Emphasis on selection for only one trait over several (10 to 20) cycles of selection can cause undesirable correlated changes in other traits (e.g., taller, later plants or ears with reduced number of kernel rows and reduced kernel depth). Multiple-trait selection could be used, but this may not be feasible. It seems a good compromise would be to emphasize mass selection initially, and then use some type of family selection to permit greater and effective control for other traits. Mass selection for adaptation, for example, has been effective in populations that include exotic germ plasm (Compton et al., 1979). After the populations have acceptable standards for use within certain areas, other breeding and selection methods can be used to control maturity, plant stature, and ear size.

Selection for percentage of oil and protein of the seed was initiated in 1896 in the open-pollinated cv. Burr's White. This is the longest continuous selection program conducted in corn, and details of the study after 76 generations of selection were reported by Dudley (1977). Divergent selection for oil and protein content was initiated by analyzing 163 open-pollinated ears (half-sib families). The 24 ears highest in protein and oil and the 12 lowest in protein and oil were used to initiate selection for strains with higher protein (IHP) and oil (IHO) and strains with lower protein (ILP) and oil (ILO). During the course of selection, different strains were developed to determine if adequate genetic variation was present for reverse selection within the respective high and low strains for protein and oil. Selection was effective in all instances. Gains after the completion of 76 generations were 292 (IHO), 92 (ILO), 133 (IHP), and 78% (ILP). Dudley and Lambert (1969) determined that significant estimates of genetic variation among half-sib families for the selected traits existed after 65 generations of selection in each of the strains. Dudley (1977) concluded that the realized gains were explainable when reasonable allele frequencies and numbers of loci involved were assumed. Frequencies of favorable alleles in the original Burr White were estimated at <0.37 for percentage of protein and <0.25 for percentage of oil. A minimum of 54 loci were estimated to differentiate IHO and ILO and a minimum of 122 loci to differentiate IHP and ILP.

Dudley (1977) discussed the results of selection for kernel oil and protein concentration relative to the genetic variation available for genetic improvement of corn. It does not seem the lack of genetic variation in corn should be a constraint for continued genetic improvement. One would assume there are more loci segregating for yield in corn populations than there were in Burr's White for percentage of oil and protein. If the yield of a corn population could be increased three to four times its original mean, as was the case for IHO and IHP, selected populations could be expected to have yields in excess of 18.8 Mg ha^{-1}. If allele frequencies were between 0.25 and 0.5 for 50 to 200 loci to permit a gain of 20 σ_A, there seems to be little concern about exhausting genetic variability for grain yield in corn. Dudley (1977) concluded that the greater concern seems to be developing methods to increase the efficiency of concentrating favorable alleles rather than whether sufficient genetic variability is available.

8–2.3.1.2 S$_1$ Progeny Recurrent Selection. Devey and Russell (1983) summarized the effects of seven cycles of selection for improved stalk quality in the open-pollinated cv. Lancaster, which was designated as BSL(S). BSL(S)C1 through BSL(S)C4 were selected on the basis of S$_0$ plant and S$_1$ progeny resistance to stalk-rot development following artificial inoculation with *Diplodia maydis* (Berk.) Sacc. After four cycles of selection, Jinahyon and Russell (1969) concluded that further gains for stalk quality based on stalk-rot resistance would be small. At this time, selection that emphasized greater mechanical strength of the stalk was initiated. BSL(S)C5 through BSL(S)C7 were derived on the basis of S$_0$ plant selection for stalk-rot resistance and S$_1$ progeny performance for improved mechanical stalk strength. After the completion of seven cycles of selection for stalk quality, the original Lancaster population (C0) and seven successively improved populations (C1 through C7) were evaluated for stalk-rot infection and mechanical stalk strength.

The incidence of stalk-rot infection and level of mechanical stalk strength in cycles of selection for improved stalk quality in the Lancaster population are illustrated in Fig. 8–7. The incidence of stalk-rot infections significantly decreased (b = −0.26 ± 0.03) over the seven cycles of selection with similar rates of gain for stalk-rot resistance based on selection for stalk-rot resistance in the first four cycles (b = −0.27) and mechanical stalk strength the last three cycles (b = −0.28). On a scale of 0.5 (no spread of disease) to 6 (premature death of plant), the level of stalk-rot infection decreased from 3.27 for the C0 to 1.33 for the C7, which compared favorably with 1.44 for the resistant check, B14A × C103. The progress for continued decrease in stalk-rot infection with selection for greater mechanical stalk strength suggests a close association between stalk-rot resistance and morphological stalk traits that contrib-

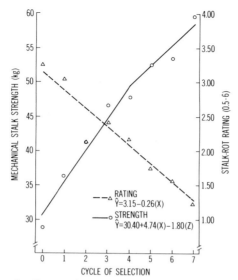

Fig. 8–7. Regression of stalk-rot rating and mechanical stalk strength on cycles of selection for Lancaster. Adapted from Devey and Russell (1983).

uted to mechanical stalk strength. Mechanical stalk strength increased from 28.7 kg for the C0 to 47.9 kg for the C4 and 59.6 kg in the C7. The estimated gain in mechanical stalk strength was 4.75 kg from C0 to C4 and 2.95 kg from C4 to C7 with 97.5% of variation among populations explained by fitting the two linear regressions.

In addition to determining the direct effects of selection for improved stalk quality, Devey and Russell (1983) also measured other plant and ear traits for the C0 through C7 (Table 8–11). Comparisons of the C7 relative to the C0 showed that selection for increased stalk strength significantly delayed flowering (5–6 d), increased plant height (11.3 cm) and internode number (1.6), and decreased internode length (1.1 cm). Average stalk lodging decreased from 31.6% in the C0 to 0.3% in the C7, compared with 1.2% for the resistant check, B14A × C103. Except for the delay in flowering and increased plant height, the correlated changes for the other traits with selection for improved stalk quality should not be critical. The greatest detrimental effects, however, were the correlated changes in grain yield and the components of yield. Yield decreased 40% from the C0 (6.65 Mg ha^{-1}) to the C7 (4.01 Mg ha^{-1}). Grain yield was maintained for the first three cycles of selection, but decreased rapidly after the C3. The 40% decrease in grain yield was reflected in each of the components with ears per plant accounting for most of the decrease in yield.

Because of the methods used for discriminating among plants and S_1 progenies, selection was effective for improving stalk quality but the correlated changes were not desirable, particularly for later maturity and reduced grain yield. Greater yields usually are correlated with later maturity. Hence, the other associated changes were too great to take ad-

Table 8–11. Means and regression coefficients for eight traits after seven cycles of recurrent selection for stalk quality in Lancaster. Adapted from Devey and Russell (1983).

Cycle of selection	Yield	Days to pollen shed†	Plant ht.	Internode		Ears per 100 plants	Kernel-row no.	Ear length
				No.	Length			
	Mg ha⁻¹	no.	cm	no.	cm	— no. —		cm
0	6.65	16.0	244	13.7	17.9	94.5	14.5	19.0
1	6.63	18.6	262	14.4	18.3	93.0	14.8	19.0
2	6.63	19.3	267	15.2	17.7	97.5	13.9	18.6
3	6.18	18.9	264	15.1	17.6	93.0	12.8	19.3
4	5.44	18.4	252	14.6	17.3	91.5	13.4	18.0
5	5.02	18.7	248	14.8	16.8	88.5	12.4	17.4
6	4.69	20.4	256	15.3	16.9	81.0	13.2	15.6
7	4.01	21.8	255	15.3	16.8	75.5	13.1	13.9
b_i‡	−0.115**	2.7**	22*	1.2**	2.4**	NS	−0.74**	−0.13**

*,** Significantly different from zero at the 0.05 and 0.01 levels, respectively.
† Beginning at 1 July.
‡ Estimates were obtained by multiple regression analysis with C4 being the joining point for the polynomials. C4 is where the selection was changed from ratings for stalk-rot infection to ratings for mechanical strength of stalks.

vantage of the later maturity. Devey and Russell (1983) suggested that the confounding effects of inbreeding depression due to small effective population size and changes in the partitioning of photosynthate, originally suggested by Dodd (1980), were the major causes for the decline in yield.

The S_1 recurrent selection program for improved stalk quality illustrates the advantages and disadvantages of the method. Selection was effective because methods for discrimination among plants and progenies for the trait of interest minimized escapes; i.e., effective screens were available. Single-trait selection, however, has obvious disadvantages for developing populations for applied breeding programs. Because effective screens are available for stalk quality, attention also needs to be given to other important traits, such as maturity and grain yield. Larger number of progenies could be included with less emphasis given to stalk quality. The rate of increase for stalk quality would be slower, but acceptable levels of maturity and grain yield could be maintained. Use of a selection index for the primary traits of interest and greater effective population sizes would be needed to reduce the undesirable effects of single-trait selection.

Penny et al. (1967) reported results from S_1 recurrent selection for leaf-feeding resistance to the European corn borer conducted in five synthetic varieties. Three cycles of selection were completed. Manual infestation of artificially reared corn borer eggs was used in each cycle of selection for each population. After the completion of three cycles of selection, 100 S_1 progenies were extracted from the C0, C1, C2, and C3 of each population and evaluated in three-replicate trials with manual infestation of corn borer egg masses. Three cycles of S_1 recurrent selection were found to be adequate to provide S_1 progenies with an acceptable level of resistance to the first-generation European corn borer. On the average, S_1 progeny ratings were reduced from 5.4 to 2.5 (1 = resistant and 9 = susceptible) with 77% of the S_1 progenies included within the resistant classes. Penny et al. (1967) concluded that differences among S_1 progenies were present after three cycles of selection, but that the nine-class visual rating scale probably was not adequate to detect individual progenies that included the greatest number of resistance genes. Russell et al. (1979) observed significant correlated changes in other agronomic traits.

The European corn borer normally has two generations per year in Iowa. Acceptable levels of resistance to first-generation feeding have been identified in most germplasm sources tested, but identifying resistance to second-generation feeding has been more difficult because methods of infestation are more difficult and time consuming and most germplasm sources have a lower frequency of factors that contribute to resistance. Klenke et al. (1986) conducted a recurrent selection study to select for resistance to both generations of feeding in BS9, a synthetic developed by intermating 10 inbred lines selected on the basis of their combining abilities and resistance to both generations of the European corn borer. General objective of the study was to determine if selection methods were effective in developing resistance to the European corn borer for the whole life of the corn plant.

S_1 recurrent selection was used with artificial infestation for both generations. After the completion of four cycles of selection, the five populations of BS9 (C0, C1, C2, C3, and C4) and the five populations crossed to four testers were evaluated to determine progress achieved in BS9 by S_1 recurrent selection and to assess worth of resistance in reducing yield losses due to infestation.

Selection was effective in reducing the level of infestation for both generations (Table 8–12). The level of infestation in the C4 was significantly less than in the BS9C0 in all instances: first-generation feeding was reduced 25% after four cycles of selection and second-generation feeding was reduced 31%. Visual ratings for second-generation feeding were corroborated by nearly a 60% reduction in cavity counts from C0 to the C4. The methods used to increase the levels of resistance were effective in BS9 even though BS9 was synthesized by intermating lines that possessed resistance to infestation by either one or both generations of European corn borer (Klenke et al., 1986). Increased levels of resistance, however, were obtained at the expense of grain yield (Table 8–12). Yield of the noninfested control populations was reduced 31.1%, comparing the yield of the C4 relative to the C0. Yields of the C4 populations infested for first- and second-generation corn borers also were reduced 21.2 to 31.8%. Genetic factors that contributed to European corn borer resistance throughout the life of the corn plant also must have affected physiological processes that are important for either the synthesis and translocation of

Table 8–12. European corn borer ratings and grain yield for BS9 and for four-cycle populations after S_1 recurrent selection for first- and second-generation resistance. Adapted from Klenke et al (1986).

		Treatments†							
		FGI		SGI		FGI & SGI		CVC	
Populations	Control‡	Rating	Yield	Rating	Yield	Rating§	Yield	SCI	FGI & SGI
	Mg ha⁻¹	1–9¶	Mg ha⁻¹	1–9¶	Mg ha⁻¹	1–9¶	Mg ha⁻¹	no.	no.
BS9C0	6.97	3.6	6.07	6.4	5.31	6.3	4.90	8.9	8.0
C1	6.34	3.6	6.50	5.9	4.75	6.2	4.87	8.7	7.1
C2	6.03	2.8	5.24	5.7	4.44	5.2	4.87	5.7	5.0
C3	5.53	2.5	5.62	4.4	4.08	4.4	4.78	3.9	4.8
C4	4.80	2.7	4.79	4.4	4.40	4.3	4.41	3.1	3.4
LSD (0.05)	1.38	0.8	1.38	1.3	1.38	1.3	1.38	2.2	2.2
Change, #	−31.1	−25.0	−21.1	−31.2	−17.1	−31.8	−10.0	−65.2	−57.5

† Abbreviations for treatments: FGI = first generation infestation; SGI = second generation infestation; and CVC = cavity counts with one cavity = 2.5 cm.

‡ Populations were not infested and were sprayed with carbofuran to control natural infestation.

§ Second generation rating.

¶ Visual ratings on 1 (resistant) to 9 (susceptible) scale.

Change of C4 relative to C0.

photosynthates or the number or size of kernels. Corn borer resistance contributes to improved plant health and has been one factor that has contributed to the genetic gains experienced in the newer hybrids (Duvick, 1984). The results of Klenke et al. (1986) are similar to those reported by Devey and Russell (1983) for improved stalk quality. High selection pressures for a single trait were effective, but the correlated responses for other important traits were not desirable.

Because of the expansion of corn growing areas in higher latitudes and elevations and the changes in tillage practices used in corn production, increased attention has been given to corn genotypes that germinate and grow in cooler soil environments. S_1 progeny recurrent selection has been used to select for greater cold tolerance in possible germplasm sources. Mock and Bakri (1976) evaluated BS13(SCT) after two cycles and BSSS2(SCT) after three cycles of S_1 progeny selection for cold tolerance. S_1 progeny selection improved percentage of emergence 30.1% and seedling dry weight 13.2% in BS13(SCT) with no improvement in BSSS2(SCT). Hoard and Crosbie (1985) evaluated BS13(SCT) and BSSS2(SCT) after five cycles of selection and reported average changes for the two populations as 2.1% cycle^{-1} for percentage of emergence, 0.04 g cycle^{-1} for seedling dry weight, and 0.3 units cycle^{-1} for seedling vigor score. Hoard and Crosbie (1985) concluded that selection would be effective with use of a selection index that included percentage of emergence and seedling dry weight, using data from more than one environment.

8–2.3.1.3 Half-sib Family and Inbred Progeny Selection. BSK is a strain of the open-pollinated cv. Krug Yellow Dent that was developed at the Nebraska Agricultural Experiment Station and designated 'Krug High I Syn. 3' (Lonnquist, 1949). In 1953, S_1 progeny and half-sib family recurrent selection for grain yield were initiated in BSK; the two strains of BSK were designated BSK(S) for S_1 progeny selection and BSK(HI) for half-sib family selection. S_1 progenies per se were tested for the first six cycles, and S_2 progenies per se for cycles 7 and 8 for BSK(S). In BSK(HI), different testers were used for different cycles of selection. The double-cross Ia4652 [(WF9 × W22) × (B14 × M14)] was used as the tester for the first three cycles, and the two parental single crosses of Ia4652 served as the testers for cycles 4 and 5. For the sixth cycle, a low-yielding related line, 'Krug 755', was used as the tester. An unrelated elite line, B73, was used as tester for cycles 7 and 8. Yield was the primary trait of selection, but attention also was given to lodging and grain moisture at harvest.

Smith (1979b) and Tanner and Smith (1987) conducted studies to determine response to selection for both methods of recurrent selection (Table 8–13). The evaluation study included populations per se, populations per se selfed one generation, population crosses between the cycle populations for both methods of selection, and population crosses selfed one generation. Positive response to selection for grain yield was realized in all comparisons (Table 8–13). After eight cycles of selection, BSK(S)C8 had 23.4% greater yield, and BSK(HI)C8 had 32.4% greater yield than BSKC0. Yield increases over cycles of selection between the two methods of selection, however, were different. The greatest yield in BSK(S) was obtained by the C4 with no further gains with four additional cycles of selection. With half-sib family selection, significant gains in grain yield were realized from the C4 to the C8. Because of the restricted genetic base of the BSKC0 population and the small effective population sizes ($N_e = 10$) used in recombination, the different rates of response among cycles of S_1-S_2 progeny and half-sib family selection may be expected. Tanner and Smith (1987) estimated the effects due to finite population

Table 8-13. Response for six traits from half-sib (HI) and S_1 (S) recurrent selection conducted in Krug Hi I Syn. 3 (BSK), their crosses, and after one generation of selfing in the populations and crosses. Adapted from Tanner and Smith (1987).

Cycle of selection	BSK(S)		BSK(S) × BSK(HI)		BSK(HI)	
	Per se	Self	Per se	Self	Per se	Self
Yield, LSD (0.05) = 0.79 Mg ha⁻¹						
C0	4.87	2.77	4.87	2.77	4.87	2.77
C4	6.21	3.90	6.16	4.08	5.29	3.19
C8	6.01	4.13	7.11	4.36	6.45	3.91
†	23.4	49.1	46.0	57.4	32.4	41.2
Grain moisture, LSD (0.05) = 1.3%						
C0	22.1	22.4	22.1	22.4	22.1	22.4
C4	21.7	22.1	21.8	21.8	21.8	22.4
C8	22.1	21.7	22.2	22.2	23.4	22.8
†	0.0	−3.2	0.4	−0.9	0.06	1.8
Root lodging, LSD (0.05) = 10.0%						
C0	25.6	24.4	25.6	24.4	25.6	24.4
C4	8.9	5.8	15.0	17.1	25.3	24.0
C8	2.6	2.4	9.5	5.2	17.0	15.1
†	−89.8	−90.2	−62.9	−78.7	−33.6	−38.1
Stalk lodging, LSD (0.05) = 8.9%						
C0	41.4	40.4	41.4	40.4	41.4	40.4
C4	39.0	41.0	48.7	46.8	39.9	39.8
C8	51.7	49.9	46.0	49.1	36.0	34.1
†	24.9	23.5	11.1	21.5	−13.0	−15.6
Plant height, LSD (0.05) = 9.4 cm						
C0	232	210	232	210	232	210
C4	227	209	231	212	230	216
C8	227	210	234	195	213	200
†	−1.2	0.0	0.9	−7.2	−8.2	−4.8
Days to pollen shed, LSD (0.05) = 1.9 d‡						
C0	21.5	23.8	21.5	23.8	21.5	23.8
C4	19.8	21.0	19.0	22.5	20.5	22.8
C8	20.3	21.8	17.5	20.5	20.6	22.5
†	−5.6	−8.4	−18.6	−13.9	−4.2	−5.5

† Percentage change for C8 relative to C0.   ‡ Beginning at 1 July.

size for BSK(S) and BSK(HI). The cumulative effects of inbreeding due to finite population size over eight cycles of selection were expected to decrease observed gain in the populations per se by 2.24 Mg ha^{-1} in BSK(S) and 1.15 Mg ha^{-1} in BSK(HI). The larger effects of finite population size in BSK(S) were attributed to recombination of S_2 progenies in C7 and C8 and the greater effectiveness of S_1 and S_2 selection in eliminating deleterious recessive alleles in BSK(S). The larger effects of drift in BSK(S) and the increased efficiency of BSK(HI) in later cycles resulted in a crossover of observed yield response (Table 8–13).

The greater effectiveness of S_1 and S_2 progeny selection in eliminating deleterious alleles also is reflected in the S_1 generation performance of the populations per se. Both methods of selection reduced inbreeding depression in the C8 compared with the C0; however, inbreeding depression was 7.9% less after eight cycles of S_1 and S_2 progeny selection compared with half-sib family selection (Table 8–13). Inbreeding depression after four cycles of S_1 progeny selection (3.90 Mg ha^{-1}) was similar to eight cycles of half-sib family selection (3.91 Mg ha^{-1}).

Crosses of populations after four and eight cycles of selection suggest that the two methods of selection increased the frequencies of different alleles. Mid-parent heterosis was 7.1% after four cycles of selection and 14.1% after eight cycles. The C4 × C4 cross yield (6.16 Mg ha^{-1}) was similar to BSK(S)C4 (6.21 Mg ha^{-1}). After eight cycles of selection, the C8 × C8 cross yielded 7.11 Mg ha^{-1} as compared with 6.01 Mg ha^{-1} for BSK(S)C8 and 6.45 Mg ha^{-1} for BSK(HI)C8. Inbreeding depression of the S_1 generation of the population crosses was similar to that for BSK(S). Inbreeding depression for the S_1 generation of BSK(S)C8 × BSK(HI)C8 was reduced 57.4% compared with the S_1 generation of BSKC0. S_1 and S_2 progeny selection were more effective, as expected, than half-sib selection for reducing the effects of inbreeding.

Except for root and stalk lodging, effective selection for greater grain yield by inbred progeny and half-sib family selection did not result in undesirable correlated responses for the other traits of interest to breeders. Changes observed with selection for grain yield did not result in taller plants with delayed maturity. Root and stalk quality are important traits in applied breeding programs, and BSK(S)C8 and BSK(HI)C8 do not have acceptable levels of root and stalk quality. Except for stalk quality in BSK(S), the observed trends are in the desired direction (Table 8–13). S_1 and S_2 progeny selection were more effective than half-sib family selection for improved root quality, but S_1 and S_2 progeny selection was not as effective as half-sib family selection for stalk lodging resistance. Stalk lodging significantly increased 24.9% in BSK(S)C8, whereas there was a nonsignificant decrease of 13.0% in BSK(HI)C8. It is not clear why the reverse trends were observed for root and stalk lodging for inbred progeny vs. half-sib family selection. Similar experimental procedures and test environments were used for both selection programs, but selection among S_1 progenies was not effective. Selection for greater yield

among S_1 and S_2 progenies seemingly directed a greater portion of photosynthate to the grain, which is the opposite effect experienced by Devey
and Russell (1983) who emphasized selection for greater stalk quality
(Table 8-11).

The response to eight cycles of selection for greater grain yield by
inbred progeny (2.9% cycle^{-1}) and half-sib family (4.0% cycle^{-1}) recurrent
selection in BSK was similar although the rates of response varied among
cycles. Except for root and stalk lodging, the indirect effects of selection
also were similar for both methods. The responses to selection for the
primary trait were similar to the summaries reported by Sprague and
Eberhart (1977) and Hallauer and Miranda (1981). Hence, the choice of
method of selection was not critical.

Mulamba et al. (1983) tested S_1 progenies extracted from BSKC0,
BSK(S)C8, BSK(HI)C8, and BSK(M)C14. BSK(M)C14 was derived from
BSKC0 by 14 cycles of mass selection for grain yield. BSK(M)C14 had
8.25% greater yield than BSKC0, or 0.58% gain per cycle of mass selection.
One-hundred S_1 progenies were obtained from BSKC0, BSK(S)C8,
BSK(HI)C8, and BSK(M)C14 and evaluated in four environments (Table
8-14). The relative changes for the means of the 100 S_1 progenies for
BSK(S)C8 and BSK(HI)C8 were similar to the selfed generations shown
in Table 8-13 for most traits. Eight cycles of inbred progeny and half-
sib family selection were more efficient than 14 cycles of mass selection
for developing germplasm sources for breeding programs. S_1 progenies
extracted from BSK(M)C14 were lower yielding, later in maturity, and
taller than the S_1 progenies extracted from BSK(S)C8 and BSK(HI)C8.
The main disturbing feature of the progeny selection methods is the
tendency to have lower estimates of σ_G^2 after eight cycles of selection,
particularly for BSK(S)C8. The estimate of σ_G^2 among S_1 progenies of
BSK(S)C8 agrees with the findings of Tanner and Smith (1987) that the
cumulative effects of inbreeding were greater in BSK(S) than in BSK(HI).

Studies comparing the relative effectiveness of half-sib family and
inbred progeny selection have been reported by Horner et al. (1973),
Horner et al. (1976), Horner (1985), and Zambezi et al. (1986). Objectives
of the studies were to compare the relative effectiveness of half-sib family
selection with different types of testers (inbred lines, single crosses, and
genetically broad base composite) and S_2 progeny selection in the improvement of populations themselves, populations selfed, and testcrosses
to different types of testers. Grain yield was the primary trait of selection,
but some attention also was given to lodging, ear height, and ear number.
Because selfed-progeny selection is expected to be more effective than
half-sib family selection, they were also interested in evaluating the relative efficiency of the two methods for changing allelic frequencies in the
populations.

Horner et al. (1973) reported data for three concurrent recurrent selection methods (half-sib family with inbred and broad-based population
as testers and S_2 progeny per se) following the suggestion of Hull (1952).

Table 8–14. Mean ($\bar{x}$), standard deviation of means (SD), ranges, and estimates of variability (σ_G^2) for six traits measured on 100 S_1 progenies of four BSK populations. Adapted from Mulamba et al. (1983).

Traits	Populations†	$\bar{x} \pm$ SD	Percentage of C0	Range	σ_G^2
Yield, Mg ha⁻¹	BSKC0	2.91 ± 0.06	--	0.49–5.72	62.5 ± 11.1
	BSK(M)C14	2.71 ± 0.06	93.1	0.88–4.37	65.5 ± 11.5
	BSK(HI)C8	4.74 ± 0.05	163.0	3.20–7.99	52.9 ± 8.5
	BSK(S)C8	4.94 ± 0.05	170.0	3.23–6.69	28.0 ± 6.1
Grain	BSKC0	16.8 ± 0.11	--	14.3–19.8	0.7 ± 0.2
moisture, %	BSK(M)C14	18.2 ± 0.16	108.0	15.4–22.2	1.7 ± 0.3
	BSK(HI)C8	18.5 ± 0.13	109.8	15.8–21.1	1.1 ± 0.3
	BSK(S)C8	17.5 ± 0.11	104.1	15.1–21.4	0.6 ± 0.2
Root	BSKC0	13.2 ± 0.33	--	7.2–20.0	6.6 ± 1.4
lodging, %	BSK(M)C14	12.9 ± 0.31	97.4	7.2–21.6	4.8 ± 1.2
	BSK(HI)C8	11.0 ± 0.36	83.2	6.3–22.9	9.3 ± 1.7
	BSK(S)C8	8.3 ± 0.18	62.8	5.9–13.9	2.2 ± 0.4
Stalk	BSKC0	10.5 ± 0.21	--	6.4–16.8	2.6 ± 0.6
lodging, %	BSK(M)C14	11.9 ± 0.28	113.3	6.2–23.1	4.7 ± 1.1
	BSK(HI)C8	9.5 ± 0.16	90.0	6.0–13.6	1.1 ± 0.4
	BSK(S)C8	10.3 ± 0.20	97.8	6.8–16.2	1.8 ± 0.6
Ear height, cm	BSKC0	112.2 ± 1.17	--	80.5–137.8	128 ± 21
	BSK(M)C14	134.0 ± 1.56	119.4	96.0–166.2	206 ± 33
	BSK(HI)C8	94.8 ± 1.12	84.5	67.8–125.8	44 ± 16
	BSK(S)C8	95.6 ± 1.03	85.2	69.0–123.0	93 ± 15
Days to silk,	BSKC0	90.3 ± 0.45	--	83.0–105.3	16.6 ± 3.0
no.	BSK(M)C14	96.7 ± 0.34	107.1	87.7–104.0	9.5 ± 1.8
	BSK(HI)C8	85.1 ± 0.28	94.4	79.3–95.5	6.4 ± 1.1
	BSK(S)C8	83.7 ± 0.25	92.7	79.5–91.7	4.9 ± 0.9

† BSKC0 is the original unselected population; BSK(M)C14 after 14 cycles of mass selection for yield; BSK(HI)C8 after eight cycles of half-sib family selection for yield; and BSK(S)C8 after eight cycles of S_1 progeny selection for yield.

Fla. 767 was the original source population. F6 was the inbred tester and Fla. 767 the broad-based tester. After five cycles of selection for each method were completed, selected populations for each method were crossed to two testers Fla. 767, the original population, and Fla. 3W, an unrelated synthetic, both of which are genetically broad-based populations. Significant linear increases in general combining ability were obtained with each method of selection, but the inbred tester method (4.4% cycle⁻¹) was more effective than the use of parental population as tester (2.4% cycle⁻¹) and S_2 progeny (2.0% cycle⁻¹) selection. Because the rate of response with use of an inbred as tester was twice the rate from S_2 progeny selection, they suggested that the inbred tester was homozygous recessive at many important loci, and, consequently, the inbred tester would have greater variation among testcrosses than the original population, which probably has intermediate allelic frequencies at most loci. The average testcross variances after five cycles of selection were 5.3 for F6 and 2.0 for Fla. 767; thus variation among F6 testcrosses was 2.65 times greater than among Fla. 767 testcrosses. Variability among S_2 progenies averaged over five cycles was 19.4, nearly four times greater than among F6 testcrosses. Hence, it seems progress for population per se should have been more effective with S_2 progeny selection than with testcross selection. It seemed, however, that S_2 progeny selection was not as effective in fixing dominant favorable alleles that combined well with the testers.

Horner et al. (1976) reported on the effectiveness of a single-cross (F44 × F6) tester for the improvement of combining ability. The source population also was Fla. 767 and six cycles of half-sib family selection were evaluated in testcrosses with F44 × F6, the tester used in selection, and FS3W, an unrelated synthetic variety. Performance over cycles of selection were similar for both testers with 18% greater grain yield, 9% lower ear height, and 35% less lodging. Horner et al. (1976) concluded that half-sib family selection increased the frequency of genes with additive effects; testers that have a genetically narrow base (i.e., single-cross hybrid) are effective for improving general as well as specific combining ability; and that it is possible to change testers in recurrent selection programs with little loss in accumulated gain.

Because the improvement in general combining ability during five cycles of selection in Fla. 767 from use of inbred F6 as tester was nearly two times greater than from the use of the parent population (Fla. 767) as tester and S_2 progeny selection, Horner (1985) reexamined the comparisons of testcross vs. S_2 progeny selection in subpopulations (A and B) derived from a different genetically broad-base synthetic, FSHmR. Grain yield was the primary trait of selection, and three cycles were completed for each method of selection. Evaluation trials to estimate response to selection indicated significant progress for both methods with no overall significant differences between testcross and S_2 selection (Table 8–15). The highest average gain (6.6% cycle^{-1}) was for the population crosses, which included the selected cycles for the two subpopulations A and B. For the average comparisons of combining ability for grain yield for three testers, gains per cycle of 4.0% (0.19 Mg ha^{-1}) for S_2 progeny selection and 4.6% (0.21 Mg ha^{-1}) for testcross selection were not significantly different. The testers included the populations and two inbred testers, one used for testcross selection and one unrelated. There was no consistent trend for combining ability between the types of testers. Zambezi et al.'s (1986) study also included genetically narrow- and broad-based testers and their data also provided further evidence that inbred testers can be used for improving general as well as specific combining ability in corn. Performance of the third-cycle populations at three levels of inbreeding (Syn-1, S_1, and S_2) indicate that S_2 progeny selection resulted in less inbreeding depression than the testcross method. Estimated rates of inbreeding depression were −0.049 Mg ha^{-1} for S_2 progeny selection and −0.057 Mg ha^{-1} for testcross selection (Table 8–15). Inbreeding depression was significantly less with S_2 selection, and the predicted yields of homozygous lines were 2.22 Mg ha^{-1} for S_2 progeny selection and 1.47

Table 8-15. Effects of testcross (TC) and S_2 recurrent selection on grain yield. Adapted from Horner (1985).

Populations and method	$C_n \times C_n$ crosses[†]	Testcross means[‡]	Bulks of selfing in C3			
			Syn. 1	S_1	S_2	S_0
			Mg ha^{-1}			
C0	4.71	4.91	--	--	--	--
C1, S2	4.94	5.00	--	--	--	--
C3, S2	5.61	5.50	6.88	4.56	3.16	2.22§
b_1	0.28**	0.19**	--	--	--	−0.049¶
C1, TC	5.28	5.15	--	--	--	--
C3, TC	5.68	5.55	6.72	4.28	2.69	1.47§
b	0.34**	0.22**	--	--	--	−0.057¶
LSD (0.05)	0.31	0.21	0.62	0.31	0.31	--

** Significantly different from zero at the 1% level.
† Crosses between A and B subpopulations.
‡ Average for A and B subpopulations crossed to C0 and two inbred testers.
§ Predicted yields of homozygous lines.
¶ Rate of inbreeding depression.

Mg ha^{-1} for testcross selection. Hence, the differences between methods for combining ability were not significant, but less inbreeding depression was expressed in populations improved by S_2 progeny selection.

Other selection programs have compared relative gains realized from S_2 progeny and half-sib family selection. In some instances, only one to three cycles of selection were completed, and the types of testers used have ranged from elite inbred lines to unimproved, open-pollinated varieties. Results and conclusions from the studies were not conclusive in that neither method was clearly superior to the other (Hallauer and Miranda, 1981). In the absence of overdominance, inbred progeny selection is expected to be superior to half-sib (or testcross) family selection for changing allelic frequencies in a population (Comstock, 1964; Wright, 1980). Theoretically, genetic variation among S_1 progenies is expected to be four times greater than among half-sib families when gene frequency is 0.5 and six times greater if S_2 progeny selection were used. Most of the evidence in corn populations suggests that genetic variation for yield in corn is primarily additive, but this does not eliminate the possibility of nonadditive variation at some loci, particularly in elite germ plasm. Under these conditions, inbred progeny selection should be more effective than half-sib family selection, which has not always been the case. The following conclusions seem valid and reasonable for the data reported for comparisons of inbred progeny and half-sib family recurrent selection: populations have responded to selection by both methods with no consistent advantage for either method; inbreeding depression was less in populations improved by inbred progeny selection and this is expected because inbred selection emphasizes contributions to homozygous loci; there was no clear evidence that combining ability was different for the two methods, though inbred progeny selection does not include testcross information in making selection; rate of response may differ among the cycles of selection for the two methods (e.g., Tanner, 1984); the choice of testers does not seem to influence response to half-sib family selection (i.e., inbred line or genetically broad-base populations); and it is possible to change testers during the sequence of selection cycles with little loss in accumulated gains. If, however, overdominance becomes of greater importance in later cycles, half-sib family selection may prove to be more effective. Jensen et al. (1983) reported S_2 progeny selection was not effective in their elite germ plasm because of nonadditive effects.

8–2.3.1.4 Iowa Stiff Stalk Synthetic.

Half-sib family and inbred progeny (S_1 and S_2) selection have been conducted in Iowa Stiff Stalk Synthetic (BSSS), but both methods were not conducted concurrently as for BSK and Fla. 767. The first sampling for half-sib family selection was in 1939 with the double-cross, Ia13 [(L317 $\times$ BL349) $\times$ (BL345 $\times$ MC401)] as the tester. After the completion of seven cycles of half-sib family selection, S_1 and S_2 progeny selection were initiated in BS13(HT)C7 to increase the variability among progenies evaluated. Details of the half-sib family selection program were provided by Eberhart et al. (1973), and estimates of the response to selection were presented by Eberhart et al. (1973), Smith (1979a, 1983, 1984), and Hallauer et al. (1983). Briefly, the response to selection in testcrosses with the tester, Ia13, (18.5%) was about 7% greater than the testcrosses of the improved cycles with BSSSC0 as tester (11.9%) and nearly 10% greater than populations per se (8.9%) for grain yield. Response to selection for improved grain yield per cycle was 0.072 Mg ha^{-1} for populations per se, 0.092 Mg ha^{-1} for BSSSC0 testcrosses, and 0.165 Mg ha^{-1} for Ia13 testcrosses. Response to selection was significant in all instances for half-sib family selection in BSSS, but Smith (1983) also estimated a significant inbreeding effect ($-0.113 \pm$ 0.047 Mg ha^{-1}) in BS13(HT) because only 10 S_1 lines were used in recombination.

Inbred progeny (S_1 and S_2) selection was initiated in BS13(HT)C7, and the population was redesignated as BS13(S)C0. Four cycles of inbred progeny selection have been completed, and Helms (1986) evaluated response to selection after seven cycles of half-sib family and four cycles of inbred progeny selection (Tables 8–16 and 8–17). Helms (1986) also included populations derived from BSSSC0 by reciprocal recurrent selection with BSCB1. Grain yield increased 38.2% after 11 cycles of selection, but 36.9% of the gain was achieved with seven cycles of half-sib family selection (BS13C0) and only 1.3% with inbred progeny selection [BS13C0 vs. BS13(S)C4]. The 11 cycles of intrapopulation selection that emphasized grain yield in BSSSC0 were similar to the 10 cycles of interpopulation half-sib selection (38.2% vs. 37.9%, Table 8–16). In both selection programs, most of the gain was realized after six cycles of selection. The main effects of the four cycles of inbred progeny selection in BS13(S) seemed to be greater fixation of favorable alleles in the homozygous state: inbreeding depression of BSSSC0 (34.8%) and BS13(S)C0

Table 8-16. Observed responses for four traits of populations per se, populations selfed one generation, and population crosses for three methods of recurrent selection conducted in Iowa Stiff Stalk Synthetic (BSSS). Adapted from Helms (1986).

Populations and crosses†	Yield		Grain moisture		Lodging			
					Root		Stalk	
	Per se	Self	Per se	Self	Per se	Self	Per se	Self
	— Mg ha⁻¹ —				%			
BSSSC0	3.85	2.51	27.6	27.8	15.7	16.0	31.0	24.6
BS13(HT)C2	4.31	2.65	27.6	27.8	20.6	15.5	27.2	24.7
BS13(HT)C4	4.64	2.91	27.1	28.7	17.9	18.4	33.1	22.6
BS13(HT)C6	4.98	3.23	28.4	29.0	30.9	24.2	25.8	19.2
BS13C0	5.27	3.37	28.6	28.7	28.8	26.6	18.7	19.1
BS13(S)C2	5.22	3.91	26.8	27.3	14.4	15.1	32.7	26.7
BS13(S)C4	5.32	4.10	25.9	26.5	15.7	19.4	30.0	29.0
‡	38.2	63.3	−6.2	−4.7	0.0	21.2	−3.2	17.9
BSSS(R)C2	4.51	2.69	25.2	25.6	17.6	15.2	33.3	24.7
BSSS(R)C4	4.56	2.76	24.7	24.7	17.9	16.4	22.4	25.4
BSSS(R)C6	5.27	3.03	27.0	27.8	16.0	14.4	20.3	20.2
BSSS(R(C8	5.09	3.06	25.8	27.1	19.7	16.9	16.4	17.2
BSSS(R)C10	5.31	3.66	26.5	27.5	16.0	12.9	16.6	19.4
‡	37.9	45.8	−4.0	−1.1	1.9	−19.4	−46.5	−21.1
BSSSC0 ×								
BSCB1C0	5.13	--	23.7	--	16.8	·	32.9	--
BSSS(R)C6 ×								
BSCB1(R)C6	6.38	--	25.3	--	16.6	--	23.1	--
BSSS(R)C10 ×								
BSCB1(R)C10	7.30	--	24.5	--	13.7	--	17.6	--
§	42.3		3.4		−18.5		−46.5	
BS13(S)C4 ×								
BSSS(R)C10	7.32	--	26.2	--	19.6	·	21.9	--
BS13(S)C4 ×								
BSCB1(R)C10	7.45	--	23.7	--	16.7	--	21.5	--
B84 × Mo17	9.48	--	25.0	--	14.7	--	16.8	--
B73 × Mo17	8.55	--	25.5	--	12.3	--	15.3	--
LSD (0.05)	0.5		1.3		6.5		7.9	

† BSSSC0 is the original strain of Iowa Stiff Stalk Synthetic; HT populations derived from BSSSC0 half-sib family selection using Ia13 as tester; S populations derived by inbred progeny selection, which was initiated in BS13(HT)C7; R populations derived from BSSSC0 by reciprocal recurrent selection with BSCB1 as the tester.
‡ Percentage change for last cycle of selection relative to BSSSC0.
§ Percentage change of cross relative to BSSSC0 × BSCB1C0.

(36.0%) was similar but reduced to 22.9% for BS13(S)C4. Average estimate of inbreeding for C6 and C8 of BSSS(R) was 41.2%, which is 5.2% greater than BS13(S)C0 [or BS13(HT)C7].

Fifty S_2 progenies derived from BSSSC0 and four selected populations were evaluated in six environments to estimate the genetic variability of the respective populations (Table 8–17). Except for grain yield of BSSS(R)C9 developed by nine cycles of reciprocal recurrent selection, the estimates of genetic variability among S_2 progenies do not suggest a significant change from BSSSC0. Average yield of S_2 progenies for each

Table 8-17. Means and estimates of genetic variance (σ^2_G) for five traits for 50 S_2 progenies derived from BSSSC0 by recurrent selection evaluated in six environments. Adapted from Helms (1986).

Populations[†]	Grain				Lodging			
	Yield		Moisture		Root		Stalk	
	$\bar{x}$	σ^2_G	$\bar{x}$	σ^2_G	$\bar{x}$	σ^2_G	$\bar{x}$	σ^2_G
	Mg ha^{-1}‡				%			
BSSSC0	2.12	41.0 ± 9.8	26.5	4.7 ± 1.2	16	59 ± 17	15	78 ± 19
BSSS(R)C5	2.62**	58.4 ± 13.4	25.4**	4.4 ± 1.0	18	53 ± 15	15	61 ± 15
BSSS(R)C9	3.40**	15.5 ± 5.0	26.0*	2.8 ± 0.7	17	62 ± 17	11**	31 ± 8
BS13(S)C0	3.32**	32.1 ± 8.0	26.1*	4.5 ± 1.1	25**	185 ± 46	10**	50 ± 13
BS13(S)C3	3.84**	44.1 ± 11.5	24.9**	3.7 ± 0.9	20**	65 ± 20	16	100 ± 25
LSD (0.05)	0.12		0.4		2.1		1.5	
LSD (0.01)	0.15		0.5		2.8		1.9	

*, ** Significantly different from BSSSC0 at the 0.05 and 0.01 levels, respectively.

† BSSSC0 is the original strain of Iowa Stiff Stalk Synthetic; R populations obtained by reciprocal recurrent selection with BSCB1 as the tester; BS13(S)C0 was obtained after seven cycles of half-sib selection with double-cross hybrid Ia13 as the tester; and BS13(S)C3 developed after three cycles of inbred progeny selection where BS13(S)C0 is equivalent to BS13(HT)C7.

‡ Mg ha^{-1} × 10^2.

population (Table 8–17) exhibited trends similar to those for the S_1 generation presented in Table 8–16. Inbreeding depression of S_2 progenies derived from populations after selection was reduced in all instances. Also, the average yields of S_2 progenies derived by half-sib family selection [BSSS(R)C9 and BS13(S)C0 or BS13(HT)C7] were similar (3.40 vs. 3.32 Mg ha^{-1}). The BS13(S)C3 S_2 progenies averaged 81.1% greater yield than the BSSSC0 S_2 progenies, or 8.1% increase cycle^{-1} of selection.

Grain yield was the primary trait in selection, and the response to selection was consistent over cycles of selection (3.8% cycle^{-1}) for the populations themselves. Grain moisture is a measure of maturity, and, in most instances, the grain moisture of the selected populations was significantly less than BSSSC0 (Tables 8–16 and 8–17). Although attention was given to root and stalk quality during selection, trends for improved root and stalk quality were not evident for either the populations or the inbred populations.

Estimates of the genetic parameters for the Smith (1983) model were obtained for both methods of selection for grain yield (Table 8–18). Changes in frequencies of alleles with additive effects (ALI) due to selection were greater in the BS13(HT) and BS13(S) than in BSSS(R). But the changes in frequencies of alleles with dominance effects (DLI) were more important in BSSS(R) than in the BS13(HT) and BS13(S) populations over cycles of selection. Significant estimates of genetic drift (DQI) over cycles of selection for grain yield were similar for BS13(HT) and BSSS(R); Smith (1979a) reported greater inbreeding depression for the BSSS(R) method, although the effective population size was the same for both methods. The estimate of genetic drift in BS13(S) was smaller and nonsignificant. Based on the estimates of the effects of genetic drift, yield of the populations was adjusted for genetic drift (Table 8–18). The observed yields for BSSS(R)C6 and BS13(HT)C7 were equal, but the ad-

Table 8–18. Estimates of genetic parameters and observed and predicted grain yield in selected populations of BSSS. Adapted from Helms (1986).

| Populations | Genetic parameters for yield† | | | Grain yield | | |
	ALI	DLI	DQI	Populations	Observed	Predicted
	——— Mg ha^{-1} ———				—— Mg ha^{-1} ——	
BS13(HT)C7	0.090**	0.082*	−0.013**	BSSSC0‡	3.85	3.93
BS13(S)C4	0.113**	--	−0.019	BS13(HT)C7	5.27	6.34
BSSS(R)C10	0.047	0.131**	−0.012**	BS13(S)C4	5.32	7.24
				BSSS(R)C6	5.27	6.06
				BSSS(R)C10	5.31	7.49

† Genetic parameters based on model used by Smith (1983) where ALI, DLI, and DQI are partial regression coefficients due to the effects of homozygous loci, heterozygous loci, and genetic drift, respectively, on cycles of selection.

‡ BSSSC0 is the original strain of Iowa Stiff Stalk Synthetic; BS13(HT)C7 after seven cycles of half-sib family selection with Ia13 tester; BS13(S)C4 after four cycles of inbred progeny selection in BS13(HT)C7; and BSSS(R) after reciprocal recurrent selection with BSCB1 as the tester.

justed yields show that seven cycles of half-sib family selection with Ia13 was 4.5% greater than six cycles of reciprocal recurrent selection. BSSS(R)C10 was only 3.4% greater than BS13(S)C4. Total response, both observed and adjusted for genetic drift, was similar for the advanced populations of BSSS.

8–2.3.1.5 Full-sib Family Selection.

One of the first recurrent selection programs used in corn was full-sib family selection within 'Jarvis' and 'Indian Chief' (Moll and Robinson, 1966). This selection program was started in the late 1940s and has continued to the present time. Periodic reports of response to selection, both direct and indirect, usually involved comparisons with reciprocal half-sib recurrent selection conducted in the same populations. Populations per se and population crosses of the respective recurrent selection programs have been evaluated to measure direct and indirect responses realized from intra- and interpopulation recurrent selection. Grain yield was the trait of selection.

Moll and Hanson (1984) reported grain yield data for two experiments (Exp. 1 and 2) that included the direct response in the Jarvis and Indian Chief populations themselves and the correlated response of their population crosses (Table 8–19). Data were available for 10 cycles of full-sib family selection. Response to selection for greater grain yield was more effective in Jarvis than in Indian Chief in both experiments. Though yields in Exp. 2 were greater than in Exp. 1, similar responses were obtained. Response seemed to have plateaued after the C8, and Moll and Hanson (1984) combined the data for C8 and C10. For the average of the two experiments, grain yield increased 2.62% cycle^{-1} for Jarvis and 0.65% cycle^{-1} for Indian Chief. Moll and Hanson (1984) also reported data for ear number, and, in both experiments, the increase in ear number was at a lower rate in Indian Chief (b = 0.031 ears cycle^{-1}) than in Jarvis (b = 0.0565 ears cycle^{-1}).

Crosses between the Jarvis and Indian Chief populations developed

Table 8–19. Responses for grain yield after 10 cycles of full-sib family selection in Jarvis and Indian Chief. Adapted from Moll and Hanson (1984).

Cycles of selection	Jarvis		Indian Chief		Jarvis × Indian Chief	
	Exp. 1	Exp. 2	Exp. 1	Exp. 2	Exp. 1	Exp. 2
				Mg ha^{-1}			
C0	5.02	7.36	5.77	8.54	6.22	8.93
C4	5.69	--	5.67	--	6.85	--
C8	6.79	9.03	6.48	8.49	7.45	10.77
C10	6.57	8.85	6.41	8.92	7.35	11.18
C8 and C10‡	--†	8.94	--†	8.70	--†	10.98
b, Mg ha^{-1} cycle^{-1}	0.176	0.166	0.081	0.025	0.122	0.226
Change, %§	30.9	21.5	11.1	1.9	18.2	23.0

† Data were not available.   § Change relative to C10 or C8 and C10.
‡ Data from C8 and C10 were combined.

by full-sib family selection were evaluated in the same experiments. Responses in the population crosses were similar to those for Jarvis; 2.06% cycle^{-1} for crosses vs. 2.62% for Jarvis (Table 8–19). Midparent heterosis increased from 13.5% in the C0 crosses to 19.7% in the C10 crosses. Response to selection in Jarvis was reflected in the population crosses. The differences in response to full-sib family selection in Jarvis and Indian Chief were discussed by Moll and Hanson (1984) relative to genetic divergence, effective population size, and number of ears plant^{-1}. It seems the effectiveness of full-sib family selection also was related to the initial yield levels and number of ears plant^{-1} in Jarvis and Indian Chief. The Indian Chief C0 had 15.6% greater yield (Table 8–19) and 34% greater ear number than the Jarvis C0 (Moll and Hanson, 1984). After 10 cycles of full-sib family selection, Jarvis was 2.6% greater yielding than Indian Chief but had fewer ears per plant than Indian Chief (1.63 for Indian Chief vs. 1.54 for Jarvis). Number of ears increased 54.5% with 10 cycles of full-sib family selection for grain yield in Jarvis and 21.6% in Indian Chief. Full-sib family selection was effective for increasing number of ears, an important component of yield, in Jarvis. Hence, a portion of the difference in response of Jarvis and Indian Chief to full-sib family selection may be due to the initial yield level in Indian Chief, enhanced by a greater frequency of ears per plant.

Full-sib family selection also has been used extensively by breeders at CIMMYT (1982). One of the problems encountered in the breeding and selection of tropical corn has been the tall, leafy nature of the plant, and, consequently, a low grain-to-stover ratio (harvest index). A selection study was initiated within and among full-sib families of 'Tuxpeno Crema 1' to improve its harvest index. Twenty cycles of selection increased the harvest index from 0.30 to 0.49, which is similar to U.S. Corn Belt materials (Table 8–20). Correlated changes with selection for an improved harvest index included 47.6% decreased plant height, 67.6% greater grain yield, and 9% less total dry matter. Full-sib family selection, therefore, was effective for improving the primary trait (harvest index), associated

Table 8–20. Response to within and among full-sib family recurrent selection for reduced plant height in Tuxpeño Crema 1. Adapted from CIMMYT (1982).

Cycles of selection	Plant ht.	Grain yield	Total dry matter	Harvest index
	cm	——— Mg ha^{-1} ———		
0	273	4.05	14.94	0.30
6	211	5.54	14.75	0.38
9	203	5.67	15.32	0.39
12	196	6.18	15.37	0.41
15	173	6.73	15.12	0.46
17	156	6.23	13.10	0.47
20	143	6.79	13.60	0.49
bl	−6.1 ± 0.5	0.12 ± 0.02	−0.07 ± 0.05	0.020 ± 0.005
Change, %	−47.6	67.7	−9.0	63.3

with changes in the desired direction for the other traits. Because harvest index is a ratio of grain to total dry matter, the correlated changes would be expected to provide an increase in the harvest index; greater grain yield and less total dry matter, which can be achieved by reducing plant stature. An index, therefore, rather than a single trait was used in selection. Johnson et al. (1986) evaluated the same population after 15 cycles of selection. Selection resulted in a linear reduction of 2.4% cycle^{-1} in plant height from 282 to 179 cm. With the reduction in plant height, optimum plant density increased from 48 000 to 64 000 plants ha^{-1}, and yield increased 2.1% cycle^{-1}. Yield improvement was correlated with a linear increase in harvest index from 0.30 for the C0 to 0.45 for the C15.

Full-sib family selection also has been used at CIMMYT (1984) to increase grain yield (Table 8–21). Data from evaluation trials after four and five cycles of full-sib family selection in eight tropical populations showed an average yield increase of 5.9 or 1.3% cycle^{-1} (Pandey et al., 1986). Response to selection, however, varied among populations, ranging from 0.2% cycle^{-1} for 'Tuxpeno Caribe' to 9.5% for 'Cogollero' and 9.1% for 'Amarillo Cristalino-1'. Rate of response to selection was related to the original yield level of the populations. Yield of Amarillo Cristalano-1 C5 was 5.27 Mg ha^{-1} (9.1% increase) vs. Tuxpeno Caribe C5, which yielded 6.21 Mg ha^{-1} (0.2% increase). A more favorable comparison was for the 'La Posta' population because yield increased from 6.12 Mg ha^{-1} for the C0 to 6.58 Mg ha^{-1} for the C4, a 7.5% yield increase at a greater yield level. On the average, full-sib family selection was effective in reducing the days-to-silk (-0.6% cycle^{-1}), plant (-1.1% cycle^{-1}) and ear (-1.8% cycle^{-1}) height, and increasing number of ears plant^{-1} (0.9% cycle^{-1}).

Singh et al. (1986) effectively used full-sib family selection to increase the level of prolificacy in the open-pollinated cv. Partap. Selection was practiced at two plant densities of 44 444 and 166 666 plants ha^{-1}. Linear response per cycle for number of ears per plant was significant at both densities, but the response at the lower density (0.06 ears or 5.5%) was

Table 8–21. Average response to full-sib family selection for grain yield, days-to-silk, and plant height for eight tropical populations. Adapted from CIMMYT (1984).

	Traits		
Cycles of selection	Grain yield	Days-to-silk	Plant ht.
	Mg ha^{-1}	no.	cm
C0	5.88	67.2	229.2
C4–C5†	6.23	65.4	218.4
Response, %	5.93	−2.6	−4.6
Range, %	0.16–9.46	−4.4–1.4	−9.0–3.8
Response cycle^{-1}, %	1.27	−0.6	−1.0
Range, %	0.03–1.89	−0.9–0.3	−1.9–0.8

† Four cycles of selection completed in three populations and five cycles completed in five populations.

greater than at the higher density (0.04 ears or 3.6%). A significant correlated increase of 4.5% cycle^{-1} in grain yield was obtained. Although there were some differences in correlated responses at the two plant densities, Singh et al. (1986) concluded full-sib family selection may be effective in developing higher-yielding, earlier-maturing, and shorter-statured genotypes.

Full-sib family selection has not been used as extensively as half-sib family or inbred progeny selection. In certain situations, full-sib family selection is effective and appropriate. In some situations (e.g., international testing), full-sib family selection is useful to provide an adequate amount of seed for testing, relative ease in producing the seeds, and progeny vigor where vigor is important to establish stands and compete with other plants. Full-sib selection has been used effectively for developing improved CIMMYT corn populations and providing flexibility in the types of cultivars that can be used in national programs; i.e., improved populations, improved full-sib families, hybrids, and extraction of inbred lines (Pandey et al., 1986).

8–2.3.2 Interpopulation Selection

Because of the importance of the phenomenon of heterosis in hybrid corn, selection methods that emphasize cross performance are of interest. Interpopulation selection methods arose from the opposing advocates of the relative importance of overdominance vs. partial-to-complete dominance of loci acting in an additive manner as the genetic basis for heterosis. Definitive evidence supporting the opposing views was not available. Thus, Comstock et al. (1949) developed reciprocal recurrent selection to permit selection of both types of genetic effects in selection among half-sib family crosses produced between two populations. From theoretical considerations, Comstock et al. (1949) concluded that under no conditions would reciprocal recurrent selection be more than slightly inferior to selection methods that emphasized selection for either specific (Hull, 1945) or general combining ability (Jenkins, 1940). Direct response for interpopulation selection methods is, therefore, measured in the population crosses, and indirect response is determined from the populations themselves. The populations for the cycles of selection are formed by intermating progenies that had superior performance in crosses with the opposing population; i.e., the opposing advanced populations are the respective testers.

Yield has been the primary trait of selection for the interpopulation selection methods. Because of the complexity for developing progenies and the greater heritability of other traits considered for selection, interpopulation selection methods have not been considered in selection for maturity, pest resistance, stalk quality, plant stature, prolificacy, and cold tolerance. Consequently, the number of interpopulation selection studies is less than for intrapopulation selection.

8–2.3.2.1 Reciprocal Recurrent Selection. Reciprocal recurrent se-

lection was the original method suggested by Comstock et al. (1949), and it has received greatest attention in corn breeding. The method includes two genetically broad-based populations (e.g., A and B) with good performance that are of interest to breeding programs. Two sets of half-sib families are produced and evaluated. Plants in a population A are selfed and crossed to a sample of plants from B. Similarly, plants in population B are selfed and crossed to a sample of plants from A. Both sets of half-sib families are evaluated in replicated trials repeated over environments. S_1 progenies of S_0 plants having superior testcross performance are intermated to form the next cycle of selection. Cycles of selection are repeated using the latest cycle populations to produce the testcrosses. Except for the modifications suggested by Paterniani (1978) and Paterniani and Vencovsky (1977) the mechanics of conducting reciprocal recurrent selection are the same as those described by Comstock et al. (1949).

Reciprocal recurrent selection programs were initiated to test the method, and the two programs that have had the longest selection history include Jarvis and Indian Chief and Iowa Stiff Stalk Synthetic (BSSS) and Iowa Corn Borer Synthetic #1 (BSCB1). Jarvis and Indian Chief are open-pollinated cultivars whereas BSSS and BSCB1 are synthetic cultivars formed by intermating 16 (BSSS) and 12 (BSCB1) selected lines. Data from both programs have been reported on a regular basis during the course of selection, and only a brief summary of the data available will be included.

Moll and Hanson (1984) reported progress following 10 cycles of reciprocal recurrent selection in Jarvis and Indian Chief for grain yield and number of ears (Table 8–22). The selection criterion was yield of ear corn, and care was taken to avoid selection for any other trait. Data from two experiments were available to estimate direct response in the population crosses. Although the yield difference between the two experiments was 1.70 Mg ha^{-1}, the estimates of linear regression coefficients (0.153 and 0.202 Mg ha^{-1}cycle^{-1}) and percentages of response (19.8 and 20.9%) following selection were similar. Direct response, therefore, was about 2% cycle^{-1} of selection. Correlated responses in Jarvis and Indian Chief were different, but consistent for the two experiments. Average response in Jarvis was 0.160 Mg ha^{-1}cycle^{-1}, whereas a negative response of -0.078 Mg ha^{-1}cycle^{-1} was realized in Indian Chief. Indian Chief C0 was 15.6% greater yielding than Jarvis C0, but following 10 cycles of reciprocal recurrent selection Jarvis C10 was 18.8% greater yielding than Indian Chief C10. Relative yields of the two populations were nearly equal at the C4. The 24.4% yield increase in Jarvis paralleled the 20.4% yield increase in the population cross. Midparent heterosis increased from 13.8% for the C0 population cross to 28.9% for the C10 population cross. High-parent heterosis also increased form 6.2 to 18.7%, but there was a reversal in the high parent.

Moll and Hanson (1984) also noted a change in response at the C8, which suggested selection reached a plateau following the eighth selection

Table 8-22. Grain yield and ear number response after 10 cycles of reciprocal recurrent selection in Jarvis and Indian Chief. Adapted from Moll and Hanson (1984).

Cycles of selection	Yield			Ear plant⁻¹		
	Jarvis	Indian Chief	Jarvis by Indian Chief	Jarvis	Indian Chief	Jarvis by Indian Chief
	——— Mg ha⁻¹ ———			——— no. ———		
Experiment 1						
C0	5.02	5.77	6.22	0.99	1.30	1.25
C4	5.49	5.57	6.48	1.23	1.41	1.37
C8	6.59	5.43	7.77	1.54	1.46	1.56
C10	6.36	5.36	7.45	1.63	1.55	1.66
b†	0.157	−0.041	0.153	0.066	0.023	0.041
Response, %‡	26.7	−7.1	19.8	64.6	19.2	32.8
Experiment 2						
C0	7.36	8.54	8.93	1.01	1.38	1.29
C8	9.31	7.76	10.77	1.63	1.50	1.75
C10	8.66	7.34	10.84	1.68	1.73	1.83
C8 + C10	8.98	7.55	10.80	1.66	1.62	1.79
b†	0.162	−0.114	0.202	0.070	0.029	0.055
Response, %‡	22.0	−11.6	20.9	64.4	17.4	38.9

† b = regression coefficient with Mg ha⁻¹ cycle⁻¹ for yield and number of ears plant⁻¹ cycle⁻¹ for ear number.
‡ Change in mean for last cycle of selection relative to the C0.

cycle. They explored several reasons for the possible plateau, including divergence, inbreeding depression, environmental effects, and changes in ears per plant (Table 8–22). Full-sib selection (Table 8–16) caused divergence for additive effects, whereas reciprocal recurrent selection utilized additive effects of Jarvis and dominance effects from Indian Chief. The changes in response between the C8 and C10 occurred when differences involving dominance occurred. This change may be related to the unique environments available for testing, but the changes occurred for both the full-sib and reciprocal recurrent selection methods, which were conducted in alternate years. Thus, the environmental effects did not seem to be a plausible explanation. Inbreeding depression did not seem reasonable because population crosses as well as the populations per se, had a similar trend. Ears plant⁻¹ have been shown to be associated with greater yields. Ears plant⁻¹ increased 64.5% in Jarvis and 18.3% in Indian Chief, but by the C8 ear number was similar for both populations (Table 8–22). Hence, they hypothesized that genetic adjustments may be required for the greater sink capacity of prolific plants. They concluded, however, that the lack of response may be transitory, and that future selection may cause changes different from those experienced following 10 cycles of selection.

Smith (1983, 1984) presented a detailed analysis following seven cycles of reciprocal recurrent selection in BSSS and BSCB1. Preliminary data for different cycles of selection and Smith's (1983, 1984) data for grain yield are summarized in Table 8–23. Grain yield was the primary trait of selection, but there was also selection for European corn borer resistance, root and stalk quality, and maturity. At the C5, individual S_1 plants from selected S_1 progenies were used to produce the half-sib families, and all evaluation trials were machine planted and harvested. Also,

Table 8–23. Grain yield response of populations per se and after one generation fo selfing following reciprocal recurrent selection in BSSS and BSCB1 and their crosses and half-sib family and inbred progeny selection in BS13 and crosses with BSSS(R) and BSCB1(R).

Cycles of selection	Smith (1983) Per se	Selfed	Martin & Hallauer (1980) Per se	Tanner (1984) Per se	Smith (1984) Per se	Helms (1986) Per se	Selfed
				Mg ha⁻¹			
BSSSC0	5.97†	3.53†	5.00†	4.81†	--	3.85†	2.51
BSSS(R)C4	6.24	3.84	5.32	--	6.43†	4.56	2.76
BSSS(R)C7	6.89	4.23	5.24	5.89§	7.11§	5.18¶	3.04¶
BSSS(R)C10	--‡	--	--	--	--	5.31	3.66
Response, %	15.4	19.8	4.8	22.4	37.9	45.8	
BSCB1C0	5.34	3.64	5.18	4.73	--	--	--
BSCB1(R)C4	5.52	3.38	5.18	--	5.68	--	--
BSCB1(R)C7	5.61	3.16	4.74	3.70†	5.10	--	--
Response, %	5.1	−13.2	−9.5	−21.8	--	--	--
BSSSC0 × BSCB1C0	7.31	4.16	5.85	5.94	--	5.13	--
BSSS(R)C4 × BSCB1(R)C4	7.90	3.60	6.74	--	8.60	--	--
BSSS(R)C7 × BSCB1(R)C7	9.13	4.95	7.07	8.34	9.08	6.38#	--
BSSS(R)C10 × BSCB1(R)C10	--	--	--	--	--	7.30	--
Response, %	24.9	19.0	20.8	40.4	--	42.3	--
BS13(HT) ×BSSSC0	6.62	4.67	--	--	--	5.39	--
BS13(HT)C7 × BSSS(R)C7	8.53	5.57	--	--	--	6.49	--
BS13(HT)C7 × BSCB1C0	7.33	4.84	--	--	--	--	--
BS13(HT)C7 BSCB1(R)C7	9.00	4.46	--	--	--	6.89	--
BS13(S)C4 ×BSSS(R)C10	--	--	--	--	--	7.32	--
BS13(S)C4 × BSCB1(R)C10	--	--	--	--	--	7.45	--
LSD (0.05)	0.588	0.588	0.532	0.656	0.590	0.469	0.469

† Each data point is an average of 20 observations for Smith (1983), 30 observations for Martin and Hallauer (1980), 16 observations for Tanner and Smith (1987), 20 observations for Smith (1984), and 30 observations for Helms (1986).
‡ No data were obtained.
§ Data were obtained in C8 by Tanner and Smith (1987) and Smith (1984).
¶ Data were averaged for C6 and C8 by Helms (1986).
# Data were for C6 by Helms (1986).

during the cycles of selection, changes were made in plant densities, amounts of fertilizer applied, types of herbicides applied, and field husbandry in seedbed preparation. A selection index that included grain yield, stand, lodging, and grain moisture was used to make selections in later cycles (Smith et al., 1981a, b). Hence, the definition of grain yield has changed with cycles of selection, and the emphasis in selection for other traits also has changed during the cycles of selection. Another important contrast in comparison with Jarvis and Indian Chief is that only 10 rather than 20, superior S_1 progenies were intermated to form the next cycle population.

Direct response for grain yield has been consistent and positive in all evaluations, ranging from 3 to 4% cycle^{-1} of selection. Indirect response in the populations themselves follows a trend similar to that reported in Jarvis and Indian Chief; BSSS responded to selection (2–3% cycle^{-1}) whereas BSCB1 did not significantly change (Smith, 1983) or had a significant decrease (Tanner and Smith, 1987). Because of the changes in experimental procedures, Smith (1983) estimated the progress for two intervals (C0-C4 and C4-C8) of selection. Improvements in grain yield for the crosses were 0.247 ± 0.033 Mg ha^{-1}cycle^{-1} for cycles C0-C4 and 0.361 ± 0.045 Mg ha^{-1}cycle^{-1} for cycles C4-C8. The difference in rate of cross improvement (0.115 ± 0.068 Mg ha^{-1}) was significant, suggesting that machine harvesting and use of S_1 plants in making testcrosses increased response to selection. The observed response, averaged over all cycles, was 4.7% cycle^{-1} or 1.4% yr^{-1} assuming 3 yr cycle^{-1}.

Smith (1983) also included crosses of BS13(HT) with BSSS(R) and BSCB1(R). Gain for grain yield of BS13(HT) $\times$ BSCB1(R) was estimated as 0.229 ± 0.020 Mg ha^{-1}cycle^{-1}, and the differences for the two intervals were not significant. This estimate is similar to 0.231 ± 0.037 Mg ha^{-1}cycle^{-1} following five cycles reported by Eberhart et al. (1973). Though BS13(HT) was developed with use of the Ia13 double cross as tester, the response to selection was similar with BSCB1(R). Crosses between the two selected strains of BSSS, BS13(HT), and BSSS(R), were estimated to be 0.219 ± 0.031 Mg ha^{-1}cycle^{-1} for cycles 0–4 and 0.586 ± 0.069 Mg ha^{-1}cycle^{-1} for cycles 4–7. The cross of BS13(HT)C7 $\times$ BSSS(R)C7 yielded 8.53 Mg ha^{-1} vs. 5.97 Mg ha^{-1} for BSSSC0. Similar responses of crosses between BSSS strains were reported by Russell and Eberhart (1975), Stangland et al. (1982), and Oyervides and Hallauer (1986). Smith (1983) also estimated a parameter, DQI, which is a measure of the loss of heterozygotes in the population per se. He estimated DQI to be -0.036 ± 0.004 Mg ha^{-1} in BSCB1(R), -0.022 ± 0.003 Mg ha^{-1} in BSSS(R), and -0.013 ± 0.003 Mg ha^{-1} in BS13(HT). The lack of response in the populations themselves could be due to the loss of heterozygotes due to drift and selection. Because only 10 progenies were recombined between cycles of selection, the effects of drift could be important. Helms (1986) also obtained a significant estimate for the loss of heterozygotes due to drift in BSSS(R) and BSCB1(R).

Other plant and ear trait data have been obtained in the evaluations of BSSS(R) and BSCB1(R). In most instances, the trends, though not generally statistically significant, are in the desirable direction: decrease in ear height, decrease in stalk lodging with no change in root lodging, greater number of ears, 1% increase in grain moisture at harvest, and an increase in ear length and kernel weight. These changes occurred in both the populations themselves and population crosses. Days to flowering decreased in BSSS(R) and the population crosses but increased in BSCB1(R). Because BSSSC0 was 5 to 7 d later flowering than BSCB1C0, the changes in flowering were a result of selection in producing the half-sib families.

Reciprocal recurrent selection has been shown to be effective for improvement of the population crosses for the limited number of studies conducted. Indirect responses in the populations themselves have not been as consistent (Martin and Hallauer, 1980). Except for the studies involving Jarvis and Indian Chief and BSSS and BSCB1 the number of cycles of selection have not been adequate to determine the long-term effects of reciprocal recurrent selection (Collier, 1959; Gevers, 1975; Darrah et al., 1978; Paterniani and Vencovsky, 1977). It would be desirable if further information were available for population types, effective population sizes, and different environments tested to determine the utility of reciprocal recurrent selection for applied corn breeding programs.

8–2.3.2.2   Reciprocal Full-sib Selection.   The principles of reciprocal full-sib selection are similar to those for reciprocal recurrent selection. The one basic difference is that full-sib families rather than half-sib families are produced for evaluation. Rather than producing reciprocal testcrosses of individual plants in one population with a sampling of individuals from the other population, reciprocal crosses (full-sib families) between individual plants are evaluated. The most effective method is to include two populations that have a strong two-ear expression (Hallauer and Eberhart, 1970). Full-sib families are produced by making reciprocal crosses between plants (one from population A and one from population B) on one ear of each plant and selfed seed is produced on the other ear. Full-sib families are evaluated, and S_1 progenies of the superior families are recombined for the respective populations. Direct selection is for the population crosses and indirect selection is for the populations themselves, which is the same as for reciprocal recurrent selection. One other suggested advantage of reciprocal full-sib selection is that the method is directly applicable for development of single crosses (Hallauer, 1967, 1973; Lonnquist and Williams, 1967).

The most extensive data available for reciprocal full-sib selection are those for 'Iowa Two-ear Synthetic' (BS10) and 'Pioneer Two-ear Composite' (BS11) following seven cycles of selection (Hallauer, 1984). Direct response for grain yield was 2.1% cycle^{-1} in the population cross; indirect response was 2.7% cycle^{-1} for BS10 and 2.4% cycle^{-1} for BS11. Heterosis increased over cycles of selection from 6.3% for the C0 population cross to 28.4% for the C7 population cross. Heritability of full-sib families averaged 61% over cycles of selection with no evidence that the variability among full-sib families had decreased from the C0 ($\sigma_G^2 = 3.53 \pm 0.50$) to the C7 ($3.33 \pm 0.62$). Six hybrid checks were included with the full-sib families in the evaluation trials for each cycle of selection. Relative to the mean of the six hybrid checks, the mean of the full-sib families was changed from three deviations below the mean of hybrid checks to three standard deviations above the mean of the hybrid checks (Fig 8–8). Grain yield was emphasized in selection, but attention also was given to maturity and standability. Relative to the common check hybrids, the changes, although not significant in all instances, have been in the desired direction (Hallauer, 1984).

Reciprocal full-sib selection has been effective for improvement of BS10, BS11, and the population cross. Rate of response to selection was similar to the other intra- and interpopulation selection methods. Originally, the method was designed to maximize selection for specific combining ability with use of prolific plants to produce the full-sib families and S_1 progenies. Prolific plants, however, are not a prerequisite for use of reciprocal full-sib selection (Hallauer, 1973). Full-sib families can be obtained by use of S_1 progenies. Marquez-Sanchez (1982) also has suggested modifications of reciprocal full-sib selection that do not require

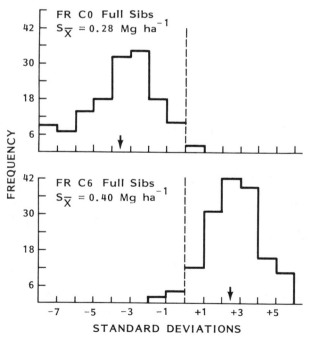

Fig. 8–8. Grain yield distribution of the C0 and C6 full-sib families relative to the mean of the six check hybrids. Arrows indicate means of the full-sib families and dashed lines indicate means of six check hybrids. Adapted from Hallauer (1984).

prolificacy and reduce the rate of inbreeding. Use of S_1 progenies requires an additional generation, but the effectiveness of selection among and within S_1 progenies may compensate for the additional generation; Smith (1983) suggested that use of S_1 progenies contributed to the continued improvement of reciprocal recurrent selection. Though specific combining ability between pairs of genotypes is emphasized, Hoegemeyer and Hallauer (1976) reported that in crosses among elite lines selected by reciprocal full-sib selection general combining ability was of greater importance than specific combining ability. Significant specific combining ability effects were more frequent among crosses selected by reciprocal full-sib selection and were of greater magnitude than among crosses of unselected lines. But the elite lines selected within pairs of genotypes also had good general combining ability with other elite lines. These results for reciprocal full-sib selection agree with the results Horner (1985) reported with recurrent selection using an inbred tester.

It seems, so far, that additive genetic effects with partial to complete dominance are of greater importance and most methods seem to respond to selection for these effects. Some methods of selection (e.g., inbred progeny) may be more effective than others, but the comparisons do not permit definite discrimination among selection methods. The results noted by Moll and Hanson (1984) following 10 cycles of reciprocal recurrent selection in Jarvis and Indian Chief may be a reflection of the genetic adjustments being made for different types of genetic effects. Hoegemeyer and Hallauer's (1976) data were derived for the C0. Different effects may be of greater importance if the single crosses were derived following 10 cycles of reciprocal full-sib selection. Comparisons of responses to selection, either direct or indirect, between reciprocal full-sib selection and other selection methods are limited.

Jones et al. (1971) compared reciprocal recurrent selection based on either half-sib or full-sib family selection algebraically and with computer simulation. The relative performance of the two methods depended on selection intensity and the environmental variance. Reciprocal full-sib selection was superior to reciprocal half-sib selection at less intense selection and when the environmental variance was large relative to the genetic variance. An example from some empirical estimates of variability among half-sib and full-sib families suggested that the selection differential should be 1.2 times greater for full-sib than for half-sib family selection to give similar response. The simulation studies indicated that full-sib family selection tended to give greater response in the mean of the population cross than half-sib family selection for the genetic models considered. For a genetic model that assumed complete dominance, gene frequencies of 0.5, and no linkage, full-sib family selection gave greater response than half-sib family selection in the population cross throughout 20 cycles of selection; the superiority of full-sib family selection increased as the number of cycles of selection increased. West et al. (1980) reported comparisons of S_1 progeny vs. reciprocal full-sib selection after two cycles of selection within and among three populations. Response to S_1 progeny selection was greater than reciprocal full-sib selection in the populations that were selfed and random mated one generation. Direct response from S_1 progeny selection was greater, therefore, than the indirect effects of reciprocal full-sib selection. But the direct effects of reciprocal full-sib selection were equal to the indirect effects of S_1 progeny selection in the population crosses. Lantin and Hallauer (1981) compared 10 cycles of mass selection for prolificacy with five cycles of reciprocal full-sib selection for yield in BS10 and BS11. Reciprocal full-sib selection was more effective than mass selection for grain yield improvement and other agronomic traits. Both methods were equally effective for increasing number of ears plant^{-1}, but the correlated response of yield with increased ear number by mass selection was not effective. Because seed on two ears was required and yield was emphasized in reciprocal full-sib selection, there was a significant response for both traits.

8–2.3.3 Relative Response Among Methods

Comparisons of the relative effectiveness of different recurrent selection methods, and the types of genetic effects affected by selection are, in most instances, confounded by the different populations included in selection. Different methods were initiated at different times with different populations. Direct comparisons of relative effectiveness of reciprocal recurrent selection in BSSS and BSCB1 are not possible with reciprocal full-sib selection in BS10 and BS11 because of different genetic backgrounds of the two pairs of populations.

The differences that arise from different methods and different populations can be illustrated from the results reported for one method of selection conducted in different populations and different methods of selection in two common populations. Paliwal and Sprague (1981) reported gains following two or three cycles of full-sib family selection for improved yield within 13 populations. Gain cycle^{-1} of selection ranged from 0.8 to 9.8%. The effectiveness of full-sib family selection obviously depended on the relative levels of grain yield and genetic variability of the populations, and, consequently, realized response to full-sib family selection. Average gain cycle^{-1} of selection for the 13 populations was 3.4%, which is similar to the average gains reported by Sprague and Eberhart (1977) and Hallauer and Miranda (1981).

Darrah (1986) summarized gains from selection for yield improvement that included five (mass, ear-to-row, S_1, half-sib, and full-sib) intrapopulation and three interpopulation methods of recurrent selection. Three populations were used: 'Kitale Synthetic II' (KSII) and 'Ecuador 573' (Ec573), which were shown to have good specific combining ability (Eberhart et al., 1967), and the population cross 'Kitale Composite A' (KCA). KCA was the base population for the intrapopulation methods that also included different levels of selection intensities for mass and ear-to-row selection methods. Grain yield was the primary trait in selection, and gains from selection were expressed on a per year basis. Averaged over selection variants, gains per year from selection in KCA were 2.3% for mass and 2.9% for ear-to-row selection for 10 cycles of selection. After five cycles of S_1, half-sib, and full-sib selection, gains from selection were 0.9, 0.71 (average of three testers), and 3.6% yr^{-1}, respectively.

Ear-to-row, S_1 progeny, and reciprocal recurrent selection were conducted using the KSII and Ec573 populations. KSII did not respond to selection, whereas Ec573 responded to ear-to-row (4.6% yr^{-1} for 10 cycles) and S_1 progeny (3.5% yr^{-1} for five cycles) but not to reciprocal recurrent selection. Hence, only Ec573 had a direct response to ear-to-row and S_1 progeny selection, and neither population had an indirect response to reciprocal recurrent selection. Direct response in the population cross of KSII and Ec573 after five cycles of reciprocal recurrent selection was 2.8% yr^{-1}, but no response was realized in the population crosses following 10 cycles of ear-to-row and five cycles of S_1 progeny selection. Reciprocal recurrent selection was effective for improving the population cross, but it was not effective in the improvement of either KCII (-0.005 Mg ha^{-1}) or Ec573 (0.066 Mg ha^{-1}). Responses to reciprocal recurrent selection were similar to those reported in other populations following five cycles of selection.

Although critical comparisons among methods of selection have not been available, the data reported by Paliwal and Sprague (1981) and Darrah (1986) suggest the rates of response, on the average, are similar among methods and among populations. Rates of response will vary among populations because of the genetic compositions of the populations (Paliwal and Sprague, 1981). But the rates of response among methods for the same populations also vary depending on how one measures the direct and indirect responses to selection.

8–2.3.4 Germ Plasm

Because genetic variability seems adequate in most populations for selection to be effective, the choice of population(s) to include for selection is important. It does not seem in most instances that adequate attention was given to the populations considered for selection. But this should not be considered a valid criticism for the populations used in past selection programs because comprehensive data were not available. BSSS and BSCB1 were included for reciprocal recurrent selection because BSSS had above average stalk quality and BSCB1 was developed by intermating inbred lines identified as having resistance to first-generation European corn borer. BS10 and BS11 were included for reciprocal full-sib selection because they both had a strong tendency for prolificacy. In neither instance, was there previous information relative to comparative mean performance with other possible populations, heterosis expressed in population crosses, inbreeding depression, total genetic variability, and data on other traits necessary for use of the populations improved by selection. Kitale Synthetic II and Ecuador 573 (Eberhart et al., 1967) and

BS10 and RSSC (Lambert, 1984) are exceptions because performance data were used to make the choice of populations to include for selection. Lonnquist and Gardner (1961) evaluated crosses of populations and how choice of population(s) can be made by performance per se and in crosses. Further information has been obtained in the past 20 yr on population performance, but data are not adequate or complete for the germplasm available to the breeders (Hallauer and Miranda, 1981). Ideally, the population(s) of choice would have performance traits that are acceptable for the target area and adequate genetic variability to permit effective selection. The only recourse is to survey populations available, glean information available, and consult with colleagues who have had experience with populations. Long-term nature of the recurrent selection methods requires a commitment for the populations chosen for selection.

8–2.4 Integration with Applied Breeding Programs

Recurrent selection methods should not be considered as separate entities from other aspects of productive applied breeding programs. If properly conducted, materials derived from recurrent selection programs can contribute to the other facets of programs dedicated to line and hybrid development (Eberhart et al., 1967). Genetic advance depends on conducting systematic selection programs that develop improved germ plasm sources for applied breeding programs. Systematic genetic improvement of germ plasm sources will contribute to realized genetic advance in the lines and hybrids extracted by conventional plant breeding methods.

Comparisons between recurrent selection techniques and pedigree selection methods were reported by Sprague (1952) and Duvick (1977). Sprague (1952) compared the increase in oil percentage of the corn kernel following five generations of pedigree selection and two cycles of recurrent selection. Depending on the comparison made, recurrent selection was 1.3 to 3.0 times more effective than pedigree selection. Duvick (1977) summarized data from four half-sib family recurrent selection programs and two pedigree selection experiments. Average rate of gain in grain yield yr^{-1} was 0.071 Mg ha^{-1} for recurrent selection and 0.068 Mg ha^{-1} for pedigree selection, assuming 3 yr to complete one cycle of recurrent selection and 13.3 yr to complete one cycle of pedigree selection. Duvick (1977) considered that rates of gain were essentially equal for the two systems, and that there was not an advantage in using one system compared with the other.

Recurrent and pedigree selection, however, should not be considered in opposition to one another. Rather, the two systems should complement each other. The goals of the two systems are different, but the ultimate objective is the same—contribute to genetic gain (Fig 8–4). The primary goal of recurrent selection is to develop improved sources of germ plasm that can be submitted to pedigree selection methods. The maximum benefits of recurrent selection programs can only be realized by the ap-

Table 8-24. Agronomic data for four single crosses evaluated at four locations for 10 yr (1976-1985) in Iowa.[†]

Cross	Yield	Grain moisture	Lodging		Dropped ears
			Root	Stalk	
	Mg ha⁻¹			%	
B14A × Mo17	7.28	20.6	11.4	7.6	1.0
B37 × Mo17	7.74	22.6	16.4	16.6	1.2
B73 × Mo17	8.51	22.4	15.2	9.8	1.7
B84 × Mo17	9.56	22.9	12.1	10.8	0.8
LSD (0.05)	0.38	0.5	4.8	3.8	--

[†] 37 location-yr environments; three tests discarded. Yield: B84 > B73 > B37 > B14A = 12.3, 10.0, and 6.3%, respectively.

plication of pedigree selection methods to isolate superior genotypes. Recurrent selection, therefore, was designed to enhance the probabilities of obtaining superior genotypes by pedigree selection. Recurrent selection was not designed to replace pedigree selection, but to supplement.

An example that illustrates the complementary benefits of recurrent selection and pedigree selection is provided by BS13 (Russell, 1986). BS13 was under half-sib family selection, and the S_1 progenies of the superior half-sib families used in recombination were also included in the breeding nursery for further selection, inbreeding, and testing. Four selections were eventually identified and released for use as possible parental stocks to produce hybrids. Lines, which have proved to be useful in hybrids, include B14 and B37 from the C0, B73 from the C5, and B84 from the C7 cycles of BS13. Each of the lines was crossed to a common inbred tester (Mo17) and evaluated at four Iowa locations for 10 yr (Table 8–24). In crosses with Mo17, B73 contributed a yield gain of 11.4% compared with B37, and B84 had a yield gain of 11.3%% over B73. Total yield gain from the first C0 release (B14) to the C7 release (B84) was 31.3%, which is 4.5% cycle⁻¹ for the lines derived from selection within BS13. It is in this context that recurrent selection can be an integral part of applied breeding programs.

8–3 HETEROSIS AND HETEROTIC PATTERNS

The pure-line hybrid concept suggested by Shull (1909) has been used to exploit heterosis in corn breeding. Heterosis in crosses between cultivars and between inbred lines has been measured and is usually expected. Although heterosis is expressed in crosses, the specific genetic basis of heterosis in corn has not been resolved. Because of the divergent views presented to explain the phenomenon of heterosis, extensive research relative to breeding methods, inbred-line development, choice of testers, and selection methods for germplasm improvement has been conducted to determine the genetic basis of heterosis. The two primary views for the genetic basis of heterosis are generally classified as being due to primarily overdominant effects at individual loci vs. loci showing partial to complete dominance. Definitive evidence supporting the opposing views has not been obtained. Studies to determine the primary importance of different types of genetic effects have been conducted in genetic materials that ranged from genetically broad-based populations to crosses between inbred lines. Relative importance of the different types of genetic effects have varied relative to the types of materials studied, which is to be expected. Estimates of genetic effects with genetically broad-based populations suggest additive effects are of greater importance than either dominance (e.g., Gardner et al., 1953; Robinson et al., 1958; Gardner and Lonnquist, 1959) or epistatic effects (e.g., Silva and Hallauer, 1975). Comparisons of different types of crosses (single, three-way, and double) among inbred lines and different generations (parents, F_1, F_2, F_3, and backcrosses) suggest nonadditive effects may be of some importance (Martin and Hallauer, 1976; Schnell and Singh, 1978; Moreno-Gonzalez and Dudley, 1981; Melchinger et al., 1986). The divergent results can be interpreted to support one of the opposing views for the cause of heterosis. Generally, it seems that the preponderance of evidence supports the view that heterosis in corn results from the accumulation of loci with alleles having partial to complete dominance. Some of the theories suggested for the expression of heterosis and evidence and interpretation supporting the different theories have been presented by East (1936), Jones (1945, 1952), Crow (1948), Brieger (1950), and Sprague (1953).

The formulation of the conditions necessary for heterosis of quantitatively inherited traits was given by Falconer (1981). He derived an expression for midparent (average of parents) heterosis (H) that considered the joint effects of all loci that differed in the cross of two particular lines or populations as $H = \Sigma dy^2$; d includes the effects due to dominance and, therefore, heterosis depends on the occurrence of dominance; and y^2 is the square of the difference in allele frequency between the lines or populations and determines the amount of heterosis expressed in the cross. Some level of dominance and differences in allele frequency, therefore, are necessary for the expression of heterosis. If either one is zero, no heterosis will be expressed, and the expression does not preclude partial, complete, or overdominant effects being the predominant types of effects. Falconer (1981) also emphasized that directional dominance is necessary, but the absence of heterosis does not preclude dominance at individual loci because of cancellation effects among loci. Heterosis is also specific for each cross, because different crosses will have different Σdy^2 values.

The differences in allele frequency and the directional dominance of the loci of the inbred lines and cultivars included in crosses are generally unknown. Hence, empirical data obtained from experiments that included the crosses and their respective parents were the only methods available to determine the level of heterosis expressed in the crosses. The estimates of heterosis in the crosses were expressed either on the basis of the midparents or the higher parents. The newer methods of analyses at the molecular level may refine the techniques for estimating heterosis of crosses in the future. Development of genetic markers either with allozymes (Kahler et al., 1986) or with restriction fragment length polymorphisms for unique DNA sequences (Helentjaris et al., 1986) provides genetic information for inbred lines and cultivars. Based on the differences for the genetic markers, the expression of heterosis may become more predictable.

Beal (1877, p. 41–59) reported the first yield data from controlled crosses of corn cultivars. After Beal's experiments, crosses among cultivars were frequently produced and compared with the parental cultivars. Richey (1922) summarized data for 244 crosses and reported 86.5% were above midparent, 13.5% were below midparent, and 67.8% exceeded the higher parent. The empirical data established that some crosses were better than the higher parent, but their predictability was not based on any observed trends. Richey (1922) stated, "In such more or less haphazard crossing, therefore, the chances seem about equal of obtaining a cross that is or is not better than the better parent." Because of the emphasis given to exploiting heterosis of crosses among inbred lines, interest in variety crosses decreased after the first two decades of the 20th century. Interest in cultivar crosses was revived when consideration was given to the selection of populations to include in recurrent selection programs and to determine the level of relationship among cultivars. Information of this nature, for example, was reported by Robinson et al. (1956) for open-pollinated cultivars adapted to southeastern USA and by Lonnquist and Gardner (1961) for open-pollinated cultivars adapted to the U.S. Corn Belt. Moll et al. (1962) and Moll et al. (1965) extended the range of inferred diversity, based on geographical origin, among the open-pollinated cultivars included for producing variety crosses. Moll et al. (1962) reported that the relative heterosis expressed in the variety crosses agreed with the original classification of the presumed genetic divergence of the parental cultivars. But the concept of genetic diversity also seemed to have limits relative to the maximum expression of heterosis. Moll et al. (1965) found that the heterosis expressed in crosses between cultivars hypothesized to be most genetically diverse was less than heterosis between cultivars considered to be less genetically diverse.

Hallauer and Miranda (1981) included summaries of the heterosis expressed between cultivar crosses, including the data summarized by Richey (1922). The expression of heterosis, on the average, was similar for the studies conducted before 1932 and after 1955. The comparisons included 611 cultivars and 1394 cultivar crosses. For the cultivar crosses tested before 1932, 80.9% exceeded the midparent, whereas 90.0% of the cultivar crosses tested after 1955 exceeded the midparent. There was no general consensus among the studies in choice of cultivars included in the crosses and how the information on heterosis of the crosses was related to the overall classification of cultivars for establishing heterotic patterns. Some evidence suggested greater heterosis was expressed more consistently by crossing cultivars having different endosperm types (Richey, 1922), but other studies that included cultivars with different endosperm types (dent, flint, and floury) showed that the expressed heterosis was as great between cultivars having similar endosperm types as between those having different endosperm types (Paterniani and Lonnquist, 1963). Estimates of heterosis and combining ability are available in the literature, but the estimates are restricted to the specific sets of parent cultivars included. If a specific variety was included with a different set of cultivars, different estimates would be obtained. Because of the manner in which the parental cultivars were chosen and the absence of common checks to compare estimates among the different trials, information is not available to suggest the primary heterotic patterns among cultivars adapted to a given area.

The preferred approach would be to cross all of the landrace cultivars in a diallel series of crosses to permit direct comparisons. This approach, however, is no more feasible than crossing all of the available inbred lines in a diallel series of crosses to determine the best single crosses. The testcross method of evaluations was developed to permit preliminary screening of inbred lines to estimate their relative combining abilities. It seems a similar approach will be needed to determine the heterotic patterns among cultivars. But the same problem exists as in the choice of testers to evaluate inbred lines; i.e., what are the best testers? Can we assume that Reid Yellow Dent and Lancaster Sure Crop are the best testers to compare U.S. Corn Belt cultivars?

An example that illustrates the problem of identifying heterotic patterns among corn cultivars was addressed by Tsotsis (1972) and Kauffmann et al. (1982). They acknowledged there was a vast number of germplasm collections available that had not been evaluated and used by U.S. corn breeders. They selected nine open-pollinated cultivars and evaluated the 36 crosses among the cultivars for yield, and calculated the midparent heterosis for each cross (Table 8–25). Because the Reid Yellow Dent by Lancaster Sure Crop heterotic pattern has received greatest use in the U.S. Corn Belt programs, they were interested in determining if other possible heterotic patterns were available. Midparent heterosis for Reid Yellow Dent by Lancaster Sure Crop was 15%, which was similar to Lancaster Sure Crop by Hays Golden (15%), Reid Yellow Dent by Osterland Yellow (14%), and Reid Yellow Dent by Hays Golden (14%). The Leaming by Midland cross showed 21% midparent heterosis while Midland by Lancaster Sure Crop (33%) and Leaming by Lancaster Sure Crop (34%) also exhibited heterosis greater than the Reid Yellow Dent by Lancaster Sure Crop. Based on the data in Table 8–25, the heterotic pattern of Midland by Leaming was chosen to develop breeding populations for future development of lines that could be used to exploit the heterosis expressed in hybrids of their crosses. One breeding population included those cultivars which in crosses to Leaming were similar to Midland, and the second breeding population included those cultivars which in crosses with Midland were similar to Leaming. In an attempt

Table 8-25. Yields (Mg ha⁻¹) of nine U.S. open-pollinated cultivars (diagonal) and their diallel crosses (above diagonal) and estimates of midparent heterosis (%, below diagonal) of the cultivar crosses. Adapted from Kauffmann et al. (1982).

					Cultivar					
Cultivar	Midland	Lancaster Sure Crop	Reid Yellow Dent	Leaming	Krug	Late Clarage	Osterland Yellow	Golden Glow	Hay's Golden	$\bar{x}$ (Mg ha⁻¹)
Midland	6.04	6.99	6.22	6.43	6.21	6.06	6.72	5.98	6.09	6.34
Lancaster Sure Crop	133†	4.49	5.79	6.05	5.71	6.17	5.62	5.67	5.41	5.93
Reid Yellow Dent	107	115	5.53	4.85	4.63	4.84	5.86	5.11	5.93	5.41
Leaming	121	134	96	4.54	5.88	5.77	6.28	5.77	6.40	5.93
Krug	112	120	88	123	5.02	5.61	6.49	5.21	6.64	5.80
Late Clarage	104	123	87	115	106	5.53	5.92	5.88	6.11	5.79
Osterland Yellow	124	121	114	134	132	115	4.80	5.72	5.71	6.04
Golden Glow	111	123	100	125	107	115	120	4.72	6.14	5.69
Hays Golden	111	115	114	136	134	117	118	128	4.89	6.05
$\bar{x}$	115.4	123.0	102.6	123.0	115.2	110.2	122.2	116.1	121.6	5.89

† Estimates of midparent heterosis calculated as $F_1[(P_1 + P_2)/]^{-1} \times 100$.

to classify other U.S. Corn Belt accessions, crosses of 111 cultivar accessions to Midland and Leaming were evaluated; Midland and Leaming were selected as the testers based on information from the diallel. Based on the crosses with Midland and Leaming, 27 accessions were assigned to the Midland population and 48 were assigned to the Leaming population. Recurrent selection was initiated within the two populations to develop useful germplasm sources for future line development that would be expected to have above average heterosis in crosses between the two populations. This approach seems logical for identifying a heterotic pattern, and then including additional germ plasm in the populations that reacted similarly to the selected heterotic pattern.

Heterotic patterns are of great concern to corn breeders, but it does not seem they were established in a systematic manner. They were established empirically by relating the heterosis observed in crosses with the origin of the parents included in the crosses. Heterotic patterns per se were not developed in an evolutionary sense, but heterotic patterns do occur because of selection, both artificial and natural, that has occurred in the development of the open-pollinated cultivars. The heterotic pattern identified by Tsotsis (1972) and Kauffmann et al. (1982) included two open-pollinated cultivars that originated in different regions of the U.S. Corn Belt. Leaming was developed in southern Ohio, and Midland was developed in southeastern Kansas. Allele frequencies affecting grain production in Leaming and Midland were undoubtedly different for many loci because of the different forces of selection in the two distinct regions. The presumed allele frequency differences for grain production were reflected in the phenotypic differences of the two open-pollinated cultivars: Midland has a later, taller, wider leaf plant type having a shorter ear with greater number of kernel rows than Leaming which was earlier, has less robust plant type, and has a more slender ear. Midland also has greater drought tolerance and greater resistance to first-generation European corn borer.

Tsotsis (1972) and Kauffmann et al. (1982) reported 15% midparent heterosis for Lancaster Sure Crop by Reid Yellow Dent, which was 50% less than for Midland by Lancaster Sure Crop (33%), Leaming by Lancaster Sure Crop (34%), Leaming by Osterland Yellow (34%), or Leaming by Hayes Golden, (34%) (Table 8-25). Average midparent heterosis for all crosses that included either Leaming or Lancaster Sure Crop as one parent was 23%. Except for Leaming and Lancaster Sure Crop, a common trend for the level of heterosis expressed in the crosses included a cultivar from the eastern areas of the U.S. Corn Belt crossed with one from the western areas. These trends seem reasonable and consistent because there would be less exchange of materials and chances of intermating of cultivars developed in the more remote areas. Hence, the chances for greater differences in allele frequencies seem reasonable.

Kauffmann et al. (1982) selected the Leaming by Midland heterotic pattern because of considerations other than the level of heterosis. The example illustrates, however, how the concept of heterotic patterns was established. They were derived by breeders based on experience, breeding, and testing. Kauffmann et al. (1982), for example, could have established other heterotic patterns. After heterotic patterns have been established, further breeding efforts are planned to enhance and optimize the selected heterotic pattern. The selected heterotic patterns have a strong impact on the breeding materials chosen for selection. It may be difficult for mature breeding programs to make significant changes in heterotic patterns if they are heavily involved with line recycling. If changes are made in heterotic groups, a significant portion of the recovered lines may not be directly applicable.

Heterotic patterns are arbitrary. Although the Lancaster Sure Crop by Reid Yellow Dent heterotic pattern has received greatest attention in the U.S. Corn Belt, other heterotic patterns that included Leaming and Midland are considered. The number of heterotic patterns considered by a research organization depends on the extent of the breeding programs. They tend to be open-ended populations with other materials being added on the basis of their tested affinities. The choice of heterotic pattern used depends on the frequency of high-performance hybrids obtained for the lines derived from the respective source populations. Lines obtained from respective heterotic patterns tend to complement one another to maximize hybrid performance. The single-cross hybrid, B73 $\times$ Mo17, illustrates how inbred-line components contribute to the single cross (Fig. 8–9). B73 was derived from Iowa Stiff Stalk Synthetic (an improved synthetic population representative of Reid Yellow Dent) and Mo17 was derived by pedigree selection from the cross of (187-2 $\times$ C103). C103 was derived from Lancaster Sure Crop whereas 187-2 was derived from Krug, an improved strain of Reid Yellow Dent. B73 having greater number of kernel rows with greater number of kernels per ear and Mo17 having greater ear length and kernel size produce a consistently high performance single cross. The example for B73 $\times$ Mo17 also illustrates that the distinction between heterotic patterns is not absolute. Mo17 was derived from a cross that included one line with Reid Yellow Dent germ plasm (187-2) and one line with Lancaster Sure Crop germ plasm (C103). Mo17 is phenotypically more similar to C103 than 187-2 and is more similar to C103 in crosses with lines having Reid Yellow Dent germ plasm. Although not as good as B73 $\times$ Mo17, B37 $\times$ B73 also is a good performance single cross, and both lines were derived from Iowa Stiff Stalk Synthetic. B37 was derived from the first sampling, whereas B73 after five cycles of half-sib family selection (Table 8–24). It seems that the effects of sampling and selection were sufficient to cause different frequencies of alleles, resulting in heterosis in the cross of B37 $\times$ B73. Heterotic patterns do not preclude identifying superior crosses within populations, but the chances are greater between populations of identified heterotic patterns.

Concerns for heterotic patterns are not limited to U.S. Corn Belt.

Fig. 8–9. An illustration of the heterotic pattern commonly used in the U.S. Corn Belt. B73 × Mo17 includes one line (B73) representative of Reid Yellow Dent and one line (Mo17) representative of Lancaster Sure Crop.

Heterotic patterns are considered in other important corn production areas of the world, where they seem to have arisen in the same manner as those for the U.S. Corn Belt. In Europe, a common heterotic pattern includes U.S. dent lines crossed with European flint lines; good seedling vigor for cool conditions with earlier maturity of the European flints complement the high productivity of U.S. dent lines. But the French single-cross, F2 × F6, included two lines derived from the same open-pollinated cultivar, and the single cross was widely used in Europe. In Mexico, crosses that include lines from ETO Composite and Tuxpeño are an important heterotic pattern, but the wealth of germ plasm available in Mexico would not preclude other important heterotic patterns. Flint-by-dent crosses are widely used in Brazil and usually include lines derived from either Cateto by Tuxpeño or Suwan I by Tuxpeño. Because of the requirement for endosperm type in Argentina, a common heterotic pattern includes crosses of flint lines with recovered flint lines, which have a dent background to enhance productivity. The heterotic pattern of ETO Composite by Tuxpeño has been widely considered in tropical regions of the world, but the heterotic pattern that includes Suwan I and Tuxpeño seems to be receiving greater attention.

Based on testcross evaluations of tropical races, Goodman (1985) listed 10 heterotic patterns that have been identified and exploited by breeders in the tropical areas: Cuban Flint by Tuxpeño, Cuban Flint by

Tuson, Tuson by Tuxpeño, Coastal Tropical Flint (Caribbean Flint) by Chandelle, Cuban Flint by Coastal Tropical Flint, Tuxpeño by Coastal Tropical Flint, Tuson by Chandelle, Tuxpeño by ETO, Chandelle by Haitian Yellow, and Cuban Flint by Perla. For the 10 heterotic patterns, only eight races are included because Cuban Flint and Tuxpeño were included in four crosses and Tuson, Coastal Tropical Flint, and Chandelle in three crosses. The crosses among the tropical races illustrated the same pattern shown by Kauffmann et al. (1982) for crosses among domestic open-pollinated cultivars; i.e., some races or cultivars expressed greater heterosis in crosses than others. One interesting heterotic pattern was Tuson by Tuxpeño because both races expressed heterosis in crosses with Cuban Flint. To reduce the number of heterotic patterns for breeding purposes in the tropical areas, it seems emphasis should be given to the races Tuxpeño, Cuban Flint, Tuson, Coastal Tropical Flint, and Chandelle. Two of the races (Tuxpeño and Caribbean Flint) also were selected by Gerrish (1983) for adaptation and use in temperate areas. For breeders in the temperate areas to exploit the heterosis among the tropical areas, the tropical materials will need to be adapted to temperate areas to provide valid comparisons with adapted materials. Oyervides-Garcia et al. (1985) and Gutierrez-Gaitan et al. (1986) compared crosses between and within cultivars from Mexico and the U.S. Corn Belt and tested in Mexico and the western U.S. Corn Belt; no useful information was obtained for crosses between Mexican cultivars and between Mexican and U.S. Corn Belt cultivars in the U.S. Corn Belt because the adverse photoperiod response masked the expression for other traits. Goodman (1985), however, identified Tuson by U.S. Southern Dents as a potentially useful heterotic pattern for use in southern U.S. corn breeding programs.

Heterotic patterns are a fact-of-life and important to corn breeders. Greater emphasis is given to the consideration of heterotic patterns by some than by others. Some heterotic patterns have been used in the past and will continue to be considered, whereas others will be identified and developed. Some heterotic patterns are transported to other areas of the world where the materials are adaptable. If heterotic patterns are important in some areas, but the materials are unadapted, efforts will be made to adapt and exploit them in crosses with native materials (Gerrish, 1983).

8–4 GENOTYPE × ENVIRONMENT INTERACTION

Genotype × environment (GE) interaction is the differential performance of genotypes across environments. The existence of GE interaction necessitates that breeders evaluate genotypes in more than one environment to obtain repeatable rankings of genotypes. The detection of GE interaction by means of an analysis of variance, however, does not indicate how the genotypes are interacting. If there are g genotypes and e environments then there are $(ge)!/g!e!$ possible types of interactions

(Allard and Bradshaw, 1964). The large number of interactions possible demonstrates the need for types of analysis that would summarize for the breeder how genotypes interact with one another across environments.

The class of methods, called *stability analysis,* has provided the tools by which breeders can summarize the overall performance of cultivars across environments. The definition of a stable cultivar varies with the type of stability analysis used, but generally breeders want cultivars with high mean yield that respond to improved environments. The predominant type of stability analysis used has been regression of cultivar means on environmental means. This type of analysis has been referred to as joint regression analysis (Freeman, 1973).

Joint regression analysis of GE interaction involves the regression of cultivar means on some index of the environment. The analysis provides an estimate of the linear response of individual genotypes to environments (b_i) and an estimate of the deviations of the observed values from the predicted values (deviations mean square). The computational methodology has been presented and will not be reviewed (Eberhart and Russell, 1966; Perkins and Jinks, 1968; Wright, 1971; Freeman and Perkins, 1971; Shulka, 1972; Hardwick and Wood, 1972; Hill, 1976; Lin et al., 1986; Westcott, 1986). Although joint regression analysis has been frequently used in many species, statistical problems have limited its application and interpretation. The primary problems with the analysis are defining the environmental index and assuming a linear relationship between GE interaction effects and the environmental index.

The environmental index is the measure of the environment used to assess its inherent productivity. For lack of a better measure, most joint regression analyses have used the mean of the cultivars grown in an environment as the index [environmental mean] (Yates and Cochran, 1938; Finlay and Wilkinson, 1963; Eberhart and Russell, 1966; Perkins and Jinks, 1968; Tai, 1971). Unbiased estimates of the regression coefficients are obtained only if the environmental index is measured without error (Freeman and Perkins, 1971; Hardwick and Wood, 1972; Hill, 1976). When the environmental mean is used as the index of the environment, the regression coefficient is biased and often underestimated (Hardwick and Wood, 1972; Wright, 1976). The bias depends on the ratio of the environmental variation to the error mean square and the number of cultivars. When the ratio and/or the number of cultivars are large the bias will be small, but not necessarily negligible. Reducing the bias to zero seems to be impossible, because all measures of environmental productivity will have an associated error. Therefore, the environments and numbers of cultivars should be selected to minimize the bias.

Freeman and Perkins (1971) criticized the use of environmental means as the index because the environmental means are not independent of the cultivar means. Freeman (1973) later qualified this criticism stating that when working with two-way tables one may consider the marginal means fixed when making inferences about values in the table. This is equivalent to working with a model containing only fixed effects (Hill, 1976). However, this does not eliminate problems associated with the distribution of degrees of freedom (df) in the analysis of variance table (Freeman and Perkins, 1971). In the Eberhart-Russell (1966) analysis, the environment and GE sums of squares (SS) are pooled (to obtain the environment within genotype SS) and the resulting g(e-1) (where there are g varieties and e environments) df are partitioned into three parts: the environment-linear SS with one df; the variety $\times$ environment-linear SS with g-1 df; and pooled deviations with g(e-1) df. The pooled deviations SS are then partitioned into g components (one for each variety) with e-2 df. This approach has been criticized because the environment-linear SS are equal to the environment SS, but they are assigned one and e-1 df, respectively (Freeman and Perkins, 1971; Freeman, 1973). The assignment of df in the Eberhart-Russell analysis should be e-1 for the environment-linear SS; g-1 for the cultivar $\times$ environment-linear SS and (g-1)(e-2) for the pooled deviations SS. This assignment of df does not allow the deviation MS for each cultivar to be tested for significance against the error MS. The deviation MS for individual cultivars, however, can be compared using Bartlett's test for comparing g variances each with e-2 df (Freeman and Perkins, 1971). Freeman and Perkins (1971) presented the appropriate analysis when using an independent index of the environment.

Several alternative measures of environmental effects are available other than the environment mean (Freeman and Perkins, 1971). One suggestion is to divide the replications into two groups and use one replication as a measure of environmental effects and use the others to measure the interaction. At least three replications would be needed to obtain an estimate of experimental error. Another suggestion is to include checks solely for the purpose of estimating environmental effects. Presumably, one would want the checks to be elite cultivars that are widely grown in the region. Many checks, however, may be needed to provide an accurate assessment of the environments. Freeman and Perkins (1971) have suggested that the coefficient obtained from regression of the mean of all cultivars on the environmental index can be tested to see if it differs significantly from one, and the residual from this regression can be tested against the experimental error. If neither of these tests is significant, the environmental index can be regarded as an estimate of the true environmental effects.

Mather and Caligari (1974) suggested that each cultivar be regressed on the mean of the other cultivars. This method avoids the criticisms made by Freeman and Perkins (1971) when regressions are done on the environmental mean. Also, additional cultivars do not need to be grown to assess environmental effects. The computational aspects of the method proposed by Mather and Caligari are increased and may be time consuming without the aid of computer software capable of matrix algebra.

Moll et al. (1978), using the modification suggested by Mather and Caligari (1974), showed that the regression coefficients are a function of responsiveness of cultivars to environments and the correlation of the responses of cultivars in different environments.

Pederson et al. (1978) suggested the gene pool concept as a measure of the environmental index. They defined the gene pool as ". . . a sample of genes representative of currently acceptable or commercially grown germ plasm for a specific geographic area." The concept was suggested to allow comparisons between cultivars grown in different locations and years. One problem associated with this approach is that environmental means will tend to increase with time, as older cultivars are replaced with improved cultivars, even though the environments may not have improved. The procedure also seems to be plagued with statistical problems, because cultivar means and stability parameters are estimated from different environments.

Perhaps the most desirable environmental index would be one composed of climatic, edaphic, and management variables (Hardwick and Wood, 1972; Westcott, 1986). Westcott (1986) states that the linear regression of cultivars on environmental means cannot be regarded as trustworthy and cannot be recommended for analysis of GE interactions. He supports further investigations into the effects of environmental variables on crop yields. Knight (1970) reached a similar conclusion, but recognized that the joint regression analysis ". . . is a valuable technique for the plant breeder when making a broad study of a collection of varieties." To use environmental variables in the study of GE interactions, variables are needed that explain a significant portion of the variation among environments. Little work has been reported along these lines because it is difficult, time-consuming, and expensive to measure these types of variables. Hardwick and Wood (1972) have shown how regression on environmental variables relates to regression on environment means.

The joint regression analysis requires the assumption that the relationship between the GE interaction and the environmental index is linear. This assumption has been the subject of criticism and is considered a valid reason for not using the analysis (Westcott, 1986). The linear relationship between cultivar and mean performance will hold when variation in cultivar performance between environments can be described by a linear function of environmental variables (climatic, edaphic, and management) and when the residuals from this regression are not significantly larger than experimental error (Hardwick and Wood, 1972). Westcott (1986) criticized the linear regression approach because outliers can influence the estimates of stability parameters for a cultivar. Westcott (1986) cited examples which supported his position, but failed to cite the many examples where the linear regression approach has performed well. To illustrate the effect of one or two environments on estimates of stability parameters, Westcott used an example with only six environments. While it is difficult to determine the number of environments needed to accurately estimate stability, clearly more than six are needed. In many applied breeding programs, cultivars may be grown in 20 to 100 environments and one or two deviant environments will have little effect on the estimates of stability parameters from the joint regression analysis.

Breeders often have data available from cultivar trials in which the cultivars vary among locations and years. These trials often contain checks which may be the same across locations within a year, but may vary with years as higher yielding checks become available. The analysis of these types of data using conventional joint regression analyses is difficult if not impossible because the experiment is unbalanced (not all genotype-environment cells contain an observation). Zhang and Geng (1986) have proposed a technique using joint regression analysis to handle this situation. Their method involves dividing the environments into three periods. Period I includes the trials in which older check cultivars are used. Period II is a transition period where older check cultivars are grown with newer check cultivars. Period III is the environments in which only the newer check cultivars are grown. The method involves regressing the check means on the environmental means in Period II. The cultivars under test are then regressed on the older check cultivars in Period I and all other cultivars are regressed on the newer check cultivars. Comparisons among cultivars are made possible by reparameterizing the stability parameters using the regression of the check cultivars on the environment means. Zhang and Geng (1986) demonstrated the use of their method for cotton (*Gossypium hirsutum* L.) cultivar trials.

Other methods for analysis of GE interaction are available. These include cluster analysis, principal components analysis, geometrical methods, and stochastic dominance. Westcott (1986) has reviewed the use of these methods and provides an inclusive reference list. He concludes his review by stating that the linear (joint) regression analysis is unsatisfactory and that the defects of this method cannot be overcome by cluster analysis or principal component analysis. Westcott (1986) recommends further research into environmental variables, stochastic dominance, multidimensional scaling, and correspondence analysis. Westcott, however, failed to recognize the plant breeding aspects of joint regression analysis and the fact that the analysis has been successful in identifying cultivars breeders wish to select.

Prior to the development of stability analyses, comparisons of cultivar stability were based primarily on GE mean squares and components of variance. These measures indicate little about how the cultivars are interacting and simply measure the magnitude of the interaction. The GE interaction SS can analytically be partitioned into differences in cultivar responsiveness and changes in rank order across environments (Cockerham, 1963; Moll et al. 1978). Corn breeders are primarily interested in discarding cultivars that show large rank order changes across environments; however, as Comstock (1977) has suggested, plant breeders and quantitative geneticists have devoted little effort to how rank order changes relate to genetic and GE variance.

Comstock and Moll (1963) emphasized the importance of defining both the cultivars and environmental reference populations when studying GE interactions. Robinson (1959) illustrated this point by comparing the results of Sprague and Federer (1951) from trials conducted in Iowa with results of yield trials conducted in North Carolina. The results of Sprague and Federer's study indicated that cultivar-year interactions were of primary importance, whereas Robinson found the second-order interaction cultivar-year-location was more important than the first-order interactions. Although the results of the two studies are not directly comparable because they involve different types of genetic material, they do indicate that results of GE interaction studies cannot be extrapolated to regions outside of the target populations of environments.

Scott (1967) demonstrated that it was possible to select for stability when defined as a cultivar that exhibits the least yield variation over all environments in the test. The response of cultivars to environments is primarily a property of the line or additive genetic effects; however, the stability of cultivars (the deviation from regression in the Eberhart-Russell model) seems to be associated with all types of gene action (Eberhart and Russell, 1966, 1969). The ability of corn to respond to environments by producing two ears seems to be a primary mechanism contributing to the stability of corn hybrids (Collins et al., 1965; Russell and Eberhart, 1968; Russell and Prior, 1975; Cross, 1977).

Eberhart and Russell (1966) analyzed several sets of corn yield trials and reported that cultivars with high mean yield generally have regression coefficients greater than one. This relationship suggests that by selecting for high mean yield, breeders are also selecting for cultivars that respond to favorable environments (Rosielle and Hamblin, 1981). Gama and Hallauer (1980) compared hybrids that were selected and unselected for grain yield and found no differences in the frequency of stable hybrids in the two groups. A significant correlation was reported between mean yield and the regression coefficient, although it was too small to be of predictive value. They suggested that hybrids should first be screened for mean yield over environments and then selection should be made among the elite hybrids for stability over environments.

The selection of the type of stability analysis to use in ranking cultivars depends on both definition of stability used and the objectives of the breeding program. Some breeders desire cultivars which perform consistently across environments (i.e., yield the same in all environments) while others desire cultivars that respond to improved environments. The first type of stability has been referred to as the "biological concept of stability" and the second type has been referred to as the "agronomic concept of stability" (Becker, 1981). Becker (1981) correlated four measures of stability using data from five different crops. The four measures of stability were variation among environments within cultivars, coefficient of regression, the deviations mean square from the Eberhart-Russell analysis, and Wricke's (1962) ecovalence. The correlations between the within variance and regression coefficient, and between ecovalence and the regression mean square were large ($r \geq 0.81**$) and consistent across crops. Becker (1981) made three points concerning these relationships: (i) the regression coefficient is equivalent to the within variance as a measure of stability according to the biological concept; (ii) the deviation mean square is equivalent to ecovalence as a measure of the agronomic concept of stability; and (iii) the use of different concepts of stability will lead to different rankings of genotypes, because the two parameters are uncorrelated with each other. Becker (1981) concluded that the two parameters from the Eberhart-Russell analysis, when used together, provide the most comprehensive analysis of stability according to the defined concepts.

Nor and Cady (1979) studied the feasibility of using physical measures of the environment as the environmental index. They had measurements on rainfall, mean daily temperature, and growing degree days for each of 36 environments. The environmental index was the first principal component from the pooled sample variance-covariance matrix of the environmental variables. The model used was the same as that suggested by Freeman and Perkins (1971) for independent environmental indices. They compared this technique with the Eberhart-Russell analysis. The rank correlation between coefficient of regressions for the two techniques was 0.69 with 16 df. There were some notable rank changes, but in general the two techniques ranked variety responses similarly. They did not compare deviation mean squares for the two techniques. The favorable results from this study indicate the need for more extensive studies on the use of environmental variables as indices of environments.

There are two differing views on the types of environments to use in developing and testing corn breeding materials (Lambert, 1984). One view contends that corn breeding materials should be developed and evaluated in environments typical of the target population of environments. The premise of this view is that some environmental factors will often be limiting and breeding materials should be developed under these conditions. The other view contends that breeding materials should be developed under nonlimiting environmental conditions and the breeding material should not be under stress for any environmental factors. The premise of this view is that nonlimiting environmental conditions will allow the expression of all genes, providing for greater genotypic variation and ultimately larger genetic gains.

Rosielle and Hamblin (1981) considered the theoretical aspects of selection for yield in stress and nonstress environments. They considered selection for tolerance to stress conditions and selection for high mean productivity. If yield in nonstress environments is defined as Y_1 and yield in stress environments is defined Y_2, then selection for tolerance is equivalent to selecting for high $Y_2 - Y_1$ and selection for mean productivity is equivalent to selecting for high $(Y_1 + Y_2)/2$. They found that selection for tolerance will normally result in a reduction in mean yield in nonstress environments (Y_1) and to obtain a yield increase in nonstress environments genetic variation in stress environments must be greater than in nonstress environments. Selection for mean productivity, however, will usually result in a yield increase in both stress and nonstress environments. This would only result in a yield decrease in nonstress environments when genetic variance in stress environments is greater than in nonstress environments, and when there is a negative genetic correlation between yield in stress and nonstress environments. Rosielle and Hamblin (1981) concluded that the most desirable approach would be to choose testing sites to be representative of population of environments for which the breeder wishes to improve mean yield.

Lambert (1978, 1984) initiated a reciprocal recurrent selection program in which testing was done under high-yield environmental conditions and under normal environmental conditions. He reported that genetic variance for grain yield was greater under high-yield environmental conditions than under normal environmental conditions, except in 1 yr when the high-yield environment was stressed by hail damage. The genetic correlations between the high-yield environment and normal environment were positive and 8 of the 12 correlations reported were significantly different from zero. These results seem to support the conclusion of Rosielle and Hamblin (1981) that selection should be conducted in environments representative of the target population of environments.

Determining the location of test sites is perhaps the most difficult challenge facing corn breeders. Generally, when a breeder is moving into a new locality little information is available on GE interaction. Corn breeders are often assigned the task of breeding for a particular maturity zone, which reduces the target population of environments considerably, although decisions on the locations of test sites still must be made so that efficient use of available resources are made and differences among cultivars are maximized. Without prior knowledge of the nature of the GE interaction in a given target population of environments, breeders must locate test sites based on prior knowledge of the germ plasm, climatic, edaphic, and management factors, and the overall objectives of the breeding program. Once information on GE interaction becomes available it can be used to add and delete locations so that available resources are used most efficiently.

The optimum allocation of test sites depends on whether breeders are developing cultivars for a specific set of environmental conditions or whether the cultivars will be grown over a wide range of environments. With corn there is a tendency for cultivars to spread geographically throughout the maturity zone to which they are adapted. The consequences of this are that corn breeders must develop cultivars that perform consistently throughout the range of environments likely to be encountered in a maturity zone.

Several criteria have been proposed for selecting test sites. Allen et al. (1978) concluded that if environments vary substantially in their value as test sites it is because of variation among them in the correlation between cultivar value in test environments and cultivar value in the target population of environments. Hamblin et al. (1980) suggested that criteria for choosing test sites should be: (i) that yields of selected cultivars at the test site consistently correspond to their yield over the range of environments for which they are intended; (ii) that the test site maximize yield differences among cultivars; and (iii) that the test site be consistently high yielding. Brown et al. (1983) presented a method to choose optimum test sites by first clustering test sites based on environmental variables and then identifying the optimum test sties within clusters by linear regression on a cultivar index. Correlations between environments and the concept of a reference set of cultivars have been suggested as a method to select test sites representative of a target population of environments (Fox and Rosielle, 1982a).

Multivariate techniques have been used extensively for grouping environments and cultivars to improve the efficiency of breeding programs. The primary technique used has been cluster analysis. The performance of the cluster technique depends on the type of data analyzed, the clustering algorithm, and the cluster method (Fox and Rosielle, 1982b; Lin, 1982; Ramey and Rosielle, 1983).

8-5 INDEX SELECTION

Corn breeders are seldom interested in improving one trait at a time. When the correlation between two traits is large and negative, selection for one trait will produce an undesirable correlated response. Klenke et al. (1986) found that four cycles of selection for European corn borer resistance resulted in a corresponding decrease in grain yield; consequently, they concluded that grain yield should be included in the selection criteria when selecting for corn borer resistance. Martin and Russell (1984) reported that three cycles of selection for stalk strength and stalk-rot resistance resulted in significantly reduced grain yields. These are just two of the many examples of undesirable correlated responses that can result from single trait selection.

Index selection is a procedure that combines all the information available on an individual or family to aid in the selection of those with the highest aggregate breeding value. When making selections, breeders often have a mental image of the type of plant or family they wish to select. They combine this image with the data obtained on the family and use the combined information to make their selections. Essentially, breeders are constructing a mental selection index. The mental selection index may work well when a small number of families is evaluated; however, with large numbers of families the procedure lacks repeatability and response to selection is difficult to predict. A formal selection index, when properly constructed, has both repeatability and predictability, which allows statements to be made about future performance before selections are made. The objective of a selection index is to find a linear combination of phenotypic values that maximizes the expected gain in aggregate breeding value.

Smith (1936) developed the first index for selecting plant lines using Fisher's (1936) discriminant function. Hazel (1943) developed the same index using the method of path coefficients and outlined methods for estimating genetic variances and covariances. This index is known as the *Smith-Hazel index*. The Smith-Hazel index is a linear index of the form $I = \Sigma_{i=1}^{n} b_i P_i$, where n is the number of traits in the index, P_i is the observed phenotypic value of the ith trait, and b_i is the weighting factor assigned to the ith trait. The b_i's are calculated to maximize the expected gain in the economic value of an individual or family (aggregate genotype). The aggregate genotype of an individual or family is defined as $H = \Sigma_{i=1}^{m} a_i G_i$, where m is the number of traits used in defining the aggregate genotype, G_i is the genotypic (breeding) value of the ith trait, and a_i is the relative economic value of the ith trait. Maximizing the expected genetic gain in the aggregate genotype is equivalent to: (i) maximizing the correlation of the sample index (I) with true breeding value (H); (ii) minimizing the expected value of the squared deviations between I and H; and (iii) maximizing the probability of correct selection (Williams, 1962). Henderson (1963), Lin (1978), and Baker (1986) reviewed the theory of the construction of selection indices.

Several modifications of the Smith-Hazel index have been developed. One modification is the restricted selection index (Kempthorne and Nordskog, 1959; James, 1968; Cunningham et al., 1970; Lin, 1985). The objective of the restricted selection index is to maximize genetic gain in some traits while holding genetic gain in other traits to zero or some fixed constant (Tallis, 1962). Smith et al. (1981a) suggested that the traits in the index be weighted by the product of their economic value and heritability. These weights are the solutions to the Smith-Hazel index equations when the genotypic and phenotypic correlations are assumed to be zero. The simplified index is nearly as efficient as the Smith-Hazel index when the absolute value of the genetic and phenotypic correlations are <0.30. Lin (1978) reported that estimated error of the genetic correlation has a larger effect on efficiency of index selection than estimated error of heritability.

Sampling errors in the estimation of genotypic and phenotypic variances and covariances can have large effects on the accuracy of the selection index and can cause biases in predicted gains (Lin, 1978). Brim et al. (1959) suggested that each trait be weighted by the relative economic value when sampling errors of parameter estimates are large. This index is called the *base index* (Williams, 1962). The Smith-Hazel index is expected to be more efficient than the base index unless sampling errors of parameter estimates are large (Williams, 1962; Lin, 1978). The primary advantages of the base index are simplicity of use, freedom from error or parameter estimation, and the index can be used in situations where estimates of genetic parameters are not available.

Economic values of the various traits breeders wish to select are rarely known and few studies have been conducted to determine how economic values should be assigned to traits. Because of these difficulties, a class of selection indices that are weight-free have been developed. Elston's (1963) weight-free index (EWF) ranks individuals on the basis of the product of their phenotypic values. Equal value is assigned to the traits by subtracting the minimum acceptable phenotype from all traits before the index is calculated. An additional advantage of EWF is that estimates of genotypic and phenotypic parameters are not needed in its construction. Because EWF is curvilinear, theory is not available to predict gains for this index. However, Baker (1974) found that EWF can be approximated by a linear index (BSD) with weights equal to the reciprocals of the phenotypic standard deviations. Approximate predicted gains can then be calculated using the theory developed by Smith (1936).

The rank summation index (RSI) suggested by Mulamba and Mock (1978) is also weight free. Rank summation index is calculated by ranking the cultivars for the traits of interest and then summing the ranks over traits. If the cultivars are ranked with one being good and there are three traits in the index, then an index value of three would represent the best variety in the sample. The primary advantages of RSI are that genotypic and phenotypic parameter estimates are not needed, the data are transformed so that the phenotypic variances for each trait are identical, and economic values are not needed, although they can be used when known (Crosbie et al., 1980). Crosbie et al. (1980) reported that predicted gains for BSD are good approximations of predicted gains for RSI. Rank summation index is most efficient when heritabilities are high and of similar magnitude among traits, and when the correlations among traits are favorable or approximately zero (Smith et al. 1981b).

The desired gain index (DGI) suggested by Pesek and Baker (1969) does not require specification of economic values, but it does require estimates of genetic variances and covariances. The DGI is calculated by substituting gains the breeder desires for each trait in the predicted gain equation for the Smith-Hazel index and solving the resulting equations for the index weights. Desired gain index is developed under the assumption that desired gains are easier to specify than economic values.

Selection index theory can also be used to make selections based on information from relatives (Henderson, 1963). Information from relatives is used to increase the accuracy of selection defined as the correlation of the sample index with the aggregate genotype. Moreno-Gonzalez and Hallauer (1982) outlined a procedure to combine information on S_2 families per se with information on full-sib families from a reciprocal recurrent selection program. The resulting selection index is superior to reciprocal full-sib selection when the heritability of the trait under selection is low and the advantage is increased when the correlations between the S_2 and full-sib families are large relative to the heritabilities.

Index selection is at least as efficient as independent culling levels and independent culling levels is at least as efficient as tandem selection (Hazel and Lush, 1942; Lin, 1978). The relative efficiency of index selection methods depends on progeny type, number of traits in the index, relative economic values assigned to the traits, selection intensity, and the relative magnitude of the genotypic and phenotypic variances and covariances among traits included in the index. As a general rule, expected genetic gain for one trait from selecting on an index containing (n) traits is only $1/\sqrt{n}$ times as great as selection for that trait alone (Hazel and Lush, 1942.

Long-term recurrent selection experiments using selection indices as the criteria of selection are rare. Generally, studies designed to compare methods of index selection in plants involve only one or two cycles of selection with a different index being used in each cycle of selection. The most common method of comparing selection indices is to use predicted gains and selection differentials. Predicted gains and selection differentials for a given trait from index selection are usually represented as a percentage of the value obtained for single trait selection. Cunningham (1969) presented a method for comparing the relative efficiencies of selection indices.

Subandi et al. (1973) compared two variations of EWF, two Smith-Hazel indices differing only in the economic values assigned to the traits, a base index, and selection for each trait alone using predicted gains. The traits were grain yield, percentage of lodged plants, and percentage of dropped ears. They concluded that EWF would be the most useful because correlations between traits were low, the index does not require specification of economic values, and is parameter free. Compton and Lonnquist (1982) reported on four cycles of intrapopulation full-sib recurrent selection using the index suggested by Subandi et al. (1973). Observed gains for yield averaged 4.7% cycle^{-1}, but no significant changes were reported for percentage of upright plants and plants without dropped ears, although trends were in the desired direction. They concluded that selection based on their index may result in yield gains similar to other studies where selection is for yield per se. West et al. (1980) studied the performance of EWF with replicated S_1 and reciprocal full-sib recurrent selection and concluded that EWF has proved its ability to change traits involved in the index simultaneously in the desired direction.

Widstrom (1974) constructed three selection indices to aid in selection for resistance to ear damage caused by corn earworm [*Heliothis zea* (Boddie)]. The traits included in the indices were corn earworm injury, husk tightness, days to 50% pollen shed, and husk extension. The first index (RS) was the Smith-Hazel index constructed using genotypic and phenotypic covariance matrices obtained from evaluating S_1 lines. The second index (RI) was constructed in the same manner except that standardized direct and correlated responses were substituted for the genotypic covariance matrix. The third index (RSI) was constructed by substituting the standardized direct and correlated responses when selection was for corn earworm injury for the index weights. The indices derived from realized gains are expected to be as efficient as the Smith-Hazel index when expected and observed responses to selection are comparable. Experimental evidence supported this conclusion.

Widstrom et al. (1982) evaluated response to four cycles of S_1 recurrent selection using the three selection indices derived by Widstrom (1974). The selection indices were not modified during the course of the recurrent selection experiment. An additional selection experiment was conducted for corn earworm injury. Significant improvement for corn earworm injury was obtained only for the RSI and RI selection indices. Selection for RI and corn earworm injury tended to increase husk tightness whereas selection for RS and RSI resulted in looser husks. The RSI and RS increased husk extension and RI and corn earworm injury decreased husk extension. All four selection methods resulted in populations that were 1 to 2 d earlier in reaching anthesis. Correlations between traits included in the index were changed over cycles of selection by all selection criteria. These changes were attributed to a breakup of genetic linkages and suggested that new indices should be constructed to exert the desired selection pressure for the traits of interest in future cycles of selection. The authors concluded that RI produced the best results.

Suwantaradon et al. (1975) compared the Smith-Hazel index, base index, and the desired gain index for S_1 recurrent selection to improve seven agronomic traits of corn. Two sets of arbitrary economic values were used with the Smith-Hazel index and in both instances the performance of the index was less than satisfactory because undesirable responses were obtained for four of the seven traits included in the indices. The base index was 95 to 97% as efficient as the Smith-Hazel index and should be used instead of the Smith-Hazel index when the relative economic weights are known, heritabilities are high, and the correlations among the traits are low. When the desired gain index was used the final goals of the program would be obtained after 14 cycles of recurrent selection. The desired gain index is preferred when relative economic values are difficult to specify.

The performance of selection indices is dependent on obtaining accurate estimates of the phenotypic and genotypic variances and covariances. Moll et al. (1975) evaluated the performance of five selection indices and concluded that nonlinear relationships between traits will have considerable effect on the prediction of correlated selection responses. The responses of traits included in the index were more variable than responses to index selection. Kauffmann and Dudley (1979) evaluated seven selection indices designed to improve corn grain yield, percentage of protein, and kernel weight simultaneously. They reported good agreement between observed and predicted responses to index selection and concluded that genetic variance and covariance estimates obtained from

200 half-sib families were sufficiently accurate to be useful in the development of selection indices. Miles et al. (1981) reached a similar conclusion, but found that selection on indices to simultaneously improve resistance to four corn diseases was no more effective than selection for disease score per se.

Crosbie et al. (1980) compared predicted gains for three cold tolerance traits of corn using several selection indices. Predicted gains for DGI were sensitive to the relative amount of economic gain specified for each trait. The Smith-Hazel and base indices ranked lines similarly. There were problems, however, with these indices because the variances for each trait differed substantially, and these indices were designed to maximize gain in the aggregate genotype. The authors suggested that RSI, EWF, or BSD be used to improve composite traits, like cold tolerance, which are composed of individual traits without logical economic values. These indices have the advantage of being parameter free, simple to use, and do not require the specification of economic values.

St. Martin et al. (1982) evaluated the use of restricted selection indices for the improvement of *opaque-2* corn. The indices were constructed to simultaneously improve agronomic and protein and kernel quality characteristics of *opaque-2* corn. They evaluated four classes of indices that differed in the traits included in the indices. The most efficient indices were those with four or five traits. When more than five traits were included the indices were less effective and singular variance-covariance matrices became more frequent. They found that the most effective trait combinations in the indices were not dependent on the recurrent selection scheme under consideration. The most efficient indices relied on direct rather than indirect selection response and these indices were generally free of the problems associated with parameter estimation. They concluded that the successful application of selection indices requires a measure of subjective judgement on the part of the breeder.

Most of the empirical work in corn involving the comparisons of selection indices have generally favored the use of indices that are parameter free and do not require specification of relative economic values. The successful application of selection indices to corn improvement will depend on the goals of the breeding program, the genetic material under selection, and the definition of the aggregate genotype. Selection indices are sensitive to inaccurate estimates of genotypic and phenotypic parameters and changes in relative economic values of the traits. More research is needed on methods of assigning economic values to traits in selection indices. Accurate estimates of variances and covariances are essential if selection indices are to be useful to corn breeders. It is particularly important to have accurate estimates of the covariances, which evidently are the most difficult to estimate. The empirical evidence reviewed suggests that it is not possible to make general statements about the best selection index.

REFERENCES

Acosta, A.E., and P.L. Crane. 1972. Further selection for lower ear height in maize. Crop Sci. 12:165–167.

Allard, R.W., and A.D. Bradshaw. 1964. Implications of genotype-environment interactions in applied plant breeding. Crop Sci. 4:503–508.

Allen, F.L., R.E. Comstock, and D.C. Rasmusson. 1978. Optimal environments for yield testing. Crop Sci. 18:747–751.

Altman, D.W., and R.H. Busch. 1984. Random intermating before selection in spring wheat. Crop Sci. 24:1085–1089.

Anonymous. 1972. Corn. Genetic vulnerability of major crops. NAS-NRC, Washington, DC.

Bailey, T.B., Jr. 1977. Selection limits in self-fertilizing populations following the cross of homozygous lines. p. 399–412. *In* E. Pollak et al. (ed.) Proc. Int. Conf. Quant. Genet., Iowa State Univ., Ames. 16–21 Aug. 1976. Iowa State Univ. Press, Ames.

––––, and R.E. Comstock. 1976. Linkage and the synthesis of better genotypes in self-fertilizing species. Crop Sci. 16:363–370.

Baker, R.J. 1974. Selection indices without economic weights for animal breeding. Can. J. Anim. Sci. 54:1–8.

––––. 1986. Selection indices in plant breeding. CRC Press, Boca Raton, FL.

Balko, L.G., and W.A. Russell. 1980a. Effects of rates of nitrogen fertilizer on maize inbred lines and hybrid progeny. I. Prediction of yield response. Maydica 25:65–79.

––––, and ––––. 1980b. Effects of rate of nitrogen fertilizer on maize inbred lines and hybrid progeny. II Correlations among agronomic traits. Maydica 25:81–94.

Bauman, L.F. 1959. Evidence of non-allelic gene interaction in determining yield, ear height, and kernel row number in corn. Agron. J. 51:531–534.

––––. 1977. Improvement of established maize inbreds. Maydica 22:213–222.

––––. 1981. Review of methods used by breeders to develop superior corn inbreds. Proc. Annu. Corn Sorghum Ind. Res. Conf. 36:199–208.

Beal, W.J. 1877. Report of the professor of botany and horticulture. Michigan Board of Agric., Lansing.

Becker, H.C. 1981. Correlations among some statistical measures of phenotypic stability. Euphytica 30:835–840.

Bogenschutz, T.G., and W.A. Russell. 1986. An evaluation for genetic variation within inbred lines maintained by sib-mating and self-pollination. Euphytica 35:403–412.

Bos, I. 1977. More arguments against intermating F_2 plants of a self-fertilizing crop. Euphytica 26:33–46.

Brieger, F.G., 1950. The genetic basis of heterosis in maize. Genetics 35:420–445.

Brim, C.A. 1966. A modified pedigree method of selection in soybeans. Crop Sci. 6:220.

––––, H.W. Johnson, and C.C. Cockerham. 1959. Multiple selection criteria in soybeans. Agron. J. 51:42–46.

Brown, K.D., M.E. Sorrells, and W.R. Coffman. 1983. A method for classification and evaluation of testing environments. Crop Sci. 23:889–893.

Brown, W.L. 1975. A broader germplasm base in corn and sorghum. Proc. Annu. Corn Sorghum Ind. Res. Conf. 30:81–89.

Burton, G.W. 1982. Developing superior inbreds from exotic germplasm of pearl millet. Crop Sci. 22:653–655.

Busch, R.H., and W.A. Russell. 1964. Hybrid expression of mutations affecting quantitative characters in inbred lines of *Zea mays* L. Crop Sci. 4:400–402.

Carlone, M.R., and W.A. Russell. 1987. Response to three plant densities and four nitrogen levels for four maize cultivars from each of seven ears of breeding. Crop Sci. 27:465–470.

Castleberry, R.M., C.W. Crum, and C.F. Krull. 1984. Genetic yield improvement of U.S. maize cultivars under varying fertility and climatic environments. Crop Sci. 24:33–36.

Centro Internacional Mejoramiento de Maiz y Trigo. 1982. CIMMYT Review 1982. CIMMYT, El Batan, Mexico.

––––. 1984. CIMMYT research highlights 1984. CIMMYT, El Batan, Mexico.

Chase, S.S. 1952. Production of homozygous diploids of maize from monoploids. Agron. J. 44:263–267.

Collier, J.W. 1959. Three cycles of reciprocal recurrent selection. Proc. Annu. Hybrid Corn. Ind. Res. Conf. 14:12–23.

Collins, W.K., W.A. Russell, and S.A. Eberhart. 1965. Performance of two-ear type of corn belt maize. Crop Sci. 5:113–116.

Compton, W.A., and R.E. Comstock. 1976. More on modified ear-to-row selection. Crop Sci. 16:122.

––––, and J.H. Lonnquist. 1982. A multiplicative selection index applied to four cycles of full-sib recurrent selection in maize. Crop Sci. 22:981–983.

––––, R.F. Mumm, and B. Mathema. 1979. Progress from adaptive mass selection in incompletely adapted maize populations. Crop Sci. 19:531–533.

Comstock, R.E. 1964. Selection procedures in corn improvement. Proc. Annu. Corn Sorghum Ind. Res. Conf. 19:87–94.

––––. 1977. Quantitative genetics and the design of breeding programs. p. 705–718. In E. Pollak et al. (ed.) Proc. Int. Conf. Quant. Genet., Iowa State Univ., Ames. 16–21 Aug. 1976. Iowa State Univ. Press, Ames.

––––. 1979. Inbred lines vs. the populations as testers in reciprocal recurrent selection. Crop. Sci. 19:881–886.

––––, and R.H. Moll. 1963. Genotype-environment interactions. p. 164–196. In W.D. Hanson and H.F. Robinson (ed.) Statistical genetics and plant breeding. Pub. 982. NAS-NRC, Washington, DC.

––––, H.F. Robinson, and P.H. Harvey. 1949. A breeding procedure designed to make maximum use of both general and specific combining ability. Agron. J. 41:360–367.

Covarrubias-Prieto, Jorge. 1987. Genetic variability in F_2 maize populations before and after random mating. Ph.D. diss. Iowa State Univ., Ames (Diss. Abstr. 48:923-B).

Crosbie, T.M. 1092. Changes in physiological traits associated with long-term breeding efforts to improve grain yield of maize. Proc. Annu. Corn Sorghum Ind. Res. Conf. 37:206–223.

––––, J.J. Mock, and O.S. Smith. 1980. Comparison of gains predicted by several selection methods for cold tolerance traits of two maize populations. Crop Sci. 20:649–655.

Cross, H.Z. 1977. Interrelationships among yield stability and yield components in early maize. Crop Sci. 6:357–360.

Crow, J.F. 1948. Alternative hypothesis of hybrid vigor. Genetics 33:477–487.

Cunningham, E.P. 1969. The relative efficiencies of selection indexes. Acta Agric. Scand. 19:45–48.

––––, R.A. Moen, and T. Gjedrem. 1970. Restriction of selection indexes. Biometrics 26:67–74.

Darrah, L.L. 1986. Evaluation of population improvement in the Kenya maize breeding methods study. p. 160–175. In To feed ourselves. Proc. 1 Eastern, Central, and Southern Africa Regional Maize Workshop, Lusaka, Zambia. 10–17 Mar. 1985. CIMMYT, El Batan, Mexico.

––––, S.A. Eberhart, and L.H. Penny. 1978. Six years of maize selection in 'Kitale Synthetic II', 'Ecuador 573', and 'Kitale Composite A' using methods of the comprehensive breeding systems. Euphytica 27:191–204.

Davis, R.L. 1927. Report of the plant breeder, p. 14–15. In Puerto Rico Agric. Exp. Stn. Annu. Rep.

Devey, M.E., and W.A. Russell. 1983. Evaluation of recurrent selection for stalk quality in a maize cultivar and effects of other agronomic traits. Iowa State J. Res. 58:207–219.

Dodd, J.L. 1980. A photosynthetic stress-translocation balance concept of corn stalk rot. Proc. Annu. Corn Sorghum Ind. Res. Conf. 32:122–130.

Doupnik, B., Jr., Les Lane, and David Wysong. 1981. Nebraska corn variety tests for reaction to corn lethal necrosis. 1981 Results. Nebraska Coop. Ext. Serv. Rep. UNL-SCS-81-151.

Dudley, J.W. 1977. Seventy-six generations of selection for oil and protein percentage in maize. p. 459–473. In E. Pollak et al. (ed.) Proc. Int. Conf. Quant. Genet., Iowa State Univ., Ames. 16–21 Aug. 1976. Iowa State Univ. Press, Ames.

––––. 1982. Theory of transfer of alleles. Crop Sci. 22:631–637.

––––. 1984a. A method of identifying lines for use in improving parents of a single cross. Crop Sci. 24:355–357.

––––. 1984b. Identifying parents for use in a pedigree breeding program. Proc. Annu. Corn Sorghum Ind. Res. Conf. 39:176–188.

————. 1984c. A method for identifying populations containing favorable alleles not present in elite germplasm. Crop Sci. 24:1053–1054.

————. 1988. Evaluation of maize populations as sources of favorable alleles. Crop Sci. 28:486–491.

————, and R.J. Lambert. 1969. Genetic variability after 65 generations of selection in Illinois high oil, low oil, high protein, and low protein strains of *Zea mays* L. Crop Sci. 9:179–181.

————, and R.H. Moll. 1969. Interpretation and use of estimates of heritability and genetic variances in plant breeding. Crop Sci. 9:257–262.

Duvick, D.N. 1974. Continuous backcrossing to transfer prolificacy to a single-eared inbred line of maize. Crop Sci. 14:69–71.

————. 1977. Genetic rates of gain in hybrid maize yields during the past 40 years. Maydica. 22:187–196.

————. 1984. Genetic contributions to yield gains of U.S. hybrid maize, 1930 to 1980. p. 15–47. *In* W.R. Fehr (ed.) Genetic contributions to yield gains of five major crop plants. Spec. Pub. 7. CSSA, Madison, WI.

Earle, E.D., and V.E. Gracen. 1985. Somaclonal variation in progeny of plants from corn tissue culture. p. 139–152. *In* R.R. Henke et al. (ed.) Tissue culture in forestry and agriculture. Plenum Press, New York.

East, E.M. 1908. Inbreeding in corn. 1907. p. 419–428. *In* Connecticut Agric. Exp. Stn. Rep.

————. 1936. Heterosis. Genetics 21:375–397.

Eberhart, S.A. 1970. Factors affecting efficiencies of breeding methods. Afr. Soils 15:669–680.

————, S. Debela, and A.R. Hallauer. 1973. Recurrent selection in the BSSS and BSCB1 maize varieties and half-sib selection in BSSS. Crop Sci. 13:451–456.

————, M.N. Harrison, and F. Ogada. 1967. A comprehensive breeding system. Zuchter 37:169–174.

————, and W.A. Russell. 1966. Stability parameters in comparing varieties. Crop Sci. 6:36–40.

————, and ————. 1969. Yield and stability for a 10-line diallel of single-cross and double-cross maize hybrids. Crop Sci. 9:357–361.

Edallo, C., C. Zucchinali, M. Perenzin, and F. Salamini. 1981. Chromosome variation and frequency of spontaneous mutants associated with in vitro culture and plant regeneration in maize. Maydica 26:39–56.

El-Hifny, M.A., M.S. Ahmund, J.D. Smith, and A.J. Bockholdt. 1969. Gamete selection with an inbred tester. Theor. Appl. Genet. 39:379–381.

El-Lakany, M.A., and W.A. Russell. 1971. Relationship of maize characters with yield in testcrosses of inbreds at different plant densities. Crop Sci. 11:698–701.

Elston, R.C. 1963. A weight free index for the purpose of ranking or selection with respect to several traits at a time. Biometrics 19:85–97.

Falconer, D.S. 1981. Introduction to quantitative genetics. Longman, New York.

Finlay, K.W., and G.W. Wilkinson. 1963. The analysis of adaptation in a plant breeding programme. Aust. J. Agric. Res. 14:742–754.

Fleming, A.A. 1971. Performance of stocks within long-time inbred lines of maize in testcrosses. Crop Sci. 11:620–622.

————, and G.M. Kozelnicky. 1965. Sibbing versus selfing in the maintenance of inbred lines of corn and the attainment of homozygosity. Crop Sci. 5:303–304.

————, ————, and E.B. Browne. 1964. Variations between stocks within long-time inbred lines of maize (*Zea mays* L.). Crop Sci. 4:291–295.

Fox, P.N., and A.A. Rosielle. 1982a. Reference sets of genotypes and selection for yield in unpredictable environments. Crop Sci. 22:1171–1175.

————, and ————. 1982b. Reducing the influence of environmental main-effects on pattern analysis of plant breeding environments. Euphytica 31:645–656.

Freeman, G.H. 1973. Statistical methods for the analysis of genotype-environment interactions. Heredity 31:339–354.

————, and J.M. Perkins. 1971. Environmental and genotype-environmental components of variability. VIII. Relation between genotypes grown in different environments and measures of these environments. Heredity 27:15–23.

Frey, K.J. 1971. Improving crop yields through plant breedings. p. 15–58. J.D. Eastin and R.D. Munson (ed.) Moving off the yield plateau. Spec. Pub. 20. ASA, CSSA, and SSSA, Madison, WI.

Gama, E.E.G.e., and A.R. Hallauer. 1977. Relation between inbred and hybrid traits in maize. Crop Sci. 17:703–706.

----, and ----. 1980. Stability of hybrids produced from selected and unselected lines of maize. Crop Sci. 20:623–626.

Gardner, C.O. 1961. An evaluation of effects of mass selection and seed irradiation with thermal neutrons on yield of corn. Crop Sci. 1:241–245.

----. 1977. Quantitative genetic studies and population improvement in maize and sorghum. p. 475–489. *In* E. Pollak et al. (ed.) Proc. Int. Conf. Quant. Genet. Univ. of Iowa, Ames, 16–21 Aug. 1976. Iowa State Univ. Press, Ames.

----. 1978. Population improvement in maize. p. 207–228. *In* D.B. Walden (ed.) Maize breeding and genetics. John Wiley and Sons, New York.

----, P.H. Harvey, R.E. Comstock, and H.F. Robinson. 1953. Dominance of genes controlling quantitative characters in maize. Agron. J. 45:186–191.

----, and J.H. Lonnquist. 1959. Linkage and the degree of dominance of genes controlling quantitative characters in maize. Agron. J. 51:524–528.

Gerrish, E.E. 1983. Indication from a diallel study for interracial maize hybridization in the Corn Belt. Crop Sci. 1082–1084.

Gevers, H.O. 1975. Three cycles of reciprocal recurrent selection in maize under two systems of plant selection. Agroplante 7:107–108.

Giesbrecht, J. 1964. Gamete selection in two early maturing corn varieties. Crop Sci. 4:653–655.

Goodman, M.M. 1985. Exotic maize germplasm: Status, prospects, and remedies. Iowa State J. Res. 59:497–527.

Goodsell, S. 1961. Male sterility in corn by androgenesis. Crop Sci. 1:227–228.

Gorsline, G.W. 1961. Phenotypic epistasis for ten quantitative characters in maize. Crop Sci. 1:55–58.

Grogan, C.O., and C.A. Francis. 1972. Heterosis in inbred source crosses of maize (*Zea mays* L.). Crop Sci. 12:729–730.

Gutierrez-Gaitan, M.A., H. Cortez-Mendoza, E.N. Wathika, C.O. Gardner, M. Oyervides-Garcia, A.R. Hallauer, and L.L. Darrah. 1986. Testcross evaluation of Mexican maize populations. Crop Sci. 26:99–104.

Hallauer, A.R. 1967. Development of single-cross hybrids from two-eared maize populations. Crop Sci. 7:192–195.

----. 1970. Zygote selection for the development of single-cross hybrids in maize. Adv. Front. Plant Sci. 25:75–81.

----. 1972. Third phase in yield evaluation of synthetic varieties of maize. Crop Sci. 12:16–18.

----. 1973. Hybrid developement and population improvement in reciprocal full-sib selection. Egypt. J. Genet. Cytol. 1:84–101.

----. 1975. Relation of gene action and type of testers in maize breeding procedures. Proc. Annu. Corn Sorghum Ind. Res. Conf. 30:150–165.

----. 1979. Corn breeding opportunities in the 1980's. Iowa Seed Dealers' Assoc., Des Moines.

----. 1981. Selection and breeding methods. p. 3–55. *In* K.J. Frey (ed.) Plant breeding II. Iowa State Univ. Press, Ames.

----. 1984. Reciprocal full-sib selection in maize. Crop Sci. 24:755–759.

----. 1985. Compendium of recurrent selection methods and their application. Crit. Rev. Plant Sci. 3:1–34.

----, and S.A. Eberhart. 1966. Evaluation of synthetic varieties of maize for yield. Crop Sci. 6:423–427.

----, and ----. 1970. Reciprocal full-sib selection. Crop Sci. 10:315–316.

----, and E. Lopez-Perez. 1979. Comparisons among testers for evaluating lines of corn. Proc. Annu. Corn Sorghum Ind. Res. Conf. 34:57–72.

----, and D. Malithano. 1976. Evaluation of maize varieties for their potential as breeding populations. Euphytica 25:117–127.

----, and J.B. Miranda, Fo. 1981. Quantitative genetics in maize breeding. Iowa State Univ. Press, Ames.

----, and J.H. Sears. 1968. Second phase in the evaluation of synthetic varieties of maize for yield. Crop Sci. 8:448–451.

----, and ----. 1969. Mass selection for yield in two varieties of maize. Crop Sci. 9:47–50.

----, W.A. Russell, and O.S. Smith. 1983. Quantitative analysis of Iowa Stiff Stalk Synthetic. Stadler Genet. Symp. 15:83–104.

Hamblin, J.H., M. Fisher, and H.I. Ridings. 1980. The choice of locality for plant breeding when selecting for high yield and general adaptation. Euphytica 29:161–168.

Hardwick, R.C., and J.T. Wood. 1972. Regression methods for studying genotype-environment interactions. Heredity 28:209–222.

Hayes, H.K., and R.J. Garber. 1919. Synthetic production of high protein corn in relation to breeding. J. Am. Soc. Agron. 11:308–318.

————, and I.J. Johnson. 1939. The breeding of improved selfed lines of corn. J. Am. Soc. Agron. 31:701–724.

Hazel, L.N. 1943. The genetic basis for constructing selection indices. Genetics 28:476–490.

————, and J.L. Lush. 1942. The efficiency of three methods of selection. J. Hered. 33:393–399.

Helentjaris, T., M. Slocum, S. Wright, A. Schaefer, and J. Nienhuis. 1986. Construction of genetic linkage maps in maize and tomato using restriction fragment length polymorphisms. Theor. Appl. Genet. 72:761–769.

Helms, T.C. 1986. Evaluation of three recurrent selection methods in corn (*Zea mays* L.). Ph.D. diss. Iowa State Univ., Ames. (Diss. Abstr. 86–27115).

Henderson, C.R. 1963. Selection index and expected genetic advances. p. 141–163. *In* W.D. Hanson and H.F. Robinson (ed.) Statistical genetics and plant breeding. Pub. 982. NAS-NRC, Washington, DC.

Hill, J. 1976. Genotype-environment interactions—a challenge for plant breeders. J. Agric. Sci. 85:477–494.

Hoard, K.G., and T.M. Crosbie. 1985. S_1 line recurrent selection for cold tolerance in two maize populations. Crop Sci. 25:1041–1045.

Hoegemeyer, T.C., and A.R. Hallauer. 1976. Selection among and within full-sib families to develop single crosses of maize. Crop Sci. 16:76–81.

Hooker, A.L. 1961. A new type of resistance to *Helminthosporium turcicum*. Planta Dis. Rep. 45:780–781.

Hopkins, C.G. 1899. Improvement in the chemical composition of the corn kernel. Bull.—Agric. Exp. Stn. (Ill.) 55:205–240.

Horner, E.S. 1985. Effects of selection for S_2 progeny versus testcross performance in corn. Proc. Annu. Corn Sorghum Ind. Res. Conf. 40:142–150.

————, H.W. Lundy, M.C. Lutrick, and W.H. Chapman. 1973. Comparison of three methods of recurrent selection in maize. Crop Sci. 13:485–489.

————, M.C. Lutrick, W.H. Chapman, and F.G. Martin. 1976. Effect of recurrent selection for combining ability with a single-cross tester in maize. Crop Sci. 16:5–8.

Hull, F.H. 1945. Recurrent selection and specific combining ability in corn. J. Am. Soc. Agron. 37:134–145.

————. 1952. Recurrent selection and overdominance. p. 451–473. *In* J.W. Gowen (ed.) Heterosis. Iowa State Univ. Press, Ames.

Humphrey, A.B., D.F. Matzinger, and C.C. Cockerham. 1969. Effects of random intercrossing in a naturally self-fertilizing species *Nicotiana tabacum* L. Crop Sci. 9:495–497.

James, J.W. 1968. Index selection with restrictions. Biometrics 24:1015–1018.

Jenkins, M.J. 1929. Correlation studies with inbred and cross-bred strains of maize. J. Agric. Res. 39:677–721.

————. 1935. The effect of inbreeding and of selection within inbred lines of maize upon hybrids made after successive generations of selfing. Iowa State Coll. J. Sci. 9:429–450.

Jenkins, M.T. 1936. Corn improvement. p. 455–522. *In* Yearbook of agriculture, 1936. U.S. Gov. Print. Office, Washington, DC.

————. 1940. The segregation of genes affecting yield of grain in maize. J. Am. Soc. Agron. 32:55–63.

————. 1978. Maize breeding during the development and early years of hybrid maize. p. 13–28. *In* D.B. Walden (ed.) Maize breeding and genetics. John Wiley and Sons, New York.

————, and A.M. Brunson. 1932. Methods of testing inbred lines of maize in crossbred combinations. J. Am. Soc. Agron. 24:523–530.

Jensen, S.D., W.E. Kuhn, and R.L. McConnell. 1983. Combining ability studies in elite U.S. maize germplasm. Proc. Annu. Corn Sorghum Ind. Res. Conf. 38:87–96.

Jinahyon, S., and W.A. Russell. 1969. Evaluation of recurrent selection for stalk-rot resistance in an open-pollinated variety of maize. Iowa State J. Sci. 43:229–237.

Johnson, E.C. 1963. Mass selection for yield in a tropical corn variety. p. 82. *In* Agronomy abstracts. ASA, Madison, WI.

————, K.S. Fisher, G.O. Edmeades, and A.F.E. Palmer. 1986. Recurrent selection for reduced plant height in lowland tropical maize. Crop Sci. 26:253–260.

Johnson, G.R. 1980. Simple quantitative theory for selection during inbred line development. Ill. Corn Breeders' School 16:1–18.

Jones, D.F. 1918. The effects of inbreeding and cross-breeding upon development. p. 5–100. *In* Connecticut Agric. Exp. Stn. Bull. 207.

————. 1945. Heterosis resulting from degenerative changes. Genetics 30:527–542.

————. 1952. Plasmagenes and chromogenes in heterosis. p. 224–235. *In* J.W. Gowen (ed.) Heterosis. Iowa State Univ. Press, Ames.

Jones, L.P., W.A. Compton, and C.O. Gardner. 1971. Comparison of full and half-sib reciprocal recurrent selection. Theor. Appl. Genet. 41:36–39.

Kahler, A.L., A.R. Hallauer, and C.O. Gardner. 1986. Allozyme polymorphisms within and among open-pollinated and adapted exotic populations of maize. Theor. Appl. Genet. 72:592–601.

Kauffmann, K.D., and J.W. Dudley. 1979. Selection indices for corn grain yield, percent protein, and kernel weight. Crop Sci. 19:583–588.

————, C.W. Crum, and M.F. Lindsey. 1982. Exotic germplasm in a corn breeding program. Ill. Corn Breeders' School 18:6–39.

Kempthorne, O., and A.W. Nordskog. 1959. Restricted selection indices. Biometrics 15:10–19.

Kermicle, J.L. 1969. Androgenesis conditioned by a mutation in maize. Science 166:1422–1424.

Klenke, J.R., W.A. Russell, and W.D. Guthrie. 1986. Recurrent selection for resistance to European corn borer in a corn synthetic and correlated effects on agronomic traits. Crop Sci. 26:864–868.

Knight, R. 1970. The measurement and interpretation of genotype-environment interaction. Euphytica 19:225–235.

Kuhn, H.C., and H.O. Gevers. 1980. Hybrid improvement in the past three decades. Proc. South African Maize Breed. Symp. 4:69–73.

Lambert, R.J. 1978. Breeding corn in a non-limiting environment. Proc. Annu. Corn Sorghum Ind. Res. Conf. 33:24–33.

————. 1984. Reciprocal recurrent selection of maize in a high-yield environment. Maydica 29:419–430.

Lamkey, K., and A.R. Hallauer. 1984. Comparisons of maize populations improved by recurrent selection. Maydica 29:357–374.

————, and ————. 1986. Performance of high × high, high × low, low × low crosses of lines from the BSSS maize synthetic. Crop Sci. 7:1114–1118.

————, and ————. 1987. Heritability estimated from recurrent selection experiments in maize. Maydica 32:61–78.

Landi, P., E. Pe, and S. Conti. 1983. Effects of selection at medium and high competition levels on the performance of local maize. (*Zea mays* L.) lines. Maydica 38:45–51.

Lantin, M.M. and A.R. Hallauer. 1981. Response to reciprocal full-sib and mass selection in corn (*Zea mays* L.). Proc. Iowa Acad. Sci. 88:172–178.

Lee, M., J.L. Geadelmann, and R.L. Phillips. 1988. Agronomic evaluation of inbred lines derived from tissue cultures of maize. Theor. Appl. Genet. 75:841–849.

Lerner, I. 1958. The genetic basis of selection. John Wiley and Sons, New York.

Lin, C.S. 1982. Grouping genotypes by a cluster method directly related to genotype-environment interaction mean square. Theor. Appl. Genet. 62:277–280.

————, M.R. Binns, and L.P. Lefkovitch. 1986. Stability analysis: where do we stand? Crop Sci. 26:894–900.

Lin, C.Y. 1978. Index selection for genetic improvement of quantitative characters. Theor. Appl. Genet. 52:49–56.

————. 1985. A simple stepwise procedure of deriving selection index with restrictions. Theor. Appl. Genet. 70:147–150.

Lonnquist, J.H. 1949. The development and performance of synthetic varieties of maize. Agron. J. 41:153–156.

————. 1950. The effect of selection for combining ability within segregating lines of corn. Agron. J. 42:503–508.

————. 1964. A modification of the ear-to-row procedure for the improvement of maize populations. Crop Sci. 4:227–228.

————. 1967. Mass selection for prolificacy in maize. Zuchter 37:185–188.

————, and C.O. Gardner. 1961. Heterosis in intervarietal crosses in maize and its implications in breeding procedures. Crop Sci. 1:179–183.

————, and D.P. McGill. 1954. Gamete selection from selected zygotes in corn breeding. Agron. J. 46:147–150.

————, and N.E. Williams. 1967. Development of maize hybrids through selection among full-sib families. Crop Sci. 7:369–370.

Mareck, J.H. and C.O. Gardner. 1979. Responses to mass selection in maize and stability of resulting populations. Crop Sci. 19:779–783.

Marquez-Sanchez, F. 1982. Modifications to cyclic hybridization in maize with single-eared plants. Crop Sci. 22:314–319.

Martin, J.M., and A.R. Hallauer. 1976. Relation between heterozygosis and yield for four types of maize inbred lines. Egypt. J. Genet. Cytol. 5:119–135.

————, and ————. 1980. Seven cycles of reciprocal recurrent selection in BSSS and BSCB1 maize populations. Crop Sci. 20:599–603.

Martin, M.J., and W.A. Russell. 1984a. Response of a maize synthetic to recurrent selection for stalk quality. Crop Sci. 24:331–337.

————, and ————. 1984b. Correlated responses of yield and other agronomic traits to recurrent selection for stalk quality in a maize (*Zea mays* L.) synthetic. Crop Sci. 24:746–750.

Mather, K., and P.D.S. Caligari. 1974. Genotype × environmental interactions. I. Regression of interaction on overall effect of the environment. Heredity 33:43–59.

Matzinger, D.F. 1953. Comparison of three types of testers for the evaluation of inbred lines of corn. Agron. J. 45:493–495.

McCoy, T.J., and R.L. Phillips. 1982. Chromosome stability in maize (*Zea mays* L.) tissue culture and sectoring in some regenerated plants. Can. J. Genet. Cytol. 24:559–565.

Meghji, M.R. J.W. Dudley, R.L. Lambert, and G.F. Sprague. 1984. Inbreeding depression, inbred and hybrid grain yield, and other traits of maize representing three eras. Crop Sci. 24:545–549.

Melchinger, A.E., H.H. Geiger, and F.W. Schnell. 1986. Epistasis in maize (*Zea mays* L.). I. Comparison of single and three-way cross hybrids among early flint and dent inbred lines. Maydica 31:179–192.

Miles, J.W., J.W. Dudley, D.G. White, and R.J. Lambert. 1981. Response to selection for resistance to four diseases in two corn populations. Crop Sci. 21:980–983.

Mock, J.J., and A.A. Bakri. 1976. Recurrent selection for cold tolerance in maize. Crop Sci. 16:230–233.

————, and R.B. Pearce. 1975. An ideotype of maize. Euphytica 24:613–623.

Moll, R.H., C.C. Cockerham, C.W. Stuber, and W.P. Williams. 1978. Selection responses, genetic-environmental interactions, and heterosis with recurrent selection for yield in maize. Crop Sci. 18:641–645.

————, and W.D. Hanson. 1984. Comparisons of effects of intrapopulation vs. interpopulation selection in maize. Crop Sci. 24:1047–1052.

————, J.H. Lonnquist, J.V. Fortuna, and E.C. Johnson. 1965. The relation of heterosis and genetic divergence in maize. Genetics 52:139–144.

————, and H.F. Robinson. 1966. Observed and expected response in four selection experiments in maize. Crop Sci. 6:319–324.

————, W.S. Salhuana, and H.F. Robinson. 1962. Heterosis and genetic diversity in variety crosses of maize. Crop Sci. 2:197–198.

————, C.W. Stuber, and W.D. Hanson. 1975. Correlated responses and responses to index selection involving yield and ear height of maize. Crop Sci. 15:243–248.

Moreno-Gonzalez, J., and J.W. Dudley. 1981. Epistasis in related and unrelated maize hybrids determined by three methods. Crop Sci. 21:644–651.

————, and A.R. Hallauer. 1982. Combined S_2 and crossbred family selection in full-sib reciprocal recurrent selection. Theor. Appl. Genet. 61:353–358.

Mulamba, N.N., A.R. Hallauer, and O.S. Smith. 1983. Recurrent selection for grain yield in a maize population. Crop Sci. 23:536–540.

————, and J.J. Mock. 1978. Improvement of yield potential of the Eto Blanco maize (*Zea mays* L.) population by breeding for plant traits. Egypt. J. Genet. Cytol. 7:40–41.

Murphy, R.P. 1942. Convergent improvement with four inbred liens of corn. J. Am. Soc. Agron. 34:138–150.

Nor, K.M., and F.B. Cady. 1979. Methodology for identifying wide adaptability in crops. Agron. J. 71:556–559.

Nordquist, P.T., O.J. Webster, C.O. Gardner, and W.M. Ross. 1973. Registration of three sorghum germplasm random mating populations. Crop Sci. 13:132.

Oyervides-Garcia, M., and A.R. Hallauer. 1986. Selection-induced differences among strains of Iowa Stiff Stalk Synthetic maize. Crop Sci. 26:506–511.

————, ————, and H. Cortez-Mendoza. 1985. Evaluation of improved maize populations in Mexico and the U.S. Corn Belt. Crop Sci. 25:115–120.

Paliwal, R.L., and E.W. Sprague. 1981. Improving adaptation and yield dependability in maize in the developing world. CIMMYT, El Batan, Mexico.

Pandey, S., A.O. Diallo, T.M.T. Islam, and J. Deutsch. 1986. Progress from selection in eight tropical maize populations using international testing. Crop Sci. 26:879–884.

Paterniani, E. 1978. Phenotypic recurrent selection for prolificacy in maize. Maydica 23:29–34.

————, and J.H. Lonnquist. 1963. Heterosis in interracial crosses of corn (*Zea mays* L.). Crop Sci. 504–507.

————, and R. Vencovsky. 1977. Reciprocal recurrent selection in maize (*Zea mays* L.) based on testcrosses of half-sib families. Maydica 22:141–152.

Pederson, A.R., E.H. Everson, and J.E. Grafius. 1978. The gene pool concept as a basis for cultivar selection and recombination. Crop Sci. 18:883–886.

Pederson, D.G. 1974. Arguments against intermating before selection in a self-fertilizing species. Theor. Appl. Genet. 45:157–162.

Penny, L.H., G.E. Scott, and W.D. Guthrie. 1967. Recurrent selection for European corn borer resistance in maize. Crop Sci. 7:407–409.

Perkins, J.M., and J.L. Jinks. 1968. Environmental and genotype-environmental components of variability. III. Multiple lines and crosses. Heredity 23:339–356.

Pesek, J., and R.J. Baker. 1969. Desired improvement in relation to selection indices. Can. J. Plant. Sci. 49:803–804.

Pinnell, E.L., E.H. Rinke, and H.K. Hayes. 1952. Gamete selection for specific combining ability. p. 378–388. *In* J.W. Gowen (ed.) Heterosis. Iowa State Univ. Press, Ames.

Ramey, T.B., and A.A. Rosielle. 1983. HASS cluster analysis: A new method of grouping genotypes or environments in plant breeding. Theor. Appl. Genet. 66:131–133.

Rawlings, J.C., and D.L. Thompson. 1962. Performance level as criterion for the choice of maize testers. Crop Sci. 2:217–220.

Richey, F.D., 1922. The experimental basis for the present status of corn breeding. J. Am. Soc. Agron. 14:1–17.

————. 1927. The convergent improvement of selfed lines of corn. Am. Nat. 61:430–449.

————. 1947. Corn breeding, gamete selection, the Oenothera method and related miscellany. J. Am. Soc. Agron. 39:403–412.

————, and G.F. Sprague. 1931. Experiments on hybrid vigor and convergent improvement in corn. USDA Tech. Bull. 267. U.S. Gov. Print. Office, Washington, DC.

Rinke, E.H., and J.C. Sentz. 1961. Moving corn-belt germ-plasm northward. Proc. Annu. Hybrid Corn Ind. Conf. 16:53–56.

Robinson, H.F. 1959. The implications of environmental effects of genotypes in relation to breeding. Proc. Annu. Corn Sorghum Ind. Res. Conf. 14:24–31.

————, C.C. Cockerham, and R.H. Moll. 1958. Studies on the estimation of dominance variance and effects of linkage bias. p. 171–177. *In* O. Kempthorne (ed.) Biometrical genetics. Pergamon Press, New York.

————, R.E. Comstock, A. Klalil, and P.H. Harvey. 1956. Dominance versus overdominance in heterosis: Evidence from crosses between open-pollinated varieties of maize. Am. Nat. 90:127–131.

Rosielle, A.A., and J. Hamblin. 1981. Theoretical aspects of selection for yield in stress and non-stress environments. Crop Sci. 21:943–946.

Russell, W.A. 1974. comparative performance for maize hybrids representing different eras of maize breedings. Proc. Annu. Corn Sorghum Ind. Res. Conf. 29:81–101.

————. 1984. Agronomic performance of maize cultivars representing different eras of maize breeding. Maydica 29:375–390.

————. 1985a. Evaluations for plant, ear, and grain traits of maize cultivars representing seven eras of maize breeding. Maydica 30:85–96.

————. 1985b. Comparison of the hybrid performance of maize inbred lines developed from the original and improved cycles of BSSS. Maydica 30:407–419.

————. 1986. Contribution of breeding to maize improvement in the United States, 1920's–1980's. Iowa State J. Res. 61:5–34.

----, and S.A. Eberhart. 1968. Testcrosses of one- and two-ear types of corn belt maize inbreds. II. Stability of performance in different environments. Crop Sci. 8:248–251.

----, and ----. 1975. Hybrid performance of selected maize lines from reciprocal recurrent and testcross selection programs. Crop Sci. 15:1–4.

----, ----, and U.A. Vega. 1973. Recurrent selection for specific combining ability in two maize populations. Crop Sci. 13:257–261.

----, G.D. Lawrance, and W.D. Guthrie. 1979. Effects of recurrent selection for European corn borer resistance on other agronomic characters in synthetic cultivars of maize. Maydica 24:33–47.

----, and Veronica Machado. 1978. Selection procedures in the development of maize inbred lines and the effects of plant densities on the relationships between inbred traits and hybrid yields. Iowa Agric. Home Econ. Exp. Stn. Res. Bull. 585.

----, and C.L. Prior. 1975. Stability of yield performance of nonprolific and prolific maize hybrids. Iowa State J. Res. 50:17–27.

----, G.F. Sprague, and L.H. Penny. 1963. Mutations affecting quantitative characters in long-time inbred lines of maize. Crop Sci. 3:175–178.

----, and A.H. Teich. 1967. Selection in *Zea mays* L. by inbred line appearance and testcross performance in low and high plant densities. Iowa Agric. Home Econ. Exp. Stn. Res. Bull. 552.

----, and U.A. Vega. 1973. Genetic stability of quantitative characters in successive generations in maize inbred lines. Euphytica 22:172–180.

Salazar, A.M., and A.R. Hallauer. 1986. Divergent mass selection for ear length in maize. Rev. Bras. Genet. 9:281–294.

Schnell, F.W., and I.S. Singh. 1978. Epistasis in three-way crosses involving early flint and dent inbred lines of maize. Maydica 23:233–238.

Scott, G.E. 1967. Selecting for stability of yield in maize. Crop Sci. 7:549–551.

Shulka, G.K. 1972. Some statistical aspects of partitioning genotype-environment components of variability. Heredity 29:237–245.

Shull, G.H. 1908. The composition of a field of maize. Am. Breeders' Assoc. Rep. 4:296–301.

----. 1909. A pure-line method in corn breeding. Am. Breeders' Assoc. Rep. 5:51–59.

----. 1910. Hybridization methods in corn breeding. Am. Breeders' Mag. 1:98–107.

Silva, J.C., and A.R. Hallauer. 1975. Estimation of epistatic variance in Iowa Stiff Stalk Synthetic maize. J. Hered. 66:290–296.

Singh, M. A.S. Khehra, and B.S. Dhillon. 1986. Direct and correlated response to recurrent full-sib selection for prolificacy in maize. Crop Sci. 26:275–278.

Smith, H.F. 1936. A discriminant function for plant selection. Ann. Eugen. 7:240–250.

Smith, J.S.C. 1988. Diversity of United States hybrid maize germplasm: Isozymic and chromatographic evidence. Crop Sci. 28:63–69.

Smith, O.S. 1979a. A model for evaluating progress from recurrent selection. Crop Sci. 19:223–226.

----. 1979b. Application of a modified diallel analysis to evaluate recurrent selection for grain yield in maize. Crop Sci. 19:819–822.

----. 1983. Evaluation of recurrent selection in BSSS, BSCB1, and BS13 maize populations. Crop Sci. 13:35–40.

----. 1984. Comparison of effects of reciprocal recurrent selection in the BSSS(R), BSCB1(R), and BS6 populations. Maydica 29:1–8.

----. 1986. Covariance between line per se and testcross performance. Crop Sci. 26:540–543.

----, A.R. Hallauer, and W.A. Russell. 1981a. Use of selection index in recurrent selection programs in maize. Euphytica 30:611–618.

----, A.R. Hallauer, W.A. Russell, and T.M. Crosbie. 1981b. Use of selection indices in maize improvement and hybrid development programs. Proc. Annu. Corn Sorghum Ind. Res. Conf. 36:95–103.

Sprague, G.F. 1946. Early testing of inbred lines. J. Am. Soc. Agron. 38:108–117.

----. 1952. Additional studies of the relative effectiveness of two systems of selection for oil content of the corn kernel. Agron. J. 44:329–331.

----. 1953. Heterosis. p. 113–136. *In* W.E. Loomis (ed.) Growth and differentiation in plants. Iowa State Univ. Press, Ames.

----. 1955. Corn breeding. p. 221–292. *In* G.F. Sprague (ed.) Corn and corn improvement. Academic Press, New York.

----, and B. Brimhall. 1950. Relative effectiveness of two systems of selection for oil content of the corn kernel. Agron. J. 42:83–88

----, and S.A. Eberhart. 1977. Corn breeding. *In* G.F. Sprague (ed.) Corn and corn improvement 2nd ed. Agronomy 18:305–363.

----, and W.T. Federer. 1951. A comparison of variance components in corn yield trials. II. Error, year × variety, location × variety, and variety components. Agron. J. 43:535–541.

----, W.A. Russell, and L.H. Penny. 1960. Mutations affecting quantitative traits in the selfed progeny of doubled monoploid stocks. Genetics 45:855–866.

----, ----, ----, T.W. Horner, and W.D. Hanson. 1962. Effect of epistasis on grain yield in maize. Crop Sci. 2:205–208.

----, and L.A. Tatum. 1942. General vs. specific combining ability in single crosses of corn. J. Am. Soc. Agron. 34:923–932.

----, and W.I. Thomas. 1967. Further evidence of epistasis in single and three-way cross yields of maize (*Zea mays* L.). Crop Sci. 7:355–356.

St. Martin, S.K., P.J. Loesch, Jr., J.T. Demopulos-Rodriguez, and W.S. Wiser. 1982. Selection indices for the improvement of opaque-2 maize. Crop Sci. 22:478–485.

Stadler, L.J. 1944. Gamete selection in corn breeding. J. Am. Soc. Agron. 36:988–989.

Stangland, G.R., and W.A. Russell. 1981. Variability within S_2 and S_8 inbred lines of maize. Maydica 24:227–238.

----, ----, and O.S. Smith. 1982. Agronomic evaluation of four maize synthetics and their crosses after recurrent selection for yield. Maydica 27:199–1212.

Stringfield, G.H. 1974. Developing heterozygous parent stocks for maize hybrids. DeKalb AgResearch, DeKalb, IL.

Stuber, C.W., W.P. Williams, and R.H. Moll. 1973. Epistasis in maize (*Zea mays* L.). III. Significance in predictions of hybrid performance. Crop Sci. 13:195–200.

Subandi, W., A. Compton, and L.T. Empig. 1973. Comparison of the efficiencies of selection indices for three traits in two variety crosses of corn. Crop Sci. 13:184–186.

Suwantaradon, K., S.A. Eberhart, J.J. Mock, J.C. Owens, and W.D. Guthrie. 1975. Index selection for several agronomic traits in the BSSS maize population. Crop Sci. 15:827–833.

Tai, G.C.C. 1971. Genotypic stability analysis and its application to potato regional trials. Crop Sci. 11:184–190.

Tallis, G.M. 1962. A selection index for optimum genotype. Biometrics 18:120–122.

Tanner, A.H., and O.S. Smith. 1987. Comparison of half-sib and S_1 recurrent selection in Krug Yellow Dent maize populations. Crop Sci. 27:509–513.

Tapper, D.C. 1983. Changes in physiological traits associated with grain yield improvement in single-cross maize hybrids from 1930 to 1970. Ph.D. diss. Iowa State Univ., Ames. (Diss. Abstr. 83–DA8316164).

Thompson, D.L. 1954. Combining ability of homozygous diploids of corn relative to lines derived by inbreeding. Agron. J. 46:133–136.

Thompson, L.N. 1975. Weather variability, climatic changes, and grain production. Science. 188:535–541.

----. 1986. Climatic change, weather variability, and corn production. Agron. J. 78:649–653.

Trifunovic, V. 1978. Maize production and maize breeding in Europe. p. 41–58. *In* D.B. Walden (ed.) Maize breeding and genetics. John Wiley and Sons, New York.

Troyer, A.F., and W.L. Brown. 1972. Selection for early flowering in corn. Crop Sci. 12:301–304.

Tsotsis, B. 1972. Objectives of industry breeders to make efficient and significant advances in the future. Proc. Annu. Corn Sorghum Ind. Res. Conf. 27:93–107.

Walejko, R.N., and W.A. Russell. 1977. Evaluation of recurrent selection for specific combining ability in two open-pollinated maize cultivars. Crop Sci. 17:647–651.

Weatherspoon, J.H. 1970. Comparative yields of single, three-way, and double crosses of maize. Crop Sci. 10:157–159.

Wellhausen, E.J. 1978. Recent developments in maize breeding in the tropics. p. 59–84. *In* D.B. Walden (ed.) Maize breeding and genetics. John Wiley and Sons, New York.

West, D.R., W.A. Compton, and M.A. Thomas. 1980. Comparison of replicated S_1 per se vs. reciprocal full-sib index selection in corn. I. Indirect response to population densities. Crop Sci. 20:35–42.

Westcott, B. 1986. Some methods of analyzing genotype-environment interaction. Heredity 56:243–253.

Widstrom, N.W. 1974. Selection indexes for resistance to corn earworm based on realized gains in corn. Crop Sci. 14:673–675.

————, B.R. Wiseman, and W.W. McMillan. 1982. Responses to index selection in maize for resistance to ear damage by corn earworm. Crop Sci. 22:843–846.

Williams, J.S. 1962. The evaluation of a selection index. Biometrics 18:375–393.

Williams, P.N., and F.M. Davis. 1983. Recurrent selection for resistance in corn to tunneling by the second-brood southwestern corn borer. Crop Sci. 23:169–170.

Wricke, G. 1962. Uber eine methode zur erfassung der okologischen streubreite in felduersuchen. Z. Pflanzenzuecht. 47:92–96.

Wright,A.J. 1971. The analysis and prediction of some two factor interactions in grass breeding. J. Agric. Sci. 76:301–306.

————. 1976. Bias in the estimation of regression coefficients in the analysis of genotype-environmental interaction. Heredity 37:299–303.

————. 1980. The expected frequencies of half-sib, testcross, and S_1 progeny testing methods in single population improvement. Heredity 45:361–376.

Yates, F., and W.G. Cochran. 1938. The analysis of groups of experiments. J. Agric. Sci. 28:556–580.

Zambezi, B.T., E.S. Horner, and F.G. Martin. 1986. Inbred lines as testers for general combining ability in maize. Crop Sci. 26:908–910.

Zhang, Q., and S. Geng. 1986. A method for estimating varietal stability for data of long-term trials. Theor. Appl. Genet. 71:810–814.

Zuber, M.S., and L.L. Darrah. 1980. 1979 U.S. corn germplasm base. Proc. Ann. Corn Sorghum Ind. Res. Conf. 35:234–249.

9

Production of Hybrid Seed Corn

ROBERT D. WYCH

Pioneer Hi-Bred International, Inc.
Johnston, Iowa

The objective of this chapter is to present a current, state-of-the-art description of seed corn (*Zea mays* L.) production as it is commercially practiced in the late 1980s. The chapter draws heavily on the treatment by Craig (1977), but will highlight changes in the industry and in technology since that chapter was written.

9–1 HISTORICAL PERSPECTIVE

The first commercial hybrids were produced and sold in the early 1920s. From that modest beginning our present-day sophisticated hybrid seed corn industry has developed. Crabb (1947) described the first production of hybrid seed corn in Iowa:

> "The first contract ever drawn for the production of seed for hybrid corn gave [George] Kurtzweil the exclusive right for all time to produce the Copper Cross hybrid, a contract which, although it hasn't been exercised for a good many years, is still one of Kurtzweil's most prized possessions."
>
> "[Henry A.] Wallace said he had foundation inbred material to plant a one-acre seed plot, and the decision was made to produce the first commercial hybrid seed corn ever grown in Iowa . . . Wallace turned the seed over to Kurtzweil [in 1923]. The old East Leaming inbred was used for the seed parent, and the meager supply of the Bloody Butcher line was used as the pollinator parent. Only by very sparse and careful planting was Kurtzweil able to plant the plot that measured almost one acre on a small farm owned by Kurtzweil's father, Mathias Kurtzweil, at Altoona, just east of Des Moines . . ."
>
> "The first detasseling of commercial hybrid seed corn in Iowa was done entirely by a woman, Ruth Kurtzweil, a sister of George . . . From the time the first tassels of the parent plants began to appear on the Leaming inbred, Miss Kurtzweil went up and down, pulling them out. Few fields of hybrid seed corn since have been detasseled with such care and interest. Now that producing hybrid seed corn has become such a tremendous enterprise, Miss Kurtzweil delights in calling her friends' attention to the fact that she once detasseled all the hybrid seed corn production fields in the State of Iowa."
>
> "Copper Cross earned another distinction in 1924 when it became the first hybrid developed in the corn belt to be purchased by farmers of Iowa and elsewhere. Approximately fifteen bushels—all that was available of Cop-

per Cross seed—was sold in the spring of 1924 at the price of $1.00 a pound, or at the rate of $56.00 a bushel."

The first hybrids to be developed were adapted primarily to the central Corn Belt; these were accepted slowly, and by 1933 approximately 1% of the Corn Belt corn acreage was planted with hybrid seed (Airy, 1955). Because of the superior performance of hybrids in the severe droughts of 1934 and 1936, farmers rapidly began accepting, and then demanding, hybrid seed.

The rapid acceptance by U.S. farmers of hybrid corn varieties in the 1930s and 1940s provided the basis on which many firms and individuals established themselves in a new and fast-growing industry. Prior to that time, only a few firms had been engaged in the hybrid seed corn business. Development of new hybrids adapted to virtually every corn-growing area of the USA and Canada helped to establish profitable corn production on hundreds of thousands of hectares outside the Corn Belt, where profitable corn production had previously been impossible on a commercial scale.

9–2 SIZE OF THE INDUSTRY

Since 1900, the area in the USA planted to corn has varied from a high of 47 million ha (116 million acres) in 1917 to a low of 24.4 million ha (60.2 million acres) in 1983 [the year of the federal government's payment-in-kind (PIK) program]. Excluding 1983, the area planted to corn between 1975 and 1985 averaged 33.4 million ha (82.5 million acres).

Planting rates vary considerably according to soil fertility levels, rainfall and irrigation availability, planting date, intended use (e.g., grain vs. silage), local custom, and finally, adaptation of specific hybrids to high plant populations. Assuming that a seed corn unit of 80 000 kernels will plant 1.4 ha (3.4 acres), it is estimated that a minimum of 24.5 million units of hybrid seed were required to plant the 1985 U.S. crop. At an estimated average retail price of $65/unit, the domestic hybrid seed corn industry has grown to a gross annual sales volume of $1.59 billion. Sales in other countries add to the total market.

9–3 TYPES OF HYBRIDS

The first hybrids produced and sold commercially were almost exclusively double crosses. However, several factors contributed to a significant transition from double crosses to single crosses within the U.S. Corn Belt, starting in the late 1950s and continuing through the 1980s. The transition to single crosses occurred because: (i) single crosses outyielded double crosses; (ii) a few companies led the way and others joined them to be competitive; (iii) farmers began to demand single crosses; and

(iv) improved agronomic practices and development by corn breeders of inbreds with higher per se yields made the production of seed of single crosses economically feasible. Single cross hybrids now comprise approximately 90% of the hybrid seed sold in North America (USA and Canada).

Modified single crosses, which are produced using related-line single crosses for either the female or male parent, were used extensively in hybrid seed corn production in the 1960s and early 1970s. Three-way crosses (single cross female parent and inbred male parent) are also a factor in the industry. Today, modified single crosses and three-way crosses account for about 10% of the North American market. While double-cross hybrids were once a significant factor in the market, their importance has decreased over the past two decades. It is estimated that they now comprise <1% of the total U.S. and Canadian market.

9–4   SEED CORN COMPANIES

Many firms have become involved in the production and sale of hybrid seed corn. Small, privately owned companies may produce and distribute only a few thousand units of seed. Operations of this size usually depend on inbred and hybrid development and research conducted by public institutions, or on that conducted by private firms that produce and sell parent seed (foundation seed) stocks. Smaller companies usually purchase foundation seed, produce their supplies of hybrid seed, and then sell it directly to farmers in their local areas.

Large companies usually carry on their own research and development programs, produce their own foundation seed stocks, produce the commercial seed, and distribute it through their own sales organizations. The majority of hybrid seed corn is sold by the various companies to farmer dealers, who, in turn, sell it to farmer customers. It is customary in the industry to deliver to dealers on a consignment basis, and to accept as "returns" seed that remains unsold by the dealer at the end of the planting season. Alternatively, the "sales agent" approach is used, with the seed remaining the property of the company until it is sold to the farmer customer (see section 9–12.2). In some geographical areas, sales are made by the seed company to jobbers or distributors who seek their own retail dealer outlets. This practice is more common in areas of relatively low sales volume.

Hybrid seed corn was at first sold in 25-kg (1-bu) packages. In the early 1960s, there began a trend to package and distribute in 23-kg (50-lb) packages. Later in that decade, the practice of packaging by kernel count became popular. At the present time, most seed corn is sold in units of 80 000 kernels.

The industry has seen both the attrition in the number of companies and great variation in the relative growth rates of individual companies. The many relatively small operations within the industry have a collective market share of 36%, while the industry's seven largest companies have in total an estimated 64% share of the U.S. hybrid seed corn market (J. Ansorge, 1987, personal communication).

9–5 PRODUCTION OF PARENT SEED STOCKS

Large quantities of parent seed stocks (foundation seed) are required annually to plant the several hundred thousand hectares of commercial hybrid seed corn production. Most larger companies have parent seed or foundation seed departments responsible for the production and inventory of inbred and single cross parents needed for commercial seed production. In recent years, many seed companies have devoted increasing attention to developing more effective techniques and procedures to assure adequate supplies of high-quality, genetically pure stocks.

Seed corn companies must forecast future commercial seed sales and seed production plans to ensure availability of adequate parent seed supplies. Since most seed companies produce and sell many different hybrids, the number and supply of different parent seed strains that must be maintained for commercial seed production requirements is often quite large.

9–5.1 Foundation Seed Stock Increase

Foundation seed stock increase involves the maintenance and increase of inbred lines and single cross parent seed used to produce commercial hybrids. Inbreds are the basic foundation seed used in hybrid seed corn production. Inbreds must therefore be maintained and increased under rigid control to ensure satisfactory final product performance. Although procedures employed may vary among organizations, at least three important steps are usually taken: (i) establishing and maintaining a supply of breeder seed; (ii) increasing inbred seed; and (iii) producing related-line and/or unrelated-line single cross parent seed.

Breeder seed is usually derived from bulked, self-pollinated seed at the F_8 to F_{10} generation of inbreeding. The breeder has the responsibility of ensuring that the inbred is homozygous, uniform for plant type, and adequately represents the genetic constitution of the inbred. All inbred increases are made from this base population of breeder seed. Some companies have established separate programs to maintain supplies of breeder seed. Increases are produced in well-isolated blocks by natural random sib mating. In turn, this initial inbred increase is used to plant subsequent inbred seed increases and production of single-cross parents.

Both types of increase are made under stringent isolation. Procedures and standards developed by certification agencies (Hutchcroft, 1957; Cowan, 1972) indicate the importance of minimum isolation distances. Commercial companies certify all foundation seed that will be exported. Much of the parent seed for domestic use is not certified, but guidelines developed over the years generally exceed, or at least equal, those of certification agencies.

Foundation seed fields are planned with isolation of 201 m (660 ft) as the base distance from other corn. Early studies by Jones and Brooks (1950, 1952) showed that: (i) the greatest contamination occurs in the 50 to 75 m (165–248 ft) nearest contaminating corn; (ii) pollen from border rows dilutes contamination; (iii) natural barriers may reduce contamination; (iv) an abundant supply of male corn pollen at the right time reduces contamination; (v) the direction of a field from contaminating pollen influences the amount of contamination; and (vi) "depth of field" in the direction of contamination source is important. Certification requirements in most states allow for substitution of additional male border rows for some portion of the 201-m isolation distance, but neither natural barriers nor time isolation are allowed to substitute for the required distances.

9–5.2 Procedures and Techniques

Generally, the equipment and procedures used in planting, detasseling, harvesting, drying, and conditioning of parent seed increases are similar to those used in commercial hybrid seed production. Some steps are applied more rigorously to ensure maximum genetic purity.

Variability among individual plants within the inbred population will sometimes occur. These off-types must be identified and removed (rogued) to avoid perpetuation of this variability from generation to generation. Careful plant removal (rogueing) must be practiced throughout the growing season to eliminate individual plants that exhibit phenotypes varying from the accepted phenotype of the inbred. As much rogueing as possible should occur prior to pollination to eliminate outcrossing resulting from pollen supplied by undesirable plants. Parent seed is usually harvested on the ear, allowing further selection (i.e., removal of off-type ears) to be practiced on the sorting table prior to drying and shelling (see section 9–9).

9–5.3 Quality Control

Rigid requirements must be used to maintain genetic purity at maximum levels. Genetic purity of parent seed not only helps ensure pure commercial hybrid seed but also reduces cost associated with rogueing commercial seed production fields and ear sorting at harvest. Parent seed is usually sized just as commercial seed corn. When genetic impurities occur, particularly those caused by outcrosses, they are often concentrated in specific kernel sizes, especially the large round kernels. As a result, certain kernel sizes within a specific lot may have unacceptably high levels of impurities, while other sizes in the same lot are acceptable. Careful selection of kernel sizes with the highest genetic purity can lead to improved purity of commercial seed corn.

Until relatively recently, the conventional approach to monitoring purity has been field "growouts". Growouts of a shelled corn composite of each seed lot from summer increase are often planted during the subsequent winter season to estimate genetic purity prior to use. In many cases more extensive growouts, sampling each kernel size in the lot, are conducted in the following summer growing season to obtain additional, more precise estimates of purity by kernel size. The accuracy of field growouts depends on: (i) securing a representative sample of the entire seed lot; (ii) a clean, uniform field to minimize volunteer corn and variation in plant height; (iii) favorable growing conditions; and (iv) knowledgeable personnel who are familiar with all the parental and hybrid plant phenotypes to score or "read" the growout.

Growouts are usually made in an area where the crop can be grown in the fall and winter months. Florida, Hawaii, Argentina, and Chile are most often used by U.S. seedsmen. Despite the use of winter growouts at these locations, it is difficult to obtain results early enough to make data-driven decisions on specific seed lots before the seed must be conditioned, bagged, and distributed. This is one of the factors that has led to increased reliance on electrophoresis results by some companies.

Starch gel electrophoresis (Cardy et al., 1980; Smith and Weissinger, 1984) is a recently developed technology that provides an additional means of purity analysis. The advantages of this technique include precision, rapidity relative to field growouts, absence of environmental influence on expression of genetically controlled characters, and the potential to make purity checks on developing embryonic samples collected prior to harvest (Smith and Wych, 1986). The disadvantages of this technique are the initial costs of the specialized equipment required and the cost of laboratory operation, or the relatively high cost per sample charged by commercial laboratories, if this alternative is chosen. Smith and Wych (1986) determined that the costs per seed lot for estimating percentage of female selfs by electrophoresis vs. growouts were approximately equivalent if both procedures were done in-house. However, if analysis for outcrosses is also conducted, the costs for electrophoresis may be somewhat higher than for estimation of selfs, only, due to the need to prepare and stain more gel slices. The urgency of the need for the purity information must be balanced against the comparative costs.

Seedsmen need to be aware that both growouts and electrophoresis provide useful information only to the extent that the samples are representative of a seed lot and adequate in size. The number and size of samples must be sufficient to provide an adequate measure of the variation within the seed lot being sampled.

Both growouts and electrophoresis can be used to identify accidental mechanical mixtures or mislabeling of foundation seed, which may occur at any point in production, conditioning, and inventory. For this application, electrophoresis has the same advantages and disadvantages mentioned above.

Another part of quality control of parent seed is germination. Various methods of measuring seed germination are employed and are generally performed on all usable kernel sizes of each seed lot. These methods are described in more detail later in the chapter (see section 9–11).

9–5.4 Storage and Inventory Control

Large inventories of parent seed are required. Accurate records of inventory supplies, genetic purity, and germination are maintained, since parent seed production is typically planned to provide an inventory adequate for 2 to 4 yr. Controlled environment storage facilities are used to maintain viability and quality (see section 9–12 for greater detail).

9–6 PRODUCTION OF COMMERCIAL HYBRID SEED

Agronomic practices in seed production fields are in general the same as those used to grow a commercial corn crop. However, there are some additional requirements unique to seed production. Acreages are determined on the basis of projected sales, utilizing yield levels based on breeders' research, production research, and past experience. The transition to the use of inbreds as female parents to produce single-cross hybrids has increased the need for planning, sound scientific and technical knowledge, and production technology to ensure economic success. Cultural practices used in production fields are planned to minimize risks while maximizing yield and seed quality.

9–6.1 Selection of Production Areas and Contract Growers

Successful commercial hybrid seed corn production begins with selection of a growing area and contract growers. Innovative farmers in cooperation with the seed companies have helped the seed corn industry grow into a sound business. Most seed corn production acreage is located in the Corn Belt. Expansion of the Corn Belt and increased technical knowledge have created opportunities for seed companies to expand in search of specific seed production areas. Production areas are chosen to provide such necessary factors as growing degree days, day length, lack of extreme temperatures, and specific farming practices, such as irrigation capability. By matching specific inbred needs to growing area characteristics, risk can be minimized and seed yields per female acre maximized.

Selecting growers within a production area is another important step. Generally, someone at the local production plant level will select growers who are among the most progressive and innovative corn growers in the area. The grower's location within the isolation block (see section 9–6.4) is also a factor. Seed companies attempt to select farms with high productivity indices and suitable soils that have been maintained in a state of high fertility with good weed control. Tillage and cultural practices must be in line with approved hybrid corn production practices. Good soil structure and tilth are important in order to avoid the adverse effects of poor drainage and crusting on inbred stands. Since approximately 90 to 95% of the seed acreage will be devoted to inbred or related-line single cross parents, seed corn growers who will give special attention to management of insect and disease pests, weed competition, and fertility are needed.

Contract growers must be willing to cooperate with seed companies to alter their cultural practices and/or timing, rate, and kind of herbicides, insecticides, or fungicides. Equipment modifications are often necessary. In some areas, the seed company furnishes equipment on a lease or rental basis to the growers. In other cases, growers may cooperate in the purchase and sharing of various specialized pieces of equipment such as unit planters and detasseling and harvesting equipment.

9–6.2 Contracts

With the advent of single-cross hybrid seed production, contract growers were not content to assume the greater risks associated with inbred parents. As a result, base guarantees are made that involve payment, up to a predesignated yield level, for complete failure of the seed crop. Incentive payments are often based on published futures or cash market prices at a specified time and place. In some instances, contracts are based on government based yield calculations or locally measured commercial hybrid corn yield checks.

Usually, the type of contract used, base guarantees, and multiplier factors are based upon anticipated yield levels and degree of difficulty encountered in the production of each individual hybrid. Factors such as fertility, herbicide or insecticide costs, seedbed preparation for split-date plantings, volunteer removal, and harvesting are items for consideration within the contract. There are considerable variations in contracts among companies.

9–6.3 Management of the Production Area

The management staff at a production plant are responsible for all aspects of production. They are assisted by trained supervisory help, especially during planting, detasseling, and harvesting periods. An area of 4000 to 6000 ha (10 000–15 000 acres) of seed production responsibility is fairly typical for a production plant manager and his/her staff. Within this acreage, regional (or area) supervisors are charged with responsibility for 400 to 800 ha (1000–2000 acres). During detasseling, additional supervisory help may be employed as crew foremen,, field foremen, and inspectors. The demand for additional supervisors during the summer months offers opportunities to utilize agriculture and science teachers, principals, and other professionally trained personnel during their school vacation periods.

Communication is essential for production plant managers and area supervisors to be effective in the management of their respective areas and for coordination of activities. Particularly during detasseling, it is critical that communication be available so that people and equipment can be effectively used and moved to high priority areas as needed. Many seed companies use a combination of mobile telephones, Citizen's Band radios, and FM two-way radios.

9–6.4 Isolation of Seed Fields

Isolation is intended to assure that the hybrid cross is produced with a high degree of genetic purity. It has often been said by seedsmen that the best isolation is a perfect nick, that is, when a pollen parent starts shedding just before the female parent's silks start to emerge beyond the husk or tip of the ear shoot. In addition, plant management personnel must work with each individual contract grower to establish the location and boundaries of each seed field to conform with isolation distance requirements. Preference is also given to crop rotation of corn following soybean [*Glycine max* (L.) Merr.] (rather than following corn), because volunteer corn problems are avoided and seed corn yield is higher.

Minimum standards for isolation of seed corn production fields have been established (Anonymous, 1971) for the USA and Canada; nevertheless, some variation exists among states. When zero or one male border row is present, minimum distances ranging from 125 to 201 m (410–660 ft) are typically required between the female parent of the hybrid being produced and any other corn of the same seed color, maturity, or endosperm type. Isolation distance of 201 m is required where possible contaminant corn may have different kernel color or endosperm type. Additional distance is sometimes employed where contaminating corn may be of decidedly different pollen shedding ability (such as tropical hybrids), and where wind velocities may be high, such as in production areas near large bodies of water.

Minimum isolation distance requirements can be modified by: (i) additional border rows (Fig. 9–1); (ii) size of field and production block; and (iii) adequate natural barriers and differential flowering dates (in some states). Jones and Brooks (1952) found that natural barriers are not as effective as border rows of corn. Differential flowering times are effective in isolation if silks of female parents are not receptive when pollen from other than the male parent is present.

To optimize genetic purity, a timely nick between receptive silks on the female parent and pollen shed by the male parent is required. Differential planting dates of seed parents are often required to achieve this. Abundant amounts of male pollen are also beneficial, and some companies utilize high population density in the male parent rows to increase pollen load.

Fig. 9–1. A commercial hybrid seed production field showing additional male parent border rows for the purpose of providing pollen saturation adequate to ensure genetic purity of the hybrid seed. The strip of soybeans on the left provides the required isolation distance.

9–7 PLANTING THE SEED FIELD

9–7.1 Planting Date

The minimum soil temperature for growth of corn is generally regarded as 10 °C (50 °F). Most agronomists would also agree that the optimum time for planting corn is as soon as the soil temperature at the 5-cm depth reaches that temperature for a relatively sustained period of time. Soil moisture and potential for compaction must also be taken into account. Numerous studies indicating the advantages of early planting upon yield were reviewed by Craig (1977). More recent work is summarized by Hicks and Wright (1987) and Johnson and Mulvaney (1980).

9–7.2 Fertility

In general, inbreds have poorer rooting ability than hybrids, and may therefore be more vulnerable to nutrient deficiencies and imbalances. In the past, it has been the tendency of contract growers to overfertilize to protect against possible fertility deficiencies, while at the same time striving for a balanced fertility program. Decreases in commodity prices (upon which contract payments are based) and hence economic pressures on seed growers, as well as growing concern about groundwater contamination, suggest the need for a closer examination of fertilizer recommendations. Contract growers are encouraged to use soil tests regularly and to apply nutrients only as necessary to maintain fertility levels.

9-7.3 Herbicides, Insecticides, and Fungicides

Control of weeds, insects, and diseases within the seed field have become an integral and necessary part of seed production. Since inbreds and related-line parents are less competitive than hybrid corn with broadleaf weeds and grasses, seed growers rely heavily on herbicides for effective weed control. Production personnel work with the grower to develop a weed control program that takes into account specific weed problems, crop rotation, soil type and organic matter, equipment, and the specific parents involved with the hybrid to be produced.

Insecticides for the control of above and below ground insects are generally a must. Most companies have formulated programs that protect against insect damage to stands, the growing plant, and the female parent ear. In recent years, some seed companies have begun to rely heavily on IPM (integrated pest management) principles and scouting of seed fields to determine if and when insecticide application is justified. Selection of the insecticide to use will depend upon the specific insect to be controlled, efficacy of alternative insecticides, the level of infestation, the development stage of the seed crop, safety considerations, and the reentry period.

Fungicides have also become a regular part of the production program for protection of the more susceptible parent lines to damaging fungal diseases. Genetic resistance to disease is preferred, but chemical protection is often needed when resistance is not adequate in the parent line. Spray programs have been effective in reducing damage from foliar disease on the more susceptible lines. Monitoring the crop for disease development is beneficial in making timely applications of chemicals. Fungicides are widely used as seed treatments to give protection against seed and seedling diseases (Shurtleff, 1980).

9-7.4 Plant Density

Plant density within the seed field is planned to produce maximum yields of high purity seed of saleable kernel size. Upper limits may be imposed by the particular germ plasm being used, the average rainfall pattern or irrigation availability in the production area, and local labor supply for detasseling. Many investigators have studied plant density effects on yield of hybrid corn (Craig, 1977; Johnson and Mulvaney, 1980). Fewer published studies of inbred response to plant density are available. Some seed companies conduct plant density trials with the female parents they are using in seed production. They evaluate the yield and kernel sizeout responses of those inbreds to increasing plant density. Plant densities in current use in seed fields typically range from 54 000 to 64 000 plants per ha (22 000–26 000 plants per acre) for inbred female parents, and often exceed that level for male parents, especially with inbred males that shed a limited amount of pollen.

9–7.5   Planting Patterns

Common planting patterns in seed production fields today include 4:1 (fours rows of female parent to one row of male parent) (Fig. 9–2), 4:2, 4:1:4:2, 6:2, and solid female with interplanted male. In the first three patterns, the female parent is never more than two rows from the male parent. One-half of the female parent rows are adjacent to a male parent in the 4:1 and 4:2 patterns, and two-thirds of the female parent rows are adjacent to a male parent in the 4:1:2:1 pattern. These contrast with the formerly conventional 6:2 pattern that was commonly used for production of double-cross hybrids. The 6:2 pattern is still used to produce some single crosses, but its use is generally restricted to male parents that shed an abundant supply of pollen.

Occasionally solid planting of the female parent in 96.5 to 101.6 cm (38–40 in.) rows is utilized with either every other or every fourth between-row space being interplanted with the male parent. This accomplishes two purposes: (i) full utilization of land area for female parent production; and (ii) placement of the male parent closer to the female parent rows. In stress environments, interplanting may lead to yield and quality problems. Solid plantings are typically limited to female parents not so aggressive as to overshadow the male parent and thereby delay pollen shed, and to reasonably short male delays. Also, it is advisable to restrict this practice to male parents of sufficient stalk and root strength to avoid stalk and root lodging, which would make it difficult to detassel the female parent or remove the male parent as soon as pollination is complete.

It is a practice of many seed companies to destroy the male parent by cutting or running it down (if it is brittle enough to break) after pollination is complete. Competition with the developing female parent for nutrients or available soil moisture should, in theory, be minimized and increased kernel size and/or seed yield may result. Production research conducted by the author's company has shown mixed results on kernel size and yield responses. Characteristics of the female and male parents involved and soil moisture availability after pollination are important factors contributing to the response observed. Destroying the male parent at this stage prevents grain formation in the male rows and eliminates the risk of seed contamination at harvest.

9–7.6   Parent Delay Techniques

Shoultz (1985) summarized the results of a recent survey of the seed corn industry's use of various parent delay techniques. Split-date planting of parents, the planting of the female and male parents on different dates, is used so that the two parents "nick", or reach the flowering stage concurrently (Fig. 9–3). This has been and continues to be the most popular method of making large alterations in flowering date, so that parents of differing maturities are brought together for a timely nick.

Fig. 9–2. (*Top*) A commercial hybrid seed production field planted in a 4:1 row pattern, with four detasseled rows (female) and one pollinator row (male). (*Bottom*) Aerial view of a commercial hybrid seed production field planted in a 4:1 row pattern, shown after detasseling. Note the border male rows on the left side of the field.

Fig. 9–3. Split-date planting of parents in a 6:2 row pattern. The female rows have emerged while the male rows are just being planted.

Split-date plantings are made on the basis of some combination of days, growth stages, and/or heat units accumulated from the time the first parent was planted (Shoultz, 1985). Most success has been realized by a combination of heat units and growth stage coupled with experience and good judgment. Male parents are often planted with a double delay to extend the pollen shedding period. Plantings are timed so that peak pollen shed coincides with maximum female parent silk exposure.

Other methods in common use for obtaining small adjustments to pollen shed are: (i) variable fertilizer rates; (ii) variable planting depths between parents; and iii) clipping (Cloninger et al., 1974) or flaming (Fowler, 1967) to retard development. These techniques can provide from 1 to 4 d delay in flowering, or extend the duration of flowering by as many as 2 to 4 d (Shoultz, 1985). Clipping and flaming are rarely used to delay the female parent because both techniques typically result in reduced seed yield. Clipping has been used effectively to save a crop when weather conditions have prevented planting the delayed parent when the early parent has already been planted. This has been particularly important when it is too risky to replant the early parent because too few heat units are left in the season or when a seed shortage exists for one or both parents.

9–8 POLLEN CONTROL

Pollen control refers to the practices employed to ensure hybridization by forced cross pollination between the female and male parents.

Pollen control in the hybrid seed corn production field is extremely critical. Various methods of pollen control in seed fields have been utilized or investigated. These were aimed primarily at reducing the cost or easing the difficulty at this critical time period, while still maintaining the desired genetic purity. The two most commonly used methods today are detasseling and cytoplasmic male sterility. Craig (1977) described two other methods, genic male sterility and chemical pollen control, which are not currently in widespread use.

9–8.1 Detasseling the Seed Field

Detasseling currently represents the most widely used method of pollen control. Detasseling involves the physical removal of the tassel from the female plant, either as a manual operation or in combination with mechanical devices. To ensure that each seed field meets the necessary quality (genetic purity) standards, tassels from the female parent rows must be removed before they shed pollen and/or before silks emerge on the ear shoots of the female parent. This is an expensive operation, currently costing the seed company from $250 to $320 per female hectare ($100 to $130 per female acre) for an average female parent. Increasing wage rates and deteriorating population demographics (labor supply and its distribution) are two factors that will continue to pose challenges to the industry.

Genetic purity of intended crosses is dependent on compliance with standards established by company management and certifying agencies (Anonymous, 1971). When the female parent has 5% receptive silks (silks emerged and turgid) the following standards, as established by certifying agencies, are employed: (i) the female parent is limited to 1% shedding tassels at any one inspection and to a total of 2% shedding tassels for three inspections at different dates; and (ii) off-types in the male not over 0.2% at any inspection. Some seed companies have established more rigorous standards; e.g., not over 0.5% female shedders allowed at any one inspection and not over 0.1% male off-types per inspection. Tassels are counted as shedding when more than 5 cm (2 in.) of the central spike and/or side branches have emerged and have shedding anthers.

Major seed corn companies hire and train seed field inspectors to observe pollen control operations, report irregularities, and assist in interpreting rules for the detasseling/rogueing supervisors. These inspectors may be assigned as many as 810 to 1620 gross ha (2000 to 4000 gross acres). Before detasseling begins, they establish compliance with isolation requirements and check for volunteer corn and/or off-type plants in both female and male parent rows. When detasseling starts, the inspectors check fields to be sure that female parent tassels and off-types in male rows are properly removed. The objective is to keep those who are responsible for achieving genetic purity (plant management, area foremen, and detasseling contractors) informed, and to prevent any violation of standards. If isolation, detasseling, or rogue removal standards are not met, inspectors report the details to plant management, so that a decision regarding corrective measures can be made.

9–8.2 Manual or Hand Detasseling

Each year thousands of workers, usually teenage youth, are employed by seed companies to perform the hand detasseling operation. This activity may last only 1 week, but may continue up to 5 weeks or more depending upon the volume of production and spread in female parent maturities planted within a seed production area. Several factors influence the magnitude and complexity of this job:

1. Tassels must be removed from all female plants in a timely manner, as previously discussed.
2. When weather conditions favor rapid corn growth, fields must be covered daily; this requires 7-d workweeks, rain or shine.
3. Some female parent plant types are easier to detassel than others.
4. Female parents whose tassels begin shedding pollen before fully emerging from the upper leaves, or which silk at about the same time as pollen shed occurs, create difficult detasseling supervision, management, and purity problems.
5. Weather conditions can greatly aid or complicate the detasseling season. A heavy rain or windstorm can lodge and tangle the female parent just as tassels emerge, making walking or driving through the field more difficult. Extreme heat can affect both the efficiency of detasselers and the emergence of silks and tassels.

Detasselers are usually organized into crews ranging from 6 up to 40 or 50 workers. The crew supervisor is responsible for recruiting, transporting, training, managing, and controlling the detasselers in his crew. With larger crews, the supervisor will have one or more assistants (sometimes called checkers) to help in crew training and managing the job to be done in the field. There will customarily be one supervisor or checker for each 6 to 10 crew members. It is important that each crew member be trained in proper detasseling technique, to minimize leaf damage and to ensure an effective detasseling job in each female parent row. The crew supervisor is also responsible for the safety and comfort of the workers while in the field.

For more effective and efficient labor utilization, detasseling carts or personnel carriers (Fig. 9–4) are frequently used, especially for detasseling taller-growing inbreds or single-cross female parents. These carts are motorized high-clearance machines equipped with platforms upon which the workers stand as they remove the tassels. The machines move slowly through the field, enabling the detasselers to look down into the plant canopy and remove the tassels more effectively and easily than if they were on foot. Usually 12 detasselers will work from each machine; for maximum effectiveness it is therefore important that all detasselers on

Fig. 9–4. A high clearance personnel carrier transporting detasselers through a seed production field. This view depicts the "second pass" through this field; during this trip, late-emerging tassels are removed.

each machine be equally skilled. It is often difficult or impossible to use these machines immediately after heavy rain or windstorms, and the detasselers must then proceed on foot.

Some seed companies employ contract detasselers for at least a part of their seed production. With this method, the contractors agree to detassel specified field areas for an established fee paid to them by the seed company. The contractors may work their own hours as long as they meet the company's established standards for timely removal of tassels. If they fail to do so, the seed company reserves the right to bring in a crew or mechanical detasselers to remove the potential problem-causing tassels before they shed pollen, and to deduct this expense from the contractor's payment. Contractors typically provide transportation for themselves and any other detasselers they employ, as well as the necessary supervision. This method often permits people employed in other jobs to earn extra income during their free time.

9–8.3 Mechanical Detasseling

Craig (1977) summarized several factors that led to increased use of mechanical detasselers in the early 1970s. Availability and cost of labor for manual detasseling continue to concern seed companies, and work to improve equipment for mechanical detasseling is ongoing.

Mechanical detasselers (Fig. 9–5) are self-propelled, high-clearance machines capable of operating even in extremely muddy fields. They fall into two basic types:

1. Cutters—a rotating cutter blade or knife cuts or shreds the top of

Fig. 9–5. (*Top*) A "wheel puller" machine used for mechanical detasseling of the female rows in a seed production field. (*Bottom*) Close-up view of the wheels in action.

the corn plant, including the tassel; the blades operate at various planes, from horizontal to vertical, and are adjustable in height.

2. Pullers—usually two counter-rotating wheels or rollers, adjustable in height, grasp the tassel and upper leaves and pull them upward in a manner approximating a hand detasseling operation.

The efficiency of mechanical detasselers is affected by many variables in the seed field, such as female parent morphology (leaf and tassel orientation), uniformity of female parent plant height and development, and skill of the operator. Mechanical detasseling produces best results when it is done in a uniform seed field in which the tassel is well exserted ahead of pollen shedding. As conditions become less favorable, percentage of tassels removed per pass will decrease and leaf damage will increase. The typical objective in the use of mechanical detasselers is to delay the operation as long as possible before silk emergence, to permit maximum exsertion of tassels, enabling their removal with minimum leaf damage. However, this delay increases the risk of leaving "sprigs" (partial tassels) or "hangers" in the leaf canopy. Hangers, as tassels that become lodged in the leaf canopy are sometimes called, are capable of shedding pollen for 2 to 3 d after removal (D. Langer and P. Downes, 1982, unpublished data). Hangers can lead to increased levels of female selfs, and are one of the chief objections that some companies have to mechanical detasseling machines. In all cases, some hand labor is required to move hangers to the ground and to pull entire tassels or sprigs remaining on missed, late, or short plants, or on tillers.

With most female parents, the combination of mechanical and hand detasseling will result in a cost savings when compared with hand detasseling alone. Current detasseling costs range from $198 to $247 per ha ($80–$100 per female acre) with a combination of mechanical and hand detasseling, compared to $296 to $321 per ha ($120 to $130 per female acre) for all hand detasseling (W. Beck, 1987, personal communication).

Cost savings attained through mechanical detasseling may be offset by seed yield reductions if the operation is not carefully managed to minimize leaf damage (Craig, 1977, unpublished data). To decide whether or not to use mechanical detasseling, seed companies and plant management consider variable production costs, especially current detasseling wages, and available labor supply, and weigh them against characteristics of the female parents involved and the size of the detasseling operation they face.

9–8.4 Effect of Detasseling on Seed Yield

The resumption in 1971 of detasseling as the primary method for pollen control (see section 9–8.5) renewed interest in the effect of detasseling on yield. The effect of detasseling on seed yield was considered more critical then, since inbred females had become involved due to the transitional adoption of single-cross hybrids. The development of various types of mechanical detasseling machines also added a new dimension. A discussion of the effect of detasseling and leaf removal on seed yields of the female parents of double-cross hybrids may be found in Craig (1977).

Published work on leaf removal with inbred lines indicates that the yield response is generally similar to that of single crosses. In theory, removal of only the tassel could result in a yield increase, due to decreased shading of upper leaves and reduced competition for photosynthate and nutrients between the ear and the tassel. Hunter et al. (1973) removed the tassel, only, from 10 inbreds and observed an average increase in yield of 6.9%. As more leaves were removed with the tassel, however, greater yield reductions typically occurred. When one, two, and three leaves were removed with the tassel, yield reductions averaged 1.5, 4.9, and 13.5% relative to the yield where the tassel alone was removed. Cantrell and Geadelmann (1981) removed the tassel with two leaves. They observed yield reductions ranging from 9 to 13% across four early maturity inbreds, with an average of 11.6% yield reduction. Several other workers have reported differences among inbreds in sensitivity to yield reduction following varying amounts of defoliation (Cantrell and Geadelmann, 1981; Hunter et al., 1973; Vasilas and Seif, 1985b).

It is common to observe greater yield reductions after mechanical detasseling than after hand detasseling. Studies conducted by seed companies with mechanical detasseling machines have shown varying results. Craig (1977) cited unpublished research in which the yield of mechanically detasseled plots was from 2 to 40% less than that of hand detasseled treatments, depending upon the inbred involved and the number of mechanical cuttings. Unpublished research by C. Carter and R. York (1979, unpublished data) compared hand detasseling with wheel pullers on inbred females. These workers observed yield reductions ranging from 2 to 46% depending on the inbred line, number of wheel pulls, and timing of the wheel pulling operation.

Measurements have been made on the yield components affected by detasseling, to determine which are primarily responsible for reduced yield (Hunter et al., 1973; Pucaric and Gotlin, 1979; Vasilas and Seif, 1985a; Craig, 1977). The variables involved in these studies included the following: (i) the time of cutting or tassel removal in relation to plant development; (ii) the climatic conditions prior to, during, and after tassel removal; (iii) morphological differences among genotypes; (iv) type of detasseling machine; (v) the number of times cut or pulled; and (vi) the skill and attention of the machine operator. Although kernel number has most often been the major contributing factor, results have varied due to the differences in severity and timing of treatments employed. These complexities mean that precise statements regarding the effect of detasseling treatments on yield components cannot be made.

9–8.5   Cytoplasmic Male Sterility

For about two decades prior to the epidemic of southern corn leaf blight that swept the USA in 1970, the conversion of inbred parents to Texas cytoplasmic male sterility (*cms*-T) replaced detasseling as the predominant form of pollen control (Craig, 1977; Ullstrup, 1972). Though other male sterile cytoplasms were available, the T source (Rogers and Edwardson, 1952) proved to be the most satisfactory, because more inbreds were completely sterilized by T cytoplasm and genetic fertility restoration was more easily accomplished in this cytoplasm.

After the 1970 epidemic, the realization that the nearly complete conversion to T cytoplasm increased the vulnerability of the corn crop (NAS, 1972; Ullstrup, 1972) prompted a retreat from the extensive use of cms as a substitute for detasseling. In addition to T cytoplasm, many other male-sterile cytoplasms had been identified (Beckett, 1971; Duvick, 1965); of these, the C and S cytoplasms were the best known (Duvick, 1972). Since the use of cms was still a cost-competitive and satisfactory technique for hybrid seed production, C and S cytoplasms became important again in the late 1970s and early 1980s.

The American Seed Trade Association (ASTA) recently conducted a survey of the type of cytoplasm used in the production of seed corn to be sold in the USA. Based on number of units of expected sales for 1987, 66.1% of the seed corn was produced using 100% normal (N) cytoplasm, 22.1% involved production with *cms*-C cytoplasm (1.9% involving 100% *cms*-C and restorers, and 20.2% involving blends with N cytoplasm), and 11.5% involved *cms*-S cytoplasm (0.4% using *cms*-S and restorers, and 11.1% involving blends with N cytoplasm) (W. T. Schapaugh, 1987, letter to member companies responding to ASTA Corn Cytoplasm Survey).

There are two major ways in which cms has been used to facilitate the crossing of two inbreds. In the first case, detasseling is eliminated through the use of a female parent for which the cms conversion is completely male sterile. No detasseling is required. The other case involves combination of C or S cytoplasms in certain genetic backgrounds that result in only partial male sterility. In this situation, anther exsertion is delayed 1 to 10 d (Duvick, 1965) and usually commences after the tassel is fully extended above the leaves. At this point, mechanical detasseling can be accomplished with minimum leaf removal.

Consider the production of the single cross, A × B. If inbred A is nonrestorer genotype (rf/rf) that has been put into a male sterile cytoplasm by backcrossing, one can plant blocks of cms female A alternating with blocks of inbred B (the male) and produce completely cross-pollinated seed on inbred A without detasseling. If inbred B is also a nonrestorer genotype, the hybrid plants in a field of commercial corn would also be pollen sterile; if inbred B carries dominant restorer genes (Rf/Rf), however, the hybrid (Rf/rf) will shed pollen.

Since restored hybrids do not always shed adequate pollen (Duvick,

1959), the use of the restorer system introduces some risk for both the farmer and the seed company. Consequently, most single cross production is likely to involve a nonrestored genotype, in which from 25 to 50% of fertile hybrid seed, produced by detasseling, is blended with 50 to 75% of seed of the same hybrid produced by the cms method. This blending results in 25 to 50% of the hybrid plants in the farmer's field that will shed pollen normally.

Various methods of blending to assure complete mixing are practiced. One method is to flank the pollinator with alternating blocks of cms and normal (fertile) cytoplasm female. Another method increases the scale by planting alternating quarters of the field in sterile or normal female. Harvesting entails making one trip across the field in the cms female and a return trip through the normal female. By the time the ear corn reaches the conditioning plant, the ears of the two cytoplasms are thoroughly mixed.

9–8.6   Other Types of Sterility

Craig (1977) described in some detail the "Patterson method", which employs genic male sterility in the production of hybrid seed corn. This method is not widely used today, however, since the conversion of inbreds is complicated, time consuming, and expensive. Furthermore, additional expenses, in the form of foundation seed production inventory and quality control, are required.

Use of chemically induced male sterility in commercial hybrid seed corn production is an idea that has received considerable attention (Craig, 1977). Despite substantial research and development effort by several agricultural chemical companies, there is essentially no recent published work on this subject for corn. Likewise, a dependable and affordable commercial application of chemical hybridizing agents for seed corn production has not yet been discovered and/or developed (S. L. Kaplan, 1987, personal communication). To date, the major stumbling blocks have been either insufficient sterility percentage (Bollinger et al., 1978) or associated female barrenness (A. J. Cavalieri, 1987, personal communication).

9–9   HARVESTING THE SEED CROP

Harvest of the hybrid seed corn crop is, by necessity, closely coordinated with the operations of conditioning facilities at the production plant. The following discussion describes the operations generally used at a typical large production plant (Fig. 9–6). There are variations among companies and among locations within a single company. All operations from husking to distribution may be done at one location. Alternatively, harvesting, sorting, drying, and shelling may be accomplished at a plant

Fig. 9–6. A modern hybrid seed corn production plant located in Iowa, with facilities for all steps in conditioning, bagged seed storage in year-round controlled atmosphere conditions, and distribution of seed.

near the growing location, while the sizing, cleaning, bagging, storage, and distribution are done at other more centralized locations.

9–9.1 Maturity and Seed Quality

Harvest of the seed crop usually begins just before the developing kernels approach physiological maturity, the stage at which the kernels have reached their maximum dry matter accumulation. The moisture percentage at which kernels of inbred corn reach physiological maturity varies with genotype and environment, and ranges from 30 to 38% (A. J. Cavalieri, 1987, unpublished data; Knittle and Burris, 1976). Generally, harvest will begin when the moisture level of the seed is between 30 and 38%. The target moisture level depends upon factors such as the female parent, environment, weather forecasts, production volume and, finally, production plant capacity.

For planning purposes, projected harvest dates are typically estimated by monitoring kernel moisture percentage and heat unit (or growing degree day) accumulation, in combination with "black layer" formation (Daynard, 1969, 1972; Daynard and Duncan, 1969) and/or progression of the "milk line" (Afuakwa and Crookston, 1984). Genetic variation for field drying rates has been observed among inbreds (Carter and Poneleit, 1973; A. J. Cavalieri, 1986, unpublished data), and may be taken into account.

Timely harvest of the seed crop provides the seed company several advantages, including minimization of: (i) risk of freeze injury; (ii) field losses from mechanical pickers; (iii) risk of harvest delays due to adverse weather conditions; and (iv) quality deterioration due to insect damage, ear molds, stalk rots, and other diseases. Each of these factors contributes to the quality of the seed crop by reduction of physical damage, preservation of physiological vigor, and enhancement of appearance.

The adverse effect of freeze damage upon seed germination is a major risk to seed corn companies (Airy, 1955; Burris and Knittle, 1985). Rossman (1949) concluded that the amount of damage by freezing depended on temperature, duration of exposure, moisture of seed, genotype, husk protection, stage of development, and rate of drying after freezing. Studies reported by Neal (1961) indicated that injury to germination from freeze damage is directly related to kernel moisture as well as intensity and duration of exposure. The higher the moisture, the greater the effect on germination at all levels of freeze treatments.

9-9.2 Field Operations

The contract grower is responsible for harvesting the seed crop and delivering it to the production plant. Most mechanical harvesters used today are self-propelled ear corn pickers with three, four, or six-row heads (Fig. 9-7). Reduction in mechanical damage from the harvesters is accomplished by removing pegs from the husking rolls and properly adjusting the husking beds. Since harvest rate is ultimately determined by dryer capacity, a well-coordinated schedule directed by the production plant management is necessary to keep field harvest operations moving smoothly and dryers at full capacity.

9-9.3 Plant Operations

The seed is weighed as it is delivered to the plant. As the load is being dumped for movement into the husking/sorting building, the ear corn is sampled to accurately represent the grower's production of each hybrid. If maturity or moisture varies within a grower's fields, more than one sample is secured. These samples are used for measurement of grain moisture percentage and the cob and husk percentage. These data are used to calculate weight of No. 2 shelled corn delivered, which is the basis of payment to the contract grower.

While final husking is still done in the field by some companies, more than 90% of the seed corn produced in the USA is transported to the plant before it is husked a final time, sorted, and then moved to the dryers (Stanfield, 1986). In a typical husking/sorting building, ear corn is conveyed from the green corn receiving area (Fig. 9-8) to storage bins above the husking bed. The action of the husking bed removes the majority of the remaining husks before the ear corn passes over the sorting table (Fig. 9-9). In some operations, a return conveyor takes unhusked ears back over the husking bed. Usually, from four to six workers per table sort the ear corn as it passes over the table. These workers remove any diseased, off-type, or off-color ears from the seed. After sorting, the seed is conveyed to the dryers.

9-10 SEED CORN CONDITIONING

Conditioning of seed corn is the series of activities that begins with drying the ear corn and ends with the seed being bagged. The primary

Fig. 9–7. (*Top*) Mechanically harvesting ear corn from the female rows using a three-row ear corn picker. (*Bottom*) The ear corn is elevated into a trailing wagon.

steps involved are drying, shelling, cleaning, sizing, treating, and bagging. These activities are accomplished in plants of all sizes and descriptions (Fig. 9–6). Although varying in engineering, all conditioning plants are designed and built to efficiently handle quantities of seed ranging from a few thousand to several million kilograms per year.

Certain objectives must constantly be addressed during the various

Fig. 9–8. Unloading seed corn at the green corn receiving area at a production plant. The ear corn is conveyed from this area to the husking and sorting building.

Fig. 9–9. The sorting operation in progress. Workers remove undesirable ears before the ear corn is conveyed to the dryer. The conveyer above the sorting table returns unhusked ears to the husking bed.

procedures of conditioning. First, the seed must be handled in a manner that minimizes mechanical damage. Any breaks that occur in the seed coat have a direct and detrimental effect on germinability and vigor of the seedling plant (Knake et al., 1986). The extent to which germinability and/or vigor are reduced depends on both the severity and location of the mechanical damage (Wortman and Rinke, 1951; Wright, 1948). The effects of seed coat damage can be only partially offset by the application of fungicidal seed treatment (Knake et al., 1986; Tatum and Zuber, 1943).

A second objective of conditioning is to achieve maximum plantability within the limitations imposed by the sizing equipment. The objectives of sizing seed are to achieve uniformity of appearance and to maximize uniformity of kernel size and/or shape so that seeds drop accurately with either plate-type or plateless planters. The contemporary corn farmer, who is optimizing soil fertility, selecting hybrids best adapted to specific population densities, and planting for most efficient production, cannot tolerate significant fluctuations in stand.

Finally, the production plant manager must carefully maintain conditioning schedules to ensure the orderly movement of seed lots through distribution channels to meet delivery and planting schedules.

9–10.1 Drying the Seed

Seed corn dryers (Fig. 9–10) vary considerably throughout the industry. The majority of the systems utilize a squirrel-cage or axial-vane fan system to draw fresh air through a burner and force the heated air through bins filled with ear corn. Most burners today are fired with natural, butane, or propane gas.

Drying temperatures vary from 35 to 46 °C (95–115 °F). The entire

Fig. 9–10. Top view of an ear corn dryer at a seed corn conditioning facility. The doors are opened during bin filling, closed during the first half of the drying cycle, and then opened again to exhaust moisture-laden air during the last half of the drying cycle.

drying procedure is closely monitored since higher temperatures are detrimental to seed quality. Temperatures in the dryer building are measured at the point of contact with the seed. Temperatures above 45 °C (113 °F) have been reported as injurious to seed viability (Navratil and Burris, 1984; Craig, 1977), and high moisture seed is best dried at temperatures of 35 to 40 °C (95–105 °F) (Navratil and Burris, 1984; R. F. Baker, N. M. Frey, and R. D. Wych, unpublished data). It is also known that the higher the initial moisture content, the more susceptible the seed is to germination damage, and that genotypes vary in dryer sensitivity. Air temperatures of 46 °C (115 °F) may be used after moisture content of the seed has decreased to 20% or less, to complete the drying with minimal risk of germination injury. The seed corn is dried to 12 to 13% moisture, at which time it is conveyed to the sheller.

The moisture level to which seed corn is dried and held in storage also is critical. Cal and Obendorf (1972) showed that imbibition of low moisture (6%) corn kernels at temperatures of 5 °C (41 °F) resulted in malformed and delayed seedling growth. Sensitivity to imbibitional chilling was reduced when the initial kernel moisture was 13 or 16%.

9–10.2 Shelling the Seed

Shellers used for seed corn are designed so that when operated at low speeds, the seed is more or less rubbed from the cob. As the sheller speed increases, the action becomes increasingly pounding, kernel damage drastically increases, and germination declines (Airy, 1955). Therefore, it is desirable that all contact edges of the moving sheller parts be well smoothed to reduce damage. Experience has shown that with adequate horsepower, shellers can be operated at lower speeds and kernel damage is reduced by keeping the sheller full at all times.

9–10.3 Conveying the Seed

Since prevention of kernel damage is one objective of conditioning seed, it follows that each step should be evaluated to determine the amount of damage chargeable to that procedure. When studies such as this were done, some of the conveying equipment formerly used was found to be directly responsible for much of the mechanical damage (Craig, 1977). Grain augers crack and scuff seed; chain conveyors crush and crack kernels; and single tube elevator legs allow seed to be caught under belts and behind cups. Perhaps the greatest single source of damage is the dropping of seed from elevated conveyors into steel bottom bins or onto concrete floors.

Today, elevator legs are the double tube type and are equipped with either all plastic or plastic-lipped buckets. Chain conveyors are seldom used anymore, and augers have been replaced by belted conveyors. Breakage from impact on bin bottoms has been nearly eliminated by using grain spirals or ladders (Fig. 9–11) to lower seed gently with minimal

Fig. 9–11. Bulk seed in storage awaiting further conditioning and bagging. The spiral chute permits filling the bin while subjecting the seed to minimal mechanical injury.

impact. Whenever the fall distances are greater than 2 to 3 m, such equipment should be considered. Lateral conveying of seed is done either on rubber belting or with vibrating trough conveyors.

9–10.4 Cleaning the Seed

Seed corn from the sheller contains varying amounts of foreign material, consisting of bits of cob, husk, silk, pieces of kernels and, on occasion, insect larvae brought in from the field with the ear corn. Storage properties, plantability, and appearance of seed are greatly enhanced by removal of such debris. If not removed, the debris encourages storage insect problems and the development of hot spots when seed is stored for long periods. Aeration and cooling are improved by removing such foreign material, and less storage space is required.

Two types of machines are used in the first steps of cleaning seed, air screen machines and scalperators. With air screen machines, shelled corn is delivered to sloping shaker screens that remove wide, extra large kernels and cob pieces (over a 24/64; see section 9–10.5 for a description of screen size nomenclature) and narrow tip kernels (through a 15/64 or a 16/64). The seed then passes through a blast of air that lifts fines, small cob pieces, and dust which have escaped the screening action. With scalperators, shelled corn is fed onto a rotating wire mesh reel. Kernels and small cob fragments pass through the mesh, thus separating them from the larger cob pieces. An air chamber is then utilized to separate fines, which are routed to a dust collector. Any grain removed is disposed of as feed or market corn.

When necessary, insects are controlled with an application of a slurry formulation of an appropriate insecticide to the shelled corn stream being conveyed into bulk storage bins. This is especially critical when there may be a delay between shelling and movement of bagged seed to cold storage following sizing, treating, and bagging.

In many operations, the shelled corn is cleaned again as the first step in the sizing towers. The air screen machines or scalperators (with a smaller mesh) are fed at a slower rate to achieve more extensive removal of fines and foreign material. A thorough cleaning prior to sizing is essential to: (i) reduce the amount of dust; (ii) ensure smooth rapid flow through the sizers; and (iii) permit cleaners (aspirators or gravity separators) at the end of the sizing system to operate more efficiently.

9–10.5   Sizing the Seed

9–10.5.1   Sizing

Sizing as used in the seed industry means separating kernels into uniform lots of sizes based on width, thickness, and length. The historic term *grading* carries a connotation of quality measurement that does not apply to the procedure. To determine screens to use in sizing, some seed companies secure a 760 to 1270 kg (30–50 bu) composite sample for each lot. These are run through a sample sizer to determine percent by size, kernel counts, plantability, and germination.

During sizing, seeds are passed through round hole cylinders in a descending series of screen sizes, which are measured in 1/128th in. (commonly referenced as one-half 64th of an inch). Screens are selected to separate the seed into large, medium, and small kernel sizes, and "tips" (narrow seeds for discard). In some systems, a divider cylinder is used to split the seed into "overs" and "throughs". The overs are separated with a larger screen into large and medium portions. A smaller screen divides the throughs into medium (combined with medium from the other separation) and small kernels. Another smaller round hole screen then removes the tips. Following this, slot screens from 12/64 to 14/64 are used to separate large kernels into large flat (LF) and large round (LR), medium kernels into MF and MR, and small kernels into SF and SR. Figure 9–12 illustrates this sequence. In contrast, some systems separate rounds and flats with slotted screens first. Then the rounds and flats are divided by round hole cylinders into large, medium, and small sizes. The goal of both systems of kernel size separations is to achieve seed with acceptable appearance and plantability.

Kernel sizes may be length sized if the range in length would be unacceptable to customers. Length sizers, called uniflows, remove shorter kernels, utilizing a revolving indented cylinder. Shorter kernels ride up higher on the inside of the cylinder before falling out of the indentations

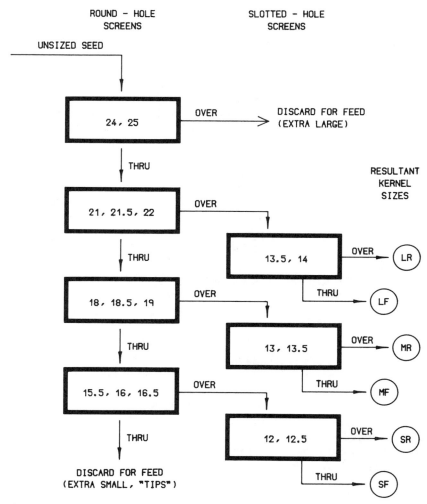

Fig. 9–12. A diagramatic outline of typical screen sizes used for sizing seed corn, using round-hole screens first and then dividing each portion (large, medium, and small) into flat and round kernels with slotted-hole screens. Screen sizes are given in 64ths of an inch.

and are captured by an adjustable tilt trough through the center of the cylinder. Uniflows may be used to remove long kernels in seed of three-way crosses and modified single crosses. Length sizing is much less common with seed from inbreds, which characteristically have rather short kernels. Length sizing generally has little effect on plantability if the shortest kernels are longer than one-half of the plate cell length.

Separation tolerances of 3/64 in. for width and thickness and 4/64 in. for length have been proposed (Bateman, 1972; McKee, 1963). The industry, however, commonly accepts a 4/64 in. range for kernel width (round hole) and up to an 8/64 in. range for length with long kerneled seeds. Bateman (1972) suggested plantability (number of kernels dropped) tolerance with plate planters of 3% under-drop to 5% over-drop. This matches well with industry standards, but under-drop must be carefully monitored to be certain that sorting does not occur. Changing round hole screens by one-half 64th of an inch is usually sufficient to greatly improve plantabilities which are heavy or light.

Since the first "plateless" planter (John Deere® 'Max-Emerge'®) was introduced in the early 1970s, sizing methods have been undergoing change. This change has been accelerated as other equipment manufacturers have also introduced plateless planters. Each of these so-called plateless planters satisfactorily plant seed without prior separation of flat from round sizes. Consequently, most seed corn firms now offer plateless sizes (flats and rounds undivided or blended together), usually sized (and designated) further as large, medium, or small. Since variation in kernel length is no problem for these planters, the short kernels removed in length sizing are often blended into plateless sizes. Current estimates indicate that 85% or more of the corn in some areas is planted with plateless planters. Consequently, up to 60% of the sales of some companies is in plateless kernel sizes.

9–10.5.2 Cleaning Sized Seed

Removal of damaged and diseased kernels, which are usually lighter in weight than sound kernels, is accomplished through the use of aspirators or specific gravity separators. Aspirators have high capacity, but the separation is not as fine as with gravity separators. Consequently, aspirators tend to discard more desirable kernels without as thorough removal of imperfect seeds. Operation of gravity separators requires more skill, because adjustments must be made not only on the feed rate and air flow, but also on the tilt and pitch of the gravity deck and on shaker speed. Quality counts before and after cleaners are vital to satisfactory operation.

Conditioning of seed corn often has little effect on germination but appearance is greatly improved. Improved equipment and a higher comprehension of seed quality by discriminating customers has resulted in excellently conditioned seed being sold in the marketplace today.

9–10.6 Planter Plate Selection

Practically all seed corn companies offer planter plate suggestions for customer convenience. The process of making planter plate checks not only identifies the plates that should be suggested to the customer, but also serves as a check on the accuracy of sizing. If the check planter will not drop the seed accurately, adjustments are made on the sizing equipment to improve accuracy. Most plate selection is done on actual planter test stands provided in recent years by the DICKEY-john® Corp. Planter stands are often electronically monitored, which makes this step faster and eliminates human error in counting drop accuracy. Planting suggestions are also made for plateless planters.

9–10.7 Treating the Seed

Most seed companies apply a fungicide or a combination fungicide/insecticide to the seed before bagging. The purpose of treating conditioned seed is to protect against seedling diseases and to give short-term protection against storage insects. Properly treating seed may also help offset vulnerability to disease caused by mechanical damage (Knake et al., 1986; Wortman and Rinke, 1951; Wright, 1948).

A typical dosage of the fungicide captan [*cis-N*-((trichloromethyl)thio)-4cyclohexene-1,2-dicarboximide] is about 0.6 g a. i. per kilogram of seed (600 ppm; 0.54 oz/bu). In areas where head smut disease is prevalent, Vitavax® or Vitavax®/thiram [bis(dimethylthio-carbamoyl)disulfide] fungicides are utilized in place of captan. A purplish or reddish dye is usually added to the fungicidal slurry to impart a distinctive color to the seed corn. This enables easy identification that treatment has been added. The treatment is spray metered on the seed in a rolling cylinder drum. A smooth uniform application is desired. During extremely cold weather, methanol may be added to prevent spotty treatment due to crystal formation.

Until recently, malathion (*O,O*-dimethyl phosphorodithoate of diethyl mercaptosuccinate) and methoxychlor [2,2-bis(p-methoxyphenyl)-1,1,1-trichloroethane] were the insecticides most commonly included in the treating mix. Use of these chemicals is now declining, due to efficacy and cost considerations, stricter governmental regulations, and the introduction of newer chemistries that are effective at lower application rates. Insecticide and fungicide use will continue to be a dynamic reflection of new chemistry, cooperative research between the chemical companies and the seed corn industry, and the regulation climate imposed by the Environmental Protection Agency and the Food and Drug Administration.

9–10.8 Bagging the Seed

Most seed corn today is packaged by automatic or semi-automatic equipment (Fig. 9–13). A specified amount of seed is weighed, the bag is hung and filled, a tag is sewn on, and the bag is coded. Only one or two operators are needed to monitor this operation and keep it running smoothly. Nearly all seed corn in the USA is packaged in multi-ply bags, most of which contain a moisture barrier of free polyethylene or a polyethylene-coated sheet to protect against external water. A crinkled outer ply with a nonslip coating improves handling and stacking ability.

A relatively new innovation is the replacement of sewing by the use of heat-sealed bags. The advantages of heat sealing are to: (i) make entry

Fig. 9–13. A typical bagging line in which the seed is weighed and dropped into the bag. Information such as bag weight, kernel size, and seed lot code is printed on the bag, and a preprinted tag is attached as the bag is sewn closed while traveling on a belt conveyor. The bags are subsequently stacked on pallets.

into the bag by moisture and insects more difficult; (ii) eliminate problems caused by malfunctioning sewing heads; and (iii) save the cost of sewing thread. Pressure sensitive labels which are preprinted by computers can be used in place of sewn in tags.

Package size has moved from the bushel bag (25 kg, or 56 lb) to units weighing 23 kg (50 lb) and, in recent years, to units with 80 000 kernels per bag. A problem with bagging all units with 80 000 kernels is that different kernel sizes neither weigh the same nor require the same volume. Bag weights may vary from 13 to 32 kg (30–70 lb) and a variety of bag sizes is necessary so that all bags will be full regardless of kernel size. In addition, palletizing bagged seed becomes difficult because of the different bag sizes. A partial solution to these problems has been achieved by some companies who have resumed varying kernel count per unit by kernel size, so that bag weight is near 22 kg (48 lb).

An important final step in conditioning is collecting and saving a representative sample of each seed lot. Trickle samplers are often used, but care must be exercised to ensure that the sampling tube draws from all the flow. Otherwise, stratification in the flow may cause the accumulation of a nonrepresentative sample. The sample thus obtained is used by quality assurance for germination and purity tests, verification of kernel counts, and checks for damaged kernels and inert material. State and federal laws require certain information to be printed on each bag or on a tag or label affixed to each bag. Requirements vary from state to state, although attempts have been made to standardize these requirements.

9–11 QUALITY ASSURANCE

During the past 10 to 15 years, many changes have taken place in the techniques, equipment, and inbred parents that affect seed corn quality. Because of higher yield goals and increased production costs, farmers demand and, in general, receive high-quality seed. It is the goal of seedsmen to supply adequate quantities of a product that retains the genetic gains incorporated into a given hybrid by the corn breeder. To help realize these goals, most companies maintain a quality assurance program to monitor all phases of seed production.

The quality assurance program should have well-defined procedures and standards that are understood by all levels of management. Data should be collected according to rules and procedures outlined in *Rules of Testing Seeds* (Anonymous, 1981), the AOSCA *Certification Handbook* (Anonymous, 1971), and the *International Rules of Seed Testing* (Anonymous, 1985). Often more strict and precise rules and procedures have been adopted by company management.

Isolation standards and tests for genetic purity were described earlier in the chapter as they pertained to production of parent seed stocks and commercial hybrid seed corn (see p. 568–571, 573). The rest of this section deals with standards for specialty corn and quality assurance procedures that are conducted during and after conditioning.

9–11.1 Specialty Corn

Seed production and quality control procedures for maintaining genetic purity of white, waxy, high-lysine, and high-amylose corn are somewhat stricter than those outlined above for yellow dent corn. These specialty corns differ from normal yellow dent by being homozygous for recessive alleles at one or more critical loci. Thus, contamination arising from any foreign pollen would mask the expression of the desired trait.

Production standards are more demanding for specialty corn. Any expression of xenia in the kernels must be removed in order to meet genetic purity standards. Most waxy and high-amylose corn is marketed with <3% normal endosperm. See Bear (1975) for a discussion of purity requirements for these specialty corns.

Isolation standards to minimize contamination in specialty seed corn have been set at 201 m (660 ft) plus four border rows when the field size is 4 ha (10 acres) or less. The distance can be decreased as field size and/or the number of border rows increases. However, many commercial companies maintain the 201 m, and some require as much as 402 m (1320 ft), as a minimum isolation distance.

When contamination does occur, such as yellow kernels in white corn, procedures have been established to remove the obviously impure seeds. The original method was to pick out the yellow kernels at the sorting tables before drying the ears. Although electronic devices sensitive to minute color changes can be used, the equipment is expensive and its capacity is limited, so few companies use color sorters. With waxy corn, a special technique to identify dent contamination is used (Jugenheimer, 1958). An iodine solution applied to exposed endosperm starch causes the waxy kernels to stain reddish brown, while normal-starch kernels stain blue-black. The iodine stain converts a chemical property to a color test that is ultimately equivalent to the detection of yellow kernels in the white seed.

9–11.2 Physical Quality

Physical quality is measured by the amount and kind of damaged kernels present and by the viability and vigor of the seed. These traits affect field emergence, establishment and uniformity, and ultimately yield (Knake et al., 1986; Wortman and Rinke, 1951; Wright, 1948; see Craig, 1977 for additional, older references).

Seed corn is said to be in its best physical condition when it has attained physiological maturity and is still in the field on the ear of the female parent plants. Many activities affecting physical quality are performed from the time the seed is harvested until it is planted by the customer. Seed left standing in the field after physiological maturity is subjected to conditions that lower quality, such as cold temperature, disease, and insect damage. Seed corn is subjected to mechanical damage during harvest, drying, shelling, cleaning, sizing, treating, and bagging. Isolating and identifying the source, nature, and extent of physical quality problems, and recommendation of preventive or corrective procedures, are responsibilities of quality assurance.

9–11.3 Sampling

Seed quality is measured by testing a representative sample of a lot or prescribed quantity of seed. Samples taken at all steps through the conditioning sequence are vital to the monitoring of seed quality. This is especially true if freezing temperatures have occurred in the field when moisture percentage of kernels exceeds the low temperature, measured in Fahrenheit degrees.

Samples should be large enough to enable running the desired test and a retest, if necessary. However, securing a new sample is usually preferable to retesting the original sample. Between the time the samples are collected and the quality tests are conducted, samples must be stored under conditions preserving the original quality as nearly as possible. Standard procedures for taking representative samples, and the necessary equipment needed, have been described (Anonymous, 1940, 1981; Justice, 1972).

9–11.4 Purity Analysis

Purity analysis for seed corn is done more for genetic purity than for determining percent of pure seed, as is practiced for quality control in small grains, soybean, and forage grasses. Beyond the endosperm purity and color checks described earlier for waxy and white hybrids, electrophoretic tests may be run to check for presence of selfs, outcrosses, off-types, or rogues. Although these tests are time consuming and expensive, they are quite accurate if the sample is representative and the isozymic patterns of the parents of the hybrid have been defined (Smith and Weissinger, 1984; Smith and Wych, 1986).

Maximum tolerances for genetic impurities have not been established by state or federal seed laws or seed certification agencies. Therefore in-house standards are employed by those seed companies that routinely conduct purity analyses. For single-cross hybrids, the presence of more than 5 to 6% selfs, or a combination of selfs and other off-types totaling 6 to 8%, are commonly used criteria for decisions to not offer a seed lot for sale. Growouts, however, might disclose that from 2 to 3% off-types would be neither detectable nor objectionable to customers, if the maturity, kernel color, and stature were similar to the hybrid. Alternatively, even 0.1% of taller off-type plants might generate considerable negative feedback from customers.

9–11.5 Germination

The germination test is the most frequently used procedure to measure product quality. Standard methods and guidelines for germination testing of seeds (Anonymous, 1981) and the necessary equipment and procedures (Justice, 1972) have been established. Most of the larger companies have established their own seed testing laboratories, but state, university, or private laboratories are also utilized.

Once a system has been established, accurate and consistent evaluation of the seedlings in the test is of greatest importance. The data collected constitute the germination percentage that is printed on the seed bag (usually on a sew-on tag), as required by both state and federal seed laws.

Standard germination tests are conducted under nearly ideal conditions; since field conditions seldom approximate the ideal, other tests have been developed to measure seed deterioration or vigor. Seed vigor is defined by the Association of Official Seed Analysts (AOSA) as "those properties which determine the potential for rapid, uniform emergence and development of normal seedlings under a wide range of field conditions" (Anonymous, 1983). Differences in vigor between two lots of seed that are otherwise genetically alike may not be obvious from percent germination in the standard warm test (Delouche, 1973; Pollock and Roos, 1972).

9–11.5.1   Cold Test

Most seed companies use some type of cold test as a routine test for vigor. The most commonly used procedures have been reviewed elsewhere (Anonymous, 1983; Martin and O'Neil, 1987; McDonald, 1975). Craig (1977) stated that cold test results indicated the ability of seed to emerge when soil conditions are cold and wet and may reflect the amount of mechanical damage a seed lot has undergone. Currently, however, uniform procedures and agreement on the value of the cold test as a measurement of quality do not exist in the seed industry. Burris and Navratil (1979) discussed the variability inherent in various cold test procedures and the consequent lack of comparability of results from one laboratory to another. Cold testing using one established technique within each seed company may nevertheless be useful for judging seed lots as to suitability for sale following carryover storage conditions, early freezes, etc.

9–11.5.2   Tetrazolium Test

This biochemical test with 2,3,5-triphenyltetrazolium chloride quickly identifies seed viability. Enzymatic activity in living tissue turns the colorless tetrazolium red; loss of enzymatic activity in dead tissue leaves the tetrazolium colorless. The tetrazolium test is further used to evaluate internal seed injury, insect injury, frost damage, and viability of dormant seed (Bennett and Loomis, 1949; Goodsell, 1948; Moore, 1958; Porter et al., 1947).

9–11.5.3   Accelerated Aging Test

In the accelerated aging test (sometimes called the *rapid aging test*), seeds are stressed prior to the germination test (Anonymous, 1983). The conditions suggested by the AOSA for seed corn are to expose the seed to nearly 100% relative humidity at 42 °C (108 °F) for 96 h. The percentage survival is an index for longevity of seed viability in storage and a good measure of seed vigor.

9–11.5.4   Electrical Conductivity Test

Electrical conductivity of steep water (seed leachate) has been studied as an index of seed quality, but has not yet received widespread use because of procedural variability.

9–12   STORAGE AND DISTRIBUTION

9–12.1   Storage

The basic requirements for seed storage space are that it be dry, free of rodents and grain storage insects, and capable of being held within certain temperature limits (Airy, 1955). Seed is at its highest quality level at physiological maturity and can only deteriorate from that point onward. The goal of seed storage is to maintain physiological quality throughout the storage period by minimizing deterioration. The best storage conditions can only maintain quality.

Storage for both bulk and bagged seed is necessary (Fig. 9–14). In some companies, facilities have been designed to take advantage of the same space for both. As the bulk seed is moved out for conditioning, the bagged seed can be moved into the vacated storage areas. At most facilities, however, the total volume of seed that must be stored exceeds bulk storage capacity; therefore, some seed must be bagged and moved to warehouse storage (often cold storage) to allow the completion of conditioning. Stored bagged seed is normally palletized and moved with forklift trucks (Fig. 9–14).

Storage of seed corn, either bulk or bagged, for prolonged periods at temperatures above 10 °C (50 °F) leads to deterioration of seed quality. For this reason, bulk seed should be cooled after the drying and shelling steps. This is usually accomplished by aeration of bulk bins with ambient air. Further, surplus bagged seed should be stored during the summer at or below 10 °C and at relative humidity levels between 45 to 55% to maintain the desired moisture content and seed quality. Early work (Airy, 1955; Sayre, 1948) indicated the influence of reduced temperature and moisture level on the maintenance of quality and longevity of stored

Fig. 9–14. Bagged seed corn in storage on pallets in preparation for distribution to sales representatives. Some seed companies now use a "stretch wrap" machine that automatically surrounds the pallet of seed corn with a protective plastic wrapping prior to storage and/or shipment. Forklift trucks are used to move pallets around the warehouse.

seed. Specifications for equipment and buildings for controlled atmosphere storage and its effects on stored seed have been reported (Beck, 1969; Dahlberg, 1967; Stanfield, 1971, 1972).

Hybrid seed corn companies must produce seed supplies over and above that which market forecasts indicate will be sold in the subsequent sales year. Some carryover seed, as this unsold seed is called, is desired as insurance against unpredictable consequences of weather, government programs, etc. Seed companies normally anticipate growing approximately 30 to 40% more seed than estimated sales requirements, to fill supply channels and to hedge against possible reduced yields from production acreage. A recent example illustrates how this practice benefits North American agriculture. The 1983 seed corn production acreage in the USA was substantially lower than in previous years, in anticipation of the impact of the federal government's PIK program on 1983 seed sales and anticipated carryover. However, drought reduced 1983 seed field yields severely in many production areas. Seed supplies for the 1984 planting season would have been critically short had it not been for adequate quantities of high-quality carryover seed inventoried in controlled-atmosphere warehouses.

9–12.2 Sales and Distribution

There are basically two common methods of sales and distribution of seed corn from the production plant or warehouse to the customer. The method used most widely throughout the Corn Belt involves farmers serving as farmer-dealers (or sales representatives or sales agents). The second method, involving seed distributors and/or dealers, is more common where corn acreage is less concentrated.

As the name implies, the farmer-dealer or sales representative is usually a farmer who is also a part-time salesman. This method of distribution depends on the local sales representative to: (i) call on his neighboring farmers to solicit their business: (ii) write the order; (iii) receive and store the seed until delivery; (iv) arrange for pick up or delivery; (v) complete the sale and collect the account; (vi) arrange for return of unsold seed to the production plant or warehouse; and (vii) provide service to the customer as needed. The sales representative is usually under the supervision of full-time company employees, commonly referred to as district sales managers. In the author's company, the sales representative never takes actual ownership of the seed corn.

In contrast, a seed distributor or a seed dealer purchases the seed corn from the seed company, and in turn sells the seed to other dealers and/or to farmer customers. Seed may be sold by the seed company directly to a seed dealer, bypassing the seed distributor. Alternatively, seed may be sold to a distributor who in turn sells it to one or more seed dealers. The dealer is often employed in related agricultural endeavors, such as fertilizer or chemicals, other seeds, livestock feeds, farm supply stores, or elevator operators. This method of operation is especially adapted to areas where sales volumes are not great enough to justify the farm-to-farm calls of the local salesman, but are compatible with the existing business of the store or elevator.

ACKNOWLEDGMENT

The author gratefully acknowledges the following co-workers in Pioneer Hi-Bred International, Inc. who contributed significantly in the preparation of this manuscript: Marc Albertsen, Jim Ansorge, Raymond Baker, Wayne Beck, Tony Cavalieri, Jack Cavanah, Irv Deihl, Don Duvick, Jack Duvick, Bill Frank, Andy Gyorgy, Helen Hoeven, Mark Johnson, Dave Langer, Curt Maas (photography), Louis Mailloux, Rick McConnell, Diane Nelson, Bill Pitzer, Nancy Risbeck, Michelle Shriver, Walt Stohlgren, and Dan Wilkinson. Constructive comments on the manuscript from Marlin Bergman, Bill Frank, Dave Langer, and John Schoper of Pioneer Hi-Bred International, Inc., Harry Leffler and Karl Knittle of DeKalb-Pfizer Genetics, and John Nelson of Asgrow Seed Co. were also greatly appreciated.

REFERENCES

Afuakwa, J.J., and R.K. Crookston. 1984. Using the kernel milk line to visually monitor grain maturity in maize. Crop Sci. 24:687–691.

Airy, J.M. 1955. Production of hybrid corn seed. In G.F. Sprague (ed.) Corn and corn improvement. Agronomy 18:379–422.

Anonymous. 1940. Federal Seed Act of August 9, 1939. (53 Stat. 1275) with amendments. U.S. Gov. Print. Office, Washington, DC.

————. 1971. Certification handbook. Pub. 23. Revised 1984. Assoc. Off. Seed Cert. Agencies, Raleigh, NC.

————. 1981. Rules for testing seeds. J. Seed Technol. 6(2). (Revised 1986).

————. 1983. Seed vigor testing handbook. Assoc. Off. Seed Anal. Handb. Contr. 32:1–88.

————. 1985. International rules for seed testing. Seed Sci. Technol. 13(2).

Bateman, H.P. 1972. Planter metering, soil and plant factors affecting corn ear populations. Trans. ASAE 15:1013–1020.

Bear, R.P. 1975. A marketing program for waxy maize. p. 101–104. In L.D. Hill (ed.) Corn quality in world markets. Interstate Printers and Publishers, Danville, IL.

Beck, J.M. 1969. Systems for controlling relative humidity and temperature. Proc. Miss. Short Course for Seedsmen 12:115–129.

Beckett, J.B. 1971. Classification of male-sterile cytoplasms in maize (Zea mays L.) Crop. Sci. 11:724–727.

Bennett, N., and W.E. Loomis. 1949. Tetrazolium chloride as a test reagent for freezing injury of seed corn. Plant Physiol. 24:162–174.

Bollinger, F.G., J.J. D'Amico, and D.J. Hansen. 1978. Use of phthalanilic acids to regulate the growth of corn plants. U.S. Patent 4 108 632. Date issued: 22 August.

Burris, J.S., and K.H. Knittle. 1985. Freeze damage and seed quality in hybrid maize. p. 51–74. In J.S. Burris (ed.) Proc. 7th Annu. Seed Tech. Conf., Ames, IA. 26–27 February. Seed Science Center, Iowa State University, Ames.

————, and R.J. Navratil. 1979. Relationship between laboratory cold-test methods and field emergence in maize inbreds. Agron. J. 71:985–988.

Cal, J.P., and R.L. Obendorf. 1972. Imbibitional chilling injury in *Zea mays* L. altered by initial kernel moisture and maternal parent. Crop Sci. 12:369–373.

Cantrell, R.G., and J.L. Geadelmann. 1981. Contribution of husk leaves to maize grain yield. Crop Sci. 21:544–546.

Cardy, B.J., C.W. Stuber, and M.M. Goodman. 1980. Techniques for starch gel electrophoresis of enzymes from maize (*Zea mays* L.). Institute of Statistics Mimeo no. 1317. North Carolina State Univ., Raleigh.

Carter, M.W., and C.G. Poneleit. 1973. Black layer maturity and filling period variation among inbred lines of corn (*Zea mays* L.). Crop Sci. 13:436–439.

Cloninger, F.D., M.S. Zuber, and R.D. Horrocks. 1974. Synchronization of flowering of corn (*Zea mays* L.) by clipping young plants. Agron. J. 66:270–272.

Cowan, R.J. 1972. Seed certification. p. 371–397. *In* T.T. Kozlowski (ed.) Seed biology, Vol. 3. Academic Press, New York.

Crabb, A.R. 1947. The hybrid corn makers. Rutgers University Press, New Brunswick.

Craig, W.F. 1977. Production of hybrid corn seed. *In* G.F. Sprague (ed.) Corn and corn improvement, 2nd ed. Agronomy 18:671–719.

Dahlberg, R.W. 1967. Seed warehousing. *In* Proc. Iowa State Univ. Seed Processors' Short Course. September. Iowa State Univ., Ames.

Daynard, T.B. 1969. The 'black layer' — its relationship to grain filling and yield. p. 49–54. *In* Proc. 24th Annu. Corn Sorghum Res. Conf. ASTA, Washington, DC.

––––. 1972. Relationship among black layer formation, grain moisture percentage, and heat unit accumulation in corn. Agron. J. 64:716–719.

––––, and W.G. Duncan. 1969. The black layer and grain maturity in corn. Crop Sci. 9:473–476.

Delouche, J.C. 1973. The problem of vigor. I. A look at the germination test. Seedsmen's Digest 24:8–24.

Duvick, D.N. 1959. Genetic and environmental interactions with cytoplasmic pollen sterility in corn. p. 42–52. *In* Proc. 14th Annu. Hybrid Corn Ind. Res. Conf. ASTA, Washington, DC.

––––. 1965. Cytoplasmic pollen sterility in corn. Adv. Genet. 13:1–56.

––––. 1972. Potential usefulness of new cytoplasmic male steriles and sterility systems. p. 197–201. *In* Proc. 27th Annu. Corn Sorghum Conf. ASTA, Washington, D.C.

Fowler, W. 1967. Cultural practices for today's seed fields. p. 53–58. *In* Proc. 22nd Annu. Hybrid Corn Ind. Res. Conf. ASTA, Washington, DC.

Goodsell, S.F. 1948. Triphenyltetrazolium chloride for viability determination of frozen seed corn. J. Am. Soc. Agron. 40:432–442.

Hicks, D.R., and D.L. Wright. 1987. Maximizing the advantages of early corn planting. Fact Sheet NCH-35. Natl. Corn Handb. Coop. Ext. Serv, Iowa State Univ. and USDA.

Hunter, R.B., C.G. Mortimore, and L.W. Kannenberg. 1973. Inbred maize performance following tassel and leaf removal. Agron. J. 65:471–472.

Hutchcroft, C.D. 1957. Contamination in seed fields of corn resulting from incomplete detasseling. Iowa State J. Sci. 31:449–450.

Johnson, R.R., and D.L. Mulvaney. 1980. Development of a model for use in maize replant decisions. Agron. J. 72:459–464.

Jones, M.D., and J.S. Brooks. 1950. Effectiveness of distance and border rows in preventing outcrossing in corn. p. 3–18. Oklahoma Agric. Exp. Stn. Tech. Bull. T-38.

––––, and ––––. 1952. Effect of tree barriers on outcrossing in corn. p. 3–11. *In* Oklahoma Agric. Exp. Stn. Tech. Bull. T-45.

Jugenheimer, R.W. 1958. Hybrid maize breeding and seed production. p. 157. *In* FAO Agric. Dev. Paper 62. FAO, Rome, Italy.

Justice, O.L. 1972. Essentials of seed testing. p. 301–370. *In* T.T. Kozlowski (ed.) Seed biology, Vol. 3. Academic Press, New York.

Knake, R.P., W.A. Beckwith, and S.C. Shen. 1986. Effect of pericarp damage and seed treatment formulations on cold test and field performance of corn. p. 106–120. *In* Proc. 41st Annu. Corn and Sorghum Res. Conf. ASTA, Washington, DC.

Knittle, K.H., and J.S. Burris. 1976. Effect of kernel maturation on subsequent seedling vigor in maize. Crop Sci. 16:851–855.

Martin, B., and M. O'Neil. 1987. Laboratory tests for the assessment of vigor in maize. p. 209–219. *In* J.S. Burris (ed.) Proc. 9th Annu. Seed Tech. Conf., Ames, IA. 24–25 February. Seed Sci. Ctr., Iowa State Univ., Ames.

McDonald, M.B., Jr. 1975. A review and evaluation of seed vigor tests. Proc. Assoc. Off. Seed Anal. 65:109–139.

McKee, G.W. 1963. Accuracy of seed corn grading and planter plate recommendations. Pennsylvania Agric. Exp. Stn. Prog. Rep. 240.

Moore, R.P. 1958. Tetrazolium tests for determination of injury and viability of seed corn. p. 13–20. In Proc. 13th Annu. Hybrid Corn Ind. Res. Conf. ASTA, Washington, DC.

National Academy of Sciences. 1972. Genetic vulnerability of major crops. U.S. NAS, Washington.

Navratil, R.J., and J.S. Burris. 1984. The effects of drying temperature on corn seed quality. Can. J. Plant Sci. 64:487–496.

Neal, N.P. 1961. The influence of freezing temperature of varying intensities and duration of the germination of seed corn at different stages of maturity. p. 67–73. In 16th Annu. Hybrid Corn Ind. Res. Conf. ASTA, Washington, DC.

Pollock, B.M., and E.E. Roos. 1972. Seed and seedling vigor. p. 313–387. In T.T. Kozlowski (ed.) Seed biology, Vol. 1. Academic Press, New York.

Porter, R.H., M. Durrell, and H.J. Romm. 1947. The use of 2,3,5-triphenyltetrazolium chloride as a measure of seed germinability. Plant Physiol. 22:149–159.

Pucaric, A., and J. Gotlin. 1979. The yield and seed size as affected by the number of leaves removed with tassel in maize inbred lines and single crosses. p. 259–266. In Proc. 10th Meet. Maize Sorghum Sect. Eucarpia, Varna, Bulgaria. 17–19 September. European Assoc. for Res. on Plant Breeding, Wageningen, Netherlands.

Rogers, J.S., and J.R. Edwardson. 1952. The utilization of cytoplasmic male-sterile inbreds in the production of corn hybrids. Agron. J. 44:8–13.

Rossman, E.C. 1949. Freezing injury of inbred and hybrid maize seed. Agron. J. 41:574–583.

Sayre, J.D. 1948. Storage tests with seed corn. p. 57–64. In Proc. 3rd Annu. Hybrid Corn Ind. Res. Conf. ASTA, Washington, DC.

Shoultz, D. 1985. An evaluation of parent delay techniques. p. 151–160. In Proc. 40th Annu. Corn and Sorghum Res. Conf. ASTA, Washington, DC.

Shurtleff, M.C. (ed.) 1980. Compendium of corn diseases. 2nd ed. Am. Phytopathological Soc., St. Paul.

Smith, J.S.C., and H.H. Weissinger. 1984. Rapid monitoring of purity in seed lots of hybrid maize: Modifications of current technologies. Maize Genet. Coop. News Lett. 58:103–105.

––––, and R.D. Wych. 1986. The identification of female selfs in hybrid maize: A comparison using electorphoresis and morphology. Seed Sci. Technol. 14:1–8.

Stanfield, Z.A. 1971. Use of seed vigor research data in design and justification of equipment and facilities. Search. 1972.

––––. 1972. Conditioned seed storage — justification, design and operation. Proc. Mississippi Short Course for Seedsmen 15:71–75.

––––. 1986. One-step husking system for seed corn. p. 121–133. In Proc. 41st Annu. Corn and Sorghum Res. Conf. ASTA, Washington, DC.

Tatum, L.A., and M.S. Zuber. 1943. Germination of maize under adverse conditions. J. Am. Soc. Agron. 35:48–59.

Ullstrup, A.J. 1972. The impacts of the southern corn leaf blight epidemic of 1970–71. Annu. Rev. Phytopathol. 10:37–50.

Vasilas, B.L., and R.D. Seif. 1985a. Defoliation effects on two corn inbreds and their single-cross hybrid. Agron. J. 77:816–820.

––––, and ––––. 1985b. Pre-anthesis defoliation effects on six corn inbreds. Agron. J. 77:831–835.

Wortman, L.S., and E.H. Rinke. 1951. Seed corn injury at various stages of processing and its effect upon cold test performance. Agron. J. 43:299–305.

Wright, H. 1948. Processing seed corn to avoid injury. p. 32–37. In Proc. 3rd Annu. Hybrid Corn Ind. Res. Conf. ASTA, Washington, DC.

10   Climate Requirement

ROBERT H. SHAW

Department of Agronomy
Iowa State University
Ames, Iowa

Corn (*Zea mays* L.), because of its many divergent types, is grown over a wide range of climatic conditions. Some cultivars grow very short, others up to 6 to 8 m in height; some require 60 to 70 d to mature the grain after emergence, others require 43 to 48 weeks. Yet, in spite of this range of characteristics, general features of the major production areas can be characterized.

10-1 WORLD-WIDE CORN PRODUCTION AND CLIMATE

Because of the wide range of climatic conditions over which corn is grown, precise limiting conditions for corn production cannot be set. The bulk of the corn is produced between latitudes 30° and 55°, with relatively little grown at latitudes higher than 47° latitude anywhere in the world (Fig. 10-1). Corn is grown in most tropical latitudes and from near sea level to several thousand meters above sea level. According to the 1982 and 1983 production statistics (USDA, 1984), 48% of the total world's corn production was grown in the USA, 19.1% in Asia, 13.8% in Europe, 7.3% in South America, 4.8% in Africa, 3.6% in Central and North America (exclusive of the USA), and 3.1% in the USSR.

Although Trewartha's climate classification system delineates the Corn Belt very well (Trewartha and Horn, 1980), it does not delineate the world areas of corn production. Corn is grown in tropical, subtropical, and temperate climates with a high percentage of the corn production in the latter two classifications. Corn is grown in woodland and grassland climates, but, without irrigation, production is limited in the drier areas where the native vegetation is short grass.

It is obvious from Fig. 10-1 that corn has a cold limit. This is a combination cool temperature, frost-free season limit. Practically no corn is grown where the mean midsummer temperature is <19°C or where the average night temperature during the summer months falls much below 13°C. The greatest production occurs where the warmest month isotherms range between 21 and 27°C and the freeze-free season lasts 120 to 180 d. Within such regions, yields generally are higher with below-

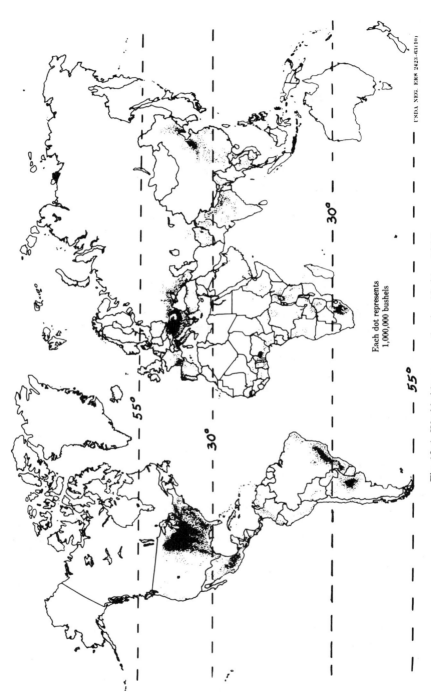

Each dot represents
1,000,000 bushels

Fig. 10–1. Worldwide corn production (Guidry, 1964).

USDA NEG. ERS 2423-63(10)

normal summer temperatures than with above-normal values. There seems to be no upper temperature limit specific for corn production, but yields usually decrease with higher temperatures. Although corn is generally called a warm weather crop, it is not a hot weather crop.

Corn is grown in areas where the annual precipitation ranges from 25 to >500 cm. Haise (1958) reports seasonal water use values of 42 to 54 cm in the Dakotas. Doss et al. (1962) reports that water use averages near 49 cm in Alabama and ranges from 45 to 56 cm. Vasquez (1961) finds a value of 47 cm for a 125-d period in Puerto Rico. The range of water use by corn is ordinarily 41 to 64 cm (Hanway, 1966), but amounts as low as 30 cm and as high as 84 cm are reported (Robins and Rhoades, 1958). To understand seasonal water use values, the evapotranspiration, runoff, and percolation components should be known, as well as the period covered.

A summer rainfall of 15 cm is approximately the lower limit for corn production without irrigation, but yield responses to irrigation are obtained with much higher summer rainfall, the response depending upon rainfall distribution and soil-moisture reserves. There seems to be no upper limit of rainfall for growing corn, but excessive rainfall will decrease yields.

As the temperate and subtropical climates merge into drier steppe climates, moisture demands of corn exceed available moisture, and wheat (*Triticum aestivum* L.), barley (*Hordeum vulgare* L.), and sorghum (*Sorghum bicolor* L.) become the important crops. When corn is grown in drier climates, yields fluctuate widely with extreme variations in rainfall.

10–2 MOISTURE STRESS CONCEPT

In discussing the effects of various climatic factors on corn growth and yield, we need to understand how these various factors affect the moisture supply of the plant. The present-day concept of soil moisture availability recognizes the importance of the amount of moisture in the soil, the texture of the soil (moisture in sand tending to be more available than moisture in clay), and the atmospheric demand for water. A number of different concepts of the availability of soil moisture have been proposed over the years (Cowan, 1965; Denmead and Shaw, 1962; Halstead, 1954; Ritchie, 1973; Thornthwaite and Mather, 1955; Veihmeyer and Henrickson, 1955). Although the individual relationships proposed seem to differ, they all fit into the theoretical concept of Philip (1957) and Gardner (1960), which includes the previously mentioned factors. The evaluation of the effect of weather factors on moisture availability must use this concept. This can be explained further by use of Fig. 10–2.

Figure 10–2 shows the relative evapotranspiration (ET) rates for corn for three different levels of atmospheric demand used in the Iowa soil moisture computer model for the period up to silking. During this period

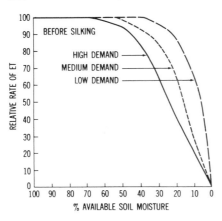

Fig. 10–2. Relative evapotranspiration rates for different atmospheric demand rates before silking. A low demand day is for Class A pan evaporation of <0.51 cm, a medium day is for pan evaporation between 0.51 and 0.76 cm, and a high demand day for >0.76 cm (Shaw, 1983).

an advancing root zone into wet soil is assumed, but excess water is not present. In poorly drained soils (Dale et al., 1982), the capillary flow component of the soil-water budget must be included. After silking, when it is assumed the root system is not advancing, which limits the amount of water available, a more limiting relation is assumed. In this program a low demand day occurs when the Class A evaporation pan has a rate of loss <0.51 cm, and a high demand day has an evaporation rate >0.76 cm. The higher the atmospheric demand placed on the corn plant, the higher is the level of soil moisture needed to meet that demand and avoid stress. Once ET drops below the 100% rate, the plant is assumed to be under some degree of moisture stress. For example, with 40% available soil moisture in the root zone and a high demand day, actual ET would be 82% of the potential ET; for a medium demand day it would be 93% of potential, while for a low demand day it would be 100% of potential. After silking, these same values for 40% available soil moisture would be 59, 83, and 100%. The degree of stress will also vary between soil types that have different moisture retention characteristics. Therefore, if the moisture relations of plants are to be understood, the available soil moisture, the soil moisture retention characteristics, and the atmospheric demand must be quantitatively evaluated. Techniques are now available that allow the water status of the plant to be monitored directly; i.e., the pressure bomb (Scholander et al., 1965), the diffusion porometer (Kanemasu et al., 1969; Washington State Univ., 1975,) and thermocouple psychrometry (Brown and van Haveren, 1972).

The atmospheric demand for water is a function of the energy available (solar radiation), the movement of moisture from the evaporating surface (wind), the dryness of the atmosphere (humidity), and air temperature. Air temperature is related to the temperature of the evaporating surface and also affects the dryness of the atmosphere by varying its capacity to hold water. Radiation is usually considered the major factor in controlling the atmospheric demand.

Moisture stress interrupts photosynthesis and checks growth until turgor is restored by removal of the moisture stress (deJager, 1968; Vaadia et al., 1961). Begg and Turner (1976) point out that, although water is the earth's most abundant compound, a deficit of water is the single most important factor limiting crop yield on a worldwide scale. Since water availability and efficient use of water in crop production are of major importance, it is not surprising that extensive information is available in the literature on water use and the physiological responses of plants to water stress (Begg and Turner, 1976; Boyer, 1970; Boyer and Mc-Pherson, 1975; Hsiao, 1973; Salter and Goode, 1967; Shaw, 1977; Slatyer, 1969). No attempt will be made here to discuss that literature.

Dale and Shaw (1965), Corsi and Shaw (1971), and Shaw (1974, 1983) developed a stress index for corn based on the daily balance between soil moisture and atmospheric demand, using the relation shown in Fig. 10–2 for the period before silking and a similar type relation for the period after silking. The daily stress index compares actual ET with potential ET for that day.

$$\text{Stress index} = 1 - \frac{\text{actual ET}}{\text{potential ET}} \qquad [1]$$

The index for each day can range from 0 (no stress) to 1 (no ET). The index is calculated for a period from 40 d before silking to 44 d after silking (85 d) with relative weighting factors assigned to each 5-d period relative to silking. The relative weighting factors were based on data accumulated by a number of researchers (Claassen and Shaw, 1970a, b; Denmead and Shaw, 1960; Mallett, 1972; Robins and Domingo, 1953; Wilson, 1968) (Fig. 10–3). The stress weighting factors used in the Iowa model are based on the average reductions shown in Fig. 3. Accumulative effects due to consecutive periods of severe stress are given additional weighting factors. Obviously, both the degree of stress and when it occurs are important in determining the final grain yield. The sum of all the 5-d weighted values is the seasonal stress index. Other ways of looking at stress have also been used; i.e., canopy temperature as a water-stress indicator (Jackson et al., 1981).

The current yield relation used for corn in Iowa is

$$y = 9682 - 118.6x \qquad [2]$$

where y is the yield in kilograms per hectare, and x is the weighted stress index. This relationship assumes a no stress yield of 9682 kg/ha and represents the yield expected by high management farmers. If excess moisture occurs, the yields will be reduced below the predicted level. This procedure is used to predict expected yields based on spring soil moisture levels and to monitor the moisture situation as the season progresses.

The water for the corn crop may come from current, crop-season

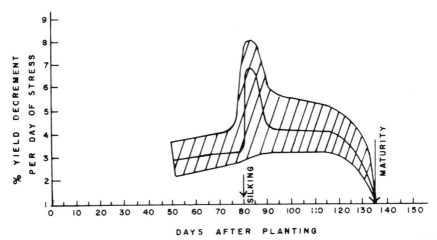

Fig. 10–3. Schematic diagram of the relationship between age of crop and percentage yield decrement due to 1 d of moisture stress. The top and bottom lines represent the highest and lowest yield reductions obtained in stress experiments, the middle line the average reduction.

rainfall, from moisture stored in the soil before planting, or from irrigation. Minor amounts may come from dew. Power et al. (1973) found that, within the range they studied, all sources were effective in enhancing crop production. Rainfall, as a variable to relate to corn growth and yield, is only as good as it is an estimator of the available soil moisture; in fact, it is only as good as it estimates the moisture status of the plant. If 50 to 64 cm of water is used to produce a high-yielding corn crop, almost half of this may be stored at the beginning of the season in a good soil that has an available moisture capacity of 5 cm per 30 cm of soil and if the crop roots to a depth of 152 cm. In the Corn Belt, soil moisture reserves at the start of the growing season will vary considerably. The normal situation is to have adequate to excess soil moisture reserves in the eastern part of the Corn Belt and adequate to deficient reserves in the western part. In Iowa, Shaw et al. (1972) found that the average centimeters of plant-available water in the top 152 cm of soil on 15 April ranged from >25 cm in eastern and southeastern Iowa to <12.5 cm in northwest Iowa. The amount of growing-season rainfall required is closely related to these reserves.

Water use varies with the stage of development of the corn crop. Early in the growing season the loss is primarily evaporation from a bare soil. As the crop cover increases, transpiration becomes an increasingly dominant factor. Denmead and Shaw (1959) found the ratio between evapotranspiration and class A open-pan evaporation shown in Fig. 10–4. This is similar to the relationship reported by Cackett and Metelerkamp (1964), Downey (1971b), and Mallett (1972), who found maximum ratios ranging from 0.75 to 1.0. Ritchie and Burnett (1971) found that a leaf area index of 2.7 was necessary for cotton (*Gossypium hirsutum* L.) and

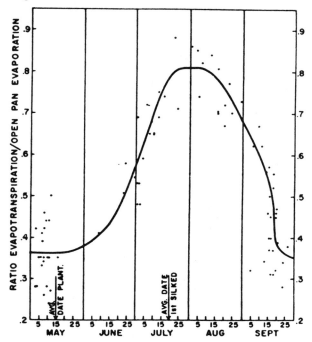

Fig. 10–4. Ratio of evapotranspiration from corn to open-pan evaporation throughout the growing season (Denmead and Shaw, 1959).

sorghum to reach an ET rate of 90% of the potential evaporation when soil evaporation was small.

Shaw (1981), in summarizing 27 yr of soil moisture and pan evaporation data in Iowa, found that the highest atmospheric demand, as expressed by Class A pan data, was measured in early July. The actual ET of corn was estimated to be 0.20 to 0.25 cm/d in May and early June, increased rapidly as the corn plant developed to an average value of 0.48 cm/d in mid-July (Fig. 10–5), then gradually decreased as the plant matured, and in many years some moisture stress developed. Other data on water use are presented in Shaw (1977). Actual water use values depend on the particular weather situation (demand) and the availability of water. Some values include only ET, others include runoff and percolation. For these reasons, seasonal water use values vary over a wide range. Harrold and Driebelbis (1951) found that ET losses from a lysimeter were 44 to 62 cm from May through September. Shaw (1983) estimated actual ET to range from 50.0 to 54.9 cm across Iowa for the 19 April to 31 October period. These were averages over a 27-yr period. Average percolation and runoff values totaled 11.4 cm.

The amount of water use may vary with stand. At very low stands water use is low. As stands increase, water use increases rapidly to a maximum and then changes slowly with increasing stands. There is a point at which increased stands will not intensify the utilization of solar

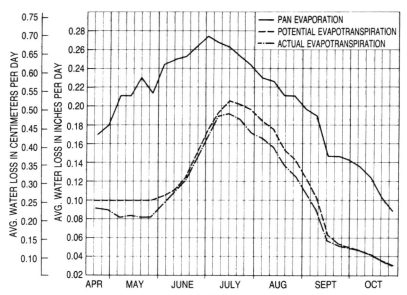

Fig. 10–5. Average pan evaporation, potential ET, and actual ET in inches and centimeters per day for Iowa (Shaw, 1981).

energy in ET. Olson (1971) found almost the same water use for stands of 35 000, 45 000, and 70 000 plants/ha. Shaw et al. (1980) found a similar relation in northwest Iowa. These results agree with a field model of evapotranspiration proposed by Viets (1966).

10–3 GROWING-DEGREE UNIT CONCEPT

Another factor that will be referred to later will be growing-degree units or heat units. The actual number of days required for corn to reach maturity varies widely with changes in the environment, although cultivars are often designated as having a certain number of days to reach maturity. The growing-degree-unit (GDU) approach has been proposed as providing a more constant maturity index for varying weather conditions as long as the other environmental conditions are not too far from optimum.

The growing-degree-unit approach is based on the use of air temperature data; thus it is not really a heat unit but a temperature unit number. It has also been called thermal units (Berbecel et al., 1964). In using it, accumulations of values above a selected base are made. The literature on GDU is extensive. Reviews by Nuttonson (1953), Holmes and Robertson (1959), and Wang (1960, 1963) are available for those interested in more extensive information.

Different approaches have been used for corn. Brown (1969) developed equations that were used to determine maturity ratings for corn in Ontario, Canada. The effect of the maximum temperature on development was obtained from the equation

$$Y_{max} = 1.85(T_{max} - 50) - 0.026(T_{max} - 50)^2 \qquad [3]$$

where Y = assigned temperature value calculated from equation, T = temperature, and units are given in degrees Farenheit. This assumes a parabolic developmental response curve to temperature. The contribution of nighttime temperatures was calculated by

$$Y_{min} = T_{min} - 40 \qquad [4]$$

Brown's growing-degree units, H, were then obtained by

$$H = (Y_{max} + Y_{min})/2 \qquad [5]$$

A remainder type index has also been used to relate GDU to corn development. It accumulates units above a base temperature. In its simplest form, it is calculated by

$$\frac{\text{daily max temp.} + \text{daily min temp.}}{2} - 10°C = GDU. \qquad [6]$$

In this example, 10 °C was assumed as the base temperature. Several systems are available, but the so-called 30 to 10 °C index (86–50 °F) will be the primary one discussed here. This is a remainder type index calculated by Eq. [6]. Any maximum temperature >30 °C is put in the equation as 30 and any minimum <10 °C is designated as 10. Growing-degree units can be calculated for any stage of development or for the total time from planting or emergence to maturity. They may also be modified to adjust for excessively high or submarginally cool temperatures (Newman and Blair, 1969). Maturity rating systems for corn are discussed by Eckert and Hicks (1985).

Cross and Zuber (1972) tested 22 different GDU methods in Missouri and found that daily measurements gave almost as good results as the use of hourly temperature data. They found the best base temperature for estimation of flowering was 10 °C with 30 °C optimum. Excess temperature above 30 °C was subtracted to account for high temperature stress. Brown (1969), in Ontario, used a threshold of 4.4 °C for nighttime and 10 °C for daytime temperatures. Rench (1973), in Iowa, found that a base temperature of 7.2 °C worked best for the planting to flowering interval and also was the best for the silking to black layer period, although 7.2 °C was only slightly better than bases of 4.4 or 10 °C.

10–4   EFFECT OF WEATHER ON CERTAIN PERIODS OF PLANT GROWTH

10–4.1   Before Planting

The influence of weather on the corn plant starts even before planting. Conditions before planting are especially important in determining soil-moisture reserves. These can reflect a carryover from the previous crop season or can be from accumulations that may occur during the fall, winter, and early spring. Neild and Richman (1981) show preseason precipitation of over 550 mm at Kokomo, IN, with the amount decreasing gradually to the west with only 186 mm at North Platte, NE. Since evaporation rates in the fall are low, precipitation during this time may be quite efficient for increasing soil-moisture reserves. In many areas, winter precipitation is low, and with a frozen ground, little moisture will enter the soil. In Iowa, Shaw (1965) found that only 25% of the precipitation that occurred when the ground was frozen ended up in the soil-moisture reserve. With the wide range of winter conditions that occur where corn is grown, changes in the soil-moisture reserve will vary greatly, depending on winter precipitation and temperature. Temperature effects are also important in insect and disease problems. Snow cover affects insect and disease problems because of the moderating effect on soil temperature. Early spring precipitation also can be quite effective in increasing the reserves, but the evaporation potential also increases as the spring progresses.

The lower the soil-moisture reserve, the greater the crop-season rainfall requirement. Thompson (1966, 1969), using regression analyses, found that the optimum preseason rainfall (September through May) for the five highest corn producing states of the Corn Belt was 68 to 71 cm, near the average for the five states. This amount usually brings the soil moisture equal to or above capacity but without too much excess. In Nebraska, Neild (1981) found that yield increased 68.5 kg/ha for each 2.5 cm of preseason precipitation above normal.

Although spring rains may help replenish soil-moisture reserves, they may also delay field operations. Spring weather determines the time when field operations can be started.

10–4.2   Planting to Emergence

The period from planting to emergence depends on soil temperature, soil moisture, soil aeration, and seed vigor. Before germination, the seed absorbs water and swells. With warmer temperatures, less water has to be absorbed (Blacklow, 1972) so that germination will start earlier and proceed faster at higher temperatures, assuming that water is available. The time from planting to emergence varies widely with environmental conditions and, to a lesser degree, with planting depth (Alessi and Power,

1971). During this stage, development is affected directly by soil temperature and indirectly by air temperatures.

Weather is a major factor in determining planting time. Relatively early planting in the USA generally shows higher yields than late planting. For example, Pendleton and Egli (1969) obtained yield decreases when planting was delayed after 30 April in Illinois. Benson and Thompson (1974) found that highest yields in Iowa were obtained with late April to early May planting, with significant yield decreases occurring with late May planting. Daynard (1972) found that delayed planting decreased the number of days from planting to midsilk and increased the number of days from midsilk to maturity. The total heat units required was reduced only slightly. The optimum planting date will vary with latitude and should consider later critical moisture periods. Early planting may not be the best in all areas of the world.

In the main crop-production areas in the USA, corn planting, until recent years, began when the average air temperature reached 12 to 14 °C (Kincer, 1919). This varied from early February in the South to the middle of May in the North. These dates represented the earliest planted fields, not when the bulk of the corn was planted. Recently there has been a trend to somewhat earlier planting in the North, when air temperature averages near 10 to 12 °C. Nield and Richman (1981) used 12.7 °C for planting temperature. Optimum germination and emergence occurs when temperatures reach 20 to 22 °C. The advent of herbicides has aided weed control for the earlier plantings. For many years the bulk of the corn planting was done when the average air temperature was near 16 °C (Wallace and Bressman, 1937) and averaged 15 May in Iowa. In recent years this has moved to 10 May (Iowa Crop Rep. Serv., 1985). Currently the air temperature averages near 14 to 15 °C.

Germination is affected by soil temperature and soil moisture. Coffman (1923) found that corn germinated best at temperatures >10 °C with a sharp decrease in germination <10 °C. Germination will be slow in the dry soil, but will speed up as soil moisture increases until saturation is reached. Then the lack of O_2 will prevent or retard germination (Wolfe, 1927).

Blacklow (1972) found that rates of elongation of the radicle and shoot were greatest at about 30 °C and effectively ceased at constant temperatures of 9 and 40 °C. The minimum time for initiation of a radicle and a shoot occurred at 30 °C with the radicle preceding the shoot. For constant temperatures, the rates of elongation of the radicle and shoot are shown in Fig. 10–6 (Blacklow, 1972). How well these represent field conditions still remains to be shown. A short duration of high temperatures >30 °C (86 °F) in the field may not show as rapid a drop in growth rate as does a constant exposure to this temperature.

According to Wallace and Bressman (1937), corn usually emerges in 8 to 10 d at an average temperature of 16 to 18 °C, but it takes 18 to 20 d at 10 to 13 °C. If the soil is moist and at an average temperature near

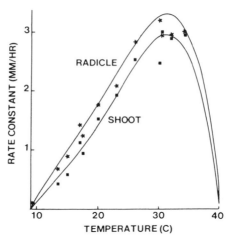

Fig. 10–6. Rate of elongation of the radicle and shoot of corn to the stage of emergence as a function of soil temperature (Blacklow, 1972).

21 °C, emergence may occur in 5 to 6 d. Alessi and Power (1971) found that emergence was delayed 1 d for each 2.6-cm increase in depth of planting. Since spring soil temperatures decrease with depth (Holmes and Robertson, 1959; Shaw, 1971), delayed emergence is a result of both cooler temperatures and a greater distance involved.

Another factor to consider is that air temperatures have been used in many studies, although the soil is the medium in which germination occurs. Air temperatures are often used because of their availability and a lack of soil-temperature data. Baker and Swan (1966) found that with an average air temperature of 10 °C, the soil temperature at the 5-cm depth was also very near 10 °C. Below 10 °C the soil was cooler; above 10 °C it was a few degrees warmer. Shaw (1971) found similar results. At shallow depths, the soil may be much warmer than air temperature during periods of intense heating, but on cloudy days, soil temperature at the planting depth closely approximates air temperature. Bright, warm days in April do not heat up the soil for rapid emergence in early May. To have a short emergence interval, daily heating of the soil must prevail during the period of germination and seeding growth.

Other aspects of the effect of weather also need to be considered. Cold, wet weather following planting favors the development of pathogens. Seed rots and seeding blight may become prevalent when corn is planted in a cold, wet soil. Germination of corn seed is greatly retarded at 10 °C [or below, but at this temperature certain species of *Pythium* are active (Ullstrup, 1966)]. However, Ullstrup states that seed rot and seedling blights occur relatively infrequently if good seed is planted and proper seed treatment is used. Later planting might be encouraged to reduce seedling diseases, but, as pointed out by Dungan (1944), this method should be used for the reduction of insect and disease damage with caution since delayed planting may decrease the yield and quality of the crop. In the South, Johns and Brown (1941) found that planting date influenced the amount of damage by southern corn rootworm (*Diabrotica undecimpunctata howardi* Barber) and corn borer (*Ostrinia nubilalis* Hübner). Practices in warmer climates may well vary from those in colder climates where the hybrids used crowd the growing season available.

10–4.3 Early Vegetative Growth from Emergence to Flower Differentiation

Shortly after emergence an important change takes place when the plant changes from dependence on stored food to self sufficiency. During the early part of its life, the corn plant requires a limited amount of moisture for the small growth that takes place. Moisture stress seldom occurs because spring rainfall is usually adequate and the moisture required is low. This is fortunate because both the initiation and differentiation of vegetative and reproductive primordia in the apical meristem and the enlargement of the cells thus differentiated are very sensitive to water stress (Slatyer, 1969). Stress shortly after emergence decreases the starch and chlorophyll content of seedlings (Maranville and Paulsen, 1970); but if the weather is somewhat dry at this time, the roots will penetrate deeper into the soil, and the plant will be better able to withstand later dry weather, which may more than offset any immediate detrimental effects of stress. In 1983 in Iowa the author calculated that a wet spring reduced yields an average of 1250 kg/ha, primarily due to poor rooting creating greater stress later in the dry summer, but the dry spring of 1985 resulted in a comparable yield increase because the better root development made more subsoil water available during the dry summer.

After emergence the plant is subjected to two different environments, the atmosphere and the soil, and the dependency on soil temperature becomes less than during the germination period (Cal and Obendorf, 1972).

Young corn plants are relatively resistant to cold weather, with an air temperature near -1 °C, generally killing exposed aboveground parts (Shaw et al., 1954). Until stage V6 (Ritchie et al., 1986) when six leaves have fully emerged, the growing point is below the soil surface. Therefore, recovery from a moderate freeze, when the growing point is below-ground, is usually rapid and almost complete. However, a late spring freeze may occasionally kill early planted corn whose growing point is at or above the soil surface (eight-leaf stage or later). Hanna (1924) found that air temperature of -1.7 °C injured corn and -4.4 °C killed the corn. Minimum soil temperatures at the 2.5-cm depth will be slightly higher than minimum air temperatures at these temperatures.

Purvis and Williamson (1972) found that very young plants were severely injured if flooded or if in a zero-O_2 atmosphere for >1 d. In a flooded soil, the O concentration approached zero in 24 h. Excess moisture in the early vegetative stage may also retard root development.

The responses of very young corn plants to root temperatures were studied extensively by Grobbelaar (1963). He subjected the roots to a range of temperatures from 5 to 40 °C, while holding constant the air temperature at 20 °C and the light intensity. He found that the initiation of crown roots was retarded progressively as root temperature decreased from 20 to 5 °C. Optimum shoot growth occurred at a temperature range of 25 to 35 °C. Root-temperature effects on plants older than 20 d, where the shoot apex was also subjected to the air temperature, were similar to those encountered with younger plants. An accelerated rate of leaf initiation at 25, 30, and 35 °C was shown to be one factor that contributed to the higher growth rate of the shoot. Rate of leaf elongation also seemed to be the most rapid in the range of 25 to 35 °C. Ultimate size of individual leaves, however, seemingly were favored by temperatures below the optimum range; the longest leaves were obtained at 15 and 20 °C. The total increase in leaf length per plant, however, proceeded most rapidly at 25, 30, and 35 °C.

The rate of increase in leaf area of corn planted very early was more highly correlated with air temperature than any other element measured (Ragland et al., 1965), while that of late planted corn was positively and equally correlated with temperature and relative humidity. Solar radiation, precipitation, black bulb evaporation, and wind were not significantly correlated with leaf area increase.

Growth during the early vegetative stage has been related to soil temperatures by several investigators. Willis et al. (1957) found that the most favorable soil temperature at the 10-cm depth for optimum growth rates and yields was around an average daily temperature of 24 °C, slightly lower than what Grobbelaar (1963) found at ages 10 and 20 d. Allmaras and Nelson (1971) found that the optimum soil temperature for growth depended on moisture conditions. When soils were dry, a mulch between the rows aided root and shoot growth even with temperatures <26 °C, but when soils were moist, treatments that reduced temperatures lower than 26 °C consistently reduced growth and yield of dry matter. Van Wijk et al. (1959) found that shoot dry weights were decreased if soil temperatures were decreased in Iowa, Minnesota, Ohio, and South Carolina. A mulch increased dry matter in South Carolina, where the early season soil temperature is sometimes above optimum, but decreased dry matter in the other states, where these temperatures are usually below optimum. Adams (1970) increased corn yields by 1000 kg/ha by use of a clear plastic mulch, the effect presumably due to faster growth in the first 4 to 6 wk. The relative dry matter production of corn plants, as related to soil temperature, was shown by Allmaras et al. (1964) to be greatest at a daily average temperature of about 27 °C (Fig. 10–7). The final effect on grain yield of early season soil temperature is difficult to evaluate because dry weight and shoot indexes of corn growth are not in phase over a range of temperatures (Allmaras et al., 1964; Arndt, 1945). The optimum temperature for shoot production is lower than that for

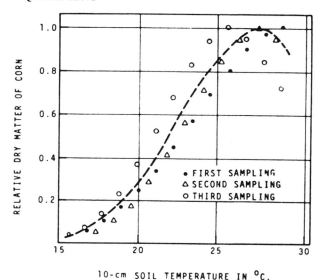

10-cm SOIL TEMPERATURE IN °C.

Fig. 10–7. Relative dry matter production of corn as related to the 10-cm soil temperature in the field. Growth measurements were taken from 13 to 38, 22 to 54, and 41 to 67 d, respectively, after planting for the first, second, and third sampling (Allmaras et al., 1964).

shoot elongation. Because elongation may be a better estimator of leaf area, it may also be a better measure of the effect of soil temperature on grain yield.

Corn growth during the vegetative stage was found to be related to both air temperature and rainfall. Hanna (1925) found that growth was more closely related to air temperature than to any other climatic variable. The best correlation between growth and air temperature occurred when remainder indices >10 °C were used. McCalla et al. (1939) also found that air temperature explained much of the growth rate variation. Loomis (1934) found that the growth rate decreased rapidly as the temperature decreased 10 °C. Most rapid growth occurred in the late afternoon and early evening and morning or on cloudy days when the air temperature was high and no water deficits developed. In general, growth rates followed the temperature curve at night and the moisture supply curve during the day. Over a 3-yr period, Kiesselbach (1950) found almost the same amount of growth during the daylight hours as at night. Wallace and Bressman (1937) estimated daily growth rates, for short periods of growth, ranging from near 8 cm at a temperature of 18 to 19 °C to >17 cm at a temperature of 25 to 26 °C.

Flooding reduces corn yields; the time and the length of the flooding period affect the yield reduction. In a greenhouse experiment, Mittra and Stickler (1961) found that flooding at the five-leaf stage reduced dry matter 7.5% if flooded for 7 d, 34% if flooded for 14 d, and 43% if flooded for 21 d. Dry matter was harvested 21 d after flooding. Corn was more susceptible than soybean [*Glycine max* (L.) Merr.] or grain sorghum.

Ritter and Beer (1969) found that flooding when corn was 15 cm in height for 72, 48, and 24 h reduced corn yields by 32, 22, and 18%, respectively, at a low N fertilizer level. At a high level, these reductions ranged from 19 to 14% in 1 yr to < 5% the following year.

Correlations between early season weather and yield have generally shown little significance. Wallace (1920) found low correlations between May temperature and yield. He estimated that an average May temperature of 15.6 °C in central Iowa resulted in average yields with higher yields occurring at higher temperatures. Rose (1936) also found that correlations between yield and May temperatures were relatively low. His results show that May temperatures in the north and northeast sections of the Corn Belt (average May temperature <15 °C) were positively correlated with yield, whereas in the southwest section (average May temperature >16.1 °C) they were negatively correlated. For Indiana, Visher (1940) found a positive correlation between yield and May temperature.

In the western part of the Corn Belt, yields generally improved with increased May rainfall (Rose, 1936; Wallace, 1920). Wallace (1920) estimated, however, that May rainfall >12.7 cm caused decreased yields. For optimum yields in Indiana, Visher (1940) found that May precipitation should be more than the normal 10 cm and be accompanied by increased temperature. Too much above normal, however, will cause yield decreases.

Thompson (1963, 1986) computed optimum June temperatures for Iowa, Illinois, Indiana, Ohio, and Missouri, assuming normal June rainfall. The optimum temperature was the normal temperature of 22 to 23 °C (Fig. 10–8). However, correlations between yield and both June temperature and June rainfall were low (Thompson, 1963). A number of researchers examined the relationships between June temperature and yield (Davis and Harrell, 1941; Rose, 1936; Visher, 1940; Wallace, 1920) and generally found positive correlations where temperatures average below the optimum values and negative correlations where they average above the optimum. Accumulated temperatures >32 °C have also shown a negative correlation with yield, except in Ohio and bordering areas where the correlations were positive.

In the southwest part of the Corn Belt, increased rainfall during June gave increased yield (Davis and Harrell, 1941; Rose, 1936; Wallace, 1920), but results conflicted in other parts of the Corn Belt. For individual years, the response to June rainfall is related to the moisture reserve in the soil, June temperature, and subsequent weather. Thompson (1966) determined the response of corn to June rainfall for the five major corn producing states in the Corn Belt, assuming other conditions were normal. The response curve for June rainfall was relatively flat but did show higher yields with below normal rainfall than with above normal rainfall. For a year with below normal soil moisture reserves, above normal rainfall could be beneficial.

In the previous discussion on early season weather effects on yield,

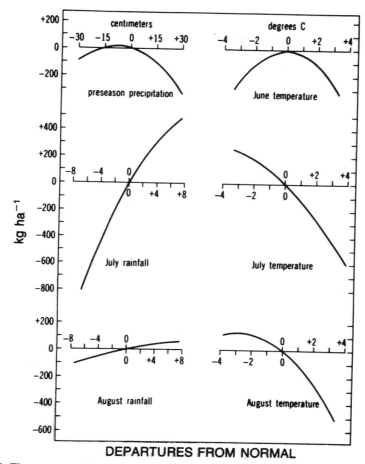

Fig. 10–8. The response of corn to weather variables in the five central Corn Belt states (Thompson, 1986).

only what would be called macro-effects are discussed, which averages out the differences among soils. It should be remembered that micro-effects, such as the difference between a poorly drained and a well-drained soil, are important for individual soils, or to individual farmers, and cannot be disregarded. These differences are probably more significant early than later in the season.

10–4.4 Late Vegetative Growth from the Beginning of Rapid Stem Elongation to Silking

In the late vegetative stage, the relationships between weather and yield are more marked and significant. In most of the Corn Belt, this growth stage occurs in late June and early July, before silking in the latter

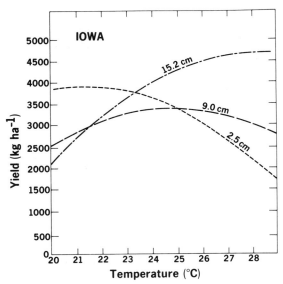

Fig. 10-9. Relation of corn yield to July temperature with different levels of rainfall in Iowa (Thompson, 1963).

part of the month. Effects of weather at silking will be covered in the next section. Wallace (1920) found that in most states, July temperature was negatively correlated with yield. Rose (1936) found that in the northwest, southwest, and southern margins of the Corn Belt, the relatively high correlation between July temperature and yield was negative; in the central part of the Corn Belt, he found low, non-significant correlations. Thompson (1962, 1963, 1966, 1986) used regression techniques to study the weather-corn yield relationships for several states. For the five major corn states, he found yields near normal when July temperatures were near the normal 24 °C (Fig. 10-8). Temperatures above normal reduced the yield sharply, while below normal temperatures gave above normal yields. The optimum temperature varies with the amount of rainfall (Fig. 10-9); the optimum average Iowa temperature is near 21 °C with only 2.5 cm of July rainfall, but is about 28 °C with 15 cm of rainfall. With more soil-moisture available, a higher water demand caused by higher temperatures can be met without stress occurring.

In the late vegetative stage, corn plants grow very rapidly. Water use is greater, and in most areas, rainfall is lower than June so that the water balance may become very important under low rainfall conditions. The optimum July rainfall (Fig. 10-8) is much above normal for the Corn Belt states (Hendricks and Scholl, 1943; Thompson, 1966, 1986). This is not surprising since atmospheric demand for water is high and the plant requires much more water to meet its needs.

Moisture stress during this period will cause yield reductions. A number of researchers (Claassen and Shaw, 1970b; Denmead and Shaw, 1960;

Table 10-1. Percentage of possible grain-yield reduction per stress day (data to nearest percent).

Growth stage	Researchers				
	Robins and Domingo (1953)	Denmead and Shaw (1960)	Wilson (1968)	Claassen and Shaw (1970a,b)	Mallett (1972)
	%				
Late vegetative	--	3-4	2	2	3
Flowering	6-8	6-8	2-3	3-13	--
Ear filling	3	3	5-6	4-7	4

Mallett, 1972; Robins and Domingo, 1953; Wilson, 1968) have studied this problem. In these experiments, corn was grown with a restricted root area and kept well watered, except when stress was imposed. At this stage, water was withheld to get the desired degree of stress. The treatments used subjected corn plants to a rather severe stress for 4 to 6 d. The results, in terms of grain yield reduction per stress day, are given in Table 10-1. Data of Mallett show a linear response of stress up to an 8-d duration for all periods.

In the experiment of Denmead and Shaw (1960), the yield reduction was due in part to some fertility stress during the late vegetative period, which decreased the leaf area below the optimum. By preventing this fertility stress in a later experiment, the yield reduction during this period was reduced to 2% per day by Claassen and Shaw (1970b). Although not measured, leaf area was much larger than for the experiment of Denmead and Shaw. Downey (1971a) found that stress stunted the growth of the plants to some degree. Hoyt and Bradfield (1962), Eik and Hanway (1966), and Mallett (1972) have all found a linear relationship between corn grain yields and leaf area for leaf area indexes (LAI) <3.3. If moisture stress reduces LAI below 3.3, yield reductions will be greater than if a larger leaf area is present. Claassen and Shaw (1970a) found that vegetative dry matter was reduced 15 to 17% by a 4-d stress treatment late in the vegetative period.

When corn at a height of 76 cm was flooded, Ritter and Beer (1969) found that 24 h of flooding, at a low level of N, reduced yields by 14%; this yield reduction increased to 30% with 96 h of flooding. With a high level of N in the soil, very little yield reduction occurred even with 96 h of flooding. When flooded near silking, no reduction in yield occurred at a high N level, but yield reductions up to 16% occurred with 96 h of flooding at the low level of N.

10-4.5 Tasseling, Silking, and Pollination

This is a very critical stage in the corn plant. The number of ovules that will be fertilized is being determined. Both moisture and fertility stresses that occur at this stage can have a serious effect on yield, with the exact stage at which it occurs also affecting the yield reduction. Barnes and Woolley (1969) found a 6 to 8% reduction in yield when stress was imposed for a period of a few days at tassel emergence. Their degree of stress cannot be directly compared with that in Table 10–1 because of a difference in the way stress was imposed.

Claassen and Shaw (1970b) found that stress imposed at 6% silking reduced yield only 3% per day, but at 75% silking the yield reduction was 7% per day with moisture stress. The data in Table 10–1 indicate that a 6 to 8% reduction per day was most common. A stress imposed at 75% silking and combined with fertility stress resulted in a yield reduction of 13% per day with a large reduction in the number of developed kernels. Voladarski and Zinevich (1960) also reported that stress could reduce the number of grains per ear. Berbecel and Eftimescu (1973) found that maximum temperatures > 32 °C around tasseling and pollination speeded up the differentiation process of the reproductive parts and resulted in higher rates of kernel abortion. High temperatures (35 °C) generally cause stress, but are usually combined with moisture stress. If too many kernels are aborted, the total sink size may limit yield, but under normal conditions the number of kernels is not as important as it is on rice (*Oryza sativa* L.) (Yoshida, 1972). The maximum size of the rice kernel is genetically determined so that a change in number will cause a change in total yield. Although there is a maximum size for corn kernels, the size $\times$ number factor limit is rarely reached. Prine (1971) also found that a poor light environment at very high plant populations could cause ear barrenness.

Barnes and Woolley (1969) subjected a "stress-sensitive" single-eared cultivar and a "stress-resistant" two-eared cultivar to severe moisture stress. At the silking and pollination stage, the two-eared cultivar was more tolerant of stress, with a yield reduction of 14%, compared with a 73% reduction for a single-eared cultivar. The two-eared type also had much greater flexibility in partly avoiding a short period of stress and in taking better advantage of later good weather. Hallauer and Troyer (1972) summarized the data from a number of experiments comparing prolific vs. single-eared hybrids and found that, over a series of environments and planting rates, the prolific hybrids had greater flexibility for adjusting to environmental stress. The prolific hybrids had less genotype $\times$ environment interaction and greater stability of performance across environments.

Little information is available regarding the effects of soil temperature at this stage. Adams and Thompson (1973), however, found that decreasing soil temperature from 26 to 22 °C during pollination and grain formation had no effect on corn yield, but reducing soil temperature to 23 °C reduced grain sorghum yield about 10% in Texas.

The time at which tasseling and silking occur are very weather dependent. Wallace and Bressman (1937) cited data showing that a so-called 115-d cultivar took 74 d from planting to tasseling with an average temperature of 20 °C, but only 54 d with an average temperature near 23 °C. Cool nights reduce the rapidity of growth before tasseling. As an average for the 60-d period after planting, they found that for each degree the temperature averaged above 21.1 °C, tasseling was hastened by 2 to 3 d. Data of Shaw and Thom (1951a) and Rench (1973) show similar variations in the length of the period to tasseling. Rench showed that the length of the period was highly correlated with temperature GDUs, but that soil moisture also needed to be considered. If a cultivar is daylength sensitive, this factor also influences time of tasseling.

Allen et al. (1973) found that a hybrid took approximately the same number of langleys (g cal/cm²) from planting to tasseling, although the number of days varied significantly. Mallett (1972) found that severe stress had little effect on the date of tasseling, although silking was delayed 6 to 8 d. Similar results were found by Shaw and Thom (1951b). Rhoades and Stanley (1973) found that both tasseling and silking occurred earlier as soil-moisture tension was decreased.

Shaw (1949, unpublished data), DuPlessis and Dijkhuis (1967), and Berbecel and Eftimescu (1973) found that stress before and during flowering caused the time between pollen shed and silking to be extended. With severe stress, silking may be delayed until after all or much of the pollen has been shed, increasing the number of barren stalks and poorly filled ears.

Rench (1973) found that a cultivar maturity rating, as well as temperature and soil moisture, were necessary to predict silking dates. Growing-degree units were a better predictor of silking date than the cultivar maturity rating in number of days, but both still showed considerable variation.

10–4.6 Grain Production From Fertilization to Physiological Maturity of the Grain

During the ear-filling stage, significant reduction in yield can occur from moisture stress. Mallett (1972) subjected corn to stress starting at 10, 20, 30, and 40 d after silking and maintained stress for up to 8 d. Four days of stress caused an average yield reduction of 4.3% per day of stress at each of the times that stress was imposed. In another experiment, Mallett found that the reduction was 4.1% per day of stress. Some yield reductions (Table 10–1) have been a little higher than this (Claassen and Shaw, 1970b; Wilson, 1968), and others have been a little lower than this (Denmead and Shaw, 1960; Robins and Domingo, 1953). Higher reductions occurred where some degree of fertility stress was confounded with the moisture stress. Data of Claassen and Shaw (1970b) also indicated that the later in the season stress is imposed, the less the yield reduction.

Barnes and Woolley (1969) obtained a yield reduction of 22% for their two-eared cultivar and 48% for their single-eared cultivar when stress was imposed at the blister-kernel stage. The 22% reduction is comparable to that found by Mallett, but the 48% reduction is much higher. The sensitivity of this particular single-eared cultivar to stress was no doubt a significant factor in its large response to stress.

August weather, which covers the first part of this period, obviously has an effect on yield. Wallace (1920), Rose (1936), Davis and Harrell (1941), Kiesselbach (1950), and Thompson (1963) have all shown that average August temperatures are higher than those associated with optimum corn yields in the Corn Belt. Thompson (1986) (Fig. 10–8) estimated that below normal temperatures were optimum for the five major producing corn states, with major decreases in yield resulting from above normal temperatures. In Missouri, Bondavelli et al. (1970) found that temperature in the last half of August had a more significant effect on corn yield than the rainfall in the same period, but in the first half of August, rainfall had a more significant effect on yield than temperature. Peters et al. (1971) in an unreplicated experiment, found that a night air temperature of 29.4 °C for the period from flowering to maturity reduced corn yield almost 40% compared with a cool temperature of 16.6 °C. The high temperature produced earlier senescence and maturity and may have induced a water stress on the plants.

In a dry year with low-soil moisture reserves, increased August rainfall will increase corn yields, but in a wet year, too much August rain may create some problems for harvesting. This may be particularly important on the more poorly drained soils in the wetter areas. Rose (1936) found that August rainfall was positively correlated with yield in most areas in the Corn Belt, but the correlations were low in the central part. Thompson (1962, 1963, 1966, 1986) found that increased August rainfall was associated with higher yields (Fig. 10–8), but correlations with yield were low for the major corn-producing states. August temperature was much more important than August rainfall in his regression techniques to predict corn yields.

In September, the corn crop is progressing toward maturity in the Corn Belt; by the end of the month much of the corn is physiologically mature. In a dry year, stress from either lack of water or high temperatures can reduce yield of long-season hybrids; severe stress may cause premature dying, an additional yield loss. In a wet year, soil-moisture reserves for the next season are increased, and the wet weather has little direct effect on yield but may delay harvesting. An early freeze before physiological maturity may cause serious yield losses, especially if the crop is late in maturing. If the crop is prematurely killed 10 to 14 d (200 GDU) before black layer maturity, a 4 to 5% grain yield reduction can be expected. If killed 3 weeks before physiologically mature, there is a 10 to 20% loss with considerable reduction in grain quality. With a freeze 30 d before maturity (30–35 d after silking), yield is reduced 35 to 50% and grain probably is not marketable (Shaw and Newman, 1985). Because of these varied effects, correlations between weather factors in September and yield have been low.

The time of physiological maturity (maximum dry weight) seems well defined in terms of the black layer development (Daynard and Duncan, 1969; Rench and Shaw, 1971). Kernel moisture at black layer development or physiological maturity varies with variety. Grain-moisture loss from early ear formation to physiological maturity is poorly correlated with weather factors (Hallauer and Russell, 1961). Degree days showed the best relationship with moisture loss, but results were not consistent. Rench (1973), using six hybrids with 85- to 135-d maturity classifications, found that longer season cultivars took more time to reach black layer maturity after silking than did the shorter season cultivars. Cooler temperatures increased the length of the period to some extent. Rench found that the best predictor for the length of this period was a cultivar maturity rating; adding a temperature variable increased the correlation slightly. The variation among the six hybrids of the length of the silking to physiological maturity period in days was much less than for the planting to silking interval. Since the grain size in corn is loosely restricted, extending the duration of the grain-filling period, or maintaining higher photosynthetic activity during this time might increase yield (Yoshida, 1972).

10–4.7 Drying of the Grain

After physiological maturity, the grain must dry to a harvestable moisture level. The rate of drying is affected by the weather and the cultivar characteristics. Dodds and Pelton (1967) found that the rate of drying of wheat in the field was influenced by vapor-pressure deficit, hours of sunshine, rate of evaporation, and wind. They determined that vapor-pressure deficit was an excellent measure for describing the causes of moisture fluctuation in wheat. Hours of sunshine have an effect on temperature and, like wind, can contribute to drying. Schmidt and Hallauer (1966) found that, before physiological maturity, kernel moisture was primarily a physiological process with the reduction showing some relationship with air temperature. Below 30% moisture, they found that the reduction in kernel moisture was related most closely to the vapor-pressure deficit, with the wet-bulb depression showing almost as good a relationship. Relative humidity gave a poorer relationship, which should be expected when using it as an expression for drying power of the air.

Rain is a major contributor to moisture increases during the early part of the drying stage, and condensation during periods of high humidity is important during later stages of maturity.

10–4.8 Seasonal Effects

The major weather effects at different growth stages on yield have been covered in earlier sections. There are some data, however, that relate yield to total seasonal effects. Total seasonal rainfall has generally not given high correlations with yield. This is partly because of negative correlations for part of the season and positive correlations for other parts of the season. Pengra (1946) found that seasonal rainfall in South Dakota was more highly correlated with corn yields ($r = 0.58$) than was preseasonal precipitation.

In Nebraska, Kiesselbach (1915) found that for each rise of 0.56 °C in mean seasonal temperature during June, July, and August a 423 kg/ha decrease in yield occurred. In more humid areas, this relationship might not be true, at least to such a degree.

Mederski and Jones (1963) in Ohio found that heated soils gave faster, earlier growth, but reduced mature plant height. Heating increased yields 15% when the soil temperature around the heating cable was maintained near 30 °C. Willis (1956) found that times of emergence, silking, and maturity were hastened by higher soil temperatures. He found that yields increased with increasing soil temperature (10-cm depth) to about 23 °C, then decreased with a further increase in soil temperature.

L. M. Thompson (1986, personal communication) has found that accumulated degrees >32.2 °C are related to yield. By using daily maximum temperature and accumulating the degrees >32.2 °C, he found that, for each 5.6 °C accumulated, yields were reduced 62.7 kg/ha for corn and one-third that amount for soybean. Schwab et al. (1958) found that the number of days with maximum temperature >32.2 °C was negatively related to irrigated corn yields in Iowa.

Duncan et al. (1973) grew corn with irrigation at Davis and Greenfield, CA, and Lexington, KY, all at the same altitude. Yields were highest at Davis, which had the highest insolation, the lowest night temperature, and the highest number of growing-degree days. Other environmental factors also were confounded in these comparisons. Maximum temperatures of 37.8 °C or higher occurred on 25 d of the growing season at Davis. Night temperatures seemed particularly significant in the yield relationship.

Using solar radiation as a treatment in controlled experiments has nearly always shown positive effects; Pendleton et al. (1967) found that increased light improved corn yields, and Duncan and Hesketh (1968) found that shading reduced yields. Mach and Dale (1983) showed that solar radiation was an important variable to consider in yield relations. Regression analyses of yield and climatic data over several years have frequently shown negative effects of increased radiation. Kiesselbach (1950) found that a seasonal 1% increase in sunshine in Nebraska reduced grain yield by 96 kg/ha (1.5 bu/acre), while an increase of 1 g cal in the seasonal mean daily total radiation reduced the yield by 24 kg/ha. In areas less dry and hot, one might expect this to be reversed, although McCalla et al. (1939) found a negative correlation between wheat growth and sunlight at Edmonton, Alberta, Canada. In the field, the effect of high radiation, often accompanied with relatively high temperatures, can well depend upon the relative magnitudes of the two factors. In Iowa in 1972 a state average corn yield that was 815 kg/ha higher than grown before was produced with excellent moisture, cooler than normal summer temperatures, and slightly below average solar radiation. Two of the western Corn Belt's best yield years (1981 and 1982) were also years with low solar radiation. Would higher radiation have increased yields because of higher photosynthetic activity or reduced yields because of greater moisture stress? We do not have a good answer to that question.

In a review on the enrichment of the plant environment, Wittwer (1966) stated, "Carbon dioxide has given the most spectacular yield increases of any growth factor yet discovered in the culture of greenhouse crops." As reported by Waggoner (1969), however, results for corn in the field have been far from spectacular. However, Harper et al. (1973) have shown a large increase in photosynthetic production in cotton with high rates of field CO_2 enrichment. Using a photosynthesis simulator, Waggoner estimated that, to increase photosynthesis substantially in full sun, it would be necessary to increase the CO_2 concentration above the canopy, as well as at the ground. This may be why addition at ground level only has been rarely successful in the field.

Currently there is considerable discussion among climatologists about possible climate changes and biological effects of increasing atmospheric CO_2 resulting from burning fossil fuels and a reduction in the world biomass from forest clearing. At the present levels of CO_2 (near 340 ppm) C_4 plants (maize and sorghum) show more photosynthesis than C_3 types (wheat and soybean). At about 0.72 mg/L (400 ppm) the rates are equal; above that C_3 plants show a higher rate (Akita and Moss, 1973). Concentrations could range from 0.77 to 1.33 mg/L (430–740 ppm) by the year 2050 (NRC, 1983). Warmer temperatures are generally predicted, but annual temperature and precipitation changes will provide little useful information relative to corn production; the distribution of these changes during the year is the important factor. Some areas are postulated to have lower summer rainfalls, which could be critical. Waggoner (1984) has discussed the various effects of possible CO_2 changes.

ACKNOWLEDGMENT

This is a paper of the Iowa Agriculture and Home Economics Exp. Stn., Ames, Iowa, Project 2397.

REFERENCES

Adams, J.E. 1970. Effects of mulches and bed configuration. II. Soil temperature and yield responses of grain sorghum and corn. Agron J. 62:785–790.

----, and D.O. Thompson. 1973. Soil temperature reduction during pollination and grain formation of corn and grain sorghum. Agron. J. 65:60–63.

Akita, S., and D.N. Moss. 1973. Photosynthetic response to CO_2 and light by maize and wheat leaves adjusted for constant stomatal aperatures. Crop Sci. 13:234–237.

Alessi, J., and J.F. Power. 1971. Corn emergence in relation to soil temperature and seeding depth. Agron. J. 63:717–719.

634   SHAW

Allen, J.R., G.W. McKee, and J.H. McGahen. 1973. Leaf number and maturity in hybrid corn. Agron. J. 65:233–235.

Allmaras, R.R., W.C. Burrows, and W.E. Larson. 1964. Early growth of corn as affected by soil temperature. Soil Sci. Soc. Am. Proc. 28:271–275.

————, and W.W. Nelson. 1971. Corn (*Zea Mays* L.) root configuration as influenced by some row-interrow variants of tillage and straw mulch management. Soil Sci. Soc. Am. Proc. 35:974–980.

Arndt, C.H. 1945. Temperature-growth relations of roots and hypocotyls of cotton seedlings. Plant Physiol. 20:200–220.

Baker, D.G., and J.B. Swan. 1966. Climate of Minnesota. Part IV. Spring soil temperatures. Minnesota Agric. Exp. Stn. Misc. Rep. 67.

Barnes, D.L., and D.G. Woolley. 1969. Effect of moisture stress at different stages of growth. I. Comparison of a single-eared and a two-eared corn hybrid. Agron. J. 61:788–790.

Begg, J.E., and N.C. Turner. 1976. Crop water deficits. Adv. Agron. 28:161–217.

Benson, G.O., and H.E. Thompson. 1974. Corn planting dates. Iowa State Univ., Coop. Ext. Serv., PM-595.

Berbecel, O., and M. Eftimescu. 1973. Effect of agrometeorological conditions on maize growth and development. (English translation.) Inst. Meteorol. Hydrology, Bucharest, Romania. p. 10–31.

————, ————, E. Gogorici, and I. Rogojan. 1964. The forecast of the vegetative phases of the self sown and cultivated flora. (English summary.) p. 347–358. *In* Culegere de lucrari. Romanian Inst. Meteorol., Bucharest, Romania.

Blacklow, W.M. 1972. Influence of temperature on germination and elongation of the radicle and shoot of corn (*Zea mays* L.). Crop Sci. 12:647–650.

Bondavalli, B., D. Colyer, and E.M. Kroth. 1970. Effects of weather, nitrogen and population on corn yield response. Agron. J. 62:669–672.

Boyer, J.S. 1970. Differing sensitivity of photosynthesis to low leaf water potentials in corn and soybeans. Plant Physiol. 46:236–239.

————, and H.G. McPherson. 1975. Physiology of water deficits in cereal crops. Adv. Agron. 27:1–23.

Brown, D.M. 1969. Heat units for corn in southern Ontario. Information leaflet. Ontario Dep. of Agric. Food, Guelph, Ontario, Canada.

Brown, R.W., and B.P. Van Haveren. 1972. Psychrometry in water relations research. Utah Agric. Exp. Stn. Rep.

Cackett, K.E., and H.R.R. Metelerkamp. 1964. Evapotranspiration of maize in relation to open-pan evaporation and crop development. Rhod. J. Agric. Res. 2:35–44.

Cal, J.P., and R.L. Obendorf. 1972. Differential growth of corn (*Zea mays* L.) hybrids seeded at cold root zone temperatures. Crop Sci. 12:572–575.

Claassen, M.M., and R.H. Shaw. 1970a. Water deficit effects on corn. I. Vegetative components. Agron. J. 62:649–652.

————, and ————. 1970b. Water deficit effects on corn. II. Grain components. Agron. J. 62:652–655.

Coffman, F.A. 1923. The minimum temperature for germination of seed. J. Am. Soc. Agron. 15:257–270.

Corsi, W.C., and R.H. Shaw. 1971. Evaluation of stress indices of corn in Iowa. Iowa State J. Sci. 46:79–85.

Cowan, I.R. 1965. Transport of water in the soil-plant-atmosphere system. J. Appl. Ecol. 2:221–239.

Cross, H.Z., and M.S. Zuber. 1972. Prediction of flowering dates in maize based on different methods of estimating thermal units. Agron. J. 64:351–355.

Dale, R.F., W.L. Nelson, K.L. Scheeringa, R.G. Stuff, and H.F. Reetz. 1982. Generalizing and testing of a soil moisture budget for different drainage conditions. J. Appl. Meteorol. 21:1417–1426.

————, and R.H. Shaw. 1965. Effect on corn yields of moisture stress and stand at two fertility levels. Agron. J. 57:475–479.

Davis, F.E., and G.D. Harrell. 1941. Relation of weather and its distribution to corn yields. USDA Tech. Bull. 806. U.S. Gov. Print. Office, Washington, DC.

Daynard, T.B. 1972. Relationships among black-layer formation, grain moisture percentage and heat unit accumulation in corn. Agron J. 64:716–719.

————, and W.G. Duncan. 1969. The black layer and grain maturity in corn. Crop Sci. 9:473–476.

deJager, J.M. 1968. Carbon dioxide exchange and photosynthetic activity in forage grasses. Ph.D. diss. Univ. of Wales, Abersystwyth.

Denmead, O.T., and R.H. Shaw. 1959. Evapotranspiration in relation to the development of the corn crop. Agron. J. 51:716–719.

----,and ----. 1960. The effects of soil moisture stress at different stages of growth on the development and yield of corn. Agron. J. 52:272–274.

----,and ----. 1962. Availability of soil water to plants as affected by soil moisture content and meteorological conditions. Agron. J. 54:385–390.

Dodds, M.E., and W.L. Pelton. 1967. Effect of weather factors on the kernel moisture of a standing crop of wheat. Agron. J. 59:181–184.

Doss, B.D., O.L. Bennett, and D.A. Ashley. 1962. Evapotranspiration by irrigated corn. Agron. J. 54:497–498.

Downey, L.A. 1971a. Effect of gypsum and drought stress on maize (Zea mays L.). I. Growth, light absorption, and yield. Agron. J. 63:569–572.

----. 1971b. Effect of gypsum and drought stress on maize (Zea mays L.). II. Consumptive use of water. Agron. J. 63:597–600.

Duncan, W.G., and J.D. Hesketh. 1968. Net photosynthetic rates, relative leaf growth rates and leaf numbers of 22 races of maize grown at eight temperatures. Crop Sci. 8:370–374.

----, D.L. Shaver, and W.A. Williams. 1973. Insolation and temperature effects on maize growth and yield. Crop Sci. 13:187–191.

Dungan, G.H. 1944. Yield and bushel weight of corn grain as influenced by time of planting. J. Am. Soc. Agron. 36:166–170.

DuPlesis, D.P., and F.J. Dijkhuis. 1967. The influence of the time lag between pollen shedding and silking on the yield of maize. S. Afr. J. Agric. Sci. 10:667–674.

Eckert, D.J., and D.R. Hicks. 1985. Maturity rating systems for corn. Purdue Univ., Coop. Ext. Serv., Natl. Corn Handb. NCH-26.

Eik, K., and J.J. Hanway. 1966. Leaf area in relation to yield of corn grain. Agron. J. 58:16–18.

Gardner, W.R. 1960. Dynamic aspects of water availability to plants. Soil Sci. 89:63–73.

Grobbelaar, W.P. 1963. Responses of young maize plants to root temperatures. Meded. Landbouwhogesch. Wageningen 63(5):1–71.

Guidry, N.P. 1964. A graphic summary of world agriculture. USDA Misc. Pub. 705. U.S. Gov. Print. Office, Washington, DC.

Haise, H.R. 1958. Irrigation. Agronomic trends and problems in the Great Plains. Adv. Agron. 6:47–56.

Hallauer, A.R., and W.A. Russell. 1961. Effects of selected weather factors on grain moisture reduction from silking to physiologic maturity in corn. Agron. J. 53:225–229.

----, and A.F. Troyer. 1972. Prolific corn hybrids and minimizing risk of stress. p. 140–158. In H.D. Loden and D. Wilkenson (ed.) Annu. Corn Sorghum Res. Conf. Proc., 27, Chicago. 12–14 December. ASTA, Washington, DC.

Halstead, M.H. 1954. The fluxes of momentum, heat and water vapor in micrometeorology. (Johns Hopkins Univ.,) Lab. of Climatology Publ. 7:326–58.

Hanna, W.F. 1924. Growth of corn and sunflowers in relation to climatic conditions. Bot. Gaz. (Chicago) 78:200–214.

----. 1925. The nature of the growth rate in plants. Sci. Agric. (Ottawa) 5:133–138.

Hanway, D.G. 1966. Irrigation. p. 155–176. In W.H. Pierre et al. (ed.) Advances in corn production: Principles and practices. Iowa State Univ. Press, Ames.

Harper, L.A., D.N. Baker, J.E. Box, Jr., and J.D. Hesketh. 1973. Carbon dioxide and the photosynthesis of field crops: A metered carbon dioxide release in cotton under field conditions. Agron. J. 65:7–11.

Harrold, L.L., and R.F. Dreibelbis. 1951. Agricultural hydrology as evaluated by monolith lysimeters. USDA Tech. Bull. 1050. U.S. Gov. Print. Office, Washington, DC.

Hendricks, W.A., and J.C. Scholl. 1943. The joint effects of precipitation and temperature on corn yields. North Carolina Agric. Exp. Stn. Tech. Bull. 74.

Holmes, R.M., and G.W. Robertson. 1959. Heat units and crop growth. Pub. 1042. Can. Dep. Agric., Ottawa, Ontario, Canada.

Hoyt, P., and R. Bradfield. 1962. Effect of varying leaf area on dry matter production in corn. Agron. J. 54:523–525.

Hsiao, T.C. 1973. Plant responses to water stress. Annu. Rev. Plant Plysiol. 24:519–570.

Iowa Crop Reporting Service. 1985. Iowa agricultural statistics. Iowa Dep. of Agric. and USDA Stn. Rep. Serv., Des Moines, IA.

Jackson, R.D., S.B. Idso, R.J. Reginato, and P.J. Pinter, Jr. 1981. Canopy temperature as a crop water stress indicator. Water Resour. Res. 17:1133–1138.

Johns, D.M., and H.B. Brown. 1941. Effect of date of planting on corn yields, insect infestation and fungous diseases. Louisiana State Bull. 327.

Kanemasu, E.T., G.W. Thurtell, and C.B. Tanner. 1969. Design, calibration and field use of a stomatal diffusion porometer. Plant Physiol. 44:881–885.

Kiesselbach, T.A. 1915. Transpiration as a factor in crop production. Nebraska Agric. Exp. Stn. Res. Bull. 8.

————. 1950. Progressive development and seasonal variation of the corn crop. Nebraska Agric. Exp. Stn. Res. Bull. 166.

Kincer, J.B. 1919. Temperature influence on planting and harvest dates. Mon. Weather Rev. 47:312–323.

Loomis, W.E. 1934. Daily growth of maize. Am. J. Bot. 21:1–6.

Mach, M.A., and R.F. Dale. 1983. A methodology for considering the effect of weather on the response of corn yields to added fertilizer: A case study in Indiana with nitrogen. Proc. Indiana Acad. Sci. 1982 92:453–462.

Mallett, J.B. 1972. The use of climatic data for maize yield predictions. Ph.D. diss. Univ. of Natal, Pietermaritzburg, South Africa.

Maranville, J.W., and G.M. Paulsen. 1970. Alteration of carbohydrate composition of corn (*Zea mays* L.) seedlings during moisture stress. Agron. J. 62:605–608.

McCalla, A.G., J.R. Weir, and K.W. Neatby. 1939. Effects of temperature and sunlight on the rate of elongation of stems in maize and gladiolus. Can. J. Res. Sect. C: 17:388–409.

Mederski, H.J., and J.B. Jones, Jr. 1963. Effect of soil temperature on corn plant development and yield. I. Studies with a corn hybrid. Soil Sci. Soc. Am. Proc. 27:186–189.

Mittra, M.K., and F.C. Stickler. 1961. Excess water effects on different crops. Trans. Kans. Acad. Sci. 64:275–286.

National Research Council. 1983. Changing climate. Natl. Acad. Press, Washington, DC.

Newman, J.E., and B.O. Blair. 1969. Growing degree days and dent corn maturity. Part II. Agronomy Dep. Purdue Univ., West Lafayette, IN.

Nield, R.E. 1981. The effect of weather on corn. Preseason precipitation and yield of unirrigated corn. Univ. of Nebraska Coop. Ext. Serv. Guide G80–526.

————, and N.H. Richman. 1981. Agroclimatic normals for maize. Agric. Meteorol. 24:83–95.

Nuttonson, M.Y. 1953. Phenology and thermal environment as a means for a physiological classification of wheat varieties and for predicting maturity dates of wheat. Am. Inst. Crop Ecology, Washington, DC.

Olson, T.C. 1971. Yield and water use by different populations of dryland corn, grain sorghum, and forage sorghum in the western Corn Belt. Agron. J. 63:104–106.

Pendleton, J.W., and D.B. Egli. 1969. Potential yield of corn as affected by planting date. Agron. J. 61:70–71.

————, ————, and D.B. Peters. 1967. Response of *Zea mays* L. to a "light rich" field environment. Agron. J. 59:395–397.

Pengra, R.F. 1946. Correlation analysis of precipitation and crop yield data for the subhumid areas of the northern Great Plains. J. Am. Soc. Agron. 38:848–849.

Peters, D.B., J.W. Pendleton, R.H. Hageman, and C.M. Brown. 1971. Effect of night air temperature on grain yield of corn, wheat and soybeans. Agron. J. 63:809.

Philip, J.R. 1957. The physical principles of soil water movement during the irrigation cycle. 32nd Congr. Int. Comm. Irrig. and Drain. Question 8:8.125–8.154.

Power, J.P., J.J. Bond, W.A. Sellner, and H.M. Olson. 1973. Effect of supplemental water on barley and corn production in a subhumid region. Agron. J. 65:464–467.

Prine, G.M. 1971. A critical period for ear development in maize. Crop Sci. 11:782–786.

Purvis, A.C., and R.E. Williamson. 1972. Effects of flooding and gaseous composition of the root environment on growth of corn. Agron. J. 64:674–678.

Ragland, J.L., A.L. Hatfield, and G.R. Benoit. 1965. The growth and yield of corn. I. Microclimate effects on the growth rates. Agron. J. 57:217–220.

Rench, W.E. 1973. Climatic influences on and indices of *Zea mays* L. growth and development. Ph.D. diss. Iowa State Univ., Ames (Diss. Abstr. 74–571).

----, and R.H. Shaw. 1971. Black layer development in corn. Agron. J. 63:303-305.

Rhoades, F.M., and R.L. Stanley, Jr. 1973. Response of three corn hybrids to low levels of soil moisture tension in the plow layer. Agron. J. 65:315-318.

Ritchie, J.T. 1973. Influence of soil-water status and meteorological condition on evaporation from a corn canopy. Agron. J. 65:893-897.

----, and E. Burnett. 1971. Dryland evaporative flux in a subhumid climate. II. Plant influences. Agron. J. 63:56-62.

Ritchie, S.W., J.J. Hanway, and G.O. Benson. 1986. How a corn plant develops. Coop. Ext. Serv. Sp. Rep. 40. (revised ed.) Iowa State Univ., Ames.

Ritter, W.F., and C.E. Beer. 1969. Yield reduction by controlled flooding of corn. Trans. ASAE 12:46-50.

Robins, J.S., and C.E. Domingo. 1953. Some effects of severe soil moisture deficits at specific growth stages in corn. Agron. J. 45:618-621.

----, and H.F. Rhoades. 1958. Irrigation of field corn in the west. USDA Leafl. 440. U.S. Gov. Print. Office, Washington, DC.

Rose, J.K. 1936. Corn yield and climate in the Corn Belt. Geogr. Rev. 26:88-102.

Salter, P.J., and J.E. Goode. 1967. Crop responses to water at different stages of growth. Res. Rev. 2. Commonw. Agric. Bur., Farnham Royal, Bucks, England.

Schmidt, J.L., and A.R. Hallauer. 1966. Estimating harvest date of corn in the field. Crop Sci. 6:227-231.

Scholander, P.F., H.T. Hammel, E.D. Bradstreet, and E.A. Hemmingsen. 1965. Sap pressure in plants. Science (Washington, DC) 148:339-346.

Schwab, G.D., W.D. Shrader, P.R. Nixon, and R.H. Shaw. 1958. Research on irrigation of corn and soybeans at Conesville and Ankeny, Iowa, 1951-1955. Iowa Agric. Home Econ. Exp. Stn. Res. Bull. 458.

Shaw, R.H. 1965. The prediction of soil moisture for the winter period in Iowa. Iowa State J. Sci. 39:337-344.

----. 1971. A comparison of soil and air temperatures in the spring at Ames, Iowa. Iowa State J. Sci. 45:613-620.

----. 1974. A weighted moisture stress index for corn in Iowa. Iowa State J. Res. 49:101-114.

----. 1977. Water use and requirements of maize—a review. p. 119-134. In Agrometeorology of the maize (corn) crop. World Meterol. Org. Publ. 481. Secretariat, WMO, Geneva, Switzerland.

----. 1981. Evaporation climatology of Iowa. Spec. Rep. 88. Iowa Agric. and Home Econ. Exp. Stn., Iowa State Univ., Ames.

----. 1983. Soil moisture and moisture stress prediction for corn in a western Corn Belt state. Korean J. Crop Sci. 28:1-10.

----, R. Felch, and E.R. Duncan. 1972. Soil moisture available for plant growth in Iowa. Iowa Agric. Home Econ. Exp. Stn. Spec. Rep. 70.

----, and J.E. Newman. 1985. Weather stress in the corn crop. Purdue Univ., Coop. Ext. Serv., Nat. Corn Handb. NCH-18.

----, K. Ross, and C. Myers. 1980. Evaluation of the management, yield, and water use interactions on corn in northwestern Iowa. Iowa State J. Res. 55:119-126.

----, and H.C.S. Thom. 1951a. On the phenology of field corn, the vegetative period. Agron. J. 43:9-15.

----, and ----. 1951b. On the phenology of field corn, silking to maturity. Agron. J. 43:541-546.

----, ----, and G.L. Barger. 1954. The climate of Iowa. I. The occurrence of freezing temperatures in the spring and fall. Iowa Agric. Exp. Stn. Spec. Rep. 8.

Slatyer, R.O. 1969. Physiological significance of internal water relations to crop yield. p. 53-83. In J.D. Eastin et al. (ed.) Physiological aspects of crop yield. ASA and CSSA, Madison, WI.

Thompson, L.M. 1962. An evaluation of weather factors in the production of corn. Center for Agric. Econ. Adjustment Rep. 12T. Iowa State Univ., Ames.

----. 1963. Weather and technology in the production of corn and soybeans. Center for Agric. Econ. Dev. Rep. 17. Iowa State Univ., Ames.

----. 1966. Weather variability and the need for a food reserve. Center for Agric. Econ. Dev. Rep. 26. Iowa State Univ., Ames.

----. 1969. Weather and technology in the production of corn in the U.S. Corn Belt. Agron. J. 61:453-456.

----. 1986. Climatic change, weather variability, and corn production. Agron. J. 78:649–653.

Thornthwaite, C.W., and J.R. Mather. 1955. The water budget and its use in irrigation. p. 346–58. *In* USDA Yearbook of Agriculture. Water. USDA Sup. of Doc. U.S. Gov. Print. Office, Washington, DC.

Trewartha, G.T., and L. Horn. 1980. An introduction to climate. 5th ed. McGraw-Hill, New York.

Ullstrup, A.J. 1966. Diseases of corn and their control. p. 419–446. *In* W.H. Pierre et al. (ed.) Advances in corn production: Principles and practices. Iowa State Univ. Press, Ames.

USDA. 1984. Agricultural statistics. USDA U.S. Gov. Print. Office, Washington, DC.

Vaadia, R., R.C. Raney, and R.M. Hagen. 1961. Plant water deficits and physiological processes. Annu. Rev. Plant Physiol. 12:265–292.

Van Wijk, W.R., W.E. Larson, and W.C. Burrows. 1959. Soil temperature and the early growth of corn from mulched and unmulched soil. Soil Sci. Soc. Am. Proc. 23:428–434.

Vasquez, R. 1961. Effects of irrigation at different growth stages and nitrogen levels on corn yields in Lajar Valley. P. R. J. Agric. 45:85–105.

Veihmeyer, F.J., and A.H. Hendrickson. 1955. Does transpiration decrease as the soil moisture decreases? Trans. Am. Geophys. Union 36:425–48.

Viets, F.G. 1966. Increasing water use efficiency by soil management, p. 259–274. *In* W.H. Pierre et al. (ed.) Plant environment and efficient water use. ASA and SSSA, Madison, WI.

Visher, S.S. 1940. Weather influences on crop yields. Econ. Geogr. 16:437–443.

Voladarski, N.I., and L.V. Zinevich. 1960. Drought resistance of corn during ontogeny. Fiziol. Rast. (Sofia) 7:176–179.

Waggoner, P.E. 1969. Environment manipulation for higher yields, p. 343–373. *In* J.D. Eastin et al. (ed.) Physiological aspects of crop yield. ASA and CSSA, Madison, WI.

----. 1984. Agriculture and carbon dioxide. Am. Sci. 72:179–184.

Wallace, H.A. 1920. Mathematical inquiry into the effect of weather on corn. Mon. Weather Rev. 48:439–446.

----, and E.N. Bressman. 1937. Corn and corn growing. John Wiley and Sons, New York.

Wang, J.Y. 1960. A critique of the heat unit approach to plant response studies. Ecology 41:785–790.

----. 1963. Agricultural meteorology. Pacemaker Press, Milwaukee.

Washington State University. 1975. Measurement of stomatal aperature and diffusive resistance. Washington State Univ. Bull. 809.

Willis, W.O. 1956. Soil temperature, mulches and corn growth. Ph.D. diss. Iowa State Univ., Ames.

----, W.E. Larson, and D. Kirkham. 1957. Corn growth as affected by soil temperature and mulch. Agron. J. 49:323–328.

Wilson, J.H. 1968. Water relations of maize. Part 1. Effects of severe soil moisture stress imposed at different stages of growth on grain yields of maize. Rhod. J. Agric. Res. 6:103–105.

Wittwer, S.H. 1966. Carbon dioxide and its role in plant growth. Proc. Int. Hortic. Congr. 17th 3:311–322.

Wolfe, T.K. 1927. A study of germination, maturity and yield in corn. Virginia State Tech. Bull. 30.

Yoshida, S. 1972. Physiological aspects of grain yield. Annu. Rev. Plant Physiol. 23:437–464.

11 Corn Production

R. A. OLSON AND D. H. SANDER

Department of Agronomy
University of Nebraska-Lincoln
Lincoln, Nebraska

Corn (*Zea mays* L.) is the major crop on the cultivated land of the USA with total production exceeding half of that for the entire world. The major portion of the national production is found in seven north central Corn Belt states where about 18.7×10^6 ha was harvested for grain in 1981 to 1983 (Table 11-1). The reason for this concentration is the combination of ideal weather and soil conditions for growth. Accordingly, it is not surprising that more research has gone into production practices for corn than for any other crop in the country. Advances in technology from that research and the foresight of industry in supplying the requisites for its efficient production have made possible the quadrupling in average corn yields of the country in the short period since World War II, now on the order of 7.0 Mg/ha.

11-1 SOIL QUALITY

Corn is grown on soils of widely different properties throughout the world, from the raw sands of the Sandhills of Nebraska and Colorado to the clays of delta regions, from strongly acid to strongly alkaline soils,

Table 11-1. Corn planted and harvested for grain in specified states and the USA, 1981-1983.†

State	Area harvested	Production
	ha	t
Illinois	4.13×10^6	2.97×10^7
Indiana	2.29×10^6	1.50×10^7
Iowa	4.78×10^6	3.38×10^7
Minnesota	2.38×10^6	1.55×10^7
Nebraska	2.50×10^6	1.68×10^7
Ohio	1.42×10^6	0.89×10^7
Wisconsin	1.24×10^6	0.81×10^7
Total	18.73×10^6	12.78×10^7
USA	26.81×10^6	17.36×10^7

† Data from Agricultural Statistics (1984).

and from shallow soils on residual material to those very deep on loess, till, or alluvium. With these ranges, however, there is corresponding variation in the crop's productivity.

11–1.1 Physical Properties

Soil texture, as it governs moisture and nutrient storage capacity, is a foremost consideration in soil quality for corn. Very sandy soils respond more rapidly to management practices than those of finer texture and can be tuned to high levels of production where water and nutrient supplies can be controlled effectively. Lacking such control, crop damage from drought or loss of nutrients (especially N) through leaching is a certainty. In the other extreme, soils high in clay content have the capacity for holding much more water, organic matter, and nutrients than the sands. They tend, however, to have problems with crusting, drainage, and aeration that can be inhibitive to plant growth. Most ideal are intermediate textures of loam to silt loam in the surface horizon and a somewhat higher clay content as silt loam to silty clay loam in the subsoil. This combination, complemented with good structural properties, allows good storage of water and nutrients and a degree of permeability favorable to water intake and air exchange.

Soil depth is an equally important criterion of soil quality from the physical property standpoint. Corn may grow very well on soil with no more than a 60-cm depth over bedrock or gravel given sufficient moisture increments throughout the growing season. But a 10-d period without rain or irrigation during the summer will almost certainly result in severe drought damage to the crop. On the other hand, the medium textured soil from the 180-cm depth wetted to field capacity can have a moisture storage in the order of 30 cm, capable of carrying the crop through a 2- or 3-wk summer dry period without harm. This is one of the important reasons why so much of U.S. corn is produced in the Corn Belt where the majority of soils are deep, having developed on mantlerock of loessial, glacial, lacustrine, or alluvial origin.

Soil drainage becomes a factor in growth of the corn crop when an excess of water prevents a sufficient flow of air for replenishing O_2 supply around the crop's roots. The volume and O_2 content of the soil air, not the quantity of water in soil, determine the need for drainage. As a general axiom, 10% is the lower limit of soil air by volume for most crops (Wesseling and Van Wijk, 1957), and the rate of diffusion of air through the soil becomes the determinant of O_2 sufficiency. Corn is one of the least tolerant among major grain crops to low air diffusion rates (Williamson, 1964). Shallow natural water tables will commonly require the establishment of some form of artificial drainage to allow aeration of an adequate volume of soil for the crop's root system. Impermeable layers such as claypan horizons in the soil profile are also responsible for perched water tables that restrict root development. Only artificial drainage can improve such situations. In addition to enhanced aeration, artificial drainage of a poorly drained soil lowers specific heat of the soil, a critical factor for early growth, especially in the more northerly latitudes of corn production. Inherent colors of the various horizons of a soil indicate present and past drainage conditions, grays and yellows suggest periods of poor aeration, while for browns and reds the converse is true. Thorough coverage of the impacts of soil aeration on crop growth and means for its improvement exist in the literature, e.g., Russell (1952) and Van Schilfgaarde (1974).

11–1.2 Topography, Physical Properties, and Erosion Control

Substantial areas of rather steeply sloping land are planted to corn in breaks to the Missouri and Mississippi Valleys, southern Illinois, and Loess Hills of Nebraska, foothills to the mountains in eastern and southeastern USA, and locally elsewhere. With a considerable portion of the annual rainfall received in the spring before and shortly after planting, runoff and erosion are accentuated with the production of corn and other summer crops. Corn being the most extensively grown cultivated crop, it bears greatest responsibility for the excessive accelerated erosion occurring in the USA. Other things being equal, the finer the texture of the surface soil and the less well aggregated, the greater the water erosion rate. The rate tends to become accelerated as erosion proceeds in exposing subsoil materials that are, as a general rule, inherently higher in clay content and less well aggregated than the original surface soil. The various factors controlling erosion by rainfall have been quantified in an equation and are reported in detail elsewhere (Wischmeier and Smith, 1978).

Runoff and water erosion are not often serious problems with very sandy soils. On these soils, wind erosion becomes of major importance, especially in the more westerly regions of corn production. Here the most critical period is in the winter and early spring months when winds are commonly strongest and no crop cover exists. The controlling factors in wind erosion have been delineated by Skidmore and Woodruff (1968). We have not been very good stewards of these sandy soils and the steeply sloping land resources of finer textured soils in this country in the past, and the present depressed agricultural economy does not foster any renewed effort toward curbing the erosion hazard. Future generations are certain to judge harshly this lack of concern for preservation of the soil, the country's foremost natural resource.

11–1.3 Chemical Properties

As with soil physical properties, corn is grown across a wide range of chemical conditions, e.g., on soils of pH 5 in the Southeast as well as those that are calcareous with pH 8 and somewhat above in the West. At and beyond these extremes, problems of toxicity with certain elements are found, as well as induced deficiencies of some of the essential nutrients. Below pH 5, toxicities of Al, Mn, and Fe may be encountered, although corn is relatively tolerant to levels of Al and Mn that are toxic to other crops (Kamprath and Foy, 1971). Thus, corn was found to grow well on soil with up to 44% Al saturation of the exchange complex, whereas cotton would tolerate no more than 10% in soils with 1:1 type clays. Otherwise at very low pH, soils are likely to be quite P deficient due to P tieup with the active Al component, and the production of NO_3^- from NH_4^+ is greatly retarded due to inactivity of the Nitrobacter organism.

At high pH levels, nutritional problems are often encountered with the elements P, Zn, and Fe. A majority of calcareous soils with pH in the range of 7.5 to 8.4 were undoubtedly P deficient for optimum corn production from the day the soil was first broken out of its native vegetation. This is due to the conversion of virtually all phosphate ions into low solubility tricalcium phosphate and carbonato-apatite forms. Zinc and Fe compounds produced in calcareous soils from native minerals are also of low solubility, commonly resulting in deficiency of those elements to the crop.

Excess soluble ions in soil, as occurs with saline conditions in dry regions, and excess Na on the soil exchange complex can be inhibitive to corn production. Salinity may have toxic effects from the excess of some ions absorbed by the root system, but the usual major damage is from moisture deprivation due to greater osmotic attraction for water molecules by the salt than is exerted by the solution within root cells. The usual ranking of crops to soil salinity is in terms of electrical conductivity (EC) of the soil saturation extract (ECe). Conductivity in the range of 1 to 4 dS/m will usually cause little or no damage to corn, but above that range decreased growth is progressively severe above an ECe of 8 (Hassan et al., 1970). Restriction in growth from excessive soil Na on the other hand, is largely a result of poor soil physical properties imposed by the deflocculation that Na effects on soil colloids, although toxicity of Na and OH ions may contribute. Water and air penetration are retarded with associated impacts on root development (Fitts et al., 1944).

11–1.4 Impacts on Rooting Patterns and Depth

Corn rooting patterns are profoundly influenced by morphological characteristics of soil as reflected in soil series classification. Horizonal factors like drainage, presence of an indurated layer or major textural discontinuity, acidity/alkalinity, salinity, and toxic components can account for the differences in rooting. A good example of differences that may exist in corn rooting on different soils is portrayed in Fig. 11–1 from nine soil series in Illinois (Fehrenbacher et al., 1967). As stated before, permeable soil of medium texture is desirable for the optimum production of corn. Available moisture must be present for the penetration and proliferation of roots to occur, and the depth of extraction will be influ-

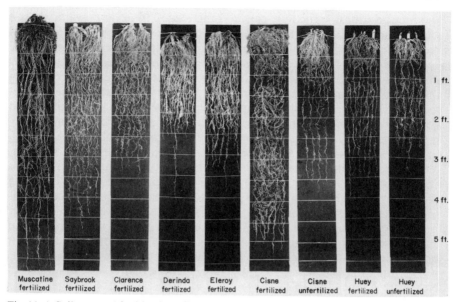

Fig. 11-1. Soil type and fertilization affects corn root penetration (Fehrenbacher et al., 1967).

enced by the accessibility of nutrients (Olson et al., 1964; Viets, 1962). Halitligil et al. (1984) and Mackay and Barber (1986) reported significant differences in rooting capacities among genotypes of corn with major yield implications. Both of these studies found the hybrid B73 × MO17 superior to the other hybrids investigated in yield and response to applied N, with a greater measured root extensity given as partial explanation.

11-2 MOISTURE REQUIREMENTS

Corn is a summer crop, appreciating a warm but not excessivly hot environment for its growth. It is slow growing under cool and wet conditions in the spring and can be damaged by early frost in the fall, thus preferring a growing season length of 150 d or more. It requires in the order of 50 to 60 cm of moisture for evapotranspiration (ET) under midtemperate conditions. These and other aspects of the climatic requirement for corn are covered in detail in Chapter 10 of this text. Accordingly, only a few of those interactions that exist among soil and climate will be touched upon here, particularly how moisture control may exist with irrigation.

As reported by Thompson (1966), the corn crop uses about 70% more moisture for ET in July and 50% more in August than is received in rainfall in the five major Corn Belt states. This means that there must be a stored reserve of around 12 cm of available moisture in the soil rooting profile at the beginning of this high water use period for optimum production unless irrigation can be practiced. This is the major reason why shallow and coarse textured soils do not have the yield potential of those that are deep and of medium texture, irrespective of fertility status.

Daily water use by corn under average summer weather conditions in the Corn Belt is on the order of 0.75 cm. Water is first extracted from the uppermost soil horizon expanding downward with added use. Therefore, in a 15-d period without rain, virtually all the available water would be removed from the surface 100 cm of a silt loam soil that was initially moistened to field capacity. Even with plentiful moisture below that depth the crop would begin to show moisture stress during the hotter and windier portions of the day because of the lesser volume of roots for moisture absorption at that depth and the greater expenditure of energy in lifting the water through the vascular system to the leaves. Most effective irrigation, therefore, will provide water to maintain a readily available supply in the surface horizon where the least energy is required for its extraction and where most nutrient feeding occurs. These considerations are built into modern irrigation scheduling programs on interactive computer networks, an example being the "Irrigate" program of the University of Nebraska Agnet (AGNET, 1984).

Not only is timing critical for the optimum irrigation of corn but rate, as it controls frequency of irrigation, has a dominating impact on N economy in the crop. Various studies showed that light and frequent irrigation is superior to heavier, less frequent irrigation involving the same seasonal total of added water. Much of the difference observed favoring a light, frequent mode of 5 cm applied weekly compared with 10 cm applied every other week can be ascribed to a greater crop utilization of fertilizer N (Russelle et al., 1981; Halitligil et al., 1984). Nitrogen losses due to denitrification and deep leaching are minimized and water use efficiency by the crop enhanced. Clearly, effective management of water and N go hand in hand. The center pivot irrigation system is readily programmed to meet the needed criteria with its capability for "fertigation," having problems only with the combination of an extended drought stress period and very sandy soil when it simply cannot supply water fast enough to meet demand.

11–3 NUTRIENT NEEDS

Corn, like all higher plants, requires at least 13 elements from the soil for its normal growth and development; another three, C, H, and O are supplied primarily by air and water. Among the 13, N, P, and K, are needed in greatest amounts, are the most likely to be deficient, and are classed as major or primary nutrients. The next three, Ca, Mg, and S, are taken up in fairly large quantity and are regarded as secondary nutrients. The remainder including Fe, Mn, Zn, Cu, B, Mo, and Cl are needed in small amounts and are classed as micronutrients. Certain of these, such as Cl, may be taken up in considerable quantity, well above

Table 11-2. Nutrients in the aboveground plant material in a 9.5 Mg/ha yield of corn grain in the Corn Belt (Barber and Olson, 1968).

| Element | Element (kg/ha) in: | |
	Grain	Stover
N	129	62
P	31	8
K	39	157
Ca	1.5	39
Mg	11	33
S	12	9
Cl	4.5	76
Fe	0.11	2.02
Mn	0.06	0.28
Cu	0.02	0.09
Zn	0.19	0.19
B	0.05	0.14
Mo	0.006	0.003

that needed for essential functions. Undoubtedly, other elements will eventually be recognized as essential to crop growth, Ni and Co having recently been so claimed. Table 11-2, assembled from data of several North Central region experiment stations, supplies average quantities of several elements in a 9.45 Mg/ha yield of corn (Barber and Olson, 1968).

Many factors influence the availability of these nutrients in soil for crop absorption, including the total nutrient supply, soil moisture and aeration, soil temperature, and soil physical and chemical properties. All of these factors are covered in detail elsewhere for each of the nutrients (Olson et al., 1971). Many soil management practices applied by the farmer are directed toward an enhancement of nutrient accessibility from the soil for the crop.

Uptake pattern for the major nutrients through the season follows rather closely that of dry matter accumulation in corn, which is expressed in Fig. 11-2 (Hanway, 1971). Note that little N, P, and K are taken up through growth stage 2, after which very rapid uptake occurs during the vegetative and grain filling stages. Whereas N and P uptake continues until near maturity, K absorption is largely completed by silking time. The major portion of the N and P taken into the early shoot, stalk, leaves, and tassel are translocated into grain, much less so with K. From two-thirds to three-fourths or more of the K remains in the stover. Thus, N and P tend to be depleted rapidly from soil with cash grain farming, but K is not. Details for the optimum management of these nutrients are presented in a subsequent section.

11-4 CROPPING SEQUENCE INTERACTIONS

Adjustments in cropping systems have long been known to have major impact on the productivity of corn. Associated factors which have

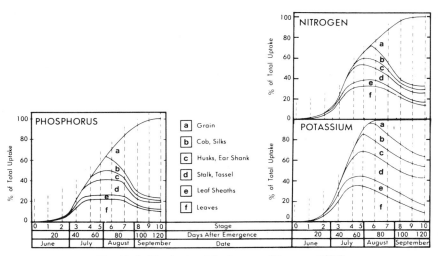

Fig. 11–2. Nutrient uptake by corn (Hanway, 1971).

been recognized include enhanced N availability, improved soil structure, water conservation, reduced soil erosion, and better pest and disease control. Recently, research provided evidence of allelochemical effects as significant contributors. No doubt, interaction existed among all of these where field benefits for cropping sequence were registered.

Much of the early work on the impact of cropping sequences concerned the role of legumes in supplying N for the corn that followed. This benefit was recognized in some of the earliest literature on agriculture, even though the element involved was not known, e.g., Zenophon of Greece and Virgil of Rome in their expressions of benefits from green manure legumes. In the modern era, long-term rotation studies report a fertilizer N equivalence in the order of 115 kg/ha in first-year corn after a good stand of legume (Haynes and Thatcher, 1955). Added benefits are apparent in second- and even third-year corn where a perennial legume was employed as a hay crop for 2 or more years. Moisture supply is a key factor in the role that the biennial and perennial legumes can serve in the N economy of corn. As a general rule, a humid climatic region is necessary or irrigation must be practiced because of the legume's long growing season and high water requirement. Because of soil moisture depletion by the legume (Brown, 1964; Shrader and Pierre, 1966), corn yields following a legume are commonly lower than after another annual grain crop in the edge of the subhumid region and extending through the semiarid zone and during dry years in humid regions.

The advent of plentiful and inexpensive fertilizer N in the generation following World War II essentially eliminated the economic feasibility of legume rotation for N gain except for farms employing an intensive livestock system, i.e., dairy farmers and beef producers and feeders. Therewith came the widely accepted practice of monoculture production of corn throughout much of the Corn Belt with farmers equipping themselves to produce corn in the most intensive and efficient way possible with modern technology. A recent growing world-wide demand for soybean [*Glycine max* (L.) Merr.] and their by-products has prompted a fairly common adjustment to a corn–soybean cropping sequence in the region with attendant soil N effects. There is no way to say with certainty how much N gain for subsequent corn accrues from the prior year of soybean because of the many other factors contributing to yield enhancement. Nonetheless, a fairly commonly accepted axiom is 1 kg/ha of added soil N availability for each 60 kg of soybean produced (1 lb of N/bu of soybean).

A number of past studies give evidence of a benefit to soil physical properties from inclusion of a legume in a rotation sequence. Improvements in soil aggregation from alfalfa were reported by many investigators (Barber, 1959; Van Bavel, 1949; Wilson et al., 1947). Few of these studies show definitive yield benefits for the change in soil physical property, in part because of confounding fertility effects. It may be conjectured, however, that yield benefits would result over longer time intervals from enhanced moisture intake, reduced erosion, and more ready root proliferation in the soil.

Yield losses due to weeds, insects, and diseases were huge until arrival of the "Chemical Age" in agriculture; e.g., the 1965 USDA estimate of losses in various crops to weeds alone in the USA was in excess of U.S.$ 5×10^9 annually (USDA-ARS, 1965). Correspondingly large losses from insects and diseases are a matter of record. A primary cultural and/or biological means of controlling or at least curbing these losses in prior times was through crop rotation, interjecting a less favorable host plant periodically for inhibiting the proliferation of such pests and diseases. Despite the ready availability of chemicals for the control of these maladies, there is increasing recognition of a need for some adjustment in cropping practice away from monoculture for maintaining or improving yield levels. Thus, corn yields in Indiana were found to decrease progressively with number of years grown away from a forage crop (Barber, 1972), and yields after sod and annual green manure crops in Georgia exceeded continuous corn even with 180 kg N/ha applied (Adams et al., 1970). Benefits, explained in part by improved soil physical conditions and reduced nematode populations, persisted for 3 to 4 yr after sod in the latter study.

Partial credit for the beneficial action noted from the alternating of crops can be given to allelochemical effects (Gajic et al., 1976; Zabyalyendzik, 1973; Bhowmik and Doll, 1982). Involved is a change in root excretions and the subsequent microbial complex of organisms that build up in the soil with a change in the organic residues returned. In monoculture, a group of microorganisms tends to develop that exude phytotoxic substances deleterious to the crop. The addition of a green manure crop such as rye (*Secale cereale* L.) before corn removes the suppressive root excretions and changes the soil microbial population that is damaging to corn in monoculture. A more favorable root environment is thereby available for the corn. The subject is not thoroughly understood, but it seemingly impacts yields even with green manure interseeding where the secondary crop is limited in time and amount of growth on the soil (Olson et al., 1986).

11–5 CULTURAL PRACTICES

11–5.1 Seed Selection and Time of Planting

Farmers are confronted with virtually hundreds of corn hybrids marketed by the many companies involved in the production of hybrid seed. Their selection must be made on the basis of comparative proven yield potential in impartially controlled trials, climatic environment of a specific locale, and disease/pest resistance needed for that locale. Fundamental principles involved with each of these issues are covered in detail in prior chapters; accordingly, nothing more than the practical aspects of making the purchase decision will be mentioned here.

Available hybrids differ widely in agronomic characteristics, including length of growing period. The one selected will of necessity mesh with the length of growing season and hopefully fit best with stress periods likely to be encountered. Stalk quality as it influences combine suitability, disease and pest resistance, and dry-down characteristics of the hybrid are added criteria to be considered. Some uncertainty exists in the literature as to the ideal maturity class for any given locality, i.e., whether full-, mid- or short-season. In any given year, by reason of varied moisture and temperature conditions, one or another may prove superior. As a general rule, the longer season hybrids have the greater yield potential where good growing conditions allow their unfettered development, by reason of the longer period involved for photosynthate production. This is no certain axiom, however, because Stringfield (1956) and Duncan (1954) found that increasing stands up to the maximum acceptable by both resulted in higher yields with early hybrids than with those of later maturity.

For dry regions, a hybrid that is both shorter than average and makes less vegetative growth is needed. In the more northerly latitudes and at higher altitudes not only is the short season attribute desirable but a degree of cold hardiness built into the hybrid will also help. The latter is a genetic quality of increasing significance as more and more cropland is brought under minimum tillage. Where a stress period can be expected at a specific time in the growing season, the choice of a hybrid that will not be in the critical flowering stage during that time should be considered. Work by Denmead and Shaw (1960) showed that 7 d of moderate moisture stress during flowering was responsible for 50% yield reduction compared with half that when the stress occurred before tasseling or after pollination. Other aspects of management will also interact when making the selection including responsiveness to fertilization and irrigation, if it is practiced (Halitligil et al., 1984). Reaction of those hybrids of a given growing season length to increased population is a further factor, as expressed in Fig. 11–3. In this study with irrigated corn, increasing plant population from 36 000 to 54 000 plants/ha was highly beneficial for N6 × N28 and B14 × N6 when N was adequate but of no help to N28 × H51 (Barber and Olson, 1968). The incidence of stress in relation to physiological stage of development undoubtedly accounts for the finding that limited irrigation in a dry region has its best impact when applied during early tasseling (Howe and Rhoades, 1955).

There is obvious interaction between a hybrid's growing season length and optimum planting date, with long-season types benefitting most from early planting and suffering most from delayed planting (Hicks et al., 1970). Results of investigations in several states through the mid-1960s revealed reduction in yields with corn planted after 15 May in the northern Corn Belt, after 10 May in the central Corn Belt, and after the first

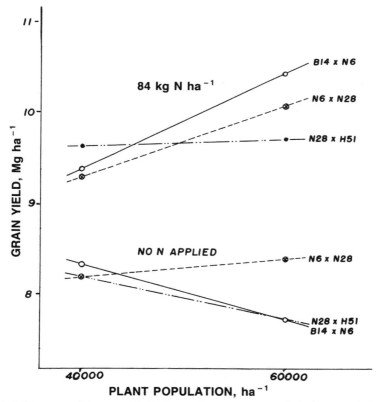

Fig. 11–3. Response of three corn hybrids as a 5-yr average to varied plant population and N rate (Barber and Olson, 1968).

week in May at the Corn Belt's southern edge (Duncan, 1966). The general guide for corn planting prepared by Sprague and Larson (1966) in Fig. 11–4 corresponds reasonably with these dates and additionally brings in the optima for the more southerly latitudes of corn production in the USA.

A more specific guide that has developed for the individual site is to plant once soil temperature persists above 15 °C in the seedling zone. Earlier planting associated with these dates and/or temperature than in the previous generation have occurred because of improved seed quality, increased cold hardiness of hybrids through breeding efforts, seed treatment for disease and pest control, and better weed control made possible by modern herbicide use (Rossman and Cook, 1966).

11–5.2 Tillage Practices and Cultivation

Since the mid-1970s, there has been a major trend away from the extensive primary and secondary tillage directed toward preparation of an ideal seedbed. A corresponding decline in the amount of cultivation for the control of weeds is evident. A combination of several factors has been responsible for this transformation, most importantly the advent of effective herbicides for weed control, the benefits from a residue cover in erosion control, and the obvious economic advantage of reduced implement performance.

Traditional moldboard plowing in the fall has commonly proved optimum for yield on fine-textured soils of the northern Corn Belt, par-

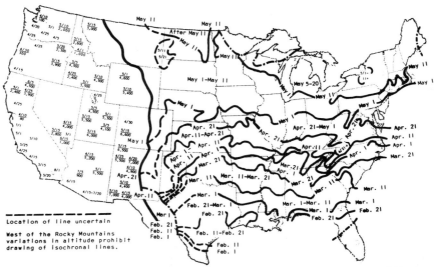

Fig. 11–4. Average dates when corn should be planted in the USA (Sprague and Larson, 1966).

ticularly those tending toward poor drainage (Triplett et al., 1973; Osch-wald, 1973; Cihacek et al., 1974). Advantage for such fall tillage comes about especially because of warmer soil temperature in the spring (All-maras et al., 1973) and a lower surface soil moisture that permits earlier secondary tillage and planting than is possible with the nontilled soil. The primary disadvantage lies with the potential that exists for water erosion during the winter and early spring months on other than level-lying sites.

For the majority of reasonably well-drained soils, however, reduced tillage systems are proving effective. Since projections indicate that, for reasons of economy and erosion control, reduced tillage will become common practice on most land producing corn in the near future, major emphasis is given to the recent literature on this issue. The required equipment development is underway by implement manufacturers, who are making the foremost limitation farmer acquaintance and experience with the measures required to make the system work.

A number of different methods are used to accomplish reduced tillage or conservation tillage. These include chisel plow-planting, disk-plant, till-planting, and no-till. All achieve the common goal of leaving much of the previous crop's residues on the soil surface. To be effective, each tillage method should accomplish as many of the following results as possible: (i) allow proper seed placement and seed-soil contact for good germination; (ii) permit ready moisture penetration, thereby limiting run-off and erosion; (iii) maintain good permeability to air and water through-out the growing season while minimizing evaporation loss; and (iv) keep weeds under control. The latter was made possible by the development of herbicides, prior to which much soil tillage had been for the express purpose of controlling weeds. With all the reduced tillage systems now in use there has been a substantial reduction in the amount of secondary tillage employed, i.e., diskings and harrowing before planting. These final operations for smoothing out the soil surface were shown to be major contributors to accelerated runoff and erosion (Duley, 1939; Meyer and Mannering, 1961). The early background for current minimum tillage systems came from the work of Duley and Russell (1942), beginning in the 1930s onward, who foresaw the significant role that crop residues should serve in soil and moisture conservation.

11–5.2.1 Chisel Plowing

This tillage procedure is accomplished by chisel points or sweeps attached to shanks spaced from 20 to 40 cm apart that allow penetration to depths of 15 to 30 cm. The soil is lifted and loosened in the tillage zone with little turnover leaving most of the prior crop's residue on the surface. When done in the fall the soil surface is left quite rough and open over winter allowing ready moisture intake and maximum frost action for ameliorating soil structure. Done under excessively wet spring weather conditions, chisel plowing can be just as deleterious to yield as moldboard plowing on wet fine-textured soils.

Joint Nebraska and Illinois studies over a 3-yr period showed slightly higher yields with moldboard than with chisel plowing (Cihacek et al., 1974). All sites received plentiful rainfall or irrigation such that known benefits of chisel plowing in moisture conservation were not reflected. A decided advantage was recorded for P placement at the depth of chisel performance in season-long feeding by the crop and reduced fertilizer P runoff.

Chisel tillage and moldboard plowing gave comparable average corn grain yields when compared over 4 yr on five soils in Indiana (Griffith et al., 1973). There were differences among soils involved, however, with chisel plowed plots outyielding those that were moldboard plowed on well-drained soil types, whereas moldboard exceeded chisel tillage on poorly drained types. A common observation at all the Indiana, Illinois, and Nebraska locations cited was that of reduced stands with the chisel system. This probably could have been alleviated with added secondary tillage before the crop was planted. However, this would have compromised the reduced tillage objective.

The chief limitation of the chisel plow among reduced tillage systems with corn production is that secondary tillage is required to provide a satisfactory seed bed. Thus, extra time, fuel consumption, and implement performance are needed and, consequently, greater costs are incurred than with some other systems. Certainly the chisel plow is an excellent erosion control tool compared to the moldboard plow (Wischmeier, 1973). It probably has its greatest application in the drier regions of wheat production, particularly in association with summer fallow practice.

11–5.2.2 Disk-plant

Disking followed by planting has been a widely used practice for corn production, especially in the western Corn Belt. Disking eliminates ridges that may exist from the previous year's between-row cultivation and those from furrow irrigation. At the same time stalk butts from the prior crop are torn loose, and remaining residues are shredded with a fair portion remaining on the soil surface. Planting follows with either surface planter type or lister. When corn was the preceding crop, a serious volunteer problem exists with surface planting for which no ready solution exists.

Lister planting following disking has been accepted extensively in the rolling to hilly areas of loess-derived soils in western Iowa and northeastern Nebraska. Grain yields have consistently exceeded moldboard plow preparation of the soil, especially in the drier years (Larson and Blake, 1966). Much of the advantage has been attributed to moisture conservation from reduced evaporation and runoff loss, the latter especially where lister furrows were established on the contour. The reduced runoff has additionally been responsible for curbing soil erosion on sloping areas (Moldenhauer and Wischmeier, 1960).

11-5.2.3 Till-plant

The till-plant system, sometimes called strip tillage, requires nothing before planting other than stalk shredding where corn or grain sorghum [*Sorghum bicolor* (L.) Moench] was the previous crop. Its sweep system of turning soil works best with an existing ridge to be split, thereby planting seed in soil that was not compacted by previous wheel tracks (Fig. 11-5). For this reason, acceptance has been greatest in furrow-irrigated monoculture fields, which are common in Nebraska. In splitting the ridges, stalk butts are lifted along with other residues partially covered in the interrow area. Volunteer corn is no problem since any existing seeds on the surface are correspondingly displaced and resulting plants readily destroyed in a following cultivation or furrowing operation. Early studies showed grain yields to be fully equivalent to those with conventional moldboard plowing plus secondary tillage in the western Corn Belt (Lane and Wittmus, 1961; Olson and Schoebert, 1970). The major advantages are lower production costs and better erosion control (Fisher and Lane, 1973; Wischmeier, 1973; Witmuss et al., 1971). Griffith et al. (1973), in studies of the eastern Corn Belt, obtained grain yields from till-plant that were equivalent or superior to moldboard plowing methods on medium- to coarse-textured and well-drained soils, but yields were inferior on poorly drained soils. A special advantage for till-planting was reported in Iowa during years of moderate to severe moisture stress (Amemiya, 1968).

A modification of the sweep system in till planting involves rotary tillage of a narrow band ahead of the planter. Essentially comparable yield results were obtained in comparisons with the sweep system. Common problems have been recognized with all till planting; for example, an accentuated weed problem with passing years (Fisher and Lane, 1973;

Fig. 11-5. Till-plant corn seeded into corn stubble. Courtesy Fleischer Mfg., Columbus, NE.

Turnquist et al., 1970) and of packed soil in interrow areas from wheel traffic (Griffith et al., 1973). Seemingly an occasional moldboard plowing would assist in alleviating these problems in most cases.

11–5.2.4 No-till

The evolution in tillage practices for corn has been inexorably toward no-till due to the energy and cost impositions of recent years (Fig. 11–6). The trend toward no-till for reducing erosion and energy input has meant a greatly modified soil-temperature-water-air environment from that with conventional tillage, approaching that of natural ecosystems. Both yield losses and reduced fertilizer use efficiency have been recorded in a number of studies on no-tillage compared with plowing, variously attributed to weed competition (Griffith et al., 1973; Fisher and Lane, 1973; Fenster and Peterson, 1979), microbial competition (Dowdell and Connell, 1975; Van Doren et al., 1976), cooler soil temperature (Griffith et al., 1973; Mock and Erback, 1977), accentuated leaching loss (Thomas et al., 1973), phytotoxic production in surface residues (Cochran et al., 1978), and denitrification (Phillips et al., 1980; Doran, 1980; Rice and Smith, 1982; Groffman, 1985). On the other hand, better yields were found with no-till than with conventional tillage in many studies (Moschler et al., 1972; Al-Darby and Lowery, 1986; Triplett et al., 1968; Phillips et al., 1980), being especially evident on medium to coarse textured soils having good internal drainage. Much of the benefit was attributed to greater soil moisture storage and preservation in the root zone (Jones et al., 1969; Triplett et al., 1968; Blevins et al., 1971) and to greater reserves of potentially mineralizable N after several years because of increased surface soil levels of organic matter, microbial biomass, and

Fig. 11–6. No-till corn seeded into wheat stubble, West Central Research and Extension Center, North Platte, NE.

aerobic organisms (Doran et al., 1987). Poorest results from no-till occurred on poorly drained soils where surface residues accentuate the cool temperature problem early in the growing season, particularly in the northern regions of corn production (Griffith et al., 1973; Triplett et al., 1973; Willis and Amemiya, 1973). The case for no-till on poorly drained soils, however, is not irreconcilable. Generally recognized advantages for early planting notwithstanding, there is recent evidence under conditions in Kentucky (Herbeck et al., 1986), which coincide with observations of Eckert (1984) in Ohio, that optimum planting date is approximately 2 weeks later with no-till than with conventional tillage on poorly drained soils without delay in corn development or yield loss.

Modifications in the soil-water-air-temperature environment induced by no-tillage compared with conventional have had a major impact on soil N transformations, with a general consensus of reduced N availability to the crop during the early years of no-tillage due to leaching, denitrification, and retarded nitrification, as previously cited. Combination of these conditions is responsible for higher N rates required for achieving maximum yields with no-tillage (Meissinger et al., 1985; Triplett and Van Doren, 1969; Moschler and Martens, 1975). With added time, however, and the gradual accretion of total N that occurs in the immediate surface soil the mineralization of N can be just as great with no-tillage as conventional. This break-even time was reached after 10 yr in the experiment of Rice et al. (1986).

11–5.3 Row Spacing and Plant Distribution in the Row

The spacing of corn rows greatly affects plant distribution within the row for any given plant density. Plants compete with each other for nutrients, light, and other growth factors. Therefore, it is reasonable that plants spaced an equal distance from each other would provide for minimum competition and maximum yield at any given plant density. However, for plant distribution to be a limiting factor for yield, other limiting factors have to be eliminated.

There have been many experiments across the Corn Belt involving plant distribution and row spacing. Excellent reviews were prepared by Dungan et al. (1958), Rossman and Cook (1966), and Larson and Hanway (1977).

Prior to 1940, the distance between rows was limited primarily by the width of a horse (*Eqqus* sp.) and the standard spacing was 100 to 112 cm. Early research included row spacing studies where rows were over 200 cm wide (Cunningham, 1914; Zook and Burr, 1923). However, after the introduction of hybrid corn, it soon became apparent that higher plant densities would be needed and that plant distribution in the row could be a limiting factor in wide rows preventing the full expression of hybrid yield potential. Corn was commonly planted in hills, with several plants per hill, in rows spaced 100 to 112 cm apart to afford weed control by cross cultivation. Early investigators concluded that there was little to gain by planting one plant per hill in a 53- × 53-cm pattern compared with four plants per hill in a 106- × 106-cm spacing (Bryan et al., 1940; Collins and Shedd, 1941).

It was not until the 1950s and 1960s when fertilizers became inexpensive, irrigation expanded, and herbicides became available for weed control that researchers and producers became seriously interested in the effect of plant distribution on corn yields. Kohnke and Miles (1951) obtained a 502 kg/ha grain yield increase for drilled compared to hilled corn, and Rounds et al. (1951) found a 7% greater yield in favor of drilled corn. Colville and McGill (1962) found significant increases for drilled compared to hilled irrigated corn. Their data compiled over 5 yr and seven locations showed that drilling increased yields 501 kg/ha over hill drop and 1066 kg/ha over checked corn when averaged across five plant desities ranging from 30 000 to 70 000 plants/ha. However, Dungan et al. (1958) averaged research results from seven corn growing states covering a total of 39 station yr and found that drilled corn averaged only 100 kg/ha or 3% more than checked corn.

As corn producers changed from animal to tractor power and cultivation became less critical for weed control because of effective herbicides, the narrower spacing of rows became a practical means of achieving nearly equidistant spacing between corn plants. By planting corn plants more nearly equidistant from one another, researchers theorized that corn could yield more than less equidistant plantings.

Results of experiments that compare different row spacings vary from large yield increases to little or no effect of decreasing row widths. Rossman and Cook (1966) reported a 14% increase in Michigan for 46- compared to 91-cm rows (Table 11–3). Stivers et al. (1971) in Indiana found a 7% increase for 51- vs. 102-cm rows, and a 4% increase from 76- compared to 102-cm rows; Stickler (1964) in Kansas reported that 51-cm rows had a 5% yield advantage over 102-cm rows under dryland and a 6% advantage for irrigated corn; and Colville (1966) found a 16% increase for over nine experiments in Nebraska in grain yield for 51- compared

Table 11–3. Average yields of corn in 46- and 92-cm row spacings at four populations for three yr, 1961 to 1963, near East Lansing, MI (Rossman and Cook, 1966).

Plants/ha	1961		1963		1963		Avg. 3 yr		Avg. increase
	46 cm	92 cm	46 cm	92 cm	46 cm	92 cm	46 cm	92 cm	
					Mg/ha				%
25 430	7.76	6.95	5.67	5.67	5.27	4.86	6.21	5.81	7
38 025	10.26	8.64	6.95	6.01	6.01	5.60	7.76	6.75	15
50 620	11.48	9.18	7.49	6.82	7.02	6.01	8.64	7.36	17
63 210	11.34	9.32	7.76	6.89	6.48	5.94	8.51	7.36	16
Avg.	10.19	8.51	6.95	6.35	6.21	5.60	7.76	6.82	14
Percentage difference	20		10		11		14		

Table 11-4. Effect of three row spacings on irrigated corn yields in Nebraska; nine experiments (Colville, 1966).

Row spacing	Plants/ha	Yield	Increase over 102 cm
cm		Mg/ha	%
51	39 500	9.72	16.1
76	39 500	9.18	9.7
102	39 500	8.37	

to 102-cm rows (Table 11-4). Investigators who found no differences in yield due to row spacing include Stickler and Laude (1960) for dryland corn in Kansas; Patterson et al. (1963) in Alabama; Lucas (1969), Rumawas et al. (1971), and Giesbrecht (1969) in Canada. Wide differences reported by various investigators for the results of various planting patterns are usually due to vastly different growing conditions, yield potential, and interactions with other management factors. The primary reason for an increase in potential yields by decreasing row spacing or providing a more equidistant planting arrangement is decreased competition among plants for light, water, and nutrients. Denmead et al. (1962) calculated that a decrease in row spacing from 100 to 60 cm would increase light energy available for photosynthesis by 15 to 20%, thus providing, theoretically at least, an increased yield potential for more equidistant plantings.

Closer row spacing also reduces energy available at the soil surface by increased shading, thereby reducing water evaporation from the soil. However, closer spacing increases the energy available in the corn canopy, providing for increased transpiration. Since evaporation is often limited by a dry soil surface, one would expect increased transpiration and, therefore, increased water use by reducing row width. Increased water use by narrow rows or more equidistant planting distribution compared to wide rows can cause yield reductions during years of water stress. This is an important factor to consider in the dryland corn production areas of the western Corn Belt where moisture stress is common.

When the soil surface is more likely to be moist such as under irrigation or in eastern Corn Belt areas, reducing row width changes the proportion of water evaporated from the soil surface compared to that transpired from the leaves. Under these conditions, reducing row width results in reduced water loss as evaporation from the soil surface because of increased shading, but transpiration is increased due to increased exposure to light energy. Therefore, reducing row width increases that portion of the soil water that can be used for growth processes and should increase productivity.

While plant distribution can greatly change the way energy is used in the crop canopy in terms of water use and photosynthesis, its effect on nutrient requirements is less well understood. Grimes et al. (1975) found that row spacing had no effect on root density (length of roots per volume of soil) or depth of root distribution. In addition, since plant roots contact only 1 or 2% of the total soil volume, changes in size and distribution of the root system would be expected to have little impact on absorption of nutrients. This would especially be true for nonmobile nutrients such as P, the uptake of which is primarily due to diffusion and root contact. However, when plant distribution affects yields positively, N requirements will increase (Barber and Olson, 1968).

There are other interactions of row spacing with management practices that affect results. Griffith (1965) reported a 6% increase from row width reduction for an early hybrid but no effect with a full-season hybrid. Brown et al. (1970) also reported hybrid differences in response to row spacing. Reducing row width favors small, less leafy hybrids because these hybrids can benefit more than large leaf hybrids from increased energy available per unit leaf area in more equidistant plantings. Early hybrids tend to be smaller than late hybrids making the early hybrids more suitable for planting in reduced row widths. Early planting opposed to late planting also causes a corresponding plant size reduction that favors reduced row spacing. As one would expect, reduced row spacings would be expected to be superior at high plant density (Table 11–5).

In summary, reducing row width to provide more equidistant planting patterns does not consistently increase corn yields because of various interactions with other management factors as well as environmental factors, especially the amount of water available either thru irrigation or precipitation. In general, the amount of yield increase is too small to measure with precision in field experiments (Duncan, 1954). This does not mean that small yield increases are not present and may well be of economic importance to corn producers. As a result, most investigators suggest that producers in the Corn Belt can expect about a 5% increase in yield for 76- compared to 96- to 102-cm rows (Aldrich et al., 1986). The advantage of 51- compared to 76-cm rows usually has been small and inconsistent. Such increases can only be expected when yield levels are high (probably >8.0 Mg/ha), which generally restricts yield increases to the eastern and central Corn Belt and to corn grown under irrigation. Even in these areas, rows of 76 cm are tending to lose favor with some larger producers. Ever increasing tractor tire sizes make sidedressing with N more hazardous, and large farm size tends to make wide row (91-cm)

Table 11–5. Effect of three row spacing and two plant populations on irrigated corn yields in experiments in Nebraska (Colville, 1966).

Row spacing	Plants/ha	Yield	Increase over 102 cm
cm		Mg/ha	%
51	39 500	9.79	15
	59 250	10.73	24
76	39 500	9.25	8
	59 250	9.45	9
102	39 500	8.51	
	59 250	8.64	

matchings of planter-cultivator-combine more advantageous than 76-cm rows.

11–6 PLANT DENSITY

11–6.1 Grain Production

Plant scientists have long speculated about and researched plant competition. It is well known that the grain yield of a single corn plant is reduced by the nearness of its neighbors (Duncan, 1984). As plant density increases, yield per plant decreases. If this were not true it would be easy to produce very high yields. Investigators agree that the yield reduction per plant is due to the effects of interplant competition for light, water, nutrients, and other yield-limiting environmental factors. Therefore, an equidistant planting arrangement theoretically will provide the highest yield for a given density. Undoubtedly, there is more to competition than simply growth factors because certain chemicals restricting plant growth may be exuded from the plant root.

There have been many studies to determine the optimum plant density for corn. Unfortunately, there is no single recommendation for all conditions because optimum density varies depending on nearly all environmental factors as well as controlled factors such as soil fertility, hybrid selection, planting date, and patterns of planting, or even the time of harvest. Dungan et al. (1958) reviewed the literature prior to 1958. Much of this review involved results from open pollinated corn grown at low levels of soil fertility, which have little application to today's hybrids. Rossman and Cook (1966) reviewed many plant characteristics affected by plant density. They indicate that published results from the various states show few instances where yields continued to increase above 45 000 to 50 000 plants/ha unless corn was irrigated. With irrigation a plant density of 50 000 to 60 000 plants/ha seemed to produce maximum yields.

Typical of data published in the early 1960s are Nebraska results of Colville et al. (1964) showing a strong interaction between hybrid maturity and optimum plant density (Table 11–6). While late hybrids have greater yield potential, early hybrids require higher plant densities for maximum yield. This occurs because early hybrids are generally smaller and have lower leaf areas per plant than the larger late hybrids. Leaf area index (LAI) excpresses the amount of leaf surface per unit of soil surface area. It is therefore an index of potential plant interception of radiation and can be used to reflect both hybrid characteristics and growing conditions (Brown et al., 1970). Larson and Hanway (1977) cite several investigators who report decreased leaf area per plant as density increases. A LAI of about 3.5 was found to be optimum over a wide range of conditions, and this is achieved by about 50 000 plants/ha when corn is grown under conditions of high management. Since early planting gen-

Table 11-6. A summary of corn yields from 10 irrigated experiments involving six corn hybrids, 1956 to 1959.

Hybrid	Days to maturity	Plants/ha			
		29 630	39 510	49 380	59 260
		Mg/ha			
Iowa 4417	100	6.14	7.16	7.70	7.97
Nebr. 201	102	6.89	7.90	8.37	8.57
Nebr. 301	104	7.36	8.37	8.71	8.64
Nebr. 401	108	7.63	8.57	9.05	8.78
Nebr. 504	112	7.63	8.51	8.98	8.91
AES† 806	120	8.37	9.32	9.38	9.11

† AES = agricultural experiment station, Nebraska.

erally results in shorter plants that have lower leaf areas per plant, increasing plant density by 5000 to 7500 plants/ha is needed to maximize yield (Aldrich et al., 1986).

In Minnesota, Hicks et al. (1970) found that planting date interacts with plant density as well as with hybrid maturity. With an 85-d maturity hybrid, yields were not maximized with 30 000 plants/ha at either an early or a late planting date (22 April vs. 31 May), while a 115-d maturity hybrid showed maximum grain yield below 24 000 plants/ha at the late planting date of 31 May compared to well over 30 000 plants/ha (the maximum plant density studied) at the early planting date of 22 April. This late maturing hybrid produced a yield of 13 500 kg/ha at the early planting date and highest plant density of 30 000 plants/ha compared to only 8000 kg/ha for the early hybrid planted at the same time and density. It made little difference when the early hybrid was planted, but highest yields were always obtained with the highest density studied. Carson et al. (1966) studied three northern Corn Belt hybrids (late, medium, and early) at densities of 48 000, 72 000, and 96 000 plants/ha with planting dates in early May and late June. The late hybrid yielded most at the early planting date, low plant density combination, whereas the earliest hybrid at the other rate-date comparisons outyielded the late combination by an average of 15%.

The above data demonstrate the presence of many interactions between various management factors that control optimum plant density as well as other controllable management factors. This makes recommendations based on mean effects often of little value. Thus, it is mandatory that studies focus on how and why various management and environmental factors affect corn yield. There is evidence that higher plant densities are required in the North compared to further south (Olson, 1930; Wiidakas, 1958). This might be expected since available light energy decreases as one proceeds north. One simple method of estimating whether plant density is optimum is by ear size. In most studies, an ear size of 220 g is associated with maximum yields. However, there is some evidence that optimum ear size may be slightly less in the northern Corn

Belt, indicating again that optimum plant densities are higher in the northern than southern Corn Belt.

It is well documented that increasing plant density increases water use and thereby generally increases plant stress. If water stress occurs during the reproductive stage, it is more detrimental to grain yield than stover yields (Tollenaar and Daynard, 1978). Frey (1981) found that a critical stage of development in corn that is highly dependent on assimilate supply is the 2- to 3-wk period after 50% silking. This is when final harvestable full kernel number is determined. According to Johnson and Tanner (1972), final kernel number is established when linear increases in grain dry weight begin. While water use is increased as plant density is increased, the increase is small and not in proportion to stand increase. Doubling the stand does not double water use (Yao and Shaw, 1964). However, small water deficits during grain fill can critically reduce kernel development (Slatyer, 1969). Similar to any factor that increases yield, increasing plant density improves efficiency of water use (kilogram of grain produced per kilogram of water used).

In order to reduce the need for planting densities matching specific management variables and to increase adaptation to variable environment factors, many studies have involved prolific hybrids (ability to produce more than one ear per plant). Zuber et al. (1960) in Missouri and Collins et al. (1965) in Iowa reported that prolific corn hybrids had more consistent yields than non-prolific types across different plant densities. Investigators have found that prolific hybrids are more consistent in yield at higher densities because they resist barrenness more than nonprolific hybrids (Duvick, 1974). However, Cross (1977) found that yield stability of prolific hybrids was related to maturity. While the prolific hybrids in the 90- to 95-d maturity group had better yield stability compared to single ear hybrids, prolific 80- to 85-d maturity hybrids were less stable and lower yielding than single-eared types. In further research, Cross et al. (1987) reported the result of studies with 16 hybrids planted at 24 000, 48 000, and 72 000 plants/ha at four locations in North Dakota. Hybrids represented two maturities and two levels of prolificacy. Data showed no significant maturity-plant density or prolificacy-plant density interactions for grain yield, grain moisture, lodging, or test weight, although early prolific hybrids outyielded late nonprolific hybrids.

In recent studies, investigators have been trying to better understand the dynamics of growing corn by measuring various components of yield during ear fill. Poneleit and Egli (1979) determined that the rate of kernel dry weight accumulation was not affected by plant density but the effective filling period was decreased 2.5 d. This resulted in smaller and fewer kernels for a 20% yield reduction per plant at the higher density. De-Loughery et al. (1979) and Genter and Camper (1973) found that the amount of dry grain in relation to total dry biomass (harvest index = HI) decreased as plant density increased, or as corn encountered greater stress. Thus the plant partitions less and less dry matter to the grain.

Plant density is composed of not only the total number of plants per hectare but also involves within-row spacing. While the in-row variability found in most farm fields is considered to have little effect on corn yields, uniformity in early plant size may be important (Glenn and Daynard, 1974). Late-emerging plants are likely to remain shorter than their neighbors (Edmeades and Daynard, 1979). Daynard and Muldoon (1983) found that increased plant density tends to increase plant to plant variability for grain weight. Plants that were initially short did not catch up in height until after flowering. Taller plants tended to shed pollen and silk earlier and produce more grain.

Plant density has been an important factor that producers have used to increase corn yields over the years. Cardwell (1982) summarized the management factors affecting corn yields in Minnesota from 1930 to 1979. He found that plant density increased from 30 740 to 49 780 plants/ha, which accounted for 21% of the gain in average grain yield (2012–6287 kg/ha) that occurred during the 50-yr period. This is similar to the 16% increase found by Shaw and Durost (1965) in Iowa from 1929 to 1962.

Probably the most important uncontrollable factor affecting optimum plant density for corn yields, especially in the western and central Corn Belt, is available water. High plant densities increase water use. Drought stress can cause complete loss of grain production if severe stress occurs during the tasseling and silking stage of reproduction. However, the yield curve as related to plant density is generally relatively flat on either side of the maximum indicating a rather broad range of plant densities can be used without great changes in yield. This is especially the case for corn grown in the eastern Corn Belt and under irrigation where water stress is not a serious factor.

Producers also need to be aware that as plant density increases, lodging increases. Lodging can increase several-fold with high densities and may result in very high harvest losses that more than negate any yield increase that may have occurred with the higher plant density. Harvest losses also increase corn volunteer problems in the succeeding year, which results in increased competition and reduced yields. Volunteer corn may be one of the most forgotten competition factors reducing corn grain yield.

11–6.2 Silage Production

Most factors that affect optimum plant densities for grain production also apply to silage production. However, there are several factors that make plant density for silage different than for grain. The increase in lodging as affected by increasing densities is much less important for silage than grain production. Therefore, plant densities can be increased to provide maximum dry matter production. Since grain moisture is not a great concern for silage, later hybrids that are more leafy and larger in size can be utilized. However, maximum dry matter will be achieved by selecting hybrids that reach physiological maturity or black layer before frost. Plant density recommendations for silage production have often been essentially the same as for grain production. Maximum grain production is important for higher dry matter yield and to optimize silage quality. The grain is the most digestible fraction of the silage.

Investigators found that higher plant densities are needed to maximize silage yields than for grain yields. How much higher, however, has not been clearly established. Daynard and Muldoon (1981) found in a 3-yr study in central and southern Ontario that silage yields were maximized for three hybrids at 63 000 plants/ha. Plant density had a negligible effect on grain percentage up to 75 000 plants/ha. Whitaker et al. (1969) reported from Missouri that silage yields were still increasing at 69 000 plants/ha, while grain yields were maximized at 59 000 plants/ha. In New York, Rutger and Crowder (1967) found a 6% increase in total dry matter yields when plant density was increased from 50 000 to 88 000 plants/ha. In Nebraska, Frank and Sander (1972) reported that with adequate applied N, irrigated silage yields were still increasing at 125 000 plants/ha. Other investigators have also reported that higher plant densities are needed to maximize silage production (Bryant and Blazer, 1968; Cummins and Dobson, 1973; Hunter, 1978).

Reduced row spacing in general has similar effects on silage yields and grain yields. Reduced row spacings more often increase silage yields at high plant densities than at low densities. However, results are variable and inconsistent (Cummins and Dobson, 1973; Rumawas et al., 1971; Rutger and Crowder, 1967).

Although total silage yields are important, the feeding quality of silage is really the deciding factor determining best management practices. Burgess and Nicholson (1980) studied the feeding value of corn silage planted at 60 000 to 65 000 plants/ha compared to 90 000 to 110 000 plants/ha. Dairy cows (*Bos taurus*) had similar dry matter intakes, milk fat, and protein percentages when fed corn from both plant densities, but the lower density silage (60–65 000 ppm) produced significantly higher body weight gains. Fattening steers also consumed more dry matter and gained weight faster when fed the low density silage compared to the high density silage. This reflects the higher energy content from the increased grain content associated with the lower density silage.

However, the higher yields of the densely seeded corn for silage supported more beef production per hectare. Muhamad et al. (1983) reported an Iowa study in which 1913 steers were fed three rations involving different ratios of high moisture corn to whole-plant corn silage as measured by estimated metabolizable energy content. Feeding treatments included ratios (high moisture corn/whole-plant corn silage) of 25:75 (Diet 1), 55:45 (Diet 2), and 85:15 (Diet 3). Steers fed Diet 1 with the lower ratio of grain had the lowest average daily gain. The bulkiness of the high silage diet prevented steers from consuming maximum dry matter and energy. In addition, Diet 3, with the highest ratio of grain, was the most efficient of the three diets. Fairey (1982, 1983) studied the effect of plant density on in vitro dry matter digestibility (IVDMD). Even though grain content varied from 0 to 50% of whole plant dry matter, there was little effect on IVDMD. Cummins and Dobson (1973) reported from the Virginia Piedmont and Mountain area no significant differences in IVDMD as a result of different plant densities or row spacings.

It appears that higher plant densities are required to maximize silage yield compared to grain yield. However, as with grain, the optimum density is a function of all other environmental and management factors. The wide variability in climatic and management factors encountered by various researchers leads to different results. While steer gains from fed silage are one important criterion for measuring silage quality, maximum beef or milk production per unit land area may be of equal or more economic importance.

11–7 FERTILIZATION

11–7.1 Measures for Estimating Nutrient Needs

Determining the kind of nutrients and the precise amounts for optimum production of corn is one of the most difficult problems confronting the farmer and those advising him. Soils vary greatly in their capacities for releasing nutrients in plant available form depending on native mineral reserves, soil pH, organic matter contents, microbiological activity, and soil oxidation-reduction potential in relation to aeration and/or drainage, all of which interact with climate. The correct choice of fertilizer kinds and amounts has far reaching implications from not only the economic standpoint but also from agronomic and environmental viewpoints. It goes without saying that either too little or too much fertilizer will result in economic loss to the farmer. Excessive amounts of fertilizer can be deleterious to yield by reaching toxic levels for certain nutrients or by inducing the deficiency of other nutrients. Excesses can also be detrimental to the environment by supporting eutrophication of surface waters and by contaminating groundwater, the latter especially with NO_3^- (FAO, 1972; Black, 1983; Keeney, 1986).

For the above reasons, the kind and amount of fertilizer to be used is far too important a decision to be left to guesswork. Measures for which research has demonstrated significant predictive capabilities are those of plant analysis and soil testing. The former has shown promise, providing that analytical data are obtained on several plant nutrients having interactive impacts, as with the DRIS system (Summer, 1977). There are serious complications involved with plant analysis interpretations by reason of varied hybrid and/or variety uptake of nutrients, differences in concentration with stage of plant growth and in plant part, and environmentally imposed impacts on plant nutrition. A further limitation is that

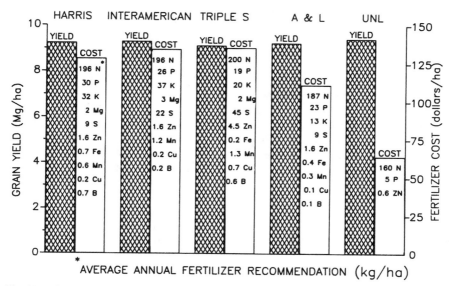

Fig. 11–7. Summary for a 13-yr study comparing yields, amounts of fertilizer, and fertilizer costs from recommendations provided by four commercial and the Univ. of Nebraska's soil testing laboratories. Average results from five experimental sites in Nebraska, 1973 to 1985.

correction for any recognized nutrient shortage can likely be made only for the following crop.

Recent progress in calibrating quick soil tests with crop response for the majority of plant nutrients has made soil testing the most widely accepted procedure for predicting fertilizer needs. Some disagreement of a philosophical nature on the interpretation of soil tests in making final recommendations remains, particularly between the concepts of "sufficiency" and "maintenance" (McLean, 1977; Olson et al., 1982). The maintenance approach is decidedly more liberal. It calls for additions equivalent to that likely to be removed in a projected crop yield. The data presented in Fig. 11–7 are indicative of how commercial laboratories have been applying the maintenance concept to their recommendations. Whatever interpretation system is used, the practice of soil testing henceforth will be expected not only to give prognosis on optimum kind and rate of fertilizer for the crop, but also to ensure that nutrient pollution of the environment is minimized.

11–7.2 Maximizing Fertilizer Use Efficiency

11–7.2.1 Nitrogen

Corn contains more N in its grain than any of the other soil derived nutrients (Table 11–2), and substantially more fertilizer N is used for its production than other primary fertilizer nutrients (Table 11–7). Certainly

Table 11-7. Average rates of N, P, and K applied for corn in the USA during 1984.†

Total corn for grian (1000 ha)	29 069
N applied, kg/ha	150
P applied, kg/ha	27
K applied, kg/ha	66

† Data from NFDC (1984), adjusted to metric units.

the advent of fertilizer N on the scene after World War II has done more toward the quadrupling of average corn yields in the USA since that time than any other factor. Nitrogen is by far the most transitory of all fertilizer nutrients, being subject to losses from both leaching and gaseous evolutions. Most N is absorbed into corn roots through mass flow of NO_3^-, a highly soluble ion that moves in the direction of moisture flow (Table 11–8). It has become the major energy and cost input among production requisites, as well as a significant contributor to groundwater NO_3^- pollution (Pratt, 1984; CAST, 1985). Thus, it is of utmost importance that fertilizer N be used in the most efficient manner possible for economic, environmental, and energy conservation reasons (Keeney, 1982; Olson and Kurtz, 1982).

In the past the corn crop's dire need for N could readily be recognized in the appearance of spindly, yellowish green colored plants. With somewhat less severe shortage a normal size plant formed, but with lower-leaf firing from shoot forming onward that started at the tip and progressed back along the midrib, initially yellow and later brown as the tissue died. Such symptoms are no longer readily seen in most producers' fields, and other means of prognosis are required for optimizing fertilizer N use. A common practice for fields 1 yr or more removed from a legume crop has been to apply the amount that would be removed from the soil by the projected yield, e.g., 10 Mg/ha × 23.2 g/kg = 234 kg of N/ha (160 bu/acre × 1.3 lb of N/bu = 208 lb of N/acre). This procedure gives no credit for any mineral N residuals that may exist in the soil at planting or for the soil's ability to nitrify a portion of the crop's N requirement from its own organic resources. A general consensus has existed that little or no carryover of NO_3^- occurs from 1 yr to the next in a humid cropping environment. There is mounting evidence to the contrary, however, com-

Table 11-8. Relative significance of root interception, mass flow, and diffusion in supplying corn with major nutrient requirements from a fertile alfisol silt loam (Barber, 1984, Table 4, p. 96).

Nutrient	Amount needed for 9500 kg/ha yield	Approximate amount supplied by:		
		Root interception	Mass flow	Diffusion
		kg		
N	190	2	150	38
P	40	1	2	37
K	195	4	35	156
S	22	1	65	0

ing first from irrigated lands (Fig. 11–8) in the western Corn Belt (Olson et al., 1964, 1976; Herron et al., 1971) and, more recently, from eastern humid regions (Peterson and Attoe, 1965; Olsen et al., 1970; Wehrmann and Scharf, 1979; Meissinger, 1984; Meissinger et al., 1985). Such residual NO_3^- is readily used by corn to depths as great as 180 cm in deep soils developed on mantlerock, providing that substantial available N does not exist at shallower depths (Gass et al., 1971). It seems reasonable to project that a measure of residual mineral N along with an estimate of the soil's N mineralization capacity (Schepers et al., 1985) in any deep, medium to fine textured, and well-drained soil will be needed for meeting current and future economic and environmental requirements. Of further

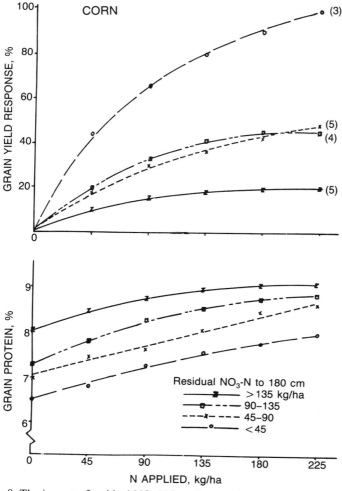

Fig. 11–8. The impact of residual NO_3-N in soil on grain yield response of irrigated corn to fertilizer N and on grain protein content (number of field experiments involved, a total of 17 experiments in Nebraska during 1962 to 1966; Olson et al., 1976).

interest in the data of Fig. 11–8 is the obvious need for a significant amount of residual mineral N in the full rooting profile for maximizing protein content of the grain. Beyond a decision on needed rate of fertilizer N for optimizing N utilization efficiency are the considerations of kind, placement, and timing of the fertilizer employed. The majority of studies comparing N carriers have shown little difference in effectiveness of materials so long as each is used in accordance with its own limitations. Thus, anhydrous NH_3 must be injected sufficiently deep with complete closure of shank slots to prevent loss. Urea materials need to be incorporated into soils, especially those with high pH, unless rain or irrigation is ensured immediately after application. Other channels of loss occur with urea, however, and it is apparent that all of the necessary details of management for this carrier are not known for all situations (Nelson, 1982; Olson et al., 1986; Fenn and Miyamoto, 1981; McInnes et al., 1986).

Timing of application is a critical factor in efficiency because of the highly transitory nature of N in soils. As a very general axiom, the latest fertilizer application possible that is commensurate with the N being in a position for ready uptake by the crop during the period of greatest need gives best results. Thus, split applications or at least a delayed summer sidedressing of much of the N is desirable for enhancing efficiency in its use (Olson et al., 1964; Miller et al., 1975; Welch et al., 1971; Russelle et al., 1981). Thereby an active root system is established for taking up the N as it is applied, and the time for losses to leaching and volatilization are minimized. The delayed N supply also results in a smaller plant with greater grain-to-stover ratio, thus less vegetative entrapment and more N for grain formation (Olson et al., 1964; Bigeriego et al., 1979). One exception to this rule appears to be anhydrous NH_3, which commonly gives almost equally good results from late fall, planting time, and summer sidedress applications. The apparent reason is that anhydrous NH_3 is in essence a delayed release material that persists as a concentrated band of adsorbed NH_4^+ in the soil until it is gradually nitrified, when temperature and moisture conditions allow.

11–7.2.2 Phosphorus

The amount of P required for corn is less than one-fourth the amount of N but a substantially greater proportion of that taken up is harvested in the grain (Table 11–2). In further contrast with N, native soil P or that added as fertilizer has very limited mobility in other than sands and organic soils because of surface adsorption and chemical reactions into low solubility forms. Its movement to plant roots is almost entirely by diffusion through short distances of millimeters in medium to fine textured soils (Table 11–8). Thus, placement in relation to presence of crop roots is essential for efficient fertilizer P utilization.

Many studies have demonstrated the benefit for early growth, i.e., the starter effect, of placing P fertilizer to the side of the seed row at planting when conventional tillage is employed. This early growth effect, especially on soils of low P availability, commonly results in maximum yield response compared with other placements (Stanford and Nelson, 1949; Spiva, 1980; Welch et al., 1966; Richards, 1977). For this effect to be realized, the soil must remain moist in that zone during most of the growing season, allowing continuous root activity. Given favorable moisture, a substantial proliferation of roots occurs in the zone, which further facilitates crop use of the fertilizer (Olson and Dreier, 1956; Duncan and Ohlrogge, 1958). Care must be exercised with near-row placements when significant amounts of N and/or K are compounded with P in complex fertilizers because of potential salt effects on germination (Raun et al., 1986; Lutz et al., 1963).

With somewhat less favorable moisture conditions, broadcasting and plowing down P fertilizer may give better results than banding because a portion of the P is located in continuously moist soil (Barber and Olson, 1968). Such applications are necessary where higher rates of P are employed in an effort to build up soil P levels for future crops. Broadcast P without incorporation is not generally an effective fertilizer practice with conventional tillage. With reduced tillage, however, surface broadcasting of P seems to be an acceptable practice, at least in humid cropping regions where root activity is high in the biomass at the soil surface throughout the growing season (Fink and Wesley, 1974; Moschler et al., 1972; Phillips et al., 1980; Singh et al., 1966). The surface placement of P reduces surface area contact with mineral soil, thereby limiting reversion reactions (Shear and Moschler, 1969; Singh et al., 1966), becoming in essence a band application (Belcher and Rayland, 1972). Such placement does, however, leave the P subject to runoff losses and consequent stream and lake pollution.

Fertilizer studies with wheat have shown promising results from dual placement (DP) of P fertilizer with anhydrous NH_3 (Leikam et al., 1983; Westerman and Edlund, 1985; Kissel, 1984). Similar studies with corn showed equally good results, and sometimes better for DP compared with other placement methods (Raun et al., 1987; Sander and Penas, 1984). A synergistic effect of the NH_4^+ ion on P uptake was recognized as a partial reason for the enhanced P utilization (Olson and Dreier, 1956; Leikam et al., 1983; Miller and Ohlrogge, 1958) with added benefit of the NH_4^+ ion in decreasing P precipitation at the soil-root interface (Miller et al., 1970). Even with no more than equivalent results from DP compared with other systems, having the fertilizer P applied along with the NH_3 injection represents a savings in time and energy requirements for the farmer.

Latitude for timing of P fertilizer application does not exist as it does with N. Because of its low mobility in mineral soils, the P must be placed in a favorable position for root uptake at or before the time of planting. Early accessibility to the plant promotes early top and root growth with greater exploitation of available soil volume for nutrient and water absorption. One study simulating delayed sidedressing by injecting fertilizer

P 5 to 7 cm to the side of corn hills and 10 cm deep gave equivalent results at any time up to the tasseling period (TVA, 1960–63). An obvious limitation is the root pruning that would occur with machine application once the crop was well established.

Even with the best P fertilizer management practices, rarely is 20% of the P utilized by the crop in the year of application because of the noted P reversion reactions and the slow diffusion rate of P ions in the soil. The best means for estimating the fertilizer P rate needed for a given soil remains that of soil testing, yield response being quite unlikely at Bray and Kurtz no. 1 values >15 mg/kg.

11–7.2.3 Potassium

This third primary nutrient is used in about the same magnitude as P for grain production (Table 11–2). A much greater amount is contained in the stover, however, usually on the order of four times as much as in the grain, such that the total K requirement of corn is substantially more than it is for P and about the same as that for N. Accordingly, soil depletion of K is much more rapid when corn is harvested for silage than for grain.

Nutrient deficiency symptoms of K in corn are quite distinctive. These deficiencies portray a marginal leaf scorch of lower leaves that progresses upward in the plant with maturity and from severe K shortage. Resulting ears are small and poorly filled at the tip. Little can be done for the current year's crop once the leaf firing condition is observed (Barber and Mederski, 1966). Severity of stalk rot was found to be closely associated with K shortage and high N application (Koehler, 1960; Long, 1953), but K fertilization is not likely to reduce stalk rot on soils of high K supplying capacity.

As with P, the major portion of root uptake of K results from diffusion of the nutrient in soil to the root surface (Table 11–8). The diffusion rate is more rapid than that of P, resulting in generally greater crop utilization of applied K fertilizer than is achieved with P fertilizer (Barber and Olson, 1968). Quite in contrast with P is that absorption by the plant is complete several weeks before crop maturity, tending to peak with the onset of ear formation (Sayre, 1948).

Much of what has been stated about P fertilizer placement applies equally to K fertilizer. Placement in a band near the seed has commonly exceeded the benefit derived from broadcast application with conventional tillage, as exemplified in experiments on several soils in Illinois (Table 11–9). Only at notably higher rates of broadcast K did yields by that method match yield results from row placement with two of the soils, and no broadcast rate achieved equality on the third soil (Welch et al., 1966). Further, as with P, the high root activity of corn in the surface biomass under minimum tillage allows effective utilization of surface broadcast K fertilizer at least in humid cropping regions (Moschler et al., 1972; Fink and Wesley, 1974; Shear and Moschler, 1969).

Table 11-9. Rate of broadcast K required to produce the same corn yield as a given rate of banded K, and the efficiency of broadcast K (K_B) in terms of banded K (K_b) for three Illinois soils[†] (Welch et al., 1966).

Banded K	Cisne, pH 6.5		Bluford, pH 6.4		Belknap, pH 6.4	
	Broadcast K	K_b/K_B	Broadcast K	K_b/K_B	Broadcast K	K_b/K_B
kg/ha	kg/ha		kg/ha		kg/ha	
11	34	0.33	32	0.35	13	0.88
22	66	0.34	64	0.35	28	0.80
34	95	0.36	98	0.34	49	0.69
45	114	0.39	137	0.33	‡	--
56	120	0.47	‡	--	≏	--

† Suborders for soils: Cisne, sil Mollic Albaqualfs; Bluford, sil Aquic Hapludolfs; Belknap, sil Aeric Fluvaquents.
‡ No rate of broadcast K equaled the yield obtained with this rate of banded K.

Principles involved in proper timing of K fertilizer are essentially the same as for P. Since most crop uptake of K results from diffusion to the root surface, it is important that fertilizer K be placed in soil that will be moist during the major portion of the crop season and in a zone of high root concentration. With conventional tillage this can be accomplished only by appropriate placement, as close and somewhat below the seed row or plowed down during or before planting. Such placement after the crop is established will cause excessive root pruning.

Soil testing by measuring the amount of exchangeable K in soil has proved a reliable means of predicting the fertilizer K requirement of corn. Various studies have revealed little probability of K response with soil test levels in excess of 100 to 120 mg of K/kg (Hanway et al., 1962; Karathanasis et al., 1980; Olson et al., 1982). Addition of K fertilizer to soils with moderate to high K levels was found to interact unfavorably with Mg on soils marginal in Mg (Foy and Barber, 1958) and with P on soils marginal in P (Shapiro et al., 1987).

11–7.2.4 Sulfur

This element is increasingly found to be limiting for the optimum production of corn world-wide and is coming to be regarded as the fourth "primary" essential nutrient. Its shortage is most commonly observed on very sandy soils, those very low in organic matter content, and in highly leached soils of warm, humid regions. Sulfur is found primarily in organic combination in most soils, as gypsum in dry regions, or as surface adsorbed sulfate on 1:1 clay minerals of semitropical and tropical regions. Sulfur deficient corn plants have an overall yellowish green coloration and in some hybrids will display striping in the leaves. Growing recognition of its shortage in the USA has come about in part because of the reduction in SO_2 effluent from industrial plants, the conversion from coal to natural gas heating of homes, higher crop yields, declining soil organic matter, and the elimination of S impurities with the production and use of increasingly high analysis N, P, and K fertilizers (Beaton and Fox, 1971). At high yield levels currently obtained, corn has one of the greatest S requirements among major crops (Table 11-2).

Beyond the direct nutritional role as a component of three essential amino acids and its supportive action in the formation of chlorophyll, vitamins, and several enzymes involved in plant growth, S compounds have commonly been used for soil acidification and the improvement of soil physical condition. Their dominant use in this respect has been in the reclamation of sodic (alkali) soils (Tisdale, 1970; Kelly, 1937). The acidification factor also proved to be important when S products are placed in fertilizer bands on calcareous soils by enhancement in availability of P and the micronutrients Mn, Zn, Cu, and Fe (Hassan and Olson, 1966; Sharpee et al., 1969; McGeorge, 1945).

Numerous S fertilizers exist on the market, a majority of which have the SO_4^{2-} ion as the S carrier. Sulfate is the ionic form of the element absorbed from the soil solution by plants and there is little difference in effectiveness of those sources to corn. The element can also be applied to soils as the SO_2 gas, much as anhydrous NH_3 is applied, with good results. Elemental S generally proves notably less effective for annual crops like corn because of the time required for oxidation in the soil by the *Thiobaccilis* organisms responsible for this enzymatic transformation.

Prediction of S fertilizer needs of corn is not as readily accomplished as with P and K even though effective testing methods for available S in soils have been developed (Fox et al., 1964b; Ensminger, 1954). The SO_4^{2-} ion, being quite mobile in most soils, requires measurements of S in the rooting profile and not just surface soil samples, just as with N. Subsoil samples are essential in warm, humid regions with predominant kaolinitic type clay minerals in the subsoil, where much of the soil's available SO_4^{2-} is adsorbed (Kamprath et al., 1956; Ensminger, 1954). Otherwise, tissue testing is being increasingly recognized as a means of prescribing S needs in corn, with critical value in the ear leaf being on the order of 0.19 (Fox et al., 1964a). Sulfur shortage for crop nutrition is rarely found in irrigated lands in the western half of the USA because of S contained in the irrigation water and gypsum accumulations in the subsoil.

11-7.2.5 Other Secondary and Micronutrients

Shortage of the remaining essential elements for corn nutrition exists on a much more limited scale than for N, P, K, and S. Responses to these lesser elements have generally been obtained in localized situations, commonly with crops other than corn. Only Zn shortages have been noted over fairly wide areas, particularly under conditions of calcareous soil, compaction from grading operations into subsoil materials, and where deficiency has been induced by P fertilization of soil that is marginal in Zn availability. Detailed treatment of all of these elements can be found in a work on corn production edited by Pierre et al. (1966) and one on micronutrients edited by Mortvedt et al. (1972).

11-8 WEED CONTROL

Weeds compete with crops for light, nutrients, water, and other growth factors. If weeds are left uncontrolled, corn simply cannot be grown successfully. Uncontrolled weeds can easily cause a complete loss of corn yield, and even small numbers of weeds can reduce yields substantially. Knake (1962) found that only one giant foxtail (*Setaria faberii* Herrm.) plant per foot of row decreased corn yield by 500 kg/ha. This is the dilemma of weed control; even relatively good weed control often results in low yield and high economic losses.

Most of the competition from weeds in corn is believed to be from root competition for the same nutrients and water. Perennial weeds may have an advantage over an annual crop like corn because of an already established root system or are able to grow faster and develop a more extensive root, complicating the competitive nature of crops and weeds.

Light is not thought to be a primary factor since most weeds do not achieve heights greater than or even equal to corn. Investigators have reported that yield reductions in corn dry matter are almost proportional to the increase in weed dry matter (Knake and Slife, 1962), which indicates a limiting factor concept of corn-weed competition. Competition for nutrients is primarily for N because, in general, all nutrients in the soil except N and water are immobile and rely on root contact and diffusion over a very small distance for uptake. Because N and water move freely in the soil, and weeds compete with corn for the available N and water supply. While it might appear possible to grow both weeds and corn by eliminating deficiencies of the mobile nutrients and water with N fertilizer and irrigation, weeds appear also to hinder crop plants by secreting a growth inhibitory substance into its environment (allelopathy). Bell and Koeppe (1972) found that giant foxtail growing in a greenhouse with corn reduced corn dry weight by 90% compared to comparable plants grown without foxtail. Simply leaching the phytotoxins from dead foxtail roots reduced corn growth by 50%. Many common weeds were found to possess inhibitory potential, but these phytotoxic effects are nearly impossible to identify under field conditions (Glaunenger and Holzner, 1982). Allelopathic affects include crop-weed, crop-crop, as well as weed-crop interactions (Rose et al., 1984).

Weed control methods involve many different aspects, some of which are indirect, while other methods are direct. Indirect methods include passive and cultural techniques, whereas direct methods involve mechanical, chemical, and biological treatment.

11-8.1 Passive Methods of Weed Control

Indirect methods of weed control are preventive in nature or provide methods that give the crop a competitive advantage over the weed. Preventive measures are those taken to disallow the introduction and spread of weed species into areas not already infested with these weeds. It is often much easier to prevent the spread of weeds than it is to control them once they are established. Practices include weed-free seed, clean harvesting and tillage equipment, weed-free hay and manures, and elimination of weed seeds in irrigation water. Other techniques include spot treatment of weed outbreaks while the infestation is low. Cultural methods for growing corn are also indirect, such as narrow rows, early planting date, and proper plant density to increase shading; planting at proper depth in good seedbeds to encourage early emergence; using rotations to reduce the buildup of certain weeds; and providing optimum nutrients for good crop growth, all of which make the crop more competitive. One way to destroy weed seed is to bury it so deeply it will not germinate. Plowing is therefore a good weed control method, although generally not a good soil conservation practice.

11-8.2   Direct Methods of Weed Control

Direct methods of weed control include mechanical, chemical, and biological methods. The oldest method is certainly mechanical, which includes hand pulling, hoeing, mowing, smothering, burning, or machine tillage. The most important for corn production is machine tillage. It is accomplished with various implements to till the soil for seedbed preparation and to cultivate the crop after emergence.

Seedbed preparation is critical for good weed control. The essential criteria of a good seedbed involve two factors. First, weeds must be destroyed immediately prior to planting. Corn must be planted into a weed-free environment to provide the corn with a competitive edge. Second, the seedbed should provide for good soil-seed contact so as to hasten the emergence of the planted corn seed. Soil other than that near the corn seed should be loose or undisturbed, delaying weed germination. It is important to note that the requirements for a good seedbed can be met by either tillage or no-tillage providing the planter has the ability to place the seed in firm contact with the soil. In a no-till system, weeds must be destroyed prior to planting by chemical means. Early preplant herbicide applications have shown promise for effective, economical weed control in no-till corn systems.

It is essential that early weed control is achieved after emergence either thru tillage (rotary hoe or harrow) or with chemicals. The first few weeks are critical for controlling weeds in corn. Even small weeds during the first weeks after emergence can reduce yields of corn substantially (Aldrich et al., 1986). Later weeds are normally controlled by cultivation most commonly with shovel cultivators. Broadleaf weeds can be controlled with applications of postemergence herbicides at the last cultivation, usually when corn is 45 to 60 cm tall.

While cultivation is a good weed control method, there is little evidence that corn needs to be cultivated other than for weed control. However, breaking up the surface soil when it is crusted may increase water infiltration (Meyer and Mannering, 1961). There is also some evidence that moving soil up to the corn plant may increase brace root development and reduce potential lodging, especially when the soil surface is very dry.

Herbicides have become a very important means of weed control in corn. In fact, without herbicides some reduced and no-till systems of corn production would be doomed to failure. However, the use of herbicides should be dictated by the cropping and tillage system used to grow corn and the weed problem. Indiscriminate use of herbicides is not only expensive but runs the risk of not controlling the weed problem. In recent years, herbicides have been especially developed for specific weed problems and specific cropping and tillage systems. Some herbicides are best applied prior to planting (preemergence) either incorporated or surface applied, while others perform better when applied after planting (postemergence), or applied as a directed application to the weed. Prominently used preemergence and postemergence herbicides include atrazine [6-chloro-N-ethyl-N'-(1-methylethyl)-1,3,5-triazine-2,4-diamine], alachor [2-chloro-N-(2,6-diethylphenyl)-N-(methoxymethyl)acetamide], and metolachlor 2-chloro - N - (2 - ethyl - 6 - methylphenyl) - N - (2 - methoxy - 1 - methylethyl) acetamide], and cyanazine {2-[[4-chloro - 6 - (ethylamino)-1,3,5 - triazin-2-yl]amino]-2-methylpropanenitrile}. Volatile herbicides that need to be incorporated include butylate [S-ethyl bis(2-methylpropyl)carbamothioate] and EPTC (S-ethyl dipropylcarbamothioate) (plus R-25788). These herbicides are often applied in combination to increase the weed control spectrum and to match particular cropping and tillage systems. The most popular postemergence herbicide for broadleaf weeds in corn remains 2,4-D [(2,4-dicholorophenoxy)acetic acid], although other herbicides for more specific weed control problems include bentazon [3-(1-methylethyl)-(1H)-2,1,3-benzothiadiazin-4(3H)-one 2,2-dioxide] and bromoxynil (3,5-dibromo-4-hydroxybenzonitrile).

Some herbicides have a long residual time that may affect the growth of succeeding crops in rotation. Such carryover is dependent on soil characteristics such as soil organic matter, temperatures, soil texture, and soil pH as well as the amount of effective precipitation received. New chemicals and new combinations are constantly being developed and tested. The reader is referred to the most recent Agricultural Extension publications for current recommendations.

Combining different herbicides as well as combining herbicides with other agricultural chemicals have several advantages over the use of single chemicals. Advantages include reduced trips over the field with reduced soil compaction and costs, increased effectiveness thereby using less chemicals, and a possible delay in the appearance of weed species resistant to selected herbicides. The problem is that although most agrochemicals act independently, others may interact to produce both antagonistic and synergistic results (Sander et al., 1987). If such results are unknown, the potential exists to either destroy the crop or a failure to destroy the weeds; either could be disastrous. Extreme care must be taken whenever herbicides are mixed with other chemicals or fertilizers. Even water quality can have an effect on herbicide phytotoxicity (Buhler and Burnside, 1983). Hatzios and Penner (1985) extensively reviewed the interaction of herbicides with other agrochemicals.

Since biological control involves the utilization of natural enemies for the control of weeds, it is generally conceived that such methods are attractive compared to the use of chemicals, which may have environmental contamination potential. However, biological controls can also pose a serious hazard to agriculture in that the biotic agent must attack only the target weed and not desirable plants. Unfortunately it is very difficult or impossible to completely guarantee desirable effects of biotic agents. Biotic control agents tend to be weed specific rather than broad spectrum.

The use of biological agents involves the use of predators, pathogens, and parasites to control weeds and is therefore sometimes referred to as "natural control." With weeds the principle biotic control agent has been the use of plant eating insects but fungi have also been used effectively (Sweetman, 1958; Templeton et al., 1976). The big advantage of biological controls in addition to not polluting the environment, is that when successful biotic agents are found to control a weed, no further control measures are required since a balance is then maintained between the weed and its agent. However, this makes biological controls less successful for short-term cropping systems such as those involved in corn production (Wapshere, 1982). Therefore, while biological controls appear to have great promise for controlling some weeds, it will be difficult to find biotic agents for controlling the wide variety of common weeds in corn. For at least the near future, producers will have to rely on other direct and indirect methods of weed control.

11–9 HARVESTING AND STORAGE

Harvesting corn should not be an event that just happens at some time in the fall, but should be planned in the spring by proper hybrid choice and planting dates (Duncan and Thompson, 1962). Early planting results in earlier black layer development, which effectively seals the kernel from the cob and the rest of the plant (Daynard and Duncan, 1969). Early maturity or black layering in the fall means a higher probability of early harvest. Harvesting earlier at lower grain moistures results in reduced grain drying costs and less field losses. One day earlier planting in the spring does not equal one day earlier to black layer. Grogan et al. (1959) found in Missouri that corn planted on 20 April took 77 d to tassel compared to 67 d when planted 17 d later on 10 May. However, the early planted corn that matured in late September when field drying conditions would be more favorable than it would for the late planted corn that matured in early October. With increased fuel costs, it is important to let the grain dry in the field as much as possible in order to hold harvest losses at a reasonable level. Models have been presented to predict the optimum moisture for beginning harvest based on the economic values of drying fuel energy, corn grain energy associated with harvest losses, drying method, and harvesting rate (Loewer et al., 1984).

While most corn hybrids mature when the grain holds about 30% moisture, the ideal moisture content to start combining is considered to be about 25%, unless severe stalk rot or European corn borer [*Ostrinia nubilalis* (Hübner)] infestations are present, causing increased lodging, ear drop, or the harvest acreage demands a long harvest season. Field losses increase rapidly as harvest is delayed. Alfrich et al. (1986) indicate, on average, grain harvest losses increase from 5 to 18% when harvest is delayed from October to December. Actual losses may range from nearly 0 to 100%, depending on weather conditions. The loss of corn associated with delayed harvest can be much greater than any savings that might be achieved through reduced drying costs. Early planting is, however, an effective way to increase field drying time and reduce drying costs.

Harvest decisions are affected to some degree by the kind of drying and storage facilities available. Commercial drying is sometimes very costly, depending on factors such as capacity to dry and the average grain moisture levels in the marketing area. When grain moisture levels are high in a marketing area, commercial drying rates increase to compensate for the greater drying times required, which reduces the capacity to dry. Management decisions to delay harvest for lower grain moisture must be based on the probability of the potential harvest losses that may occur.

Proper management of stored corn depends on future plans for the grain. If the corn is to be stored for a long period of time (>1 yr), grain moisture must be down to 14%. Since field drying to 14% is not probable regardless of harvest time, most corn in the Corn Belt is dried artificially. Corn that is stored above 15% moisture is subject to heating from the natural respiration of the grain and mold growth present in the grain. For every 10 °C that grain temperature increases due to heating, the rate of biological activity doubles. As temperatures rise in storage, humidity also increases, and mold, insect, and bacterial growth is even faster. Therefore, if grain in storage begins to heat, severe spoilage will result unless the grain is aerated to reduce and control temperature. The higher the storage grain moisture, the greater the difficulty in keeping the grain cool and controlling hotspot development.

Even if grain moisture is at 14%, aeration is needed to control moisture migration. As outside temperature changes in relation to stored grain temperature, air convection currents and water vapor diffusion cause moisture to accumulate in the cold grain at the top center of the bin. As temperatures warm, this grain will spoil and create a favorable environment for insect reproduction. In a warm- and cold-season climate, it is desirable to keep the grain temperature to average outside air temperature differential to <5 to 10 °C. Ideally, the grain should be cooled in the fall to 4 °C or less for winter and warmed to 10 to 15 °C in the spring for summer storage.

When aerating grain, it is important to recognize that the cooling rate is proportional to airflow. A typical aeration airflow of 0.1 m^3/(min Mg) of corn requires about 120 h for a one degree temperature change, whereas natural air drying airflow rates of 1.0 m^3/(min Mg) can do the same job in about 12 h. Therefore, fan management strategies require adjustment to reflect air delivery rates (McKenzie, 1984).

When holding wet corn with aeration, grain moisture content and temperature are critical for determining safe storage periods. For example, at 4 °C corn can be stored safely for 55 d at 22% moisture but only 20 d at 30% moisture. At 15 °C corn can be stored safely for only 15 d at 22% moisture and only 5 d at 30% moisture (Aldrich et al., 1986). Corn at 18 to 20% moisture can be stored for several months during the winter if it is aerated to keep grain temperatures at 4 °C, but must be fed to animals or otherwise disposed of before temperatures rise in the spring. For feeding, corn can also be placed into an air-tight structure when corn is physiologically mature (usually around 30%) and ensiled.

Chemical treatment can also be used instead of drying to prevent mold growth in high moisture grain. The most common preservative chemicals are propionic acid and a mixture of acetic and propionic acids, neither of which is toxic to animals. When properly applied, the acid type preservatives kill all microorganisms and even the germ of the grain, preventing respiration (Larson and Hanway, 1977). The usual method of applying the acid is to spray the grain at harvest as it is augered into the bin. The amount of acid needed varies from 0.005 L/kg at 15% moisture to 0.015 L/kg at 30% moisture (Hyde and Burrell, 1973).

While acid preservatives appear to have promise, they have failed to gain acceptance in the USA. Primary disadvantages are that they corrode unprotected metal bin surfaces, are a safety hazard, and there is no market for treated corn except as livestock feed (Aldrich et al., 1986).

REFERENCES

Adams, W.E., H.D. Morris, and R.N. Dawson. 1970. Effect of cropping systems and nitrogen levels on corn (*Zea mays*) yields in the Southern Piedmont region. Agron. J. 62:655–659.

AGNET. 1984. The first decade. Central AGNET, Univ. of Nebraska, Lincoln.

Agriculture Statistics. 1984. USDA. U.S. Gov. Print. Office, Washington, DC.

Al-Darby, A.M., and B. Lowery. 1986. Evaluation of corn growth and productivity with three conservation tillage systems. Agron. J. 78:901–907.

Aldrich, S.R., W.O. Scott, and R.G. Hoeft. 1986. Modern corn production. A and L Publ., Champaign, IL.

Allmaras, R.R., A.L. Black, and R.W. Rickman. 1973. Tillage soil environment, and root growth. p. 62–86. *In* Conservation tillage. Proc. Natl. Conf., Des Moines, IA. 28–30 March. Soil Conserv. Soc. of Am., Ankeny, IA.

Amemiya, M. 1968. Tillage-soil water relations of corn as influenced by weather. Agron. J. 60:534–537.

Barber, S.A. 1959. The influence of alfalfa, bromegrass and corn on soil aggregation and crop yield. Soil Sci. Soc. Am. Proc. 23:258–259.

––––. 1972. Relation of weather to influence of hay crops on subsequent corn yields on a Chalmens silt loam. Agron. J. 64:8–10.

––––. 1984. Soil nutrient bioavailability: A mechanistic approach. John Wiley and Sons, New York.

––––, and H.J. Mederski. 1966. Potassium fertility requirements. p. 259–284. *In* W.R. Pierre et al. (ed.) Advances in corn production: Principles and practices. The Iowa Univ. Press, Ames.

––––, and R.A. Olson. 1968. Fertilizer use on corn. p. 163–188. *In* L.B. Nelson et al. (ed.) Changing patterns in fertilizer use. SSSA, Madison, WI.

Beaton, J.D., and R.L. Fox. 1971. Production, marketing, and use of sulfur products. p. 335–379. *In* R.A. Olson et al. (ed.) Fertilizer technology and use. 2nd ed. SSSA, Madison, WI.

Belcher, C.R., and J.L. Rayland. 1972. Phosphorus absorption by sod-planted corn (*Zea mays* L.) from surface applied phosphorus. Agron. J. 64:754–756.

Bell, D.T., and D.E. Koeppe. 1972. Noncompetitive effects of giant foxtail on the growth of corn. Agron. J. 64:321–325.

Bigeriego, M., R.D. Hauck, and R.A. Olson. 1979. Uptake, translocation and utilization of N^{15}-depleted fertilizer in irrigated corn. Soil Sci. Soc. Am. J. 43:528–533.

Black, C.A. 1983. The double-edged sword of nitrogen fertilizer. Comments from CAST, 1983–3. Counc. for Agric. Sci. and Technol., Ames, IA.

Blevins, R.L., D. Cook, S.H. Phillips, and R.E. Phillips. 1971. Influence of no-tillage on soil moisture. Agron. J. 63:593–596.

Bhowmik, P.S., and J.D. Doll. 1982. Corn and soybean response to allelopathic effects of weed and crop residues. Agron. J. 74:601–606.

Brown, P.L. 1964. Legumes and grasses in dryland cropping systems in the northern and central great plains. USDA-ARS Misc. Pub. 952. U.S. Gov. Print. Office, Washington, DC.

Brown, R.H., E.R. Beaty, W.J. Ethredge, and D.D. Hayes. 1970. Influence of row width and plant population on yield of two varieties of corn (*Zea mays* L.). Agron. J. 62:767–770.

Bryan, A.A., R.C. Echkardt, and G.F. Sprague. 1940. Spacing experiments with corn. J. Am. Soc. Agron. 32:707–714.

Bryant, H.T., and R.E. Blazer. 1968. Plant constituents of an early and a late corn hybrid as affected by row spacing and plant population. Agron. J. 60:557–559.

Buhler, D.D., and O.C. Burnside. 1983. Effect of water quality carrier volume, and acid on glyphosate phytotoxicity. Weed Sci. 31:163–169.

Burgess, P.L., and J.W.G. Nicholson. 1980. Yield and feeding value of densely planted corn for silage. Can. J. Anim. Sci. 60:1071.

Cardwell, V.B. 1982. Fifty years of Minnesota corn production: Sources of yield increase. Agron. J. 74:984–990.

Carson, P.L., R.C. Ward, D.B. Shank, and D.W. Beatty. 1966. Stable corn yields sought in Northern Great Plains. Crops Soils Mag. 19(2):19–20.

CAST. 1985. Agriculture and groundwater quality. Rep. 103. Counc. Agric. Sci. and Technol., Ames, IA.

Cihacek, L.J., D.L. Mulvaney, R.A. Olson, L.F. Welch, and R.A. Wiese. 1974. Phosphate placement for corn in chisel and moldboard plowing systems. Agron. J. 665:665–668.

Cochran, V.L., R.L. Warner, and R.I. Papendick. 1978. Effect of nitrogen depth and application rate on yield, protein content and quality of winter wheat. Agron. J. 70:964–968.

Collins, E.V., and C.K. Shedd. 1941. Results of row spacing experiments with corn. Agric. Eng. 22:177–178.

Collins, W.K., W.A. Russell, and S.A. Eberhart. 1965. Performance of two-ear types of corn belt maize. Crop. Sci. 5:113–116.

Colville, W.L. 1966. Plant populations and row spacing. p. 55–62. *In* Rep. 21 Hybrid Corn Ind. Res. Conf., Chicago, IL. 14–15 December. ASTA, Washington, DC.

––––, A. Dreier, D.P. McGill, P. Grabouski, and P.E. Ehlers. 1964. Influence of plant population hybrid, and "productivity level" on irrigated corn production. Agron. J. 56:332–335.

————, and D.P. McGill. 1962. Effect of rate and method of planting on several plant characters and yield of irrigated corn. Agron. J. 54:235–238.

Cross, H.Z. 1977. Interrelationships among yield stability and yield components in early maize. Crop Sci. 17:741–745.

————, K.J. Tonye, and L. Brun. 1987. Plant density, maturity and prolificacy effects on early maize. Can. J. Plant Sci. 67:35–42.

Cummins, D.G., and J.W. Dobson, Jr. 1973. Corn silage as influenced by hybrid maturity, row spacing, plant population, and climate. Agron. J. 65:240–243.

Cunningham, C.C. 1914. A new method of growing corn. J. Am. Soc. Agron. 6:84–88.

Daynard, T.B., and W.G. Duncan. 1969. The black layer and grain maturity in corn. Crop Sci. 9:473–476.

————, and J.F. Muldoon. 1981. Effects of plant density on the yield maturity and grain content of whole-plant maize. Can. J. Plant Sci. 61:843–849.

————, and ————. 1983. Plant to plant variability of maize plants grown at different densities. Can. J. Plant Sci. 63:45–59.

DeLoughery, R.L., and R.K. Crookston. 1979. Harvest index of corn affected by population density, maturity rating and environment. Agron. J. 71:577–580.

Denmead, O.T., L.J. Fritschen, and R.H. Shaw. 1962. Spatial distribution of radiation in a corn field. Agron. J. 54:505–510.

————, and R.H. Shaw. 1960. The effects of soil moisture stress at different stages of growth on development and yield of grain. J. Am. Soc. Agron. 52:272–274.

Doran, J.W. 1980. Soil microbial and biochemical changes associated with reduced tillage. Soil Sci. Soc. Am. J. 44:765–771.

————, L.N. Mielke, and J.F. Power. 1987. Tillage/residue management interactions with soil environment, organic matter, and nutrient cycling. INTECOL 15:33–39.

Dowdell, R.J., and R.Q. Connell. 1975. Effect of plowing and direct drilling on soil nitrate content. Soil Sci. 26:53–61.

Duley, F.L. 1939. Surface factors affecting the rate of intake of water by soils. Soil Sci. Soc. Am. Proc. 4:60–64.

————, and J.C. Russell. 1942. Effect of stubble mulching on soil erosion and runoff. Soil Sci. Soc. Am. Proc. 7:77–81.

Duncan, E.R. 1954. Influences of varying plant population, soil fertility and hybrid on corn yield. Soil Sci. Soc. Am. Proc. 18:437–440.

————. 1966. Problems relating to selection of hybrid seed: Calendarization a consideration. p. 104–119. In W.H. Pierre et al. (ed.) Advances in corn production: Principles and practices. Iowa State Univ. Press, Ames.

————, and A.J. Ohlrogge. 1958. Principles of nutrient uptake from fertilizer bands: II. Root development in the band. Agron. J. 50:605–608.

————, and H.E. Thompson. 1962. Calendarized row crop production. Iowa Farm Sci. 16:3–5.

Dungan, G.H., A.L. Leng, and J.W. Pendleton. 1958. Corn plant population in relation to soil productivity. Adv. Agron. 10:435–473.

Duvick, D.N. 1974. Continuous backcrossing to transfer prolificacy to a single-eared inbred line of maize. Crop Sci. 14:69–71.

Edmeades, G.O., and T.B. Daynard. 1979. The development of plant-to-plant variability in maize at different planting densities. Can. J. Plant Sci. 59:561–576.

Ekert, D.J. 1984. Tillage system × planting date interactions in corn production. Agron. J. 76:580–582.

Ensminger, L.E. 1954. Some factors affecting the adsorption of sulfates by Alabama soils. Soil Sci. Soc. Am. Proc. 18:259–264.

Fairey, N.A. 1982. Influence of population density and hybrid maturity on productivity and quality of forage maize Zea mays. Can. J. Plant Sci. 62:157–168.

————. 1983. Yield quality and development of forage maize (Zea mays) as influenced by dates of planting and harvesting. Can. J. Plant Sci. 63:157–168.

FAO. 1972. Effects of intensive fertilizer use on the human environment. Soils Bull. 16. Food and Agric. Org., Rome.

Fehrenbacker, J.B. B.W. Ray, and J.D. Alexander. 1967. Root development of corn, soybeans, wheat and meadow in some contrasting Illinois soils. Illinois Research (spring), Univ. of Illinois, Urbana.

Fenn, L.B., and S. Miyamoto. 1981. Ammonia loss and associated reactions of urea in calcareous soils. Soil Sci. Soc. Am. J. 45:537–540.

Fenster, C.R., and G.A. Peterson. 1979. Effects of no-tillage fallow as compared to conventional tillage in a wheat-fallow system. Nebraska Agric. Exp. Stn. Res. Bull. 289.

Fink, R.J., and D. Wesley. 1974. Corn yield as affected by fertilization and tillage system. Agron. J. 66:70–71.

Fisher, W.F., and D.E. Lane. 1973. Till-planting. p. 187–194. *In* Conservation tillage. Proc. Natl. Conf., Des Moines, IA. 28–30 March. Soil Conserv. Soc. of Am., Ankeny, IA.

Fitts, J.W., E.S. Lyons, and H.F. Rhoades. 1944. Chemical treatment of "slickspots." Soil Sci. Soc. Am. Proc. 8:432–436.

Fox, R.L., H.M. Atesalp, D.H. Kampbell, and H.F. Rhoades. 1964a. Factors influencing the availability of sulfur fertilizers to alfalfa and corn. Soil Sci. Soc. Am. Proc. 28:406–408.

––––, R.A. Olson, and H.F. Rhoades. 1964b. Evaluating the sulfur status of soils by plant and soil tests. Soil Sci. Soc. Am. Proc. 28:243–246.

Foy, C.D., and S.A. Barber. 1958. Magnesium deficiency and corn yield on two acid Indiana soils. Soil Sci. Soc. Am. Proc. 22:145–148.

Frank, K.D., and D.H. Sander. 1972. Plant population—how high is high. Farm, Ranch Home Q. 9:9–10.

Frey, N.M. 1981. Dry matter accumulation in kernels of maize (*Zea mays* L.). Crop Sci. 21:118–122.

Gajic, D., S. Malencic, M. Vrbaski, and S. Vrbaski. 1976. Study of the possible quantitative and qualitative improvement of wheat yield through agrostemin as an allelopathic factor. Fragm. Herb. Jugosl. 63:121–141. (As cited in Rice, E.L. 1983. Pest control with nature's chemicals: Allelochemics and pheromones in gardening and agriculture. Univ. of Oklahoma Press, Norman.

Gass, W.B., G.A. Peterson, R.D. Hauck, and R.A. Olson. 1971. Recovery of residual nitrogen by corn (*Zea mays* L.) from various soil depths as measured by N[15] tracer techniques. Soil Sci. Soc. Am. Proc. 35:290–294.

Genter, C.F., and H.M. Camper, Jr. 1973. Component plant part development in maize as affected by hybrids and population density. Agron. J. 65:669–671.

Giesbrecht, J. 1969. Effect of population and row spacing on the performance of four corn (*Zea mays* L.) hybrids. Agron. J. 61:439–441.

Glauninger, J., and W. Holzner. 1982. Interference between weeds and crops: A review of literature. p. 149–154. *In* W. Holzner and M. Numata (ed.) Biology and ecology of weeds. Kluwer Boston, Hingham, MA.

Glenn, F.B., and T.B. Daynard. 1974. Effect of genotype, planting pattern, and plant density on plant-to-plant variability and grain yield of corn. Can. J. Plant Sci. 54:323–330.

Griffith, D.R. 1965. Effect of planting date and row width on yield of short season and full season corn hybrids in northwestern Indiana. Indiana Agric. Exp. Stn. Res. Prog. Rep. 171.

––––, J.V. Mannering, H.M. Galloway, S.D. Parsons, and C.B. Richey. 1973. Effect of eight tillage-planting systems on soil temperature, percent stand, plant growth, and yield of corn on five Indiana soils. Agron. J. 65:321–326.

Grimes, D.W., R.J. Miller, and P.L. Wiley. 1975. Cotton and corn root development in two fields of different strength characteristics. Agron. J. 67:519–523.

Groffman, P.M. 1985. Nitrification and denitrification in conventional and no-tillage soils. Soil Sci. Soc. Am. J. 49:329–334.

Grogan, C.O., M.S. Zuber, N. Brown, D.C. Peters, and H.E. Brown. 1959. Date-of-planting studies with corn. Missouri Agric. Exp. Stn. Bull. 706.

Halitligil, M.B., R.A. Olson, and W.A. Compton. 1984. Yield, water use, and nutrient uptake of corn hybrids under varied irrigation and nitrogen regimes. Fert. Res. 5:321–333.

Hanway, J.J. 1971. How a corn plant develops. Iowa State Univ. Spec. Rep. 48. revised ed.

––––, S.A. Barber, R.H. Bray, A.C. Caldwell, M. Fried, L.T. Kurtz, K. Lawton, J.T. Pesek, K. Pretty, M. Reed, and F.W. Smith. 1962. North central regional potassium studies. III. Field studies with corn. Iowa Agric. Exp. Stn. Res. Bull. 503.

Hassan, N., and R.A. Olson. 1966. Influence of applied sulfur on availability of soil nutrients for corn (*Zea mays* L.) nutrition. Soil Sci. Soc. Am. Proc. 30:284–286.

Hassan, N.A.K., J.V. Drew, D. Knudsen, and R.A. Olson. 1970. Influence of soil salinity on production of dry matter and uptake and distribution of nutrients in barley and corn. II. Corn (*Zea mays* L.) Agron. J. 62:46–48.

Hatzios, K.K., and D. Penner. 1985. Interactions of herbicides with other agrochemicals and higher plants. Rev. Weed Sci. 1:1–63.

Haynes, J.L., and L.E. Thatcher. 1955. Crop rotations and soil nitrogen. Soil Sci. Soc. Am. Proc. 19:324–327.

Herbeck, J.H., L.W. Murdock, and R.L. Blevins. 1986. Tillage system and date of planting effects on yield of corn on soils with restricted drainage. Agron. J. 78:824–826.

Herron, G.M., A.F. Dreier, A.D. Flowerday, W.L. Colville, and R.A. Olson. 1971. Residual mineral N accumulation in soil and its utilization by irrigated corn. Agron. J. 63:322–327.

Hicks, D.R., S.D. Evans, R.D. Frazier, W.E. Luschen, W.W. Nelson, H.J. Otto, C.J. Overdahl, and R.H. Peterson. 1970. Corn management studies in Minnesota 1967–68–69. Minnesota Agric. Exp. Stn. Misc. Rep. 96.

Howe, O.W., and H.F. Rhoades. 1955. Irrigation practice for corn production in relation to stage of plant development. Soil Sci. Soc. Am. Proc. 19:94–98.

Hunter, R.B. 1978. Selection and evaluation procedures for whole-plant corn silage. Can. J. Plant Sci. 58:661–678.

Hyde, M.B., and N.J. Burrell. 1973. Some recent aspects of grain storage technology. p. 313–341. In R.N. Sinha and W.E. Muir (ed.) Grain storage: Part of a system. The AVI Publ. Co., Westport, CT.

Johnson, D.R., and J.W. Tanner. 1972. Calculation of the rate and duration of grain filling in corn. Crop Sci. 12:485–486.

Jones, J.N., Jr., J.E. Moody, and J.H. Lillard. 1969. Effects of tillage, no-tillage and mulch on soil water and plant growth. Agron. J. 61:719–721.

Kamprath, E.J., and C.D. Foy. 1971. Lime-fertilizer-plant interactions in acid soils. p. 105–151. In R.A. Olson et al. (ed.) Fertilizer technology and use. SSSA, Madison, WI.

––––, W.L. Nelson, and J.W. Fitts. 1956. The effect of pH, sulfate and phosphate concentrations on the adsorption of sulfate by soils. Soil Sci. Soc. Am. Proc. 21:463–466.

Karathanasis, A.D., V.A. Johnson, G.A. Peterson, D.H. Sander, and R.A. Olson. 1980. Relation of soil properties and other environmental factors to grain yield and quality of winter wheat grown at international sites. Agron. J. 72:329–336.

Keeney, D.R. 1982. Nitrogen management for maximum efficiency and minimum pollution. In F.J. Stevenson (ed.) Nitrogen in agricultural soils. Agronomy 22:605–649.

––––. 1986. Sources of nitrate to groundwater. CRC Crit. Rev. Environ. Control 16(3):257–304.

Kelley, W.P. 1937. The reclamation of alkali soils. California Agric. Exp. Stn. Bull. 617.

Kissel, D.E. 1984. Effects of P source and method of N–P application on phosphorus availability of winter wheat. J. Fert. Issues 1:125–129.

Knake, E.L. 1962. Losses caused by weeds. Proc. North Cent. Weed Control Conf. 19:1.

––––, and F.W. Slife. 1962. Competition of Setaria faberii with corn and soybeans. Weeds 10:26–29.

Koehler, B. 1960. Corn stalk rots in Illinois. Illinois Agric. Exp. Stn. Bull. 658.

Kohnke, H., and S.R. Miles. 1951. Rates and patterns of seeding corn on high-fertility land. Agron. J. 43:488–493.

Lane, D.E., and H. Witmuss. 1961. Nebraska till-plant system. Nebraska Ext. Circ. 61–714.

Larson, W.E., and G.R. Blake. 1966. Seedbed and tillage requirements. p. 28–52. In W.H. Pierre et al. (ed.) Advances in corn production: Principles and practices. Iowa State Univ. Press, Ames.

––––, and J.J. Hanway. 1977. Corn production. In G.F. Sprague (ed.) Corn and corn improvement. 2nd ed. Agronomy 18:625–669.

Leikam, D.F., L.S. Murphy, D.E. Kissel, D.A. Whitney, and H.C. Moser. 1983. Effects of nitrogen and phosphorus application method and nitrogen source on winter wheat grain yield and leaf tissue phosphorus. Soil Sci. Soc. Am. J. 47:530–535.

Loewer, O.J., T.C. Bridges, G.M. White, R.B. Razor. 1984. Optimum moisture content to begin harvesting corn as influenced by energy cost. Trans. ASAE 27(2):362–365.

Long, O.H. 1953. Nitrogen and spacing experiments with corn. Tennessee Agric. Exp. Stn. Bull. 232.

Lucas, R.E. 1969. Cultural trials on irrigated corn. Michigan State Univ. Res. Rep. 84.

Lutz, J.A., Jr., H.M. Camper, J.D. Jones, and M.T. Carter. 1963. Fertilizer placement effects on stand, growth, maturity and yield of corn. Virginia Exp. Stn. Bull. 549.

Mackay, A.D., and S.A. Barber. 1986. Effect of nitrogen on root growth of two corn genotypes in the field. Agron. J. 78:699–703.

McClean, E.O. 1977. Contrasting concepts in soil test interpretation: Sufficiency levels of available nutrients vs. basic cation saturation ratios. p. 39–54. *In* T.R. Peck et al. (ed.) Soil testing: Correlating and interpreting the analytical results. Spec. Pub. 29. ASA, Madison, WI.

McGeorge, W.T. 1945. Sulphur: A soil corrective and soil builder. Arizona Agric. Exp. Stn. Tech. Bull. 201.

McInnes, K.J., R.B. Ferguson, D.E. Kissel, and E.T. Kanemasu. 1986. Ammonia loss from applications of urea–ammonium nitrate solution to straw residues. Soil Sci. Soc. Am. J. 50:969–974.

McKenzie, B. 1984. Aeration for long term storage. Grain Storage and Handling 6(3):28–30.

Meissinger, J.J. 1984. Evaluating plant-available nitrogen in soil-crop systems. p. 391–416. *In* R.D. Hauck (ed.) Nitrogen in crop production. ASA, CSSA, and SSSA, Madison, WI.

————, V.A. Bandell, G. Stanford, and J.O. Legg. 1985. Nitrogen utilization of corn under minimal tillage and moldboard plow tillage: I. Four year results using labeled N fertilizer on an Atlantic Coastal Plain soil. Agron. J. 77:602–611.

Meyer, L.D., and J.V. Mannering. 1961. Minimum tillage for corn: Its effect on infiltration and erosion. Agric. Eng. 42:72–75, 86.

Miller, H.F., J. Kavanaugh, and G.W. Thomas. 1975. Time of N application and yields of corn in wet alluvial soils. Agron. J. 67:401–404.

Miller, M.H., C.F. Marmil, and G.J. Blair. 1970. Ammonium effects on phosphorus absorption through pH changes and phosphorus precipitation at the soil-root interface. Agron. J. 62:524–527.

————, and A.J. Ohlrogge. 1958. Principles of nutrient uptake from fertilizer bands: 1. Effect of placement of nitrogen fertilizer and the uptake of band-placed phosphorus at different soil phosphorus levels. Agron. J. 50:95–97.

Mock, J.J., and D.C. Erback. 1977. Influence of conservation tillage environments on growth and productivity of corn. Agron. J. 69:337–340.

Moldenhauer, W.C., and W.H. Wischmeier. 1960. Soil and water losses and infiltration rates on Ida silt loam as influenced by cropping systems, tillage practices and rainfall characteristics. Soil Sci. Soc. Am. Proc. 24:409–413.

Mortvedt, J.J., P.M. Giordano, and W.L. Lindsay (ed.). 1972. Micronutrients in agriculture. SSSA, Madison, WI.

Moschler, W.W., G.M. Shear, D.C. Martens, G.D. Jones, and R.R. Wilmouth. 1972. Comparative yield and fertilizer efficiency of no-tillage and conventionally tilled corn. Agron. J. 64:229–231.

Moschler, N.W., and D.C. Martens. 1975. Nitrogen, phosphorus and potassium requirement in the no-tillage and conventionally tilled corn. Soil Sci. Soc. Am. Proc. 39:886–891.

Muhamad, Y.B., M.P. Hoffman, and H.L. Self. 1983. Influence of different ratios of corn and corn silage, housing systems and seasons on performance of feedlot stress. J. Anim. Sci. 56:747–754.

Nelson, D.W. 1982. Gaseous losses of nitrogen other than through denitrification. *In* F.J. Stevenson (ed.) Nitrogen in agricultural soils. Agronomy 22:327–363.

NFDC. 1984. Fertilizer summary data. Natl. Fert. Dev. Ctr., TVA, Muscle Shoals, AL.

Olsen, R.J., R.H. Hensler, O.J. Attoe, S.A. Witzel, and L.A. Peterson. 1970. Fertilizer nitrogen and crop rotation in relation to movement of nitrate nitrogen through soil profiles. Soil Sci. Soc. Am. Proc. 34:448–452.

Olson, P.J. 1930. Planting rates for early varieties of corn. North Dakota Agric. Exp. Stn. Cir. 43:8–9.

Olson, R.A., and A.F. Dreier. 1956. Nitrogen, a key factor in fertilizer phosphorus efficiency. Soil Sci. Soc. Am. Proc. 20:509–514.

Olson, R.A., T.J. Army, J.J. Hanway, and V.J. Kilmer (ed.). 1971. Fertilizer technology and use. 2nd ed. SSSA, Madison, WI.

————, A.F. Dreier, C. Thompson, K. Frank, and P.H. Grabouski. 1964. Using fertilizer nitrogen effectively on grain crops. Nebraska Agric. Exp. Stn. Res. Bull. 479.

————, K.D. Frank, E.J. Deibert, A.F. Dreier, D.H. Sander, and V.A. Johnson. 1976. Impact of residual mineral N in soil on grain protein yields of winter wheat and corn. Agron. J. 68:769–772.

————, ————, P.H. Grabouski, and G.W. Rehm. 1982. Economic and agronomic impacts of varied philosophies of soil testing. Agron. J. 74:492–499.

----, and L.T. Kurtz. 1982. Crop nitrogen requirements, utilization and fertilization. *In* F.J. Stevenson (ed.) Nitrogen in agricultural soils. Agronomy 22:567–604.

----, W.R. Raun, Y.S. Chun, and J. Skopp. 1986. Nitrogen management and interseeding effects on irrigated corn and sorghum and on soil strength. Agron. J. 78:856–862.

----, C.A. Thompson, P.H. Grabouski, D.D. Stukenholtz, K.D. Frank, and A.F. Dreier. 1964. Water requirement of grain crops as modified by fertilizer use. Agron. J. 56:427–432.

Olson, T.C., and L.S. Schoebert. 1970. Corn yields, soil temperature and water use with four tillage methods in the western Corn Belt. Agron. J. 62:229–232.

Oschwald, W.R. 1973. Chisel plow and strip tillage systems. p. 194–202. *In* Conservation tillage. Proc. Natl. Conf., Des Moines, IA. 28–30 March. Soil Conserv. Soc. of Am., Ankeny, IA.

Patterson, R.M., C.S. Hoveland, O.N. Andrews, Jr., and H.L. Webster. 1963. Thick silage spacing—good practice or highly overrated? Highlights Agric. Res. 10(1):9.

Peterson, L.A., and O.J. Attoe. 1965. Importance of soil nitrates in determination of need and recovery of fertilizer nitrogen. Agron. J. 57:572–574.

Phillips, R.E., R.L. Blevins, G.W. Thomas, W.W. Frye, and S.H. Phillips. 1980. No-tillage agriculture. Science (Washington, DC) 208:1108–1113.

Pierre, W.H., S.A. Aldrich, and W.P. Martin (ed.). 1966. Advances in corn production: Principles and practices. Iowa State Univ. Press, Ames.

Poneleit, C.G., and D.B. Egli. 1979. Kernel growth rate and duration in maize as affected by plant density and genotype. Crop Sci. 19:305–388.

Pratt, P.F. 1984. Nitrogen use and nitrate leaching in crop production. p. 319–333. *In* R.D. Hauck (ed.) Nitrogen in crop production. ASA, CSSA, and SSSA, Madison, WI.

Raun, W.R., D.H. Sander, and R.A. Olson. 1986. Emergence of corn as effected by source and rate of solution fertilizers applied with the seed. J. Fert. Issues 3:18–24.

----, ----, and ----. 1987. Phosphorus fertilizer carriers and their placement for minimum till corn under sprinkler irrigation. Soil Sci. Soc. Am. J. 51:1055–1062.

Rice, C.W, and M.S. Smith. 1982. Denitrification in no-till and plowed soils. Soil Sci. Soc. Am. J. 46:1168–1173.

----, ----, and R.L. Blevins. 1986. Soil nitrogen availability after long-term continuous no-tillage and conventional tillage corn production. Soil Sci. Soc. Am. J. 50:1206–1210.

Richards, G.E. (ed.). 1977. Band application of phosphatic fertilizers. Olin Corp., Little Rock, AR.

Rose, S.J., O.C. Burnside, J.E. Specht, and Beth Swisher. 1984. Competition and allelopathy between soybeans and weeds. Agron. J. 76:523–528.

Rossman, E.C., and R.L. Cook. 1966. Soil preparation and date, rate, and pattern of planting. p. 53–101. *In* W.H. Pierre et al. (ed.) Advances in corn production: Principles and practices. Iowa State Univ. Press, Ames.

Rounds, W.T., E.C. Rossman, William Zurakowski, and E.E. Down. 1951. Rate, method, and date of planting corn. Michigan Agric. Exp. Stn. Qt. Bull. 33(4):372–387.

Rumawas, F., B.O. Blair, and R.J. Bula. 1971. Microenvironment and plant characteristics of corn (*Zea mays* L.) planted at two row spacings. Crop Sci. 11:320–323.

Russell, M.B. 1952. Soil aeration and plant growth. *In* B.T. Shaw (ed.) Soil physical conditions and plant growth. Agronomy 2:254–301.

Russelle, M.P., E.J. Deibert, R.D. Hauck, M. Stevanovich, and R.A. Olson. 1981. Effects of water and nitrogen management on yield and ^{15}N-depleted fertilizer use efficiency of irrigated corn. Soil Sci. Soc. Am. J. 45:553–558.

Rutger, J.N., and L.V. Crowder. 1967. Effect of row spacing on corn silage yields. Agron. J. 59:475–476.

Sander, D.H., and E.J. Penas. 1984. Effect of different methods of P fertilizer placement on fertilizer efficiency for winter wheat. p. 219. *In* Agronomy abstract. ASA, Madison, WI.

Sander, K.W., O.C. Burnside, and J.I. Bucy. 1987. Herbicide compatibility and phytotoxicity when mixed with liquid fertilizers. Agron. J. 79:48–52.

Sayre. 1948. Mineral accumulation in corn. Plant Physiol. 23:267–281.

Schepers, J.S., K.D. Frank, and D.G. Watts. 185. Influence of irrigation and nitrogen fertilization on groundwater quality. p. 21–32. *In* F.X. Dunin et al. (ed.) Rotation of groundwater quantity and quality. Proc. Int. Assoc. Hydrological Sci. Symp., Hamburg and Koblenz, West Germany. 25–26 Aug. 1983. IAHS Press, Inst. of Hydrology, Wallingford, Oxfordshire, England.

Shapiro, C.A., D.L. McCallister, W.R. Raun, F.N. Anderson, G.W. Rehm, O.P Engelstad, M.P. Russelle, and R.A. Olson. 1987. Rate of phosphorous and potassium buildup/decline with fertilization for corn and wheat on Nebraska Mollisols. Soil Sci. Soc. Am. J. 51:1646–1652.

Sharpee, K.W., A.E. Ludwick, and O.J. Attoe. 1969. Availability of zinc, copper and iron in fusions with sulfur. Agron. J. 61:746–749.

Shaw, L.H., and D.D. Durost. 1965. The effect of weather and technology on corn yields in the Corn Belt, 1929–1962. USDA Econ. Res. Serv. Agric. Econ. Rep. 80. U.S. Gov. Print. Office, Washington, DC.

Shear, G.M., and W.W. Moschler. 1969. Continuous corn by the no-tillage and conventional tillage methods: A six year comparison. Agron. J. 61:524–526.

Schrader, W.D., and J.J. Pierre. 1966. Soil suitability and cropping systems. p. 1–25. In W.H. Pierre et al. (ed.) Advances in corn production: Principles and practices. Iowa State Univ. Press, Ames.

Singh, T.A., G.W. Thomas, W.W. Moschler, and D.C. Martens. 1966. Phosphorus uptake by corn (Zea mays L.) under no-tillage and conventional practices. Agron. J. 58:147–148.

Skidmore, E.L., and N.P. Woodruff. 1968. Wind erosion forces in the United States and their use in predicting soil loss. USDA Agric. Handb. 346. USDA, Washington, DC.

Slatyer, Ro.O. 1969. Physiological significance of internal water relations to crop yields. p. 53–79. In J.D. Eastin et al. (ed.) Physiological aspects of crop yield. Proc. Am. Soc. of Agron., CSSA and Univ. of Nebraska, Lincoln. 20–24 January. ASA, Madison, WI.

Spiva, C. 1980. The case for banding. Solutions 24(5):14–24.

Sprague, G.F., and W.E. Larson. 1966. Corn production, USDA Agric. Handb. 322. U.S. Gov. Print. Office, Washington, DC.

Stanford, G., and L.B. Nelson. 1949. Utilization of phosphorus as affected by placement: I. Corn in Iowa. Soil Sci. 68:129–135.

Stickler, F.C. 1964. Row width and plant population studies with corn. Agron. J. 56:438–441.

————, and H.H. Laude. 1960. Effect of row spacing and plant population on performance of corn, grain sorghum, and forage sorghum. Agron. J. 52:275–277.

Stivers, R.K., D.R. Griffith, and E.P. Christmas. 1971. Corn performance in relation to row spacings, populations, and hybrids on five soils in Indiana. Agron. J. 63:580–582.

Stringfield, G.H. 1956. Corn culture. In G.F. Sprague (ed.) Corn and corn improvement. Agronomy 5:343–378.

Sumner, M.E. 1977. Use of the DRIS system in foliar diagnosis of crops at high yield levels. Commun. Soil Sci. Plant Anal. 8:251–268.

Sweetman, H.L. 1958. The principles of biological control. Wm. C. Brown Co., Dubuque, IA.

Templeton, G.E., D.O. Tebeest, and R.J. Smith, Jr. 1976. Development of an endemic fungal pathogen as a mycoherbicide for biological control of northern joint vetch in rice. p. 214–216. In Proc. 4 Int. Symp. Biol. Control Weeds. Center for Environ. Prog., Inst. of Food and Agric. Sci., Gainesville, Fl. 30 August–2 September. Univ. of Florida, Gainesville.

Thomas, G.W., R.L. Blevins, R.E. Phillips, and M.A. McMohan. 1973. Effect of killed sod mulch on nitrate movement and corn yield. Agron. J. 65:736–739.

Thompson, L.M. 1966. Regional weather realtions. p. 143–154. In W.H. Pierre et al. (ed.) Advances in corn production: Principles and practices. Iowa State Univ. Press, Ames.

Tisdale, S.L. 1970. The use of sulphur compounds in irrigated soil-land agriculture. Sulphur Inst. 6(1):2–7.

Tollenaar, M., and T.B. Daynard. 1978. Relationship between assimilate source and reproductive sink in maize grown in a short-season environment. Agron. J. 70:219–223.

Triplett, E.B., Jr., and D.M. Van Doren, Jr. 1969. Nitrogen, phosphorus and potassium fertilization of non-tilled maize. Agron. J. 61:637–639.

————, ————, and S.W. Bone. 1973. An evaluation of Ohio soils in relation to no-tillage corn production. Ohio Agric. Res. and Dev. Ctr. Res. Bull. 1068.

————, ————, and B.L. Schmidt. 1968. Effect of corn (Zea mays L.) stover mulch on no-tillage corn yield and water infiltration. Agron. J. 60:236–239.

Turnquist, P.K., H. Waelti, and L.A. Mathison. 1970. Till planting corn. South Dakota State Univ. Bull. 567.

Van Bavel, C.H.M. 1949. Mean weight-diameter of soil aggregates as a statistical index of aggregation. Soil Sci. Soc. Am. Proc. 14:20–23.

Van Doren, D.M., Jr., G.B. Triplett, Jr., and J.E. Henry. 1976. Influence of long term tillage, crop rotation, and soil type combinations on corn yield. Soil Sci. Soc. Am. J. 40:100–105.

Van Schilfgaarde, J. 1974. Drainage for agriculture. Agronomy 17.

Viets, F.G., Jr. 1962. Fertilizers and the efficient use of water. *In* A.G. Norman (ed.) Adv. Agron. 14:223–261.

Wapshere, A.J. 1982. Biological control of weeds. p. 47–56. *In* W. Holzner and M. Numata (ed.) Biology and ecology of weeds. Kluwer Boston, Hingham, MA.

Wehrmann, J., and H.C. Scharf. 1979. The mineral nitrogen of soil as a measure of fertilizer nitrogen requirement. Plant Soil 52:109–126.

Welch, L.F., P.E. Johnson, G.E. McKibben, L.V. Boone, and J.W. Pendleton. 1966. Relative efficiency of broadcast versus banded potassium for corn. Agron. J. 58:618–621.

––––, D.L. Mulvaney, L.V. Boone, G.E. McKibben, and J.W. Pendleton. 1966. Relative efficiency of broadcast versus banded phosphorus for corn. Agron. J. 58:283–287.

––––, ––––, M.G. Oldham, L.V. Boone, and J.W. Pendleton. 1971. Corn yields with fall, spring, and sidedress nitrogen. Agron. J. 63:528–533.

Wesseling, J., and W.R. Van Wijk. 1957. Soil physical conditions in relation to drain depth. *In* J.N. Luthin (ed.) Drainage of agricultural lands. Agronomy 7:461–504.

Westerman, R.L., and M.G. Edlund. 1985. Deep placement effects of nitrogen and phosphorus on grain yield, nutrient uptake and forage quality of winter wheat. Agron. J. 77:803–809.

Whitaker, F.D., H.C. Heinemann, and W.E. Larson. 1969. Plant populations and row spacing influence on corn yield. Missouri Agric. Exp. Stn. Res. Bull. 961.

Wiidakas, W. 1958. Is early maturing corn more dependable? N.D. Farm Res. 20(5):4–10.

Williamson, R.E. 1964. The effect of root aeration on plant growth. Soil Sci. Soc. Am. Proc. 28:86–90.

Willis, W.O., and M. Amemiya. 1973. Tillage management principles. Soil temperature effects. p. 22–42. *In* Conservation tillage. Proc. Natl. Conf. Des Moines, IA. 28–30 March. Soil Conserv. Soc. Am., Ankeny, IA.

Wilson, H.A., R. Gish, and G.M. Browning, 1947. Cropping systems and season as affecting aggregate stability. Soil Sci. Soc. Am. Proc. 12:36–38.

Wischmeier, W.H. 1973. Conservation tillage to control water erosion. p. 133–141. *In* Conservation tillage. Proc. Natl. Conf., Des Moines, IA. 28–30 March. Soil Conserv. Soc. Am., Ankeny, IA.

Wischmeier, W.J., and D.D. Smith. 1978. Predicting rainfall erosion loss. A guide to conservation planning. USDA Agric. Handb. 537. USDA, Washington, DC.

Witmuss, H.D., D.E. Lane, and B.R. Somerholder. 1971. Strip till planting of row crops through surface residues. Trans. ASAE 14:60–63, 68.

Yao, A.Y.M., and R.H. Shaw. 1964. Effect of plant population and planting pattern of corn on water use and yield. Agron. J. 56:147–152.

Zabyalyendzik, S.F. 1973. Allelopathic interaction of buckwheat and its components through root excretions. Vyestsi Akad. Nauuk BSSR Syer Biyal Nauuk 5:31–34. (As cited in Rice, E.L. 1974. Pest control with nature's chemicals: Allelochemics and pheromones in gardening and agriculture. Univ. of Oklahoma Press, Norman.

Zook, L.L., and W.W. Burr. 1923. Sixteen years' grain production at the North Platte Substation. Nebraska Agric. Exp. Stn. Bull. 193.

Zuber, M.S., C.O. Grogan, and D.V. Singleton. 1960. Rate of planting studies with prolific and single ear corn hybrids. Missouri Agric. Exp. Stn. Res. Bull. 737.

12 Diseases of Corn

D. R. SMITH

DEKALB-PFIZER GENETICS
DeKalb, Illinois

D. G. WHITE

University of Illinois
Urbana, Illinois

Human sustenance relies on plants. Nourishment depends upon either direct consumption of cereal or tuber crops or their indirect consumption as they are passed through animals in the food chain. The three major cereals are wheat (*Triticum aestivum* L.), rice (*Oryza sativa* L.), and corn (*Zea mays* L.). Each of these cereals has had notable epiphytotics (plant disease epidemics). Wheat has been plagued with its rusts, rice with brown spot, and corn with southern corn leaf blight (caused by *Bipolaris maydis*). The results of these epiphytotics have ranged from the loss of human life due to famine to the loss of monetary returns to societies growing these crops.

Disease is the result of a condition in which the use or structure of any part of an organism is impaired. While corn is considered a relatively healthy plant, it rarely, if ever, is grown in the absence of disease. Losses that do occur are expressed in a reduction in either the quantity or quality of the harvested crop. This is true for corn grown for cash grain as well as silage, popcorn, sweetcorn, decorative corn, or the inbred parents used in the production of hybrid corn seeds. Corn is affected by both biotic and abiotic agents. In this chapter both types of causal agents will be addressed. The use of illustrations will be limited; excellent visual representation of more corn diseases are available elsewhere (De Leon, 1984; Shurtleff, 1980) and their use is highly recommended.

Estimates made of disease losses for corn in the USA caused by all pathogens have ranged from 2 to 7 (Ullstrup, 1955) to 7 to 17% yearly (Shurtleff, 1980). The year of greatest deviation was 1970. In that year the estimated loss of the corn crop credited to a single pathogen was 15%. The pathogen involved was a previously undescribed race of a well-known fungus, *B. maydis*, which causes southern corn leaf blight. The monetary loss from this disease was a staggering $1 billion loss to the agricultural economy of the USA. In food chain equivalents it has been expressed as a loss equating to over 30 billion quarter-pound hamburgers (Horsfall, 1975). While the economic losses incurred during 1970 were great, a point of extreme significance is that there was no loss of human life due to famine which has accompanied major epiphytotics on other crops. With the existing corn reserves and by moving other staples into the food chain, adquate foodstuffs were available to nourish citizens of the USA.

It is the responsibility of the plant pathologist to assist in attempts to minimize crop losses caused by disease. Because of its stature as a food and feed crop, its genetics, and its adaptability to most environments, corn and its diseases can serve as a model system by which certain principles of plant disease development and disease control can be understood and practiced to accomplish the pathologist's responsibility.

12-1 INTRODUCTION

12-1.1 Principles of Disease Development

The initiation of disease caused by biotic agents depends upon three main factors, the host, the environment, and the pathogen. The severity of disease development is dependent on the degree of interaction of these factors in a time frame conducive to further reproduction or replication, dissemination, and reinfection by the pathogen. Epiphytotics develop only when all variables work together.

12-1.1.1 Host

The inherent susceptibility of the host is often the determining factor in disease development. Susceptibility implies no impediment to a pathogen by the host. Resistance is a form of susceptibility that measurably impedes a pathogen when appropriate comparisons are made. Some common comparisons qualifying that the host exhibits resistance include lesion type differences, lesion number differences, pathogen reproduction differences, lack of response by the host to pathotoxins, structural formation differences of a host in response to a pathogen, and/or the production of a phytoalexin by the host when challenged by a pathogen. A host that exhibits restricted or fewer lesions, retards reproduction of a pathogen, does not respond to pathotoxins, forms structures to hinder a pathogen, or produces a phytoalexin is considered to be more resistant than a host that does not. The degree of resistance expressed is dependent on the ability to scale the differences observed.

Resistance is heritable. For corn, three types of resistances, based on their inheritance, are exploited to reduce disease. These are oligogenic, polygenic, and cytoplasmic types of resistances.

Oligogenic resistances are simply inherited and in theory are easy to incorporate into existing varieties. They are usually dramatic in their level of protection against a specific pathogen or race of a pathogen, but suffer because they are more prone to being negated as the pathogen changes. They are usually completely dominant or recessive in their action. Dominant oligogenic resistances are more useful than recessives, especially in hybrid corn, because only one of the inbred parents or one side of the pedigree requires the presence of the resistance to protect the resulting hybrid.

Polygenic resistances are controlled by a number of genes. Their incorporation into existing varieties is much more complex, but these resistances are considered to be more stable and enduring than oligogenic resistance.

Cytoplasmic resistance resides in the hereditary units within the cytoplasm. These units are believed to be located primarily within the chloroplasts and mitochondria. Inheritance is through the maternal parent. This type of resistance can easily be incorporated into existing varieties by backcrossing the recurrent parent onto the cytoplasmic sources desired.

Currently, most corn germ plasm used in hybrids in the USA is being selected in regular corn breeding nurseries for acceptable levels of resistance to common diseases to which the resulting hybrids would be most likely exposed. However, certain diseases occur in such restricted geographic areas that specialized nurseries and breeding efforts are required to identify resistant germ plasm to satisfy those markets. As these and other diseases become more widespread or important they are generally incorporated as a screening tool into the routine germplasm selection process. Since the acceptance of hybrid corn, vast progress has been made in the development of varieties with acceptable levels of resistance to many diseases. The degree of improvement has not been documented largely because growers readily substitute resistant varieties with equal or superior performance over varieties that may be susceptible to a disease in their growing area.

12.1.1.2 Environment

Corn and the biotic agents capable of causing diseases have coevolved throughout the millennia. It is logical to assume that those environments conducive to corn growth also favor the pathogens that can attack corn.

Corn pathogens and the diseases they cause fit specific environmental niches. Northern corn leaf blight is most commonly seen in humid areas where temperatures are moderate, whereas southern corn leaf blight is favored by warmer temperatures. Common corn rust occurs in most of the environments where corn is grown, while southern corn rust is usually restricted in its development to warmer climates. Goss's wilt is associated with geographic areas of the USA where hail is common because of the type of plant injury required for this disease to become established. For crazy top to develop, complete soil saturation or flooding of the young corn crop is required. Therefore, its occurrence is commonly associated with low, poorly drained fields. While the pathogens causing these diseases may be widespread, their particular environmental adaptation may limit the ability of the disease they cause to develop further.

Factors such as rainfall, temperature, hail, wind damage, the presence of insect vectors, and humidity can have a pronounced effect on disease initiation and its subsequent development. Most fungal pathogens require free water at favorable temperatures on corn tissues for germination and active penetration into the corn plant. Hail or wind damage resulting in tissue injury in combination with free water allows passive entry of many bacterial pathogens into the corn plant. Insect vectors that serve as reservoirs of some bacterial or viral pathogens can introduce these pathogens into corn when they are feeding. Conditions of high humidity favor reproduction of many fungal pathogens that cause local lesions and greatly influences further disease development.

Fertility, soil drainage, pH, light levels, tillage practices, and cropping sequence can have an indirect effect on disease development. Corn grown at less than optimum fertility, soil aeration levels, pH, or light levels is more stressed than corn grown at optimum levels of these factors. These stresses can result in higher disease development by the corn being predisposed to infection and less hearty than when grown under less stress. Tillage practices and cropping sequence can influence the amount of disease development by providing an overseasoning site of many pathogens in sufficient numbers to establish infection in the new crop. Reduced tillage that allows corn debris to remain on the soil surface and the continuous cropping of corn greatly increase the chances of many corn pathogens becoming established, surviving between cropping seasons, and increasing in their severity across years.

12.1.1.3 The Pathogen

A pathogen is a reproducing or replicating disease-inciting agent. Certain fungi, bacteria, viruses, nematodes, and at least one mycoplasma, one spiroplasma, and one parasitic seed plant are pathogens of corn in the USA. These pathogens may vary in their pathogenicity, race, or strain constituency within a single species, adaptability to specific environments, and geographic area of recognized occurrence.

Before a reproducing or replicating entity is described as being a corn pathogen, it must be shown to satisfy four main criteria. These are: (i) the biotic entity suspected of being a pathogen must be associated with a particular symptom of a diseased plant; (ii) it must be isolated and/or cultured and characterized under artificial conditions away from the infected plant; (iii) when inoculated back onto the same genotype, it must produce the same type of symptom as was initially observed; and (iv) it must be reisolated and exhibit the same traits as characterized under (ii). While symptoms of the disease and signs of the suspected pathogen are important aids in disease diagnosis, only when the previous criteria are met is the proof of pathogenicity completed and the suspected disease-inciting agent classified a pathogen.

In reality, what is generally considered to be a specific pathogen is probably a mixture of races or strains that are morphologically indistinguishable. The term *race* or *strain* denotes the observation of measurable differences between isolates of the same pathogen. These may be seen as pathogenicity differences between isolates inoculated across a set of dissimilar hosts or between isolates inoculated across a set of different genotypes within a single host. The term race is usually associated with fungal pathogens where a gene for gene relationship has been shown. That is, for each gene-conditioning resistance in the host there is a corresponding gene-conditioning virulence in the pathogen (Flor, 1942, 1955). The formation of races can negate advances made in breeding for disease resistance. The term strain is usually associated with viral pathogens where differences of pathogenicity have been observed between viral isolates but where a gene for gene relationship has yet to be conclusively demonstrated.

Corn pathogens vary in their area of occurrence, shifting geographically with time. The fungus, which causes sorghum downy mildew of corn, was originally observed in India during 1907. It was observed in the USA in 1963. Since 1963, it has been identified in Alabama, Arkansas, Florida, Georgia, Illinois, Indiana, Kentucky, Louisiana, Mississippi, Missouri, Nebraska, New Mexico, Oklahoma, and Tennessee. This example of the movement of a pathogen of foreign origin has been monitored closely because of the potential severity of the disease it causes. Pathogen movement has also been documented for the fungus causing Helminthosporium leaf spot. This fungus was originally described in the eastern USA and has recently been shown to be moving westward. While these examples do demonstrate the movement of pathogens into/or across the USA, some care should be taken in assuming that the occurrence of a disease from a locality where it was previously undescribed indicates the recent movement of the pathogen into that locality. It may be that the pathogen was present for a number of cropping seasons prior to its detection and that either the environment or corn germ plasm grown in that locality suppressed the development of the disease below recognizable levels. By monitoring the movement of corn pathogens as an adjunct to observing disease development, epiphytotics may be avoided by employing appropriate control measures (Smith, 1977, 1984; Young et al., 1978).

12-1.2 Principles of Disease Control

Five principles of controlling corn diseases are exclusion, eradication, avoidance, protection, and the use of resistant corn cultivars.

Exclusion is an attempt to prevent the introduction of a pathogen into an area in which that pathogen did not previously exist. Quarantines are the primary regulatory vehicle by which exclusion is practiced. Currently, the USA imposes quarantines against the routine importation of corn from various parts of the world. The most common corn diseases of potential concern cited in these quarantines are downy mildews and the parasitic seed plant, witchweed [*Striga asiatica* (L.) Ktze]. Internal quarantines within a country are also sometimes imposed. A recent example is the regulation of articles (soil, roots with soil, grass sod, root crops with soil attached, mechanized farm equipment used for soil tillage, custom farm equipment used for soil treatment, or mechanized soil-moving equipment used to move or transport soil) that might spread the corn cyst nematode out of the localized areas of Maryland in which it presently exists into other corn-growing areas.

Eradication is an attempt to eliminate or greatly reduce the pathogen after it has become established in a specific area. Crop rotation, sanitation, and the elimination of overseasoning hosts of corn pathogens are commonly used methods of eradication. The use of crop rotation can reduce the perpetuation and intensification of many corn pathogens when compared to the practice of continuous cropping of corn. Sanitation, which consists of the removal of diseased plants or plant parts prior to further dissemination of the pathogen, is rarely used in the USA as a means of eradication. An example of sanitation is the removal of plants infected with head smut prior to release of the fungal spores from the galls. This practice has been used in Mexico to attempt to reduce the incidence of the head smut pathogen in certain fields. The eradication of overseasoning hosts of corn pathogens can also lower the probability of occurrence of certain corn diseases. By removing or controlling johnsongrass [*Sorghum halepense* (L.) Pers.], a perennial weed that harbors many viruses capable of attacking corn, the source of inoculum is eliminated or greatly reduced.

Avoidance is a means of escaping infection or reducing the intensity of disease. If corn is grown in areas free of specific pathogens then the diseases caused by these pathogens are avoided. The movement of the major sweet corn growing areas into the mid- to northern Corn Belt of the USA avoids major outbreaks of bacterial wilt and bacterial leaf blight. By planting in a timely fashion or at a time unfavorable to a corn pathogen's infection or disease development, the crop can be managed and harvested prior to disease buildup, and potential losses due to disease may be avoided.

Protection of the corn crop from diseases is accomplished largely through the use of chemical control measures. These are targeted to reduce the intensity of disease development by adversely affecting the pathogen, or when a disease is spread by an insect vector, controlling that vector. The cost of protecting the crop, as compared to that crop's value, determine the extent of use of chemical control measures. The seed of commercial corn cultivars is treated with fungicides to help prevent losses from seed rots and seedling blights that can occur if adverse environmental conditions occur shortly after planting. Foliar fungicides are used on seed production fields, commercial popcorn, and sweet corn fields to protect them from potential yield losses caused by foliar diseases. This is justified because of the value of these types of corn crops. Currently, no routine chemical control of diseases on grain or silage crops is used because of the narrow margin of profitability of these crops. Similar types of decisions are involved in protecting the various corn crops against insects that vector certain corn diseases.

The principles of exclusion, eradication, avoidance, and protection attempt to exclude or limit the corn pathogen prior to its coming into contact with the corn plant. Methods involved in utilizing these principles of disease control can be affected by weather conditions, mechanical failure of equipment, misapplication of chemicals, subtle changes in the distribution of pathogens, and improper planning.

The use of resistant cultivars allows intimate contact between the pathogen and the corn plant. Resistance is less affected by external factors or management decisions than other disease control measures. Resistant cultivars offer the most feasible control of corn diseases and are the most widely used method of corn disease control. No one commercially acceptable corn cultivar expresses resistance to all corn diseases. However, numerous cultivars are available that contain satisfactory resistance to the most common diseases in the area in which these cultivars are most likely to be marketed. As well-known pathogens change or as new pathogens are identified, additional types of resistance will be needed and incorporated into commercially acceptable corn cultivars.

12–2 DISEASES INDUCED BY BIOTIC AGENTS

12–2.1 Seed Rots and Seedling Blights

Seed rot and seedling blight diseases are not usually of widespread importance, but are a problem in localized areas every year. Seed may be rotted prior to or shortly after germination. Seedlings that do emerge may have rotted roots and stems resulting in less vigorous plants which may die. Seed rot and seedling blights are usually more prevalent when seed produced in drought years or years with early frosts is planted in cool soil (below 13 °C) or wherever misplacement of fertilizer or misuse of herbicides and other pesticides are involved. Seedling blight and seed rot rarely occur when injury-free seed of high germination (produced under favorable environment) is planted in a well-prepared seed bed with warm, moist soil.

A number of factors interact to determine the germination of seed under adverse conditions. These include genetics, environment in which the seed was produced, stage of maturity at harvest, seed size, seed weight, structural integrity, deterioration (after harvest), and pathogens present. No standardized test exists whereby percent germination in all types of adverse conditions can be predicted. Various types of cold tests or vigor tests have been developed and are being used to predict germination in adverse conditions (McDonald, 1975; AOSA, 1983). Improved methods of hybrid seed production and handling, improved mechanical planters, and the use of fungicide seed treatments have greatly reduced losses from seed rot and seedling blights. Since high-quality seed with rapid emergence is demanded by farmers, improvements should continue.

A large number of fungi and bacteria may be involved in seed rot and seedling blight diseases. These organisms can be divided into two groups. One group being those pathogens that are in or on the seed at planting and the other being those pathogens that are in soil in which the seed is planted.

Fungi associated with seed at planting are usually ear-rotting fungi. The most common fungus associated with seed is *Fusarium moniliforme* Sheld. This fungus can be found associated with a large number of kernels but rarely causes problems with seed germination of dent corn. To a lesser extent, other fungi such as *Penicillium* spp., *Aspergillus* spp., *Rhizoctonia* spp., *Drechslera* spp., *Alternaria* spp., *Nigrospora* spp., *Trichoderma* spp., *F. graminearum* Schw., and *Diplodia maydis* (Berk.) Sacc. are also found associated with hybrid seed. The amount of damage caused by these fungi depends on the extent of rotting that has occurred before harvest and conditioning of seed. If rot is extensive, the embryo may be killed and the seed will not germinate. Usually severely rotted seed is removed from hybrid seed lots with gravity tables. Seed lots containing rotted seed are also easily detected by warm germination tests. In many cases, seed that is not severely rotted will germinate when planted into environments that are favorable for germination. When this seed is planted in unfavorable environments, germination is slow and the internal fungi have an opportunity to rot the developing seedling. Since most fungicides that are used on seed corn are not systemic, those fungi established within seed at planting are not controlled.

The second group of organisms that are involved with seed rot and seedling blights are those that are found in soil in which the seed is planted. These organisms would include those which are also involved in kernel rots as well as other fungi. The species involved with seed rot and seedling root rot depend on location, soil conditions, and crop sequence. The most common soil fungi that can cause seed rot and decay of seedling roots are *Pythium* spp. Pythium seed rot and seedling blight is most serious in cool, wet soils, particularly with pericarp damaged seed. Cool conditions slow the growth of the plant and allow fungi more time to kill the seedling plant. High moisture results in an increase of leachates that stimulate germination of oospores as well as low oxygen conditions that favor the growth of *Pythium* spp. and reduce root development. Pericarp damaged seed is more readily attacked by fungi because of increased leachates and damaged areas that serve as sites for penetration by fungi. Some of the *Pythium* spp. that have been associated with seed rot and seedling blight include: *Pythium irregulare* Buisman, *P. debaryanum* Hesse, *P. ultimum* Trow., *P. rostratum* Butler, *P. paroecandrum* Drechs., and *P. vexans* de Bary (Hoppe and Middleton, 1950).

More than likely *Pythium* spp. and other fungi interact to attack the seed and root system of a plant rather than acting as a single organism.

Control of soil organisms is provided by selecting high-quality seed and seed treatments. Nonsystemic fungicidal seed treatments surround the seed when it is planted. This provides a barrier between the seed and soilborne fungi. As soon as roots grow away from the soil zone in which the seed treatment is found, they are subject to attack by fungi. The use of cold testing of hybrid seed provides some indication as to how seed will germinate in cool wet conditions, however, cold tests are not uniform in that different methods are used. Most take into account the genetic susceptibility of the hybrid and pericarp damage, and provide some indication of potential seed rot and seedling blight in cool soils.

Another occasionally observed seedling blight disease is caused by *Penicillium oxalicum* Thom. (Johann et al., 1931). Unlike most other seed rot and seedling diseases, this disease is favored by higher temperatures. Symptoms are normally a necrosis of the leaf tip which may occur in streaks or large areas. Later these areas will become brittle. Another symptom is that entire plants are chlorotic and these seedlings usually die. This condition has been associated with damage to the pericarp and penetration of *P. oxalicum*. Plants that survive are usually stunted and yellow.

Another condition that is occasionally observed, particularly from damaged seed produced during a drought year, are plants with striped leaves. These stripes are narrow and white and usually occur only on young plants. Upper leaves of the plant are free from striping, particularly those above the ear shoot. This disease was first described as being caused by *Aspergillus flavus* Link and *A. tamarii* Kita (Koehler and Woodworth, 1938). Virescence due to *Aspergillus* spp. may be confused with genetic virescence. Symptoms are basically the same in that striping occurs on leaves of seedlings. In the case of virescence caused by *Aspergillus* spp., however, the condition is associated with pericarp damage and the penetration of *Aspergillus* spp. into the embryo. Normally plants that are not severely affected will outgrow this condition. This condition has been noted in Illinois since 1976 with seed produced during drought years. The fungus isolated from affected seed was *A. flavus*.

Rapid seedling emergence and resistance to various seed rot and seedling blight diseases are heritable characteristics. Breeding efforts in this area are complicated by the large number of organisms and environmental factors involved. No single method can be used in evaluation of particular genotypes for rapid emergence in all conditions and for resistance to seed and seedling diseases. However, those hybrids that have potential problems are identified in the testing of experimental hybrids over numerous locations and are seldom advanced to the commercial level.

12-2.2 Midseason Foliar and Other Local Infection Diseases

Regardless of the pathogens that attack corn foliage, their effect on the plants is largely the same. Initially, there is a reduction of total leaf area. This alone can account for significant losses to the corn crop grown for silage. If enough tissue is destroyed in the grain crop, the leaves will not be able to produce sufficient photosynthate to satisfy the plants' needs. With plants exposed to high levels of foliar infection, the grain-filling process can be impaired to the point that direct losses will result. Even under marginal infection levels there is an effect on the infected plants. Grain filling may be nearly normal but the ear will develop at the expense of the stalk. This results in the plants affected by the foliar disease becoming more susceptible to common stalk rotting pathogens.

Since the corn-disease information was prepared for the second edition of *Corn and Corn Improvement*, two additional races of *Exserohilum turcicum*, which causes northern corn leaf blight, and one additional race of *Bipolaris zeicola*, which causes Helminthosporium leaf spot, have been described within the USA. Gray leaf spot of corn, caused by *Cercospora zeae-maydis*, is still increasing in its prevalence; but *Phyllosticta maydis*, which causes yellow leaf blight, and race T of *Bipolaris maydis*, which causes southern corn leaf blight, have declined dramatically.

12–2.2.1 Bacterial Leaf Blight and Stalk Rot

A disease expressing symptoms of bacterial leaf blight and a soft stalk rot in the upper part of the stalks was first reported in 1929 (Johnson et al., 1929). Since then, it has been reported as occurring sporadically in many southern and central states of the USA (Johnson et al., 1945).

A bacterium, *Pseudomonas avenae* Manns [Syn. = *Pseudomonas alboprecipitans* Rosen; *Bacterium alboprecipitans* Rosen; *Phytomonas alboprecipitans* (Rosen) Bergey et al.] is the disease-inciting agent (Schaad et al., 1975). It is a polar-flagellated, Gram-negative rod which measures $0.6 \times 1.6 \ \mu$m.

Symptoms of this disease on corn include water-soaked linear lesions on the leaves as they emerge from the whorl. The lesions become necrotic with straw-colored centers and brown margins as they age. Shredding of the leaves is common. Stalks which become infected exhibit a soft rot usually around or above the node of ear attachment. Tops of plants with infected stalks may die.

Bacterial leaf blight and stalk rot have been of minor importance. Infection is favored by periods of overcast and wet weather (Sumner and Schaad, 1977). Contaminated farm equipment and ditchbank weeds have been implicated as reservoirs of primary inoculum (Gitaitis et al., 1978).

While most corn cultivars appear resistant to the bacterium (Sumner and Schaad, 1977), further control could be obtained from the utilization of clean cropping practices and controlling weeds bordering fields.

12–2.2.2 Bacterial Stripe

Bacterial stripe of corn was first reported in 1960 even though the disease occurred years earlier (Ullstrup, 1960). Since its original description, the disease has been observed sporadically in the western and northern Corn Belt states (Vidaver and Carlson, 1978).

The disease-inciting agent is a Gram-negative, motile by a single polar-flagellum, bacterial rod measuring 1.5 to 2.5 × 0.5 to 0.8 μm. It is named *Pseudomonas andropogonis* (Smith) Stapp [Syn. = *Bacterium andropogoni* Smith; *Phytomonas andropogoni* (Smith) Bergey et al.].

Two types of symptoms seem to be associated with this disease. The first symptom described involved corn leaves which expressed amber- to olive-colored, oil-soaked, translucent lesions which were elongate, generally parallel-sided and tending to coalesce (Plate 12-1). Infected tissue was gorged with bacteria. Extremely susceptible inbred lines of corn exhibited chlorotic striping of the whorl leaves and distortion of the upper internodes (Ullstrup, 1960). In 1978, symptoms, consisting of circular to ellipsoidal, tan to brown spots, 1 to 4 mm in diameter, with one or more darker brown rings within the lesions, were observed. Some of these spots were surrounded by a chlorotic ring. Sometimes the spots coalesced into irregular, elongated blotches. These symptoms were atypical of previous descriptions of bacterial stripe but the pathogen was determined as being *P. andropogonis* (Vidaver and Carlson, 1978). These observations indicate different strains of the bacterium may be involved in this disease.

This disease is favored by warm, wet weather, and infection is through stomata of water-soaked leaves. It is considered to be of little economic importance on corn.

12-2.2.3 Bacterial Wilt and Bacterial Leaf Blight

Bacterial wilt and bacterial leaf blight, first reported in the USA in 1897 (Stewart, 1897), has also been called bacterial wilt, Stewart's wilt, Stewart's disease, Stewart's leaf blight and maize bacteriosis. Since its initial identification, it has been found in most corn-growing areas of the USA and many other parts of the world. It most often occurs in the south central Corn Belt eastward to the Atlantic coast in the USA. An entire monograph has been devoted to this disease (Pepper, 1967).

This disease is caused by the bacterium, *Erwinia stewartii* (E.F. Smith) Dye. Other synonyms which have been associated with this bacterium include: *Pseudomonas stewarti* E.F. Smith; *Bacterium stewarti* E.F. Smith; *Aplanobacter stewarti* (E.F. Smith) McCulloch; *Bacillus stewartii* (E.F. Smith) Holland; *Phytomonas stewarti* (E.F. Smith) Bergey et al.; and *Xanthomonas stewarti* (E.F. Smith) Dowson. The bacterium is a nonflagellate, nonmotile, nonspore-forming, Gram-negative rod measuring 0.4 to 0.8 × 0.9 to 2.2 μm. Colonies on nutrient-glucose agar are cream-yellow to orange-yellow. Virulence has been shown to be correlated with colony appearance (Ivanoff et al., 1938; Lindstrom, 1938; Wellhausen, 1937a). Those colonies exhibiting most virulence were large, watery, smooth, spreading, and mucoid; avirulent colonies were small, raised, and nonmucoid. Virulence can be increased through successive passage of the bacterium through resistant corn stocks (Wellhausen, 1937a) or at least maintained by culturing on media having sources of inorganic N (McNew, 1938).

Two phases of this disease have been described. One phase affects young plants which can become systemically infected and exhibit pale green-gray linear water-soaked lesions with irregular-wavy margins, stunting, and wilting leading to death of the plants. Cavities may form in severely infected plants in the stalk pith near the soil line. Bacterial masses ooze from the cut end of infected stalks or leaves. Kernels from severely infected plants have been shown to harbor the bacterium, resulting in low levels of seed transmission (Frutchey, 1936). Sweet corn hybrids are generally more susceptible to the wilting phase than are other corn hybrids. The other and more common phase of this disease is a leaf-blighting phase. This phase, if present, is usually seen after tasseling. Lesions which are gray-green to yellow-green will develop as streaks on the leaves (Plate 12–1). These lesions are almost always associated with flea beetle feeding scars.

The corn flea beetle (*Chaetocnema pulicaria* Melsheimer) is the primary vector and overwintering site of the bacterium (Elliott and Poos, 1934). The ability of the beetle to survive mild winters is closely linked to the severity of the disease the next growing season (Castor et al., 1975; Haenseler, 1937; Stevens, 1934; Stevens and Haenseler, 1941). This finding leads to accurate forecasting of the severity of bacertial wilt and leaf blight based on winter temperatures. The disease severity is expected to be great following winters whose sum of mean temperatures (°C) for December, January, and February exceed 37 to 38 °C while the disease will be absent or occur only slightly when the sum of mean temperatures for those months is 32 °C or below.

Following artificial inoculations many diverse host plants were identified (Pepper, 1967). However, under conditions of natural infection only corn, teosinte (*Z. mays* ssp. *mexicana* (Schrad.) Iltis], and eastern gamagrass [*Tripsacum dactyloides* (L.)] have been reported as hosts of *E. stewartii*.

In the absence of natural disease occurrence, artificial inoculations have been developed to evaluate corn materials. Techniques include a leaf cut with immediate application of a bacterial suspension (Lockwood and Williams, 1957) and a pinprick method of inoculation (Blanco et al., 1977; Chang et al., 1977).

To control this disease; insecticides can be used to reduce feeding by the corn flea beetles (Heichel et al., 1977), but the most practical means of control is the use of resistant cultivars. In fact, after the epiphytotic of bacterial wilt and leaf blight of 1932 and 1933, resistant sweet corn hybrids were developed and quickly replaced the more susceptible cultivars in the marketplace (Smith, 1940). In corn, resistance to *E. stewartii* is highly heritable, appears to be mostly dominant with some additive gene action, and is controlled by relatively few genes (Blanco et al., 1979; Forgey et al., 1982; Parker, 1980; Smith, 1971; Wellhausen, 1937b). Resistance has also been correlated to vigor, lateness, plant height, resistance to northern corn leaf blight, and resistance to Goss's wilt (Ivanoff, 1936; Ivanoff and Riker, 1936; Koehler, 1955; Pataky, 1985). Currently, the use of resistant cultivars of all corns and the northward movement of the sweet corn canning industry has reduced the significance of bacterial wilt and leaf blight.

12–2.2.4 Chocolate Spot

Chocolate spot was first reported from corn grown in Wisconsin in 1971. Since that initial occurrence it has been seen elsewhere, but always in fields deficient in K or in plants which are exhibiting K deficiency. The pathogen involved is a bacterium with the proposed name of *Pseudomonas coronafaciens* pathovar *zeae* (Ribeiro et al., 1977). The bacterium is a Gram-negative rod, motile by one to five polar flagella. It measures 0.6 × 1.0 to 2.7 μm.

The symptoms of chocolate spot on corn leaves are dark brown, elongated spots up to 3-cm long surrounded by a pronounced, broad yellow halo. A toxic material was present in culture filtrates of the pathogen. This material was heat-liable with the chlorotic effect being light dependent as is characteristic of a tabtoxin. Injury to the leaves appears to promote infection. Correcting K deficiency controls the disease.

12–2.2.5 Goss's Wilt

Goss's wilt has also been known as leaf freckles and wilt of corn, Nebraska bacterial wilt and leaf freckles, and Goss's bacterial wilt and blight. The disease was first found in Nebraska during 1969. Since then it has also occurred in Kansas, Colorado, South Dakota, Iowa, Minnesota, Illinois, and Wisconsin. It is not known to occur outside this area of the USA.

The pathogen causing Goss's wilt is a bacterium, *Clavibacter michiganense* ssp. *nebraskense* (Schuster, Hoff, Mandel, and Lazar) emend. Vidaver and Mandel (Syn. = *Corynebacterium nebraskense*). It is a nonflagellate, Gram-positive, nonmotile rod measuring 1.6 to 2.0 × 0.5 μm. The bacterium is white to cream in color on potato dextrose agar. On nutrient dextrose agar plus thiamine, the bacterium is capucine to apricot-orange in color, mucoid, and has convex colonies (Schuster et al., 1972). Virulence can be maintained through lyophilization of cultures or storing infected leaf tissue (Vidaver, 1977).

Systemically infected seedlings or young plants exhibit symptoms of wilting leading to plant death. The vascular bundles of these plants are discolored. While seedlings and young plants are quite susceptible to the pathogen, infection occurs more commonly later in the season. This later-season infection results in plants that exhibit dull gray-green to orange lesions containing water-soaked streaks with irregular margins (Plate 12–1). The main diagnostic symptom for Goss's wilt is the presence of "freckles". These freckles are small, irregularly shaped, dark water-soaked areas seen within developing lesions. Early in the morning, droplets of a bacterial exudate are often visible on the leaf surface. The pathogen can invade developing kernels. A maximum of 4% seed transmission has been obtained from artificially inoculated plants (Biddle et al., 1985).

Plant injury, usually resulting from hail or severe winds, is required for the bacterium to become established in corn tissues. No insect vectors have been found. All types of corn and green foxtail [*Setaria viridis* (L.) Beauv.], shattercane [*Sorghum bicolor* (L.) Moench], sorghum, eastern gamagrass, sugarcane (*Saccharum officinarum* L.), sudangrass [*Sorghum sudanense* (Piper) Stapf], and teosinte have been demonstrated as being hosts of the bacterium either naturally or through artificial inoculations (Schuster et al., 1972). Pinprick methods of inoculation are satisfactory in establishing artificial infections (Pataky, 1985).

The control of Goss's wilt can be obtained through the use of good cultural practices and resistant cultivars. Since the bacterium overwinters in corn debris, deep plowing in combination with crop rotation can greatly reduce the bacterial population. In areas where this is not a feasible method of control, resistant corn hybrids are available and should be grown (Wysong et al., 1981). In inheritance studies on Goss's wilt in corn, responses of progenies were intermediate to parental reactions or slightly more susceptible than the midparent reaction, with more than one gene for resistance being involved (Gardner and Schuster, 1973; Martin et al., 1975). Goss's wilt resistance appears to be correlated with resistance to northern corn leaf blight and bacterial wilt and leaf blight resistance (Pataky, 1985).

12–2.2.6   Holcus Spot

Holcus spot of corn was observed in Iowa during the growing season of 1916. Since that time, the disease has occurred sporadically in many corn-growing areas of the USA.

Holcus spot is caused by a bacterium, *Pseudomonas syringe* van Hall [Syn. = *P. holci* (Kendrick) Bergey et al.; *Xanthomonas holcicola* (Elliott) Starr and Burkeholder]. It is a Gram-negative, short rod measuring 0.6 to 1.2 × 1.5 to 3.0 μm. It is motile with one or more polar flagella (Kendrick, 1926).

Symptoms of the disease are small circular to oblong water-soaked lesions on corn leaves. As the lesions mature, they can reach 10 mm in diameter with reddish brown margins. Viewed in transmitted light a yellow halo surrounding the lesions is often apparent. The symptoms are similar to those caused by the herbicide paraquat (1,1'-dimethyl-4,4'-bipyridinium ion). Rainstorms accompanied with wind seem to be a prerequisite for infection (Weihing and Vidaver, 1967).

Hosts other than corn include sudangrass, johnsongrass, broom corn, pearl millet [*Pennisetum americanum* (L.) Leeke], and foxtail. The bacterium can overwinter in the soil and crop debris. To date the disease is of such little economic importance that control measures have not been investigated.

12–2.2.7 Anthracnose

Anthracnose of corn consists of a leaf blight phase and a stalk rot phase. The leaf blight phase has been of less importance than the stalk rot phase in the USA. The disease occurs in warm, humid corn-growing areas throughout the world. In the USA, the disease occurs in the central through southern Corn Belt to the Atlantic Coast and in the southeastern States.

Anthracnose is caused by the fungus, *Colletotrichum graminicola* (Ces.) G.W. Wils. Preliminary investigations suggest that the perfect stage is of a Glomerella type (Politis and Wheeler, 1972). Conidia are one-celled, hyaline, crescent-shaped with pointed ends, borne singly at the tips of short conidiophores, and measure approximately 5×28 μm. Conidiophores develop from acervuli that are erumpent, cushion-like masses of hyphae. Setae, which are long, rigid, dark, unbranched, hair-like structures, also develop from acervuli, and their presence aids in the diagnosis of this disease.

Host specific races of the pathogen exist. Some isolates of the fungus are able to infect corn but not sorghum and vice versa (Dale, 1963; Messiaen et al., 1959). In one study, some *C. graminicola* isolates were able to attack corn, sorghum, and sudangrass (Wheeler et al., 1974). While physiologic races of *C. graminicola* in corn have been reported (Forgey et al., 1978), further investigations did not substantiate their existence (Nicholson and Warren, 1981).

The symptoms of the leaf blight phase of anthracnose on susceptible corn appear as oval to broad spindle-shaped lesions that are tan to brown with from yellow to reddish brown borders and measure 12×40 mm. Lesions may be seen on leaves of corn seedlings early in the growing season and late in season on the upper leaves. There is little disease development during the mid-growing season when the plant is actively growing. The fungus can overwinter on corn debris (Lipps, 1982) with surface residue providing more inoculum than buried residues (Lipps, 1985). It can survive on corn kernels (Warren and Nicholson, 1975; Warren, 1977). The disease is favored by warm temperatures and extended periods of high humidity.

Resistance to the foliar phase of anthracnose is evidenced by a variety of symptoms from chlorotic flecks to restricted lesion development (Nicholson and Warren, 1976). Lesion size and sporulation are decreased under high light intensity (Hammerschmidt and Nicholson, 1977; Jenns and Leonard, 1985). Resistance is based predominantly upon additive gene effects with partial dominance being expressed at some loci (Carson and Hooker, 1981a; Lim and White, 1978). Resistance to the leaf blight phase of anthracnose in corn appears to be a different genetic mechanism than that which affects the stalk quality of corn (Zuber et al., 1981).

Control of the leaf blight phase of anthracnose can be accomplished through crop rotation, conventional tillage, and the use of resistant corn cultivars.

12–2.2.8 Eyespot

Eyespot of corn was first observed in the USA in 1968 (Ullstrup et al., 1969). It was first reported in Japan, where the disease is called brown spot (Narita and Hiratsuka, 1959). In the USA, the disease has been observed in areas of South Dakota, Minnesota, Wisconsin, Iowa, Illinois, Indiana, Ohio, Michigan, and New York (Carson, 1985; Smith, 1984). While eyespot has not reached epiphytotic proportions, yield losses up to 44% have been obtained from artificial inoculations (Reifschneider and Arny, 1983).

The disease is caused by a fungus, *Kabatiella zeae* Narita and Hiratsuka. The perfect stage is *Aureobasidium zeae* (Narita and Hiratsuka) Dingley. Conidia are hyaline, slightly curved, nonseptate, pointed at their ends and measure 3 to 4 $\times$ 18 to 33 μm. Conidia are produced on short, simple conidiophores. Sporulation readily occurs under conditions of high relative humidity.

Symptoms of the disease are the presence of small, circular, translucent lesions from 1 to 4 mm in size. The lesions are usually surrounded by a margin which can vary from yellow to purple in color. Lesions occur on the foliage, sheath tissue, and husks. These symptoms mimic some other abiotic leaf spots which seem to be genetically inherited. Cool, moist conditions favor disease development. The fungus overwinters on plant debris (Arny et al., 1971). Through artificial inoculations, the fungus has been shown to infect corn seed internally. This may be a contributing factor in its dissemination into other parts of the world (Reifschneider and Arny, 1979). Besides corn, *Z. diploperennis*, *Z. mays* spp. *luxurians*, *Z. mays* ssp. *mexicana*, and *Z. perennis* have been shown to be hosts for *K. zeae* (Reifschneider and Arny, 1980).

Genetic resistance is partially dominant and a few genes control resistance (Reifschneider and Arny, 1983). Since the fungus overwinters in corn debris and resistances to the fungus are known, logical control measures include the use of crop rotation, conventional tillage practices, and resistant corn cultivars.

12–2.2.9 Gray Leaf Spot

Gray leaf spot of corn was first described from samples taken in Illinois (Tehon and Daniels, 1925). Localized epiphytotics occurred in eastern Tennessee and Kentucky during 1943 (Hyre, 1943) and in South Carolina during 1962 (Kingsland, 1963). Recently, the disease has been increasing in its occurrence and severity in localized areas of Iowa eastward to the Atlantic Coast in the USA. Its increase in severity has usually been associated with the continuous culturing of corn and the use of minimum tillage practices (Latterall and Rossi, 1983a).

While the fungi *Cercospora zeae-maydis* Tehon and Daniels and *Cercospora sorghi* Ell. and Ev. have been implicated in gray leaf spot of corn (Chupp, 1953; Hyre, 1943), only *C. zeae-maydis* has been shown to be the causal agent of this disease (Latterall and Rossi, 1974). Accounts of infection of *C. sorghi* on corn have not been substantiated (Mulder and Holliday, 1974). Conidia of *C. zeae-maydis* are hyaline, 6 to 10 septate, slightly curved, and measure 5 to 6 × 70 to 180 μm, tapering to 2 to 3 μm at the apex. A species of *Mycosphaerella* is believed to be the sexual stage of *C. zeae-maydis* (Latterell and Rossi, 1983a). *Cercospora zeae-maydis* is a slow-growing fungus that sporulates best on decoction media made from corn leaves and V-8 juice agar under a diurnal light regime (Beckman and Payne, 1983). Corn is the only known host of *C. zeae-maydis* (Chupp, 1953).

Symptoms of gray leaf spot on susceptible corn are gray to tan linear-rectangular lesions delimited by the major veins on the corn leaf (Plate 12–2). The lesions are completely opaque when viewed through transmitted light. Leaf, sheath, and husk tissue can be infected by the fungus. Disease development is favored by extended periods of overcast days and high relative humidity (Beckman and Payne, 1982; Rupe et al., 1982).

Corn genotypes with resistance to *C. zeae-maydis* have been identified (Hilty et al., 1979). Resistance is largely due to additive genetic effects (Bergquist, 1985), and resistant corn cultivars are available for areas where gray leaf spot is of concern to grain or silage corn producers (Stromberg, 1985).

To minimize potential losses due to gray leaf spot, crop rotation, conventional tillage, and resistant corn cultivars can be used.

12–2.2.10   Helminthosporium Leaf Spot

Helminthosporium leaf spot, also known as northern leaf spot of corn, was first seen and isolated from corn during the 1938 growing season (Ullstrup, 1941).

The disease is caused by a fungus, *Bipolaris zeicola* (Stout) Shoemaker, [Syn. = *Helminthosporium carbonum* Ullstrup; *Drechslera zeicola* (Stout) Subram. and Jain.]. The sexual stage is *Cochliobolus carbonum* Nelson (Nelson, 1959). Conidia are golden-yellow to dark olive-brown, slightly curved, having rounded ends, 2 to 12 septate, and measuring 7 to 8 × 25 to 100 μm. The sexual stage exhibits perithecia which when mature are black, beaked, globose to ellipsoidal, and measure 355 to 550 μm in height by 320 to 430 μm in diameter. The asci are cylindrical to clubshaped and hyaline. They contain one to eight ascospores arranged in a helicoid manner, and measure 23 to 197 μm. Ascospores are filiform, hyaline, five to nine septate, and measure 6 to 10 × 180 to 300 μm.

Initially described as a physiologic race of *B. maydis* (Ullstrup, 1941), *B. zeicola* was later determined to be distinct from *B. maydis* and was named *H. carbonum* (Ullstrup, 1944). Within *B. zeicola*, three races have been described and designated race 1, race 2 (Ullstrup, 1944), and race 3 (Nelson et al., 1973).

Bipolaris zeicola race 1 exhibits lesions which are tan, oval, and measuring 15 × 25 mm on susceptible corn. Ear rots which can develop result in a black charred appearance of the ear. The disease is devastating on susceptible corn with all aboveground plant tissue being affected. Race 1 produces a host-specific toxin (Pringle and Scheffer, 1967; Scheffer and Ullstrup, 1965; Walton et al., 1982). Few corn inbreds are susceptible to race 1. Some publicly available inbreds susceptible to *B. zeicola* race 1 are Pr, K61, K44, MO21A, N31, NC37, GA203, and GA209. Also the corn synthetic BS13, which has served as a breeding source of some elite corn germ plasm, segregates for susceptibility to race 1 (Smith et al., 1985). Susceptibility is controlled by two recessive genes, one of which is designated *hm* and is located on chromosome 1 and the other being designated *hm2* and is located on chromosome 9 (Nelson and Ullstrup, 1964). Resistance to *B. zeicola* is common and is the primary factor used in controlling this race of the fungus.

Race 2 of *B. zeicola* is characterized by oblong to blocky, tan to chocolate-brown lesions measuring 5 × 25 mm on susceptible corn. The ear rot phase caused by race 2 is indistinguishable from that caused by race 1. Corn inbreds are more susceptible than hybrids. This race is widely distributed in the USA, but causes little economic loss (Smith, 1984).

Race 3 of *B. zeicola* exhibits narrow, linear lesions measuring 0.5 to 2 × 15 to 20 mm on susceptible corn. The lesions are grayish tan and are surrounded by a light to darkly pigmented border. Race 3 occurs primarily from Illinois eastward to the Atlantic Coast. Resistance appears to be polygenically inherited, with additive gene action being more important than nonadditive gene action (Hamid et al., 1982a). Isolates of race 3 differ in their degree of virulence when evaluated across different corn inbred lines (Hamid et al., 1982b). The parasitic fitness of race 3 populations are host genotype dependent (Gregory et al., 1984).

Since many similar fungi can overwinter on corn debris, it is logical that crop rotation and conventional tillage practices, in combination with the use of resistant cultivars, will control this disease situation.

12–2.2.11 Northern Corn Leaf Blight

Northern corn leaf blight is found in humid climates wherever corn is grown. In the USA, the blight has occurred primarily from the eastern Corn Belt to the Atlantic Coast, including many southern states. Localized epiphytotics can occur when the pathogen is present and environmental conditions favorable. Periods of major injury by the disease were during the early 1940s, 1951, in localized areas of western North Carolina and the coastal bend of Texas during 1985, and often on sweet corn grown in Florida.

The disease is caused by the fungus *Exserohilum turcicum* (Pass.) Leonard and Suggs [Syn. = *Helminthosporium turcicum* Pass.; *Bipolaris*

turcica (Pass.) Shoemaker; *Drechslera turcica* (Pass.) Subram. and Jain.].
The perfect stage of the pathogen is named *Septosphaeria turcica* (Luttrell)
Leonard and Suggs (Syn. = *Trichometasphaeria turcica* Luttrell). The
conidia are sometimes slightly curved, spindle-shaped, olive-gray, three
to nine septate, with a protruding hilum, and measuring 20 × 105 μm.
Germination is by polar germ tubes. The conidiophores are olivaceous,
two to four septate, and 7 to 9 × 150 to 250 μm in size. The sexual stage
has been induced in the laboratory by pairing appropriate mating types
on a suitable media (Lim et al., 1974; Luttrell, 1958). The sexual stage
has not been found in field environments. The perithecia are ellipsoidal,
black, 360 to 720 μm in height, and 350 to 500 μm in diameter. Asci are
long and cylindrical and measure 27 × 200 μm, while bearing one to
eight ascospores. Ascospores are hyaline, fusoid, typically three septate
measuring 15 × 62 μm. Sporulation of the fungus from susceptible genotypes readily occurs at moderate temperatures under conditions of high
humidity (Leach et al., 1977).

Symptoms of northern corn leaf blight on susceptible corn consist of
long, elliptical, gray-green lesions measuring from 2.5 to 15 cm in length
(Plate 12–2). As the lesions age they become tan-brown. Under field
conditions, the disease is first noticed in the lower canopy of the crop
and progresses upward on the plant throughout the growing season. Potential grain loss due to the disease can vary. Under severe disease conditions direct loss can result. Under moderate levels of infection, plants
are predisposed to attack by common stalk rotting pathogens, and losses
from this disease complex can result (Fajemisin and Hooker, 1974; Raymundo and Hooker, 1981).

Exserohilum turcicum can overseason on corn debris either as dormant mycelium (Robert and Findley, 1952) or as chlamydospores (Boosalis et al., 1967). Disease development is favored by conditions of high
humidity at moderate temperatures. It is retarded by hot, dry weather.

Both host-specific races and physiologic races of the fungus exist. The
presence of host-specific races was shown by obtaining single-ascospore
recombinants of fungal isolates which could attack corn, sorghum, sudangrass, and johnsongrass and inoculating them back onto the appropriate set of host differentials (Rodriguez and Ullstrup, 1962). Prior to
1974, only one physiologic race of *E. turcicum* was known to exist. During
1974, a race designated race 2 was identified from Hawaii (Bergquist and
Masias, 1974), and in 1980 was reported as occurring in the conterminous
USA (Turner and Johnson, 1980). Since 1980, the occurrence of *E. turcicum* race 2 has greatly increased in the USA (Jordan et al., 1983; Smith,
1984). Race 3 of *E. turcicum* was described in 1980 from fungal samples
collected from the 1976 corn-growing season (Smith and Kinsey, 1980).
These physiologic races were identified based on their differential virulence across sets of various chlorotic-lesion sources of resistance. Virulence for race 2 is determined by a single gene in the pathogen (Lim et
al., 1974).

Both oligogenic and polygenic sources of resistance have been found and are being exploited to minimize losses from northern corn leaf blight. Oligogenic resistances include various chlorotic-lesion resistances (Hooker, 1961, 1977b; Hooker et al., 1964; Ullstrup, 1963), and a type of resistance that usually produces lesion-free plants (Gevers, 1975; Raymundo et al., 1981). The chlorotic-lesion sources of resistance identified are inherited as single dominant genes (Hooker, 1963, 1975, 1977). Three gene loci seem to be involved as sites of inheritance of chlorotic-lesion resistance. Most of the genes involved are on chromosome 2 occurring at a locus designated *Ht1* (=*Ht*). Another gene locus designated *Ht2*, independent of *Ht1*, has been described (Hooker, 1977b). The gene *Ht3* segregates independent of both *Ht1* and *Ht2* (Simone, 1978). *HtN* is the proposed designation for the single dominant gene in which resistance is not a chlorotic-lesion type, but rather results in lesion-free plants until shortly after pollination (Gevers, 1975). Based on their virulence formula (effective/ineffective genes) when evaluated across the chlorotic-lesion resistances, the three races of *E. turcicum* would be expressed as *E. turcicum* race 1 (*Ht1, Ht2, Ht3/0*), *E. turcicum* race 2 (*Ht2, Ht3/Ht1*), and *E. turcicum* race 3 (*Ht1/Ht2, Ht3*).

Symptoms of *E. turcicum* on plants containing chlorotic-lesion resistances include irregularly sided lesions, surrounded by a yellow chlorotic margin. Sporulation within these lesions is greatly reduced when compared to wilt-type necrotic lesions (Hilu and Hooker, 1964). These resistances are believed to be due to the production of phytoalexins (Lim et al., 1968, 1970), H ion concentration (Mace and Veech, 1973), and/or cyclic hydroxamic acid production (Couture et al., 1971).

Polygenic inheritance of resistance is expressed as a reduction of lesion numbers and size (Hughes and Hooker, 1971; Jenkins and Robert, 1959; Jenkins and Robert, 1961; Jenkins et al., 1952). This type of resistance is effective in reducing losses in corn to northern corn leaf blight (Ullstrup, 1970a). Resistance of northern corn leaf blight, bacterial wilt and leaf blight, and Goss's wilt appear to be correlated (Pataky, 1985). Polygenic resistance functions regardless of the races of *E. turcicum* present.

The conrol of northern corn leaf blight can be accomplished through the exploitation of available genetic resistance and the application of fungicides whose use is warranted on high value corn crops such as sweet corn or hybrid seed production fields The disease may also be minimized through the use of crop rotation and clean tillage practices.

12–2.2.12 Physoderma Brown Spot

Physoderma brown spot occurs from Texas northward through South Dakota and eastward to the Atlantic Coast in the USA (Tisdale, 1919). While this disease is not considered to be devastating in the USA, some severely affected fields have been observed (Burns and Shurtleff, 1973). Brown spot is usually more severe in humid, tropical corn-growing areas of the world.

Physoderma brown spot is caused by the fungus, *Physoderma maydis* Miyabe [Syn. = *P. zeae-maydis* Shaw; *Cladochytrium maydis* Miyabe (nom. nud.)]. The sporangia are produced in pustules within areas of infected tissue and are brown, smooth, and thick-walled. They measure 18 to 24 × 20 to 30 μm. They are flattened on one side in which a circular lid is formed that opens upon germination to release zoospores. The sporangia germinate only under diffuse light conditions (Voorhees, 1933), and at relatively high pH's (Hebert and Kelman, 1958). The zoospores, which are thin-walled and measure 3 to 4 × 5 to 7 μm, have flagella that are three to four times longer than the zoospore. Infection on young corn tissue is established by the germination of zoospores formed between 0800 and 1600 h (Broyles, 1962). This results in bands of infection across the leaf blade.

Symptoms of Physoderma brown spot first appear as small yellow spots on the leaf blade. As the spots mature, they become brown in color. These spots eventually coalesce to form chocolate-brown to reddish, irregular blotches (Plate 12–3). Leaf sheath, husk, tassels, and stalks may exhibit symptoms of the disease late in the season. Under severe infections, stalks infected at the nodes frequently break at the site of infection.

Besides corn, teosinte is the only other known host for *P. maydis* (Eddins, 1933).

Varying degrees of resistance in corn to *P. maydis* have been observed (Eddins, 1933; Harvey et al., 1955). Most genetic variation for the *P. maydis* reaction is additive (Moll et al., 1963; Thompson, 1969; Thompson et al., 1963).

Control of Physoderma brown spot can be accomplished with the use of clean tillage practices (Burns and Shurtleff, 1973), systemic fungicides (Lal and Chakravarti, 1977), and resistant corn cultivars.

12–2.2.13 Southern Corn Leaf Blight

Southern corn leaf blight is generally distributed over the world in warm-temperate and tropical corn-producing areas. During most of its history in the USA, southern corn leaf blight was not of major significance. It reached epiphytotic proportions during 1970 when a previously undescribed physiologic race of the causal pathogen became prevalent. This race was designated race T because it was especially virulent on corn which contained the cytoplasmic male-sterile source from Texas (*cms*-T).

From the discovery of *cms*-T and until 1970 much of the hybrid seed corn was produced using *cms*-T to avoid detasseling of the female parent in seed production fields. The use of *cms*-T reduced the cost of seed corn production and produced a high-quality product of excellent uniformity. The resulting savings could be passed on to the consumer. Reacting to the epiphytotic of 1970, the vast majority of the seed industry quickly reverted to the use of "normal" (nonsterile) cytoplasm resistant to race T. By 1972, *cms*-T corn was largely a thing of the past and the frequency of occurrence of race T rapidly declined (Leonard, 1977; Smith, 1977, 1984).

The disease is caused by the fungus *Bipolaris maydis* (Nisik.) Shoem. [Syn.= *Helminthosporium maydis* Nisik. and Miyake; *Drechslera maydis* (Nisik.) Subram. and Jain.] The perfect stage is *Cochliobolus heterostrophus* (Drechs.) Drechs. (Syn. = *Ophiobolus maydis* Drechs.). Conidia are curved, spindle-shaped, tapering to rounded ends, olivaceous-brown, 3 to 13 septate, and measuring 15×90 μm. Germination is by polar germ tubes and the hilum does not protrude. Perithecia formed through the pairing of appropriate mating types of the fungus (Nelson, 1957a) are globose, black, 0.4 to 0.6 mm in diameter, with beaks. Asci are cylindrical, hyaline, straight to slightly curved, bearing four to eight ascospores, and measuring 24 to 28×160 to 180 μm. Ascospores are dark with five to nine septations, measure 6 to 7×130 to 340 μm, and occur in a helicoid arrangement in the ascus (Drechsler, 1925). While the sexual stage was reported as occurring naturally in field collections of corn in Florida (Schenck, 1970), the perithecia described were found later to be from a fungus other than *B. maydis* (Schenck, 1972). Two physiologic races of *B. maydis* have been reported (Hooker et al., 1970b; Smith et al., 1970). *Bipolaris maydis* race 0 was the predominant race that occurred prior to 1970 in the USA while *B. maydis* race T was the race to which *cms*-T corn exhibited preferential susceptibility. The observation of increased susceptibility of *cms*-T corn was reported earlier, but the possibility of physiologic races was not investigated by using isolates of the fungus from where the observations were made (Mercado and Lantican, 1961; Scheifele et al., 1970; Villareal and Lantican, 1965). Based on morphological characteristics, the two races are indistinguishable except when grown on malt extract agar, where race T producees sclerotia while race 0 does not (Locci and Locci, 1972).

Bipolaris maydis has been reported as occurring on corn, teosinte, and sorghum under field conditions (Tarr, 1962). Studies involving artificial inoculations of various other members of the Gramineae have implicated many of them as potential hosts of *B. maydis* (Ullstrup, 1970c).

The symptoms of *B. maydis* race 0 on susceptible corn are the presence of elongated parallel-sided lesions, which are tan in color and measure 2 to 6×3 to 22 mm long. Race 0 of the fungus attacks primarily the leaves of the corn plant. *Bipolaris maydis* race T on *cms*-T corn exhibits spindle-to-elliptical-shaped lesions, which measure 0.6 to 1.2×0.6 to 2.7 cm and are surrounded by a chlorotic halo (Plate 12–2). Race T can infect all aboveground plant parts. Under severe infections on *cms*-T corn, an ear rot of *B. maydis* race T can develop. On "normal" cytoplasm or resistant *cms* stocks, race T exhibits much smaller lesions than race 0. Race T produces a pathotoxin which accounts for the acute susceptibility of *cms*-T corn (Hooker et al., 1970b; Lim et al., 1971). The specific pathotoxin production of race T is due to a single gene in the pathogen (Lim and Hooker, 1971). The site of the race T pathotoxin activity is the mitochondrial membrane of *cms*-T plants (Miller and Koeppe, 1971) which accounts for the cytoplasmic inheritance of disease reaction.

The disease cycle of *B. maydis* is well studied. It is favored by conditions of high relative humidity and warm temperatures. The conidia are largely wind blown but can be moved by splashing rain to uninfected leaves (Waggoner et al., 1972). The conidia germinate and infect mainly the mesophyll, lesions are formed, sporulation occurs, and the process repeats itself. The fungus has been shown to be seed-borne (Boothroyd, 1971; Crosier and Braverman, 1971; Kommedahl et al., 1971) and can overwinter in crop debris (Futrell and Scott, 1971; Gudauskas et al., 1971; Littrell and Sumner, 1971; Schenck, 1971; Thompson and Hebert, 1971; Ullstrup, 1971b).

Control of southern corn leaf blight can be achieved through the use of fungicides (Comstock et al., 1974). This is only warranted on high value corn crops such as fresh market winter-produced sweetcorn or production fields that contain parental inbreds used in the production of hybrids. The most logical means of control is the use of resistant cultivars.

Resistances to *B. maydis* race 0 are both polygenically and oligogenically inherited. Polygenic resistance has been shown in one case to be partially dominant (Pate and Harvey, 1954). In other cases, additive gene action was much greater than nonadditive effects (Lim, 1975b; Lim and Hooker, 1976; Thompson and Bergquist, 1984), and additive genetic effects were greater than dominant genetic effects. Epistasis was of minor importance (Burnette and White, 1985). Oligogenic resistance was initially reported as being controlled by two linked recessive genes (Craig and Fajemisin, 1969). From these seedstocks a single, recessive gene was isolated and designated *rhm* (Smith and Hooker, 1973). The expression of resistance in corn to *B. maydis* race 0 is a reduction of lesion size and number being typical for polygenic resistance, while chlorotic lesions with greatly reduced sporulation within the lesions result from oligogenic resistance (Craig and Daniel-Kalio, 1968; Smith, 1975).

Resistance to *B. maydis* race T is inherited cytoplasmically, polygenically, and oligogenically. The most effective means of control of race T is through the use of various resistant cytoplasms (Hooker et al., 1970a; Smith et al., 1971). Both polygenic and oligogenic resistance can modify the expression of disease reaction of *cms*-T corn to race T (Johnson, 1975; Lim, 1975a; Scott and Futrell, 1975; Smith, 1975), but because of the use of resistant cytoplasms, the nuclear resistances have not been exploited.

The influence of tillage practices on southern corn leaf blight has been investigated. Conventional tillage reduces the amount of initial infection due to *B. maydis*, but by tasseling time infection was nearly identical to that in minimum-tillage or no-tillage plots (Bekele and Sumner, 1983).

The 1970 southern corn leaf blight epiphytotic caused by *B. maydis* race T served to alert and remind us of our dependency on relatively few crops and their potential vulnerability. Never had a disease caused so much economic loss in such a short period of time with no direct loss of human life and been controlled so quickly. Two publications of paramount importance resulted from this disease. One was the report of *Genetic Vulnerability of Major Crops* (NAS, 1972) and the other was *A Plant Pathologist's View of Germplasm Evaluation and Utilization* (Hooker, 1977a). These two works address concerns, offer guidance, and can serve as a foundation in the building and strengthening of pathological research programs regardless of crop or disease. While agreement on all the topics discussed in these publications is not expected, they do challenge the reader's thinking process and should be included in any file related to plant disease.

12–2.2.14 Yellow Leaf Blight

Yellow leaf blight of corn was first reported from Wisconsin during 1967 (Arny et al., 1970), from Pennsylvania during 1968 (Scheifele and Nelson, 1969), and from Ontario, Canada during 1969 (Gates and Mortimore, 1969). During the period 1967 through 1971, the disease was found to occur mainly in the northern and northeastern corn-growing areas of the USA.

Yellow leaf blight is caused by a fungus, *Phyllosticta maydis* Arny and Nelson. The sexual stage is *Mycosphaerella zeae-maydis* Mukunya and Boothroyd. Pycnidia are dark reddish brown, subglobose, embedded within diseased tissues with ostioles protruding from the leaf surface, and measure 60 to 150 μm in diameter. Conidia are oblong to ellipsodial, nonseptate, hyaline with two oil droplets near each end. Conidia measure 3 to 7.5 $\times$ 8 to 20 μm. The perfect stage was initially observed occurring in naturally infected corn leaf debris (Mukunya and Boothroyd, 1973). Psuedothecia are dark brown, globose, measure 86 to 192 μm in diameter, and are embedded in leaf tissue with their ostioles exposed. Asci are straight or curved, cylindrical or clavate, have thick hyaline walls, measure 10 to 12 $\times$ 45 to 65 μm, and bear eight biseriately arranged ascospores. Ascospores are straight or curved, tapered toward the ends, are hyaline, two celled with a constriction at the cell wall, and measure 5 $\times$ 16 μm.

The symptoms of yellow leaf blight on susceptible corn are the presence of rectangular to oval lesions that measure 7 to 10 $\times$ 15 to 20 mm. These lesions are yellow, cream, or buff colored with necrotic centers and are surrounded by a brown border. Lesions initially are seen on the lower leaves. They may coalesce, progress upward on the plant, and late in the season may be observed on the leaf sheaths and outer husks. While the production of pycnidia within mature lesions aids in the diagnosis of this disease, their presence alone does not conclusively verify the occurrence of yellow leaf blight caused by *P. maydis*. The presence of pynicidia in combination with conidial measurements, is the best diagnostic tool in lieu of a proof of pathogenicity. Conidia from fungal isolates which measure 1.5 to 3 $\times$ 5 to 7 μm may be produced by the fungus *Phyllosticta zeae* Stout, which is weakly pathogenic on corn. Conidia from isolates which measure 3 to 7.5 × 8 to 20 μm result in symptoms typical of yellow leaf blight when these isolates are inoculated onto appropriate corn differentials. Therefore, these do represent isolates of *P. maydis* (McFeeley, 1971; Smith, 1984).

Dissemination of the pathogen is primarily by rainsplash and wind. The disease is most prevalent during the seedling-growth stage and again after tasseling. These periods coincide with cool and wet corn-growing periods. The fungus can overseason on corn debris and can be reduced by rotation and conventional tillage practices (Castor et al., 1977; Sutton et al., 1972).

Phyllosticta maydis was the first pathogen to which *cms*-T corn exhibited differential susceptibility when compared to "normal" cytoplasm counterparts (Arny et al., 1970; Ayers et al., 1970; Scheifele and Nelson, 1969; Scheifele et al., 1969). The cause of the differential pathogenicity of *P. maydis* on various sources of cytoplasmic male sterility is due to the production of a host-specific toxin by the fungus (Comstock et al., 1973; Yoder, 1973).

Resistance in corn to *P. maydis* is available in the form of various cytoplasmic sources (Nelson et al., 1971) and in the existence of at least one dominant gene pair in the nucleus (Mukunya et al., 1975). Since the epiphytotic of southern corn leaf blight caused by *B. maydis* race T and the shift from the use of *cms*-T to normal cytoplasm or resistant male-sterile cytoplasms in hybrid seed production, yellow leaf blight has been of little economic importance on the corn crop.

12–2.2.15 Common Corn Rust

Common corn rust is widespread over the USA wherever corn is grown. Its severity varies widely across years. The earlier the infection becomes established the more severe the disease is likely to become. It can be a problem on certain inbred parents used in the production of hybrid seed corn, but has not been prevalent on hybrid corn itself in the USA since 1950 (Wallin, 1951). It is a continuing problem with sweetcorn.

The fungus causing common corn rust is *Puccinia sorghi* Schw. It is an obligately parasitic, macrocyclic, heteroecious fungus. Uredial and telial spore stages are produced on corn. Urediospores are cinnamon-brown in color, spherical to ellipsoid, moderately echinulate, with three or four equatorial pores, and measure 21 to 30 × 24 to 33 μm. Urediospores are dispersed by wind and rain and continue to reinfect corn throughout the growing season. Late in the growing season, as the corn matures, teliospores develop within the pustules. These spores are chestnut-brown to black, oblong to ellipsoid, two-celled with a constriction at the septum, measuring 14 to 25 × 28 to 54 μm, and are attached to a pedicel which is once to twice the length of the spore. Cells of teliospores are binucleate, but prior to germination the two haploid nuclei fuse to form the diploid phase of the fungus. Teliospores usually germinate in the spring or early summer under warm, moist conditions. Basidiospores that contain one haploid nucleus are produced from germinating teliospores. The basidiospores cannot infect corn but can parasitize a number of species of wood sorrel (*Oxalis* spp.), the alternate hosts of the pathogen (Mains, 1934). Spermagonia are formed on the upper surface of the wood sorrel leaves. Spermatia are formed within the spermagonia and are exuded in a gelatinous matrix. Spermatia are uninucleate, haploid spores which fuse with paraphyses of the opposite mating type and protrude from the ostioles of the spermagonia. Without fusion between spermatia and paraphyses of the opposite mating type, the mycelium remains haploid and further development of the fungus is halted. After karyogamy occurs, binucleate aeciospores are produced in "cluster-cups" on the lower surface of the wood sorrel leaves. The aeciospores are pale-yellow, verrucose, globoid to ellipsoid, and measure 13 to 19 × 18 to 26 μm. Aeciospores are able to infect corn, on which urediospores are produced. Urediospores may be able to overwinter in the southern USA and serve as the initial inoculum on corn in the spring. Because of the infrequent occurrence of infection of wood sorrel by *P. sorghi* in the U.S. Corn Belt, it is unlikely that the alternate host has a primary role in the epidemiology of common corn rust.

The symptoms of common corn rust on susceptible corn are the presence of cinnamon-brown, powdery pustules that may occur on any aboveground plant tissues but are most often seen on the leaves (Plate 12–3). The pustules are formed on both leaf surfaces. In contrast, the pustules caused by the southern corn rust fungus are most prevalent on the upper leaf surface. Also, pustules of common corn rust are circular to elongate. These pustules become darker brown to black late in the growing season when the urediospores are replaced by teliospores.

The disease is favored by moderate temperatures, with 17 to 25 °C being optimum for urediospore germination (McKeen, 1951; Weber, 1922). Disease development is slowed below 8 °C and almost no sporulation occurs above 32 °C (Headrick and Pataky, 1986). Saturated atmospheres also greatly enhance germination with 100% germination occuring in fully saturated conditions, but only 3% germination occurring at 97.5% relative humidity (Smith, 1926).

The resistance of corn to common corn rust is of two distinct types, specific and general.

Specific resistance to common rust is pathogen race specific and is seen as a hypersensitive reaction by the host resulting in restricted pustule development. Inheritance of specific resistance is oligogenic. Five different gene loci, occurring on three chromosomes, have been identified as possessing alleles for specific resistance (Hooker and Saxena, 1971; Saxena and Hooker, 1974).

General resistance to *P. sorghi* results in a reduction of pustule number and size and in leaf necrosis (Kim, 1974). This resistance is observed best on older plants and is often referred to as "mature" or "adult plant" resistance. The degree of expression of various sources of this resistance appears to be dependent upon the environments in which the material is evaluated. The environments more favorable to severe epiphytotics of common rust negate some sources of resistance which were identified in milder rust environments (Kim and Brewbaker, 1976). High heritabilities and low gene number estimates are associated with general resistance (Kim and Brewbaker, 1977).

Fungicide control of common corn rust is warranted for dent corn seed production fields and sweet corn hybrid fields when the disease is severe.

12–2.2.16 Southern Corn Rust

In 1891, southern corn rust from eastern gamagrass was first observed in the USA (Underwood, 1897). Normally, this rust is not a serious disease in the USA, but it did cause losses of the corn crop during the years 1972 through 1974 on late-planted corn in the lower Mississippi River Valley (Futrell, 1975) as well as in Texas and Kansas during 1979 (Rodriquez-Ardon et al., 1980). The rust has been observed as far north as Wisconsin (Pavgi and Flangas, 1959). Southern corn rust was severe in areas of Africa (Cammack, 1954; Rhind et al., 1952) until resistant cultivars were developed (Storey et al., 1958).

Southern corn rust is caused by the fungus *Puccinia polysora* Underw. It is an obligate pathogen. The aecial stage of the pathogen has not been found. The urediospores are yellow to golden, ellipsoid to obovoid, and measure 20 to 29 × 29 to 40 μm. The urediospore walls are sparsely echinulate, 1 to 1.5 μm thick with four or five equatorial pores. Teliospores are chestnut brown, smooth, angular to ellipsoid or oblong, two-celled, rounded at both ends, and measure 18 to 27 × 29 to 41 μm. They are borne on short, persistent, yellow to brown pedicels.

Symptoms of southern rust on susceptible corn are small, circular, orange to red pustules on the leaves and leaf sheaths (Plate 12–3). Pustule development occurs more readily on the upper than the lower surface of corn leaves and can measure 0.2 to 2.0 mm in diameter.

Southern corn rust is favored by warm, humid environments (Hollier and King, 1985a, b). In Africa, *P. polysora* is most prevalent at lower altitudes, while *P. sorghi* is more prevalent at higher altitudes. This is believed to be due to warmer temperatures favoring the development of southern corn rust (Nattrass, 1953; Schall et al., 1983).

In addition to corn, *P. polysora* also infects *Erianthus alopecuroides* (L.) Ell., *Tripsacum dactyloides* L., *T. lanceolatum* Rupr., *T. laxum* Nash., and *T. pilosum* Scrib. and Merr. (Robert, 1962; Schieber and Dickson, 1963; Ullstrup, 1977).

Twelve physiologic races of *P. polysora* are known (Lallmahomed and Craig, 1968; Robert, 1962; Ryland and Storey, 1955; Storey and Howland, 1967; Ullstrup, 1965). Specific resistance in corn to *P. polysora* has been identified and 11 genes controlling that resistance have been designated *Rpp1* to *Rpp11* (Ullstrup, 1977). *Rpp9* occurs on chromosome 10 (Ullstrup, 1965) and may contain numerous alleles (Scott et al., 1984). It is closely linked to *Rp1d*, which confers resistance to some races of *P. sorghi*. General resistance, while not having been shown experimentally, probably exists.

12–2.2.17 Common Corn Smut

Common smut of corn, also known as boil smut or blister smut, is worldwide in its distribution and can occur wherever corn is grown. Its frequency and severity in the USA varies widely from year to year, with losses usually being <2%. An extensive summary of this disease is available in another monograph (Christensen, 1963).

The fungus which causes common smut is a heterobasidiomycete, *Ustilago maydis* (DC.) Cda. (Syn. = *Ustilago zeae* Ung.). *Ustilago maydis* produces teliospores (often called chlamydospores) which are olive-brown to black, spherical to ellipsoidal, heavily echinulate, and measure 8 to 12 μm in diameter. The diploid teliospores germinate by the formation of a septate promycelium on which four or more small hyaline, fusiform, ellipsoid sporidia are produced. Sporidia are usually uninucleate and haploid. They fuse to form binucleate infection hyphae that are dikaryotic and capable of establishing infection. The infection hyphae can survive in the host but they die on artificial substrates. Diploid thalli can be induced on certain culture media (Puhalla, 1969). Sometimes the diploid nucleus in the teliospore is not reduced during germination and a diploid thallus results. Single sporidia from these cultures are pathogenic. Haploid sporidia are nonpathogenic (Chilton, 1940; Christensen, 1931).

Infection of meristematic tissue can occur by binucleate infection hyphae resulting from sporidial fusion, or by infection hyphae developing directly from germinating teliospores (Walter, 1934). Infection can be by direct penetration of the thin-walled meristematic cells or through injury to the plant produced by hail, insects, or mechanical injury resulting from the normal husbandry of the crop. The fungal mycelium stimulates host cells to increase in size and number with galls resulting. The galls are composed of hypertrophied and hyperplasic host and fungal tissue. Most research leads to the conclusion that the galls result from local infections (Itzerott, 1938; Piemeisel, 1917). Since most galls disperse their teliospores when the host is reaching maturity and mature plants possess little meristematic tissue, there is little, if any, secondary infection within the normal cropping season. Most infections result from inoculum that survived the previous growing season.

The most conspicuous symptom of common smut on corn is the development of galls (Plate 12–4). All aboveground plant parts are susceptible at some time during the growing season. However, the apical meristem can become infected when the plants are young and galls can develop beneath the soil surface. Galls develop only from infections of meristematic tissues. At first, galls are glistening and white. Their interior consists of soft white tissue that may show black streaks as a result of teliospore formation. As the host matures the entire gall becomes a powdery mass of teliospores. Under conditions of rapid cell maturation, gall formation is halted and the galls remain small, hard, and develop only a few teliospores. Corn and teosinte are the only known hosts of *U. maydis*.

The number, size, location of galls on the plants, and the age of plants at the time of infection determine the actual losses resulting from common smut. The greatest losses result from infection of the apical meristem in seedlings. Galls develop and the infected seedlings die (Ullstrup and Britton, 1968). In some tests, smut affected yield only when barrenness was induced, and plants in which only the tassel was infected yielded more than noninfected plants (Garber and Hoover, 1928). In seed production fields where smut gall size effects on yield loss were studied, galls under 5 cm in diameter reduced yield about 9%, galls from 5 to 7.6 cm reduced yield about 14%, and galls more than 7.6 cm in diameter resulted in 40% yield loss of the corn inbred studied (Ullstrup, 1977).

Reports of investigations of factors favoring smut infection result in contradictory lists of variables. Most reports indicate that rainy, humid weather is the most critical environmental factor essential for infection (Christensen, 1963). Fertilization with barnyard manure tends to increase the frequency of smut and fertilization with phosphate (PO_4^3) reduces the incidence of smut. In some tests the addition of K alone increased smut levels. The increase of smut in this case was associated with a decrease in reducing sugars and an increase in N in the pith (Martens and Arny, 1966). Crop rotation does not appear to greatly influence the incidence of smut across years, but soil moisture during tasseling and silking does seem to be an important factor contributing to smut severity (Maric et al., 1969).

The most practical method of controlling common corn smut is the use of resistant corn cultivars. While few artificially inoculated evaluations are conducted on corn germ plasm for reaction to *U. maydis*, there is enough natural infection to identify and eliminate from a breeding program those genotypes that may be acutely susceptible to the pathogen. Heritable differences in the reaction of corn to *U. maydis* were first reported in 1918 (Jones, 1918). Recent studies indicate that resistance is polygenic in inheritance and breeding for resistance could be accomplished by crossing developmental material to a susceptible tester and evaluating the resulting hybrid (Bojanowski, 1969).

The use of chemical control methods aimed directly at the pathogen or at insects that predispose the plants to infection have been unsuccessful. Also, because of the widespread occurrence of the pathogen, sanitation is not a practical method of controlling common corn smut.

12–2.2.18 Other Foliar or Local Infection Diseases

Many other foliar or local infection diseases have been reported on corn. Those that occur infrequently or are of little importance in the USA include:

1. Alternaria leaf blight caused by *Alternaria alternata* (Fr.) Keissler.
2. Ascochyta leaf and sheath spots caused by various *Ascochyta* spp.
3. Curvularia leaf spots caused by various *Curvularia* spp.
4. Diplodia leaf streak caused by *Stenocarpella macrospora* (Earle) Sutton.
5. False smut caused by *Ustilaginoidea virens* (Cke.) Tak.
6. Helminthosporium leaf disease caused by *Exserohilum rostratum* (Drechs.) Leonard and Suggs emended Leonard.
7. Purple sheath spot caused by various bacteria and fungi.
8. Septoria leaf blotch caused by *Septoria* spp.
9. Zonate leaf spot caused by *Gloeocercospora sorghi* D. Bain and Edg. (Shurtleff, 1980).

Since these diseases are of little concern in the USA, no specific control measures have been investigated. However, based on the similarity of the pathogens causing these diseases with pathogens that cause diseases of concern, logical control measures would be the use of clean tillage practices and crop rotation. If any of these diseases were to become more important in the USA, the screening of corn germ plasm would probably identify sources of resistance, as has been done for other disease situations.

12–2.3 Systemic Diseases

Systemic diseases are those in which the pathogen develops from its infection site systemically throughout the corn plant. For the USA this includes diseases caused by one smut fungus, three downy mildews, numerous viruses, one spiroplasma, and one mycoplasma.

While the pathogens which cause systemic diseases in corn consist of organisms of widely diverse origin, their effects on the corn plants are similar. When early or severe infections occur from these diseases, corn plants are barren, have their reproductive structures replaced by vegetative structures, or produce only rudimentary ears. Therefore, yield losses from systemic diseases are largely proportional to the percentage of the plants infected within a field.

12–2.3.1 Head Smut

Head smut of corn was first observed in Kansas during the 1890 growing season (Norton, 1895). Since that time it has been observed in the western states of California, Washington, Oregon, and Idaho (Potter, 1914; Simpson, 1966). More recently, head smut has been reported from the high plains of Texas (Frederiksen et al., 1976); Ontario, Canada (Lynch, 1980); and Minnesota (Stromberg, 1981). It has been known to exist in Mexico and other parts of the world for many years (Duran, 1970; Halisky, 1962). Smut incidences as high as 80% have been observed (Frederiksen, 1977).

Sphacelotheca reiliana (Kühn) Clint. (Syn. = *Sorosporium reilianum*

(Kühn) McAlp.; *Ustilago reiliana* Kühn) is the fungus that causes head smut of corn. Teliospores are reddish brown to black, densely and conspicuously spiny, and measure 9 to 12 μm in diameter. They germinate to form a septate promycelium that bears small, hyaline, thin-walled, single-celled, haploid sporidia measuring 7 to 15 μm. Seedling infection occurs by way of direct penetration by the promycelium or from binucleate infection hyphae that form following the fusion of sporidia of opposite mating types. While young seedling infection is the most common mode of infection, postseedling infection has been experimentally demonstrated (Fenwick and Simpson, 1969). The morphology and life cycle of *S. reiliana* is similar to *U. maydis*, which causes common smut. However, *S. reiliana* can be distinguished by its seedling infection resulting in systemic infection of the fungus, and the formation of sori almost exclusively in the tassels and ears.

Two cultivars of the pathogen have been demonstrated (Al-Sohaily et al., 1963b). One cultivar infects sorghum and is comprised of four physiologic races that can be sorted out by selected sorghum differentials. When the sweetcorn cv. North Star is included as an additional differential, five races can be distinguished. The other pathogen cultivar infects only corn with no physiologic races being identified. There is evidence that hybrids made between the two main cultivars are pathogenic to both hosts (Al-Sohaily et al., 1963a).

The initial disease symptom of head smut is the presence of chlorotic flecks within the leaves of infected seedling plants (Foster and Frederiksen, 1977; Matyac and Kommedahl, 1985a; Tyler and Shumway, 1935). These are subtle symptoms. More obvious symptoms of infection are evident as infected plants reach tasseling and during ear formation. Tassels of infected plants are replaced by smut sori or exhibit phylloidy (Plate 12-4). While each sorus is covered by a periderm, it soon ruptures to expose a black mass of teliospores. Ears are rounded in their shape and are replaced with sori. Vascular elements remain relatively intact and appear as black fibrous strands of tissue that remain as the teliospores are released. Occasionally, a partially developed ear with a few kernels will be observed. Infected plants are usually stunted to some degree.

Environmental factors favoring infection include high soil temperatures of 23 to 30 °C and dry soil conditions (Matyac and Kommendahl, 1985b). Smut incidences decrease with the application of urea, ammonium sulfate, triple superphosphate, and calcium nitrate [$Ca(NO_3)_2$] (Matyac and Kommendahl, 1985b).

Resistance to *S. reiliana* has been found in corn (Frederiksen, 1977; Fuentes, 1963; Stromberg et al., 1984). Inheritance of resistance appears to be partially dominant and there are commercial dent corn cultivars presently available with resistance to head smut.

In-furrow soil treatment of some fungicides has been shown to be an effective means of chemical control (Fenwick and Simpson, 1967; Simpson and Fenwick, 1968, 1971; Stienstra et al., 1985). Foliar applications of fungicides have had no effect in controlling head smut (Stienstra et al., 1985). Since the teliospores of the fungus can persist in the soil, crop rotation is not an effective control practice.

12–2.3.2 Crazy Top

Crazy top was first observed in Italy in 1902 (Cugini and Traverso, 1902). In 1939, it was reported to be in the USA (Koehler, 1939). It is now widespread and occurs globally (Frederiksen and Renfro, 1977). While it is considered a minor corn disease, localized severe infections can result in significant yield losses.

Crazy top is caused by *Sclerophthora macrospora* (Sacc.) Thirum., Shaw & Naras [Syn. = *Sclerospora macrospora* Sacc.; *Phytophthora macrospora* (Sacc.) Ito & Tanaka]. The sporangia, measuring 60 to 100 × 30 to 65 μm, are hyaline, operculate, lemon-shaped, and attached to simple, short hyphoid sporangiophores emerging from stomata. The sporangia germinate with the release of zoospores. The zoospores are biciliate, hyaline, and subspherical to reinform. The oospores, measuring 45 to 75 μm, are hyaline to yellowish, multinucleate, and globose with granular contents. When stained with Zn chloriodide, the oogonia and oospores appear as darkly stained "nests" of several spores. The nests appear in the vascular bundles or their parenchymatous sheath cells in thickened leaves and leaf sheaths of infected plants. The oospores germinate by the formation of a thin-walled tube bearing a sporanguim, which releases zoospores.

Infection is accomplished by zoospores released by oospores germinating under saturated soil conditions. After a short period of motility, the zoospores encyst and produce germ tubes. The mycelium becomes systemic but is most abundant in meristematic tissues. Sporangia are produced sparsely in corn, but oogonia are produced abundantly.

Since *S. macrospora* is an obligate parasite, its role as the causal agent of crazy top has only recently been established (Semeniuk and Mankin, 1964; Ullstrup, 1970b).

Initial symptoms include excessive tillering of infected plants with rolling and twisting of the newer leaves. The tassel usually exhibits phyllody, hence the name crazy top (Plate 12–5). Leaves of infected plants are often narrow, thick, and straplike in appearance. Occasionally, "giant" plants are observed within severely affected fields.

The fungus has a wide host range, with 140 grass species other than corn serving as hosts (Frederiksen and Renfro, 1977).

The pathogen is systemic and infection of the seed by *S. macrospora* has been shown (Ullstrup, 1970b; Ullstrup and Sun, 1969). There is, however, no evidence that seed transmission is involved in the epidemiology of crazy top. The pathogen is readily killed during the grain-drying process and rapidly loses viability in stored seed.

While some corn hybrids exhibit resistance to *S. macrospora* (Graves et al., 1980), little has been done in specific breeding for resistance. This is due to the fact that a narrow range of environmental conditions must be met to establish infections. The soil must be waterlogged for a period of about 2 d sometime between germination of the seeds and the time the plants are 20-cm high. The most effective control measure to reduce crazy top is improved soil drainage. Since the oospores are long lived in the soil, sanitation and crop rotation have little effect on the disease. The recent development of fungicides targeted for Oomycetes may offer an alternative control measure for the future.

12–2.3.3 Sorghum Downy Mildew

Sorghum downy mildew was first observed in India during 1907. The causal pathogen was correctly determined in 1932 (Weston and Uppal, 1932). The disease occurs on corn in Asia, Africa, Central America, Europe, South America, and North America (Frederiksen and Renfro, 1977). Sorghum downy mildew was first observed in the USA in Texas during 1963 (Reyes et al., 1964). From 1963 to 1987, the disease has been found to occur in Alabama, Arkansas, Florida, Georgia, Kansas, Kentucky, Illinois, Indiana, Louisiana, Mississippi, Missouri, Nebraska, New Mexico, Oklahoma, and Tennessee (Frederiksen, 1980). Losses of up to 90% have been reported from experimental nurseries (Frederiksen and Bockholt, 1969).

The cause of sorghum downy mildew is a fungus, *Peronosclerospora sorghi* (Weston and Uppal) C.G. Shaw (Syn. = *Scelerospora sorghi* Weston and Uppal; *S. graminicola* var. *andropogonis-sorghi* Kulk). The conidiophores that emerge from stomata are 180 to 300 μm in length, and are fragile, erect, and usually dichotomously branched. The conidia are hyaline, obovate, nonpapillate, nonporoid, borne on sterigmata, and 15 to 27 × 15 to 29 μm. Oogonia are spherical, embedded among mesophyll cells between the fibrovascular bundles, and 40 to 55 μm in diameter. Oospores are spherical, hyaline to yellow, enclosed in a thickened, brown oogonial wall and 25 to 43 μm in diameter.

Initial infection of plants is usually by oospores which can persist in the soil for at least 3 yr. Conidial infection can be important as an avenue of secondary infection between plants within a field. Conidia are viable for only a few hours. Susceptible corn plants develop systemic infections from oospore infections and from conidial infection in plants which are 4 weeks old or younger. In older plants, conidial infections result in local-lesion development. Within host tissues oospores are produced less frequently in corn than in sorghum.

The symptoms of systemic infection of sorghum downy mildew in corn are first seen as a "half-diseased" leaf, followed by chlorosis of the leaves, stunting, white-striping of the leaves, replacement of the ear with leafy structures, and phyllodied tassels (Plate 12–5). Sporulation of the fungus appears as a white downy growth on both leaf surfaces. Sometimes a few plants develop ears with scattered kernels. Seed produced on systemically infected plants may be internally infected, but because the fungus is short lived in these tissues it is unlikely that seed transmission is important in the dissemination of this disease (Dange, 1976; Jones et al., 1972).

Hosts of *P. sorghi* other than corn include sorghum, *Zea mays* spp. *mexicana, Heteropogon contortus*, and *Panicum typheron* (Frederiksen and Renfro, 1977).

Control of sorghum downy mildew in corn can be accomplished in many ways. The most logical control is through the use or development of resistant cultivars. From the evaluation of corn germ plasm used in the USA, it was evident that there were excellent sources of resistance to sorghum downy mildew available (Frederiksen et al., 1971). The inheritance of resistance may be dominant (Schmitt et al., 1977) or recessive depending on the resistant source (Frederiksen and Ullstrup, 1975). Physiologic races of *P. sorghi* on corn have yet to be identified (Craig and Frederiksen, 1980). Resistance of corn to *P. sorghi* may be a result of inhibition of the pathogen's progress from its entry point toward the meristematic tissues (Craig, 1980, 1982).

Disease resulting from conidial infections may be avoided by planting corn at times when other hosts of the pathogen are not present to provide a source of conidia (Siradhana et al., 1978). Chemical control has been used to control sorghum downy mildew on sorghum in many regions of the world and this would be an effective control measure for corn if needed (Frederiksen and Odvody, 1979).

12–2.3.4 Maize Dwarf Mosaic Virus

A corn disease, believed to be caused by a virus, was seen in the USA during the 1962 growing season (Janson and Ellett, 1963). In 1965, the causal agent was named maize dwarf mosaic virus (MDMV) (Williams and Alexander, 1965). Since MDMV's initial discovery in Ohio in 1962, the virus has been reported throughout most of the USA where corn is grown with the exception of the Pacific Northwest (Forster et al., 1980; Gordon et al., 1978; Singh and Gordon, 1980).

Maize dwarf mosaic virus is a filamentous particle 12 to 15 nm in diameter and 750 to 800 nm long. It is a RNA virus in the potyvirus group. It can be transmitted mechanically or by aphids in a nonpersistent manner (Bancroft et al., 1966). Seven strains of MDMV have been identified and designated strain A, B (MacKenzie et al., 1966); C, D, E, F (Louis and Knoke, 1975), and O (McDaniel and Gordon, 1985). Maize dwarf mosaic virus strains A, C, D, E, F, and O infect johnsongrass, while strain B does not. Strain O infects oat (*Avena sativa* L.), while the other strains do not. Strains A, C, D, E, and F can be separated using characteristic symptoms that develop on the susceptible corn inbred N20, by a differential host response across a selected set of corn genotypes, and by a differential rate of transmission using the aphids, *Acyrthosipon pisum* and *Myzus persicae*. While these strains can be separated based on their characterizations within the MDMV group, their synonymy with other viruses is likely (Gordon et al., 1974; Gordon, 1976; Tosic and Ford, 1972).

Maize dwarf mosaic virus strains that infect johnsongrass are usually found in areas coinciding with the johnsongrass. Recently, however, MDMV strain A has been identified from areas much further north than where johnsongrass overwinters. Its occurrence in these areas has been attributed to viruliferous aphids from the southern USA being blown northward by low level jet-stream winds (Stromberg et al., 1978; Timian et al., 1978; Zeyen et al., 1978). However, the time required for the aphids to be introduced into the more northern corn-growing areas takes longer than the aphids have been shown to be viruliferious (Thongmeearkom et al., 1976). Hence, a second possible mechanism for the northern distribution of MDMV strain A is seed transmission. While low incidences of seed transmission of MDMV have been shown (Hill et al., 1974; Mikel et al., 1984; Shepherd and Holdeman, 1965; Williams et al., 1968), it has been stated that these results are adequate to account for the occurrence of MDMV strain A in northern corn-growing areas (Gordon et al., 1978). A third possibility involves overwintering of MDMV in other perennial grassy weeds (Ford and Tosic, 1972). It is also possible that annual weeds would exhibit enough seed transmission to serve as sources of MDMV inocula (Timian et al., 1978). These various explanations as to the distribution of MDMV strain A are still being investigated.

The symptoms of MDMV include the development of mosaic or mottle on the younger leaves, progressing into narrow, light green to yellowish streaks along the veins (Plate 12–6). Symptoms may develop on leaves, leaf sheaths, and husks. Infected plants may be slightly stunted with the ear being reduced in size and functional seed set. As the temperature rises, the mosaic symptoms become less noticeable. Early infection results in the most severe symptom development, yield loss (Mikel et al., 1981; Rosenkraz and Scott, 1978), and an increased susceptibility to root rots (Tu and Ford, 1971).

Control or reduction of MDMV can be accomplished through the use of resistant corn cultivars, eliminating overwintering hosts, planting early to avoid exposure to insect vectors, and controlling insect vectors themselves.

Genetic resistance in corn to MDMV has been demonstrated to be dominant (Johnson, 1971; Josephson and Naidu, 1971; Loesch and Zuber, 1972; Naidu and Josephson, 1976). Depending on the germ plasm studied, from two to five genes appear to be involved in resistance to MDMV (Mikel et al., 1984; Rosenkranz and Scott, 1984). Using chromosomal translocation stocks, genes for resistance have been located on both arms of chromosomes 6, 7, and 10; the long arms of chromosomes 1 and 2; and the short arms of chromosomes 3 and 8 (Findley et al., 1973; Scott and Nelson, 1971; Scott and Rosenkranz, 1973). The most commonly occurring genes are on both arms of chromosome 6. Since the inheritance of resistance is mainly dominant and relatively few genes are involved, a backcross breeding program under artificially induced epi-phytotics would be effective in introgressing resistance into more agron-omically acceptable corn genotypes. While the majority of the research concerning the inheritance of resistance in corn to MDMV uses john-songrass-infecting strains, there is evidence that resistance to MDMV strain B in corn is different than that for strain A (Scheifele and Wernham, 1969), and that *Zea diploperennis* possesses good resistance to MDMV strain B (Nault et al., 1982). Resistance to MDMV is also independent of resistance to other corn-stunting agents (Scott and Rosenkranz, 1974).

The use of resistant corn cultivars and the control of johnsongrass have been the two most important factors in reducing losses in corn to MDMV.

12–2.3.5 Maize Chlorotic Dwarf Virus

While "corn-stunting agents" were being aggressively investigated in the USA during the mid-1960s, it was not until 1972 that initial reports sorting out particle morphology and mode of transmission (Bradfute et al., 1972a, 1972b; Pirone et al., 1972) lead to the naming of maize chlo-rotic dwarf virus (MCDV) (Nault et al., 1973). Since the identification of MCDV, it has been found to occur from Texas eastward to the Atlantic Coast with northern movement being mostly limited to southern Illinois, Indiana, Ohio, and Pennsylvania (Ayers et al., 1978; Damsteegt, 1976; Gordon and Nault, 1977). The distribution of MCDV is more limited than MDMV, but where MCDV occurs it is detected more frequently than MDMV (Gordon and Nault, 1977) and is more damaging than MDMV (Kingsland and Barnett, 1985).

Maize chlorotic dwarf virus is an isometric virion 31 nm in diameter and containing RNA. It is transmitted by the leafhoppers *Graminella nigrifrons* and *G. sonora* in a semipersistent manner. Following feeding on plants infected with MCDV, the leafhoppers remain viruliferous for up to 48 h. The virus cannot be transmitted mechanically. While the main overwintering host of MCDV is johnsongrass, other hosts include broomcorn, millet, sorghum, sudangrass, wheat, crabgrass, and foxtail (Shurtleff, 1980).

Symptoms of MCDV infections include chlorosis of the leaves emerg-ing from the whorl, chlorotic banding of secondary veins, and chlorotic striping of tertiary veins. General chlorosis or reddening of the leaves and stunting of plants through the compaction of upper internodes are evident later in the growing season. Severely affected plants will be barren or produce only rudimentary ears. While symptoms of plants infected with viral agents are similar, the main diagnostic symptom separating MCDV from other viral diseases is the veinbanding that appears as nar-row bands of green next to the secondary veins with fine chlorotic striping over the smaller veins (Louie et al., 1974).

Genetic resistance in corn to MCDV is available (Naidu and Jo-sephson, 1976; Scott and Rosenkranz, 1981). General combining-ability estimates are higher than those for specific combining ability, with some degree of dominance being expressed. Agronomically elite hybrids which possess adequate resistance to MCDV are presently being marketed in areas where MCDV is of concern to farmers. Recently, immunity to MCDV was described as occurring in *Z. diploperennis* (Nault et al., 1982). Other factors associated with control of this disease include the control of johnsongrass and the use of systemic insecticides to reduce leafhopper populations (Kuhn et al., 1975).

12–2.3.6 Corn Lethal Necrosis

In 1976, a previously undescribed disease was observed in Norton County, KS. This disease was the result of viral infections, and was named corn lethal necrosis (CLN) (Niblett and Claflin, 1978). Since its discovery the disease has been primarily associated with the river-basin systems of the Republican or Little Blue Rivers in south central Nebraska and north central Kansas (Uyemoto, 1983). Seven counties in Nebraska and six counties in Kansas have had fields affected by CLN. On highly susceptible dent corn hybrids, yields have been reduced up to 70% (Uyemoto et al., 1980).

Corn lethal necrosis is caused by the synergistic interaction between maize chlorotic mottle virus (MCMV) and either maize dwarf mosaic virus (MDMV) or wheat streak mosaic virus (WSMV). Both MDMV and WSMV were known to occur in the areas affected by CLN prior to 1976. Maize dwarf mosaic virus in combination with MCMV is probably the more commonly occurring situation encountered in the field (Niblett and Claflin, 1978). Maize chlorotic mottle virus was unknown in the USA before 1976.

While MCMV was originally described from Peru (Castillo and Herbert, 1974; Castillo-Loayza, 1976), the strains which occur in Peru are serologically distinguishable from USA strains (Niblett and Claflin, 1978). Maize chlorotic mottle virus is an isometric virus particle about 30 nm in diameter. Based on its physical properties, it may be a member of the sobemovirus group (Lommel, 1985). It is transmitted by six species of chrysomelid beetles (*Oulema melanopa, Chaetocnema pulicaria, Systena frontalis, Diabrotica undecimpunctata, D. longicornis,* and *D. virgifera*). Virus retention in adults is 6 d following acquisition (Jensen, 1985; Nault et al., 1978). Maize chlorotic mottle virus is also mechanically transmitted. Nineteen grass species have been shown to be systemic hosts of the Kansas serotype of MCMV and 15 grass species were hosts for the Peru serotype (Bockelman et al., 1982). Seed-transmission studies involving corn have been negative (Bockelman et al., 1982).

Symptoms of the disease include mosaic patterns developing on the leaves and husks of infected corn plants, leaf necrosis progressing inward from the margins, and premature death of the plants. In maturing plants, necrosis starts at the tassel and progresses downward. Barrenness often results in severely affected plants. If ears are produced, they are small, distorted, poorly filled, and exhibit "popping" of the scattered grain. Distribution patterns of CLN within a field suggests that a soilborne phase exists for CLN (Uyemoto, 1983).

Control of CLN can be accomplished through the use of resistant corn cultivars and crop rotation. Fall plowing does not seem to be an effective control measure (Uyemoto, 1983). No studies of the inheritance of resistance of CLN in corn have been conducted; however, resistant corn sources have been identified and tolerant cultivars are available where the disease is of concern. Immunity to MCMV from *Zea diploperennis* and *Z. perennis* has been reported (Nault et al., 1982).

12–2.3.7 Maize White Line Mosaic Virus

During 1979, a severe stunting and mosaic of plants in both dent and sweet corn fields was observed in New York. The infective agent was a virus which was designated maize white line mosaic virus (MWLMV) (Boothroyd and Israel, 1980). Since its discovery it has been found to occur in seven other northeastern and north central states (Louie et al., 1983b).

Maize white line mosaic virus is a 30-nm isometric viral particle which has a 17 nm satellite-like virus particle in association with the larger particle (Gingery and Louie, 1985). These particles appear to be serologically related to particles described for maize dwarf ringspot virus. Maize white line mosaic virus seems to be soilborne (deZoeten et al., 1980; Louie et al., 1981). No vectors have been positively identified, it is not mechanically transmitted, and seed-transmission studies have been negative (Louie et al., 1982).

Symptoms of plants infected by MWLMV include a mosaic of the leaves and stunting of the plants. The main diagnostic symptom is the development of chlorotic white lines, primarily within veinal tissue. Symptomless infections do occur and symptom development may depend upon some other factor in addition to MWLMV infection (Louie et al., 1983a). Hosts other than corn include green foxtail and winter wheat (Grau et al., 1981).

The only experimental controls at this time are autoclaving the soil or applying benomyl as a soil drench (Louie et al., 1982). Due to the difficulty associated with screening germ plasm against MWLMV, no studies have been conducted screening for resistance.

12–2.3.8 Corn Stunt

Corn stunt was first described from the Rio Grande Valley of Texas in 1945 (Altstatt, 1945). Initially this disease was thought to be caused by a virus (Kunkel, 1946), but later this proved to be incorrect (Davis and Worley, 1973; Granados, 1969). The causal agent of corn stunt is a spiroplasma (Chen and Liao, 1975; Davis, 1973, 1976; Williamson and Whitcomb, 1975). Since its initial discovery from Texas, CSS has also been observed in Louisiana (Bradfute and Robertson, 1974) and southern

Florida (Bradfute et al., 1981; Davis et al., 1984), in both plants and leafhoppers from Mexico (Davis, 1973; Gordon et al., 1985), and as far south as Argentina (Nault and Knoke, 1981).

The CSS is a minute, filterable bacterium in the class Mollicutes. It is procaryotic, smaller than common bacteria, and lacks a rigid cell wall. It is helical, motile, and measures from 250 nm in diameter to 15 μm in length.

The spiroplasma is transmitted by the leafhoppers *Dalbulus maidis, D. elimatus, Graminella nigrofrons, Exitianus exitiosus, Stirellus bicolor, D. tripsacoides, D. gelbus, D. guevarai, D. quinquenotatus,* and *Baldulus tripsaci* (Gordon et al., 1985; Madden and Nault, 1983).

Hosts other than corn include *Zea mays* ssp. *mexicana, Z. perennis,* and *Z. diploperennis* (Nault, 1980) and *Vinca rosea* and *Vicia faba* (Markham et al., 1977).

The symptoms of corn stunt start as chlorosis of the leaf margins of the whorl leaf. This is followed by reddening of the older leaves. Chlorotic spots develop at the base of newly developing leaves. These spots coalesce to form chlorotic stripes which extend to the leaf tips. Plants are stunted and produce numerous small ear shoots (Plate 12–6). Root systems of infected plants are less extensive than those in healthy plants.

The most logical means of control would be the development of resistant corn cultivars for areas where the disease is of concern.

12–2.3.9 Maize Bushy Stunt

Maize bushy stunt is caused by a mycoplasma. Prior to its identification as the maize bushy stunt mycoplasma (MBSM), it may have been the cause of the diseases known as the corn stunt Mesa Central strain, the corn stunt Louisiana strain (Gordon et al., 1978), and achaparramiento-M in Mexico. Maize bushy stunt mycoplasma is currently known to occur only in Texas (Bradfute et al., 1977), Mexico, Peru, and Columbia.

The MBSM, a member of the class Mollicutes, is a mycoplasmalike body 0.15 to 3.0 μm in diameter. It has yet to be cultured in vitro. It is transmitted by the leafhoppers: *Baldulus tripsaci, Dabulus elimatus, D. gelbus, D. guevarai, D. maidis, D. quinguenotatus, D. sonorus, D. tripsacoides,* and *Graminella nigrofrons* (Madden and Nault, 1983; Nault, 1980). Besides corn, the only other known host of MBSM is teosinte, *Z. mays* ssp. *mexicana.*

The symptoms caused by the MBSM are similar to those produced by the corn stunt spiroplasma (CSS), except that the MBSM causes more severe plant stunting and reddening of older leaves than CSS, but does not produce chlorotic stripes at the base of younger leaves. The MBSM also can cause a proliferation of auxiliary and basal shoots (Nault, 1980).

The most logical means of controlling maize bushy stunt would be the development of resistant corn cultivars where the disease is of concern.

12-2.3.10   Other Systemic Diseases

Other systemic diseases of corn reported from the USA include one downy mildew and numerous viruses or virus-like diseases. These diseases are limited in their occurrence or minor in their damage to the corn crop.

Green ear disease or Graminicola downy mildew, caused by the fungus *Sclerospora graminicola* (Sacc.) Schroet, has been reported from the USA (Melhus et al., 1928; Weston, 1929). This disease is extremely rare in its occurrence. While only three downy mildews have been reported from the USA, numerous other downy mildews reported from other parts of the world cause significant yield losses in corn (Frederiksen and Renfro, 1977; Shurtleff, 1980).

Many more diseaes of viral origin or suspected viral origin have been reported from the USA than is in the scope of this chapter to discuss. They are currently limited in their distribution and occurrence within the USA. Discussions of these viruses are presented elsewhere (Gordon et al., 1978; Shurtleff, 1980).

12-2.4   Stalk and Root Rots

Stalk rot continues to be the most serious, widespread, corn disease. Even though the incidence and severity of stalk rot varies from year to year, some stalk rot occurs in every field every year. The term stalk rot is often used to include stalk breakage, stalk lodging, premature death of the plant, and occasionally even root lodging. For purposes of this discussion, however, stalk rot is the decay of the internal pith tissues of the stalk. Typically the first sign of stalk rot is plant wilting. Within several days, leaves become gray, the ear will droop, and the outer rind of the lower stalk will turn brown. When the outer stalk tissue is brown, the pith tissue in the lowest internode is rotted and pulled away from the rind. As the rotting pith tissue pulls away from the rind, the structural integrity of the plant changes from that of a solid rod to a tube. With the structural integrity destroyed, the "plant tube" will more readily lodge. Plants are weakened and those with rotted stalks almost always have rotted roots. The stalk rot complex is complicated in that a number of fungi and sometimes bacteria are involved in the decay of the pith. This is further confounded in that stalk rot is generally regarded as a disease of senescence with factors involved in acceleration of senescence altering the susceptibility of the plant.

Losses due to stalk rot may occur in several different ways. One type of yield loss results from premature plant death, thus stopping normal grain fill. Total grain weight on stalk-rotted plants is usually less than grain weight on healthy plants. Another component of yield loss is that plants with stalk rot may lodge and not be harvested with mechanical equipment. Harvest is slowed if stalk rot is severe and losses also occur due to loss of valuable time during harvest. Another loss occurs with ear rots as a result of ears on lodged plants coming in contact with the soil. This results in reduced grain quality and potential dockage when the grain is marketed. Because losses due to stalk rot may occur in several different ways, yield loss estimates are difficult to obtain. Additionally, no control is available to establish plots completely free from stalk rot.

Different techniques have been used in an attempt to estimate losses due to stalk rot. Yields of hybrids during years with little natural stalk rot incidence have been compared to yields in years when stalk rot is severe (Koehler, 1960). These types of studies are confounded by year-to-year variation in average yield. Another technique that is used is comparing inoculated vs. uninoculated plots (Michaelson and Christensen, 1953; Michaelson, 1957; Wilcoxson, 1962; White et al., 1979). These studies, however, are confounded by natural infection in uninoculated plots, and by the fact that inoculation does not exactly duplicate the natural stalk rot condition. A third technique that has been used is paired plant comparisons whereby grain yields of adjacent diseased and healthy plants are compared (Hooker and Britton, 1962; Perkins and Hooker, 1979; Wysong and Kerr, 1969). These studies have problems in that kernel number on diseased plants is normally much higher than on healthy plants. The final problem with yield loss studies on corn stalk rot is that in a number of studies, losses are estimated on the basis of hand-harvested yield and do not take into account those losses due to lodging or ear rots.

Considerable research has been done on factors that influence stalk rot. Obviously the most important factor is the inherent susceptibility of the hybrid. A hybrid that is considered susceptible, however, may have stalk rot problems in some locations and/or years but not others. Several factors may alter the susceptibility of the hybrid. These include weather conditions, moisture availability, grain fill and kernel number, cultural practices, plant densities, leaf disease damage, cloud cover, and insect damage. Factors that affect stalk rot development have been reviewed (Dodd, 1977, 1980a, 1980b) and a photosynthetic stress-translocation balance concept of predisposition of corn to stalk rot was proposed. In general, whenever growing conditions are favorable early in the growing season, corn plants will develop a large number of kernels. After flowering, the kernels will be a sink for carbohydrates within the plant. Whenever the plant does not produce enough carbohydrates for maintenance of all tissues, the grain sink has priority over other tissues. With intraplant competition for carbohydrates, tissues in the root and lower stem have low priority and cells in those tissues will senesce. As cells start to senesce those tissues become more susceptible to colonization by stalk rot organisms.

A review of all the factors involved in plant stress and their relationship to stalk rot would be too lengthy for the space allowed for this chapter. Therefore, a brief review of some factors that can be manipulated to provide control are discussed. These include soil fertility, tillage, and plant density.

In general, stalk rot is more severe and the incidence greater with increased fertility. A number of studies evaluated the effects of various nutrients on stalk rot. The most widely studied nutrient has been N, which has been reported to both increase (Christensen and Wilcoxson, 1966) and decrease stalk rot severity (Kruger, 1970; Nelson, 1963). The variable effect of N on stalk rot appears to be influenced by factors such as the stalk rot pathogen, susceptibility of the plant, source of N, and relative availability of other nutrients. Most research would indicate that when N is in excess in relation to K, stalk rot is increased. Other research indicates that if N levels are high early in the growing season and N is lost through denitrification and leaching, stalk rot is increased. This would imply a need for a balanced and continuous N supply throughout the growing season to maintain cells in the pith for a longer period of time. A balanced and continuous N supply helps to explain the reduction of stalk rot with the use of nitrification inhibitors such as 2-chloro-6(trichloromethyl)pyridine(nitrapyridin) when mixed with anhydrous ammonia (Warren et al., 1975; White et al., 1978). Also, stalk rot was reduced following a top-dress application on a field with large amounts of residue on the surface (Kruger, 1970). Therefore, the effect of N may not be dependent upon how much is applied at the beginning of the season, but whether it is available throughout the season.

Effects of K have also been related to stalk rot. Potassium is involved in stomatal functions as well as metabolic pathways. When plants are deficient in K the photosynthesis rate is lower and may result in more rapid pith senescence. When adequate K is present, stalk rot severity is reduced (Christensen and Wilcoxson, 1966).

The response of corn to P varies with the season, hybrid, and the pathogen (Christensen and Wilcoxson, 1966). While P does not decrease stalk rot severity when applied at high levels, it seems to afford some protection against stalk rot (Thayer and Williams, 1960).

A number of studies have related tillage practices to the occurrence of plant diseases. In general, debris that is left on the surface of the soil may favor some foliar diseases. This is because many fungi that cause foliar diseases overwinter in association with debris on the soil surface and are disseminated to the foliage of the next crop. The presence of foliar diseases increases the possibility of stalk rots. In the absence of leaf blight diseases, however, reduced tillage has been shown to actually reduce most stalk rot diseases (Parker and Burrows, 1959; White and Yanney, 1981; Doupnick and Boosalis, 1980). The reduction in stalk rot with reduced tillage may be due to the reduced evaporation of soil moisture that would result in less stress.

As plant populations are increased, the incidence and severity of stalk rot increases. This increase is greater with hybrids that are susceptible to stalk rot. If cloudy weather, foliar diseases, or unbalanced fertility occur within a field, plant populations become an even more critical contributing factor to stalk rot.

12-2.4.1 Gibberella Stalk Rot

Gibberella stalk rot is the predominant stalk rot in the midwestern Corn Belt. Symptoms of this disease are similar to those with other stalk rots. Affected plants wilt, the leaves change from bright to dull green and the lower stalk becomes straw colored. The internal pith tissue disintegrates leaving only the vascular bundles. A diagnostic sign of Gibberella stalk rot is the reddish discoloration that occurs on the inside of the stalk (Plate 12-7). Another characteristic sign of Gibberella stalk rot is the superficial, small, round, black perithecia that can be easily scraped from the stalk surface.

Gibberella zeae (Schw.) Petch. is the causal agent of Gibberella stalk rot. Perithecia of the fungus are bluish black, superficial, containing eight ascospores arranged obliquely in one row. The ascospores are hyaline, three-septate, tapering uniformly at the ends, slightly curved, and 3 to 5 $\times$ 20 to 30 μm. Perithecia are often seen in the fall, but usually spores contained in those perithecia are not mature until the following spring or summer. The asexual stage of *G. zeae, Fusarium graminearum* (Schwabe), produces macroconidia that are hyaline, slightly curved, with pointed ends, three to five septate, and 4 to 6 $\times$ 30 to 60 μm. Some isolates of the fungus produce chlamydospores.

Under warm, wet conditions, the perithecia will produce ascospores that are wind-borne and may infect corn plants. Inoculum may also be produced as conidia during the summer. Stalk infections usually occur shortly after pollination, developing at the origin of the leaf sheaths or around the brace roots. The fungus may also enter through the roots and grow through the roots to the lower stem. *Gibberella zeae* is also the causal agent of Gibberella ear rot of corn. It also infects wheat, barley (*Hordeum vulgare* L.), oat, and rye causing scab and seedling blights. The fungus is common and the incidence and severity of Gibberella stalk rot is not limited by inoculum in much of the Midwest.

12-2.4.2 Diplodia Stalk Rot (Stenocarpella Stalk Rot)

This disease was considered to be the most important stalk rot pathogen of corn until the late 1960s and early 1970s. At that time, the incidence and severity of Diplodia stalk rot declined and the incidence and severity of Gibberella stalk rot and anthracnose stalk rot increased (Hooker and White, 1976). This trend appears to be reversing during the last several years. Symptoms of Diplodia stalk rot are similar to those of Gibberella stalk rot. Symptoms include a straw-brown discoloration of the lower, inner nodes and a disintegration of the pith, leaving only the vascular bundles intact (Plate 12-7). As with Gibberella stalk rot, plants are prematurely killed. A characteristic sign of Diplodia stalk rot is the presence of subepidermal, minute, dark-brown to black pycnidia embedded in the rind tissue of the lower stem.

The causal agent of Diplodia stalk rot is *Stenocarpella maydis* (Berk.)

Sutton [Syn. = *Diplodia maydis* (Berk.) Sacc.; *Diplodia zeae* (Schw.) Lev.]. The recent revision of the coelomycetes indicate that the common corn stalk rot pathogen will be included in the genus *Stenocarpella* Syd. (Sutton, 1980). This will be supported by phytopathologists in spite of the fact that *Diplodia* is used as the genus name in a considerable amount of literature (Latterell and Rossi, 1983b). The most recent list of "Common Names for Plant Diseases" uses *D. maydis* and Diplodia stalk rot (Committee on Standardization of Common Names for Plant Diseases, 1985). For that reason the name Diplodia will be retained here. The fungus produces globose or flask-shaped pycnidia containing olive to brown colored elliptical, two-celled, straight to slightly curved conidia, 5 to 6 × 25 to 30 μm in size. Less commonly, pycnidia contain colorless, long, narrow thread-like spores, 1 to 2 × 25 to 35 μm. No sexual stage of the fungus is known.

Diplodia maydis overwinters as conidia in pycnidia associated with debris. Under warm, moist conditions, the spores are extruded from the pycnidia and disseminated by rain and wind. Infection of plants occurs mainly through the crown, mesocotyl, and roots. Occasional infections may occur at the nodes between the crown and the ear.

Corn is the only host for *D. maydis* and the disease is most common where debris from a previous crop is on the soil surface. This may help explain the reduced incidence of Diplodia stalk rot in the 1960s and 1970s as Fall tillage was widely practiced. With reduced tillage coming back into practice, the incidence of diplodia stalk rot has increased.

12–2.4.3 Anthracnose Stalk Rot

Since 1855, anthracnose stalk rot has been known to occur in the USA (Wilson, 1914). The disease, however, was not considered to be important until sometime after 1970. The prevalence and severity of the disease has increased and it is now considered to be one of the more important stalk rot diseases in the southeastern portions of the USA extending north into Wisconsin and west into Iowa. Stalk infections become evident at various stages of growth, depending on the susceptibility of the plant. The lower stalk tissues of acutely susceptible inbreds and hybrids may be so severely rotted in early growth stages that plants are killed well before pollen production. In most inbreds and hybrids, however, symptoms are not visible until just prior to normal senescence. Unlike other common stalk rot diseases, the pathogen may rot several internodes of the plant. Usually, the entire plant is prematurely killed and lodging is likely to occur. In some cases, portions of the plant above the ear will die prematurely while the lower portions of the plant will remain green. Later, the prematurely killed top portions of the plant may lodge and fall off the plant. Anthracnose stalk rot is easily recognized late in the season by the shiny black color on the outer stalk (Plate 12–7). This discoloration may be uniform or blotchy, and may occur on the bottom few internodes or the entire length of the stalk. Occasionally, the discoloration may be seen only near the nodal plate. The black color is due to the presence of what appear to be masses of fungal mycelium just under the rind surface. The internal stalk tissues are often blackened or discolored and the stalk may be easily crushed between the thumb and forefinger. With many plants, discoloration may be present on the outer stalk surface but internal tissues are not discolored or rotted. When this occurs, it is assumed that infection occurred late in the season and the fungus was not able to penetrate the pith tissues.

Colletotrichum graminicola is the causal agent of anthracnose stalk rot. The fungus is described in the midseason foliar disease section 12–2.2 of this chapter.

The mechanisms of penetration and infection of stalk tissues are not completely understood. This fungus is the only stalk rot pathogen that also causes a leaf blight and some researchers postulate that spores produced in lesions on the leaves are washed behind the leaf sheath and penetrate into the stalk (Williams and Willis, 1963). The fungus may also penetrate the stalk through wounds or insect feeding sites (Keller et al., 1986). Anthracnose leaf blight and stalk rot appears to be more severe where corn residues are on the soil surface with the stalk rot incidence decreasing with increased distance from crop residue (Lipps, 1985). The occurrence of the disease in fields without apparent sources of inoculum could be explained by wind dissemination of conidia associated with dry leaf fragments (Nicholson and Moraes, 1980) or by penetration of the roots by buried inoculum. The host range for *C. graminicola* includes corn, sorghum, wheat, barley, oat, and rye. However, most isolates of the fungus that attack corn do not attack other grasses and vice versa. Therefore, it is doubtful that inoculum produced on other graminus crops would be involved in the disease cycle on corn.

12–2.4.4 Charcoal Rot

Charcoal rot is a common stalk rot disease in warm, dry areas of the USA. Initial symptoms are similar to Diplodia, Gibberella, and Fusarium stalk rot. A characteristic sign of the disease is the presence of numerous, minute, black sclerotia, particularly on the vascular bundles and inside the rind of the stalk (Plate 12–7). This may cause the stalk to appear gray-black and from this symptom the name of the disease is derived.

Charcoal rot is caused by *Macrophomina phaseolina* (Tassi) G. Goid. [Syn. = *Macrophomina phaseoli* (Maubl.) Ashby; *Botryodiplodia phaseoli* (Maub.) Thirum; and *Sclerotium bataticola* Taub.]. Some strains of the fungus produce conidia; however, isolates from corn are sterile and do not form spores. Sclerotia of the fungus are generally smooth, black, and range from 0.05 to 0.22 mm in size.

Charcoal rot is favored by soil temperatures that range from 30 to 42 °C and low soil moisture. The fungus overwinters as sclerotia and may penetrate roots and lower stems during the growing season. The fungus also attacks sorghum and soybean. The disease is more common on soybean than corn in much of midwestern USA. The survival of the fungus on crops, such as soybean [*Glycine max* (L.) Merr.], may help explain why the disease is widespread on corn in years that are hot and dry.

12-2.4.5 Fusarium Stalk Rot

Fusarium stalk rot seems to be more important in the dryer, warmer areas where corn is grown even though the causal agent may be found wherever corn is grown. The symptoms of Fusarium stalk rot are not easily distinguished from those of Diplodia or Gibberella stalk rot. There are no signs of the fungus that make it easily recognizable when associated with corn stalks. Usually, Fusarium stalk rot is diagnosed when no signs are found of Gibberella stalk rot, Diplodia stalk rot, anthracnose stalk rot, or charcoal rot (Plate 12-7). Several workers have considered it to be of minor importance in comparison to other stalk rots. *Fusarium moniliforme*, the causal agent of Fusarium stalk rot, may be isolated from rotted as well as healthy stalks near the end of the growing season. Thus, some researchers have concluded that *F. moniliforme* is not a stalk rot pathogen, but rather an organism that is usually associated with corn stalks. However, *F. moniliforme* has been shown to cause severe stalk rot when inoculated into plants using the toothpick method (Young, 1943); and, reports from warmer, dryer areas indicate that *F. moniliforme* is an important stalk rot of corn in those areas.

The causal agent of Fusarium stalk rot is *Fusarium moniliforme* Sheld., [perfect stage *Gibberella moniliforme* (Sheld.) Wineland; Syn. = *G. fujikuroi* (Saw.) Wr.]. The perfect stage of the pathogen of *F. moniliforme* is rarely observed in the USA. The imperfect stage produces conidia on mycelium. Macroconidia of the fungus are sparse. They are hyaline 2.5 to 5 $\times$ 15 to 60 μm in size, curved near the tips, and are three to five septate. Microconidia are abundant and are 2 to 3 $\times$ 5 to 12 μm in size and single celled. Another Fusarium species, *F. moniliforme* var. *subglutins* (Wr. and Reink) has been frequently isolated from corn plants with symptoms of Fusarium stalk rot. The major difference between these two organisms is that *F. moniliforme* bears microconidia in chains and *F. moniliforme* var. *subglutins* has microconidia borne in false heads, never in chains.

The fungus survives on crop residue in or on the soil surface. Under favorable conditions, the fungus may infect roots or stalks. Some workers speculate that *F. moniliforme* may actually have been present throughout the life cycle of the plant and may have first been present in seedling plants. Other workers dispute this.

12-2.4.6 Pythium Stalk Rot

This stalk rot occurs during extended hot and wet conditions. The disease is not considered to be of economic importance because it occurs on individual plants in localized areas and does not become severe over extensive areas. Unlike many other stalk rot diseases, Pythium stalk rot may occur prior to flowering. The disease is usually confined to the first internode above the soil line with the roots and tops of the plant becoming infected. The outer rind and pith tissues are rotted with only the vascular bundles remaining intact.

The causal agents of Pythium stalk rot are *Pythium aphanidermatum* (Eds) Fitzp. and/or *P. butleri* Subr. The two species have been placed in synonymy with *P. aphanidermatum* as the preferred name (Middleton, 1943). Both species are favored by high temperature and for the purposes of this chapter *P. aphanidermatum* is considered to be synonymous with *P. butleri*. The hyphae are hyaline and nonseptate. Sporangia are inflated filamentors, branched or unbranched, measuring 50 to 1000 $\times$ 4 to 20 μm usually forming complexes. Zoospores are arereniform, laterally biciliate, measuring 12 $\times$ 7.5 μm. Oogonia are spherical, terminal, rarely intercalary, measuring 22 to 27 μm in diameter. Antheridia are usually monoclinous, typically intercalary though often terminal. Oospores are aplerotic, single measuring 17 to 19 μm in diameter.

12–2.4.7 Bacterial Stalk Rot Diseases

Several bacterial stalk rot diseases with soft rot-type symptoms have been reported. At least two distinct causal agents have been identified. Bacterial stalk and top rot is the most commonly reported bacterial stalk rot disease. The disease involves both stalk and leaf tissue and is found predominantly where corn is grown with overhead irrigation (Hoppe and Kelman, 1969; Kelman et al., 1957). Symptoms include wilting of leaves in the whorl of the plant, followed by rapid, soft rotting of the uppermost stalk tissues. The causal agent has been assigned a number of different names but has the greatest taxonomic affinity for the *Erwinia chrysanthemi* Burkholder, McFadden and Dimoock group (Syn. = *E. carotovora* f. sp. *zeae* Sabet). The bacterium is a Gram-negative rod with peritrichous flagella.

Another bacterial stalk rot disease is usually referred to as bacterial stalk rot. This stalk rot disease was reported in a series of papers between 1919 and 1926 (Rosen, 1921, 1922, 1926). The symptoms include a soft rot of stalk tissue usually at or near the soil surface followed by rapid wilting and death of the plant. The vascular bundles remain intact. Only scattered plants are affected and the disease is of little significance. The causal agent of bacterial stalk has been placed in several generi, but may be taxonomically nearer to *Klebsiella* spp. than to *Erwinia dissolvens* (Rosen) Burkholder which is used in more recent literature (Dye, 1969).

12–2.4.8 Other Stalk Rot Diseases

Black bundle disease caused by *Cephalosporium acremonium* Cda. was reported in several studies conducted from 1920 to 1930 but is not currently considered to be a problem in the midwestern Corn Belt of the USA. Symptoms include reddening of the leaves and stalk at dough stage with blackening of the vascular bundles extending through several inter-nodes. Infected plants are often barren, have excessive tillers or multiple ears at one node.

Nigrospora stalk rot caused by *Nigrospora oryzae* (Berk. & Br.) Peth is also occasionally found on corn. The symptoms include black streaking on the exterior of the stalk with black discoloration of the pith. The fungus is more often found in association with cobs and grain and is not con-sidered to be an aggressive stalk invader.

Pyrenochaeta terrestris (Hansen) Gorenz, Walker and Larsen may be found associated with shallow, dark-brown, blotchy lesions at or just below the soil surface. Lesions are reddish on dead stalks and may be confused with Gibberella stalk rot. The fungus is also commonly asso-ciated with roots and causes reddening of the brace roots. Infection can occur prior to tasseling.

Phaeocytostroma ambiguum (Mont.) Petr. (Syn. = *Phaecytosporella zeae* Stout.) is found associated with lesions on maturing stalks at or below ground level. The fungus produces pycnidia resembling those of *Diplodia maydis* except that they are enlongated rather than round. The organism is not known to cause economic damage as a stalk-rotting path-ogen.

Other fungi associated with stalks are usually regarded as secondary stalk invaders. They may cause decay of pith tissue when stalks are in-oculated. Some of the more common genera include: Alternaria, Asper-gillus, Bipolaris, Cladosporium, Curvularia, Mucor, Penicillium, Rhi-zoctonia, Rhizopus, and Trichoderma.

It is apparent, therefore, that breeding for resistance to corn stalk rot is greatly complicated by relatively large numbers of fungi that may rot stalks and the effect of various environmental factors that predispose plants to stalk rot. Additionally, a hybrid could be resistant to pith decay but have lodging problems due to poor rind and/or root strength.

Resistance to *Diploidia maydis* and *Colletotrichum graminicola* is inherited in a complex manner (Carson and Hooker, 1981b; Christensen and Wilcoxson, 1966; Hooker, 1974; Kappelman and Tompson, 1966; and Lim and White, 1978). Resistance to Fusarium stalk rot in inbred 61C is reportedly due to two genes (Younis, 1969; Younis et al., 1969) and resistance to anthracnose stalk rot in inbred Mp305 is dominant and simply inherited (Carson, 1980; White et al., 1979).

Even though stalk rot and lodging continue to be serious problems, considerable gains have been made with improved hybrids. To illustrate the progress made for stalk lodging resistance, the percent lodging of a popular hybrid widely grown in the 1940s (US13) was compared with other hybrids grown in Missouri yield trials from 1938 to 1972 (Zuber, 1973). The average stalk lodging of US13 increased in trials in the late 1950s to the early 1970s as a result of higher fertility and plant popula-tions. Hybrids that were recent commercial releases had consistently lower amounts of lodging, suggesting that new hybrids with better stalk quality were replacing older ones with poorer stalk quality even though gains were often masked by increased fertility and plant populations.

12–2.4.9   Root Rots

Corn root rot diseases are among the least studied and understood diseases of corn. Root rot occurs on every corn plant in every field every year. The amount of yield loss cannot be estimated because techniques are not available where yield comparisons can be made on healthy vs. diseased plants. Many of the studies concerning root rots have been based on the isolation of various fungi from roots during the growing season and in some cases followed by inoculation of plants in the greenhouse for determination of pathogenicity. Fungi recovered from root systems are dependent on the media used for isolation. Pathogenicity studies may be difficult to interpret since inoculations of plants under stress, or where fungi are introduced into sterilized soil where no competition with other organisms exist, may result in root rot that does not occur in the field.

All researchers agree that (i) root rot is a complex involving many different fungi, bacteria, and nematodes; (ii) different groups of organisms occur on roots depending on the stage in the life cycle of the host, environmental conditions, genotype, and previous crops; and (iii) fungi vary in their ability to cause root rot.

Pythium spp. and *Fusarium* spp. are the most common genera of fungi isolated from corn roots grown in the USA. Pythium root rot is widely distributed and can be most severe during wet years in poorly drained soils. *Pythium graminicola* Subr. and *P. arrhenomanes* Drechs. have been most frequently isolated from corn roots and are often reported to be the most pathogenic. These two fungi have been considered synonymous by some and considered as distinct species by others (Middleton, 1943). *Pythium graminicola* and/or *P. arrhenomanes* is most frequently associated with root rot prior to flowering (Rao et al., 1978). Other *Pythium* spp. have been isolated from corn roots but are not considered to be as destructive. Apparently *P. graminicola* and/or *P. arrhenomanes* do not move from roots to stalks causing stalk rot. Control of Pythium root rot is best achieved by improved drainage.

Fusarium graminearum, F. moniliforme, F. tricinctum, F. oxysporum, and *F. solani* are also isolated from corn roots. *Fusarium graminearium* and *F. moniliforme* are pathogenic on corn, while *F. oxysporum* and *F. tricinctum* are secondary invaders (Palmer and Kommedahl, 1969).

Fungi isolated from roots include common seedling blight and stalk rot pathogens as well as a number of other pathogens and secondary invaders. Other than the previously discussed organisms a partial list includes *Rhizoctonia solani*, other *Fusarium* spp., *Drechslera rostrata*, *Pyrenochaeta terrestris, Phaeocytostroma ambiguum, Rhizopus* spp., *Penicillium* spp., *Trichoderma viride, Curvularia* spp., *Mortierella* spp., and *Sclerotium rolfsii*. It is clear from the number of genera involved that root rot diseases (much like stalk rot diseases) are the result of activity of numerous organisms. This greatly complicates the study of these diseases.

12–2.5 Ear Rots, Storage Molds, and Mycotoxins

Ear, kernel, and cob rots occur wherever corn is grown. These diseases rarely cause severe yield losses over wide geographical areas. However, they have been important in localized areas of the USA. Losses result from reduced test weight, poor grain quality and mycotoxins that may contaminate feeds and food. Mycotoxins have been reviewed in detail elsewhere (Wyllie and Morehouse, 1978). Ear, kernel, and cob rots vary greatly between years depending on preharvest environment and damage from insects, hail, and frost. These diseases may also reduce the allowable storage time of corn grain.

12–2.5.1 Fusarium Kernel or Ear Rot

Fusarium kernel or ear rot is the most widespread disease of corn ears. It can be found in virtually every field, every year, and is more prevalent in drier parts of the Corn Belt (Hoppe, 1942). Symptoms of the disease are scattered or groups of randomly infected kernels over the entire ear (Plate 12–8). Whitish pink to lavendar fungal growth is typical of Fusarium ear and kernel rot. Infection is also frequent at the tip of the ear where it is often associated with earworm and other types of damage.

Fusarium ear and kernel rot is caused by *Fusarium moniliforme* and the closely related *F. moniliforme* var. *subglutinans*. Characteristics of these two fungi are described in section 12–2.4.5 on Fusarium stalk rot.

Spores of the pathogen may enter through the silk channel at the tip of the ear and infect immature kernels (Koehler, 1959). Additional infections occur following injury to the ear. The fungus is also found where seed coats are broken as a consequence of "silk-cut or popped-kernel." The fungus may also be isolated from symptomless kernels. It is difficult to find grain lots where *F. moniliforme* cannot be found associated with at least a small percentage of the kernels.

Hybrids differ in susceptibility to Fusarium ear rot. Greater susceptibility occurs in high-lysine, brown midrib, *cms*-T male-sterile hybrids, and sweetcorn (Nicholson et al., 1976; Ooka and Kommedahl, 1977; Ullstrup, 1971a; Warmke and Schenck, 1971).

Acute toxicity in different animals has been reported with various mycotoxins produced by *F. moniliforme*. One interesting problem associated with the fungus was first described as moldy corn poisoning of horses in the latter part of the 19th century. Clinical signs of the syndrome may vary but are usually characterized by leucoencephalomalacia. Symptoms in horses (*Equus caballus*) occur several weeks after they have consumed moldy corn. Symptoms manifest a variety of neurologic disturbances and animals usually die.

12–2.5.2 Gibberella Ear Rot

Gibberella ear rot occurs throughout the Corn Belt but is more prevalent in the northern parts of this region. The disease is favored by cool, humid weather particularly with heavy rainfalls following silking of the crop. The symptoms of the disease are a reddish color that usually begins at the tip of the ear and progresses toward the butt (Plate 12–8). The rot rarely involves the entire ear. Husks may also be rotted and cemented to the ear with black perithecia formed on husk tissue. Usually perithecia do not produce ascospores until the following spring. In some cases, the rot will occur at the base of the ear and progress upward. Gibberella ear rot is easily distinguished from Fusarium ear rot. In Fusarium ear rot, scattered kernels on an ear are affected; whereas with Gibberella ear rot large groups of kernels on an ear are affected.

The causal agent of Gibberella ear rot is *Gibberella zeae*, the same fungus that is responsible for Gibberella stalk rot. The morphology of the fungus is described in the section on Gibberella stalk rot.

Gibberella ear rot is more severe when wet weather occurs 14 to 21 d following flowering (Tuite et al., 1974). The fungus infects silks and grows into the ear progressing down the ear during grain fill. Those hybrids with extremely tight husks appear to be more severely affected than those hybrids that have loose husks. Infections may also occur when heavy rainfall occurs late in the season, especially on hybrids where the ears do not turn down and water collects at the base of the ear.

Yield losses due to Gibberella ear rot are from both the damage of the grain per se as well as those losses that occur to animals (particularly swine, *Sus domesticus*) when grain is fed. *Gibberella zeae* produces several mycotoxins. One toxin that is produced is zearalenone, also referred to as F-2. This toxin is responsible for estrogenic mycotoxicoses with symptoms including enlargement of the uteri and mammary glands, vulvar swelling, vaginal prolapse, and atrophy of testes. Another toxin that is produced is deoxynivalenol, a cytotoxic tricothecene, which can be responsible for emesis and feed refusal in swine. Many other mycotoxins are produced by strains of *G. zeae*, however, zearalenone and deoxynivalenol are the most common and most studied. Ruminant animals and poultry do not seem to be as affected by these toxins as are swine.

Marked differences in resistance to Gibberella ear rot and mycotoxin formation have been reported among inbred lines and hybrids (Gendloff et al., 1986; Hart et al., 1984; Cullen et al., 1983; Shannon et al., 1980; Hart et al., 1984; Caldwell and Smalley, 1981). However, no reliable methods have been developed to produce inbred lines that are highly resistant when in hybrid combination.

12–2.5.3 Diplodia Ear Rot (Stenocarpella Ear Rot)

Diplodia ear rot is widely distributed throughout the Corn Belt but is present most often in fields where reduced tillage is used and corn follows corn. One of the earliest symptoms of ear rot is the bleaching of husks. When husks are opened, a white mold is seen on the ear. By harvest infected ears are completely rotted with husks tightly adhering to the ear. Pycnidia are embedded in the white mycelium at the base of rotted kernels and in cob tissue (Plate 12–8). Diplodia may cause destruction of the entire ear or just the butt or the upper tip.

Diplodia ear rot is caused by *Diplodia maydis*, which is the same fungus that causes Diplodia stalk rot. For a description of the fungus see section 12–2.4.2 on Diplodia stalk rot.

Diplodia maydis may infect the ear at any time; however, ears are most susceptible to infection 21 to 28 d after full silk. Spores produced in pycnidia associated with debris on the soil surface are splashed onto the silks. Early infection often results in complete rotting of the ear, whereas late infections result in only partial rotting of the ear. Diplodia ear rot is usually found close to sources of inoculum (Ullstrup, 1964) and is rarely found where inoculum has been buried by tillage or where inoculum is reduced following rotation with another crop.

Husk coverage and time of ear declination may contribute to the susceptibility or resistance of hybrids. Open husk hybrids and those in which ears are held in an upright position for a long time have been reported as susceptible (Koehler, 1951). In contrast, another report indicates tight husk coverage was a factor in reduced susceptibility (Boewe, 1936). Therefore, the effects of condition of husk coverage and ear declination may not have been completely resolved. The fungus does not appear to produce mycotoxins that have caused problems with animals under natural infection conditions in the USA. Toxins have been reported to be produced by the fungus in culture.

12–2.5.4 Aspergillus Ear and Kernel Rot

Several species of Aspergillus cause ear and kernel rots of corn. However, ear and kernel rots caused by *Aspergillus flavus* is the most serious. Symptoms include a greenish or yellowish tan discoloration on and between individual kernels. Often, kernels at the tip of the ear are infected. This is seen on those hybrids where husk coverage does not protect ears from damage due to insects, hail, and other factors.

Aspergillus flavus Link is charcterized by conidial heads that produce conidia in chains from uniseriate sterigmata. Conidia are finely roughened and variable in size and shape. Sclerotia are often present and reddish brown. Colonies are green-yellow to yellow-green, remaining green on Czapek's agar.

Aspergillus ear rot is important due to the production of several mycotoxins referred to as aflatoxins. Prior to the early 1970s aflatoxin contamination of corn grain was generally considered to be a problem resulting from growth of the fungus and toxin production in storage. This is still true in most years in the upper midwest areas of the USA. Several reports in the late 1960s and early 1970s indicated the presence of aflatoxin in freshly harvested corn with the first definitive report of toxin production in the field in 1975 (Anderson et al., 1975). Aflatoxins are extremely toxic having a number of effects on mammals. The carcinogenic, as well as toxic properties of the compounds, has caused great concern about the potential hazards not only to animals but also to human health. Aflaxtoxin contamination of corn is a serious problem, particularly in the southern and southeastern USA. Several factors have been associated with fungal infection and aflatoxin production in preharvested corn. These include high temperatures, insect damage, and plant stress and have been reviewed in more depth elsewhere (Widstrom et al., 1984). *Aspergillus flavus* is a thermotolerant fungus, thus making it more competitive at higher temperatures encountered during dry years. The fungus increases inoculum in debris and pollinated silk tissue. The disease may be reduced by irrigation and tillage (Payne et al., 1986).

12–2.5.5 Other Ear and Kernel Rots

A number of other ear and kernel rots have been reported on corn. Usually these are of little economic importance because of their restricted occurrence.

Nigrospora cob and ear rot is widespread, but rarely important. There is no conspicuous fungal growth between rows or on the surface of kernels as is often seen with other ear rot diseases. Infection usually starts at the butt of the ear resulting in kernels that are loose on the cob (Plate 12–8). The kernels exhibit bleached or whitish streaks and masses of small, round, black spores at their base. Rotted cob and shank tissue is easily broken during combining. This results in shelling problems and pieces of cob tissue mixed with the grain. The causal fungus is *Nigrospora oryzae* (Berk. & Br.) Petch. (Syn. = *Basidiosporium gallarum* Moll.). The fungus is considered to be a weak parasite. Ears are attacked after plants are weakened or killed by frost, drought, or poor fertility.

Gray ear rot usually is only found when warm wet weather occurs for several weeks following silking. The disease was common in seed fields where double-cross hybrids were being made in the 1940s but has virtually disappeared since then (Ullstrup, 1977). Symptoms begin with grayish white growth on and between kernels that resembles that of Diplodia ear rot. Later, ears become more or less solid slate gray to black in color rather than the shades of brown that occur with Diplodia ear rot. The causal organism is *Botryosphaeria zeae* (Stout), von Arx & Muller (Syn. = *Physalospora zeae* Stout), asexual stage *Macrophoma zeae* Tehon and Daniels.

Penicillium rot occurs on ears and kernels especially following injury (Plate 12–8). Several species of Penicillium may be isolated from kernels at harvest but *P. oxalicum* is the only one that causes definite ear rot damage following inoculation (Caldwell et al., 1981).

Cladosporium kernel or ear rot is often associated with insect injury on kernels and may occur following frost damage. Symptoms include greenish black striations or blotches on the kernels scattered on the ear. When the seed coat is broken, greenish black mycelium of the causal fungus may develop on exposed starch surfaces. The disease is caused by *Cladosporium herbarum* Lk. ex Fr. and *C. cladosporioides* (Fres.) De Varies (Syn. = *Hormodendrum cladosporioides* (Fres.) (Sacc.).

Rhizoctonia ear rot may be found following extended periods of warm, wet weather. Symptoms include salmon-pink mold growth on the ear followed by the development of dark brown to black sclerotia developing on the outer husks. The causal fungus is *Rhizoctonia zeae* Voorhees.

Trichoderma ear rot usually occurs when corn is under stress. The disease is caused by *Trichoderma viride* Pers. and is recognized by the bright green powdery growth of the fungus on and between the kernels. The entire ear may be covered with the fungus.

Other fungi such as *Alternaria* spp., *Rhizopus* spp., *Corticium sasakii, Sclerotium rolfsii, Gonatobotrys zeae, Aspergillus niger, Fusarium tricinctum*, and *Cephalosporium acremonium* have been associated with ear and kernel rots. In other cases, fungi that are more often associated with diseases of other parts of the plant may be associated with ear and kernel rots. Examples of these include *Colletotrichum graminicola, Bipolaris zeicola, Bipolaris maydis*, and *Stenocarpella macrospora*.

12–2.5.6 Storage Molds

The fungal kernel rots of corn can be divided into two groups. The first group includes the field fungi that require higher moisture (above 18% grain moisture) in order to grow and reproduce. These fungi cause ear rots in the field. The second group, referred to as storage fungi, grow best below 18% grain moisture. Storage and storage molds are reviewed in greater depth elsewhere (Christensen, 1974; Tuite and Foster, 1979). The importance of storage fungi has increased with the change from harvesting ear corn to harvesting shelled grain. The corn combine allows for rapid harvest and reduced field losses, but does result in more damage to corn kernels, especially when corn is harvested at high moistures. Storing shelled grain rather than ear corn has improved the ability to store and ship grain, but has increased problems with storage fungi.

Normally storage fungi are not present in high numbers in grain at harvest. The most important storage fungi are in the genera Penicillium and Aspergillus. Of the species of Penicillium, *P. oxalicum* is the most common species associated with grain at harvest. With *Aspergillus* spp., *A. flavus*, and *A. niger* are the most common species associated with grain at export points and on-farm storage. A study of fungal populations in USA farm-stored grain indicated that *A. glaucus* was associated with 84% of the corn samples taken from farm bins in 27 states in 1980. It had infected an average of 26% of the kernels (Sauer et al., 1984). A similar study with corn samples at export terminals associated *A. glaucus* with nearly all samples taken (Sauer et al., 1982). Usually, storage fungi are found associated with dead plant materials, soil, and in places where moisture levels are relatively low. Spores of these fungi are spread during mechanical combining of the grain crop. Grain becomes coated with additional spores during the drying processes as air with spores is passed over the grain. More spores become coated on the grain during loading, unloading, and the blending of contaminated grain lots into good grain lots. The incidence and severity of damage caused by *Aspergillus* spp. and *Penicillium* spp. is dependent upon a number of factors, including storage temperature, grain moisture, relative humidity of air in the grain mass, fungal species present, levels of preharvest infection, and mechanical damage. After a kernel is infected by a storage fungus, the fungus begins to rot the kernel any time that moisture and/or temperature conditions become favorable for fungal growth. In general, under favorable temperature conditions, *Aspergillus* spp. can grow at moisture levels as low as 13.5% with rapid growth above that level. Penicillium species will grow at moisture exceeding 16.5%. As these fungi grow they produce metabolic heat and moisture. This creates conditions for growth of field fungi that may be present in the grain lot, thus speeding the decay process.

Symptoms of damage due to storage fungi include discoloration of the embryo, blackening of kernels, a musty odor, and in some cases the production of mycotoxins.

Currently, control of storage molds relies on the integration of three controls. These include: (i) the prevention of mechanical damage during harvest and transportation (an intact kernel of corn is more resistant to penetration by fungi than a kernel that has been cracked or broken); (ii) keeping moisture levels below those that are optimum for fungal growth; and (iii) using cool temperatures for control of storage fungi as is done much of the upper midwest Corn Belt. During the winter months, cool air is blown through the grain and the grain mass becomes cold enough to prevent fungal growth.

With these three controls available, the common practice is to dry corn to 15 to 16% moisture and maintain this moisture as long as temperatures are cool. Corn can be stored in much of the Midwest from harvest to the next spring using a combination of cool temperature and moistures of 15 to 17%. During the spring, however, some kernels which have higher moisture due to moisture migration in the bin or uneven drying may begin to decay. To prevent fungal growth at warmer temperatures, corn in the summer is often dried to 13.5 to 14% moisture, thus moving grain moisture levels to those that are less conducive for fungal growth.

Economic losses due to storage molds are obscured by the grain grading system used in the USA and the blending of good and damaged lots of grain. The grading system allows for a certain amount of damaged kernels with premiums sometimes being paid for corn with less damage. High damage corn can be purchased for a reduced price and blended with grain with low damage, resulting in grain that is at the allowable damage level. Therefore, damaged grain that represents an economic loss to the seller may be a source of profit to the purchaser. Mold-damaged grain that is fed to animals may not result in measurable adverse effects to animals when mycotoxins are not produced at high levels. Therefore, damaged grain may be satisfactory animal feed and the damage does not represent an economic loss to a livestock farmer.

Even in the absence of extensive data on the economic losses due to storage molds, the losses are significant enough to warrant additional research (Christensen, 1980). Controls of storage molds in addition to those previously discussed include chemical control and genetic improvement (Tuite and Foster, 1979).

With chemical control technique, proprionic acid has been the most effective and widely used. The advantage of proprionic acid is that corn can be stored at relatively high moistures. The disadvantages are that this treatment is expensive, corrosive to metal, and treated grain has an odor. Proprionic acid has its widest use on exposed piles of animal feed in the drier regions of the USA. Recent research has shown that low rates of fungicides such as thiabendazole may be effective in preventing penetration of corn kernels by storage fungi during drying and storage.

Control of storage molds by genetic resistance may have promise, but does not have application at this time. Breeding for resistance to storage fungi is complicated by the lack of usable methods for screening for resistance and the number of different fungi involved.

12–2.6 Nematode Diseases

Nematodes are small invertebrate animals also known as roundworms or eelworms. All plant-parasitic nematodes possess a stylet used to injure roots and through which the nematode feeds. Many nematodes have been associated with corn roots. The most common indigenous nematodes damaging to corn include the root-lesion nematodes (*Pratylenchus* spp.), root-knot nematodes (*Meloidogyne* spp.), lance nematodes (*Hoplolaimus* spp.), stunt nematodes (*Tylenchorhynchus* spp.), stubby-root nematodes (*Trichodorus* spp.), needle nematodes (*Longidorus* spp.), daggar nematodes (*Xiphinema* spp.), sting nematodes (*Belonolaimus* spp.), awl nematodes (*Dolichodorus* spp.), and spiral nematodes (*Helicotylenchus* spp.). In 1981, the corn cyst nematode (*Heterodera zeae* Kosky, Swarup, and Sethi) identified only from Egypt and India, was also found on corn in Maryland (Sardanelli et al., 1981).

The geographic distribution of corn nematodes is probably more a result of their environmental adaptation than their host range. Most of the nematodes attacking corn are known to have wide host ranges. Within a field the population of nematodes is influenced by cropping history, tillage practices, local climatic conditions, soil structure, soil texture, pH, fertility, organic matter, cation exchange capacity, soil osmotic pressure, soil moisture, and the presence of predators or parasites (Norton, 1978).

Nematodes affect corn primarily through mechanical damage to the roots caused by the stylet and through digestive enzymes injected from the nematodes into the corn roots. The injury to the corn roots has been reported to create avenues of entry for other root-rotting pathogens (Kisiel et al., 1969; Palmer et al., 1967). Nematodes can be separated by their feeding patterns. Ectoparasitic nematodes feed on the roots through their stylet which penetrates the epidermal and cortical cells while their main body remains outside the root. Semiendoparasitic nematodes penetrate but do not embed their whole body in the root tissue. Migratory endoparasitic nematodes completely penetrate roots, feed on cortical cells, and migrate throughout the roots. Sedentary endoparasitic nematodes penetrate the roots, find a good feeding site, and remain at that site for the remainder of their feeding.

Aboveground symptoms of nematode injury may resemble symptoms caused by nutrient deficiency in localized areas of a field. Also the wilting of the plants during a hot day, followed by recovery at night, is common. When these types of symptoms are observed, root systems of affected plants should be examined. The stubbing of roots, root systems with fine feeder roots, and/or the presence of root lesions indicate the possiblity of nematode activity. The only way to verify the existence of a nematode problem is by taking soil and plant samples, identifying the presence of the specific nematode, and quantifying the population level to see if the populations are high enough to warrant concern.

While the mechanism of resistance has been studied for many nematodes across a wide spectrum of crops (Giebel, 1982), little is known about corn. Differences in susceptibility of corn inbreds and hybrids have been observed (Baldwin and Barker, 1970; Johnson, 1975; Nelson, 1957b). However, the potential resistance in corn to nematodes has yet to be exploited.

Nematodes can be controlled through the use of crop rotation and soil application of nematicides. Crop rotation has been an effective control of some nematodes, but the actual species of the nematode involved must be known so the correct cropping sequence can be used (Nusbaum and Ferris, 1973; Tarte, 1971). Nematicides can be used to reduce populations of nematodes in the soil. To maximize effectiveness, treatment should be after specific identification of the actual nematode species causing the problem. If this is not possible, a trial treatment of nematicides in strips across the field is advised. The actual amount of chemical control used is dependent on the value of the type of corn crop involved.

12–2.7 Witchweed

Witchweeds, *Striga asiatica* (L.) Kuntze (Syn. *S. lutea* Lour.) and *S. hermonthica* Benth., are parasitic seed plants that attack corn and many other economic grass plants. They are obligate parasites. Their distribution is primarily in Africa, Australia, India, Southeast Asia, and Indonesia. *Striga asiatica* occurs in localized areas within North and South Carolina in the USA (Eplee, 1981).

Corn plants infected by witchweed exhibit symptoms of drought stress and nutrient deficiencies even though moisture is adequate and the fertility program is good. Losses can range from slight to severe, depending on the amount of parasitism across the affected field.

Striga asiatica is a flowering plant with square stems, small bright green leaves, and flowers ranging in color from near-white to brick-red with yellow centers and undersides. A single plant can produce 500 000 seeds <0.25-mm long. Seeds are dormant for 3 to 18 months prior to germination. The parasite overseasons as seeds. These seeds remain viable for 15 to 20 yr in the soil. They are disseminated by water, wind, or contaminated farm equipment.

For the seeds to germinate a chemical stimulant supplied by hosts and some nonhosts is required. Stimulated by the chemical supplied by a host, the seeds germinate, the rootlets contact the host roots, the rootlets join the host roots by producing haustoria within the host-root cells, and the infection process is completed. The witchweed feeds off of the host until seed production is completed (60–90 d) and then dies. If the chemical stimulant for germination is supplied by a nonhost such as soybean, peanut (*Arachis hypogaea* L.), or cotton (*Gossypium hirsutum* L.), the witchweed seedling rootlets cannot join with the nonhost roots and the witchweed dies.

Nothing is known about potential resistances or their inheritances for corn. A major problem is in establishing uniform infestations of witchweed to evaluate material. Research is progressing on obtaining uniform germination of witchweed seeds by selecting seeds of uniform size (Bebawi et al., 1984). This should allow for the success of more definitive research in the future.

Currently, witchweed in the USA is being contained by imposing both federal and state quarantines for infested areas. Two main areas of activity are being addressed in an attempt to eradicate witchweed: (i) controlling the witchweed plant prior to its reproduction and (ii) devitalizing the seeds in the soil.

Control of the witchweed plant is accomplished through the use of herbicides. The chemicals 2,4-D (2,4-dichlorophenoxyacetic acid), paraquat, trifluralin (*a, a, a*-trifluoro-2,6-dinitro-*N,N*-dipropyl-*p*-toluidine), and oxyfluorfen [2-chloro-1-(3-ethoxy-4-nitrophenoxy)-4-(trifluoromethyl) benzene] (Eplee and Langston, 1970; Langston et al., 1976; Shaw et al., 1962) can be used singly or in various combinations to control witchweed.

The research involving devitalizing of witchweed seed has lead to the isolation and identification of the chemical stimulant required for germination of the witchweed seeds. This chemical has been named *strigol* (Cook et al., 1972) and has been chemically synthesized (Heather et al., 1974), but is not considered as a practical soil treatment. Ethylene gas has also been shown to induce the germination of witchweed seeds (Egley and Dale, 1970) and its use has been succesful, but limited, due to funding of this endeavor. The use of nonhost trap crops that stimulate witchweed seed germination but do not allow parasitism can also reduce the amount of seeds in the soil. To effectively use trap crops as a control measure, all other grassy-weed hosts must be eliminated from the field and cropping of these nonhosts should be maintained over a period of 4 to 5 yr.

12–2.8 Diseases of Exotic Occurrence

The major emphasis of this chapter has been devoted to corn disease that occurs within the USA. However, corn diseases from outside the USA have been described and some can be economically significant on corn grown in other areas of the world.

At least eight foliar diseases and one additional race of a pathogen which exists within the USA have been described from outside the USA. These diseases are horizontal banded blight (Syn. = banded leaf and sheath blight) caused by *Rhizoctonia microsclerotia* Matz, the imperfect stage of *Corticium solani* (Prill and Delacr.) [Syn. = *Thanatephorus cucumeris* (Frank) Donk]; vertical banded blight caused by *Marasmiellus paspali* (Petch) Singer; Didymella leaf spot caused by *Didymella exitialis* (Mor.) Muller; Hyalothyridium leaf spot caused by *Hyalothyridium* spp.; Leptosphaeria leaf spot caused by *Leptosphaeria* spp.; Phaeosphaeria leaf spot caused by *Phaeosphaeria maydis* (P. Henn.) Rane, Payak, and Renfro (Syn. = *Sphaerulina maydis* P. Henn.); tar spot caused by *Phyllachora maydis* Maubl.; and tropical rust caused by *Physopella zeae* (Mains) Cummings and Ramachar (Syn. = *Angiospora zeae* Mains). All of these diseases are caused by fungi. Their occurrence is mostly in tropical areas of the world where moderate temperatures and conditions of high humidity prevail (De Leon, 1984; Payak and Sharma, 1986; Shurtleff, 1980). An additional race of *Bipolaris maydis* designated race C has been reported from the People's Republic of China (Wei et al., 1988) which appears to preferentially attack *cms*-C stocks as race T was able to preferentially attack *cms*-T corn stocks. Normal cytoplasm, *cms*-S, and *cms*-T stocks offer resistance to this race C of *B. maydis*.

Ergot (also known as horse's tooth) is caused by *Claviceps gigantea* Fuentes, de la Isla, Ullstrup and Rodrigues and occurs in some humid valleys of central Mexico.

At least seven systemic diseases in addition to those described within the USA are known to exist. Six of these are downy mildews and are brown stripe downy mildew caused by *Sclerophthora rayssiae* Kenneth, Kaltin, and Wahl var. *zeae* Payak and Renfro; Java downy mildew caused by *Peronosclerospora maydis* (Racib.) C.G. Shaw (Syn. = *Sclerospora maydis* (Racib.) Butl.; leaf splitting downy mildew caused by *Peronosclerospora miscanthi* (T. Miyake) C.G. Shaw (Syn. = *Sclerospora miscanthi* T. Miyake); Philippine downy mildew caused by *Peronosclerospora philippinensis* (Weston) C.G. Shaw (Syn. = *Sclerospora philip-

pinensis Weston); Spontaneum downy mildew caused by *Peronosclerospora spontanea* (Weston) C.G. Shaw (Syn. = *Sclerospora spontanea* Weston); and sugarcane downy mildew caused by *Peronosclerospora sacchari* (T. Miyake) C.G. Shaw (Syn. = *Sclerospora sacchari* T. Miyake). Using a combination of eradication of infected plants, good husbandry, rotation to nonhosts, and resistant cultivars, these diseases have been reduced in their severity. Resistance to brown stripe downy mildew and Java downy mildew is expressed polygenically largely through additive gene action. Resistance to Philippine downy mildew varies from being partially dominant to quantitatively inherited to fully dominant with overdominance being expressed. Resistance appears to be influenced by inocula density and seedling vigor (Frederiksen and Renfro, 1977).

The other important systemic disease is maize streak caused by an isometric virion 20 nm in diameter. The infective entity is a circular, single-stranded DNA. It is vectored by five *Cicadulina* spp., leafhoppers. It is widespread throughout much of Africa, Mauritius, Madagascar, India, and Reunion. Resistance to maize streak has been found and varies from being monogenic—to being controlled by three genes—to being expressed as additive gene action depending on the corn germ plasm being studied (Gelaw, 1986).

Late wilt is a stalk rot caused by the fungus *Cephalosporium maydis* Samra, Sabet, and Hingorain [Syn. = *Gaeumannomyces graminis* (Sacc.) Arx and Olivier]. Late wilt is known to occur in India and Egypt. Symptoms of wilting can be as early as flowering. Resistance has been identified with additive genetic effects being the most important (Galal et al., 1985).

12–3 DISEASES INDUCED BY ABIOTIC FACTORS

Abiotic diseases of corn are caused by noninfectious entities. Two main types of abiotic diseases affect corn. One type of disease is the result of internal genetic factors within the plant. The other is a result of external stimuli being exerted upon the corn plant. This type of disease can be further grouped into climatically induced diseases, management practice-induced diseases, and diseases caused by air pollutants.

12–3.1 Genetically Induced Abiotic Diseases

Genetically induced diseases, other than those genes or alleles conditioning susceptibility to an infectious agent, are usually seen only in corn breeders' developmental nurseries. Most are simple recessives in their inheritance (Neuffer et al., 1968) with only a few shown to be dominant (Neuffer and Calvert, 1975). Some are genes that limit or alter the ability of the corn plant to produce chlorophyll. Examples include genes for white to yellow virescent seedlings, striate, stripe, or various other variegations. Some mimic infectious diseases and are lethal to the plants with these genes. Others, such as polymitotic, nuclear genetic male steriles, and cytoplasmic male steriles affect pollen production. Affecting seed set are genes for barrenness, defective endosperms, vivipary, and asynaptic. Also, the conditions of "silk-cut" and "popped kernels" are associated with the development of certain corn inbreds and appear to be under genetic control. Since the majority of these genetic traits are undesirable, they are usually discarded from corn breeder's nurseries. Two notable exceptions exist. These are the nuclear genetic and cytoplasmic male-sterility factors (Duvick, 1972; Patterson, 1973). Their use is in providing sterile females in seed production fields. This allows the seed industry to produce a quality product with less expense, because these fields either do not require detasseling or require less detasseling than fields where a fully fertile female is used. Since the epiphytotic of southern corn leaf blight in 1970 when *cms*-T plants were found to be more vulnerable to infection than those with "normal" cytoplasm or other *cms* sources, these alternatives are closely monitored for their reaction to many corn diseases.

12–3.2 Abiotic Diseases of External Origin

Climatically induced diseases can occur regardless of precautions taken by farmers. From planting to harvest, the corn crop is exposed to the potential problems of excessive moisture, soil crusting, Faris banding, sun scald, late frost, wind injury resulting in root lodging or desiccation, drought, high temperatures, hail, lightning, and early frosts. Excessive moisture and soil crusting can have an effect in stand establishment of the corn crop. Faris banding can result in bands of yellow across the leaves due to inhibition of chloroplast development when exposed to low night temperatures (Slack et al., 1974). Sun scald occurs in the spring when night temperatures are cool, followed by clear sunny mornings. Symptoms are a silvery-gray appearance to the leaves. A late frost in the spring or an early frost in the fall can kill plants. In the spring if the growing point is still underground usually only the leaves are damaged and the plants will recover. Winds can result in lodging of corn plants or desiccation of leaf tissue. Hail or lightning can occur at any time during the growing season. Both are usually localized in their occurrence. Hail, which shreds the leaves and bruises the sheath and stalk tissue, occurs more often than lightning. Plants affected by hail are more susceptible to stalk rots, common smut, and Goss's wilt.

Abiotic diseases induced by management practices in crop production are usually either due to nutrient deficiencies (Krantz and Melsted, 1964; Mortvedt et al., 1972) or herbicide toxicities (Jugenheimer, 1976; Shurtleff, 1980).

The most common nutrient deficiencies involve N, P, K, Mg, and Zn. Nitrogen-deficient corn plants are usually stunted and spindly with yellow-green leaves. As plants mature they may develop a V-shaped yellowing around the midrib of the lower leaves. Under N-deficient conditions, ears do not tip-fill. Phosphorus deficiency is usually expressed as purpling of the leaves of young plants. If the deficiency is not corrected, ears of affected plants will be small, poorly filled at the tips, and twisted. Potassium deficiency results in yellowing and necrosis of the leaf margins of lower leaves. Stalk lodging at harvest may be prevalent in fields low in K. Ears may be small with poorly developed tips and possess small, poorly filled kernels. The initial expression of Mg deficiency is usually a yellowing of the upper leaves. Later, yellow-white interveinal striping is evident. Corn plants short of Zn exhibit symptoms shortly after emergence. Affected plants lack vigor, have shorter internodes and develop elongated pale strips between the midrib and margin. Other nutrient deficiencies which have been reported for corn but are seldom seen include Ca, S, Fe, Cu, B, and Mo deficiencies. After a specific nutrient problem is identified, it can be corrected by the application of the required nutrient. Monitoring available nutrients can be accomplished through soil- or plant-tissue analysis.

Selective herbicides are chemicals that inhibit targeted weeds, but usually not crop plants for which the herbicides are registered. Nonselective herbicides affect all plants. Misapplication accounts for the majority of herbicide injuries to corn. However, under certain environments, herbicides registered for use on corn and applied properly can injure corn.

The triazines, acetanilides, and phenyluresas can cause damage to corn when very cool and wet conditions follow planting. The damage is largely due to the inability of the corn plant under these stress environments to metabolize the active component of the herbicide into nontoxic substances. Symptoms of triazine and phenyluresas injury are similar in that the leaves turn yellow and brown, die back from the tips, and under severe injury the plants will die. Damage from the acetanilides is seen in plants which have stunted or malformed shoots which leaf out underground. Excessive rainfall favors thiocarbamate injury. These products are commonly marketed with a herbicide antidote to protect corn added to the active compound. Problems can result during periods of excessive rainfall, which leaches out the antidote faster than the active component. When this occurs there is a twisting of the plants and ear malformation may occur. Benzoic acid and 2,4-D both tend to act like growth stimulants. Conditions favoring injury to corn are hot days for 2,4-D and unfavorable seedling emergence conditions for benzoic acid. Symptoms of affected plants are similar and may include buggy-whipping, malformation of roots, or lodging. Timing of application and soil placement of the herbicide affect damage to corn by the dinitroanilines. When placed in the root zone of young seedlings the dinitroanilines can cause stunting, uneven plant height, stubbing of roots, and reduced stands.

Resistance in corn to some herbicides has been investigated. Atrazine resistance in corn is conditioned by a single dominant allele (Grogan et al., 1963), while resistance to Eradicane is controlled by a single recessive allele (Pfund and Crum, 1977).

Air pollutants can damage corn. Sweet corn is more sensitive to pollutants than corn grown for grain or silage. Chlorine fluorides, ozone, peroxyacetyl nitrate, and sulfur dioxide are examples of pollutants known to affect corn. The severity of symptoms is dependent on the concentration of the pollutant and the environmental factors of light, temperature, humidity, soil moisture, and plant nutrition (Heck, 1968). When these environmental conditions are optimal for plant growth, they are also optimal for potential injury to corn by air pollutants. Differences in resistance by sweet corn to ozone have been observed (Cameron, 1975), and techniques using peroxidase banding patterns show promise as a screening procedure for ozone sensitivity (Podleckis et al., 1984).

REFERENCES

Association of Official Seed Analysts. 1983. Seed vigor testing handbook. Assoc. Off. Seed Anal. Handb. Contr. 32:1–88.

Al-Sohaily, I.A., C.J. Mankin, and G. Semeniuk. 1963a. Pathogenicity to sorghum and corn of a hybrid between the head smut fungi on each of these crops. Phytopathology 53:360–361.

——, ——, and ——. 1963b. Physiologic specialization of *Sphacelotheca reiliana* to sorghum and corn. Phytopathology 53:723–726.

Alstatt, G.E. 1945. A new corn disease in the Rio Grande Valley. Plant Dis. Rep. 29:533–534.

Anderson, H.W., E.W. Nehring, and W.R. Wichser. 1975. Aflatoxin contamination of corn in the field. J. Agric. Food Chem. 23:775–782.

Ark, P.L. 1940. Bacterial stalk rot of field corn caused by *Phytomonas lapsa*. Phytopathology 30:1 (Abstr.).

——. Persistence of *Phytomonas lapsa* on seed of field corn. Plant Dis. Rep. 25:202.

Arny, D.C., E.B. Smalley, A.J. Ullstrup, G.L. Worf, and R.W. Ahrens. 1971. Eyespot of maize, a disease new to North America. Phytopathology 61:54–57.

——, G.L. Worf, R.W. Ahrens, and M.F. Lindsey. 1970. Yellow leaf blight of maize in Wisconsin: Its history and the reactions of inbreds and crosses to the inciting fungus (*Phyllosticta* sp.). Plant Dis. Rep. 54:281–285.

Ayers, J.E., J.S. Boyle, and D.T. Gordon. 1978. The occurrence of maize dwarf and maize dwarf mosaic viruses in Pennsylvania in 1977. Plant Dis. Rep. 62:820–821.

——, R.R. Nelson, Carol Koons, and G.L. Schiefele. 1970. Reactions of various maize inbreds and single crosses in normal and male-sterile cytoplasm to the yellow leaf blight organism, (*Phyllosticta* sp.). Plant Dis. Rep. 54:277–280.

Baldwin, J.C., and K.R. Barker. 1970. Host suitability of selected hybrids, varieties, and inbreds of corn to populations of *Meloidogyne* spp. J. Nematol. 2:345–350.

Bancroft, J.B., A.J. Ullstrup, M. Messieha, C.E. Bracker, and T.E. Snazelle. 1966. Some biological and physical properties of a Midwestern isolate of maize dwarf mosaic virus. Phytopathology 56:474–478.

Bebawi, F.F., R.E. Eplee, and R.S. Norris. 1984. Effect of age, size, and weight of witchweed seeds on host/parasite relations. Phytopathology 74:1074–1078.

Beckman, P.M., and G.A. Payne. 1982. External growth, penetration, and development of *Cercospora zeae-maydis* in corn leaves. Phytopathology 72:810–815.

——, and ——. 1983. Cultural techniques and conditions influencing growth and sporulation of *Cercospora zeae-maydis* and lesion development in corn. Phytopathology 73:286–289.

Bekele, E., and D.R. Sumner. 1983. Epidemiology of southern corn leaf blight in continuous corn culture. Plant Dis. 67:738–742.

Bergquist, R.R. 1985. Inheritance estimates of resistance in maize (*Zea mays*) to gray leaf spot (*Cercospora zeae-maydis*). Phytopathology 75:1310 (Abstr.).

————, and O.R. Masias. 1974. Physiologic specialization in *Trichometasphaeria turcica* f. sp. *zeae* and *T. turcica* f. sp. *sorghi* in Hawaii. Phytopathology 64:645–649.

Biddle, J.A., E.J. Braun, and D.C. McGee. 1985. Epidemiology and seed transmission of Goss's wilt in corn. p. 962. *In* Phytopathology abstracts. Am. Phytopathological Soc., St. Paul.

Blanco, M.H., M.G. Johnson, T.R. Colbert, and M.S. Zuber. 1977. An inoculation technique for Stewart's wilt disease of corn. Plant Dis. Rep. 61:413–416.

————, M.S. Zuber, J.R. Wallin, D.V. Loonan, and G.F. Krause. 1979. Host resistance to Stewart's disease in maize. Phytopathology 69:849–853.

Bockelman, D.L., L.E. Claflin, and J.K. Uyemoto. 1982. Host range and seed-transmission studies of maize chlorotic mottle virus in grasses and corn. Plant Dis. 66:216–218.

Boewe, G.H. 1936. The relation of ear rot prevalence in Illinois corn fields to ear coverage by husks. State of Ill. Nat. Hist. Surv. Div. Contrib. Sec. of Applied Bot. Plant Pathol. Pub. 273.

Bojanowski, J. 1969. Studies of inheritance of reaction to common smut in corn. Theor. Appl. Genet. 39:32–42.

Boosalis, M.G., D.R. Sumner, and A.S. Rao. 1967. Overwintering of conidia of *Helminthosporium turcicum* on corn residues and in the soil in Nebraska. Phytopathology 57:990–996.

Boothroyd, C.W. 1971. Transmission of *Helminthosporium maydis* race T by infected corn seed. Phytopathology 61:747–748.

————, and H.W. Israel. 1980. A new mosaic disease of corn. Plant Dis. 64:218–219.

Bradfute, O.E., R.E. Gingery, D.T. Gordon, and L.R. Nault. 1972a. Tissue ultrastructure, sedimentation and leafhopper transmission of a virus associated with a maize dwarfing disease. J. Cell. Biol. 55:25a.

————, R. Louie, and J.K. Knoke. 1972b. Isometric virus-like particles in maize with stunt symptoms. Phytopathology 62:748 (Abstr.).

————, L.R. Nault, D.C. Robertson, and R.W. Toler. 1977. Maize bushy stunt—a disease associated with a non-helical mycoplasma-like organism. Proc. Am. Phytopathol. Soc. 4:171 (Abstr.).

————, and D.C. Robertson. 1974. Identification of the Mississippi corn stunt agent by electron microscopy. Proc. Am. Phytopathol. Soc. 1:35–36 (Abstr.).

————, J.H. Tsai, and D.T. Gordon. 1981. Corn stunt spiroplasma and viruses associated with a maize disease epidemic in southern Florida. Plant. Dis. 65:837–841.

Broyles, J.W. 1962. Penetration of meristematic tissues of corn by *Physoderma maydis*. Phytopathology 52:1013–1016.

Burnette, D.C., and D.G. White. 1985. Inheritance of resistance to *Bipolaris maydis* race 0 in crosses derived from nine resistant inbred lines of maize. Phytopathology 75:1195–1200.

Burns, E.E., and M.C. Shurtleff. 1973. Observations of *Physoderma maydis* in Illinois: Effects of tillage practices in field corn. Plant Dis. Rep. 57:630–633.

Caldwell, R.W., and E.G. Smalley. 1981. Effect of host genotype on zearalenone contamination of corn. Pythopathology 71:211 (Abstr.).

————, J. Tuite, and W.W. Carlton. 1981. Pathogenicity of *Penicillia* to corn ears. Phytopathology 71:175–180.

Cameron, J.W. 1975. Inheritance in sweet corn for resistance to acute ozone injury. J. Am. Soc. Hortic. Sci. 100:577–579.

Cammack, R.H. 1954. Observations in *Puccina polysora* Underwood in West Africa. West Afr. Maize Rust Res. Unit Annu. Rep. 1:16–31.

Carson, M.L. 1980. Sources and inheritance of resistance to anthracnose stalk rot of corn. Ph.D. thesis. Univ. of Illinois, Urbana-Champaign (Diss. Abstr. 81–08459).

————. 1985. First report of eyespot (Kabetiella zeae) of corn in South Dakota. Plant Dis. 69:117.

————, and A.L. Hooker. 1981a. Inheritance of resistance to anthracnose leaf blight in five inbred lines of corn. Phytopathology 71:488–491.

————, and ————. 1981b. Inheritance of resistance to stalk rot of corn caused by *Colletotrichum graminicola*. Phytopathology 71:1190–1196.

Castillo, J., and T.T. Herbert. 1974. Nueva enfermedad virosa afectando al maiz en al Peru. Fitopatologia 9:79–84.

Castillo-Loayza, J. 1976. Maize virus and virus-like diseases in Peru. p. 40–44. *In* L.E.

Williams et al. (ed.) Proc. Maize Virus Dis. Colloq. Workshop. 16–19 August. Ohio Agric. Res. Dev. Ctr., Wooster.

Castor, L.L., J.E. Ayers, A.A. MacNab, and R.A. Krause. 1975. Computerized forecasting system for Stewart's bacterial disease on corn. Plant Dis. Rep. 59:533–536.

———, ———, and R.R. Nelson. 1977. Controlled-environment studies on the epidemiology of yellow leaf blight of corn. Phytopathology 67:85–90.

Chang, C.-M., A.L. Hooker, and S.M. Lim. 1977. An inoculation technique for determining Stewart's bacterial leaf blight reaction in corn. Plant Dis. Rep. 61:1077–1079.

Chen, T.A., and C.H. Liao. 1975. Corn stunt spiroplasma: Isolation, cultivation, and proof of pathogenicity. Science (Washington, DC) 188:1015–1017.

Chilton, S.P. 1940. Delayed reduction of the diploid nucleus in the promycelia of *Ustilago zeae*. Phytopathology 30:622–623.

Christensen, C.M. (ed.) 1974. Storage of cereal grains and their products, Vol. 2. Am. Assoc. of Cereal Chemists, St. Paul.

Christensen, C.M. 1980. Needed: Research on storage molds in grains, seeds, and their products. Plant Dis. 64:1067–1070.

Christensen, J.J. 1931. Studies on the genetics of *Ustilago zeae*. Phytopathol. Z. 4:129–188.

———. 1963. Corn smut caused by *Ustilago maydis*. Monogr. 2. Am. Phytopathol. Soc., St. Paul.

———, and R.D. Wilcoxson. 1966. Stalk rot of corn. Monogr. 3. Phytopathol. Soc., St. Paul.

Chupp, C. 1953. A monograph of the fungus genus *Cercospora*. Ronald Press, Ithaca, NY.

Committee on Standardization of Common Names for Plant Diseases. 1985. Common names for plant disease. Plant Dis. 69:649–676.

Comstock, J.C., C.A. Martinson, and A.H. Epstein. 1974. Fungicidal control of southern corn leaf blight on Texas male-sterile corn. Plant Dis. Rep. 58:104–107.

———, ———, and B.G. Gengenbach. 1973. Host specificity of a toxin from *Phyllosticta maydis* for Texas cytoplasmically male-sterile maize. Phytopathology 63:1357–1361.

Cook, C.E., P. Wichard, M.E. Wall, G.H. Egley, P. Coggan, R.A. Luban, and A.T. McPhall. 1972. Germination stimulants II. The structure of strigol—a potent seed germination stimulant for witchweed (*Striga lutea* Lour.). J. Am. Chem. Soc. 94:6198–6199.

Couture, R.M., D.G. Routley, and G.M. Dunn. 1971. Role of cyclic hydroxamic acids in monogenic resistance of maize to *Helminthosporium turcicum*. Physiol. Plant Pathol. 1:515–521.

Craig, J. 1980. Comparative reactions of corn inbreds to oospore and conidial inoculum of *Peronosclerospora sorghi*. Phytopathology 70:313–315.

———. 1982. Identification of sorghum downy mildew resistance in corn by leaf reaction to conidial inoculum. Plant Dis. Rep. 72:351–352.

———, and L.A. Daniel-Kalio. 1968. Chlorotic lesion resistance to *Helminthosporium maydis* in maize. Plant Dis. Rep. 52:134–136.

———, and J.M. Fajemisin. 1969. Inheritance of chlorotic lesion resistance to *Helminthosporium maydis* in maize. Plant Dis. Rep. 53:742–743.

———, and R.A. Frederiksen. 1980. Pathotypes of *Peronosclerospora sorghi*. Plant Dis. 64:778–779.

Crosier, W.F., and S.W. Braverman. 1971. *Helminthosporium maydis* in seeds of Minnesota-grown field corn. Phytopathology 61:427–428.

Cugini, G., and G.B. Traverso. 1902. La *Sclerospora macrospora* Sacc. parassita della *Zea mays* L. Stn. Sper. Agrar. Ital. 35:46–49.

Cullen, D., R.W. Caldwell, and E.B. Smalley. 1983. Susceptibility of maize to *Gibberella zeae* ear rot: Relationship of host genotype, pathogen virulence and zearalenone contamination. Plant Dis. 67:89–91.

Dale, J.L. 1963. Corn anthracnose. Plant Dis. Rep. 47:245–249.

Damsteegt, V.D. 1976. A naturally occurring corn virus epiphytotic. Plant Dis. Rep. 60:858–861.

Dange, S.R.S. 1976. Sorghum downy mildew (*Sclerospora sorghi*) of maize in Rajasthan, India. Kasetsart J. 10:121–127.

Davis, R.E. 1973. Occurrence of a spiroplasma in corn stunt-infected plants in Mexico. Plant Dis. Rep. 57:333–337.

———. 1976. Spiroplasma: Role in the diagnosis of corn stunt disease. p. 92–98. *In* L.E. Williams et al. (ed.) Proc. Maize Virus Dis. Colloq. Workshop. 16–19 August. Ohio Agric. Res. Dev. Ctr., Wooster.

————, J.H. Tsai, and R.E. McCoy. 1984. Isolation of the corn stunt spiroplasma from maize in Florida. Plant Dis. 68:600–604.

————, and J.F. Worley. 1973. Spiroplasma: Motile, helical micro-organisms associated with corn stunt disease. Phytopathology 63:403–408.

De Leon, C. 1984. Maize diseases, a guide for field identification. 3rd ed. CIMMYT, Mexico City.

Dodd, J.L. 1977. A photosynthetic stress-translocation balance concept of corn stalk rot. p. 122–130. In H.D. Loden and D. Wilkinson (ed.) Proc. Annu. Corn Sorghum Res. Conf., 32, Chicago. 6–8 Dec. ASTA, Washington, DC.

————. 1980a. The role of plant stresses in development of corn stalk rots. Plant Dis. 64:533–537.

————. 1980b. Grain sink size and predisposition of Zea mays to stalk rot. Phytopathology 70:534–535.

Doupnick, B., and M.B. Boosalis. 1980. Ecofallow—a reduced tillage system—and plant diseases. Plant Dis. 64:31–35.

Drechsler, C. 1925. Leaf spot of maize caused by Ophiobolus heterostrophus n.sp. the ascigerous stage of a Helminthosporium exhibiting bipolar germination. J. Agric. Res. 31:701–726.

Duran, R. 1970. Hosts and distribution of Mexican smut fungi. Mycologia 62:1094–1105.

Duvick, D.N. 1972. Potential usefulness of new cytoplasmic male steriles and sterility systems. p. 192–201. In H.D. Loden and D. Wilkinson (ed.) Proc. Annu. Corn Sorghum Res. Conf., 27, Chicago. 12–14 December. ASTA, Washington, DC.

Dye, D.W. 1969. A taxonomic study of the genus Erwinia IV. "Atypical" Erwinias. N. Z. J. Sci. 12:833–839.

deZoeten, G.A., D.C. Arny, C.R. Grau, S.M. Saad, and G. Gaard. 1980. Properties of the nucleoprotein associated with maize white line virus in Wisconsin. Phytopathology 70:1019–1022.

Eddins, A.H. 1933. Infection of corn plants by Physoderma zeae-maydis Shaw. J. Agric. Res. 46:241–253.

Egley, G.H., and J.E. Dale. 1970. Ethylene, 2-chloroethylphosphonic acid and witchweed germination. Weed Sci. 18:586–589.

Elliott, C., and F.W. Poos. 1934. Overwintering of Aplanobacter stewarti. Science N.S. (Washington, DC) 80:289–290.

Eplee, R.E. 1981. Striga's status as a plant parasite in the United States. Plant Dis. 65:951–954.

————, and M.A. Langston. 1970. Paraquat efficacy and application in witchweed (Striga lutea) control. Proc. South. Weed Sci. Soc. 23:127.

Fajemisin, J.M., and A.L. Hooker. 1974. Predisposition to Diplodia stalk rot in corn affected by three Helminthosporium leaf blights. Phytopathology 64:1496–1499.

Fenwick, H.S., and W.R. Simpson. 1967. Suppression of corn head smut by infurrow application of pentachloronitrobenzene. Plant Dis. Rep. 51:626–628.

————, and ————. 1969. Evidence of postseedling infection by Sphacelotheca reiliana. Phytopathology 59:1026 (Abstr.).

Findley, W.R., E.J. Dollinger, R. Louie, and J.K. Knoke. 1973. Locating genes for maize dwarf mosaic resistance by means of chromosomal translocations in corn (Zea mays L.). Crop Sci. 13:608–611.

Flor, H.H. 1942. Inheritance of pathogenicity in Melamspora lini. Phytopathology 32:653–669.

————. 1955. Host-parasite interaction in flax rust—its genetics and other implications. Phytopathology 45:680–685.

Ford, R.E., and M. Tosic. 1972. New hosts of maize dwarf mosaic virus and sugarcane mosaic virus and a comparative host range study of viruses infecting corn. Phytopathol. Z. 75:315–348.

Forgey, W.M., M.H. Blanco, L.L. Darrah, and M.S. Zuber. 1982. Prediction of Stewart's wilt disease in single and three-way crosses of maize. Plant Dis. 66:1159–1162.

————, and ————, and W.Q. Loegering. 1978. Differences in pathological capabilities and host specificity of Colletotrichum graminicola on Zea mays. Plant Dis. Rep. 62:573–576.

Forster, R.L., R.L. Stoltz, H.S. Fenwick, and W.R. Simpson. 1980. Maize dwarf mosaic virus in Idaho. Plant Dis. 64:410–411.

Foster, J.H., and R.A. Frederiksen. 1977. Symptoms of head smut in maize seedlings and evaluation of hybrids and inbreds. Texas Agric. Exp. Stn. Rep. PR3432.

Frederiksen, R.A. 1977. Head smuts of corn and sorghum. p. 89–105. *In* H.D. Loden and D. Wilkinson (ed.) Proc Annu. Corn Sorghum Res. Conf., 32, Chicago. 6–8 December. ASTA, Washington, DC.

————. 1980. Sorghum downy mildew in the United States: Overview and outlook. Plant Dis. 64:903–908.

————, R.W. Berry, and J.H. Foster. 1976. Head smut of maize in Texas. Plant Dis. Rep. 60:610–611.

————, and A.J. Bockholt. 1969. *Sclerospora sorghi*, a pathogen of corn in Texas. Plant Dis. Rep. 53:566–569.

————, A.J. Bockholt, L. Reyes, and A.J. Ullstrup. 1971. Reaction of selected midwestern corn inbred lines to *Sclerospora sorghi*. Plant Dis. Rep. 55:202–203.

————, and G. Odvody. 1979. Chemical control of sorghum downy mildew. Sorghum Newsl. 22:129

————, and B.L. Renfro. 1977. Global status of maize downy mildew. Annu. Rev. Phytopathol. 15:249–277.

————, and A.J. Ullstrup. 1975. Sorghum downy mildew in the United States. Trop. Agric. Res. Ser. 8:39–43.

Frutchey, C.W. 1936. A study of Stewart's disease of sweet corn caused by *Phytomonas stewarti*. Michigan Agric. Exp. Stn. Tech. Bull. 152.

Fuentes, S. 1963. Resistance to head smut in Mexican races of corn. Phytopathology 53:24 (Abstr.).

Futrell, M.C. 1975. *Puccina polysora* epidemics on maize associated with cropping practice and genetic homogeneity. Phytopathology 65:1040–1042.

————, and G.E. Scott. 1971. Overwintering and early season development of *Helminthosporium maydis* in Mississippi. Plant Dis. Rep. 55:954–956.

Galal, A.A., F.M.E. Omar, A.A. Ismail, and F.A. El-Seir. 1985. Genetic analysis of resistance to late wilt disease in single crosses of maize. Egypt. J. Genet. Cytol. 14:309.

Garber, R.J., and M.M. Hoover. 1928. The relation of smut infection to yield in maize. J. Am. Soc. Agron. 20:735–741.

Gardner, C.O., and M.L. Schuster. 1973. Genetic studies on the susceptibility to bacterial leaf freckles and wilt, *Corynebacterium nebraskense*. Maize Genet. Coop. News Lett. 47:155–157.

Gates, L.F., and C.G. Mortimore. 1969. Three diseases of corn (*Zea mays*) new in Ontario: Crazy top, a Phyllosticta leaf spot, and eyespot. Can. Plant Dis. Surv. 49:128–131.

Gelaw, B. (ed.). 1986. To feed ourselves: A proceedings of the first eastern, central and southern Africa regional maize workshop. CIMMYT, Mexico City.

Gendloff, E.H., E.C. Rossman, W.L. Casale, T.G. Isleib, and L.P. Hart. 1986. Components of resistance to Fusarium ear rot in field corn. Phytopathology 76:684–688.

Gevers, H.O. 1975. A new major gene for resistance to *Helminthosporium turcicum* leaf blight of maize. Plant Dis. Rep. 59:296–299.

Giebel, J. 1982. Mechanism of resistance to plant nematodes. Annu. Rev. Phytopathol. 20:257–279.

Gingery, R.E., and R. Louie. 1985. A satellitelike virus particle associated with maize white line mosaic virus. Phytopathology 75:870–874.

Gitaitis, R.D., R.E. Stall, and J.O. Strandberg. 1978. Dissemination and survival of *Psuedomonas alboprecipitans* ascertained by disease distribution. Phytopathology 68:227–231.

Gordon, D.T. 1976. Maize virus diseases in the United States. p. 45–48. *In* L.E. Williams et al. (ed.) Proc. Maize Virus Dis. Colloq. Workshop. 16–19 August. Ohio Agric. Res. Dev. Ctr., Wooster.

————, O.E. Bradfute, R.E. Gingery, J.K. Knoke, and L.R. Nault. 1978. Maize virus disease complexes in the United States: Real and potential disease problems. p. 102–133. *In* H.D. Loden and D. Wilkinson (ed.) Proc. Annu. Corn Sorghum Res. Conf., 33, Chicago. 12–14 December. ASTA, Washington, DC.

————, W.R. Findley, J.K. Knoke, R. Louie, L.R. Nault, O.E. Bradfute, E.J. Dollinger, and R.E. Gingery. 1974. Distinguishing symptoms and latest research findings on corn virus diseases in the United States. p. 153–173. *In* H.D. Loden and D. Wilkinson (ed.) Proc. Ann. Corn Sorghum Res. Conf., 29, Chicago. 10–12 December. ASTA, Washington, DC.

————, and L.R. Nault. 1977. Involvement of maize chlorotic dwarf virus and other agents in stunting diseases of *Zea mays* in the United States. Phytopathology 67:27–36.

----, ----, N.H. Gordon, and S.E. Heady. 1985. Serological detection of corn stunt spiroplasma and maize rayado fino virus in field-collected *Dalbulus* spp. from Mexico. Plant Dis. 69:108–111.

Granados, R.R. 1969. Electron microscopy of plants and insect vectors infected with corn stunt disease agent. Contrib. Boyce Thompson Inst. 24:173–187.

Grau, C.R., G.A. deZoeten, D.C. Arny, S.M. Saad, and G. Gaard. 1981. Maize white line mosaic—A new disease of corn in Wisconsin. Phytopathology 71:220 (Abstr.).

Graves, C., T. McCutehen, and D. West. 1980. Corn hybrids evaluated for resistance to downy mildew (crazy top) diseases. Tenn. Farm Home Sci. 113:24–25.

Gregory, L.V., J.E. Ayers, and R.R. Nelson. 1984. Effect of host genotype on estimating relative parasitic fitness among populations of *Helminthosporium carbonum* race 3. Phytopathology 74:1024–1026.

Grogan, C.O., E.F. Eastin, and R.D. Palmer. 1963. Inheritance of susceptibility of a line of maize to simazine and atrazine. Crop Sci. 3:451.

Gudauskas, R.T., D.H. Teem, W. To, and T.L. Whatley. 1971. Overwintering of *Helminthosporium maydis* in Alabama. Plant Dis. Rep. 55:947–948.

Haenseler, C.M. 1937. Correlation between winter temperature and incidence of sweet corn wilt in New Jersey. Plant Dis. Rep. 21:298–301.

Halisky, P.M. 1962. Prevalence and pathogenicity of *Sphacelotheca reiliana* causing head smut of field corn in California. Phytopathology 52:199–202.

Hamid, A.H., J.E. Ayres, and R.R. Hill, Jr. 1982a. The inheritance of resistance in corn to *Cochliobolus carbonum* race 3. Phytopathology 72:1173–1177.

----, ----, and ----. 1982b. Host × isolate interactions in corn inbreds inoculated with *Cochliobolus carbonum* race 3. Phytopathology 72:1169–1173.

Hammerschmidt, R., and R.L. Nicholson. 1977. Resistance of maize to anthracnose: Effect of light intensity on lesion development. Phytopathology 67:247–250.

Hart, L.P., E. Gendloff, and E.C. Rossman. 1984. Effect of corn genotype on ear rot infection by *Gibberella zeae*. Plant Dis. 68:296–298.

Harvey, P.H., D.L. Thompson, and T.T. Herbert. 1955. Reaction of inbred lines of corn to brown spot. Plant Dis. Rep. 39:973–976.

Headrick, J.M., and J.K. Pataky. 1986. Effects of night temperature and mist period on infection of sweet corn by *Puccinia sorghi*. Plant Dis. 70:950–953.

Heather, J.B., R.S.D. Mittal, and C.F. Sih. 1974. The total synthesis of distrigol. J. Am. Chem. Soc. 96:1976–1977.

Hebert, T.T., and A. Kelman. 1958. Factors influencing the germination of resting sporangia of *Physoderma maydis*. Phytopathology 48:102–106.

Heck, W.W. 1968. Factors influencing expression of oxidant damage to plants. Annu. Rev. Phytopathol. 6:165–168.

Heichel, G.H., D.C. Sands, and J.B. King. 1977. Seasonal patterns and reduction by carbofuran of Stewart's bacterial wilt of sweet corn. Plant Dis. Rep. 61:149–153.

Hill, J.H., C.A. Martinson, and W.A. Russell. 1974. Seed transmission of maize dwarf mosaic and wheat streak mosaic viruses in maize and response of inbred lines. Crop. Sci. 14:232–235.

Hilty, J.W., C.H. Hadden, and F.T. Garden. 1979. Response of maize hybrids and inbred lines to gray leaf spot disease and the effects on yield in Tennessee. Plant Dis. Rep. 63:515–518.

Hilu, H.M., and A.L. Hooker. 1964. Host-pathogen relationship of *Helminthosporium turcicum* in resistance and susceptible corn seedlings. Phytopathology 54:570–575.

Hollier, C.A., and S.B. King. 1985a. Effect of dew period and temperature on infection of seedling maize plants by *Puccinia polysora*. Plant Dis. 69:219–220.

----, and ----. 1985b. Effects of temperature and relative humidity on germinability and infectivity of *Puccinia polysora* uredospores. Plant Dis. 69:937–939.

Hooker, A.L. 1961. A new type of resistance in corn to *Helminthosporium turcicum*. Plant Dis. Rep. 45:780–781.

----. 1963. Inheritance of chlorotic-lesion resistance to *Helminthosporium turcicum* in seedling corn. Crop Sci. 660–662.

----. 1974. Selection for stalk rot resistance in corn and its effect on grain yield. Genetika (Zemun, Yugosl.) 6:27–32.

----. 1975. *Helminthosporium turcicum* as a pathogen of corn. Rep. Tottori Mycol. Inst. (Jpn.) 12:115–125.

––––. 1977a. A plant pathologist's view of germplasm evaluation and utilization. Crop Sci. 17:689–694.

––––. 1977b. A second major gene locus in corn for chlorotic-lesion resistance to *Helminthosporium turcicum*. Crop Sci. 17:132–135.

––––, and M.P. Britton. 1962. The effects of stalk rot on corn yields in Illinois. Plant Dis. Rep. 46:9–13.

––––, H.M. Hilu, D.R. Wilkinson, and C.G. Van Dyke. 1964. Additional sources of chlorotic-lesion resistance to *Helminthosporium turcicum* in corn. Plant Dis. Rep. 48:777–780.

––––, and K.M.S. Saxena. 1971. Genetics of disease resistance in plants. Annu. Rev. Genet. 5:407–424.

––––, D.R. Smith, S.M. Lim, and J.B. Beckett. 1970a. Reaction of corn seedlings with male-sterile cytoplasm to *Helminthosporium maydis*. Plant Dis. Rep. 54:708–712.

––––, ––––, ––––, and M.D. Musson. 1970b. Physiological races of *Helminthosporium maydis* and disease resistance. Plant Dis. Rep. 54:1109–1110.

––––, and D.G. White. 1976. Prevalence of corn stalk rot fungi in Illinois. Plant Dis. Rep. 60:1032–1034.

Hoppe, P.E. 1942. Fusarium ear rot in sweet corn. Plant Dis. Rep. 26:458.

––––, and A. Kelman. 1969. Bacterial top and stalk rot disease of corn in Wisconsin. Plant Dis. Rep. 53:66–70.

––––, and J.T. Middleton. 1950. Pathogenicity and occurrence in Wisconsin soil of Pythium species which cause seedling diseases in corn. Phytopathology 40:13.

Horsfall, J.G. 1975. The fire brigade stops a raging corn epidemic. p. 105–114. *In* USDA Yearbook. U.S. Gov. Print. Office, Washington, DC.

Hughes, G.R., and A.L. Hooker. 1971. Gene action conditioning resistance to northern corn leaf blight in maize. Crop Sci. 11:180–183.

Hyre, R.A. 1943. New records and occurrences of plant diseases. Plant Dis. Rep. 27:553–554.

Itzerott, D. 1938. On the germination and growth of *Ustilago zeae* with special reference to infection. Phytopathol. Z. 1:155–180.

Ivanoff, S.S. 1936. Resistance to bacterial wilt of open-pollinated varieties of sweet, dent and flint corn. J. Agric. Res. 53:917–926.

––––, and A.J. Riker. 1936. Resistance to bacterial wilt of inbred strains and crosses of sweet corn. J. Agric. Res. 53:937–954.

––––, ––––, and H.A. Dettwiler. 1938. Studies on cultural characteristics, physiology and pathogenicity of strain types of *Phytomonas stewarti*. J. Bacteriol. 35:235–253.

Janson, B.F., and C.W. Ellett. 1963. A new corn disease in Ohio. Plant Dis. Rep. 47:1107–1108.

Jenkins, M.T., and A.L. Robert. 1959. Evaluating the breeding potential of inbred lines of corn resistant to the leaf blight caused by *Helminthosporium turcicum*. Agron. J. 51:93–96.

––––, and ––––. 1961. Further genetic studies of resistance to *Helminthosporium turcicum* Pass. in maize by means of chromosomal translocations. Crop Sci. 1:450–455.

––––, ––––, and W.R. Findley, Jr. 1952. Inheritance of resistance to Helminthosporium leaf blight in populations of F₃ progenies. Agron. J. 44:438–442.

Jenns, A.E., and K.J. Leonard. 1985. Effect of illuminance on the resistance of inbred lines of corn to isolates of *Colletotrichum graminicola*. Phytopathology 75:281–286.

Jensen, S.G. 1985. Laboratory transmission of maize chlorotic mottle virus by three species of corn rootworms. Plant Dis. Rep. 69:864–868.

Johann, H., J.R. Holbert, and J.G. Dickson. 1931. Further studies on Penicillium injury to corn. J. Agric. Res. 43:757–790.

Johnson, A.G., L. Cash, and W.A. Gardner. 1929. Preliminary report on a bacterial disease of corn. Phytopathology 19:81–82 (Abstr.).

––––, A.L. Robert, and L. Cash. 1945. Further studies on bacterial leaf blight and stalk rot of corn. Phytopathology 35:486–487 (Abstr.).

––––, ––––, and ––––. 1949. Bacterial leaf blight and stalk rot of corn. J. Agric. Res. 78:719–732.

Johnson, A.W. 1975. Resistance of sweet corn cultivars to plant-parasitic nematodes. Plant Dis. Rep. 59:373–376.

Johnson, G.R. 1971. Analysis of genetic resistance to maize dwarf mosaic disease. Crop Sci. 11:23–24.

————. 1976. Analysis of nuclear genetic resistance in maize to race T of southern corn leaf blight. Crop Sci. 16:340–343.

Jones, B.L., J.C. Leeper, and R.A. Frederiksen. 1972. *Sclerospora sorghi* in corn: Its location in carpellate flowers and mature seeds. Phytopathology 62:817–819.

Jones, D.F. 1918. Segregation of susceptibility to parasitism in maize. Am. J. Bot. 5:295–300.

Jordan, E.G., J.M. Perkins, R.A. Schall, and W.L. Pedersen. 1983. Occurrence of race 2 of *Exserohilum turcicum* on corn in the central and eastern United States. Plant Dis. 67:1163–1165.

Josephson, L.M., and B. Naidu. 1971. Reaction in diallel crosses of corn inbreds (*Zea mays* L.) to maize dwarf mosaic virus. Crop Sci. 11:664–667.

Jugenheimer, R.W. 1976. Corn improvement, seed production, and uses. John Wiley and Sons, New York.

Kappelman, A.J., Jr., and D.L. Tompson. 1966. Inheritance of resistance to Diplodia stalk rot in corn. Crop. Sci. 6:288–290.

Keller, N.P., G.C. Bergstrom, and R.E. Carruthers. 1986. Potential yield reductions in maize associated with an anthracnose European corn borer pest complex in New York. Phytopathology 76:586–589.

Kelman, A., L.H. Person, and T.T. Herbert. 1957. A bacterial stalk rot of irrigated corn in North Carolina. Plant Dis. Rep. 41:798–802.

Kendrick, J.B. 1926. Holcus bacterial spot of *Zea mays* and *Holcus* species. Iowa Agric. Exp. Stn. Bull. 100:301–334.

Kim, S.K. 1974. Quantitative genetics of *Puccinia sorghi* resistance and husk number in *Zea mays*. Ph.D. diss. Univ. of Hawaii, Honolulu.

————, and J.L. Brewbaker. 1976. Sources of general resistance to *Puccinia sorghi* on maize in Hawaii. Plant Dis. Rep. 60:551–555.

————, and ————. 1977. Inheritance of general resistance in maize to *Puccinia sorghi* Schw. Crop Sci. 17:456–461.

Kingsland, G., and O.W. Barnett. 1985. Effect of two viruses on components of yield of corn in South Carolina. Phytopathology 75:1299 (Abstr.).

Kingsland, G.C. 1963. Cercospora leaf blight of corn: A case history of a local epiphytotic in South Carolina. Plant Dis. Rep. 47:724–725.

Kisiel, M., K. Deubert, and B.M. Zuckerman. 1969. The effect of *Tylenchus agricola* and *Tylenchorhynchus claytoni* on root rot of corn caused by *Fusarium roseum* and *Pythium ultimum*. Phytopathology 59:1387–1390.

Koehler, B. 1939. Crazy top of corn. Phytopathology 29:817–820.

————. 1951. Husk coverage and ear declination in relation to corn ear rots. Phytopathology 41:22 (Abstr.).

————. 1955. Correlation between resistance to Stewart's leaf blight and northern leaf blight in corn. Plant Dis. Rep. 39:164–165.

————. 1959. Corn ear rots in Illinois. Illinois Agric. Exp. Stn. Bull. 639.

————. 1960. Cornstalk rots in Illinois. Illinois Agric. Exp. Stn. Bull. 659.

————, and C.M. Woodworth. 1938. Corn seedling virescences caused by *Aspergillus flavus* and *A. tamarii*. Phytopathology 28:811–823.

Kommedahl, T., D.S. Lang, and K.L. Blanchard. 1971. Detection of kernels infected with *Helminthosporium maydis* in commercial samples of corn produced in 1970. Plant Dis. Rep. 55:726–729.

Krantz, B.A., and S.W. Melsted. 1964. Nutrient deficiencies in corn, sorghum, and small grains. p. 25–57. *In* H.B. Sprague (ed.) Hunger signs in crops. David McKay Co., New York.

Kruger, W. 1970. Wurzel-und stammfaule bei mais. (In German.) Phytopathol. Z. 68:334–345.

Kuhn, C.W., M.D. Jellum, and J.N. All. 1975. Effect of carbonfuran treatment on corn yield, maize chlorotic dwarf and maize dwarf mosaic virus diseases, and leafhopper populations. Phytopathology 65:1017–1020.

Kunkel, L.O. 1946. Incubation period of corn stunt virus in the leafhopper *Baldulus maidis* (DeL. and W.). Am. J. Bot. 33:830–831 (Abstr.).

Lal, B.B., and B.P. Chakravarti. 1977. Root and collar inoculation and control of brown spot of maize by post-infection spray and soil application of systemic fungicides. Plant Dis. Rep. 61:334–336.

Lallmahomed, G.M., and J. Craig. 1968. Races of *Puccinia polysora* in Nigeria. Plant Dis. Rep. 52:136–138.

Langston, M.A., R.E. Eplee, and T.J. English. 1976. Witchweed control in corn with oxyflurorfen , RH-2915. Proc. South. Weed Sci. Soc. 29:163.

Latterell, F.M., and A.E. Rossi. 1983a. Gray leaf spot of corn: A disease on the move. Plant Dis. Rep. 67:842–847.

————, and ————. 1974. Evidence that *Cercospora zeae-maydis* is the causal agent of gray leaf spot of corn. Proc. Am. Phytopathol. Soc. 1:40 (Abstr.).

————, and ————. 1983b. *Stenocarpella macrospora* (=*Diplodia macrospora*) and *S. maydis* (=*D. maydis*) compared as pathogens of corn. Plant Dis. 67:725–729.

Leach, C.M., R.A. Fullerton, and K. Young. 1977. Northern leaf blight of maize in New Zealand: Relationship of *Drechslera turcica* airspora to factors influencing sporulation, conidium development, and chlamydospore formation. Phytopathology 67:629–636.

Leonard, K.J. 1977. Races of *Bipolaris maydis* in the southeastern U.S. from 1974–1976. Plant Dis. Rep. 61:914–915.

Lim, S.M. 1975a. Diallel analysis for reaction of eight corn inbreds to *Helminthosporium maydis* race T. Phytopathology 65:10–15.

————. 1975b. Heterotic effects of resistance in maize to *Helminthosporium maydis* race 0. Phytopathology 65:1117–1120.

————, and A.L. Hooker. 1971. Southern corn leaf blight: Genetic control of pathogenicity and toxin production in race T and race 0 of *Cochliobolus heterostrophus*. Genetics 69:115–117.

————, and ————. 1976. Estimates of combining ability for resistance to *Helminthosporium maydis* race 0 in a maize population. Maydica 21:121–128.

————, ————, and J.D. Paxton. 1970. Isolation of phytoalexins from corn with monogenic resistance to *Helminthosporium turcicum*. Phytopathology 60:1071–1075.

————, ————, and D.R. Smith. 1971. Use of *Helminthosporium maydis* race T pathotoxin to determine disease reaction of germinating corn seed. Agron. J. 63:712–713.

————, J.G. Kinsey, and A.L. Hooker. 1974. Inheritance of virulence in *Helminthosporium turcicum* to monogenic resistant corn. Phytopathology 64:1150–1151.

————, J.D. Paxton, and A.L. Hooker. 1968. Phytoalexin production in corn resistant to *Helminthosporium turcicum* Phytopathology 58:720–721.

————, and D.G. White. 1978. Estimates of heterosis and combining ability for resistance of maize to *Colletotrichum graminicola*. Phytopathology 68:1336–1342.

Lindstrom, E.W. 1938. Genetic investigations of bacterial wilt resistance in corn. p. 46–47. *In* Report on agricultural research. Iowa Agric. Exp. Stn. Rep. (1937–38).

Lipps, P.E. 1982. Survival of *Colletotrichum graminicola* in infested corn residues in Ohio. Plant Dis. 67:102–104.

————. 1985. Influence of inoculum from buried and surface corn residues on the incidence of corn anthracnose. Phytopathology 75:1212–1216.

Littrell, R.H., and D.R. Sumner. 1971. Overwintering of *Helminthosporium maydis* in Georgia. Plant Dis. Rep. 55:951–953.

Locci, R., and J.R. Locci. 1972. Possible means of differentiating, on malt agar, between physiologic races of "T" and "O" of *Helminthosporium maydis*. Riv. Patol. Veg. 8(4):232–238.

Lockwood, J.L., and L.E. Williams. 1957. Inoculation and rating methods for bacterial wilt of sweet corn. Phytopathology 47:83–87.

Loesch, P.J., and M.S. Zuber. 1972. Inheritance of resistance to maize dwarf mosaic virus. Crop Sci. 12:350–352.

Lommel, S.A. 1985. Partial characterization of maize chlorotic mottle virus. Phytopathology 75:1292 (Abstr.).

Louie, R., D.T. Gordon, J.K. Knoke, R.E. Gingery, O.E. Bradfute, and P.E. Lipps. 1982. Maize white line mosaic virus in Ohio. Plant Dis. 66:167–170.

————, ————, and P.E. Lipps. 1981. Transmission of maize white line mosaic virus. Phytopathology 71:1116 (Abstr.).

————, ————, L.V. Madden, and J.K. Knoke. 1983a. Symptomless infection and incidence of maize white line mosaic. Plant Dis. 67:371–373.

————, and J.K. Knoke. 1975. Strains of maize dwarf mosaic virus. Plant Dis. Rep. 59:518–522.

————, ————, and D.T. Gordon. 1974. Epiphytotics of maize dwarf mosaic and maize chlorotic dwarf diseases in Ohio. Phytopathology 64:1455–1459.

————, ————, ————, and R.E. Gingery. 1983b. Maize white line mosaic and maize subtle mosaic viruses. p. 139–140. *In* D.T. Gordon et al. (ed.) Proc. Int. Maize Virus Dis. Colloq. Workshop. 2–6 Aug. 1982. Ohio Agric. Res. Dev. Ctr., Wooster.

Luttrell, E.S. 1958. The perfect stage of *Helminthosporium turcicum*. Phytopathology 48:281–287.

Lynch, K.V., L.V. Edgington, and L.V. Busch. 1980. Head smut, a new disease of corn in Ontario. Can. J. Plant Pathol. 2:176–178.

Mace, M.E., and J.A. Veech. 1973. Inhibition of *Helminthosporium turcicum* spore germination by leaf diffusates from northern leaf blight—susceptible or resistant—corn. Phytopathology 63:1393–1394.

MacKenzie, D.R., C.C. Wernham, and R.E. Ford. 1966. Differences in maize dwarf mosaic virus isolates of the northeastern United States. Plant Dis. Rep. 50:814–818.

Mack, H.J., J.R. Bagett, and P.A. Koepsell. 1980. Cultural practices affected corn smut. Oregon Veg. Dig. 29:1–2.

Madden, L.V., and L.R. Nault. 1983. Differential pathogenicity of corn stunting mollicutes to leafhoppers vectors in *Dalbulus* and *Baldulus* species. Phytopathology 73:1608–1614.

Mains, E.B. 1934. Host specialization of *Puccinia sorghi*. Phytopathology 24:405–411.

Maric, A., Z. Markovic, P. Drezgic, and D. Varga. 1969. Agricultural practice and the epiphytotic of corn smut [*Ustilago maydis* (DC) Corda] in Vojvodina during 1968. Savrem. Poljoprivr. 17:385–394.

Markham, P.G., R. Townsend, K. Plaskitt, and P. Saglio. 1977. Transmission of corn stunt to dicotyledonous plants. Plant Dis. Rep. 61:342–345.

Martens, J.W., and D.C. Arny. 1966. The effect of potassium fertilization on the incidence of smut in a susceptible corn inbred. Plant Dis. Rep. 50:12–13.

Martin, P.R., C.O. Gardner, A.G. Calub, and M.L. Schuster. 1975. Inheritance of susceptibility and tolerance to leaf freckles and wilt (*Corynebacterium nebraskense*) of corn. Maize Genet. Coop. News Lett. 49:137–138.

Matyac, C.A., and T. Kommedahl. 1985a. Occurrence of chlorotic spots on corn seedlings infected with *Sphacelotheca reiliana* and their use in evaluation of head smut resistance. Plant Dis. 69:251–254.

————, and ————. 1985b. Factors affecting the development of head smut caused by *Sphacelotheca reiliana* on corn. Phytopathology 75:577–581.

McDaniel, L.L., and D.T. Gordon. 1985. Identification of a new strain of maize dwarf mosaic virus. Plant Dis. 69:602–607.

McDonald, M.B., Jr. 1975. A review and evaluation of seed vigor tests. Proc. Assoc. Off. Seed Anal. 65:109–139.

McFeeley, J.C. 1971. Comparison of isolates causing yellow leaf-blight of corn in Ohio. Plant Dis. Rep. 55:1064–1068.

McNew, G.L. 1938. The relation of nitrogen nutrition to virulence in *Phytomonas stewarti*. Phytopathology 28:769–787.

Melhus, I.W., F.H. VanHaltern, and D.E. Bliss. 1928. A study of *Sclerospora graminicola* on *Setaria viridis* and *Zea mays*. p. 297–338. *In* Iowa Agric. Exp. Stn. Res. Bull. 1111.

Mercado, A.C., Jr., and R.M. Lantican. 1961. The susceptibility of cytoplasmic male sterile lines of corn to *Helminthosporium maydis* Nisik. & Miy. Philipp. Agric. 45:235–243.

Messiaen, C.M., R. Lafon, and P. Malot. 1959. Necroses de racines, pourritures de tiges, et verse parasitaire du mais. Ann. Epiphyt. 4:441–474.

Michaelson, M.E. 1957. Factors affecting development of stalk rot of corn caused by *Diplodia zeae* and *Gibberella zeae*. Phytopathology 47:499–503.

————, and J.J. Christensen. 1953. Reduction in yield of corn due to stalk rot. Phytopathology 43:479 (Abstr.).

Middleton, J.T. 1943. The taxonomy, host range and geographical distribution of the genus Pythium. Mem. Torrey Bot. Club. 20:1–171.

Mikel, M.A., C.J. D'Arcy, A.M. Rhodes, and R.E. Ford. 1981. Yield loss in sweet corn correlated with time of inoculation with maize dwarf mosaic virus. Plant Dis. 65:902–904.

————, ————, ————, and ————. 1984. Genetics of resistance of two dent corn inbreds to maize dwarf mosaic virus and transfer of resistance into sweet corn. Phytopathology 74:467–473.

Miller, R.J., and D.E. Koeppe. 1971. Southern corn leaf blight: Susceptible and resistant mitochondria. Science (Washington, DC) 173:67–69.

Mortvedt, J.J., P.M. Giordano, and W.L. Lindsay. (ed.). 1972. Micronutrients in agriculture. SSSA, Madison, WI.

Mukunya, D.M., and C.W. Boothroyd. 1973. *Mycosphaerella zeae-maydis* sp. n., the sexual stage of *Phyllosticta maydis*. Phytopathology 63:529–532.

----, ----, and C.O. Grogan. 1975. Genetic nature of resistance in corn to yellow leaf blight. Cro Sci. 15:495–499.

Mulder, J.L., and P. Holliday. 1974. *Cercospora sorghi* C.M.I. Descriptions of pathogenic fungi and bacteria. 419. The Eastern Press, London.

Naidu, B., and L.M. Josephson. 1976. Genetic analysis of resistance to the corn virus disease complex. Crop Sci. 16:167–172.

Narita, T., and Y. Hiratsuka. 1959. Studies on *Kabatiella zeae* n. sp., the causal fungus of a new leaf spot disease of corn. Ann. Phytopathol. Soc. Jpn. 24:147–153.

National Academy of Sciences. 1972. Genetic vulnerability of major crops. NAS, Washington, DC.

Nattrass, R.M. 1953. Occurrence of *Puccinia polysora* in east Africa. Nature (London) 171:527.

Nault, L.R. 1980. Maize bushy stunt and corn stunt: A comparison of disease symptoms, pathogen host ranges, and vectors. Phytopathology 70:659–662.

----, D.T. Gordon, V.D. Damsteegt, and H.H. Iltis. 1982. Response of annual and perennial teosintes (*Zea*) to six maize viruses. Plant Dis. 66:61–62.

----, and J.K. Knoke. 1981. Maize vectors. p. 77–84. *In* D.T. Gordon et al. (ed.) Virus and viruslike diseases of maize in the United States. Ohio Agric. Res. Ctr., South. Coop. Serv. Bull. 247.

----, W.E. Styer, M.E. Coffey, D.T. Gordon, L.S. Negi, and C.L. Niblett. 1978. Transmission of maize chlorotic mottle virus by chrysomelid beetles. Phytopathology 68:1071–1074.

----, W.E. Styer, J.K. Knoke, and H.N. Pitre. 1973. Semipersistent transmission of leaf-hopper-borne maize chlorotic dwarf virus. J. Econ. Entomol. 66:1271–1273.

Nelson, D.W. 1963. The relationship between soil fertility and the incidence of Diplodia stalk rot and northern corn leaf blight in *Zea mays*. M.S. thesis. Univ. of Illinois, Urbana.

Nelson, O.E., and A.J. Ullstrup. 1964. Resistance to leaf spot in maize: Genetic control of resistance to race 1 of *Helminthosporium carbonum* U11. J. Hered. 55:195–199.

Nelson, R.R. 1957a. Heterothallism in *Helminthosporium maydis*. Phytopathology 47:191–192.

----. 1957b. Resistance in corn to *Meloidogyne incognita*. Phytopathology 47:25–26 (Abstr.).

----. 1959. *Cochliobolus carbonum*, the perfect stage of *Helminthosporium carbonum*. Phytopathology 49:807–810.

----, J.E. Ayers, and J.B. Beckett. 1971. Reactions of various corn inbreds in normal and different male-sterile cytoplasms to the yellow leaf blight organism (*Phyllosticta* sp.). Plant Dis. Rep. 55:401–403.

----, M. Blanco, S. Dalmacio, and B.S. Moore. 1973. A new race of *Helminthosporium carbonum* on corn. Plant Dis. Rep. 57:822–823.

Neuffer, M.G., and O.H. Calvert. 1975. Dominant disease lesion mimics in maize. J. Hered. 66:265–270.

----, L. Jones, and M.S. Zuber. 1968. The mutants of maize. CSSA, Madison, WI.

Niblett, C.L., and L.E. Claflin. 1978. Corn lethal necrosis—a new virus disease in Kansas. Plant. Dis. Rep. 62:15–19.

Nicholson, R.L., L.F. Bauman, and H.F. Warren. 1976. Association of *Fusarium moniliforme* with brown midrib maize. Plant Dis. Rep. 60:908–910.

----, and W.B.C. Moraes. 1980. Survival of *Colletotrichum graminicola*: Importance of the spore matrix. Phytopathology 70:255–261.

----, and H.L. Warren. 1976. Criteria for evaluation of resistance to maize anthracnose. Phytopathology 66:86–90.

----, and ----. 1981. The issue of races of *Colletotrichum graminicola* pathogenic to corn. Plant Dis. 65:143–145.

Norton, D.C. 1978. Ecology of plant-parasitic nematodes. John Wiley and Sons, New York.

Norton, J.B.S. 1895. *Ustilago reiliana* on corn. Bot. Gaz. (Chicago) 5:463.

Nusbaum, C.J., and H. Ferris. 1973. The role of cropping systems in nematode population management. Ann. Rev. Phytopathol. 11:423–440.

Ooka, J.J., and T. Kommedahl. 1977. Kernels infected with *Fusarium moniliforme* in corn cultivars with opaque-2 endosperm or male-sterile cytoplasm. Plant Dis. Rep. 61:161–165.

Palmer, L.T., and T. Kommedahl. 1969. Root-infecting Fusarium species in relation to rootworm infestations in corn. Phytopathology 59:1613–1617.

––––, D. MacDonald, and T. Kommedahl. 1967. The ecological relationship of *Fusarium moniliforme* to *Pratylenchus scribneri* in seedling blight of corn. Phytopathology 57:825 (Abstr.).

Parker, D.T., and W.C. Burrows. 1959. Root and stalk rot in corn as affected by fertilizer and tillage treatment. Agron. J. 51:414–417.

Parker, G.B. 1980. Inheritance of resistance in dent corn to wheat streak mosaic virus and *Erwinia stewartii*. Ph.D. diss. Univ. of Illinois, Urbana. (Diss. Abstr. 81–08622).

Pataky, J.K. 1985. Relationships among reactions of sweet corn hybrids to Goss's wilt, Stewart's bacterial wilt, and northern corn leaf blight. Plant Dis. 69:845–848.

Pate, J.R., and P.H. Harvey. 1954. Studies on the inheritance of resistance in corn to *Helminthosporium maydis* leaf spot. Agron. J. 46:442–445.

Patterson, E. 1973. Procedures for use of genic male sterility in production of commercial hybrid maize. U.S. Patent 3 710 511. Date issued: 16 January.

Pavgi, M.S., and A.L. Flangas. 1959. Occurrence of Southern corn rust in Wisconsin. Plant. Dis. Rep. 43:1239–1240.

Payak, M.M., and R.C. Sharma. 1986. Vertical banded blight—an unusual Marasmiellus disease of maize. Curr. Sci. 55:1135–1137.

Payne, G.A., D.K. Cassel, and C.R. Adkins. 1986. Reduction of aflatoxin contamination in corn by irrigation and tillage. Phytopathology 76:679–684.

Pepper, E.H. 1967. Stewart's bacterial wilt of corn. Am. Phytopathol. Soc. Monogr. 4. Am. Phytopathological Soc., St. Paul.

Perkins, J.M., and A.L. Hooker. 1979. The effects of anthracnose stalk rot on corn yields in Illinois. Plant Dis. Rep. 63:26–30.

Pfund, J.H., and C.W. Crum. 1977. Inheritance of tolerance to eradicane in maize. p. 66. *In* Agronomy abstract. ASA, Madison, WI.

Pirone, T.P., O.E. Bradfute, P.H. Freytag, M.C.Y. Lung, and C.G. Poneleit. 1972. Virus-like particles associated with a leafhopper transmitted disease of corn in Kentucky. Plant. Dis Rep. 56:652–656.

Podleckis, E.V., C.R. Curtis, and H.E. Heggestad. 1984. Peroxidase enzyme markers for ozone sensitivity in sweet corn. Phytopathology 74:572–577.

Politis, D.J., and H. Wheeler. 1972. The perfect stage of *Colletotrichum graminicola*. Plant Dis. Rep. 56:1026–1027.

Potter, A.A. 1914. Head smut of sorghum and maize. J. Agric. Res. 2:339–371.

Pringle, R.B., and R.P. Scheffer. 1967. Isolation of the host-specific toxin and a related substance with nonspecific toxicity from *Helminthosporium carbonum*. Phytopathology 57:1169–1172.

Puhalla, J.E. 1969. The formation of diploids of *Ustilago maydis* on agar media. Phytopathology 59:1771–1772.

Rao, B.A., A.F. Schmitthenner, R. Caldwell, and C.W. Ellett. 1978. Prevalence and virulence of Pythium species associated with root rot of corn in poorly drained soil. Phytopathology 68:1557–1563.

Raymundo, A.D., and A.L. Hooker. 1981. Measuring the relationship between northern corn leaf blight and yield losses. Plant Dis. 65:325–327.

––––, ––––, and J.M. Perkins. 1981. Effect of gene *HtN* on the development of northern corn leaf blight epidemics. Plant Dis. 65:327–330.

Reifschneider, F.J.B., and D.C. Arny. 1979. Seed infection of maize (*Zea mays*) by *Kabatiella zeae*. Plant Dis. Rep. 63:352–354.

––––, and ––––. 1980. Host range of *Kabatiella zeae*, causal agent of eyespot of maize. Phytopathology 70:485–487.

––––, and ––––. 1983. Yield loss of maize caused by *Kabatiella zeae*. Phytopathology 73:607–609.

Reyes, L.D., T. Rosenow, R.W. Berry, and M.C. Futrell. 1964. Downy mildew and head smut diseases of sorghum in Texas. Plant Dis. Rep. 48:249–253.

Rhind, D., J.M. Waterson, and F.C. Deighton. 1952. Occurrence of *Puccinia polysora* Underw. in West Africa. Nature (London) 169:631.

Ribeiro, R.L.D., R.D. Durbin, D.C. Arny, and T.F. Uchytil. 1977. Characterization of the bacterium inciting chocolate spot of corn. Phytopathology 67:1427–1431.

Robert, A.L. 1962. Host ranges and races of the corn rusts. Phytopathology 52:1010–1012.

————, and W.R. Findley. 1952. Diseased corn leaves as a source of infection and natural epidemics of *Helminthosporium turcicum*. Plant Dis. Rep. 36:9–10.

Rodriguez, A.E., and A.J. Ullstrup. 1962. Pathogenicity of monoascosporic progenies of *Trichometasphaeria turcica*. Phytopathology 52:599–601.

Rodriquez-Ardon, R., G.E. Scott, and S.B. King. 1980. Maize yield losses caused by southern corn rust. Crop Sci. 20:812–814.

Rosen, H.R. 1921. Further observations on a bacterial root and stalk rot of field corn. Phytopathology 11:74–79.

————. 1922. The bacterial pathogen of corn stalk rot. Phytopathology 12:497–499.

————. 1926. Bacterial stalk rot of corn. Arkansas Agric. Exp. Stn. Bull. 209. (Also in: Phytopathology 16:241–267.)

Rosenkranz, E., and G.E. Scott. 1978. Effect of plant age at time of inoculation with maize dwarf mosaic virus on disease development and yield in corn. Phytopathology 68:1688–1692.

————, and ————. 1984. Determination of the number of genes for resistance to maize dwarf mosaic virus strain A in five corn inbred lines. Phytopathology 74:71–76.

Rupe, J.C., M.R. Siegal, and J.R. Hartman. 1982. Influence of environment and plant maturity on gray leaf spot of corn caused by *Cercospora zeae-maydis*. Phytopathology 72:1587–1591.

Ryland, A.K., and H.H. Storey. 1955. Physiological races of *Puccinia polysora* Underw. Nature (London) 176:655–656.

Sardanelli, S., L.R. Krusberg, and A.M. Golden. 1981. Corn cyst nematode, *Heterodera zeae*, in the United States. Plant Dis. 65:622.

Sauer, D.B., C.L. Storey, O. Ecker, and D.W. Fulk. 1982. Fungi in U.S. export wheat and corn. Phytopathology 72:1449–1452.

————, ————, and D.E. Walker. 1984. Fungal populations in U.S. farm-stored grain and their relationship to moisture, storage time, regions, and insect infestation. Phytopathology 74:1050–1053.

Saxena, K.M.S., and A.L. Hooker. 1974. A study on the structure of gene *Rp3* for rust resistance in *Zea mays*. Can. J. Genet. Cytol. 16:857–860.

Schaad, N.W., C.I. Kado, and D.R. Sumner. 1975. Synonymy of *Psuedomonas avenae* Manns 1905 and *Psuedomonas alboprecipitams* Rosen 1922. Int. J. Syst. Bacteriol. 25:133–137.

Schall, R.A., J.W. McCain, and J.F. Hennen. 1983. Distribution of *Puccinia polysora* in Indiana and absence of a cool weather form as determined by comparison with *P. sorghi*. Plant Dis. 67:767–770.

Scheffer, R.P., and A.J. Ullstrup. 1965. A host-specific toxic metabolite from *Helminthosporium carbonum*. Phytopathology 55:1037–1038.

Scheifele, G.L., and R.R. Nelson. 1969. The occurrence of Phyllosticta leaf spot of corn in Pennsylvania. Plant Dis. Rep. 53:186–189.

————, ————, and Carol Koons. 1969. Male sterility cytoplasm conditioning susceptibility of resistant inbred lines of maize to yellow leaf blight caused by *Phyllosticta zeae*. Plant Dis. Rep. 53:656–659.

————, and C.C. Wernham. 1969. Further evidence supporting the hyposthesis that two genetic systems control disease reaction to maize dwarf mosaic virus strain A and strain B. Plant Dis. Rep. 53:150–151.

————, W. Whitehead, and C. Rowe. 1970. Increased susceptibility to southern leaf spot (*Helminthosporium maydis*) in inbred lines and hybrids of maize with Texas male-sterile cytoplasm. Plant Dis. Rep. 54:501–503.

Schenck, N.C. 1970. Perithecia of *Cochliobolus heterostiophus* on corn leaves in Florida. Plant Dis. Rep. 54:1127–1128.

————. 1971. Overwintering of *Helminthosporium maydis* in Florida. Plant Dis. Rep. 55:949–951.

————. 1972. *Phaeosphaeria herpotricha* on southern corn leaf blight-infected plants in Florida. Plant Dis. Rep. 56:276.

Schieber, E., and J.G. Dickson. 1963. Comparative pathology of three tropical corn rusts. Phytopathology 53:517–521.

Schmitt, C.G., G.E. Scott, and R.E. Freytag. 1977. Response of maize diallel cross to *Sclerospora sorghi*, cause of sorghum downy mildew. Plant Dis. Rep. 61:607–608.

Schuster, M.L., B. Hoff, M. Mandel, and I. Lazar. 1972. Leaf freckles and wilt, a new corn disease. p. 176–191. *In* H.D. Loden and D. Wilkinson (ed.) Proc. Annu. Corn Sorghum Res. Conf., 27, Chicago. 12–14 December. ASTA, Washington, DC.

Scott, G.E., and M.C. Futrell. 1975. Reaction of diallel crosses of maize in T and N cytoplasms to *Bipolaris maydis* race T. Crop Sci. 15:779–782.

----, S.B. King, and J.W. Armour, Jr. 1984. Inheritance of resistance to southern corn rust in maize populations. Crop Sci. 24:265–267.

----, and L.R. Nelson. 1971. Locating genes for resistance to maize dwarf mosaic in maize seedlings by using chromosomal translocations. Crop Sci. 11:801–803.

----, and E.E. Rosenkranz. 1973. Use of chromosomal translocations to determine similarity of maize genotypes for reaction to maize dwarf mosaic. Crop Sci. 13:724–725.

----, and ----. 1974. Independent inheritance of resistance to corn stunt and maize dwarf mosaic in corn. Crop Sci. 14:104–106.

----, and ----. 1981. Effectiveness of resistance to maize dwarf mosaic and maize chlorotic dwarf viruses in maize. Phytopathology 71:937–941.

Semeniuk, G., and C.J. Mankin. 1964. Occurrence and development of *Sclerophthora macrospora* on cereals and grasses in South Dakota. Phytopathology 54:409–416.

Shannon, G.M., O.L. Shotwell, A.J. Lyons, D.G. White, and G. Garcia-Aguirre. 1980. Laboratory screening for zearalenone formation in corn hybrids and inbreds. J. Assoc. Off. Anal. Chem. 63:1275–1277.

Shaw, W.C., D.R. Robinson, and P.F. Sand. 1962. Advances in witchweed control. Weeds 10(3):182–191.

Shepherd, R.J., and Q.L. Holdeman. 1965. Seed transmission of the johnsongrass strain of the sugarcane mosaic virus in corn. Plant Dis. Rep. 49:468–469.

Schurtleff, M.C. (ed.). 1980. Compendium of corn diseases. 2nd ed. Am. Phytopathol. Soc., St. Paul.

Simone, G.W. 1978. Inheritance of resistance in fifteen corn selections to *Helminthosporium turcicum*. Ph.D. diss. Univ. of Illinois, Urbana. (Diss. Abstr. 78–11293).

Simpson, W.R. 1966. Head smut of corn in Idaho. Plant Dis. Rep. 50:215–217.

----, and H.S. Fenwick. 1968. Chemical control of corn head smut. Plant Dis. Rep. 52:726–727.

----, and ----. 1971. Suppression of corn head smut with carboxin seed treatment. Plant Dis. Rep. 55:501–503.

Singh, B.P., and D.T. Gordon. 1980. Maize dwarf mosaic virus in Michigan. Plant Dis. 64:704–705.

Siradhana, B.S., S.R.S. Dange, R.S. Rathore, and S.D. Singh. 1978. Ontogenic predisposition of *Zea mays* to sorghum downy mildew. Plant Dis. Rep. 62:467–468.

Slack, C.R., P.G. Roughan, and H.C.M. Bassett. 1974. Selective inhibition of mesophyll chloroplast development in some C4-pathway species by low night temperatures. p. 499–504. *In* R.L. Bieleski et al. (ed.) Mechanisms of regulation of plant growth. Bull. 12. The Royal Soc. of New Zealand, Wellington.

Smith, D.R. 1971. Inheritance of reaction to Stewart's disease (bacterial wilt) in dent corn. M.S. thesis. Univ. of Illinois, Urbana.

----. 1975. Expression of monogenic chlorotic-lesion resistance to *Helminthosporium maydis* in corn. Phytopathology 65:1160–1165.

----. 1977. Monitoring corn pathogens. p. 106–121. *In* H.D. Loden and D. Wilkinson (ed.) Proc. Annu. Corn Sorghum Res. Conf., 32, Chicago. 6–8 December. ASTA, Washington, DC.

----. 1984. Monitoring corn pathogens nationally. p. 101–136. *In* D.E. Alexander (ed.) Proc. 20 Annu. Illinois Corn Breeders School, Univ. of Illinois, Champaign. 6–8 March. Univ. of Illinois, Champaign.

----, and A.L. Hooker. 1973. Monogenic chlorotic-lesion resistance in corn to *Helminthosporium maydis*. Crop Sci. 13:330–331.

----, ----, and S.M. Lim. 1970. Physiologic races of *Helminthosporium maydis*. Plant Dis. Rep. 54:819–822.

----, ----, ----, and J.B. Beckett. 1971. Disease reaction of thirty sources of cytoplasmic male-sterile corn to *Helminthosporium maydis* race T. Crop Sci. 11:772–773.

----, and J.G. Kinsey. 1980. Further physiologic specialization in *Helminthosporium turcicum*. Plant Dis. 779–781.

----, J.G. Kinsey, and K.D. Kauffmann. 1985. Segregation of *Helminthosporium carbonum* race 1 susceptibility in the corn synthetic BS 13. Plant Dis. 69:1101.

Smith, G.M. 1940. Wilt resistance in new sweet corn hybrids and inbreds. p. 61–62. *In* Fifty-second annual report Indiana Agric. Exp. Stn. 1939.

Smith, M.A. 1926. Infection and spore germination studies with *Puccinia sorghi*. Phytopathology 16:69.

Stevens, N.E. 1934. Stewart's disease in relation to winter temperature. Plant Dis. Rep. 18:141–149.

----, and C.M. Haenseler. 1941. Incidence of bacterial wilt of sweet corn, 1935–1940: Forecast and performance. Plant Dis. Rep. 25:152–157.

Stewart, F.C. 1897. A bacterial wilt of sweet corn. N. Y. (Geneva) Agric. Exp. Stn. Bull. 130:423–439.

Stienstra, W.C., T. Kommedahl, E.L. Stromberg, C.A. Matyac, C.E. Windels, and F. Morgan. 1985. Suppression of corn head smut with seed and soil treatments. Plant Dis. 69:301–302.

Storey, H.H., and A.K. Howland. 1967. Resistance in maize to a third race of *Puccinia polysora*. Ann. Appl. Biol. 60:297–303.

----, ----, J.S. Hemingway, J.D. Jameson, B.S.T. Baldwin, H.C. Thorp, and G.E. Dixon. 1958. East African work on breeding maize resistant to the tropical American rust, *Puccinia polysora*. Empire J. Exp. Agric. 26:1–17.

Stromberg, E.L. 1981. Head smut of maize, a new disease in Minnesota. Phytopathology 71:906 (Abstr.).

----. 1985. Evaluation of gray leaf spot resistance in selected corn hybrids in Virginia. Phytopathology 75:629 (Abstr.).

----, W.C. Stienstra, T. Kommendahl, C.A. Matyac, C.E. Windels, and J.L. Geadelmann. 1984. Smut expression and resistance of corn to *Sphacelotheca reiliana* in Minnesota. Plant Dis. 68:880–884.

----, R.J. Zeyen, and H.G. Johnson. 1978. An epidemic of maize dwarf mosaic virus in sweet corn in Minnesota. Phytopathol. News. 12:225–226 (Abstr.).

Sumner, D.R., and N.W. Schaad. 1977. Epidemiology and control of bacterial leaf blight of corn. Phytopathology 67:1113–1118.

Sutton, B.C. 1980. The Coelomycetes. Commonwealth Mycological Inst., Kew, Surrey, England.

Sutton, J.C., A. Bootsma, and T.J. Gillespie. 1972. Influence of some cultural practices on yellow leaf blight of maize. Can. Plant Dis. Surv. 52:89–92.

Tarr, S.A.J. 1962. Disease of sorghum, sudan grass and broom corn. Commonwealth Mycological Inst., Kew, Surrey, England.

Tarte, R. 1971. The relationship between preplant populations of *Pratylenchus zeae* and growth and yield of corn. J. Nematol. 3:330–331.

Tehon, L.R., and E. Daniels. 1925. Notes on parasitic fungi of Illinois. Mycologia 17:240–249.

Thayer, P., and L.E. Williams. 1960. Effect of nitrogen, phosphorus and potassium concentrations on the development of Gibberella stalk and root-rot of corn. Phytopathology 50:212–214.

Thompson, D.L., and R.R. Bergquist. 1984. Inheritance of mature plant resistance to *Helminthosporium maydis* race 0 in maize. Crop Sci. 24:807–811.

----, and T.T. Hebert. 1971. Winter survival of *Helminthosporium maydis* in North Carolina. Plant. Dis. Rep. 55:956–959.

Thongmeearkom, P., R.E. Ford, and H. Jedlinski. 1976. Aphid transmission of maize dwarf mosaic virus strains. Phytopathology 66:332–335.

Timian, R.G., V.L. Jons, and H.A. Lamey. 1978. Maize dwarf mosaic virus in North Dakota. Plant Dis. Rep. 62:674–675.

Tisdale, W.H. 1919. Physoderma disease of corn. J. Agric. Res. 16:137–154.

Tosic, M., and R.E. Ford. 1972. Grasses differentiating sugarcane mosaic and maize dwarf mosaic viruses. Phytopathology 62:1466–1470.

Tu, J.C., and R.E. Ford. 1971. Maize dwarf mosaic virus predisposes corn to root rot infection. Phytopathology 61:800–803.

Tuite, J., and G.H. Foster. 1979. Control of storage diseases of grain. Annu. Rev. Phytopathol. 17:343–366.

----, G. Shaner, G. Rambo, J. Foster, and R.W. Caldwell. 1974. The Gibberella ear rot epidemics of corn in Indiana in 1965 and 1972. Cereal Sci. Today 19:238–241.

Turner, M.T., and E.R. Johnson. 1980. Race of *Helminthosporium turcicum* not controlled by *Ht* genetic resistance in corn in the American Corn Belt. Plant Dis. 64:216–217.

Tyler, L.J., and C.P. Shumway. 1935. Hybridization between *Sphacelotheca sorghi* and *Sorosporium reilianum*. Phytopathology 25:375–376.

Ullstrup, A.J. 1941. Two physiologic races of *Helminthosporium maydis* in the Corn Belt. Phytopathology 31:508–521.

————. 1944. Further studies on a species of Helminthosporium parasitizing corn. Phytopathology 34:214–222.

————. 1955. Diseases of corn. *In* G.F. Sprague (ed.) Corn and corn improvement. Agronomy 5:465–536.

————. 1960. Bacterial stripe of corn. Phytopathology 50:906–910.

————. 1963. Sources of resistance to northern corn leaf blight. Plant Dis. Rep. 47:107–108.

————. 1964. Observations on two ephiphytotics of Diplodia ear rot of corn in Indiana. Plant Dis. Rep. 48:414–415.

————. 1965. Inheritance and linkage of a gene determining resistance in maize to an American race of *Puccinia polysora*. Phytopathology 55:425–428.

————. 1970a. A comparison of monogenic and polygenic resistance to *Helminthosporium turcicum* in corn. Phytopathology 1597–1599.

————. 1970b. Crazy top of maize. Indian Phytopathol. 23:250–261.

————. 1970c. Hosts of *Helminthosporium maydis*. Plant Dis. Rep. 54:1103.

————. 1971a. Hyper-susceptibility of high-lysine corn to kernel and ear rots. Plant Dis. Rep. 55:1046.

————. 1971b. Overwintering of race T of *Helminthosporium maydis* in midwestern United States. Plant Dis. Rep. 55:563–565.

————. 1977. Diseases of corn. *In* G.F. Sprague (ed.) Corn and corn improvement. Agronomy 18:391–500.

————, and M.P. Britton. 1968. An unusual epiphytotic of common corn smut in Indiana and Illinois. Plant Dis. Rep. 52:922–923.

————, E.B. Smalley, G.L. Worf, and R.W. Ahrens. 1969. Eyespot: A serious new disease of corn in the USA. Phytopathology 59:105 (Abstr.).

————, and M.H. Sun. 1969. The prevalence of crazy top of corn in 1968. Plant Dis. Rep. 53:246–250.

Underwood, L.M. 1897. Some new fungi chiefly from Alabama. Bull. Torrey Bot. Club 24:81–86.

Uyemoto, J.K. 1983. Biology and control of maize chlorotic mottle virus. Plant Dis. 67:7–10.

————, D.L. Bockelman, and L.E. Claflin. 1980. Severe outbreak of corn lethal necrosis disease in Kansas. Plant Dis. 64:99–100.

Vidaver, A.K. 1977. Maintenance of viability and virulence of *Corynebacterium nebraskense*. Phytopathology 67:825–827.

————, and R.R., Carlson. 1978. Leaf spot of field corn caused by *Psuedomonas andropogonis*. Plant Dis. Rep. 62:213–216.

Villareal, R.L., and R.M. Lantican. 1965. The cytoplasmic inheritance of susceptibility to Helminthosporium leaf spot in corn. Philipp. Agric. 49:294–300.

Voorhees, R.K., 1933. Effect of certain environmental factors on the germination of the sporangia of *Physoderma zeae-maydis*. J. Agric. Res. 47:609–615.

Waggoner, P.E., J.G. Horsfall, and R.J. Lukens. 1972. EPIMAY, a simulator of southern corn leaf blight. Connecticut Agric. Exp. Stn. Bull. 729.

Wallin, J.R. 1951. An epiphytotic of corn rust in the north central region of the United States. Plant Dis. Rep. 35:207–211.

Walter, J.M. 1934. The mode of entrance of *Ustilago zeae* into corn. Phytopathology 24:1012–1020.

Walton, J.D., B.W. Gibson, and E.D. Earle. 1982. Purification and characterization of *Helminthosporium carbonum* race 1 toxin. Plant Physiol. 69:144 (Abstr.)

Warmke, H.E., and N.C. Schenck. 1971. Occurrence of *Fusarium moniliforme* and *Helminthosporium maydis* on and in corn seed related to T cytoplasm. Plant Dis. Rep. 55:486–489.

Warren, H.L. 1977. Survival of *Colletotrichum graminicola* in corn kernels. Phytopathology 67:160–162.

————, D.M. Huber, D.W. Nelson, and O.W. Mann. 1975. Stalk rot incidence and yield of corn as affected by inhibiting nitrification of fall-applied ammonium. Agron. J. 67:655–660.

––––, and R.L. Nicholson. 1975. Kernel infection, seedling blight, and wilt of maize caused by *Colletotrichum graminicola*. Phytopathology 65:620–623.

Weber, G.F. 1922. Studies on corn rust. Phytopathology 12:89–97.

Wei, J., K. Lui, J. Chen, P. Luo, and O. Young Lee-Stadelmann. 1988. Pathological and physiological identification of race C of *Bipolaris maydis* in China. Phytopathology 78:550–554.

Weihing, J.L., and A.K. Vidaver. 1967. Report of holcus leaf spot (*Pseudomonas syringae*) epidemic on corn. Plant Dis. Rep. 51:396–397.

Wellhausen, E.J. 1937a. Effect of the genetic constitution of the host on the virulence of *Phytomonas stewarti*. Phytopathology 27:1070–1089.

––––. 1937b. Genetics of resistance to bacterial wilt in maize. Iowa Agric. Exp. Stn. Res. Bull. 224:69–114.

Weston, W.H., Jr. 1929. The occurrence of *Sclerospora graminicola* on maize in Wisconsin. Phytopathology 19:391–397.

––––, and H.N. Uppal. 1932. The basis for *Sclerospora sorghi* as a new species. Phytopathology 22:573–586.

Wheeler, H., D.J. Politis, and C.G. Poneleit. 1974. Pathogenicity, host range, and distribution of *Colletotrichum graminicola* on corn. Phytopathology 64:293–296.

White, D.G., R.G. Hoeft, and J.J. Touchton. 1978. Effect of nitrogen and nitrapyrin on stalk rot, stalk diameter, and yield of corn. Phytopathology 68:811–814.

––––, and J. Yanney. 1981. Conservation tillage and plant diseases. p. 164–166. *In* Crop production with conservation tillage in the 80's. ASAE, St. Joseph, MI.

––––, J. Yanney, and T.A. Natti. 1979. Anthracnose stalk rot. p. 1–15. *In* H.D. Loden and D. Wilkinson (ed.) Proc. Annu. Corn Sorghum Res. Conf., 34, Chicago, 11–13 December. ASTA, Washington, DC.

Widstrom, N.W. 1979. The role of insects and other plant pests in aflatoxin contamination of corn, cotton and peanuts—a review. J. Environ. Qual. 8:5–11.

––––, W.W. McWilliams, and D.M. Wilson. 1984. Contamination of Preharvest Corn by Aflatoxin. p. 68–83. *In* H.D. Loden and D. Wilkinson (ed.) Proc. Annu. Corn Sorghum Res. Conf., 39, Chicago. 5–6 December. ASTA, Washington, DC.

Wilcoxson, R.D. 1962. Stalk rot in relation to yield in corn. Phytopathology 52:416–418.

Williams, L.E., and L.J. Alexander. 1965. Maize dwarf mosaic, a new corn disease. Phytopathology 55:802–804.

––––, W.R. Findley, E.J. Dollinger, and R.M. Ritter. 1968. Seed transmission studies of maize dwarf mosaic virus in corn. Plant Dis. Rep. 52:863–864.

––––, and G.M. Willis. 1963. Disease of corn caused by *Colletotrichum graminicolum*. Phytopathology 53:364–365.

Williamson, D.L., and R.F. Whitcomb. 1975. Plant mycoplasmas: A cultivable spiroplasma causes corn stunt disease. Science (Washington, DC) 188:1018–1020.

Wilson, G.W. 1914. The identity of the anthracnose of grasses in the United States. Phytopathology 4:106–112.

Wyllie, T.D., and L.G. Morehouse. (ed.) 1978. Mycotoxic fungi, mycotoxins, mycotoxicoses: An encyclopedic handbook. Marcel Dekker, New York.

Wysong, D.S., B. Doupnik, Jr., and L. Lane. 1981. Goss's wilt and corn lethal necrosis—can they become a major problem? p. 104–152. *In* H.D. Loden and D. Wilkinson (ed.) Proc. Annu. Corn Sorghum Res. Conf., 36, Chicago. 9–11 December. ASTA, Washington, DC.

––––, and E. Kerr. 1969. Hybrid corn yield reduction by stalk rot and root rot in Nebraska. Plant Dis. Rep. 53:326–329.

Yoder, O.C. 1973. A selective toxin produced by *Phyllosticta maydis*. Phytopathology 63:1361–1366.

Young, H.C., Jr. 1943. The pathogenicity of certain fungi, singly and in combination, on the various inbred lines and crosses of corn. M.S. thesis. Univ. of Minnesota, St. Paul.

––––, J.M. Prescott, and E.E. Saari. 1978. Role of disease monitoring in preventing epidemics. Annu. Rev. Phytopathol. 16:263–285.

Younis, S.E.A. 1969. Locating genes determining resistance to Fusarium stalk-rot in maize. Genetika 1:123–129.

––––, M.K. Abo-El Dahb, and G.S. Mallah. 1969. Genetic studies of the resistance to Fusarium stalk-rot in maize. Indian J. Genet. Plant Breed. 29:418–425.

Zeyen, R.E., E. Stromberg, and E. Kuehnast. 1978. Research links MDMV epidemic to aphid flights. Minn. Sci. 33:10–11.

Zuber, M.S. 1973. Evaluation of progress in selection for stalk quality. p. 110–122. *In* H.D. Loden and D. Wilkinson (ed.) Proc. Annu. Corn. Sorghum Res. Conf., 28, Chicago. 4–6 December. ASTA, Washington, DC.

————, T.C. Ainsworth, M.H. Blanco, and L.L. Darrah. 1981. Effect of anthracnose leaf blight on stalk rind strength and yield in F_1 single crosses in maize. Plant Dis. 65:719–722.

13   The Most Important Corn Insects

F. F. DICKE AND W. D. GUTHRIE

USDA-ARS
Iowa State University
Ankeny, Iowa

In recent decades, there have been substantial changes in crop production practices. Such changes as decline in oat (*Avena sativa* L.) acreage, ascendancy of soybean [*Glycine max* (L.) Merr.] acreage, upsurge in the use of commercial fertilizer, improved corn (*Zea mays* L.) hybrids, changes in tillage practices, and effective pesticides have had an impact on insect populations. Collective improvements and generally favorable climatic conditions have made it possible to about double the average per-hectare yield of corn in the USA in this period.

Certain insects such as chinch bugs (*Blissus* spp.) and grasshoppers (locusts), which in the past have been serious pests, in recent years had relatively low populations in most corn-producing areas. Environmental conditions characterized by sustained below-normal rainfall and above-normal temperatures, which are regarded favorable for epizootics of these pests, have not prevailed since the drought years of 1930 to 1936. Effective insecticides are available to cope with local insect problems should they occur.

Nevertheless, the corn crop is subject to attack by a complex of insects from the time it is planted until it is utilized as food or feed. Other crops, particularly small grains, forage grasses, and legumes are sources of insects that attack corn and are also sources of prey that help keep the population complex in balance. This ecological relationship is a part of the corn insect problem. It is important to recognize the universal biological variability within species, their hosts, and where diseases are involved, in pathogens.

The most important corn insect pests (common and scientific names with authors are listed in the appendix) and areas where they occur are: the European corn borer [*Ostrinia nubilalis* (Hübner)] in North America, Europe, Mideast, and North Africa; the Asian corn borer (*O. furnacalis*) in Asia and Philippines; the spotted stem borer (*Chilo partellus*) in Asia and Africa; the Asiatic rice borer [*C. suppressallis* (Walker)] in Asia; the Oriental corn borer (*C. agamemnon*) and the pink borer (*Sesamia cretica*) in Mid-East and Africa; the African maize borer (*S. calamistis*) in Africa; the pink stem borer (*S. inferens* in Asia, *S. nonagrioides* in Mid-East and

Africa); the African maize stalk borer (*Busseola fusca*) and the African sugarcane borer (*Eldana saccarina*) in Africa; the American sugarcane borer (*Diatraea saccharalis*) in the Americas; the neotropical corn borer (*D. lineolata*) in Central and South America; the southwestern corn borer (*D. grandiosella*) in southern USA and Mexico; the lesser cornstalk borer [*Elasmopalpus lignosellus* (Zeller)], the *Heliothis* spp., and the *Diabrotica* complex in the Americas; the fall armyworm [*Spodoptera frugiperda* (J.E. Smith)] and *Dalbulus* spp. in southern USA and Latin America; the African armyworm (*S. exempta*) and *Cicadulina* spp. throughout Africa south of the Sahara; and the corn leaf aphid [*Rhopalosiphum maidis* (Fitch)], and *Sitophilus* spp. throughout the world (Ortega et al., 1980; Mihm, 1985). Most borer species in the early larva instars, are leaf feeders on corn plants in the seedling to whorl stage. Later instar-larvae attack stems and other plant parts. Larvae attacking corn plants at anthesis feed on tassels, pollen, leaf sheaths, collars, mid-ribs, developing ear shanks and stems (Mihm, 1985).

It is customary to classify the injurious species according to their habitat or to plant structures that they commonly infest. The stage of plant development is frequently an important factor in determining what structures are attacked.

In general, this chapter has been arranged in sections based on a seasonal host-insect biological relationship as follows: (i) research trends; (ii) soil insects; (iii) insects attacking the leaf, stalk, and ear; (iv) lesser recognized groups; (v) insects in relationship to corn diseases; (vi) stored grain insects; (vii) insect resistance in corn; and (viii) chemical control status. In addition, a list of common and scientific names of insects mentioned in this chapter is given in an appendix.

Specific identification is essential. When questions of identity arise it is desirable to collect specimens and preserve them in a 70% alcohol solution for future reference. An attempt has been made to briefly describe the injurious forms and the typical injury to the plant structures involved. Literature citations have been more or less limited to publications that include data and supporting references.

Many early records on distribution, abundance, and biology of corn insects were assembled by USDA entomologists and state entomologist of several states, especially New York, Illinois, and Missouri. The most complete special reports are those of Forbes (1893, 1904) in Illinois. In discussing sources of American corn insects, Neiswander (1931) listed fewer than 400 species. Many of these species do not have a proven host relationship. Because of the expansion of corn culture throughout the world, we have included species in tropical areas that directly and indirectly exert severe stress on corn culture. An effort has been made to discuss protective traits, particularly those that are highly developed on the ear.

13-1   RESEARCH TRENDS

Records of identity, prevalence, and biology of corn insects in America prior to the establishment of official entomology in 1854 are scattered and fragmentary. The complex of insects before the days of systematic records, however, was similar to that of today. Major groups infesting different parts of plants and grain were well represented. Some species have extended their range, whereas some species have adapted themselves as they became exposed to corn culture.

Epizootics of many important species show a periodicity pattern, although not necessarily in regular cycles. Populations may remain relatively stable for several years and then suddenly increase. Limiting factors in such periodicity are environmental. The variable pattern of the environment, therefore, affects the general corn-insect complex from year to year.

Much of the research to control corn insects has centered around applied biological and ecological methods. A good deal of emphasis was placed on natural enemies. Efforts were mainly directed toward methods of limiting populations through cultural adjustments such as plowing or seedbed preparation and planting time, crop rotation, and sanitation. The effect of compatible cultural practices to reduce insect abundance is perhaps of greater significance than is commonly appreciated. Through usage many such practices have become established procedure. Others, such as indiscriminate burning of crop residue to destroy overwintering forms, have been discarded.

During the period 1930 to 1950, there was practically a complete turnover from open-pollinated to hybrid cultivars of corn. With this conversion the development of new inbred lines and hybrid combinations became a continuing process. Extensive breeding, with improved techniques and exposure to varying environmental conditions, has resulted in new hybrids with improvements in yields, standing ability, and resistance to insects and diseases (Russell, 1974; Guthrie, 1974; Duvick, 1977).

Over the last 30 yr, there has been a significant adjustment in research activities on the corn insect complex. A group of factors have contributed to stimulating an increase in host and insect relationship studies, namely: (i) the upsurge in use of commercial fertilizers, particularly N, which resulted in increased monoculture of corn and corn Diabrotica rootworm problems; (ii) development of strains of rootworms resistant to insecticides, which intensified search for new insecticides and tolerant corn hybrids; (iii) dispersal of the western corn rootworm (*Diabrotica virgifera virgifera*) and southwestern corn borer to new areas; (iv) the widespread increase in virus and spiroplasma diseases in corn and the vector-host relationships; (v) aflatoxin outbreaks in corn; (vi) insect pathology and pheromone research; and (vii) a significant increase in a regional and interdisciplinary approach in research. The overall outlook appears to be promising for improvements in practical control of corn insects under a wide range of environmental conditions.

13–2 SOIL INSECTS

Soil insects are those that inhabit soil while they are in some way causing plant injury. Soil insects may be injurious to roots or other subterranean parts of plants, or, as with some cutworms and beetles, they may sever or feed on aboveground plant parts. Many of these species ordinarily escape attention when immature because they are hidden in the soil, but may be well known in the adult stage. Plant injury symptoms aboveground are commonly the first indications of infestation. With a knowledge of insect adaptations and habits one can usually detect where certain species are apt to be most abundant. The economic species of soil insects have been treated more in groups than those feeding on aerial parts of plants, perhaps because of the large number of species involved. Thus, cutworms, wireworms, and white grubs have been grouped, although there may be deviations in biology among the species within a group.

13–2.1 Northern Corn Rootworm — Description and Biology

Larvae of the northern corn rootworm (NCR) (*Diabrotica barberi*) are slender, white to pale yellow, with a yellowish brown head, and about 10-mm long when full grown. Young larvae may be found feeding on root hairs and on or in young lateral roots, causing them to turn reddish or brown. Infestations by larvae follows a more or less definite pattern related to development of crown roots. Apple and Patel (1963) showed the larvae feeding on progressively higher rings of crown roots as they emerged at the nodes and as the season advanced. Feeding habits on roots of seedlings are shown in Fig. 13–1. Later stages may be found on young crown root buds near the leaf sheath attachment. The pupae, naked and white, are located in earthen cells in soil near plants. Adults are about 5-mm long and pale green. Emerging during mid-summer, the beetles feed on silks and tips of ears and may also be found on other flowering plants in other crop fields. When abundant on newly emerged silk they may interfere with full pollination. The NCR has been predominantly a pest in the Central states, but also occurs in Ontario, Canada, and the Eastern and Southern states (Forbes, 1893; Webster, 1913; Chiang, 1973; Hill and Mayo, 1980).

The NCR has a single generation annually. Adults emerge in summer and are prevalent in corn fields until fall. The feed gregariously on silks and also on pollen of corn and other plants. There is a tendency for the beetle population to shift to later silking fields in which oviposition is likely to be more concentrated. Eggs are deposited in soil mostly in corn fields in the latter part of summer. This habit is an important factor in the fate of progeny the following year. When corn follows corn, a favorable

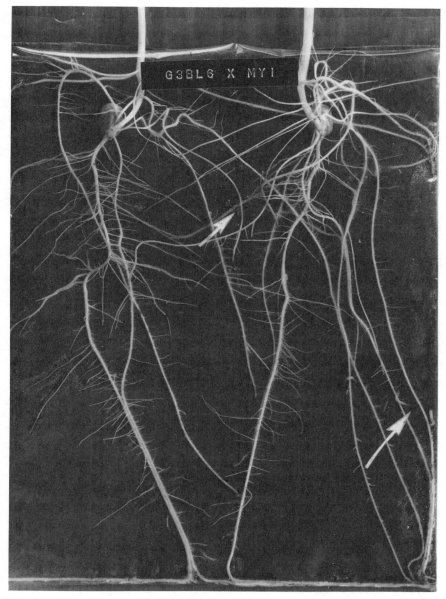

Fig. 13–1. Immature larvae of Diabrotica feeding on lateral roots of corn growing in plastic bags.

environment is provided for development of larvae of the next generation. Although indicated many years ago in Illinois (Bigger, 1932), there are extensive areas in Minnesota, South Dakota, and Iowa where eggs of *D. barberi* extend diapause over a second winter. This results in hatching and attack on roots of corn planted after an intervening small grain or soybean crop. Where this prevails a longer rotation or an insecticide application is desirable to avoid significant yield loss (Krysan et al., 1984). Feeding on or in lateral roots results in poor root growth or "root pruning" as shown in Fig. 13–2, producing varying degrees of fibrous secondary root growth. Injured roots are commonly infected with root rots, a con-

Fig. 13–2. Root pruning by northern and western corn rootworms, and regrowth trait.

dition that may be implicated in varietal responses (Forbes, 1893; Palmer and Kommedahl, 1969).

Under heavy infestation, plants are poorly anchored and are susceptible to root lodging. Because of interference with machine harvesting, lodging may be as important in the rootworm problem as direct loss of yield. According to Tate and Bare (1946), in Nebraska, continuous crops of corn and moist soil conditions favor development and survival of larvae.

13-2.2 Western Corn Rootworm — Description and Biology

In early publications, the western corn rootworm (WCR) (*Diabrotica virgifera virgifera*) was usually referred to as the Colorado corn rootworm. Periodically, it was a pest of corn in Colorado, western Nebraska, and Kansas (Gillette, 1912; Tate and Bare, 1946). This species began to dominate the rootworm population with its rapid spread eastward in the 1960s. The distribution extended to parts of Indiana, Michigan, and Ohio in 1976. By 1985, the species had spread into Ontario and to eastern areas of the USA. It is generally accepted that high populations of both the western and northern species are principally associated with insecticide failure and monoculture of corn. The latter was made possible by rapid increase in use of commercial fertilizers, particularly N.

Larva of the WCR is similar in appearance and feeding habits to the northern species (Fig. 13-1). Specific characters for identification of mature larvae of three species of *Diabrotica* have been described by Mendoza and Peters (1964). The adult female is dark greenish and is identified by horizontal stripes on the wing covers; males are dark and usually are lacking in wing stripes. The life history is similar to the NCR and the same control practices are advocated. Beetles feed vigorously on leaves of "whorl stage" corn and likewise attack florets of emerging tassels. Leaves of some genotypes are more susceptible than others.

Branson and Ortman (1970) made extensive studies of the host range of larvae of both the northern and western species. Corn was found to be the favored host for completing the life cycle. Limited populations were recovered from green [*Setaria viridis* (L.) Beav.] and yellow foxtail [*Silutescens* (Weigel) Hubb], foxtail millet [*S. italica* (L.) Beauv.], wheat (*Triticum aestivum* L.), barley (*Hordeum vulgare* L.), spelt (*T. spelta* L.), intermediate wheatgrass [*Agropyron intermedium* (Host) Beav.] and pubescent wheatgrass [*A. trichophorum* (Link) Richt.]. There is a tendency for the WCR beetles to remain in cornfields (Hill and Mayo, 1980).

Tate and Bare (1946), working in Nebraska, found less lodging after fall plowing, listed planting, and timely irrigation than after other cropping practices; excessive irrigation at tasseling and thereafter increased lodging. In further tests in Nebraska, Hill et al. (1948) reported increased yields and reduction in lodging under irrigation when corn was grown in rotation with sweet clover, or when it was fertilized with N, or when manure was applied. Nitrogen did not decrease rootworm populations but stimulated root recovery. The practice of short rotation, particularly with an intervening crop of soybean, has become common in the Corn Belt. Where monoculture of corn is practiced, several effective insecticides are available to ensure against appreciable yield losses.

13–2.3   Southern Corn Rootworm — Description and Biology

The southern corn rootworm (SCR) (*Diabrotica undecimpunctata*) also known as the spotted cucumber beetle, injures corn in both larval and adult stages. Young larvae are slender, white to yellowish, becoming greenish yellow as they mature. The full-grown larva is about 12-mm long and has a brownish head shield and brown dorsal shield on the ninth abdominal segment. Larvea and pupae resemble those of the NCR and WCR and are easily confused with them. The adult is about 6-mm long, green, with 11 or 12 black spots on the wings. Symptoms of larval injury are holes through the base of small plants, tillering following growing point injury and root injury is similar to that described for the other species (Forbes, 1893; Webster, 1913).

The SCR has many hosts among the grasses, cucurbits, and legumes. It is widely distributed east of the Rocky Mountains, including southern Canada, but is most serious as a pest in the southeastern states and in the lower and middle Mississippi Valley. In the middle Corn Belt, beetles appear on alfalfa (*Medicago sativa* L.) or young corn in the latter part of May. There is as yet no evidence that any form overwinters in this area. It is presumed that populations of beetles are migrants from more southern areas. In warm climates, the SCR overwinters as an adult under debris but may be active or feed on green plants on warm days in winter. It is not known to have an inherent diapause system in any of its stages of development. In spring, the beetles fly to legumes, cucurbits, or grasses, where they feed and deposit their eggs in soil. In southern areas, according to Isely (1929) and Arant (1929), the main source of injury to young corn is from early stage larvae that were present in soil prior to seedbed preparation and corn planting. However, oviposition has been observed after corn emergence. In areas where this species is a pest, cool and wet springs are favorable for building up populations in winter legumes and on lowlands where favorable hosts are prevalent.

First-generation larvae feed in or on young roots and also burrow through plants near the base. This feeding stunts or kills the growing point of plants and frequently induces tillering. Luginbill (1918) reported the first generation of larvae as the most important on corn in South Carolina. However, there appears to be an overlapping of generations, and Isely (1929) concluded that in Arkansas the number of generations was indeterminate. In the northern areas there are thought to be one or two generations. Forbes (1893) reported root pruning and subsequent root lodging after the bud-feeding stage and presence of larvae from June to August. On older corn, larval feeding was found in the base of stalks, on young brace roots, and on lower leaf sheaths.

Injury in northern states is easily confounded with that of the northern and western corn rootworms. In southern areas the injury may be mistaken for that of *Diatraea* spp., the sugarcane beetle (*Euetheola humilis rugiceps*), or wireworms. Adults commonly feed on leaves of corn from the seedling to later whorl growth stages and on silks. Feeding on whorl leaves may be confused with that of some lepidopterous budworms.

In southern areas, various cultural practices have been advocated for reducing rootworm injury, such as crop rotation, thick planting, fertilization, green manure crops, clean tillage, and adjustment of planting dates. Good soil and fertilization practices minimize rootworm injury. Isely (1929) recommended elimination of wild grasses, on which larval infestations begins, about a month before the planting of corn. Similarly, Arant (1934) and Eden and Arant (1953) suggested turning under winter legumes on or before 15 April and planting early in May in areas with a climate similar to that in Alabama. Cultural practices are not known to have an effect on populations in Corn Belt areas where infestations originate from a migrant population.

13–2.4   Cutworms — Description and Biology

Cutworms are larvae of noctuid moths. The typical cutworm found attacking corn has a plump, curled-up appearance. The color of the larvae varies with the species from a light-glassy to a grayish black or brown. Larvae feed at night and their presence in soil is indicated by plants cut off at or below surface of the ground. Moths are usually gray to brown. They fly at night and congregate at lights, where they may be readily trapped to determine their abundance in a locality. Among the most important species on corn in the USA are the black cutworm (*Agrotis ipsilon*), the glassy cutworm (*Crymodes devastator*), the dingy cutworm (*Feltia ducens*), and the claybacked cutworm (*A. gladiaria*). These species are widely distributed in the USA and Canada, but vary in abundance in different areas. The black cutworm (Fig. 13–3) is worldwide in distribution and is of general importance on other crops (Forbes, 1904; Stanley, 1936; Walkden, 1950).

The incidence of cutworm larvae in corn fields is usually dependent on the population present in the previous season and practices followed

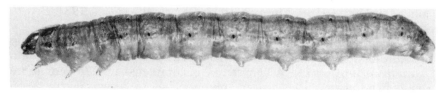

Fig. 13–3. Larva of the black cutworm.

for seedbed preparation. Moths deposit their eggs in hay or sod land early in the fall. Larvae generally develop on grass or clover and pass the winter about half-grown. Typical areas for cutworm infestation in corn are in grassy river or creek bottoms to which moths are attracted for oviposition.

Recent extensive research has produced convincing evidence that early spring flights of black cutworm moths in Iowa and northern Missouri are of southern origin (Domino et al., 1983; Kaster and Showers, 1982).

Moths may be carried several hundred kilometers to Iowa in one to three nights by strong southerly winds. More numerous southerly wind events seemed to make northern Missouri more subject to moth invasions. The black cutworm, however, overwinters in the pupal stage in southern areas. It has two or more generations, depending on the bioclimate, whereas the other three species have one generation. Immature larvae are usually present in the field when the crop is planted. The larvae occupy burrows in the soil, feeding on plant parts that they have severed and pulled in from the surface. Girdling of plants is, therefore, a means to an end and results in a loss of plants out of proportion to the food requirements of the larvae. Advanced larval stages may burrow into plants near the soil surface, causing plants to produce tillers or die. Loss of stand may be substantial even with a low population (Crumb, 1929; Forbes, 1904; Fairchild et al., 1981; Munson et al., 1984).

Late summer or early fall plowing to eliminate young larvae has been recommended for many years. This practice, however, is not desirable in hilly areas, where grass sod serves to prevent erosion of soil through winter. Under such conditions spring plowing is the logical practice. Most farmers replant when stands have been depleted by cutworm infestation.

13-2.5 Wireworms — Description and Biology

Wireworms are larvae of the common click beetles. They are slender, shiny, rather sluggish, buff to reddish brown, heavily chitinized, and usually from 12- to 40-mm long. Figure 13–4 shows a typical wireworm specimen. Typical symptoms of their presence in corn are poor stands, dying seedlings, and tillering of young plants. In addition to corn, wireworms are injurious to small grains, forage grasses, and vegetable crops. The widely distributed species on corn are the wheat wireworm (*A. mancus*), the sand wireworm (*Horistonotus uhlerii*), *Melanotus cribulosus*, *Aeolus mellillus*, and *M. communis* (Forbes, 1893; Glen et al., 1943; Tenhet and Howe, 1939; Thomas, 1940; Riley and Keaster, 1981; Brown and Keaster, 1986).

The wireworm problem in corn is inherited from the previous crop of pasture or forage grasses and, in some cases, small grain and potato (*Solanum tuberosum* L.). A generation is completed in 1 to 3 or more years, depending on the species and climatic factors. A typical generation develops as follows: Larvae pupate in earthen cells in middle summer.

Fig. 13—4. Wireworm larva.

Adults emerge in late summer and early fall. In some species pupae remain in cells in soil and adults emerge in spring. Eggs are deposited in grass or small-grain fields and hatch in about 14 d. Young larvae feed on roots until fall, when they burrow deeper into soil for hibernation. They resume feeding on roots or sod during the following summer, go again into hibernation and complete their feeding in the following spring. When corn is planted on infested ground, immature larvae migrate to the germinating seed or young plants, burrow through the seed, and feed on the developing roots and crown. Loss of stand, therefore, is the initial effect, particularly if large populations are present.

Tenhet and Howe (1939) found a 1-yr cycle of the sand wireworm in South Carolina, and Jewett (1942) reported a full and a partial second generation of *A. mellilus* in Kentucky, with most injury from overwintered larvae in spring. *Agriotes mancus, M. communis,* and *M. cribulosus* are long-cycle species that sometimes injure corn (Hawkins, 1936; Hyslop, 1915). In south Florida, *M. communis* has a single generation annually. Adults emerge in summer and deposit their eggs on grass areas. Fall-planted corn is subject to attack under these conditions. There appears to be general agreement that wireworms attacking corn and wheat are favored by a moist, clay soil with liberal amounts of organic matter. However, *H. uhlerii,* an important species in the South, thrives in light, sandy soils low in organic matter. In the Pacific Northwest, several species of wireworms attack corn and other crops (Lane, 1941).

Prior to the introduction of effective insecticides, cultural practices were considered the only means of relief for wireworm infestations. These practices varied with the species involved. Hawkins (1936) in Main reported that a short rotation and use of crimson clover or buckwheat as a green manure crop reduced reinfestation. Clean cultivation and summer plowing or fallowing, regular crop rotation, and soil drainage have also been recommended, the objective being to eliminate susceptible vegetation and to disturb the insect activities as much as possible.

13–2.6 Billbugs — Description and Biology

Billbugs are snout beetles. Most of them are reddish or brown, but they may appear grayish when covered with mud. They vary from about 5 to 25 mm in length. The larvae are white with a brownish head, rather plump, and legless. Injury on young corn plants shows up as a series of transverse oblong or round holes in leaves and some destruction of the growing point which results in tillering, stunting, or loss in stand.

As pests of corn, billbugs are widely distributed. The species most injurious to corn in the USA are the maize billbug (*Sphenophorus maidis*), timothy billbug (*S. zeae*), bluegrass billbug, (*S. parvulus*), and the southern corn billbug (*S. callosus*) (Forbes, 1904; Kelly, 1911; Satterthwait, 1919).

Most of the billbugs normally inhabit moist or swampy soil areas, where larvae develop on various species of grasses such as rushes, sedges, reeds, timothy, and bluegrass (*Poa* spp.). Infestations on corn, therefore, are likely to occur when this crop is planted in or near ground that had these conditions and plant associations in previous seasons. In some species only adults are injurious, whereas in others, notably the maize and southern corn billbugs, larvae also infest corn. Only a single generation occurs annually in the species commonly recorded on corn, the adults overwintering among roots or in roots or culms of their hosts.

In spring, adults feed on bulbous parts of rhizomes of grasses. They begin to infest corn during the seedling and postseedling growth stages, eating small holes into plants at about the soil surface, thereby piercing the rolled leaves in the bud. As leaves unroll they show typical transverse series of holes, which increase in size with the growth of leaves. Severe injury in seedlings may cause distortion of young leaves or even the death of plants. In a study of the habits of *S. callosus* on corn in North Carolina, Metcalf (1917) found eggs deposited in plants near or below the soil surface and also among roots. Eggs were laid in May or June. Larvae were found feeding in plants and externally on roots. This feeding resulted in death of young plants and stunting when older plants were attacked. Injury caused by larvae in the lower part of stems was more serious than that caused by adults. Similar observations were reported by Cartwright (1929) from South Carolina for *S. maydis*.

Drainage of swampy areas and elimination of the common wild host grasses associated with them has lessened the incidence of infestations on corn. Rotation of crops, early planting, clean cultivation, and use of fertilizer are normal practices that reduce injury and stimulate plant growth to overcome it (Cartwright, 1929; Metcalf, 1917; Satterthwait, 1919).

13-2.7 Webworms — Description and Biology

Adults of webworms are crambid or close-wing moths (*Crambus* spp.). The larvae are slender, yellow to pink with regular dark spots, and about 25 mm in length when full grown. When injury on young plants is first noticed, the larvae, then about 12-mm long, are located in silken-web-lined burrows in soil near plants. Typical attack at or belowground level shows gnawed places, pits, or sometimes cut off plants, somewhat resembling cutworm injury. Above the soil surface infested plants have distorted leaves with ragged feeding areas. Sod webworms are occasionally injurious to corn in the Corn Belt following spring plowing of sod land. The most common species injurious to corn are the corn root webworm (*Crambus caliginosellus*), striped webworm (*C. mutabilis*), and larger sod webworm (*C. trisectus*) (Ainslie, 1922; Forbes, 1904).

According to Ainslie (1922), the corn root webworm has a single generation annually, whereas the striped webworm and larger sod webworm have at least two full generations. All three species pass the winter as partly grown larvae. Webworm moths drop their eggs in flight on bluegrass (*Poa pratensis* L.), timothy,(*Phleum pratense* L.), and other grass sod. Thus, development of larvae is closely tied up with grass sod and perhaps with legumes commonly found with it. Corn is a host only where it follows sod. Eggs from which overwintering larvae develop are deposited in summer. Young larvae establish themselves within their flimsy cocoons or webs in sod, feed on foliage during late summer and early fall, and establish themselves in burrows in soil before winter. They are about 12-mm long. With warm weather in spring, feeding is resumed and there may be some migration to corn along edges of fields. Larvae complete their development in about 30 d. When corn is planted on spring-plowed sod land infested with webworms, the seedling stage is attacked, resulting in loss of stand (Ainslie, 1922, 1927).

Cultural practices for controlling sod webworms have not been evaluated for many years. Late summer or early fall plowing has been recommended for eliminating partially grown larvae before they enter hibernation. However, fall plowing would not be an acceptable practice on soils that are subject to erosion. Since most of the larvae become full grown while corn is in the seedling stage, serious crop injury does not usually occur in corn that is replanted (Ainslie, 1922).

13-2.8 White Grubs — Description and Biology

White grubs are larvae of brown beetles commonly known as May or June beetles. The larvae are sluggish, white, with a brown head and rather prominent legs. They have two slightly curved, narrowly spaced rows of spines on the ventral side of the last abdominal segment. Larvae feed on roots of corn seedlings, causing stunted, wilted, or dying plants.

There are many species of white grubs, which vary in abundance in different sections of the country. Chamberlain and Callenbach (1943) found the following species to be most numerous on cereal and forage crops in Wisconsin: *Phyllophaga rugosa, P. hirticula, P. fusca,* and *P. tristis.* According to Luginbill and Painter (1953), these species are widely distributed and may be involved in crop damage.

The primary source of white grubs in cornfields is soil that has been in grass and in some instances in soybean. Bluegrass and timothy sods are particularly favorable for their development. The beetles ordinarily prefer to feed on foliage of trees, but they also feed on weeds and crop plants.

Most of the important species of May beetles require 3 yr to complete a generation. Of the four species listed only *P. tristis* has a 2-yr cycle. Adults emerge from soil in spring and lay their eggs a few centimeters below the surface. Eggs hatch in about 21 d. Young larvae feed through the first season on living roots and decaying vegetable matter at about plow-sole level or in the top soil. In late fall they burrow deeper into soil and remain inactive during winter. Second-year larvae feed throughout the growing season on roots of plants and are the most injurious to corn when it is planted on infested sod ground. In the fall the larvae again go deep into the soil to overwinter. The feeding period in the 3rd yr is relatively short. Pupation takes place in cells in midsummer. Adults emerge in early fall but remain in earthen cells over winter and emerge from the soil in spring. There is an overlapping of broods which results in beetle flights each year. For 3-yr-cycle species these broods are designated as A, B, and C. Brood A is by far the most abundant and is the one present in outbreak years. Brood B is usually unimportant, but Brood C may be injurious in certain areas.

When corn is planted in infested ground the grubs congregate near the base of plants, where they feed on and sever the young roots. Because adults concentrate in wooded areas, likely places of infestations are on high ground near such areas. Thus, important infestations are often associated with poorer soils in an area (Davis, 1922; Luginbill and Chamberlain, 1953).

In areas where white grubs are periodically a problem, Luginbill and Chamberlain (1953) proposed certain cropping practices utilizing crop that are least susceptible to attack. They suggest avoiding common grasses as much as possible and using alfalfa and clovers as the dominant pasture and hay crops.

An effective method of eliminating grubs from infested fields to be planted to corn is through pasturing by swine (*Sus scrofa*). This practice is not desirable on permanent pastures because of serious uprooting of sod. Crows, blackbirds, skunks, and opossums are effective predators of white grubs.

13–2.9 Corn Root Aphid — Description and Biology

The corn root aphid (*Anuraphis maidiradicis*) is bluish green and about the size of a pinhead. It sucks the sap from corn roots and weeds.

Typical external evidence of injury are dwarfing and yellowing and reddening of plants before they are knee-high. This aphid is widely distributed in the USA but is most abundant in the Corn Belt (Davis, 1949; Forbes, 1915).

The corn root aphid is dependent on ants for survival, principally the cornfield ant (*Lasius alienus*). This aphid has both sexual egg laying and parthenogenetic viviparous forms. The sexual form deposits eggs in the fall, whereupon the ants transfer eggs to their nests and nurture them during winter. When the eggs hatch in spring, the ants transfer young aphids to roots of cornfield weeds and later, after corn is planted, to roots of corn. The ants feed on sweetish fluids excreted from cornicles of aphids. During spring and summer the aphids reproduce viviparously, some of the offspring begin winged forms. Winged aphids emerge from soil and fly to other fields where with attending ants new colonies are produced (Davis, 1949). Successive crops of corn, satisfactory spring host plants, and a favorable environment for the cornfield ant are important factors in building up populations.

The corn root aphid is of economic importance only on corn (Davis, 1949). Therefore, rotation of crops will hold down both aphid and ant populations. In the presence of both insects, Bigger and Bauer (1939) found that plowing shortly before planting reduced aphid infestations. Early plowing and tillage to keep favored wild hosts under control before planting corn was the most desirable practice. In connection with the other cultural practices, Davis (1949) advocated thorough cultivation and maintenance of a high fertility level to stimulate plant growth.

13–2.10 Seedcorn Maggot — Description and Biology

The adult of the seedcorn maggot (*Delia platura*) is a grayish fly similar to the housefly but with a more prominent thorax. The larvae are pearly white, almost conical, tapering anteriorly, and have black hook-like mandibles (about 7-mm long when full grown). The larvae mine into germinating seed and subsequently attack young seedlings. The species is worldwide in distribution. In addition to corn, it is an important pest of many vegetable crops (Forbes, 1893; Hawley, 1922).

Habits and biology of the seedcorn maggot have been studied mostly on vegetable crops. Adults are attracted to decaying vegetable or animal matter on which eggs are deposited. Maggots attack sprouting seed and seedlings. In warmer parts of the country, adults are widely distributed throughout the year. Reid (1940) reported that diapause was not observed in North and South Carolina, where he trapped adults every month of the year. He found puparia in fields and also observed oviposition in winter months. Hawley (1922) in New York reported collecting adults on wheat stubble in spring and assumed that the insect spends winter in the puparium. It is generally agreed that the maggots become injurious on seeds and seedlings under cool, moist soil conditions. As a pest of corn, infestations are most prevalent in early plantings on soils with liberal amounts of plowed-under decaying plant material. Under such conditions, Hawley (1922) suggested that shallow planting and use of seed with good viability with rapid germination is a means of avoiding stand failure.

13–2.11 Grape Colaspis — Description and Biology

Grubs of grape colaspis (*Colaspis brunnea*) are white with brownish heads and thoracic shields and about 3 mm in length when full grown. Compared with the common white grubs, they are not as slender, have less prominent legs, and lack the two rows of spines on the ventral side of the last abdominal segment. The adults are small, pale brown beetles, which have many hosts but commonly feed on clover (*Trifolium* spp.), bean (*Phaseolus* spp.), grape (*Vitus* spp.), and strawberry (*Fragaria* spp.) foliage.

The species is widely distributed east of the Rocky Mountains. It has been reported as injurious to young corn mainly in the North Central states (Bigger, 1928; Lindsay, 1943; Petty and Apple, 1966).

Grubs found on young corn originate from infestations in ground planted to clover, soybean, or alfalfa. The beetles emerge in midsummer and deposit their eggs in soil. Incubation requires 7 to 14 d. Young larvae commonly become established and feed on roots of clovers during the latter part of summer and early fall. Winter is passed as immature larvae. With appearance of warm weather in spring the larvae feed on roots, completing their development late in the spring.

Bigger (1928) reported the larvae to be most abundant on red clover, sweet clover, soybean, and timothy, in the order named. The most severe injury on corn occurred when red clover ground was plowed late in spring. Similarly, Lindsay (1943) in season-history studies in Iowa also reported damage to corn following red clover.

13–2.12 Seedcorn Beetles — Description and Biology

The adult of the seedcorn beetle (*Stenolophus lecontei*) is oblong, about 6-mm long, and dark with two brown stripes on its wing covers. The adult of the slender seedcorn beetle (*Clivina impressifrons*) is about 6-mm long, shiny dark red with a constricted articulation between the first and second thoracic segments. In characteristic injury, the germinating seed is attacked by adults of both species. One observes holes into or hollowed out kernels with dead or stunted sprouts. Both species are widely distributed in the USA and Canada (Forbes, 1893; Phillips, 1909).

The two species hibernate as adults. They are attracted to light in large numbers, especially on warm evenings in spring. Presence of beetles throughout the season indicates that there are one or more overlapping generations annually. Little is known of habits of immature stages. It is believed that larvae are predaceous on other soil insects and may also inhabit sod. Adults of *S. lecontei* are sometimes pests in lawns and golf greens. Both species occur in wet grassy ground (Forbes, 1893; Hamilton, 1935; Phillips, 1909). In soils inhabited by these beetles (Phillips, 1909) suggested delaying planting until there is assurance of quick germination. Recent experience has shown that deep planting should be avoided.

13–3 INSECTS ATTACKING THE LEAF, STALK, AND EAR

Most insects injurious on the leaf, stalk, and ear may at some time feed on any major structures of the corn plant. There is a degree of similarity among species in that corn parts attacked depend to a large extent on stage of plant development and on life history of the insect. Some species may develop on foliage and partially on tassels in one generation, but in a subsequent generation mostly on ear structures. This group, predominantly lepidoptera, includes some of the most important corn insects.

13–3.1 Corn Earworm — Description and Biology

Newly hatched larvae of the corn earworm (*Heliothis zea*) are light gray with conspicuous small dark hairs. Full-grown larvae range in color from red and brown to green with a striped appearance. They may be located among whorl leaves or on emerging tassels but are most frequently found feeding in the tip of ears. Figure 13–5 shows a full-grown larva in the tip of the ear with inserts of the moth and eggs. Moths vary in color from a light olive green to buff. Eggs, laid singly on leaves, emerging tassel, and silks are off-white, dome-shaped, with ribs converging at the top. Because it also damages cotton (*Gossypium* spp.), tomato (*Lycopersicon esculentum* Mill.), legume, and other crops, entomologists rate it as one of our most injurious insects.

For many years, the corn earworm received a great deal of attention by entomologists. Quaintance and Brues (1905) assembled early information on biology, distribution, and control of the insect as a pest of cotton. Many of the studies reported by them are useful in understanding the problem on corn.

The corn earworm hibernates as a pupa in a burrow prepared in soil by the larva. Moths emerge from early spring to early summer, depending on the bioclimate (Barber, 1936a; Phillips and Barber, 1929). Early in the season moths oviposit on corn leaves and emerging tassel, but as silks appear, a high proportion of the eggs are deposited on fresh silks. Depending on stage of plant development, young larvae become established on leaves in the whorl, on florets of the tassel, or on silks.

As the larvae hatch on silks, or migrate there from other parts of the plant, feed, and grow they gradually infest the tip of ears. When husks are loose, feeding extends along the side of the ear. This type of feeding, illustrated in Fig. 13–6, is especially prevalent on field corn in the more northern areas when corn is in the dough stage. If the ear has a long husk extension, and silk channel, larvae sometimes mature on the silk. When feeding is completed, the larva leaves the ear, usually from the tip end or through an exit hole made through the husk, drops to the ground and

Fig. 13–5. Full-grown earworm on ear tip with inset of moth and eggs.

pupates in the soil. In summer, pupation takes place within a few days and moths emerge in 14 to 21 d, or they may have a period of aestivation. Hibernating pupae become established in late summer and early fall. In warm climates there may be as many as five or six generations annually. In the central Corn Belt area there may be one or two generations, or

Fig. 13–6. Typical grain injury caused by the earworm on loose-husked variety.

perhaps there may be some infestations that originate from migrant moths from more southern areas (Barber, 1936b; Blanchard, 1942; Ditman and Cory, 1931; Garman and Jewett, 1914).

The attraction of moths to fresh silk for oviposition causes them to move from less attractive older silks to more attractive new silks. This tends to limit larval development to corn which has not reached the dough stage for much of the growing season. Callahan (1957) presented evidence of oviposition response of moths to various wavelengths of light. On late-maturing corn there is a more prolonged oviposition, and more larvae mature on dough stage corn. Because larvae are cannibalistic, usually only one larva completes its development in an ear. Under high levels of infestation there may be a succession of larvae infesting ears, particularly in late summer and early fall. Eggs laid after the first 7 d in September in Virginia are considered to be of little significance in the development of overwintering pupae (Dicke, 1939; Phillips and Barber, 1929, 1933).

As corn becomes unattractive, moths move to other hosts for oviposition, particularly to cotton, tomato, and legumes. The importance of cotton or tomato in building up populations is not well known. Isely (1935) found that the reproductive capacity was highest when the insect was reared on corn and lowest when reared on tomato. In records covering 25 yr, he observed that this insect was most serious where acreages of corn and cotton were about equal.

Hibernation and overwintering of the earworm has received a great deal of attention because it has a bearing on the general abundance of the insect, at least early in the growing season. Conditions that determine whether or not larvae will develop into aestivating or hibernating pupae, the extent of successful hibernation, and seasonal abundance have been investigated in different parts of the country. Maturity of corn on which larvae feed may determine whether or not pupae will hibernate and may affect the rate of overwinter survival. Phillips and Barber (1929) found that larvae maturing on dough stage corn late in summer developed into pupae that most successfully survived winter. In hibernation studies conducted in southeast Georgia under cage conditions, Barber (1941) reported that an average of 51% of the individuals that entered soil for pupation in late summer and early fall survived to the following summer.

Ditman (1938) studied water and fat relations of prepupae and pupae that developed from larvae reared on silk and dough stage corn. He concluded that reduced percentages of water, increased percentage of fat, and reduced saturation of fat are intensified by a diet of dough stage corn, and that these factors are associated with the ability of the earworm to withstand temperature hazards of hibernating conditions. Some pupae from larvae reared on dough stage corn were able to survive and produce moths after an exposure to temperatures of -6 to -10 °C for 10 d.

Experimental evidence shows that dry soil conditions favor survival of aestivating as well as hibernating pupae (Barber, 1941; Barber and

Dicke, 1939). From a study conducted near the District of Columbia, it was concluded that a mean temperature of 0 °C or less from December through February was thought to reduce the abundance of the earworm the following season (Dicke, 1939). Blanchard (1942) summarized results of cooperative hibernation experiments conducted in 15 Central and Northeastern states during the period 1935 to 1939. Survival of hibernating pupae was recorded in all states except Iowa. In Ohio and Indiana, larvae entering the soil in October and early November under cool soil temperatures showed a low rate of pupation. Eichmann (1940) reported a similar experience in Washington. Information at hand indicates that under conditions favorable for development and with a mild winter the earworm may hibernate farther north than has been supposed.

There is a considerable mortality of hibernating pupae throughout the period from fall to summer. In soils where earthworms are abundant, mortalities may be high when pupae become embedded in droppings deposited in burrows. Diseases, particularly fungus, take a small toll. There is a rather low rate of parasitism and predation on larvae infesting the ear. *Trichogramma minutum* frequently parasitizes a high proportion of eggs, parasitism reaching a peak in the fall. Among the predators *Orius insidiosus* is responsible for destroying a considerable proportion of eggs deposited on silks (Phillips and Barber, 1929, 1933).

One of the earliest recommendations for control of the corn earworm was plowing. It was recommended many years before definite evidence of its effectiveness for destroying hibernating pupae was available. Experiments in Virginia (Barber and Dicke, 1937) showed that fall plowing resulted in a high mortality of overwintering pupae. Spring plowing and fall disking were less effective.

The effect of planting date on amount of earworm injury has been studied at several locations. In Virginia, early planted corn produced the best yield and had a low rate of earworm damage. Similar observations in Georgia confirmed these results (Barber, 1936a; Phillips and Barber, 1934).

13–3.2 European Corn Borer — Description and Biology

Newly hatched larvae of the European corn borer (*Ostrinia nubilalis*) are about 2 mm in length, light-greenish after early feeding, with a brown to black head. The larvae take on a more opaque greenish gray or pink cast in later stages and have light longitudinal lines along the body. The full-grown larva is about 25-mm long and varies in color, usually grayish to light brownish, and frequently has a reddish tinge.

Pupae are 12- to 20-mm long, slender and brown; they may be located on foliage, in ears, or in stalks, and in surface debris in the spring. Moths are buff to brownish, frequently with reddish wing veins and a wing expanse of about 25 mm. Detailed descriptions of all stages were published by Vinal and Caffrey (1919). Early in the season, characteristic injury indicating the presence of larvae are shot-hole and elongated lesions on leaf blades, in midribs and behind sheaths. Later, broken tassels, and holes and burrows in the stalk become prominent.

The presence of the European corn borer in the USA was first reported by Vinal (1917) in Massachusetts. Infestations were found in New York and Pennsylvania in 1919; in Ontario, Canada in 1920; and Ohio in 1921. Separate points of introduction from foreign sources or spread through transportation were indicated in this rapid westward establishment. Severe damage occurred in Kent and Essex Counties, Ontario in 1925 and 1926, and caused an appreciable reduction of corn acreage (Caffrey and Worthley, 1927; Stirrett, 1938). Movement westward and southward was gradual between 1927 and 1936. After the drought year of 1936, the spread into Southern states and across the North Central region proceeded rapidly and the insect reached the Rocky Mountain area in northern Colorado in 1950. Currently in North America, the European corn borer is found in most states east of the Rocky Mountains and in several Canadian provinces, including Prince Edward Island (Brindley et al., 1975; Thompson and White, 1977). The number of generations/yr ranges from one to four depending upon location (Showers, 1979; Thompson and White, 1977). The general abundance of the borer reached a peak in 1949 when there were high populations over much of the central Corn Belt.

There are numerous published accounts on the biology and habits of the European corn borer. Results of experiments and observations reported from some areas may seem at variance with other areas. These differences are primarily due to differences in the environment and the population complexes produced in it. The fact that the species is of economic importance in such diverse environments as those prevailing in Canada and northern USA, and Israel and Egypt is positive evidence that a versatile genetic mechanism is an important factor in developing these adaptations. In an extensive interregional study of populations, Brindley et al. (1975) reported that diapause is controlled by multigenic factors that respond to temperature and photoperiod.

The first extensive report on life history studies in the USA was made by Vinal and Caffrey (1919). Most of this work was done on sweet corn and with an insect that was predominantly two-brooded. Their descriptions of the biology are in general still applicable to a two-generation infestation similar to that encountered in Massachusetts. Under a single generation, which was predominant for many years in the Great Lakes area, similar data were brought together by Crawford and Spencer (1922), Caffrey and Worthley (1927), and Huber et al. (1928).

The European corn borer hibernates as a full-grown larva in cornstalks or plant debris. Time of pupation and moth emergence depends on weather conditions and to some extent on whether or not the prevailing population is single or multiple-brooded. For most of the infested area moth emergence begins in May or June. Most of the eggs are deposited between dusk and midnight. The important factors limiting moth activity are low temperatures and high winds. Earliest planted corn is most attractive to moths of the first generation for oviposition, whereas late-planted or late-maturing corn is more attractive to moths of subsequent generations. The stage of development of corn is therefore an important factor in the rate of oviposition and figures prominently in determining the need for insecticides (Barber, 1925; Huber et al., 1928; Stirrett, 1938). In a given area, stage of development of corn varies widely during the first-generation, egg-laying period. The vegetative or whorl stage of growth increases progressively in attractiveness and susceptibility to larval establishment and survival as plant growth increases.

The most significant increase in larval survival occurs with exposure of the tassel. A high susceptibility to larval survival persists throughout reproductive stages of plants but recedes significantly about 14 d after silking. This condition prevails in early market sweet corn during the first generation oviposition period in varying degrees and in late-maturing fields and sweet corn during the second generation oviposition period. The pattern of larval survival during vegetative and reproductive stages of growth is shown in Fig. 13–7.

In vegetative or whorl stages of plant growth the primary place of larval establishment is near the upper limits of the surface moisture level within spirally rolled leaves. Larvae are predominantly sheath and midrib feeders during the third and fourth stages, whereas later larval stages invade the stalk, shank, and ear.

Aggregation of second-generation European corn borers in dense vegetation at edges of cornfields was first reported by Caffrey and Worthley (1927). Microclimate produced by foxtailgrass (*Setaria* spp.) and other tall, dense vegetation readily allows formation of dew and the retaining of droplets from rainfall (DeRozari et al., 1977); the moist habitat is ideally suited for mating and resting of adults (Showers et al., 1976). The habit of second-generation European corn borers moving from cornfields to nearby grassy areas to rest and mate offers a possible control strategy, i.e., to treat grassy waterways, roadways, etc. with an insecticide to kill adults (Showers et al., 1980).

When corn is in the reproductive stage during either first or second generation oviposition, young larvae become established largely on structures associated with inflorescence, in florets, on pollen accumulations at the axils of leaves, or on ear structures. The pattern of feeding by middle and late stage larvae is about the same for both generations, with perhaps a higher concentration of young larvae in the upper region of the plant during the second generation infestation. Full-grown larvae have a habit of establishing themselves in the lower part of the stalk (Batchelder, 1949; Caffrey and Worthley, 1927; Dicke, 1954).

For control of the European corn borer, USDA established its program of foreign parasite introduction into the USA from Europe in 1919 and from the Orient in 1927; 24 exotic species of parasites were imported but only 6 species became established (Baker et al., 1949; Brindley et al.,

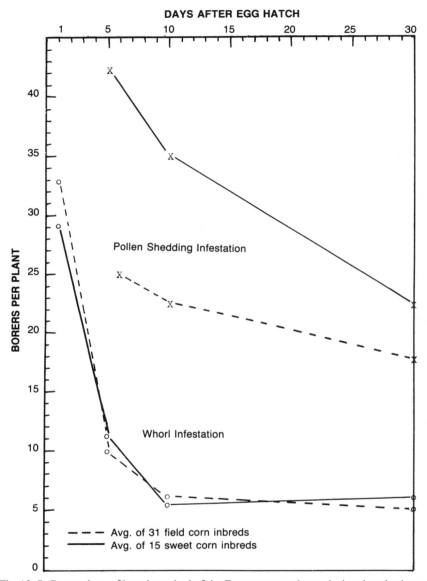

Fig. 13–7. Comparison of larval survival of the European corn borer during the whorl stage period (first brood) and the pollen-shedding period (second brood).

1975). Federal and state agencies participated in recovery and redistribution of the most effective parasites. Arbuthnot (1953) reported that *Lydella thompsoni* (formerly *L. stabulans*), *Eirborus tetebrons* (formerly *Horogones punctorius*), *Simpiesis viridulus*, and *Macrocentrus grandii* to be widely established, and *L. thompsoni* to be abundant over most of the infested area. Since 1966, however, *L. thompsoni* has not been found in Iowa (Lewis, 1982); this species has recently been reintroduced and established in Delaware (Burbutis et al., 1981). A group of tiny wasps (*Trichogramma* spp.) attacks the eggs of many lepidopterous insects including the European corn borer. *Trichogramma* spp. have been released in Switzerland (Bigler, 1983), German Federal Republic (Hassan et al., 1984), USSR (Pargamin and Grigorenko, 1977), and other countries for controlling the European corn borer. *Trichogramma nubilalae*, native to the USA, has been evaluated in Delaware for controlling the European corn borer (Burbutis et al., 1977).

During some years, insect predators such as *Orius insidiosus*, coccinellids, chrysopids, and fungus beetles reduce corn borer populations (Brindley et al., 1975). During some seasons, fungi (*Beauveria bassiana, Metarrhizium anisopliae*), bacteria (*Bacillus thuringiensis*), and microsporidia (*Nosema pyrausta*) kill considerable numbers of European corn borers. No biological agents, however, at present are consistently operative at a sufficient level to control the European corn borer in North America (Hudon, 1963; Hill et al., 1967; Lewis and Lynch, 1974, 1976, 1978; Brindley et al., 1975; Lynch et al., 1977).

The reduction of population levels through the disposal of infested crop residues was advocated in central Europe as early as 1897 (Babcock and Vance, 1929). Similar practices were later adopted in the USA and Canada (Caffrey and Worthley, 1927; Vinal and Caffrey, 1919). Much of the larval population of a given season is destroyed by the usual farm tillage and harvesting practices. The most effective reductions of overwintering populations can be obtained through ensiling and stalk chopping, followed by plowing under crop residue (USDA, 1962).

Based on a 10-yr study on effect of farm practices on reduction of corn borer populations from October to June in Illinois, Bigger and Petty (1953) showed that the general practice of disking stalk fields for oat is an important factor contributing to the continued threat for corn borer damage. Eighty percent of the larval population in spring after tillage were found in disked fields. They advocated the proper adjustment of corn picker rolls and heavy pasturing in stalk fields as supplementary to good plowing as the most effective cultural control practice. The effect of minimum or no-tillage practices on population survival has yet to be determined.

In early biological studies of the European corn borer, it was established that under univoltine (single-brooded) infestation, the earliest planted corn receives the highest rate of egg deposition and infestation and the latest planted corn the least. In areas subject to univoltine infestation, delayed planted was encouraged. This practice was never well received because over a period of years early planted corn has a yield advantage and is less subject to attack by second-generation borers and to stalk breakage.

13-3.3   Corn Leaf Aphid — Description and Biology

The corn leaf aphid (*Rhopalosiphum maidis*) is small, dark bluish green in color. Its wingless colonies first become conspicuous on emerging leaves and tassel tip (Fig. 13–8). The winged form becomes abundant in large crowded colonies on leaves and tassels at about anthesis. Before tassel emergence early nymphal (all females) infestation occurs typically on the moist part of leaves in the whorl, where the insects suck nutrients from phloem elements (Fig. 13–9). When infestations begin relatively early in the season on mid-whorl corn and build up large colonies by the time of tassel eclosion, anthesis is impeded and may result in varying

Fig. 13–8. Corn leaf aphid infestation on top leaves and lower part of tassel.

degrees of barrenness. The species occurs on all continents and has been identified as a vector of virus disease in corn and other species of grasses (Wildermuth and Walter, 1932). The role of the corn leaf aphid in virus transmission is discussed in a later section.

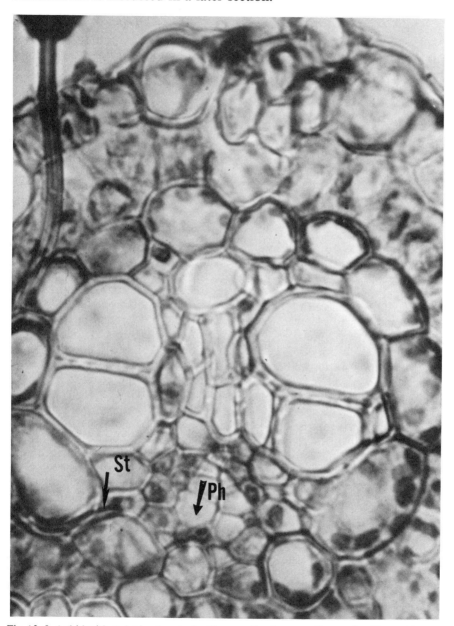

Fig. 13-9. Aphid with stylet in place to feed in vascular elements. St = stylet; Ph = phloem.

As far as we know the corn leaf aphid overwinters successfully only in warmer climates. Wildermuth and Walter (1932) reported corn, sorghum (*Sorghum* spp.), and barley as preferred cultivated hosts with abundant populations on winter barley in the southwestern states. Forbes (1893) recognized the species as distinct from the corn root aphid and failed to find an oviparous form or any winter survival of viviparous forms in Illinois. In Wisconsin, Orlob and Medler (1961) failed to find any forms in winter but found colonies with mature apterous forms on barley in mid-May. Similarly, Foott (1977) reported an alate and small colonies on 26 April in southwestern Ontario, Canada. Source of infestation in the northern areas stems from populations of the winged form carried in by southerly air currents. In southern Indiana, Saugstad and Everly (1967) found reproducing populations on winter barley during the winter months of 1965 to 1966. In airplane collections in eastern Kansas, Taylor and Berry (1968) captured the corn leaf aphid and other cereal crop aphid species at an altitude of 670 m.

Alatae have been observed to be attracted to emerging seedlings (Dicke, 1969). They have a habit of crawling into the small opening of emerging spirally rolled leaves where they feed and start an occasional colony. Heavy rains during the seedling and early whorl stage decimate alatae and young colonies. With favorable conditions of temperature early colony establishment has the potential of developing a large apterous population as successive internodes elongate and whorl leaves emerge culminating in tassel and ear shoot emergence and infestation. The population is typically sessile on the plant unless crowded conditions occur. Steiner et al. (1985) using electrophoretic procedures in a genetic study on migration in North American populations found the most variable population at a Hillsboro, TX location. They reported a lack of heterozygosity in Illinois populations and suggested that the Illinois population with which they worked were not of southern origins. Different biotypes were recognized in studies in Kansas (Cartier and Painter, 1956; Maxwell and Painter, 1962).

Feeding activities of large colonies in the vascular system results in an accumulation of carbohydrates in leaves and abnormal synthesis of anthocyanin and reddening of leaves (McCulloch, 1921; Wildermuth and Walter, 1932).

In detailed biological studies, Randell (1970) found that crowded colonies of first and second instar nymphs produced a high proportion of winged forms which he interpreted to be a postnatal effect. Late whorl and tassel infestations yields much of the alate summer population.

Climatic conditions play an important role in determining the rate of colony development and yield reduction. Triplehorn (1959), in a comparison of yield losses in Ohio, reported severe reduction in yield mainly through barrenness, under stress of high infestation and soil moisture in 1957; whereas in 1958 under high infestation with abundant moisture supply, yield losses were light. Everly (1960a) reported similar results on high yield loss under soil moisture stress.

Extremes of temperature are unfavorable for aphid development. Aphids seem to reach their maximum reproductive capacity in periods of cool temperatures which are unfavorable for some of their important predators and parasites. Wildermuth and Walter (1932) observed this relationship in the Southwestern states and Walter and Brunson (1940) reported similar observations in Indiana. *Lysiphlebus testaceipes*, a small hymenopterous parasite, the common lady beetles (*Hippodamia convergens* and *Ceratomegilla fuscilabris*) and the lacewing (*Chrysopa* spp.) are the dominant natural enemies (Wildermuth and Walter, 1932).

13-3.4 Fall Armyworm — Description and Biology

Young larvae of the fall armyworm (*Spodoptera frugiperda*) are slightly greenish with black heads. They are commonly found feeding on leaves in whorls of young corn plants. With the emergence of the tassel they feed on tassel florets and surrounding leaves. Later the ear is favored.

Mature larvae vary from greenish to a grayish brown, have a light-colored inverted 'Y' on the head, and dorsal lines running lengthwise of the body. The moth has variegated gray forewings, which are held at an angle over the back when at rest.

The fall armyworm is an important pest of corn and other grasses in the South Atlantic and Gulf states. Periodically it spreads to the Middle Atlantic states and the southern part of the North Central region, where it becomes prevalent in later-maturing corn in August and September. It has been observed as far north as Canada (Forbes, 1893; Luginbill, 1950). It is frequently a limiting factor in profitable corn production in tropical America unless protective insecticides are used.

The fall armyworm overwinters in subtropical and tropical America and migrates northward each year by moth flight as the weather warms up. Diapause or aestivation is not known to occur in any of its life stages. On corn, eggs are usually deposited on the under side of leaves in large masses covered with scales and hair of the moth. In the whorl stage of growth young larvae feed on tender parts of whorl leaves. Upon tassel, eclosion florets are a preferred site of feeding. In successive growth stages, larvae feed on leaf sheath and ear parts. The stage of plant development is therefore an important factor in feeding habits of larvae. When the larvae become established in the whorl, the unfurled leaves show irregular elongated feeding areas as shown in Fig. 13-10.

With appearance of the ear, larvae feed on husks, silks, kernels, and in the shank. Injury at the tip of ears can easily be confused with that caused by the corn earworm. On becoming full grown the larvae leave the plant and prepare short tunnels in soil in which to pupate.

It requires about 30 d to complete a generation. In the South there may be as many as six generations annually, whereas in more northern areas there may be only a single generation of larvae resulting from migrant moths (Burkhardt, 1952; Dicke and Jenkins, 1945; Luginbill, 1928, 1950).

Fig. 13–10. Typical whorl stage damage by the fall armyworm.

The fall armyworm has several important hymenopterous and dipterous parasites as well as hemipterous and coleopterous predators. Some of the common entomogenous fungi have also been recorded in several southern localities (Luginbill, 1928; Vickery, 1929).

13–3.5   Other Corn Borers — Description and Biology

Larval forms of the southern cornstalk borer (*Diatraea crambidoides*) and the southwestern corn borer (*D. grandiosella*) and the injuries they cause are similar. The young larvae are dull white to yellowish with black heads, about 2-mm long, with prominent transverse, closely spaced dark spots, giving the general appearance of a ring around each segment. With successive molts the dark spots are further apart, becoming pale shortly before pupation. In the winter form larvae practically lose their spots, leaving prominent black spiracles.

Larvae of the American sugarcane borer (*D. saccharalis*) and Neotropical corn borer (*D. lineolata*) are superficially similar. Ordinarily they can be differentiated from the southern cornstalk borer by their brown spots. Typical injury by larvae of these species in the whorl stage of corn growth is at first on unrolled leaves. As leaves unfold midribs and sheaths are the main points of attack, followed by burrowing in ear parts and stalks. Holes across leaves and broken midribs are characteristic of later stages of leaf injury similar to that shown for the European corn borer in Fig. 13–25.

Severe injury to young plants may kill the growing point, causing dead heart and subsequent tillering. Holes are made in stalks by older larvae. Symptoms of second or third-generation feeding on corn that has tasseled are sheath and ear part injury, and holes and burrows in the stalk. Girdled stalks in lower internodes are more typical for the southwestern corn borer than for the other species. Similarity of plant injury sometimes confuses their identity with the corn earworm and fall armyworm.

Moths of the four species are of pale to medium straw color with white hindwings and a spread of about 25 to 30 mm. They are generally distinguished by spots on the forewings. The southern cornstalk borer moths have a prominent black spot in the middle of the wing and seven similar spots along the margin. These spots are 'V'-shaped on moths of the sugarcane borer but not conspicuous on moths of the southwestern corn borer.

The southern cornstalk borer is generally distributed along Atlantic coastal areas and Gulf states. It occurs as far west as Texas and north to Kansas. It has been ranked among the important pests of the corn crop in the South Atlantic coastal region. The southwestern corn borer has spread from the Southwestern states and has northern limits of survival in Colorado, Kansas, Missouri, and Illinois. It is a hazard in corn production in parts of Texas and the Southeastern states. The sugarcane borer is of most importance on corn in sugarcane areas and is frequently a pest in Central and South America and in rice-producing areas of the Gulf states. The Neotropical corn borer is generally distributed in Central and northern South America and in the Caribbean Islands. In the USA, the borer occurs in southern Texas (Ainslie, 1919; Leiby, 1920; Cartwright, 1934; Ingram and Bynum, 1941; Wilbur et al., 1950; USDA, 1966).

Habits and biology of the four species of *Diatraea* are sufficiently similar in the corn crop to discuss them together. The southern cornstalk borer and the southwestern corn borer hibernate as full-grown larvae in stalks near the base in corn, sometimes erroneously called the tap root. Figure 13-11 shows the usual position of hibernating larva of the southwestern corn borer. Pupation and moth emergence occur in May or June, depending on the bioclimate. Larvae of the sugarcane borer overwinter in various parts of the stalk, as shown in Fig. 13-12, but seldom below the level of the ground. Overwintered larvae pupate in spring, the pupal stage requiring about 21 d. Time of first-generation pupation and moth emergence varies with the bioclimate from April to June.

Eggs of the four species are normally deposited in masses on leaves or in sheaths in fish-scale fashion. Young larvae feed in whorls of unfolding leaves, following a pattern similar to several of the other lepidopterous caterpillars occurring on young corn. They invade the growing point and cause dead heart or they burrow in the stalk. There is a tendency for the larvae to leave the upper part of the stalk and to reenter at lower points. Larvae of Neotropical corn borer have adapted to aestivate during dry seasons and pupate after rains resume (USDA, 1966).

Fig. 13–11. Typical position of the overwinter hibernating larva of the southwestern corn borer in the base of the stalk.

Fig. 13–12. Sugarcane borer burrowing in stalk.

On late-planted corn, in the whorl stage of growth, the habits are the same as those of the first generation. On older tasseled corn there is little feeding on the leaf blade, but there is considerable feeding on sheaths, husks of the primary ear, and ear shoots (Fig. 13–13). Again older larvae feed and burrow in the stalk. A detailed study of feeding habits of larvae of the southwestern corn borer on two stages of corn growth has been reported by Davis et al. (1972).

Phillips et al. (1921) reported two generations for *D. crambidoides* in Virginia, and Cartwright (1943) recorded mostly two or three overlapping generations in South Carolina, which is similar to the observations on *D. grandiosella* by Walton and Bieberdorf (1948) and Wilbur et al. (1950). When three generations occurred, each of the first two produced some hibernating larvae. Henderson and Davis (1970) directed insecticide tests against second and third generation infestation of the southwestern species. In the sugarcane borer, Ingram and Bynum (1941) report from two to four generations. Of particular significance in the second- and third-generation infestations of the southwestern corn borer is the

Fig. 13–13. Husk penetration and ear injury by the southwestern corn borer.

severe breakage caused by larvae girdling the rind of the stalk, usually below the ear. This has not been reported as serious with the other species.

Procedures advocated for reducing populations of the southern cornstalk borer and the southwestern corn borer are similar. They are both aimed at eliminating as many overwintering larvae as possible by exposure of corn stubble, which they inhabit below the soil surface, to freezing temperatures on the soil surface. A high percentage of larvae are killed by subfreezing temperatures. Stubble or stalks should be plowed or disked out in the fall and allowed to remain on the surface until March. High mortalities among hibernating larvae also result when stalks are scattered and broken up in such operations. Moths fail to reach the soil surface when stalks are plowed under to a depth of 10 cm (Cartwright, 1934; Davis et al., 1972; Phillips et al., 1921; Wilbur et al., 1950).

The southwestern corn borer has been most troublesome in areas where grain sorghums are better adapted than corn. Wilbur et al. (1950) therefore advocated the substitution of sorghum for corn. This has become a common practice in Oklahoma (Walton and Bieberdorf, 1948). In a study of planting dates, a partial escape from infestation by first generation was observed by these workers. This practice has been further discussed by Davis et al. (1973). In South Carolina, Cartwright (1934) observed lower infestations of the southern cornstalk borer in late-planted corn, but discouraged this practice in areas where billbugs and the lesser cornstalk borer (*Elasmopalpus lignosellus*) are important factors. He also observed that properly fertilized corn will outgrow injury and produce fair yields.

Ingram and Bynum (1941) regarded the source of the sugarcane borer as a pest of corn to be sugarcane (*Saccharum officinarim* L.) debris and rice (*Oryza sativa* L.) stubble. A high percentage of the overwintering larvae may be destroyed by burning sugarcane trash. In rice stubble, hibernating larvae are materially reduced by grazing, burning, flooding, and dragging.

13–3.6   Armyworm — Description and Biology

Young larvae of the armyworm (*Pseudaletia unipuncta*) are pale green with alternate brown to reddish and light longitudinal stripes, which become more conspicuous in successive instars. The anterior prolegs of the first two instars are poorly developed. In these stages the larvae are similar to measuring worms. Late-instar larvae vary in color from green to light brown and red. The head is pale brown with a mottled area on each side of the median suture. When feeding in corn ears, mature larvae may easily be mistaken for the fall armyworm or the corn earworm.

Most of the armyworm are brownish with a white spot near the center of the forewing. They are nocturnal in their flight habits, but are attracted to light in large numbers during outbreak years.

Injury on young corn is at first on leaves and in the whorl; later older larvae feed more on the edge of leaves. Later injury is common when migrations occur from adjoining small grain. A typical infestation shows plants with elongated lesions on and along the edge of leaves.

The armyworm is widely distributed over the USA and Canada as well as in foreign countries. Outbreaks are frequently local and sporadic, but high general populations have at times occurred over large sections of the eastern parts of the USA and Canada (Forbes, 1904; Walton and Packard, 1951; USDA, 1961).

The primary host plants of the armyworm are wheat, oat, barley, rye (*Secale cereale* L.), and forage grass. Forbes (1904) reported that winter is passed as partially grown larvae; this fact was confirmed by Davis and Satterthwait (1916) and Knight (1916). Overwintering larvae complete their development early in spring and then burrow into soil to pupate. The first generation of moths are abroad from April to June, depending on the bioclimate. They commonly deposit their eggs in bead-like clusters behind sheaths and on leaves of small grain near the base of plants. On hatching, larvae hide among leaves during the day and feed on upper leaves at night.

Presence of an infestation does not become conspicuous until the later instars, or about the time the heads of the grain appear. Under conditions of overpopulation, migration to contiguous cornfields occurs from May to July depending on the locality and may extend a considerable distance into a field. Some infestations have been observed on early planted corn that resulted directly from first-generation oviposition. Forbes (1904) and Davis and Satterthwait (1916) estimated three complete generations in Illinois and Indiana, respectively. Knight (1916) observed two generations in New York. At about the roasting-ear stage of corn, larvae cause injury to ears typical of the corn earworm.

Musick and Tuttle (1973) observed a high infestation of the armyworm in corn planted by the no-tillage method (Fig. 13–14). A maximum reduction of severe damage was obtained by an application of carbofuran granules placed in the furrow at the rate of 68.6 g (2.4 ounces) per 304.4 m (1000 feet) of row.

During an armyworm outbreak large numbers of larvae fall prey to parasites, predators, and diseases. Knight (1916) recorded two species of tachinid flies, four of Hymenoptera, and five of predaceous beetles in western New York. Among other predators, the most common feeders are blackbirds, sparrows, domestic fowls, skunks, and toads (Walton and Packard, 1951).

13–3.7 Lesser Cornstalk Borer — Description and Biology

Full-grown larva of the lesser cornstalk borer (*Elasmopalpus lignosellus*) is about 25 mm in length, and greenish with conspicuous brown longitudinal stripes. The body colors of young larvae vary from pale yellow to pale green. Larvae have a distinctive habit of jerking and skipping when disturbed.

Fig. 13–14. Armyworm infestation under no-till planting conditions.

Typical injury in young plants is characterized by tunnels into plants at or slightly below the surface of soil (Fig. 13–15). Heavy populations may cause loss of stand, stunting, and tillering. In older plants injury in stems is of a girdling nature near the ground, and consequently plants are subject to stalk breakage. Presence of earthen-like, silk-webbed tubes attached at the entrance of tunnels into the plant is evidence of an infestation. These tubes are occupied by larvae when they are not feeding in plants (Kirk, 1960; Luginbill and Ainslie, 1917).

The species is widely distributed over the warmer parts of North and South America and the islands of the West Indies. In addition to corn, the more important crops attacked in the Southern states are sugarcane, sorghum, cowpea [*Vigna unguiculata* (L.) Walp.], and bean. Among weeds, nut grasses (*Cyperus* spp.) are sources of seasonal populations. Moths have been recorded in the Northern states, but infestations of economic

Fig. 13–15. Corn plant showing typical injury by the lesser corn stalk borer with full-grown larvae on right.

importance have been reported only as far north as Arkansas (Isely and Miner, 1944).

According to Luginbill and Ainslie (1917), only larvae survive winter in their stalk burrows, and pupation and moth emergence take place late in winter and in early spring. At Columbia, SC, the first-generation larvae on corn were nearly full grown by the first week of June. Based on rearing experiments, they concluded that the insect developed four generations in that latitude. Records of outbreaks on various crops showed that infestations are most likely to occur under weedy conditions on sandy upland soils.

Cultural control practices suggested by Luginbill and Ainslie (1917) are aimed primarily at destroying the overwintering population through elimination of crop debris by clean plowing in late fall or early winter. Early planting and fertilization are advocated as a means of producing vigorous growth and tolerance to an infestation. Isely and Miner (1944) reported that corn was the preferred host in an outbreak in Arkansas in 1943. This infestation followed heavy rains in May and June, and resulted in abundant growth of crabgrass. They concluded that clean cultivation before planting would prevent outbreaks of this insect.

13–3.8 Chinch Bug — Description and Biology

The adult chinch bug (*Blissus leucopterus leucopterus*) is about 4 mm in length with a black, finely pubescent body with whitish wings. The wings have a triangular black area near the middle of the outer edge, and there is a triangular black scutellum between them at the anterior. The egg is reddish, elongate-oval, and about 0.7-mm long. Nymphs, the primary source of injury through sucking plant sap, are light red at first, becoming darker red in each instar, until after the fourth molt they are practically black (Forbes, 1904; Luginbill, 1922).

The chinch bug has been recorded from Central America and Mexico and is generally distributed over the major corn-growing areas of USA and southern Canada. Leonard (1966) reviewed the status of several species of *Blissus* in relation to distribution and biology. He concluded that *B. hirtus* is a subspecies of *B. leucopterus* but does not infest corn. Although *B. leucopterus* has many hosts, corn figures prominently in population build-up. Outbreaks have occurred periodically for more than 150 yr. The most serious losses on corn have occurred in the upper Mississippi Valley, with Illinois being about the center of the region of periodic outbreaks. Shelford and Flint (1943) made a study of factors involved in the fluctuation of chinch bug populations in the upper Mississippi Valley from 1823 to 1940. They concluded that population levels were correlated with meteorological conditions. Populations sufficient to cause crop damage were associated with above-normal temperatures and below-normal rainfall between March and October. No adverse effect could be attributed to below-normal winter temperatures.

So far as known the chinch bug feeds exclusively on plants belonging to the grass family. They attack wheat, barley, rye, oat, corn, and sorghum. Adult chinch bugs overwinter deep in clumps of sod of perennial grasses and in accumulations of leaves or debris, concentrating in fence rows and southern or western exposure of wooded areas. They fly to such cover in the fall from corn, sorghum, or other hosts (Forbes, 1904; Headlee and McColloch, 1913). In spring the bugs fly to small grains. In Illinois, Benton and Flint (1938) found wheat, rye, and barley most attractive to the bugs in spring, and oat least attractive. Early planted corn may also be a host to the spring brood, especially in the Southwest.

Eggs are deposited around the base of plants and behind sheaths of lower leaves, where they hatch in 7 to 14 d. The bugs obtain their food by sucking sap from plants, thereby causing serious injury to small grain under heavy infestations. Painter (1928), in a histological study of tissues pierced by sucking mouth parts of nymphs and adults, established that the stylets were thrust into vascular bundles. He concluded that food was obtained chiefly from phloem and that the plant's conductive tissues became clogged through the feeding process.

Small grain begins to ripen before much of the first generation reaches the adult stage and results in the well-known, on-the-foot migration from small-grain fields to adjoining corn, where nymphs complete their development. Adults become abundant a few weeks later and distribute themselves by flight on corn, sorghum, or other grasses. Second generation bugs complete their development on these crops in late summer and early fall. A third generation has been observed in the southern areas. Flight to their overwintering cover occurs in late summer and fall, being heaviest at temperatures above 38°C following cool nights. Among important natural control agents that have been recorded are two fungus diseases, *Beauveria bassiana* and *Erynia aphidis*, which are most effective when rainfall is abundant. A minute egg parasite, *Eumicrosoma benefica*, is also considered to be of importance.

Various cropping practices have long been advocated when a chinch bug problem is threatened. The spectacular migration from small-grain fields to adjoining corn led to recommendation to avoid planting corn next to small grain whenever possible. Cultural practices that produce good, vigorous stand of small grain and legumes are unfavorable for development of chinch bugs (USDA, 1954).

13–3.9 Grasshoppers — Description and Biology

Many species of grasshoppers attack corn but only several of these cause serious crop losses during epidemic years. Of foremost importance on corn is the differential grasshopper (*Melanoplus differentialis*). This species is about 38-mm long, dorsally dark-greenish to olive-brown to yellow underneath. Its distribution extends from the Great Plains States to the Atlantic Coast and north to the southern part of Canada.

Of almost equal importance to corn is the slightly smaller two-striped grasshopper (*M. bivittatus*). It is distinguished by two yellow stripes which extend back from the eyes along the sides to the end of the abdomen. The body is generally olive-brown above to yellow underneath. *Melanoplus bivittatus* is generally distributed over the USA and north into the Canadian provinces.

Of lesser importance on corn are the migratory grasshopper (*M. sanguinipes*) and the redlegged grasshopper (*M. femurrubrum*). These are about the same size and general appearance, being about 25 mm and reddish brown to gray dorsally to greenish yellow beneath. The redlegged grasshopper has highly colored red hind tibiae. Both species are distributed throughout most of North America and are most specific on small grain, clover, alfalfa, and pasture.

In the Southern states, the American grasshopper (*Schistocera americana*) is a large species 50- to 75-mm long and of reddish brown color and is occasionally a pest on corn (Blatchley, 1920; Parker and Connin, 1964; Shotwell, 1958).

Eggs of these species are deposited sometime during late summer and early fall in pods 25 to 50 mm below the surface of the soil. Depending upon the species, pods are 25- to 400-mm long and contain 15 to 100 eggs/pod. The differential and two-striped grasshoppers concentrate their egg pods among roots of weeds or grass along fence rows, roadsides, ditch banks, and other margins of cropped fields and pastures. Egg pods of migratory and the redlegged species are deposited in more open areas of small grain stubble and bare spots in alfalfa and clover fields. The American grasshopper deposits its pods in old weedy pastures, stump, and abandoned lands typical among cropped fields in the Southeastern states (Blatchley, 1920; Parker and Connin, 1964; Shotwell, 1941).

Eggs of grasshoppers found on corn hatch in spring, sometime between 1 April and 1 July, depending upon weather conditions and species. Young nymphs at first are <6-mm long and develop in stages by five to seven molts at intervals of 4 to 8 d. Most of the injury to corn is done after midsummer by adults or nymphs in the last two stages of development which migrate to corn from newly harvested small grain, hay fields, and roadsides (Shotwell, 1941, 1952).

Grasshoppers show a distinct preference for corn silks and eat them down to the cob, a practice which may interfere with pollination. A population of 15 to 30 m² will devour leaves to the midrib or cut them off at the axils, leaving bare stalks. Grasshoppers thrive under moderately dry climatic conditions. Fungus and bacterial diseases are effective in population control in areas that have a rainy climate (Parker and Connin, 1964).

Tillage practices, where they are compatible with good cropping procedures, are helpful in destroying egg pods of cropland species. This can be accomplished either in fall or spring by disking or moldboard plowing. Laying soil open to wind erosion should be avoided (USDA, 1964).

13–3.10   Corn Flea Beetle — Description and Biology

The adult is the primary injurious form of the corn flea beetle (*Chaetocnema pulicaria*). It is oblong, very dark, shiny green, and averages about 2-mm long. Feeding lesions on leaves form a pattern of narrow, closely spaced lines which normally run parallel with the veins. On the average lesions are about 6 mm in length. They are the points of origin of bacterial wilt, which in its more advanced stages, may obscure the beetle lesions in susceptible varieties. The role of this beetle as a vector of disease is discussed elsewhere (Poos and Elliott, 1936).

Large populations of the corn flea beetle occur periodically in sections from the Atlantic states to as far west as Colorado. Infestations on field and sweet corn are sometimes severe. Forbes (1905), in discussing the importance of this insect in several states, indicated that wilting was associated with plant injury and that the beetles were especially fond of sweet corn.

Other species of flea beetles are commonly found on corn and cause similar injury. The toothed flea beetle (*C. denticulata*) which is metallic green and about twice as large as *C. pulicaria*, is more closely associated with wild grasses that persist in cornfields. This species is also capable of transmitting Stewart's disease but with less virulence (Elliott and Poos, 1940; Poos and Elliott, 1936). In the Southwestern states, the desert corn flea beetle (*C. ectypa*) is generally distributed as a pest of corn (Wildermuth, 1917). Evidence of its ability to harbor and transmit Stewart's disease has not been established.

Adults of the corn flea beetle feed on many different plants. Forbes (1905) and Elliott and Poos (1940) list a wide host range but the cereal and forage grasses, wheat, oat, barley, rye, bluegrass, timothy, and orchardgrass are probably the most important. Poos (1955) for several years investigated the biology of the species and its relationship to transmission of bacterial wilt.

In the vicinity of Washington, DC., the insect was found to overwinter as an adult, mostly in the top 25 mm of soil and primarily in bluegrass sod. On days when the air temperature near the surface of the soil reached 35 to 48°C for a period of a few hours, adults became active during winter. In spring they became generally dispersed. New generations of adults were observed at various times during the season. Emergence of a generation was concentrated after a good rainfall following dry soil conditions. This was observed as early as 9 June and as late as 8 August, making it evident that at least two generations of this insect were completed each season. Under laboratory and greenhouse conditions a generation was completed in about 30 d.

Small larvae were found developing on 21 species of grains and grasses, including corn (both field and sweet), barley, oat, wheat, orchardgrass, timothy, redtop, and Italian ryegrass. Larvae would not feed on alfalfa and adults lived only about 10 d when confined to this host plant. Evidence obtained in 1940 indicated that a generation developed on wheat and timothy before corn was available in the field.

13–3.11 Japanese Beetle — Description and Biology

The injurious form of the Japanese beetle (*Popillia japonica*) on corn is the adult. It is about 12-mm long, oval, with a metallic green body and brownish wing covers. The beetle can readily be identified by six conspicuous tufts of white hair along the outer edge of each wing cover. Typical injury is scatter-grain, particularly at the tip of ears, due to continuous beetle feeding on emerging silks (Coon, 1951; Hawley and Metzger, 1940; Fleming, 1972). As a pest of corn this beetle is most important in the Middle Atlantic and Southern New England states. The Japanese beetle was discovered in New Jersey in 1916. In approximately 70 yr it has extended its range as far south as the Gulf States, west to western areas of the North Central region. Colonies have become established by hitchhiking beetles on conveyances moving out of heavily infested areas. Larvae are sod feeders and have their optimum survival in sandy soil. The polyphagous nature of beetles readily permits situations for successful establishment of colonies in grassy areas (Fleming, 1970, 1972).

The emergence period of beetles extends from June to July and there is but one generation annually. Egg deposition is predominantly in grass sod. On hatching larvae feed on fine plant roots and organic matter in soil until fall and again in spring. Pupation occurs in May and early June. Favorable situations for development of larvae are lawns or short grass pastures. Host selection is odoriferous in nature. Adults feed on many species of plants, corn in the silking stage being one of the preferred hosts. The beetles have a gregarious feeding habit and when large populations concentrate in a field with emerging silks, pollination and seed set is interfered with to varying degrees.

13–4 LESSER RECOGNIZED GROUPS

13–4.1 Thrips

Several species of thrips are almost invariably present on corn, particularly in the early stage of growth. The authors have recorded varietal resistance under high populations of the grass thrips (*Anaphothrips obscurus*) and lesser populations of *Frankliniella tenuicornis* in northern Ohio. Everly (1960b) observed the same species and *F. fusca* and *Aeolothrips bicolor* as injurious to seedling corn. Thrips injury is characterized by a silvery mottled appearance of lower leaves which is sometimes more intense along the edges of leaves. Young larvae are primarily located in the moist, rolled leaves of the bud, whereas adults commonly occur under fully exposed leaves. Sources of corn resistant to *F. occidentalis* and *F. williamsi* have been evaluated by Granados (1970). Elliott and Poos (1940) reported on tests with *A. obscurus, A. fasciatus*, and *Heliothrips femoralis* as possible vectos of bacterial wilt. A single isolation was obtained from *A. obscurus*. In Italy, Grancini (1963) reported *Limathrips cerealium*, injury to corn and resultant serious infections of smut (*Ustilago maydis*).

13–4.2 Leafhoppers

Many species of leafhoppers have been recorded on corn. Neiswander (1931) lists 59 species. The significance of their injury, with the exception of several species, is not well established. The corn delphacid (*Peregrinus maidis*) is a pest of corn in tropical and semitropical areas. Nymphal instars concentrate feeding activity on bud leaves. This species and several others are discussed in a subsequent section as virus and spiroplasma vectors. Leafhoppers are nearly always abundant on small grain, pasture and other grasses. Some of the same species commonly occur on corn. A pale-green mirid (*Trigonotylus brevipes*) feeding on leaf blades has been observed to be abundant on early to mid-whorl stages of growth for several years in Ohio and Iowa.

13–4.3 Western Bean Cutworm

The western bean cutworm (*Loxagrotis albicosta*) has been a pest of field bean for many years and has been recorded as injurious to corn in several Western states. In recent years it has extended its range eastward in Nebraska and Kansas. Injurious infestations have occurred on corn in the Platte River Valley, mainly in the Grand Island area. Raun et al. (1968) reported on extensive losses to about 121 600 ha of corn, primarily in central Nebraska.

Full-grown larva, about 40-mm long, tunnels into soil where it passes winter in a cell. Pupation takes place in early summer followed by moth emergence shortly thereafter. The moth is brown with creamy white stripes near the front of the forewing. The wing expanse is about 40 mm and the body is brown to tan in color. Eggs are deposited in masses in July on upper surface of leaves. The stage of corn growth during this period ranges from late whorl to tasseling. Upon hatching the brownish larvae feed on whorl leaves and on developing tassels. The pattern of larval feeding progresses to leaf sheaths, husks, and developing ears. Injury to ears can be severe (Fig. 13–16). There is a single generation annually.

Full-grown larvae leave plants to enter the soil from late summer to early fall. The end result of ear infestation is not only the actual grain devoured but also an increase in moldy grain (Douglas et al., 1957).

The spread eastward of the western bean cutworm has been rapid. In its normal habitat it prefers field bean as a host. On corn the highest populations have occurred in irrigated areas. Whether or not the large area of nonirrigated corn beyond the present distribution limits will restrict further spread remains to be seen.

Fig. 13–16. Illustration of husk penetration and ear injury by advanced stage larvae of the western bean cutworm.

13–4.4 Corn Blotch Leaf Miner

The corn blotch leaf miner (*Agromyza parvicornis*) attracts attention in some localities each year. This insect belongs to a large family of Diptera in which larvae develop in between epidermal layers of leaves. As larvae develop the "mines" increase in size and appear as irregular, dead, or blighted spots. Full-grown larvae are about 6-mm long and pale green in color. They pupate in soil. Adults emerge from 14 to 21 d later. Egg deposition is on leaves. Larvae enter the leaf directly as soon as they hatch.

The species has several host plants among the Gramineae but appears to have a preference for corn. Under high populations blotched leaves may occur from the seedling to the top leaves of plants. After several generations during the growing season the insect enters diapause as a puparium, although continuous breeding has been reported from Florida.

Phillips (1914) lists 20 species of parasites reared at several locations. Infestations are usually not noticed until damage is almost complete. For this reason, chemical control practices are believed to be of doubtful value.

13–4.5 Spider Mites

Mites are small, light to dusky arthropods (four pairs of legs) that vary in size from <1 mm for the newly hatched to about 2 mm when full grown. Eggs are minute, spherical and off-white in color. The normal feeding site is under leaves and injury first appears as small stippled areas in the leaf. As mite numbers increase, chlorophyhll breaks down and leaves take on a grayish color. Mites are vigorous spinners of silk, which forms a protective webbing over feeding areas on leaves. Disruption of the silk webbing through rains is an important factor in natural control of populations.

Infestations of spider mites have become commonplace in drier western corn-growing areas, particularly on irrigated ground. When populations begin to build up on young corn, severe stunting may occur. Ehler (1973) reported on the identity of mites collected on corn and sorghum in three areas of Texas. The species most frequently collected on corn was the Banks grass mite (*Oligonychus pratensis*) which has a wide distribution over the Great Plains area. The other species identified were the two-spotted spider mite (*Tetranychus urticae*), the carmine spider mite (*T. cinnabarinus*), and *O. stickneyi*. He emphasized the importance of proper identification in field observations and experimentation.

13–4.6 Pink Scavenger Caterpillar

The injurious form of the pink scavenger caterpillar (*Pyroderces rileyi*) is a pink to rose-colored larva about 10-mm long when full grown. Larvae begin to infest ears in fields and continue to feed on ears after harvest in storage. The moth has mottled yellow, brown, and black forewings and long-fringed narrow hindwings. It is smaller than the Angoumois grain moth (*Sitotroga cerealella*) with which its populations may be mixed. In typical injury the ear is webbed with grass between rows of grain and in the larval cavities. The injury and the silk webbing are not unlike that of the Indianmeal moth (*Plodia interpunctella*). The species is tropical and subtropical in distribution and is a pest of corn, sorghum, and cotton in the South Atlantic and Gulf States (Chittenden, 1916).

According to records published by Chittenden (1916), the pink scavenger caterpillar worm infests corn in fields that have been infested with earworms or has had the husk cover broken in some other way. He observed ears infested about milk stage or a little later. Breeding is continuous throughout the fall and into storage. Larvae feed also on husks and cobs but have a habit of feeding in the grain on embryos and endosperms. Douglas et al. (1962) found a positive correlation between infestation of ears by the corn earworm and the pink scavenger caterpillar. Good husk cover gave partial protection against infestation. Wiseman et al. (1970) in studies in Georgia, similarly concluded that husks of selected hybrids provided significant protection against the earworm and the pink scavenger caterpillar and that there was a close connection between damage incurred from the two insects.

13–4.7   Garden Symphylan

The garden symphylan (*Scuttigerella immaculata*) is a "centipede-like" soil arthropod that has been frequently observed as a pest of corn in recent years. Eggs are deposited in runways in moist soil. Newly hatched larvae are white with six pairs of legs. There are six molts and the number of legs increase to 12 pairs by the last molt. Adults are about 6-mm long, white, sometimes grayish in the abdominal segments. They have prominent, protruding antennae. This "centipede" has many hosts among the vegetable crops. It feeds on roots and underground stems, with asparagus (*Asparagus officinalis* L.) and sprouting seeds being favored hosts (Wymore, 1931).

13–4.8   Hop-Vine Borer and Potato Stem Borer

From 1920 to 1975, populations of the hop-vine borer (*Hydraecia immanis*) remained localized. For many years this pest was considered a grass/hop specialist but recently the insect has successfully and significantly switched to a corn diet and has caused heavy localized damage in at least 50 countries in Wisconsin, Illinois, Iowa, and Minnesota. The first two to four instars feed on grass stems then move to adjacent corn plants to complete their feeding. Increasing trends toward reduced- and conservation-tillage practices in the Midwest may contribute to spread of the hop-vine borer in the future. The potato stem borer (*H. micacea*) has a similar biology as the hop-vine borer but has a wider range of host plants, including potato, corn, and many other plants as well as hops. The potato stem borer, introduced into North America about 82 yr ago, has only recently spread across Canada from New York State and is present in Wisconsin where it is separated in noticeable economic damage from the hop-vine borer by only a single county (Giebink et al., 1984, 1985).

13–5   INSECTS IN RELATIONSHIP TO DISEASES

In crop improvement, primary consideration has to be given to yield, quality, and harvestability under a range of environmental conditions. Experimental experience through which our goals are achieved is a continuing process. An inbred line or cultivar may be reasonably homozygous or uniform but well utilized under a wide array of environments. Plant breeders may have to compromise by using genetic factors that will best meet this variable environment. In order to achieve cultivar improvements we need to have knowledge of the components that contribute to these end results.

The role of insects in transmission or dissemination of pathogenic organisms is an important part of an interdisciplinary corn development program. These problems are encountered each year to varying degrees from the time of germination to plant maturity and storage of the grain.

Soil is a complex environment abounding in microorganisms, particularly fungi, that may infect plant parts injured by soil-inhabiting arthropods. During vegetative growth stages there are many species of insects that become involved directly or indirectly in fungal, bacterial, viral, mycoplasma, and spiroplasma diseases of corn plants.

To obtain an understanding of the insect or mite-related diseases of corn, basic research on biological relationships between the host and its parasites is essential. Information developed through such studies builds stepping-stones of methodology for evaluating many qualities needed to withstand hazards present in the environment. In recent years, there has been an increasing cooperative effort in this direction by state, federal, and private agencies. It is the purpose of this section to review some of the contributions made on the status of the more important insect-related diseases.

13–5.1 Fungal Diseases

In much of the Corn Belt, pathogenic fungi probably pose more problems in corn production than any of the other groups of organisms. Primary roots of the seedling and the radical and seminal roots are commonly infected with *Fusarium* spp. after they have served their function and become senescent. Thus, inoculum of root-invading pathogens is normally present and in close proximity to any later root injury that may occur.

Diabrotica rootworms are generally prevalent in much of the corn-growing areas of North and Central America. Periodically, populations reach high levels. Habits of larvae encompass feeding on root hairs, small rootlets, burrowing in tender portions of roots, and removal of rings of young crown roots. Palmer and Kommedahl (1969) reported on the *Fusarium* spp. associated with roots of corn infested with *D. barberi*. They isolated *F. oxysporum, F. moniliforme, F. roseum, Cerealis graminearum,* and *F. tricinctum. Fusarium roseum* and *F. moniliforme* were pathogenic, whereas *F. oxysporum* and *F. tricinctum* were secondary invaders and grew only on tissues damaged by the rootworm. Both larvae and adults were vectors of *Fusarium* spp. Eggs and frass also harbored these organisms.

On sweet corn, Pepper and Haenseler (1944) observed less corn smut (incited by *Ustilago maydis*) where the European corn borer was controlled with insecticides, indicating that the organism gained entrance in plants at sites of larval injury. Smut infection may be a cause of barrenness and poor ear development in corn.

The corn pathogens associated with stalk rots are of significant importance in determining the quality, yield, and harvestability of corn. Interference with translocation of nutrients in the vascular system predisposes stalks for development of common stalk rot organisms, such as *Stenocarpella (Diplodia) maydis* and *Gibberella zeae*. In a study of losses caused by varying levels of infestation by the European corn borer, Patch et al. (1941) reported increased stalk breakage below the ear as the level of larval population increased. Christensen and Schneider (1950) in Minnesota, investigated organisms that developed in stalks and ears after infestation with the European corn borer. Christensen and Schneider (1950) found that species of *Fusarium* were the most common pathogens isolated from injured points in the stalk, shank, and ear following infestation with European corn borers. Among the fungi isolated from rotted internodes of corn infested with European corn borer larvae were *Alternaria* spp., *Aspergillus* spp., *Mucor* spp., *Rhizopus* spp., *Penicillium* spp., *S. maydis*, and *G. zeae*. Substantially the same group of fungi were isolated from internal parts of living and dead larvae. They indicated that weak pathogens may play an important role in disease development of injured stalks.

Resistance to stalk rot is negated under high infestations by second-generation European corn borers. Stalk rot resistance did not break down in genotypes that were also resistant to the borer. Stalk rot infection did not affect the borer but European corn borer infestation greatly increased the incidence of stalk rot (Jarvis et al., 1982, 1984).

The most important insects associated with ear injury (kernel) are the corn earworm, European corn borer, and the fall armyworm. In years of general infestation by these insects, ear fungi take a substantial toll in kernel damage and quality. Koehler (1942) found that ear rot incited by *F. moniliforme* was increased by corn earworm damage. *Gibberella zeae* infection increased somewhat less, and *Nigrospora* spp. and *Cephalosporium* spp. increased only slightly through earworm infestation. Earworm injury did not increase *S. maydis* infection.

Lillehoj et al. (1975) reported the presence of aflatoxin, produced by *Aspergillus flavus*, on corn in diverse locations in the USA. There is a relationship between the concentration of aflatoxin and the incidence of ear infestation by the European corn borer, the fall armyworm, the corn earworm, and the maize weevil (Widstrom et al., 1975; McMillian et al., 1980a, 1985; Barry et al., 1985). Corn earworms were most susceptible to aflatoxin (incorporated into a meridic diet) than were the European corn borer and fall armyworm (McMillian et al., 1980b). Concentrations of aflatoxin B_1 that occur under field conditions would at times be great enough to adversely affect the European corn borer, especially ear-infesting larvae, but would probably have only a minimal influence on population fluctuations of the insect (Jarvis et al., 1984). Field corn, sweet corn, and popcorn have been evaluated for ear resistance to field aflatoxin contamination (Widstrom et al., 1978, 1984; Guthrie et al., 1981; McMillian et al., 1982a). A corn hybrid (B86 × SC213) highly resistant to sheath-collar and stalk-feeding damage by European corn borer larvae did not prevent aflatoxin contamination in ears (Guthrie et al., 1981). Evaluation and selection for plant resistance to infection by *A. flavus* and aflatoxin production will probably be difficult (Widstrom et al., 1978).

13–5.2 Bacterial Diseases

Bacterial leaf blight incited by *Erwinia stewartii* (sometimes called Stewart's bacterial blight) has been recognized mainly as a disease of sweet corn. However, some susceptible cultivars of field corn do exist. According to the *Compendium of Corn Diseases* (American Phytopathological Society, 1973), this disease has been reported from Europe and Asia. All of these reports are apparently from warm climate areas. Likewise, in the Western Hemisphere, bacterial leaf blight is annually present in the Southern states and the southern fringe of the central Corn Belt east to the Atlantic Coast. In 1972 and 1973, this blight was prevalent as far west as Kansas. Stevens (1936) monitored bacterial leaf blight in relation to winter temperature for a series of years and predicted increased severity of the disease in seasons following mean temperature for December, January, and February that totaled 68 °C or more. The relationship of insects to this disease was observed by Rand and Cash (1933). They were able to transfer the organism from diseased plants to healthy plants under cage conditions with the corn flea beetle and the southern corn rootworm.

The importance of the corn flea beetle in incidence of bacterial leaf blight was investigated extensively by Elliott and Poos (1934) and Poos and Elliott (1936), particularly in connection with overwintering of the bacterium. They found that at least 19% of the overwintered corn flea beetles carried the bacterium. In tests of some 40 species of insects as possible vectors, they concluded that only the corn flea beetle and the toothed flea beetle were vectors of the pathogen under field conditions. From May to September in 1934 they found 40% of the corn flea beetles harboring the pathogen. Under experimental conditions, the southern corn rootworm transferred the pathogen from diseased to healthy corn. An association between winter temperatures and abundance of the corn flea beetle and incidence of bacterial leaf blight was indicated in 1934 in New York and the New England states. In that year, the corn flea beetle was scarce north of central Pennsylvania. Bacterial leaf blight was also reduced compared to its existence in 1932 and 1933.

Favored overwintering habitat of the corn flea beetle is in grass sod and in well-drained areas. During warm periods in early spring they can be collected from a variety of grasses and small grain, particularly wheat. Although information on the biology of larval and pupal development is fragmentary, the evidence is that the first generation may be completed on these grasses although some of the overwintering population of beetles may feed upon and infect early planted corn. A short life-cycle is indicated and populations may reach high concentrations by midsummer, when elongated feeding scars and wilt lesions can be readily observed. Poos (1955) recovered larvae of the corn flea beetle from soil surrounding 21 species of Gramineae belonging to 17 genera. Poos (1939) reported that Kentucky bluegrass (*Poa pratensis* L.), orchardgrass (*Dactylis glomerata* L.), and wheat, which do not show symptoms, probably provide inoculum for the vector before corn is available in fields. The pathogen was recovered from these species after beetles exposed to diseased corn plants fed upon them. Little information has been developed on the host-vector relationship of this wilt disease since these reports were published. After many years of experience and observation on this problem the authors suspect that the lack of symptomless hosts such as winter wheat and corn flea beetle relation thereto could be one of the factors involved in the low incidence of the corn flea beetle and bacterial wilt in central Iowa where little wheat is produced.

13–5.3 Virus and Viruslike Disease Vectors

Most of the insect vectors of virus and viruslike diseases in corn belong to the aphid and leafhopper families. Until recently, virus diseases were not regarded as threatening problems of corn production in the USA. For many years virus diseases encompassed those maladies whose pathogens could be transmitted by biological or mechanical techniques but could not be observed by maximum magnification of available microscopes. The electron microscope has made it possible to describe the configuration of these pathogens, which has aided in the identification and classification process. This has also resulted in separating many pathogens from viruses and establishing an additional hierarchy of classification currently designated as mycoplasmalike or spiroplasms. Some of the cicadelid leafhopper-transmitted pathogens now fall into the spiroplasma group and are causal agents of yellows disease.

A sugarcane-mosaic pathology program identified the corn leaf aphid as a vector of sugarcane mosaic in corn (Brandes, 1920). About the same time, Kunkel (1921) reported the corn delphacid (*Peregrinus maidis*) (a Fulgorid) as a possible vector of maize mosaic virus also referred to as corn stripe. This disease was later determined to be distinct from sugarcane mosaic (Stahl, 1927; Kunkel, 1927). Later Kunkel's studies were confirmed by Carter (1941) and McEwen and Kawanishi (1967).

Maize virus disease of corn has had a long history in many parts of Africa. Storey (1939) made detailed studies of the vector relationships of *Cicadulina mbila, C. zeae,* and *C. storeyi* in epidemiology of what was identified as a virus disease and was successful in transmitting the pathogen only with these species of leafhoppers. The disease has been limited to where the leafhoppers are present.

In 1963, a new regime in virus investigations began primarily in corn and sorghum and other Gramineae, as a result of pockets of virus disease outbreaks in Mississippi, Louisiana, and Ohio. Stoner (1968) compiled reports from many investigators representing practically all of the corn- or sorghum-producing states and provinces in Canada. The Ohio Agricultural Research and Development Center (1973) issued a list of the many references pertaining to maize virus diseases and corn stunt.

Samples from Mississippi led to a determination of corn stunt virus (CSV) (Maramorosch, 1963) with *Dalbulus maidis* as the vector. Many years of investigation with leafhopper vectors established that CSV (now classified as a spiroplasma) was a persistent pathogen with an incubation period of about 14 d. Working with an Ohio source of disease, Stoner et al. (1964) established that the corn leaf aphid was a nonpersistent vector of the virus infecting corn in southern Ohio. They were able to mechanically transmit the pathogen and to observe that the disease was different from known virus diseases of corn. The disease, as it prevailed in the southern area, first became known as corn stunt and that found in the Ohio river areas, maize dwarf mosaic virus (MDMV). Research soon established that johnsongrass served as a winter host of the virus. This grass is a favored host of the corn leaf aphid. Figure 13–17 shows a typical mosaic virus of corn and johnsongrass [*Sorghum halepense* (L.) Pers.] and the relation to sugarcane mosaic virus. Detailed studies on properties of the virus and the vector relationship were reported by Bancroft et al. (1966) and Messieha (1967). The virus was found to be transmissable by 11 species of aphids in the laboratory, namely *Dactynotus* spp., *Brevicoryne brassicae, Rhopalosiphum padi, R. maidis, Aphis maidiradicis, Myzus persicae, Rhopalomyzus poae, Therioaphis maculata, Acyrthosiphon pisum, Aphis gossypii,* and *A. craccivora.* The acquisition period of the virus was short (10–20 s) and the retention period by the aphids was only 10 to 20 min. Effective sources of host-vector relationship were shown in 10 species of Gramineae. In tests of many grasses, Ford (1967) determined that 10 species of perennial grasses found in Iowa were susceptible to MDMV when the grasses were mechanically inoculated.

There has been extensive research on a number of species of aphids as vectors of MDMV and a group of strain isolates thereof. Because of the need for isolation under controlled conditions much of this has been done in cages in the laboratory or greenhouse with apterous forms. When a species has been exposed to an infected plant for feeding and probing and is able to transmit the disease to a healthy noninfected plant it may be designated a vector. Knoke and Louie (1981) aptly pointed out that aphid behavior may be quite different under field conditions and suggested that using field-collected alate aphids on test plants directly would partially compensate for such deviations.

Fig. 13–17. Inbred line infected with mosaic virus.

The short retention period of MDMV inoculum by aphids under laboratory procedures was investigated by Berger (1983). By immobilization methods to prevent spending of inoculum, simulating what happens in flight, they were able to extend retention from minutes to more than 21 h in *Schizaphis graminum* and 18 h in several other species. The feeding habits of *R. maidis* were discussed in a previous section. Several other species sometimes occur on corn. However, none actively infest the emerging whorl, a vulnerable position for introducing the virus to the growing point of leaves. *Rhopalosiphum maidis* is generally accepted as the primary source for establishing MDMV (Shaunak and Pitre, 1971; Straub and Boothroyd, 1980).

A series of contributions on vector-host, and pathogen relationships were made in succeeding years (Choudhury and Rosenkranz, 1973; Davis et al., 1972; Granados et al., 1966, 1968; Maramorosch et al., 1968; Nault and Bradley, 1969; Nault et al., 1973; Pitre, 1968; Pitre and Hepner, 1967; Rosenkranz, 1969; Tu and Ford, 1971; Niblett et al., 1981). What were once thought to be different diseases (Mississippi corn stunt and Ohio corn stunt) are now recognized as different isolates of the same virus transmitted primarily by *Graminella nigrifrons*. Maize chlorotic dwarf virus (MCDV) does not occur independently of MDMV in any state (Knoke and Louie, 1981).

An isometric virus causing chlorosis and stunting was recovered from corn, johnsongrass, sweet sorghum, giant foxtail (*Setaria faberi* Herrm.), and yellow foxtail [*S. glauca* (L.) Beauv.] and was transmitted to corn. This virus, a new recovery, was named MCDV (Bradfute et al., 1972; Nault et al., 1973). Investigators working with *G. nigrifrons* identified johnsongrass as a reservoir for two viruses, MCDV as only transmissible biologically by *G. nigrifrons*, and MDMV as aphid-borne and mechanically transmissible.

Periodically wheat streak mosaic virus (WSMV) has been prevalent in corn, but the disease caused by this pathogen has not been as virulent as in wheat. Slykhuis (1953), in transmission work, established that *Eriophyes tulipae*, an eriophyd mite, was an efficient vector. Oldfield (1970) published a review of the literature on mite transmission of plant viruses. The vector, *E. tuplipae*, is widely distributed and has been recorded on a variety of hosts. On corn, *E. tulipae* causes kernel red streak which is mostly concentrated on the tip end of ears. This kernel condition was at first thought to be the result of WSMV infection. Later nonviruliferous as well as viruliferous mites were shown to be able to induce the red streaks through their feeding activity on kernels (Nault et al., 1967). The WSMV has been shown to be a component of the disease known as corn lethal necrosis.

Uyemoto and Claflin (1981) presented information on the relationship between maize chlorotic mottle virus (MCMV) originally described from Peru and corn lethal necrosis. The MCMV in combination with MDMV transmitted by aphids or WSMV transmitted by the wheat curl mite (*E. tulipae*) was observed to severely damage corn in north central Kansas and south central Nebraska.

The classification of pathogens causing yellows diseases in plants, usually transmitted by leafhoppers, as viruses was questioned by Doi et al. (1967). Their studies of electron microscope sections of mulberry (*Morus* spp.) infected with dwarf disease showed microorganisms in the phloem elements that they described as mycoplasma-like agents. Ishiie et al. (1967) reported that some tetracycline antibiotics had a suppressive and therapeutic effect on mulberry dwarf infected plants. Similarly, Granados (1969b) reported such effects with the corn stunt pathogen in corn and in the leafhopper vector, *Dalbulus elimatus*. These events set in motion the reexamination of many diseases, classified as viruses, transmitted by leafhoppers. An extensive literature has developed in this area of pathology. Maramorosch et al. (1968, 1970) and Granados (1969b) described mycoplasma-like structures in diseased plants and in insect vectors. Whitcomb and Davis (1970) published a review of literature on this matter. The generic name *Spiroplasma* was assigned to the spiral-like or helical pathogens that have been referred to as mycoplasma-like agents (Davis and Worley, 1973; Whitcomb et al., 1973). Corn stunt, transmitted by leafhoppers of *Dalbulus* spp., falls into this classification (Davis, 1973). Granados (1969a) obtained suppressive effects with tetracycline antibiotics on corn stunt symptoms and in the ability of the leafhopper vector (*D. eliminatus*) to transmit the pathogen.

Dalbulus leafhoppers have long been associated with corn stunt and its reservoir close relatives of corn, *Zea mays mexicana*, *Z. perennis*, *Z. diploperennis*, *Z. luxurians*, and *Tripsacum* spp. (Davis et al., 1981; Nault and Knoke, 1981). In our collections on corn in Jamaica and Nicaragua, *D. maidis* was by far the most abundant leafhopper species but was exceeded in numbers by *R. maidis*. The latter is attracted to emerging seedlings. The important questions in tropical corn-growing areas are pathogen hosts and what vector gets there first.

A number of virus or spiroplasma diseases, commonly referred to as noneconomic, found in small grain and other grasses, have been transmitted to corn. A list of these diseases is given in a book published by the American Phytopathology Society (1973). The potential of such causal pathogens and their vectors should not be discounted. Carter (1973) assembled a large mass of information on insects in relation to plant diseases. An appreciation of the extensive research activities in the area of virus and viruslike diseases on corn on an international basis can be gained by consulting Gordon et al. (1981).

13–6 STORED-GRAIN INSECTS

The most injurious insects found in stored corn also infest other grain, cereal products, and stored food or feed. The problems of controlling these insects on corn are frequently related to those on other grain and products in which culture infestations are unknowingly maintained. Cotton et al. (1953) reported significant information on causes of outbreaks of stored-grain insects. To a considerable extent this information applies to the heavy grain-producing region of the North Central states but much of it also applies to other regions (Bulla et al., 1979).

Stored-grain insect infestations in corn are most intense in warm climates and tropical areas where the problem begins in the field and continues on through the storage period. Cultivars with good husk cover are helpful in protection against heavy field infestation. The following section gives only some of the more general information on a group of the most important forms encountered in corn storage and conditions under which they occur.

13–6.1   Rice Weevil and Maize Weevil — Description and Biology

The rice weevil (*Sitophilus oryzae*) and the maize weevil (*S. zeamais*) are dark reddish brown snout beetles usually about 4-mm long, with light spots on each wing cover. The thorax is densely pitted, legs are prominent, and the wings are well developed. The larvae which feed in corn and small grain are white, legless, thick-bodied grubs. These weevils are warm-climate insects and infest grain in the field and continue reproducing in storage until the grain is used. In the lower temperate zone and in tropical areas they are classed among the most important economic insects. In the USA, field infestations of the rice weevil extend into the southern part of the North Central states region following mild winters. The primary source of infestations in stored corn by this species in colder areas is from the transportation of infested grain or from small local cultures located in favorable spots for surviving the winter (Dean, 1913; Cotton, 1920; Kuschel, 1961; Widstrom et al., 1972a).

It is typical for *Sitophilus* adults to eat small cavities in grain in which eggs are deposited. Under favorable temperature and humidity, egg deposition by the rice weevil may extend over 120 or 150 d. Upon hatching, larvae feed in grain on both germ and endosperm. Pupation takes place in grain in the cavity made by the larva during its feeding. During summer months, 35 d were required to complete a generation (Cotton, 1920). There were as many as seven generations annually in the South. However, this number is dependent on the bioclimate and would be considerably less in northern areas. Figure 13–18 shows a mature ear infested with rice weevil (also some Angoumois grain moth) and typical grain with adult emergence holes.

Adult beetles are strong fliers, an important factor in dissemination and establishment of field infestations where there is normally an overwinter survival in stored grain. Cotton (1920) observed that infestations in corn in the field began after grain became firm. This corresponds closely to the time earworms have emerged from ears and left openings favorable for weevil access. The relationship between poor husk protection and increased injury by the corn earworm and rice weevil in the field and in storage was reported by several workers (Cartwright, 1930; Cotton, 1920; Eden, 1952; Floyd and Powell, 1958; Hinds, 1914; Kyle, 1918; Wiseman et al., 1970).

The relationship between injury of ears in storage and field infestations by the rice weevil is further supported by results on control of earworms by insecticides. Douglas and Smith (1953) reported almost complete absence of the rice weevil in ear corn until November harvest in local fields where they had practically eliminated the corn earworm and fall armyworm with a DDT-mineral oil spray.

Fig. 13–18. Rice weevil infestation originating in the field.

13–6.2 Granary Weevil — Description and Biology

Granary weevil (*Sitophilus granarius*) is closely related to and easily confused with the rice weevil. Light spots on wing covers, typical of the rice weevil, are lacking, however, and the wings are reduced to a vestige. The larva inhabits grain like the rice weevil. It has a wide range among cereal grains and products, in which it has become a cosmopolitan pest (Dean, 1913).

The granary weevil has a life history similar to that of the rice weevil. Observations in corn storage bins have shown that it is not as widespread a pest of stored corn as the rice weevil. It is somewhat more tolerant to colder climates than the rice weevil (Decker, 1941) and is not considered a serious pest of corn. In Kansas, Dean (1913) reported four or five generations annually. Because of their inability to fly, beetles become disseminated only through transport of grain and other infested products stored under conditions favorable for their multiplication and survival.

13–6.3 Flour Beetles — Description and Biology

The flour beetles (*Tribolium* spp.) are flat, reddish brown, and about 4-mm long. The larvae are about 6-mm long when full grown and have a forked termination of the last abdominal segment. Although they are usually associated with flour and meal storage they are commonly found in stored corn. Like most of the other stored-product insects they are worldwide in distribution and thrive on a variety of seed and food products. In the extreme northern states and Canada, survival is believed to occur only in heated buildings. The most common species are the red flour beetle (*T. castaneum*) and the confused flour beetle (*T. confusum*) (Good, 1936). In late summer, *T. castaneum* becomes abundant in shelled corn stored in the corn area of the USA.

Both adults and larvae feed on stored corn but prefer broken kernels to undamaged grain. Because they shun light they are seldom noticed when populations are low. Adults are long-lived, but the developmental stages are short. The oviposition period may extend for as long as a year. The number of generations produced annually depends on the bioclimate. Continuous breeding is believed to occur in the Gulf states where *T. castaneum* may be associated with infestations of other grain insects in the field. Dissemination by flight for a short distance is considered possible only for *T. castaneum*. For this reason this species is the predominant one in farm-stored grain. *Tribolium confusum* has been extensively used as a test insect for nutrition research.

13–6.4 Flat Grain Beetle — Description and Biology

The flat grain beetle (*Cryptolestes pusillus*) is flat, reddish brown, and about 1.5-mm long, with long antennae extending 'V'-shaped from the head. Adults feed mostly on grain dust or broken kernels, whereas larvae burrow into the germ. This species has been noticeable for its presence in large numbers in out-of-condition corn in storage. Infestations show grain with the germ eaten out and association with primary infestations by the rice weevil and the cadelle beetle (*Tenebroides mauritanicus*) (Cotton, 1947; Cotton et al., 1953).

The flat grain beetle is attracted to and breeds in grain that is in poor condition. Decker (1941) and Cotton et al. (1953) report the species as among the most abundant form in shelled corn stored in steel bins. It has, however, not been regarded as a serious pest in sound corn. The rusty grain beetle (*C. ferrugineus*) is similar in appearance and habits to *C. pusillis*. Cotton (1947) states that it is more resistant to cold weather and more commonly found in stored grain in Northern states.

13–6.5 Sawtoothed Grain Beetle — Description and Biology

The saw-toothed grain beetle (*Oryzaephilus surinamensis*) is readily identified by the six tooth-like projections on each side of the thorax. These also occur on the pupa. It is dark brown and about 2.5-mm long. The larva is slender and yellowish white, with three pair of legs. Both adult and larva are free feeders upon or in grain, injuring more seeds than they consume. The species is worldwide in distribution and infests many grains, seeds, and foodstuffs.

Adults of this beetle are long-lived, whereas immature forms develop relatively fast requiring only about 21 d under favorable conditions. The egg deposition period ranged from 180 to 300 d, according to Back and Cotton (1926). On completing development, the larva transforms into a pupa in a light cocoon bound together with foodstuff fragments. Because of the long and variable adult life, it is difficult to determine the number of generations. In the vicinity of Washington DC, Back and Cotton (1926) estimated from four to five generations and believed breeding to be continuous in subtropical and tropical climates. Winter is passed in the adult stage. Under low humidity in heated buildings, development of larvae was much inhibited.

13–6.6 Cadelle — Description and Biology

The cadelle beetle (*Tenebroides mauritanicus*) is one of the largest of the common stored-grain pests. The adult is dark reddish brown, oblong, flat, and about 8-mm long with a conspicuous constriction just ahead of the wings. The mature larva is about 20-mm long, white, with a black head and two caudal spines. The head and thoracic segments are narrower than the abdominal segments. Both adults and larvae prefer the germ for food.

The larva has a habit of burrowing into wooden structures before pupation, a habit which is an important factor in control practices in some areas. Other grain insects usually follow up its attack. The species is worldwide in distribution. It has a wide host range among grains and stored products (Back and Cotton, 1926). It is not one of the abundant species in shelled corn stored in steel bins.

Among the important stored-grain insects the cadelle is probably the most hardy under winter temperatures in the more northern corn-growing areas. The overwintering population is made up of both adults and larvae. Infestations in spring result from the beetles and larvae that survive winter. In life history studies, Back and Cotton (1926) reported oviposition throughout the spring and summer months. Continuous breeding occurs in warm climates.

13–6.7 Angoumois Grain Moth — Description and Biology

The injurious form of the Angoumois grain moth (*Sitotroga cerealella*) is a small white caterpillar with yellowish head that feeds within the grain. Pupation occurs in the cavity hollowed out by the larva. Typical indication of an infestation are kernels with round holes or with small channels stopping just below the seed coat. Moths are buff-colored with pointed hair-fringed wings measuring about 12 mm when spread (Fig. 13–19). As a pest of grain the Angoumois grain moth is ranked next to the rice weevil in economic importance. It is distributed throughout the world, infesting grain in storage and in the field in lower temperate and tropical areas. It only occurs in outbreak numbers in the southern part of the central Corn Belt after a series of warm winters allow populations to build up. In the southern area it is never as troublesome in corn as the rice weevil (Cotton et al., 1953; Simmons and Ellington, 1933).

In areas where the Angoumois grain moth is a pest, corn serves as an important source for building up infestations in other grains, particularly in fields and in storage. As with the rice weevil corn becomes

Fig. 13–19. Angoumois grain moth showing long hair at the end of the wings, and kernels with emergence holes.

infested in the field, ears with loose husks and exposed tips being most susceptible to attack. In warm climates, there is a continuing infestation in cribbed corn. In stored shelled corn, the infestation is concentrated near the top of the bin. Simmons and Ellington (1933) reported on the life history and host activity of the insect in Maryland. In that area, they observed winter survival primarily in the full-grown larval stage in grain in storage and in wheat straw piles, baled straw, and in litter. Light infestations were present in corn with exposed ear tips at harvest time. Cartwright (1930) presented data that showed an inverse relationship between damage and husk extension beyond the tip of ears.

The effect of infestation by the Angoumois grain moth on germination and stand was investigated by Everly et al. (1963). Infested popcorn was found to be unsuitable for seed, and germination was not increased by an application of a fungicide. Unless dent corn was highly infested, germination and final stand reduction was not serious. Treatment of dent corn seed with a fungicide decreased loss in stand. Infestation in seed reduced seedling vigor by 50 and 90% in dent and popcorn, respectively.

Different levels of amylose content in the endosperm and their effect on biology of the Angoumois grain moth were studied by Peters et al. (1972a). They found highly significant differences in weight of moths when larvae were reared in strains of corn with endosperm differing in levels of amylose, but there was no difference in number of moths emerged per kernel. A decreasing rate of infestation resulted when moths collected from certain strains were used to infest noninfested ears. In further tests, Peters et al. (1972b) reported that amylose and fat content of corn kernels were negatively correlated with weight of moths. However, kernel hardness had a significant effect on weight of male moths. Size of female moths appeared to be reduced by the size and weight of kernels of a strain of popcorn.

13–6.8 Indianmeal Moth — Description and Biology

Full-grown larvae of the Indianmeal moth (*Plodia interpunctella*) are about 12-mm long and vary in color from whitish to green or pink. When at rest moths are easily recognized by their brown color and a light, transverse band on the forepart of the wings (Fig. 13–20). In typical injury the embryo of corn kernels is devoured, and silken webs are spun over infested grain or meal. It breeds in ear, shelled, and ground corn and on a wide variety of grain and cereal products. It is widely distributed in grain-growing countries (Dean, 1913).

In the southern areas, the Indianmeal moth breeds in ear corn through most of the year. In the North Central states moths fly to bins of shelled corn in midsummer and lay their eggs on surface grain. In some years this insect is so abundant that the entire surface of bins are covered with a sheet of silk. In 1972, damaging infestations of bulk and bagged seed corn in commercial warehouses were observed in Iowa. Survival of large

Fig. 13–20. Indian meal moth showing the typical whitish cross-band on the wings.

numbers of larvae exposed in an unheated building was observed at Johnston, IA in January 1974 following a week of near and below −32 °C. In this case, larvae pupated shortly after being brought into the laboratory, indicating a nondiapause condition. What appeared to be normal moths emerged. In chemical control this species has shown high resistance to the commonly used malathion (*O, O*-dimethyl phosphorodithoate) seed treatment.

13–6.9 Other Stored Grain Insects

Among other insect pests of stored grain, the foreign grain beetle (*Ahasverus advena*), the hairy fungus beetle (*Typhaea stercorea*), and the larger black flour beetle (*Cynaeus augustus*) are often quite abundant in shelled corn stored in the North Central states. They are attracted to corn that is slightly out of condition, but seldom cause appreciable damage to corn in good condition.

13–6.10 Control of Stored Grain Insects

The practices recommended for controlling infestations of insects in stored corn or small grain vary with the environmental conditions under which the crop is produced, the handling of the crops, storage facilities, and insect species present. In the environment, temperature and moisture are important limiting factors in the prevailing abundance of these pests in different regions.

Cotton (1938) related storage problems in the USA based on climatic conditions. In Region 1, which comprises the northern corn-growing areas, crib-stored corn is free of these problems overwinter. In shelled corn, the sources of infestation are from old grain and feed situated in places favorable for winter survival. Farm storage is considered to be relatively safe. Region 2 comprises the central part of the commercial corn-growing area. Monthly inspection of grain during the warm months is advised. In Region 3, which consists of a zone from Pennsylvania to Virginia, the southern part of the North Central region and the northern part of the Southern region, grain corn storage becomes more hazardous because of more favorable conditions for winter survival in susceptible products stored in protected places. In the southern part of this region, field infestations of the Angoumois grain moth and rice weevil — beginning in wheat before harvest and continuing in corn later in the season — make crib and bin storage on the farm hazardous. Under these conditions monthly inspection, except in the winter is advised. In the southern corn-growing areas, designated as Region 4, conditions are favorable for the development of storage pests and for their winter survival. Field and storage infestations at varying levels are chronic under farm conditions. Immediate treatment when grain is placed in storage, and monthly inspection for possible treatment is essential in this area.

Systematic application of preventive measures and chemical treatment are effective in keeping stored grain pests in check. Practices for farm-stored grain have been discussed by Cotton et al. (1953) and Walkden et al. (1954). The following are effective preventive measures. Store in weather-tight rodent-proof bins, preferably of steel; clean out all bins before loading with grain; spray walls and floor of bins and adjacent woodwork of farm buildings with an approved and registered insecticide; clean up and dispose of litter, waste grain, and feed that have accumulated in and around farm buildings; and store only dry grain (12% moisture or less).

Insecticides registered for treatment of stored grain insects are labeled with ample information about the insects, dosage, use of the material, and handling hazards. Methods and materials are not static. When a grain insect problem is encountered it is advisable to seek the advice of a state extension service or research personnel who are familiar with species identity and current control practices (Foster et al., 1984).

13–7 INSECT RESISTANCE IN CORN

In the first edition of this monograph, George Sprague stated, "The lack of regular infestations has proved to be a serious deterrent to studies on inheritance of resistance or breeding for resistance." The effectiveness in breeding for resistance to insects is directly related to the efficiency in rearing insects for artificial infestations and in efficient evaluation of plant damage. These methods have been developed for several species of corn insects and are discussed later in this section.

Insect resistance factors in corn are heritable and have become established through an evolutionary process of mutation, natural selection, and selection by man. Painter (1951) defined three general types of insect resistance in plants: (i) antibiosis, (ii) tolerance, and (iii) nonpreference (antixenosis). In relative antibiosis, the host plant has a varying degree of effect on the development and survival of insect species. Relative tolerance is repair, recovery, or ability of the host plant to withstand an insect infestation; whereas, nonpreference involves a degree of avoidance of the host for oviposition or food. These three types of resistance may, to some degree, occur in the same host variety.

Because of its wide variability, corn has adaptations that permit it to survive in different environments. Husk protection qualities on the ear are well developed in southern and tropical areas where hazards from earworms and grain-infesting insects can be severe. In more northern areas, where these hazards are minor or do not exist, the selection pressure has been for shorter seasoned cultivars with relatively loose husks adapted for fast drying, ease of hand or machine-harvesting, and safe storage of grain. Biological as well as physical hazards play an important role in the cultivar development process in a particular environmental area.

Breeding for insect resistance in corn and other crops has received an increasing amount of attention in recent years. Perhaps some of this emphasis was generated by the development of strains of insects resistant to insecticides. The stress of epidemics has a positive effect on efforts for cultivar improvement. Probably the most important factor in recent advances is the interdisciplinary approach to cultivar development. In these programs, entomologists assume major responsibility for biological relationship studies between host and pest and for exploration in collections of cultivars for locating resistance factors. Plant breeders have primary responsibility for utilizing resistance factors and determining the genetic nature of inheritance. Methods of evaluating relative resistance are a by-product of biological relationship research. Efficient methods to evaluate relative infestations are needed by plant breeders.

In temperate regions, borer species (Lepidoptera) attack corn for relative short and irregular intervals, thus resistance may be relatively easy to locate and/or develop. In subtropical and tropical areas, most of the borer species have three or more overlapping generations per year or cropping cycle, and corn plants are attacked and damaged from the early seedling stages to near maturity. Plants must, therefore, possess resistance for their whole life or in several key parts (leaf tissue, stalks, sheaths, collars, shanks, ears). It may take longer to develop genotypes that will withstand multiple attacks by borers (Mihm, 1985). For example, the task of finding resistance to multiple generations of the European corn borer and southwestern corn borer continues to be formidable (Guthrie et al., 1971; Williams and Davis, 1983). Most host plant resistance projects have focused on resistance to one species. Some projects have selected for resistance to two species. Few projects have attempted to develop multiple resistance (three or more species) to corn insects (Mihm, 1985).

13–7.1   Insect Rearing Techniques

In the USA, USDA-ARS and state experiment stations have for many years cooperated to improve hybrids for resistance to a number of corn insects. For example, host plant resistance studies on the European corn borer have been conducted for 60 yr (from 1927 through 1931 under natural infestation conditions, from 1932 to the present under artificial infestation conditions). For many years, the source of infestation was egg masses produced in the laboratory by moths that emerged from infested cornstalks stored in cages (Dicke, 1932, 1954; Patch, 1947; Guthrie et al., 1965).

There are now numerous institutions that have research projects on insect nutrition, insect pathology, antibiotics, and artificial diets involving many species of insects (especially Diptera, Lepidoptera, and Coleoptera).

The first work on an artificial diet and chemical nature of resistance was reported by Bottger (1940, 1942, Bottger collaborated with J. D. Sayre); Beck et al. (1949); Beck and Stauffer (1950, 1957); Chippendale and Beck (1964). The use of wheat germ marked the advent of practical artificial diets for rearing plant-feeding Lepidoptera. Slight modifications in existing wheat-germ diets have been successful for rearing other species away from their natural host plants. At present, several species of plant-feeding Lepidoptera are reared on artificial diets in large numbers. Examples are the corn earworm and fall armyworm (Burton, 1969; Perkins et al., 1973; Mihm, 1982, 1983a); the southwestern corn borer (Jacob and Chippendale, 1971; Reddy and Chippendale, 1972; Davis et al., 1973; Davis, 1976; Mihm, 1983b); the American sugarcane borer, the African sugarcane borer, the neotropical corn borer, the lesser cornstalk borer, the African maize stalk borer, the Asiatic rice borer, the spotted stem borer, the Asian corn borer (Ortego et al., 1980; Mihm, 1983b, 1985), and the European corn borer (Guthrie et al., 1971). Both public and private researchers and national and international institutes are rearing large numbers of some Lepidopterous species for host plant resistance and other biological studies. For example, in 1986, about 50 million European corn borer egg masses (ca. 1.5 billion eggs) were produced.

Soil insects, such as rootworms (Coleoptera) and sucking forms, particularly Homoptera (leafhoppers and aphids), are more difficult to rear on artificial diets. Some species of aphids, however, have been reared on artificial media (Auclair, 1963).

Some species, such as adult northern and western rootworms are attracted to special late-planted, trap-crop corn for oviposition of the overwintering diapausing egg population. Succeeding corn plantings on such trap-crop ground usually develop infestations that are adequate for evaluation of root injury (Owens et al., 1974). The variability in egg distribution, however, makes it difficult to screen for antibiosis type of resistance in segregating populations (Owens et al., 1974). At present, large numbers of eggs can be produced in the laboratory, and artificial field infestation techniques have been developed (Palmer et al., 1977; Sutter and Branson, 1980). The artificial infestation technique should accelerate progress on breeding for resistance to corn rootworms.

Currently, about 200 000 *Cicadulina* leafhoppers are reared in the laboratory for screening 50 000 corn plants per week for resistance to maize streak virus at the International Institute of Tropical Agriculture, Ibadan, Nigeria. Millet plants are used to rear the leafhoppers because corn leaves containing 400 to 500 eggs die even before all nymphs are hatched, whereas millet plants affected by leafhopper feeding and oviposition on the main shoots develop a large number of tillers that are used later by the nymphs (Soto et al., 1982; Dabrowski, 1983, 1984a, b, c).

13–7.2 Artificial Insect Infestation and Plant Evaluation Techniques

The European corn borer illustrates the efficiency in artificial insect infestation and evaluation of plant damage caused by insect feeding. For screening corn germ plasm for resistance to leaf feeding by first-generation European corn borers, egg masses, or larvae (mixed in corncob grits) are dropped into plant whorls (midwhorl stage of plant development). For screening corn germ plasm for resistance to sheath-collar feeding by second-generation borers discs of waxed paper containing egg masses are pinned through the leaf midrib under the ear leaf and under the leaf above and below the ear during anthesis; with larval infestations, the larval-corncob grit mixture is placed around collars of plants. Female moths oviposit on sheets of waxed paper. Discs of waxed paper (1.25 cm in diam) each containing an egg mass are punched out with a specially designed machine and pinned into celotex boards for ease of infestation. In larval infestation of plants, egg masses are removed from waxed sheets and allowed to hatch in quart jars for case of mixing with corncob grits. The larval-corncob grit mixture is placed on plants with a specially designed inoculator. Six to 10 plants in each plot are infested with 100 to 200 eggs or 100 to 200 larvae per plant (in two to four applications of 50 eggs or 50 larvae each, spaced 1 to 3 d apart).

A nine-class rating scale (Guthrie et al., 1960) is used for evaluating the amount of injury to leaf tissue caused by first-generation borers. Genotypes that rate 1 and 2 are considered highly resistant, genotypes that rate 3 and 4 are considered resistant, genotypes that rate 5 and 6 are considered intermediate in resistance, and genotypes that rate 7 to 9 are considered susceptible. Classification into a highly resistant, resistant, intermediate, or susceptible class is dependent upon the size and shape of leaf injuries, and rating within each class is determined by the number of holes or amount of feeding. Genotypes are rated on a plot or individual-plant basis, depending on the type of material under tests, before pollination (about 21 d after egg hatch). This system preserves the resistant material for pollination and progeny testing, and is particularly valuable in individual plant selection in segregating populations to study inheritance of resistant factors. This is an excellent method for evaluating a large amount of material. One person (with someone to record) can rate 5000 to 6000 plots in an 8-h day. Our breeders discard 25 to 75% of the material on the basis of ratings; rating plots before pollination, therefore, saves much labor.

Because second-generation borers (all five instars) are primarily sheath-collar feeders for at least 25 to 30 d after egg hatch, a rating scale should be useful in evaluating corn germ plasm for resistance. Phenotypic and genotypic correlations between sheath-collar feeding ratings (1 = no damage to 9 = extensive damage) and cavity counts (centimeter of damage in the stalk) showed that visual sheath-collar ratings can be used to screen genotypes of corn for resistance to second-generation borers (Guthrie et al., 1978). At present, we use the nine-class rating technique on all plots. Ratings are made on a plot basis 45 to 60 d after egg hatch. Susceptible material can easily be detected and discarded. Under high levels of artificial infestation, we consider genotypes that rate 5 or 6 to be good. If desired, cavity counts may be used to detect differences among genotypes with ratings of 1 to 6. One person can rate 3000 plots in an 8-h day.

13–7.3 Corn Rootworms

Three main species of corn rootworms, *Diabrotica virgifera virgifera* (western), *D. barberi* (northern), and *D. undecimpunctata howardi* (southern), cause varying degrees of damage to corn in the U.S. Corn Belt (Chiang, 1973). The Mexican corn rootworm (*D. virgifera zeae*) (Branson et al., 1986), the banded cucumber beetle (*D. balteata*), *D. speciosa,* and others damage corn in Latin America (Ortego et al., 1980). Larvae damage subterranean parts and adults feed on leaves and silks.

Root lodging, size of root system, secondary root development, vertical pulling resistance of roots, and root damage rating (scale of 1–6 or 1–9) have been used for evaluation of rootworm resistance. Most researchers use a combination of these techniques. Data are usually taken at the time of maximum root damage (at or shortly after anthesis). Tolerance is the primary form of resistance to larval feeding that has been identified thus far. Tolerance to corn rootworms is probably multigenic (Ortman et al., 1974). When using root damage ratings or root pulling as criteria of tolerance, the breeding technique must be based on family evaluations because plants are destroyed during the evaluation process. Three experimental hybrids are the only genotypes of corn reported to have some degree of antibiosis (or at least some mechanism other than tolerance) to corn rootworms (Branson et al., 1983).

To obtain detailed data on root injury, it is necessary to dig and clean roots by pressure washing. Estimates of injury can be readily made by a rating system. A system in common use for evaluating relative cultivar resistance qualities is the nine-class system. Figure 13–21 illustrates dif-

Fig. 13–21. Characteristic root types representing six inbred lines, from right to left: (1) strong, spreading, deep system with excellent lodging resistance; (2) vertical, deep, weak resistance to lodging under rootworm attack; (3) intermediate in root numbers and spread, disease resistant; (4) relatively high root numbers with dark lower portion disease-infested; (5 and 6) relatively poor root system, susceptible to lodging under rootworm attack.

ferent root types. Figure 13–22 shows high susceptibility in lodged row (class 9) and excellent tolerance in row to the right (class 1). Vertical-pull devices have been successfully used to obtain comparative tolerance ratings by Ortman et al. (1968), Zuber et al. (1971), Rogers et al. (1976a), and Penny (1981). These researchers found a highly significant correlation among root-pulling resistance, root volume, and root classification, indicating that any of the three characteristics would be suitable for tolerance evaluations. Fitzgerald et al. (1968) evaluated roots of commercial hybrids through mechanical damage and concluded that root pruning could be useful in selecting for root regrowth potential in breeding for tolerance or resistance to rootworms in the absence of an infestation.

Some of the early records on rootworm tolerance or resistance were reported from Ohio and Illinois (Anonymous, 1937–1938; Bigger et al., 1938, 1941). In these tests, involving the southern corn rootworm, inbreds Oh56 and 38-11 were least damaged. In a 1952 test of 200 topcrosses in Iowa, the parent lines 38-11, B2, and B14, or derivatives of crosses involving these lines, regenerated their roots and had good lodging resistance under a high level of northern corn rootworm infestation.

With the rapid dispersion of the western corn rootworm, much of the recent resistance research has been done under the population dominance of this species in Iowa, Missouri, and South Dakota. Eiben and Peters (1965), and Ortman et al. (1974) reported the following inbred lines as being above average in performance under rootworm infestation: SD10, Hy, B9A, B14, B45, B46, B57, B67, B69, OhO5, and N38A. Fitzgerald and Ortman (1964) tested many inbred lines, single crosses, synthetic variety derivatives, and plant introductions at different locations in South Dakota and Iowa. Several inbreds had consistently high levels of performance under infestation and transmitted these qualities to single

Fig. 13–22. Difference in susceptibility to corn rootworm infestation; center row very susceptible; right row with good resistance.

crosses. They also found wide differences in leaf feeding on inbred lines by western corn rootworm beetles. Sifuentes and Painter (1964), in Kansas tests, estimated that resistance to leaf feeding by western corn rootworm beetles had a monogenic type of inheritance.

In a study of the performance of 22 inbred lines, using nine different measurements, Ortman and Gerloff (1970), concluded that correlations with field performance are best for a root growth index and root-pulling resistance. Tolerance may also be expressed in relative degree of stunting (Fig. 13–23).

In a survey of 2000 plant introductions, Wilson and Peters (1973) selected 441 entries for a retest. Among the retest entries the following showed the best response to infestations: PI 177606, PI 239099, PI 214288,

Fig. 13–23. Inbred line showing stunting effect from rootworm attack (*foreground*); rear of row treated with insecticide.

PI 177245, PI 303923, and PI 257625. Corn populations have also been improved for rootworm tolerance through recurrent selection (Rogers et al., 1976b, 1977; Kahler et al., 1985). Several populations of corn with some tolerance to the Mexican corn rootworm in Mexico also had some tolerance to the western corn rootworm in South Dakota (Branson et al., 1986).

Resistance in sorghum roots to western corn rootworm larval attack has been attributed to a cyanogenic glucocide. Cyanide is liberated by the enzymatic action of a hydrolytic glucosidase (Branson et al., 1969). In a study of root resistance to larval feeding of the western corn rootworm, reciprocal crosses between corn and *Tripsacum dactyloides* gave mixed results. Roots of *T. dactyloides* were highly resistant to larval attack. *Zea mays* × *T. dactyloides* was susceptible, whereas the reciprocal cross was resistant. Branson and Guss (1972) explained these results as indicating that the resistance was either inherited through the cytoplasm or that the resistance genes were on the lost *Tripsacum* genome in the *Z. mays* × *T. dactyloides* cross.

13-7.4 Corn Earworm

Through a long period of ear selection under stress of earworm populations, protective husk qualities became fairly well fixed in tropical and southern open-pollinated cultivars. In contrast, these qualities were not well developed in Corn Belt cultivars. Evidence of this is apparent in results of some varietal tests made by Garman and Jewett (1914). Hinds (1914) pointed out that extension and tightness of husks provided protection against earworm injury and subsequent field infestation by the rice weevil. Collins and Kempton (1917) demonstrated that characters for resistance to ear infestation could be transferred from field corn to sweet corn and that husk extension and number of husk layers were associated with protection against earworm injury. Kyle (1918) reported selections with such characters in Georgia. In a comparison of cultivars with different types of husk cover and extension, Phillips and Barber (1931) concluded that ears protected by a long, tight husk had less earworm damage and suffered less from grain beetles, grain moths, and birds. Cultivars of southern origin gave the best protection against earworm injury.

With establishment of many corn-breeding programs and development of hybrids in the 1930s by federal and state agencies, evaluations of inbred lines and hybrid combinations for resistance to the earworm and associated field infestation of grain insects became a cooperative, routine procedure. Information on relative resistance of numerous inbred lines and hybrid combinations came from many locations in Southern and Corn Belt areas and have been reported by Painter and Brunson (1940), Blanchard et al. (1941), Richey (1944), Dicke and Jenkins (1945), Douglas (1948), Blanchard and Douglas (1953), and Douglas and Eckhardt (1957). Mass selection, recurrent selection, or the use of a selection index have been used to develop corn resistant to the corn earworm (Painter and Brunson, 1940; Widstrom et al., 1970; Widstrom, 1974). The chemical nature of resistance factors in corn silk, which is a primary structure for establishment of newly hatched larvae, has been investigated. Walter (1957) presented evidence of a lethal factor in silks of sweet corn. Nutritional factors in silks as a source of relative resistance have not been conclusive. However, total reducing sugars were reported to be higher in susceptible single crosses by Knapp et al. (1965). In a comparison of silks of the resistant inbred Ab18 and the susceptible inbred Ab34, McCain et al. (1963) found no qualitative differences in free amino acids, but quantitative analyses were not made. Maysin, a flavone glycocide identified from the silks of Zapalote Chico, retards growth of corn earworm larvae (Waiss et al., 1979). No relationship has been established, however, between maysin concentration of fresh silks and the weight of larvae. The suspected biochemical basis for resistance of Z. Chico silks to corn earworm, therefore, remains unknown (Wiseman, 1985).

The area of preference as a feeding response in larvae of the corn earworm on plant parts of corn and other hosts has received extensive attention in recent years. Starks et al. (1965) in preference experiments with fourth-instar larvae showed that water extracts of silks and kernels possessed a feeding stimulus. In pursuing this phase of host plant resistance, McMillian and Starks (1966) found a differential larval-feeding response in water extracts from primary and secondary hosts, corn silks and kernels being preferred over extracts from sorghum, cotton, tomato, and tobacco (*Nicotiana tabacum* L.) plant parts. Such differential feeding responses were also found between corn lines (Starks and McMillian, 1967).

Some resistance mechanisms and other factors giving genotypes of corn resistance to the corn earworm are: Dixie 18 is tolerant, has tight husks, and large quantity of silk (Wiseman et al., 1972, 1977). Zapalote Chico 2451 contains a larval growth inhibitor and the mechanism of resistance is antibiosis and nonpreference (Wiseman et al., 1972, 1983; Waiss et al., 1979); and Antiqua 2D-118 has less pubescence and the mechanism of resistance is nonpreference (Widstrom et al., 1979). Two synthetics (GT-CEW-RS8, GT-R14) with corn earworm resistance have recently been released (Widstrom et al., 1975, 1984).

In a study of husk qualities among hybrids, significant protection against several insect species resulted in increased yields. The corn earworm and the pink scavenger caterpillar were more damaging than the maize weevil (Wiseman et al., 1970). The various facets in Fig. 13–24 shows the protective effect of husk qualities in a comparison where the exposure to a corn insect complex was on slit and nonslit husks. Earworm resistance in corn and other related biological problems were comprehensively reviewed by McMillian and Wiseman (1972).

13–7.5 European Corn Borer

Early tests on varietal resistance showed that early cultivars of sweet and flint corn supported higher populations of larvae than the longer

Fig. 13–24. Illustration of the effect of protective husk qualities under earworm infestation; five ears on the left with unslit husks and light injury; five ears on right on which husks were slit to expose the ear, resulting in severe infestation.

seasoned dent cultivars (Crawford and Spencer, 1922; Caffrey and Worthley, 1927). Huber et al. (1928) found differences in larval populations between cultivars of corn and the ability of some cultivars to tolerate damage. In tests of F_3 and F_4 lines extracted from crosses of 'Maize Amargo' and local Michigan cultivars, Marston (1931) reported higher populations of larvae on local cultivars than on recovered lines.

With the advent of extensive breeding programs by federal and state agencies in field, sweet, and popcorn there was continued testing of inbred lines and hybrid combinations of them. Results of these tests were reported by Patch et al. (1942), Patch and Everly (1945), Schlosberg and Baker (1948), Meyers et al. (1937), and in numerous special reports of federal and state agencies.

Resistance and tolerance qualities of certain lines were transmitted to their crosses and there was a significant correlation between stalk breakage in the absence and presence of an infestation. Hybrids had less stalk breakage than open-pollinated cultivars and lost less yield as a result of a first-generation infestation (Patch, 1937; Patch et al., 1941). In a comparison of the development of first-generation larvae on susceptible and resistant crosses, Patch (1943) reported slower development and smaller larvae on resistant cross. Patch (1943) also reported that with tassel appearance, pollen shedding, and silking, plants became highly susceptible to larval survival. This condition applies to early market sweet corn during the first-generation infestation and to varying degrees in late-planted sweet corn and field corn during the second-generation period. Everly (1947) and Everly et al. (1979) reported that inbred lines varied in attractiveness to moths for oviposition and that this trait was heritable in crosses.

Resistance factors to first-generation European corn borers are located in leaf tissue (Dicke, 1950, 1954; Guthrie et al., 1960). Resistance factors to second-generation borers are located primarily in sheath-collar tissue (Guthrie et al., 1978).

High resistance to first-generation borers is conditioned by at least six genes (Scott et al., 1966). High resistance to second-generation borers is conditioned by at least seven genes (Onukogu et al., 1978). Gene action for both types of resistance is primarily additive (Scott et al., 1964; Jennings et al., 1974a, b). Resistance in corn germ plasm to first-generation borers has been easy to find (Guthrie and Dicke, 1972) and several lines have been released. Resistance to second-generation borers has been more difficult to locate (Guthrie et al., 1971). Pesho et al. (1965) found only one inbred, B52, with good resistance to second-generation borers. B86 was the first inbred released with resistance to both generations of borers (Russell and Guthrie, 1979). A void, therefore, exists in corn germ plasm for resistance to second-generation borers and to both generations combined. Recurrent selection has proved successful in improving resistance to first-generation borers (Penny et al., 1967; Tseng et al., 1984) and to second-generation borers (Barry et al., 1983, 1985; Barry and Zuber, 1984). BS9 (CB)C4 was the first-released Corn Belt synthetic specifically selected (through four cycles of S_1 line recurrent selection) for resistance to the European corn borer for the whole life of the plant (Russell and Guthrie, 1982; Klenke et al., 1986a, b, c, 1987).

Figures 13–25 and 13–26 show differences between a high level of susceptibility and a high level of resistance to a first-generation infesta-

Fig. 13–25 and 13–26. Fig. 13–25. (*Left*) Inbred line highly susceptible to first brood (whorl stage infestation) European corn borer. Fig. 13–26. (*Right*) Inbred line showing high level of resistance to first brood European corn borer (whorl stage infestation).

tion. Figure 13–27 shows a severely broken inbred line in contrast to a sister line resistant to second-generation European corn borers. In a worldwide cooperative effort by the International Working Group on

Fig. 13–27. Broken row in foreground shows high susceptibility to second brood European corn borer (late summer) infestation and lodging; background, comparable row, a sister line, with good resistance.

Ostrinia (14 countries), several hundred genotypes of corn have been evaluated for resistance to the European corn borer (Hudon and cooperators, 1973; Hudon et al., 1979; Hudon and Chiang, 1976, 1985). The genetic yield gains in commercial hybrids of 92 kg/ha per year from 1930 to 1980 were accompanied by large and consistent improvements in resistance to root lodging, stalk lodging, premature plant death, and barrenness. Successive hybrid released were increasingly tolerant to feeding by second-generation European corn borers with small improvements to feeding by first-generation borers (Duvick, 1984). Other advances in resistance research have been reported by Penny and Dicke (1956), Chiang and Holdaway (1960), and Guthrie and Stringfield (1961), Zuber and Dicke (1964), Scott et al. (1967), and Guthrie et al. (1970).

The basis of resistance has been investigated by histological and chemical procedures. Bell (1956), working with whorl stage, first-generation infestations, determined that the primary feeding point by first instar larvae is on the upper leaf surface and that the bulliform cells are the initial point of attack. He observed that the outer walls of the bulliform cells were thinner than the inner walls and that staining reaction of the walls differed between WF9 (susceptible) and L317 (resistant).

The chemical nature of resistance has been studied for many years. Early workers associated resistance to leaf feeding by first-generation borers with the compound 6-methoxybenzoxazolinone,MBOA (Beck and Smissman, 1960, 1961; Beck and Stauffer, 1957; Loomis et al., 1957).

Later studies revealed that MBOA is an end product of DIMBOA (2,4-dihydroxy-7-methoxy-1, 4-benzoxaxine-3-one), and that the latter, a labile substance, is actually the chemical factor that is present in resistant strains of corn in the whorl stage of development (Wahlroos and Virtanen, 1959; Klun and Brindley, 1966; Klun et al., 1967). In a study of a group of inbred lines, Klun and Robinson (1969), found a significant correlation between the concentration of DIMBOA, as measured by the end product MBOA, and the resistance rating of inbreds when grown and infested in the whorl stage of growth in the field. These results were further confirmed by Klun et al. (1970) in a test that showed a high correlation between concentration of DIMBOA in 11 inbreds and a set of diallel crosses, and their resistance ratings. General and specific combining ability effects were also highly significant. Russell et al. (1975), using a simple inbreeding and selection technique for DIMBOA in a cross of WF9 (susceptible × CI.31A resistant) made progress in selecting lines that had resistance to leaf feeding by first-generation borers. Tseng et al. (1984) found that levels of resistance to first-generation borers in a synthetic cultivar of corn were improved with recurrent selection procedures when selection was made on the basis of insect damage and also when selection was made by chemical analysis for DIMBOA in leaf tissue. Each method of selection accumulated about the same level of resistance. Russell et al. (1975) and Scriber et al. (1975) found that selection only on the basis of DIMBOA may cause the eventual loss of other European corn borer resistance factors in corn breeding populations. Sullivan et al. (1974) found that whorl leaves of some exotic genotypes of corn low in DIMBOA were resistant to leaf feeding by first-generation borers. Rojanaridpicked et al. (1984) found that resistance to second-generation European corn borers was significantly correlated with silica content in leaf sheath and collar tissues of some lines and therefore, DIMBOA has a secondary role in second-generation resistance of some lines. Klun and Robinson (1969) and Guthrie et al. (1986), however, found little DIMBOA in sheath-collar tissues.

13–7.6 Fall Armyworm

An increasing amount of effort has been devoted to searching for sources of resistance to fall armyworm infestations in recent years. Some inbred lines are less subject to ear attack through husks and through the silk channel than others. In areas where the fall armyworm is important the corn earworm is usually dominant. Therefore, it is necessary to consider resistance of corn to both insects. In Virginia, northern inbred lines in general were much more subject to fall armyworm attack on husks, ears, and in the shank than some lines having southern or tropical corn in their parentage.

In greenhouse tests with seedlings of several hybrids, Wiseman et al. (1967a) were able to adapt a numerical rating system for detecting significant differences in plant damage 3 and 5 d after first instar larvae were introduced. In field tests in Kansas with 81 Latin American lines, Wiseman et al. (1967b) found 'Cuba Honduras 46-J', 'Eto Amarillo', and some 'Antigua' lines to be least damaged. Widstrom et al. (1970), from a test of 36 inbred lines, concluded that of 14 characters considered the mechanical protection of tight husks reduced damage considerably.

In a study of eight inbred lines and their F_1 progeny, Widstrom et al. (1972a) concluded that general combining ability was highly significant in conditioning resistance. Dominance and/or specific combining ability added little to resistance but heterosis contributed substantially to F_1 progenies. They suggested recurrent selection based on selfed progeny performance as a procedure for developing resistant plant populations. Corn inbreds, or germplasm lines with resistance to the fall armyworm have been developed by the pedigree method. Mp496, Mp701, Mp702, Mp703, Mp704, Mp705, Mp706, Mp707, and MpSWCB-4 are resistant to the fall armyworm and have recently been released (Scott et al., 1981a, b, 1982; Williams and Davis, 1980, 1982, 1984). It may be possible to combine leaf-feeding resistance to fall armyworm and silk resistance to corn earworms into a single corn germ plasm which would permit growers in the southeast to vary planting dates, thus reducing devastating populations of two pest species (Wiseman, 1985).

13–7.7 Southwestern Corn Borer

Resistance to first-generation southwestern corn borers is leaf-feeding resistance because larvae feed within whorl leaves for about 10 d and then tunnel into stalks (Williams et al., 1983). Genotypes of corn with intermediate levels of resistance to leaf-feeding damage (MpSWCB-4, Mp496, Mp701, Mp702, Mp703, Mp704, Mp705, Mp706, and Mp707) have been released (Scott and Davis, 1981a; Scott et al., 1982; Williams and Davis, 1980, 1982, 1984). Some of these genotypes are also resistant to the fall armyworm. Southwestern corn borer larvae weighed less and grew more slowly on corn callus initiated from crosses of resistant lines (leaf-feeding resistance) than from crosses of susceptible lines. Lines indicating the factors present in leaves that imparted resistance were likely present in callus also. Evaluation of larval growth on callus could provide means of evaluating corn genotypes throughout the year (Williams et al., 1983; Williams and Davis, 1985). Second generation southwestern corn borers (infestation of corn plants at or after anthesis) first feed within husks and developing ears and then bore into stalks (Davis et al., 1972). Corn germ plasm resistant to damage by second-generation borers has not been released. Genotypes of corn resistant to leaf feeding by first-generation borers are not necessarily resistant to stalk tunneling by second-generation borers (Williams and Davis, 1983). Genotypes are needed with resistance throughout the whole life of the plant. Recurrent selection based on S_1 progeny evaluation was effective in increasing levels of leaf-feeding resistance (Scott and Davis, 1981a). Recurrent selection for resistance in corn to tunneling by second-generation borers, however, was not effective (Williams and Davis, 1983).

13–7.8 Spotted Stem Borer

Genotypes of corn resistant to the spotted stem borer have been reported (Chatterji et al., 1973; Sarup et al., 1974; Dabrowski and Nyangiri, 1983; Omolo, 1983; Siddiqui et al., 1984). Different parts of plants such as whorls, stems, cobs, and tassels show varying degrees of antibiosis. Little is known of the genetics of resistance to the spotted stem borer but inheritance seems to be multigenic (Sharma and Chatterji, 1972) and both additive and nonadditive effects are involved (Singh, 1967).

13–7.9 Other Borers

At present, resistance investigations are conducted on the Asian corn borer, Oriental corn borer, pink borer, African maize borer, African maize stalk borer, African sugarcane borer, American sugarcane borer, neotropical corn borer, and pink stem borer. Few sources of resistance have been found thus far (Patanakamjorn et al., 1978; Ortega et al., 1980; Onukogo, 1984, 1985; Barrow, 1985; Mihm, 1985).

13–7.10 Black Cutworm

Resistance to black cutworm larvae probably cannot be used as a component in management of this insect pest because resistance is needed to fourth-, fifth-, or sixth-instar larvae (cutting stage larvae), and geno-types of corn resistant to half-grown larvae will be difficult if not im-possible to find. Resistance in corn plants to lepidopterous larvae is al-most always against first instar larvae. For example, more than 95% mortality of European corn borer larvae occur within 5 d after egg hatch; genotypes of corn highly resistant to first-instar larvae were not resistant to third- and fourth-instar larvae (Guthrie, 1981). Black cutworm adults migrate into the Corn Belt states of the USA from Southern states in early spring prior to corn planting (Domino et al., 1983). Newly hatched larvae probably become established on winter annual and perennial weeds. Many larvae develop to the fourth, fifth-, or sixth-instars before emi-grating to corn (Sherrod et al., 1979), thus the need for resistance to half-grown larvae instead of resistance to first-instar larvae.

The frequency of genes resistant to first- or third-instar larvae (leaf-feeding larvae) seems to be extremely low because 6388 genotypes of corn were evaluated and all were susceptible (Wilson et al., 1983). Frequency of genes resistant to half-grown larvae would undoubtedly be even lower.

13–7.11   Corn Leaf Aphid

Differences in varietal response to the corn leaf aphid have been recorded over a period of years. McColloch (1921) observed that there was a tendency for later-maturing cultivars to be most heavily infested although there were exceptions. Walter and Brunson (1940) found no plant characters that could be consistently correlated with resistance; al-though in many inbreds and hybrids, large and compact tassels were attractive to aphids. With some exception, hybrids were less heavily in-fested than the parental lines.

Snelling et al. (1940) tested a large number of inbred lines at different places in Illinois and observed little barrenness in plants with no infes-tation, whereas in aphid-infested plants there was a high rate of barren-ness. Huber and Stringfield (1942) presented data showing a correlation between resistance to corn leaf aphid and the European corn borer in a group of lines tested in single-cross combinations. Coon et al. (1948) reported a significant correlation between the carotene content of seed and the degree of aphid infestation, high carotene parent lines being more susceptible. Such a correlation seemed to depend on the reactions and resistance balance among the lines under test. From tests of many inbred lines and hybrids differences in relative degree of resistance to aphid development and infestations were found (Dicke, 1969; Everly, 1967; Neiswander and Triplehorn, 1961; Rhodes and Luckman, 1967).

13–7.12   Rice Weevil, Maize Weevil, Wireworm, and Pink Scavenger Caterpillar

There are wide differences in response of corn genotypes to the maize weevil (*Sitophilus zeamais*) and the rice weevil (*Sitophilus oryzae*) (Kyle,

1918; Eden, 1952; VanDerSchaff, 1969; Wiseman et al., 1970; Widstrom et al., 1972b). Maize weevil-resistant genotypes are available that can be used to minimize losses to this insect pest (Davis and Scott, 1973; Widstrom et al., 1983). Ten eight-line sets of dent maize inbreds were tested for seed resistance to maize weevils in a design II experiment (Widstrom et al., 1975). Dominance effects were important for seed resistance among sources segregating for maternal and endosperm genotypes. Most of the additive variation originated from maternal tissues, while cytoplasmic effects were unimportant. A procedure of recurrent selection within two breeding populations, with attention to crossbred performance, was suggested. Some corn germ plasm has been found with resistance to a wireworm (*Conoderus falli*) (Wiseman et al., 1976) and to the pink scavenger caterpillar (*Pyroderces rileyi*) (McMillian et al., 1982b).

13–7.13 Chinch Bugs

Flint (1921) reported the open-pollinated cv. Champion White Pearl and Golden Beauty as resistant or tolerant to attack by second-generation chinch bugs. In further tests in Illinois, Holbert et al. (1934) demonstrated that inbred lines resistant to second-generation bugs transmitted these qualities to top, three-way, and double-cross hybrids. In a comparison of hybrids and open-pollinated cultivars Holbert et al. (1935), under an infestation of second-generation bugs, found 'Illinois Hybrid 391' to be superior in standing ability and yield. In tests under second- and third-generation infestations conducted in Kansas and Oklahoma, Painter et al. (1935) reported F_1 hybrids to be more resistant on the average than their inbred parents, which they thought to be due to one or both of two conditions, namely, specific inherited resistance and tolerance or escape from injury associated with heterosis. They considered heterosis to be an important factor. Hybrids in general were superior to open-pollinated cultivars but a wide range of resistance was found in both groups. The pattern on corn appeared to be similar to that found on sorghum. With populations at relatively low levels, little emphasis has been placed on breeding for resistance to chinch bugs in recent years.

13–7.14 Grasshoppers — Many Species

General outbreaks of grasshoppers occur periodically, and, similar to chinch bugs have been associated with a continued period of dry weather conditions. High populations are prevalent in some parts of the world each year. Little information has become available on resistance in corn since the drought years of 1930 to 1936. Brunson and Painter (1938) reported on differential feeding of grasshoppers on corn and sorghum in Kansas. They estimated the percent defoliation in open-pollinated cultivars, inbred lines in uniform top crosses, and in double and three-way hybrids. Extreme contrasts in grasshopper injury were found. In their tests, cultivars and inbred lines of corn showing the greatest resistance originated in areas where grasshoppers are a natural element of the environment. Because of generally low levels of "crop hopper" populations, exploration and breeding for resistance has occupied a low priority in cultivar development programs for many years.

13-8 CHEMICAL CONTROL STATUS

The importance of development of strains of insects resistant to insecticides should not be underestimated in varietal development. Resistance to arsenicals, for example, was well documented for the codling moth (*Cydia pomonella*) long before organochlorine, organophosphorus, and carbamate compounds became available. Strains of the housefly (*Musca domestica* L.) resistant to DDT (dichloro diphenyl trichloroethane) were recognized a few years after DDT came into general use. Ball and Weekman (1963) reported on resistance of field populations of the western corn rootworm to aldrin. The horn fly (*Haematobia irritans*) developed resistance to synthetic pyrethroids after 2 to 3 yr of usage (Sparks et al., 1985).

McGaughey (1985) reported that in tests with *Bacillus thuringiensis* for the control of the Indianmeal moth (*Plodia interpunctella*), two generations of exposure resulted in 30-fold resistance and 15 generations of exposure resulted in 100-fold resistance. In collections from treated field bins, *P. interpunctella* was more resistant than from nontreated bins. The resistance was inherited as a recessive trait.

Failures of insecticides (applied in soil) to control soil insects, particularly the *Diabrotica* group appeared about as soon as these materials came into use in a diversity of soils and environments. Extensive studies traced such degradation to action by soil microorganisms and their metabolites (Gorder et al., 1982; Kaufman and Edwards, 1983; Harris et al., 1984).

Brown (1968) summarized information on cross-resistance of different types of compounds and on the genetic nature of resistance in various species. Of 224 species of insects and acarines known to have developed resistance, 127 attack field or forest crops or stored products.

Chemical companies have made major contributions in research and development of new chemicals and in providing monetary grants to state and federal agencies for evaluating formulations. In spite of the high cost of development and official registrations, new compounds have been introduced by the chemical industry with considerable frequency, particularly in the area of synthetic pyrethroids. Considerable effort is being devoted to sex attractants (pheromones) and hormones. These materials have been synthesized for many species and practical application has received increased attention.

Probably the most significant development in application of chemical control of corn insects was the development of granular formulations. Farrar (1953) pointed out the advantages of granular materials in uniformity of distribution, ease of handling, adaptation, avoiding drift and for controlling soil and whorl-inhabiting insects.

Although such materials as bran, cornmeal, and sawdust had been used for many years as carriers of insecticides for control of cutworms, grasshoppers, etc., the impregnation of granular clay materials generated a great deal of research activity that extended into a wide aspect of handling pesticides and equipment to apply them. Because of the simplicity of procedures and relatively low cost of application equipment, this development has met with favorable response from growers.

Detailed biological and comparative studies of formulations have been conducted with many chemicals for control of the European corn borer. These studies emphasized equipment, development of infestation on corn plants, dosages, and timing of applications, relative toxicity to plants and insects, and position and amount of residual toxicant at intervals after application. Over a period of many years DDT was the standard of comparison. Because of persistent residue problems, these materials have given way to pyrethroids, organophosphorus and carbamate materials which provide satisfactory performance.

There has been an active regional participation by state and federal agencies in the chemical control program. Large numbers of formulations have been tested each year and the results published or processed. Reports are available to growers with information on their acceptance and registry status.

All institutions, public and private, strongly emphasize that users of chemicals adhere closely to the instructions provided on each container label. These instructions are specific for target species; however, nontarget pests are not included.

ACKNOWLEDGMENT

This chapter is a joint contribution of the Corn Insects Research Unit, USDA-ARS, and Journal Paper J-12278 of the Iowa Agric. and Home Econ. Exp. Stn., Ames, IA 50011 and Ankeny, IA 50021, Project 2513.

Photo Credits. Figures 3, 14, Ohio Agricultural Research and Development Center (14 by Musick); Fig. 4, 19, 20, Univ. of Missouri (4, 19 by Paul S. Szopa and 20 by Lee Jenkins); Fig. 5, 6, 7, 12, 24, ARS-USDA (24 by Wiseman, McMillian, and Widstrom at Insect Biology and Population Management Research Laboratory, Tifton, GA); Fig. 9, Saxena and Chada, Oklahoma State Univ.; others from Pioneer Hi-Bred International, Inc., workers and the authors. We thank D. Barry, G. Beland, F. Davis, R. Wilson, B. Wiseman, and M. Zuber for reviewing this chapter.

We appreciate the assistance of Helen Hoeven, Pioneer Hi-Bred International Inc., for computer search of the literature.

APPENDIX

Common and Scientific Names† of Corn Insects

African armyworm, *Spodoptera exempta* (Walker)‡
African maize borer, *Sesamia calamistis* Hmps‡
African maize stalk borer, *Busseloa fusca* Fuller‡
African sugarcane borer, *Eldona saccarina* Walker‡
American black flour beetle, *Tribolium audax* Halstead
American grasshopper, *Schistocerca americana* (Drury)
Angoumois grain moth, *Sitotroga cerealella* (Oliver)
Armyworm, *Pseudaletia unipuncta* (Haworth)
Asian corn borer, *Ostrinia furnacalis* (Guenee)‡
Asiatic rice borer, *Chilo suppressalis* (Walker)‡
Banded cucumber beetle, *Diabrotica balteata* LeConte
Banks grass mite, *Oligonychus pratensis* (Banks)
Billbugs, *Spenophorus* spp. (snout beetles)
Black cutworm, *Agrotis ipsilon* (Hugnagel)
Blackfaced leafhopper, *Graminella nigrifrons* (Forbes)
Bluegrass billbug, *Spenophorus parvulus* Gyllenhal
Cadelle beetle, *Tenebroides mauritanicus* (Linnaeus)
Carmine spider mite, *Tetranychus cinnabarinus* (Boisduval)
Chinch bug, *Blissus leucopterus leucopterus* (Say)
Claybacked cutworm, *Agrotis gladiaria* Morrison
Codling moth, *Cydia pomonella* (Linnaeus)
Confused flour beetle, *Tribolium confusum* Jacquelin du Val
Corn blotch leafminer complex, *Agromyza parvicornis* Loew and other species
Corn delphacid, *Peregrinus maidis* (Ashmead)
Corn earworm, *Heliothis zea* (Boddie)
Corn flea beetle, *Chaetocnema pulicaria* Melsheimer
Corn leaf aphid, *Rhopalosiphum maidis* (Fitch)
Corn root aphid, *Anuraphis maidiradicis* (Forbes)
Corn root webworm, *Crambus caliginosellus* Clemens
Corn sap beetle, *Carpophilus dimidiatus* (Fabricius)
Cornfield ant, *Lasius alienus* (Foerster)
Desert Corn flea beetle, *Chaetocnema ectypa* Horn
Differential grasshopper, *Melanoplus differentialis* (Thomas)
Dingy cutworm, *Feltia ducens* Walker
Dusky sap beetle, *Carpophilus lugubris* Murray
English grain aphid, *Macrosiphum avenae* (Fabricius)
European corn borer, *Ostrinia nubilalis* (Hübner)
Fall armyworm, *Spodoptera frugiperda* (J.E. Smith)
Flat grain beetle, *Cryptolestes pusillus* (Schönherr)

---

†Most of the common and scientific names in this list are from the 1982 revision approved by the Committee on Common Names of Insects, Entomological Society of America; Spec. Publ. ISBN 0-938522-18-3, F.G. Werner, chair. Several other arthropods pests are included.
‡Important pests on corn in Asia, Africa, and mid-East.

Flower thrips, *Frankliniella tritici* (Fitch)
Foreign grain beetle, *Ahasverus advena* (Waltl)
Garden symphylan, *Scutigerella immaculata* (Newport)
Glassy cutworm, *Crymodes devastator* (Brace)
Granary weevil, *Sitophilus granarius* (Linnaeus)
Grape colaspis, *Colaspis brunnea* (Fabricius)
Grass thrips, *Anaphothrips obscurus* (Müller)
Hairy fungus beetle, *Typhaea stercorea* (Linnaeus)
Hop-vine borer, *Hydraecia immanis* (Guenée)
Indianmeal moth, *Plodia interpunctella* (Hübner)
Japanese beetle, *Popillia japonica* Newman
Larger black flour beetle, *Cynaeus angustus* (Leconte)
Lesser cornstalk borer, *Elasmopalpus lignosellus* (Zeller)
Maize billbug, *Sphenophorus maidis* Chittenden
Maize weevil, *Sitophilus zeamais* Motschulsky
Mediterranean flour moth, *Anagasta kuehniella* (Zeller)
Mexican corn rootworm, *Diabrotica virgifera zeae* Krysan & Smith
Migratory grasshopper, *Melanoplus sanguinipes* (Fabricius)
Neotropical corn borer, *Diatraea lineolata* (Walker)
Northern corn rootworm, *Diabrotica longicornis barberi* Smith & Lawrence
Oriental corn borer, *Chilo agamemnon* Bteszynski‡
Pale western cutworm, *Agrotis orthogonia* Morrison
Pink borer, *Sesamia cretica* Led‡
Pink scavenger caterpillar, *Pyroderces rileyi* (Walsingham)
Pink stem borer, *Sesamia inferens* Walker‡
Pink stem borer *Sesamia nonagrioides* Tams & Bowden‡
Potato stem borer, *Hydraecia micacea* (Esper)
Redlegged grasshopper, *Melanoplus femurrubrum* (De Geer)
Rice weevil, *Sitophilus oryzae* (Linnaeus).
Rusty grain beetle, *Cryptolestes ferrugineus* (Stephens)
Rusty plum aphid, *Hysteroneura setariae* (Thomas)
Sand wireworm, *Horistonotus uhlerii* Horn
Sawtoothed grain beetle, *Oryzaephilus surinamensis* (Linnaeus)
Seedcorn beetle, *Stenolophus lecontei* (Chaudoir)
Seedcorn maggot, *Delia platura* (Meigen)
Slender seedcorn beetle, *Clivinia impressifrons* LeConte
Southern corn billbug, *Sphenophorus callosus* (Olivier)
Southern corn rootworm, *Diabrotica undecimpunctata howardi* Barber
Southern cornstalk borer, *Diatraea crambidoides* (Grote)
Southwestern corn borer, *Diatraea grandiosella* (Dyar)
Spotted stem borer, *Chilo partellus* Swinhow‡
Stalk borer, *Papaipema nebris* (Guenée)
Striped webworm, *Crambus mutabilis*
Sugarcane beetle, *Euetheola humilis rugiceps* (LeConte)
Sugarcane borer, *Diatraea saccharalis* (Fabricius)
Toothed flea beetle, *Chaetocnema denticulata* (Illiger)
Twospotted spider mite, *Tetranychus urticae* Koch
Twostriped grasshopper, *Melanoplus bivittatus* (Say)

Western bean cutworm, *Loxagrotis albicosta* (Smith)
Western corn rootworm, *Diabrotica virgifera virgifera* LeConte
Wheat curl mite, *Eriophyes tulipae* Keifer
Wheat wireworm, *Agriotes mancus* (Say)
White grubs, *Phyllophaga* spp.

REFERENCES

Ainslie, G.G. 1919. The larger corn stalk-borer. USDA Farmers' Bull. 1025. U.S. Gov. Print. Office, Washington, DC.

————. 1922. Webworms injurious to cereal and forage crops and their control. USDA Farmers' Bull. 1258. U.S. Gov. Print. Office, Washington, DC.

————. 1927. The larger sod webworm. USDA Agric. Tech. Bull. 31. U.S. Gov. Print. Office, Washington, DC.

American Phytopathological Society. 1973. A compendium of corn diseases. *In* M.C. Schurtleff (chm.) Advisory committee to the maize (corn) disease compendium project. Am. Phytopathol. Soc., St. Paul.

Anonymous. 1937–1938. Ohio Agric. Exp. Stn. Annu. Rep. Bull. 600.

Apple, J.W., and K.K. Patal. 1963. Sequence of attack by northern corn rootworm on the crown roots of corn. Proc. North Cent. Branch Entomol. Soc. Am. 18:80–81.

Arant, F.S. 1929. Biology and control of the southern corn rootworm. Alabama Exp. Stn. Bull. 230.

————. 1934. Time of turning legumes and planting corn to avoid injury from the southern corn root worm. Alabama Polytechnic Inst. Agric. Exp. Stn. Cir. 65.

Arbuthnot, R.D. 1953. Present status and potential value of parasites of the European corn borer. Proc. North Cent. Branch Entomol. Soc. Am. 8:30–32.

Auclair, J.L. 1963. Aphid feeding and nutrition. Annu. Rev. Entomol. 8:439–490.

Babcock, K.W., and A.M. Vance. 1929. The corn borer in Central Europe. USDA Tech. Bull. 135. U.S. Gov. Print. Office, Washington, DC.

Back, E.A., and R.T. Cotton. 1926. Biology of the sawtoothed grain beetle, *Oryzaephilus surinarnensis* Linne. J. Agric. Res. 33:435–452.

Baker, W.A., W.G. Bradley, and C.A. Clark. 1949. Biological control of the European corn borer in the United States. USDA Tech. Bull. 983. U.S. Gov. Print. Office, Washington, DC.

Ball, H.J., and G.T. Weekman. 1963. Differential resistance of corn rootworms to insecticides in Nebraska and adjoining states. J. Econ. Entomol. 56:553–555.

Bancroft, J.B., A.J. Ullstrup, M. Messieha, C.E. Bracker, and T.E. Snazelle. 1966. Some biological and physical properties of a midwestern isolate of maize dwarf mosaic virus. Phytopathology 56:474–478.

Barber, G.W. 1925. A study of the cause of the decrease in the infestation of the European corn borer (*Pyrausta nubilalis*, Hubn.) in the New England area during 1923. Ecology 6:39–47.

————. 1936a. The corn earworm in southeastern Georgia. Georgia Exp. Stn. Bull. 192.

————. 1936b. The cannibalistic habits of the corn earworm. USDA Tech. Bull. 499. U.S. Gov. Print. Office, Washington, DC.

————. 1941. Hibernation of the corn earworm in southeastern Georgia. USDA Tech. Bull. 791. U.S. Gov. Print. Office, Washington, DC.

————, and F.F. Dicke. 1937. The effectiveness of cultivation as a control for the corn earworm. USDA Bull. 561. U.S. Gov. Print. Office, Washington, DC.

————, and ————. 1939. Effect of temperature and moisture on overwintering pupae of the corn earworm in the northeastern states. J. Agric. Res. 59:711–723.

Barrow, M.R. 1985. The effect of different maize genotypes on the maize stalk-borer, *Busseola fusca* (Fuller) (Lepidoptera: Noctuidae), feeding in whorl tissue. J. Entomol. Soc. South. Afr. 48:113–119.

Barry, D., and M.S. Zuber. 1984. Registration of MOECB2(S1)C5 maize germplasm. Crop Sci. 24:213.

————, ————, and L.L. Darrah. 1985. Registration of MO-2ECB-2 maize germplasm. Crop Sci. 25:715–716.

————, ————, A.O. Antonio, and L.L. Darrah. 1983. Selection for resistance to the second generation of the European corn borer (Lepidoptera: Pyralidae) in maize. J. Econ. Entomol. 76:392–394.

————, ————, E.B. Lillehoj, W.W. McMillian, N.J. Adams, W.F. Kwolek, and N.W. Widstrom. 1985. Evaluation of two arthropod vectors as inoculators of developing maize ears with *Aspergillus flavus*. Environ. Entomol. 14:634–636.

Batchelder, C.H. 1949. European corn borer location on the corn plant as related to insecticidal control. USDA Bull. 976. U.S. Gov. Print. Office, Washington, DC.

Beck, S.D., J.H. Lilly, and J.F. Stauffer. 1949. Nutrition of the European corn borer, *Pyrausta nubilalis* (Hbn.). I. Development of a satisfactory purified diet for larval growth. Ann. Entomol. Soc. Am. 42:483–496.

————, and E. Smissman. 1960. The European corn borer *Pyrausta nubilalis* and its principal host plant. VIII. Laboratory evaluation of host plant resistance to larval growth and survival. Ann. Entomol. Soc. Am. 53:755–762.

————, and ————. 1961. The European corn borer, *Pyrausta nubilalis*, and its principal host plant. IX. Biological activity of chemical analogs of corn resistance Factor A (6-methoxybezoxazolinone). Ann. Entomol. Soc. Am. 54:53–61.

————, and J.F. Stauffer. 1950. An aseptic method for rearing European corn borer larvae. J. Econ. Entomol. 43:4–6.

————, and ————. 1957. The European corn borer, *Pyrausta nubilalis* (Hubn.), and its principal host plant. III. Toxic factors influencing larval establishment. Ann. Entomol. Soc. Am. 50:166–170.

Bell, M.E. 1956. Histology of the maize plant in relation to susceptibility of the European corn borer. Iowa State Coll. J. Sci. 31:9–17.

Benton, C., and W.P. Flint. 1938. The comparative attractiveness of various small grains to the chinch bug. USDA Cir. 508. U.S. Gov. Print. Office, Washington, DC.

Berger, P.H. 1983. The retention of maize dwarf mosaic virus by the greenbug, *Schizaphis graminum* Rondoni. Ph.D. diss. Texas A&M Univ., College Station.

Bigger, J.H. 1928. Hibernation studies of *Colaspis (beumea) flavida* (Fab.). J. Econ. Entomol. 21:268–273.

————. 1932. Short rotation fails to prevent attack of *Diabrotica longicornis* Say. J. Econ. Entomol. 25:196–199.

————, and F.C. Bauer. 1939. Plowing dates as they affected the abundance of corn root aphids at Clayton, Illinois, 1929–1932. J. Am. Soc. Agron. 31:695–697.

————, J.R. Holbert, W.P. Flint, and A.L. Lang. 1938. Resistance of certain corn hybrids to attack of southern corn root worm. J. Econ. Entomol. 31:102–107.

————, and H.B. Petty. 1953. Reduction of corn borer numbers from October to June. Univ. of Illinois Bull. 566.

————, R.O. Snelling, and R.A. Blanchard. 1941. Resistance of corn strains to the southern corn rootworm *Diabrotica duodecimpunctata* F. J. Econ. Entomol. 34:605–613.

Bigler, E. 1983. Experience in the biological control of the European corn borer (*Ostrinia nubilalis* Hbn.) with *Trichogramma* wasps in Switzerland. Mitt. Schweiz. Landwirtsch. 31(1):4–22.

Blanchard, R.A. 1942. Hibernation of the corn earworm in the central and northeastern parts of the United States. USDA Tech. Bull. 838. U.S. Gov. Print. Office, Washington, DC.

————, J.H. Bigger, and R.O. Snelling. 1941. Resistance of corn strains to the corn earworm. J. Am. Soc. Agron. 33:344–350.

————, and W.A. Douglas. 1953. The corn earworm as an enemy of field corn in the eastern states. USDA Farmers' Bull. 1651. U.S. Gov. Print. Office, Washington, DC.

Blatchley, W.S. 1920. Orthoptera of northeastern America, with especial reference to the faunas of Indiana and Florida. Nature Publ. Co., Indianapolis, IN.

Bottger, G.T. 1940. Preliminary studies of the nutritive requirements of the European corn borer. J. Agric. Res. 60:249–257.

————. 1942. Development of synthetic food media for use in nutrition studies of the European corn borer. J. Agric. Res. 65:493–500.

Bradfute, O.I., T.P. Pirone, P.H. Freytag, and M.C.Y. Lung. 1972. Virus-like particles associated with a leafhopper-transmitted disease of corn in Kentucky. Plant Dis. Rep. 56:652–656.

Brandes, E.W. 1920. Artificial and insect transmission of sugar-cane mosaic. J. Agric. Res. 19:131–138.

Branson, T.F., and P.L. Guss. 1972. Potential for utilizing resistance from relatives of cultivated crops. Proc. North Cent. Branch Entomol. Soc. Am. 27:91–95.

————, ————, and E.E. Ortman. 1969. Toxicity of sorghum roots to larvae of the western corn rootworm. J. Econ. Entomol. 62:1375–1378.

————, and E.E. Ortman. 1970. The host range of larvae of the western corn rootworm: Further studies. J. Econ. Entomol. 63:800–803.

————, H. Valdes, and A.L. Kahler. 1986. Evaluation of Mexican populations of maize for resistance to larvae of *Diabrotica virgifera* (Coleoptera:Chrysomelidae). Maydica 31:173–177.

————, V.A. Welch, G.R. Sutter, and J.R. Fisher. 1983. Resistance to larvae of *Diabrotica virgifera virgifera* in three experimental maize hybrids. Environ. Entomol. 12:1509–1512.

Brindley, T.A., A.N. Sparks, W.B. Showers, and W.D. Guthrie. 1975. Recent research advances on the European corn borer in North America. Annu. Rev. Entomol. 20:221–239.

Brown, A.W.A. 1968. Insecticide resistance comes of age. Bull. Entomol. Soc. Am. 14:3–9.

Brown, E.A., and J. Keaster. 1986. Activity and dispersal of adult *Melanotus depressus* and *Melanotus verberans* (Coleoptera:Elateridae) in a Missouri cornfield. J. Kans. Entomol. Soc. 59(1):127–132.

Brunson, A.M., and R.H. Painter. 1938. Differential feeding of grasshoppers on corn and sorghums. J. Am. Soc. Agron. 30:334–346.

Bulla, Lee A. Jr., R.B. Mills, J.R. Pederson, and R.G. Strong. 1979. Proceedings of symposium on prevention and control of insects in stored-food products. Manhattan, KS.

Burbutis, P.P., G.D. Curl, and C.P. Davis. 1977. Host searching behavior by *Trichogramma nubilalae* on corn. Environ. Entomol. 6:400–402.

————, N. Erwin, and L.R. Ertle. 1981. Reintroduction and establishment of *Lydella thompsoni* and notes on other parasites of the European corn borer in Delaware. Environ. Entomol. 10:779–781.

Burkhardt, C.C. 1952. Feeding and pupating of fall armyworm in corn. J. Econ. Entomol. 45:1035–1037.

Burton, R.L. 1969. Mass rearing the corn earworm in the laboratory. p. 33–134. *In* USDA-ARS(Ser.), U.S. Gov. Print. Office, Washington, DC.

Caffrey, D.J., and L.H. Worthley. 1927. A progress report on the investigations of the European corn borer. USDA Bull. 1476. U.S. Gov. Print. Office, Washington, DC.

Callahan, P.S. 1957. Oviposition response of the imago of the corn earworm, *Heliothis zea* (Boddie), to various wave lengths of light. Ann. Entomol. Soc. Am. 50:444–452.

Carter, W. 1941. *Peregrinus maidis* (Ashm) and the transmission of corn mosaic. I. Incubation period and longevity of the virus in the insect. Ann. Entomol. Soc. Am. 34:551–556.

————. 1973. Insects in relation to plant diseases. 2nd ed. John Wiley and Sons, New York.

Cartier, J.J., and R.H. Painter. 1956. Differential reaction of two biotypes of the cornleaf aphid to resistant and susceptible varieties, hybrids, and selections of sorghums. J. Econ. Entomol. 49:498–508.

Cartwright, O.L. 1929. The maize billbug in South Carolina. South Carolina Agric. Exp. Stn. Bull. 257.

————. 1930. The rice weevil and associated insects in relation to shuck length and corn varieties. South Carolina Agric. Exp. Stn. Bull. 266.

————. 1934. The southern corn stalk borer, (*Diatraea crambidoides* (Grote) in South Carolina. South Carolina Agric. Exp. Stn. Bull. 294.

Chamberlain, T.R., and J.A. Callenbach. 1943. Oviposition of June beetles and the survival of their offspring in grasses and legumes. J. Econ. Entomol. 36:681–688.

Chatterji, S.M., P. Sarup, K.K. Marwaha, V.P.S. Panwar, K.H. Siddique, and M.W. Bhamburkar. 1973. Studies on insect-plant relationship-comparative tolerance of some elite indigenous maize lines to *Chilo partellus* (Swinhoe) under artificial infestation. Indian J. Entomol. 35:156–159.

Chiang, H.C. 1973. Bionomics of northern and western rootworms. Annu. Rev. Entomol. 18:47–72.

----, and F.G. Holdaway. 1960. Relative effectiveness of resistance of field corn to the European corn borer, *Pyrausta nubilalis*, in crop protection and in population control. J. Econ. Entomol. 53:918–924.

Chippendale, G.M., and S.D. Beck. 1964. Nutrition of the European corn borer, *Ostrinia nubilalis* (Hubn.) V. Ascorbic acid as the corn leaf factor. Entomol. Exp. Appl. 7:241–248.

Chittenden, F.H. 1916. The pink corn-worm: An insect destructive to corn in the crib. USDA Bull. 363. U.S. Gov. Print. Office, Washington, DC.

Choudhury, M.M., and E. Rosenkranz. 1973. Differential transmission of Mississippi and Ohio corn stunt agents by *Graminella nigrifrons*. Phytopathology 63:127–133.

Christensen, J.J., and C.L. Schneider. 1950. European corn borer (*Pyrausta nubilalis* Hbn.) in relation to shank, stalk, and ear rots of corn. Phytopathology 40:284–291.

Collins, G.N., and J.H. Kempton. 1917. Breeding sweet corn resistant to the corn earworm. J. Agric. Res. 11:549–572.

Coon, B.F. 1951. Japanese beetle damage in field corn. Pennsylvania Agric. Exp. Stn. Prog. Rep. 55.

----, R.C. Miller, and L.W. Aurand. 1948. Correlation between the carotene content of corn and infestation by the corn leaf aphid. Pennsylvania Agric. Exp. Stn. J. Ser. 1436.

Cotton, R.T. 1920. Rice weevil (Calandra) *Sitophilus oryzae*. J. Agric. Res. 20.

----. 1938. Control of insects attacking grain in farm storage. USDA Farmers' Bull. 1811. U.S. Gov. Print. Office, Washington, DC.

----. 1947. Insect pests of stored grain and grain products. 3rd print. Burgess Publ. Co., Minneapolis.

----, H.H. Walkden, G.D. White, and D.A. Wilbur. 1953. Causes of outbreaks of stored-grain insects. North Cent. Region Pub. 35.

Crawford, H.G., and G.J. Spencer. 1922. The European corn borer *Pyrausta nubilalis* (Hubn.): Life history in Ontario. Annu. Rep. Entomol. Soc. Ontario 52:22–26.

Crumb, S.E. 1929. Tobacco cutworms. USDA Tech. Bull. 88. U.S. Gov. Print. Office, Washington, DC.

Dabrowski, Z.T. 1983. Identifying and collecting *Cicadulina* for maize streak resistance screening. Int. Inst. Trop. Agric. Res. Briefs (Ibadan, Nigeria) 4(4):2–3.

----. 1984a. Handling new *Cicadulina* colonies. Int. Inst. Trop. Agric. Res. Briefs (Ibadan, Nigeria) 5(1):2–4.

----. 1984b. Rearing *Cicadulina*: Technical methods, equipment needed. Int. Inst. Trop. Agric. Res. Briefs (Ibadan, Nigeria) 5(2):2–3.

----. 1984c. Releasing *Cicadulina* for maize streak resistance screening. Int. Inst. Trop. Agric. Res. Briefs (Ibadan, Nigeria) 5(3):4–5.

----, and E.O. Nyangiri. 1983. Some field and screenhouse experiments on maize resistance to *Chilo partellus* under western Kenya conditions. Inst. Sci. Applic. 4:109–118.

Davis, E.G., J.R. Horton, C.H. Gable, E.V. Walter, and R.A. Blanchard. 1933. The south-western corn borer. USDA Tech. Bull. 388. U.S. Gov. Print. Office, Washington, DC.

Davis, F.M. 1976. Production and handling of eggs of southwestern corn borer for host plant resistance studies. USDA Tech. Bull. 74. U.S. Gov. Print. Office, Washington, DC.

----, C.A. Henderson, and G.E. Scott. 1972. Movement and feeding of larvae of the south-western corn borer on two stages of corn growth. J. Econ. Entomol. 65:518–521.

----, and G.E. Scott. 1973. Evaluating corn hybrids for maize weevil resistance. Mississippi Agric. For. Exp. Stn. Info. Sheet 1207.

----, ----, and C.A. Henderson. 1973. Southwestern corn borer: Preliminary screening of corn genotypes for resistance. J. Econ. Entomol. 66:503–506.

Davis, J.J. 1922. Common white grubs. USDA Farmers' Bull. 940. U.S. Gov. Print. Office, Washington, DC.

----. 1949. The corn root aphid and methods of controlling it. USDA Farmers' Bull. 891. U.S. Gov. Print. Office, Washington, DC.

----, and A.F. Satterthwait. 1916. Life-history studies of *Pseudaletia* (Cirphis) *unipuncta*, the true armyworm. J. Agric. Res. 6:799–812.

Davis, R.E. 1973. Occurrence of a spiroplasma in corn stunt-infected plants in Mexico. Plant Dis. Rep. 57:333–337.

----, T.A. Chen, and J.F. Worley. 1981. Corn stunt spiroplasma. p. 40–50. *In* D.T. Gordon et al. (ed.) Virus and viruslike diseases of maize in the United States. Ohio Agric. Res. Dev. Ctr. South. Coop. Ser. Bull. 247.

----, R.F. Whitcomb, T.A. Chen, and R.R. Granados. 1972. Current status of the aetiology of corn stunt disease. p. 205–225. *In* Pathogenic mycoplasmas. CIBA Found. Symp., 25–27 January.

----, and J.F. Worley. 1973. Spiroplasma: Motile, helical microorganism associated with corn stunt diseases. Phytopathology 63:403–408.

Dean, G.A. 1913. Mill and stored-grain insects. Kansas Agric. Exp. Stn. Bull. 189.

Decker, G.C. 1941. Protect Iowa's grain crop. p. 168–176. *In* Iowa State College 42nd Yearbook (Part 4), Ames.

DeRozari, M.B., W.B. Showers, and R.H. Shaw. 1977. Environment and the sexual activity of the European corn borer. Environ. Entomol. 6:657–665.

Dicke, F.F. 1932. Studies on the host plants of the European corn borer, *Pyrausta nubilalis* Hübner, in southeastern Michigan. J. Econ. Entomol. 24:868–878.

----. 1939. Seasonal abundance of the corn earworm. J. Agric. Res. 59:237–257.

----. 1950. Response of corn strains to European corn borer infestation. Proc. North Cent. Branch Entomol. Soc. Am. 5:47–49.

----. 1954. Breeding for resistance to European corn borer. Proc. Annu. Corn Res. Conf. 9:44–53.

----. 1969. The corn leaf aphid. Proc. Annu. Corn Sorghum Ind. Res. Conf. 24:61–70.

----, and M.T. Jenkins. 1945. Susceptibility of certain strains of field corn in hybrid combinations to damage by corn earworms. USDA Tech. Bull. 898. U.S. Gov. Print. Office, Washington, DC.

Ditman, L.P. 1938. Metabolism in the corn earworm I. Studies on fat and water. Maryland Agric. Exp. Stn. Bull. 414.

----, and E.N. Cory. 1931. The corn earworm biology and control. Maryland Agric. Exp. Stn. Bull. 328.

Doi, Y., M. Terenaka, K. Yora, and H. Asuyama. 1967. Mycoplasma — or PLT group-like microorganisms found in the phloem elements of plants infected with mulberry dwarf, potato witches' broom, aster yellows, or paulownia witches' broom. Ann. Phytopathol. Soc. Jpn. 33:259–266.

Domino, R.P., W.B. Showers, S.E. Taylor, and R.H. Shaw. 1983. Spring weather pattern associated with suspected black cutworm moth (Lepidoptera:Noctuidae) introduction to Iowa. Environ. Entomol. 12:1863–1871.

Douglas, J.R., J.W. Ingram, K.E. Gibson, and W.E. Peay. 1957. The western bean cutworm as a pest of corn in Idaho. J. Econ. Entomol. 50:543–545.

Douglas, W.A. 1948. The effect of husk extension and tightness on earworm damage to corn. J. Econ. Entomol. 40:661–664.

----, and R.C. Eckhardt. 1957. Dent corn inbreds and hybrids resistant to the corn earworm in the South. USDA Tech. Bull. 1160. U.S. Gov. Print. Office, Washington, DC.

----, C.A. Henderson, and J.A. Langston. 1962. Biology of the pink scavenger caterpillar and its control on corn. J. Econ. Entomol. 55:651–655.

----, and C.E. Smith. 1953. Control of the corn earworm and rice weevil in dent corn with DDT-mineral oil emulsions. J. Econ. Entomol. 46:683–684.

Duvick, D.N. 1977. Genetic rates of gain in hybrid maize yields during the past 40 years. Maydica 22:187–196.

----. 1984. Genetic contributions to yield gains of U.S. hybrid maize, 1930 to 1980. p. 15–47. *In* W.R. Fehr (ed.) Genetic contributions to yield gains of five major crop plants. Spec. Pub. 7. CSSA and ASA, Madison, WI.

Eden, W.G. 1952. Effect of huskcover of corn on rice weevil damage in Alabama. J. Econ. Entomol. 45:543–544.

----, and F.S. Arant. 1953. Control of corn rootworm in corn. Alabama Agric. Exp. Stn. Leafl. 34.

Ehler, L.E. 1973. Spider mites associated with grain sorghum and corn in Texas. J. Econ. Entomol. 66:1220–1222.

Eiben, G.J., and D.C. Peters. 1965. Varietal response to rootworm infestation in 1964. Proc. North Cent. Branch Entomol. Soc. Am. 20:44–46.

Eichmann, R.D. 1940. Corn earworm hibernates in Washington State. J. Econ. Entomol. 33:951–952.

Elliott, C., and F.W. Poos. 1934. Overwintering of *Aplanobacter stewarti*. Science 80:289–290.

––––, and F.W. Poos. 1940. Seasonal development, insect vectors, and host range of bacterial wilt of sweet corn. J. Agric. Res. 60:645–686.

Everly, R.T. 1947. Studies on the attractiveness of dent corn to moths of the European corn borer. Ind. Acad. Sci. Proc. for 1946. 56:145 (Abstr.).

––––. 1960a. Loss in corn yield associated with the abundance of the corn leaf aphid, *Rhopalosiphum maidis*, in Indiana. J. Econ. Entomol. 53:924–932.

––––. 1960b. Insecticidal control of thrips on corn. Proc. North Cent. Branch Entomol. Soc. Am. 15:89–91.

––––. 1967. Establishment and development of corn leaf aphid populations on inbred and single cross dent corn. Proc. North Cent. Branch Entomol. Soc. Am. 22:80–84.

––––, W.D. Guthrie, and F.F. Dicke. 1979. Attractiveness of corn genotypes to ovipositing European corn borer moths. Agric. Rev. and Manuals, USDA-SEA. ARM-WC-8.

––––, P. Sandberg, and B. Weaver. 1963. The effect of infestation of the Angoumois grain moth on the germination and vigor of corn. Proc. North Cent. Branch Entomol. Soc. Am. 18:76–79.

Fairchild, M.L., E.E. Ortman, and Cooperators. 1981. Development of pest management strategies for soil insects on corn. Fourth Annu. Rep. and Final Rep. EPA Grant R805429-04. U.S. Gov. Print. Office, Washington, DC.

Farrar, M.D. 1953. The granulated type insecticide for soil treatment. J. Econ. Entomol. 46:377–379.

Fitzgerald, P.J., and E.E. Ortman. 1964. Breeding for resistance to western corn rootworm. Proc. Annu. Corn Res. Conf. 19:1–15.

––––, E.E. Ortman, and T.F. Branson. 1968. Evaluation of mechanical damage to roots of commercial varieties of corn (*Zea mays* L.). Crop Sci. 8:419–421.

Fleming, W.E. 1970. The Japanese beetle in the United States. USDA Handb. 236. U.S. Gov. Print. Office, Washington, DC.

––––. 1972. Biology of the Japanese beetle, USDA Tech. Bull. 1449. U.S. Gov. Print. Office, Washington, DC.

Flint, W.P. 1921. Chinch bug resistance shown by certain varieties of corn. J. Econ. Entomol. 14:83–85.

Floyd, E.H., and J.W. Powell. 1958. Some facts influencing the infestation in corn in the field by the rice weevil. J. Econ. Entomol. 51:23–26.

Foott, W.H. 1977. Biology of the corn leaf aphid, *Rhopalosiphum maidis* (Homoptera:Aphididae), in southwestern Ontario. Can. Entomol. 109:1129–1135.

Forbes, S.A. 1893. Noxious and beneficial insects in the state of Illinois. Illinois State Entomologist Rep. 18.

––––. 1904. The more important insect injuries to Indian corn. Illinois Agric. Exp. Stn. Bull. 95.

––––. 1905. Monograph of insect injuries to Indian corn. 23rd Rep. Ill. State Entomol.

––––. 1915. Recent Illinois work on the corn root-aphid and the control of its injuries. Illinois Agric. Exp. Stn. Bull. 178.

Ford, R.E. 1967. Maize dwarf mosaic virus susceptibility of Iowa native perennial grasses. Phytopathology 57:450–451.

Foster, D.E., L.E. Sandvol, and H.G. Raney. 1984. Preventing insect problems in farmstored Corn. Purdue Univ. Coop. Ext. Serv. Nat. Corn Handb., NCH-7.

Garman, H., and H.H. Jewett. 1914. The life-history and habits of the corn-earworm (*Chloridea obsoleta*). Kentucky Agric. Exp. Stn. Bull. 187.

Giebink, B.L., J.M. Scriber, and J.L. Wedberg. 1984. Biology and phenology of the hopvine borer, *Hydraecia immanis* Guenee, and detection of the potato stem borer, *H. micacea* (Esper) (Lepidoptera:Noctuidae), in Wisconsin. Environ. Entomol. 13:1216–1224.

––––, ––––, and D.B. Hogg. 1985. Developmental rates of the hop-vine borer, and potato stem borer (Lepidoptera:Noctuidae): Implications for insecticidal control. J. Econ. Entomol. 78:311–315.

Gillette, C.P. 1912. *Diabrotica virgifera* Lec., a corn rootworm. J. Econ. Entomol. 5:364–366.

Glen, R., K.M. King, and A.P. Arnason. 1943. The identification of wireworms of economic importance in Canada. Can. J. Res. 21:358–387.

Good, N.E. 1936. The flour beetles of the genus *Tribolium*. USDA Tech. Bull. 498. U.S. Gov. Print. Office, Washington, DC.

Gorder, G.W., P.A. Dahm, and J.J. Tollefson. 1982. Carbofuran persistence in cornfield soils. J. Econ. Entomol. 75(4):637–642.

Gordon, D.T., J.K. Knoke, and G.E. Scott (ed.) 1981. Virus and viruslike diseases of maize in the United States. Ohio Agric. Res. Dev. Ctr. South. Coop. Ser. Bull. 247.

Granados, R.G. 1970. Sources of corn, *Zea mays* L. resistance to thrips, *Frankliniella occidentalis* (P.) and *F. williami* H., in Mexico. Ph.D. diss. Kansas State Univ., Manhattan.

––––. 1969a. Chemotherapy of the corn stunt disease. Phytopathology 59:1556 (Abstr.).

––––. 1969b. Electron microscopy of plants and insect vectors infected with the corn stunt disease agent. Contrib. Boyce Thompson Inst. 24:173–187.

––––, K. Maramorosch, T. Everett, and T.P. Pirone. 1966. Contrib. Boyce Thompson Inst. 23:275–280.

––––, and E. Shikata. 1968. Mycoplasma: Suspected etiologic agent of corn stunt. Proc. Natl. Acad. Sci. USA 60:841–844.

Grancini, P. 1963. Damages by thrips on maize. Maydica 8:90–94.

Guthrie, W.D. 1974. Techniques, accomplishments and future potential of breeding for resistance to European corn borers in corn. p. 359–380. *In* F.G. Maxwell and F.A. Harris (ed.) Biological control of plant insects and diseases. Jackson Miss. Univ. Press, Jackson.

––––. 1981. Maize whorl stage resistance to the first four instars of European corn borer larvae (Lepidoptera:Pyralidae). J. Kans. Entomol. Soc. 54:737–740.

––––, and F.F. Dicke. 1972. Resistance of inbred lines of dent corn to leaf feeding by first-brood European corn borers. Iowa State J. Sci. 46:339–357.

––––, ––––, and C.R. Neiswander. 1960. Leaf and sheath feeding resistance to the European corn borer in eight inbred lines of dent corn. Ohio Agric. Exp. Stn. Res. Bull. 860.

––––, J.L. Huggans, and S.M. Chatterji. 1970. Sheath and collar feeding resistance to the second brood European corn borer in six inbred lines of dent corn. Iowa State J. Sci. 44:297–311.

––––, E.B. Lillehoj, W.W. McMillian, D. Barry, W.F. Kwolek, A.O. Franz, E.A. Catalano, W.A. Russell, and N.W. Widstrom. 1981. Effect of hybrids with different levels of susceptibility to second-generation European corn borers on aflatoxin contamination in corn. J. Agric. Food Chem. 29:1170–1172.

––––, E.S. Raun, F.F. Dicke, G.R. Pesho, and S.W. Carter. 1965. Laboratory production of European Corn borer egg masses. Iowa State J. Sci. 40:65–83.

––––, W.A. Russell, and C.W. Jennings. 1971. Resistance of maize to second-brood European corn borers. Proc. Annu. Corn Sorghum Ind. Res. Conf. 26:165–179.

––––, ––––, G.L. Reed, A.R. Hallauer, and D.F. Cox. 1978. Methods of evaluating maize for sheath-collar feeding resistance to the European corn borer. Maydica 23:45–53.

––––, and G.H. Stringfield. 1961. Use of test crosses in breeding corn for resistance to the European corn borer. J. Econ. Entomol. 54:784–787.

––––, C.T. Tseng, W.A. Russell, J.R. Coats, J.C. Robbins, and J.J. Tollefson. 1986. DIMBOA content at seven stages of plant development in a maize synthetic cultivar. J. Kans. Entomol. Soc. 59:356–360.

Hamilton, C.C. 1935. The control of insect pests of lawns and golf courses. New Jersey Exp. Stn. Circ. 347.

Harris, C.R., R.A. Chapman, C. Harris, and C.M. Tu. 1984. Biodegradation of pesticides in soil: Rapid induction of carbamate degrading factors after carbofuran treatment. J. Environ. Sci. Health, B19(1):1–11.

Hassan, S.A., E. Koch, and G. Neuffer. 1984. Control of the European corn borer with *Trichogramma*. Angewandte Wissenschaft 299.

Hawkins, J.H. 1936. The bionomics and control of wireworms in Maine. Maine Agric. Exp. Stn. Bull. 381.

Hawley, I.M. 1922. Insects and other animal pests injurious to field beans in New York. Cornell Univ. Agric. Exp. Stn. Memo 55.

––––, and F.W. Metzger. 1940. Feeding habits of the adult Japanese beetle. USDA Circ. 547. U.S. Gov. Print. Office, Washington, DC.

Headlee, T.J., and J.W. McColloch. 1913. The chinch bug. Kansas Agric. Exp. Stn. Bull. 191.

Henderson, C.A., and F.M. Davis. 1970. Four insecticides tested in the field for control of *Diatraea grandiosella*. J. Econ. Entomol. 63:1495–1497.

Hill, E., and Z.B. Mayo. 1980. Distribution and abundance of corn rootworm species as influenced by topography and crop rotation in eastern Nebraska. Environ. Entomol. 9:122–127.

––––, E. Hixon, and M.H. Muma. 1948. Corn rootworm control tests with benzene hexachloride, DDT, nitrogen fertilizers and crop rotation. J. Econ. Entomol. 41:392–401.

––––, A.N. Sparks, C.C. Burkhardt, H.C. Chiang, M.L. Fairchild, and W.D. Guthrie. 1967. European corn borer, *Ostrinia nubilalis* (Hub.) populations in field corn, *Zea mays* (L.) in the North Central United States. Nebraska Agric. Exp. Stn. Res. Bull. 225.

Hinds, W.E. 1914. Reducing insect injury in stored corn. J. Econ. Entomol. 7:203–211.

Holbert, J.R., W.P. Flint, and J.H. Bigger. 1934. Chinch bug resistance in corn — an inherited character. J. Econ. Entomol. 27:121–124.

––––, ––––, ––––, and G.H. Dungan. 1935. Resistance and susceptibility of corn strains to second brood chinch bugs. Iowa State J. Sci. 9:413–425.

Huber, L.L., C.R. Neiswander, and R.M. Salter. 1928. The European corn borer and its environment. Ohio Agric. Exp. Stn. Bull. 429.

––––, and G.H. Stringfield. 1942. Aphid infestation of strains of corn as an index of their susceptibility to corn borer attack. J. Agric. Res. 64:283–291.

Hudon, M. 1963. Further field experiments on the use of *Bacillus thuringiensis* and chemical insecticide for the control of the European corn borer, *Ostrinia nubilalis*, on sweet corn in Southwestern Quebec. Econ. Entomol. 56:804–808.

––––, and M.S. Chiang. 1976. Resistance of maize lines to leaf feeding by the European corn borer, *Ostrinia nubilalis* (Hubner) in Quebec, Canada. Rep. Int. Proj. on *Ostrinia nubilalis*, Phase III:73–80.

––––, and ––––. 1985. Resistance and tolerance of maize germplasm to the European corn borer, *Ostrinia nubilalis* (Hubner) and its maturity in Quebec. Maydica 30:329–337.

––––, ––––, and D. Chez. 1979. Resistance and tolerance of maize inbred lines to the European corn borer, *Ostrinia nubilalis* (Hubner), and their maturity in Quebec. Phytoprotection 60:1–22.

––––, and Cooperators. 1973. International reactions of dent corn inbred lines to European corn borer populations. Canadian vs. pooled international data. Rep. Int. Proj. on *Ostrinia nubilalis*. Phase I:62–86.

Hyslop, J.A. 1915. Wireworms attacking cereal and forage crops. USDA Bull. 156. U.S. Gov. Print. Office, Washington, DC.

Ingram, J.W., and E.K. Bynum. 1941. The sugarcane borer. USDA Farmers' Bull. 1884. U.S. Gov. Print. Office, Washington, DC.

––––, E.K. Bynum, R. Mathes, W.E. Haley, and L.J. Charpentier. 1951. Pests of sugar cane and their control. USDA Circ. 878. U.S. Gov. Print. Office, Washington, DC.

Isely, D. 1929. The southern corn rootworm. Arkansas Agric. Exp. Stn. Bull. 232.

––––. 1935. Relation of hosts to abundance of cotton bollworm. Arkansas Agric. Exp. Stn. Bull. 320.

––––, and F.D. Miner. 1944. The lesser cornstalk borer, a pest of fall beans. J. Kans. Entomol. Soc. 17:51–57.

Ishiie, T., Y. Doi, K. Yora, and H. Asuyama. 1967. Suppressive effects of antibiotic of tetracycline group on symptom development of mulberry dwarf disease. Ann. Phytopathol. Soc. Jpn. 33:267–275.

Jacob, D., and G.M. Chippendale. 1971. Growth and Development of the southwestern corn borer, *Diatraea grandiosella* on meridic diet. Ann. Entomol. Soc. Am. 64:485–488.

Jarvis, J.L., R.L. Clark, and W.D. Guthrie. 1982. Effect of second-generation European corn borers on resistance of maize to *Diplodia maydis*. Phytopathology 72:1149–1152.

––––, ––––, ––––, E.C. Berry, and W.A. Russell. 1984. The relationship between second-generation European corn borers and stalk rot fungi in maize hybrids. Maydica 29:247–263.

––––, W.D. Guthrie, and E.B. Lillehoj. 1984. Effect of Aflatoxin B1 on European corn borer survival and development in the laboratory. J. Agric. Entomol. 1:17–22.

Jennings, C.W., W.A. Russell, and W.D. Guthrie. 1974a. Genetics of resistance in maize to first and second brood European corn borer. Crop Sci. 14:394–398.

----, ----, ----, and R.L. Grindeland. 1974b. Genetics of resistance in maize to second-brood European corn borers. Iowa State J. Res. 48:267–280.

Jewett, H.H. 1942. Life history of the wireworm *Aeolus mellillus* (Say). Kentucky Agric. Exp. Stn. Bull. 425.

Kahler, A.L., R.E. Telkamp, L.H. Penny, T.F. Branson, and P.J. Fitzgerald. 1985. Registration of NGSDCRW1(S2)C4 maize germplasm. Crop Sci. 25:202.

Kaster, L. Von, and W.B. Showers. 1982. Evidence of spring immigration and autumn reproductive diapause of the adult black cutworm in Iowa. Environ. Entomol. 11:306–312.

Kaufman, D.D., and D.F. Edwards. 1983. Pesticide/microbe interaction effects on persistence of pesticides in soil. p. 177–182. *In* J. Miyamoto et al. (ed.) IUPAC, Pesticide Chemistry.

Kelly, E.O.G. 1911. Papers on cereal and forage insects. The maize billbug. USDA Bur. Entomol. Bull. 95 (Part II). U.S. Gov. Print. Office, Washington, DC.

Kirk, V.M. 1960. Corn insects in South Carolina. South Carolina Agric. Exp. Stn. Bull. 478.

Klenke, J.R., W.A. Russell, and W.D. Guthrie. 1986a. Recurrent selection for resistance to European corn borer on a corn synthetic and correlated effects on agronomic traits. Crop Sci. 26:864–886.

----, ----, ----. 1986b. Grain yield reduction caused by second-generation European corn borer in 'BS9' corn synthetic. Crop Sci. 26:859–863.

----, ----, ----. 1986c. Distributions for European corn borer (Lepidoptera:Pyralidae) ratings of S1 lines from 'BS9' corn synthetic. J. Econ. Entomol. 79:1076–1081.

----, ----, ----. C.A. Martinson, and W.L. Pedersen. 1987. Disease resistance in five cycles of 'BS9' corn synthetic selected for resistance to two generations of European corn borer. Phytopathology 77:735–739.

Klun, J.A., and T.A. Brindley. 1966. Role of 6-methoxybenzoxazolinone in inbred resistance of host plant (maize) to first-brood larvae of European corn borer. J. Econ. Entomol. 59:711–718.

----, W.D. Guthrie, A.R. Hallauer, and W.A. Russell. 1970. Genetic nature of the concentration of 2,4-dihydroxy-7-methoxy 2*H*-1,4-benzoxazin-3(4*H*)-one and resistance to the European corn borer in a diallel set of eleven maize inbreds. Crop Sci. 10:87–90.

----, and J.F. Robinson. 1969. Concentration of two, 1,4-benzoxazinones in dent corn at various stages of development of the plant and its relation to resistance of the host plant to the European corn borer. J. Econ. Entomol. 62:214–220.

----, C.L. Tipton, and T.A. Brindley. 1967. 2,4-dihydroxy-7-methoxy-1, 4-benzoxazin-3-one (DIMBOA), an active agent in the resistance of maize to the European corn borer. J. Econ. Entomol. 60:1529–1533.

Knapp, J.L., P.A. Hedin, and W.A. Douglas. 1965. Amino acids and reducing sugars in silks of corn resistant or susceptible to corn earworm. Ann. Entomol. Soc. Am. 58:401–402.

Knight, H.H. 1916. The army-worm in New York in 1914 *Leucania unipuncta* Haworth: Order, *Lepidoptera* Family, *Noctuidae*. Cornell Univ. Agric. Exp. Stn. Bull. 376.

Knoke, J.K., and R. Louie. 1981. Epiphytology of maize virus diseases. p. 92–102. *In* D.P. Gordon et al. (ed.) Virus and viruslike diseases of maize in the United States. Ohio Agric. Res. Dev. Ctr. Coop. Ser. Bull. 247.

Koehler, B. 1942. Natural mode of entrance of fungi into corn ears and some symptoms that indicate infection. J. Agric. Res. 64:421–442.

Krysan, J.L., J.J. Jackson, and A.C. Lew. 1984. Field termination of egg diapause in *Diabrotica* with new evidence of extended diapause in *D. barberi* (Coleoptera:Chrysomelidae). Environ. Entomol. 13:1237–1240.

Kunkel, L.O. 1921. A possible causative agent for the mosaic disease of corn. Bull. Exp. Stn. Hawaii Sugar Planters Assoc. 3:44–58.

----. 1927. The corn mosaic of Hawaii distinct from sugar cane mosaic. Phytopathology 17:41 (Abstr.).

Kuschel, G. 1961. On problems of synonymy in the *Sitophilus oryzae* complex (3rd contribution Col. Curculionoidea). Cent. Inv. Zool. Univ. Chile. Am. Mag. Nat. Hist. 13:241–244.

Kyle, C.H. 1918. Shuck protection for ear corn. USDA Bull. 708. U.S. Gov. Print. Office, Washington, DC.

Lane, M.C. 1941. Wireworms and their control on irrigated land. USDA Farmers' Bull. 1866. U.S. Gov. Print. Office, Washington, DC.

Leiby, R.W. 1920. The larger corn stalk borer in North Carolina. North Carolina Dep. Agric. 41 (274).

Leonard, D.E. 1966. Biosystematic of the "Leucopterus Complex" of the genus *Blissus*. Connecticut Agric. Exp. Stn. Bull. 677.

Lewis, L.C. 1982. Present status of introduced parasitoids of the European corn borer, *Ostrinia nubilalis* (Hübner), in Iowa. Iowa State J. Res. 56:429–436.

――――, and R.E. Lynch. 1974. Lyophilization, vacuum drying and subsequent storage of *Nosema pyrausta* spores. J. Invertebr. Pathol. 24:149–153.

――――, ――――. 1976. Influence of the European corn borer of *Nosema pyrausta* and resistance in maize to leaf feeding. Environ. Entomol. 5:139–142.

――――, ――――. 1978. Foliar application of *Nosema pyrausta* for suppression of populations of European corn borer. Entomophaga 23:83–88.

Lillehoj, E.B., W.F. Kwolek, E.E. Vandegraft, M.S. Zuber, O.H. Calbert, N. Widstrom, M.C. Futrell, and A.J. Bockholt. 1975. Aflatoxin production in *Aspergillus flavus* inoculated ears of corn grown at diverse locations. Crop Sci. 15:267–270.

Lindsay, D.R. 1943. The biology and morphology of *Colaspis flavida* (Say). Iowa State Coll. J. Sci. 18:60–61.

Loomis, R.S., S.D. Beck, and J.F. Stauffer. 1957. The European corn borer, *Pyrausta nubilalis* (Hübn.), and its principal host plant. V.A. chemical study of host plant resistance. Plant Physiol. 32:379–385.

Luginbill, P. 1918. The southern corn rootworm and farm practices to control it. USDA Farmers' Bull. 950. U.S. Gov. Print. Office, Washington, DC.

――――. 1922. Bionomics of the chinch bug. USDA Bull. 1016. U.S. Gov. Print. Office, Washington, DC.

――――. 1928. The fall armyworm. USDA Tech. Bull. 34. U.S. Gov. Print. Office, Washington, DC.

――――. 1950. Habits and control of the fall armyworm. USDA Farmers' Bull. 1990. U.S. Gov. Print. Office, Washington, DC.

――――, and G.G. Ainslie. 1917. The lesser corn stalk-borer. USDA Bull. 539. U.S. Gov. Print. Office, Washington, DC.

――――, and T.R. Chamberlain. 1953. Control of white grubs on cereal and forage crops. USDA Farmers' Bull. 1978. U.S. Gov. Print. Office, Washington, DC.

――――, and H.R. Painter. 1953. May beetles of the United States and Canada. USDA Tech. Bull. 1060. U.S. Gov. Print. Office, Washington, DC.

Lynch, R.E., L.C. Lewis, E.C. Berry, and J.F. Robinson. 1977. European corn borer: Granular formulations of *Bacillus thuringiensis* for control. J. Econ. Entomol. 70:389–391.

Maramorosch, K. 1963. The occurrence in Arizona of corn stunt disease and of the leafhopper vector *Dalbulus maidis*. Plant Dis. Rep. 47:858.

――――, R.R. Granados, and H. Hirumi. 1970. Mycoplasma disease of plants and insects. Adv. Virus Res. 16:135–193.

――――, E. Shikata, and R.R. Granados. 1968. Structures resembling mycoplasma in diseased plants and in insect vectors. Trans. N.Y. Acad. Sci. Ser. 2:841–855.

Marston, A.R. 1931. Breeding European corn borer resistant corn. J. Am. Soc. Agron. 23:950–964.

Maxwell, F.G., and R.H. Painter. 1962. Auxin content of extracts of host plants and honeydew of different biotypes of corn leaf aphid, *Rhopalosiphum maidis* (Fitch). Kans. Entomol. Soc. 35:2.

McCain, F.S., W.G. Eden, B.W. Arthur, and M.C. Carter. 1963. Amino acid content of corn silks in relation to resistance to corn earworm. J. Econ. Entomol. 56:902.

McColloch, J.W. 1921. The corn leaf aphid (*Aphis maidis* Fitch) in Kansas. J. Econ. Entomol. 14:89–94.

McEwen, F.L., and C.Y. Kawanishi. 1967. Insect transmission of corn mosaic: Laboratory studies in Hawaii. J. Econ. Entomol. 60:1413–1417.

McGaughey, H. 1985. Insect resistance to the biological insecticide *Bacillus thuringiensis*. Science 229:193–195.

McMillian, W.W., and K.J. Starks. 1966. Feeding responses of some noctuid larvae (Lepidoptera) to plant extracts. Ann. Entomol. Soc. Am. 59:516–519.

――――, N.W. Widstrom, and D.M. Wilson. 1982a. Aflatoxin production on various popcorn genotypes. Agron. J. 74:156–157.

――――, ――――, and B.R. Wiseman. 1982b. Pink scavenger caterpillar resistance among selected dent corn hybrids. J. Ga. Entomol. Soc. 17:93–96.

----, ----, D.M. Wilson, and R.A. Hill. 1980a. Transmission by maize weevils of *Aspergillus flavus* and its survival on selected corn hybrids. J. Econ. Entomol. 73:793–794.

----, D.M. Wilson, N.W. Widstrom, and W.D. Perkins. 1980b. Effects of Aflatoxin B1 and G1 on three insect pests of maize. J. Econ. Entomol. 73:26–28.

----, ----, and N.W. Widstrom. 1985. Aflatoxin contamination of preharvest corn in Georgia: A six-year study of insect damage and visible *Aspergillus flavus*. J. Environ. Qual. 14:200–203.

----, and B.R. Wiseman. 1972. Host plant resistance: A Twentieth Century look at the relationship between *Zea mays* L. and *Heliothis Zea* (Boddie). Florida Agric. Exp. Stn. Monogr. Ser. 2.

Mendoza, C.E., and D.C. Peters. 1964. Species differentiation among mature larvae of *Diabrotica undecimpunctata* Howardi, *D. virgifera* and *D. longicornis*. J. Kans. Entomol. Soc. 37:123–125.

Messieha, M. 1967. Aphid transmission of maize dwarf mosaic virus. Phytopathology 57:956–959.

Metcalf, Z.P. 1917. Biological investigation of *Spenophorus callosus* Oliv. North Carolina Agric. Exp. Stn. Tech. Bull. 13.

Meyers, M.T., L.L. Huber, C.R. Neiswander, F.D. Richey, and G.H. Stringfield. 1937. Experiments on breeding corn resistant to the European corn borer. USDA Tech. Bull. 583. U.S. Gov. Print. Office, Washington, DC.

Mihm, J.A. 1982. Techniques for efficient mass rearing and infestation in screening for host plant resistance to corn earworm, *Heliothis zea*. CIMMYT, El Batan, Mexico.

----. 1983a. Efficient mass-rearing and infestation techniques to screen for host plant resistance to fall armyworm, *Spodoptera frugiperda*. CIMMYT, El Batan, Mexico.

----. 1983b. Efficient mass rearing and infestation techniques to screen for host plant resistance to maize stem borers, *Diatraea* sp. CIMMYT, El Batan, Mexico.

----. 1985. Breeding for host plant resistance to maize stem borers. Inst. Sci. Applic. 6:369–377.

Munson, G., A.J. Keaster, R.N. Story, and J.A. Grundler. 1984. Corn cutworm control. Agric. Guide Univ. of Missouri Ext. Div.

Musick, G.J., and P.J. Tuttle. 1973. Suppression of armyworm damage to no-tillage corn with granular carbofuran. J. Econ. Entomol. 66:735–737.

Nault, L.R., and R.H.E. Bradley. 1969. Acquisition of maize dwarf mosaic virus by the greenbug, *Schizaphis graminum*. Ann. Entomol. Soc. Am. 62:403–406.

----, M.L. Briones, L.E. Williams, and B.D. Barry. 1967. Relations of the wheat curl mite to kernel red streak of corn. Phytopathology 57:986–989.

----, and J.K. Knoke. 1981. Maize vectors. p. 77–84. *In* D.T. Gordon et al. (ed.) Virus and viruslike diseases of maize in the United States. Ohio Agric. Res. Dev. Ctr. South. Coop. Bull. 247.

----, W.E. Styer, J.K. Knoke, and H.N. Pitre. 1973. Semi-persistent transmission of leafhopper-borne maize chlorotic dwarf virus. J. Econ. Entomol. 66:1271–1273.

Neiswander, C.R. 1931. The sources of American corn insects. Ohio Agric. Exp. Stn. Bull. 473.

----, and C.A. Triplehorn. 1961. Differential resistance of dent corn strains to the corn leaf aphid, *Rhopalosiphum maidis* (Fitch), in Ohio. Ohio Agric. Exp. Stn. Res. Bull. 898.

Niblett, C.L., J.H. Tsai, and B.W. Falk. 1981. Virus and Mycoplasma Diseases of Corn in Florida. Proc. Annu. Corn Sorghum Ind. Res. Conf. 36:78–88.

Ohio Agricultural Research and Development Center. 1973. A list of references: Maize virus diseases and corn stunt. Maize Virus Information Serv. Library of OARDC, Wooster, OH.

Oldfield, G.N. 1970. Mite transmission of plant viruses. Annu. Rev. Entomol. 15:343–380.

Omolo, E.O. 1983. Screening of local and exotic maize lines for stem borer resistance with special reference to *Chilo partellus*. Inst. Sci. Applic. 4:105–108.

Onukogu, F.A. 1984. Oviposition behavior, biology, and host plant resistance studies of the western African maize borer, *Sesamia calamistis* Hmps. Maydica 29:121–132.

----. 1985. West African maize borer (*Sesamia calamistis* Hmps.): Evaluation of techniques for artificial infestations assessing resistance to leaf feeding/dead heart damage. Maydica 30:281–284.

----, W.D. Guthrie, W.A. Russell, G.L. Reed, and J.C. Robbins. 1978. Location of genes that condition resistance in maize to sheath-collar feeding by second-generation European corn borer. J. Econ. Entomol. 71:1–4.

Orlob, G.B., and J.T. Medler. 1961. Biology of cereal and grass aphids in Wisconsin. Can. Entomol. 93:703–714.

Ortega, A., S.K. Vasal, J. Mihm, and C. Hershey. 1980. Breeding for insect resistance in maize. p. 371–419. *In* F.G. Maxwell and P.R. Jennings (ed.) Breeding plants resistance to insects. John Wiley and Sons, New York.

Ortman, G.E., T.F. Branson, and E.D. Gerloff. 1974. Techniques, accomplishments, and future potential of host plant resistance to *Diabrotica*. p. 344–358. *In* F.G. Maxwell and F.A. Harris (ed.) Proceedings of the summer institute on biological control of plant insects and diseases. Univ. of Mississippi Press, Jackson.

––––, and E.D. Gerloff. 1970. Rootworm resistance: Problems in measuring and its relationship to performance. Proc. Annu. Corn Sorghum Ind. Res. Conf. 25:161–174.

––––, D.C. Peters, and P.J. Fitzgerald. 1968. Vertical-pull technique for evaluating tolerance of corn root systems to northern and western rootworms. J. Econ. Entomol. 61:373–375.

Owens, J.C., D.C. Peters, and A.R. Hallauer. 1974. Corn rootworm tolerance in maize. Environ. Entomol. 3:767–772.

Painter, R.H. 1928. Notes on the injury to plant cells by chinch bug feeding. Ann. Entomol. Soc. Am. 21:232–242.

––––. 1951. Insect resistance in crop plants. Macmillan Publ. Co., New York.

––––, and A.M. Brunson. 1940. Differential injury within varieties, inbred lines, and hybrids of field corn caused by the corn earworm *Heliothis armigera* (Hbn.). J. Agric. Res. 61:81–100.

––––, R.O. Snelling, and A.M. Brunson. 1935. Hybrid vigor and other factors in relation to chinch bug resistance in corn. J. Econ. Entomol. 28:1025–1030.

Palmer, D.F., M.B. Windel, and H.C. Chiang. 1977. Artificial infestation of corn with western corn rootworm eggs in agar-water. J. Econ. Entomol. 70:277–278.

Palmer. L.T., and T. Kommedahl. 1969. Root-infecting *Fusarium* species in relation to rootworm infestations in corn. Phytopathology 59:1613–1617.

Pargamin, G.D., and A.N. Grigorenko. 1977. Increasing the effectiveness of using *Trichogramma*. Zashchita Rastenii 7.

Parker, J.R., and R.V. Connin. 1964. Grasshoppers: Their habits and damage. USDA Info. Bull. 287. U.S. Gov. Print. Office, Washington, DC.

Patanakamjorn, S., W.D. Guthrie, and W.R. Young. 1978. Biology of the tropical corn borer, *Ostrinia furnacalis*, in relation to host plant resistance research. Iowa State J. Res. 52:371–385.

Patch, L.H. 1937. Resistance of a single-cross hybrid strain of field corn to European corn borer. J. Econ. Entomol. 30:271–278.

––––. 1943. Survival, weight and location of European corn borers feeding on resistant and susceptible field corn. J. Agric. Res. 66:7–19.

––––. 1947. Manual infestations of dent corn to study resistance to European corn borer. J. Econ. Entomol. 40:667–671.

––––, J.R. Holbert, and R.T. Everly. 1942. Strains of field corn resistant to the survival of the European corn borer. USDA Tech. Bull. 823. U.S. Gov. Print. Office, Washington, DC.

––––, and R.T. Everly. 1945. Resistance of dent corn inbred lines to survival of first-generation European corn borer larvae. USDA Tech. Bull. 893. U.S. Gov. Print. Office, Washington, DC.

––––, G.W. Still, B.A. App, and C.A. Crooks. 1941. Comparative injury by the European corn borer to open-pollinated and hybrid field corn. J. Agric. Res. 63:355–368.

Penny, L.H. 1981. Vertical-pull resistance of maize inbreds and their testcrosses. Crop Sci. 21:237–240.

––––, and F.F. Dicke. 1956. Inheritance of resistance in corn to leaf feeding of the European corn borer. Agron. J. 48:200–203.

––––, G.E. Scott, and W.D. Guthrie. 1967. Recurrent selection for European corn borer resistance in maize. Crop Sci. 7:407–409.

Pepper, B.B., and C.M. Haenseler. 1944. Control of European corn borer and ear smut on sweet corn with dusts and sprays. New Jersey Agric. Exp. Stn. Circ. 486.

Perkins, W.D., R.L. Jones, A.N. Sparks, B.R. Wiseman, J.W. Snow, and W.W. McMillian.

1973. Artificial diets for mass rearing the corn earworm (*Heliothis zea*). USDA Prod. Res. Rep. 154. U.S. Gov. Print. Office, Washington, DC.

Pesho, G.R., F.F. Dicke, and W.A. Russell. 1965. Resistance of inbred lines of corn (*Zea mays* L.) to the second brood of the European corn borer (*Ostrinia nubilalis* (Hubner). Iowa State J. Sci. 40:85–98.

Peters, L.L., M.L. Fairchild, and M.S. Zuber. 1972a. Effect of corn endosperm containing different levels of amylose on Angoumois grain moth biology. 1. Life cycle, certain physiological responses, and infestation rates. J. Econ. Entomol. 65:576–581.

––––, M.S. Zuber, and M.I. Fairchild. 1972b. Effect of corn endosperm containing different levels of amylose on Angoumois grain moth biology. 2. Physical and chemical properties of experimental corn. J. Econ. Entomol. 65:581–584.

Petty, H.B., and J.W. Apple. 1966. Insects. p. 351–417. *In* W.H. Pierre et al. (ed.) Advances in corn production: Principles and practices. Iowa State Univ. Press, Ames.

Phillips, W.J. 1909. The slender seed-corn ground-beetle. USDA Bur. Entomol. Bull. 85.

––––. 1914. Corn-leaf blotch miner. J. Agric. Res. 2:15–41.

––––, and G.W. Barber. 1929. A study of the hibernation of the corn earworm in Virginia. Virginia Agric. Exp. Stn. Bull. 40.

––––, and ––––. 1931. The value of husk protection to corn ears in limiting corn earworm injury. Virginia Agric. Exp. Stn. Tech. Bull. 43.

––––, and ––––. 1933. Egg-laying habits and fate of eggs of the corn earworm moth and factors affecting them. Virginia Agric. Exp. Stn. Tech. Bull. 47.

––––, and ––––. 1934. Ear-worm injury in relation to date of planting field corn in central Virginia. Virginia Agric. Exp. Stn. Tech. Bull. 55.

––––, G.W. Underhill, and F.W. Poos. 1921. The larger corn stalk-borer in Virginia. Virginia Agric. Exp. Stn. Tech. Bull. 22.

Pitre, H.N. 1968. Systemic insecticides for control of the blackfaced leafhopper, *Graminella nigrifrons*, and effect on corn stunt disease. J. Econ. Entomol. 61:765–768.

––––, and L.W. Hepner. 1967. Seasonal incidence of indigenous leafhoppers (Homoptera, Cicadellidae) on corn and several winter crops in Mississippi. Ann. Entomol. Soc. Am. 60:1044–1055.

Poos, F.W. 1939. Host plants harboring *Aplanobacter stewarti* without showing external symptoms after inoculation by *Chaetocnema pulicaria*. J. Econ. Entomol. 32:881.

––––. 1955. Studies of certain species of *Chaetocnema*. J. Econ. Entomol. 48:555–563.

––––, and C. Elliott. 1936. Certain insect vectors of *Aplanobacter stewarti*. J. Agric. Res. 52:585–608.

Quaintance, A.L., and C.T. Brues. 1905. The cotton bollworm. USDA Bull. 50. U.S. Gov. Print. Office, Washington, DC.

Rand, F.V., and L.C. Cash. 1933. Bacterial wilt of corn. USDA Tech. Bull. 362. U.S. Gov. Print. Office, Washington, DC.

Randell, R. 1970. The bionomics of the corn leaf aphid, *Rhopalosiphum maidis* Fitch. Ph.D. diss. Univ. of Illinois, Urbana.

Raun, E.S., R.E. Hill, and D.L. Keith. 1968. Western bean cutworm. Univ. Nebraska Coll. Agric. Home Econ. Quart. Bull. 14:16–17.

Reddy, G.P.V., and G.M. Chippendale. 1972. Nutritional requirements of the southwestern corn borer, *Zea diatrea grandiosella*. Entomol. Exp. Appl. 15:51–60.

Reid, W.J., Jr. 1940. Biology of the seed-corn maggot in the coastal plain of the south Atlantic States. USDA Tech. Bull. 723. U.S. Gov. Print. Office, Washington, DC.

Rhodes, A.M., and W.H. Luckmann. 1967. Survival and reproduction of the corn leaf aphid on twelve maize genotypes. J. Econ. Entomol. 60:527–530.

Richey, F.D. 1944. Maize hybrids susceptible to earworm. J. Hered. 35:327–328.

Riley, T.J., and A.J. Keaster. 1981. A pictorial field key to wireworms attacking corn in the Midwest. Univ. of Missouri MP517.

Rogers, R.R., W.A. Russell, and J.C. Owens. 1976a. Evaluation of vertical-pull technique in population improvement of maize for corn rootworm tolerance. Crop Sci. 16:591–594.

––––, ––––, and ––––. 1976b. Relationship of corn rootworm tolerance to yield in BSSS maize population. Iowa State J. Res. 51:125–129.

––––, ––––, and ––––. 1977. Expected gains from selection in maize for resistance to corn rootworms. Maydica 22:27–36.

Rojanaridpicked, C., V.E. Gracen, H.L. Everetts, J.G. Coors, B.F. Pugh, and P. Bouthyette.

1984. Multiple factor resistance in maize to European corn borer. Maydica 29:305–315.

Rosenkranz, E. 1969. A new leafhopper—transmissable corn stunt disease agent in Ohio. Phytopathology 59:1344–1346.

Russell, W.A. 1974. Comparative performance for maize hybrids representing different eras of maize breeding. Proc. Annu. Corn Sorghum Ind. Res. Conf. 29:81–101.

––––, and W.D. Guthrie. 1979. Registration of B85 and B86 germplasm lines of maize. Crop Sci. 19:565.

––––, and ––––. 1982. Registration for BS9(CB)C4 maize germplasm. Crop Sci. 22:694.

––––, ––––, J.A. Klun, and R. Grindeland. 1975. Selection for resistance in maize to first-brood European corn borer leaf-feeding damage by the insect and chemical analysis for DIMBOA in the plant. J. Econ. Entomol. 68:31–34.

Sarup, P., B.K. Mukherjee, K.K. Marwaha, V.P.S. Panwar, K.H. Siddiqui, and N.N. Singh. 1974. Identification of a source of resistance to Chilo partellus (Swinhoe) in Columbia maize hybrid H207 and formulation of a suitable breeding procedure for the utilization. Indian J. Entomol. 36:1–5.

Satterthwait, A.F. 1919. How to control billbugs destructive to cereal and forage crops. USDA Farmers' Bull. 1003. U.S. Gov. Print. Office, Washington, DC.

Saugstad, E.S., and R.T. Everly. 1967. Overwintering populations of the corn leaf aphid on barley and grasses in Indiana. Proc. North Cent. Branch Entomol. Soc. Am. 22:69–73.

Schlosberg, M., and W.A. Baker. 1948. Tests of sweet corn lines for resistance to European corn borer larvae. J. Agric. Res. 77:137–156.

Scott, G.E., and F.M. Davis. 1981a. Registration of MpSWCB-4 population of maize. Crop Sci. 21:148.

––––, and ––––. 1981b. Registration of Mp496 inbred of maize. Crop Sci. 21:353.

––––, ––––, and W.P. Williams. 1982. Registration of Mp701 and Mp702 germplasm of maize. Crop Sci. 22:1170.

––––, F.F. Dicke, and L.H. Penny. 1966. Location of genes conditioning resistance to corn to leaf feeding of the European corn borer. Crop Sci. 6:444–446.

––––, W.D. Guthrie, and G.R. Pesho. 1967. Effect of second-brood European corn borer infestation on 45 single cross hybrids. Crop Sci. 7:229–230.

––––, A.R. Hallauer, and F.F. Dicke. 1964. Types of gene action conditioning resistance to European corn borer leaf feeding. Crop Sci. 4:603–604.

Scriber, J.M., W.M. Tingey, V.E. Gracen, and S.L. Sullivan. 1975. Leaf-feeding resistance to the European corn borer in genotypes of tropical (Low-DIMBOA) and U.S. inbred (High-DIMBOA) maize. J. Econ. Entomol. 68:823–826.

Sharma, V.K., and S.M. Chatterji. 1972. Further studies on the nature of antibiosis in maize (Zea mays Linn) against the maize borer, Chilo zonellus (Swinhoe). Indian J. Entomol. 34:11–19.

Shaunak, K.K., and H.N. Pitre. 1971. Seasonal alate aphid collections in yellow pan traps in northeastern Mississippi: Possible relationship to maize dwarf mosaic disease. J. Econ. Entomol. 71:1105–1109.

Shelford, V.E., and W.P. Flint. 1943. Populations of the chinch bug in the upper Mississippi Valley from 1823–1940. Ecology 24:435–455.

Sherrod, D.W., J.T. Shaw, and W.H. Luckmann. 1979. Concepts on black cutworm field biology in Illinois. Environ. Entomol. 8:191–193.

Shotwell, R.L. 1941. Life history and habits of some grasshoppers of economic importance on the Great Plains. USDA Tech. Bull. 774. U.S. Gov. Print. Office, Washington, DC.

––––. 1952. Tests with sprays for controlling grasshoppers on farmlands in North Dakota and Texas, 1950–51. USDA Bur. Entomol. Plant Quarantine E-845. U.S. Gov. Print. Office, Washington, DC.

––––. 1958. The grasshopper your sharecropper. Missouri Agric. Exp. Stn. Bull. 714.

Showers, W.B. 1979. Effect of diapause on the migration of the European corn borer into the southeastern United States. p. 420–429. In R.L. Rabb and G.G. Kennedy (ed.) Movement of highly mobile insects: Concepts and methodology in research. North Carolina State Univ. Press, Raleigh.

––––, E.C. Berry, and L. Von Kaster. 1980. Management of 2nd-generation European corn borer by controlling moths outside the cornfield. J. Econ. Entomol. 73:88–91.

––––, G.L. Reed, J.F. Robinson, and M.B. DeRozari. 1976. Flight and sexual activity of the European corn borer. Environ. Entomol. 5:1099–1104.

Siddiqui, K.H., K.K. Marwaha, and P. Sarup. 1984. Location of sources of resistance amongst elite and local maize germplasm to the stalk borer, *Chilo partellus* (Swinhoe) under artificial infestation. J. Entomol. Res. 8:25–28.

Sifuentes, J.A., and R.H. Painter. 1964. Inheritance of resistance to western corn rootworm adults in field corn. J. Econ. Entomol. 57:475–477.

Simmons, P., and G.W. Ellington. 1933. Life history of the Angoumois grain moth in Maryland. USDA Tech. Bull 351. U.S. Gov. Print. Office, Washington, DC.

Singh, J. 1967. Studies on breeding in maize for resistance to top shoot borer (*Chilo zonellus* Swin). Ph.D. diss. P.G. School, Indian Agric. Res. Inst., New Delhi.

Slykhuis, J.T. 1953. The relation of *Aceria tulipae* (K.) to streak mosaic and other chlorotic symptoms of wheat. Phytopathology 43:484–485.

Snelling, R.O., R.A. Blanchard, and J.H. Bigger. 1940. Resistance of corn strains to the leaf aphid *Aphis maidis* Fitch. J. Am. Soc. Agron. 32:371–381.

Soto, P.E., I.W. Buddenhagen, and V.L. Asnani. 1982. Development of streak virus resistant maize populations through improved challenge and selection methods. Ann. Appl. Biol. 100:539–546.

Sparks, T.C., S.S. Quisenberry, J.A. Lockwood, R.L. Byford, and R.T. Rouch. 1985. Insecticide resistance in the horn fly, *Haematobia irritans*. J. Agric. Entomol. 2(3):217–233.

Stahl, C.F. 1927. Corn stripe disease in Cuba not identical with sugar cane mosaic. Trop. Plant Res. Found. Bull. 7:3–11.

Stanley, W.W. 1936. Studies of the ecology and control of cutworms in Tennessee. Tennessee Agric. Exp. Stn. Bull. 159.

Starks, K.J., and W.W. McMillian. 1967. Resistance in corn to the corn earworm and fall armyworm. Part II. Type of field resistance to the corn earworm. J. Econ. Entomol. 60:920–923.

––––, W.W. McMillian, A.A. Sekul, and H.C. Cox. 1965. Corn earworm larval feeding response to corn silk and kernel extracts. Ann. Entomol. Soc. Am. 58:74–76.

Steiner, W.M., J. Voegtlin, and M.E. Irwin. 1985. Genetic differentiation and its bearing on migration in North American populations of the corn leaf aphid, *Rhopalosiphum maidis* (Fitch) (Homoptera:Aphididae). Ann. Entomol. Soc. Am. 78:518–525.

Stevens, N.E. 1936. Second experimental forecast of the incidence of bacterial wilt of corn. Plant Dis. Rep. 20:241–244.

Stirrett, G.M. 1938. A field study of the flight, oviposition and establishment periods in the cycle of the European corn borer *Pyrausta nubilalis* Hbn., and the physical factors affecting them. Sci. Agric. 18:355–369, 536–557, 568–585, 656–683.

Stoner, W.N. (ed.) 1968. Corn (maize) viruses in the Continental United States and Canada. USDA-ARS 33-118. U.S. Gov. Print. Office, Washington, DC.

––––, L.E. Williams, and L.J. Alexander. 1964. Transmission by the corn leaf aphid, *Rhopalosiphum maidis* (Fitch) of a virus infecting corn in Ohio. Ohio Agric. Exp. Stn. Res. Circ. 136.

Storey, H.H. 1939. Investigations of the mechanism of the transmission of plant viruses by insect vectors. III. The insect's saliva. Proc. R. Soc. London, B 127:526–543.

Straub, R.W., and C.W. Boothroyd. 1980. Relationship of corn leaf aphid and maize dwarf mosaic disease to sweet corn yields in southeastern New York. J. Econ. Entomol. 73:92–95.

Sullivan, S.L., V.E. Gracen, and A. Ortega. 1974. Resistance of exotic maize varieties to the European corn borer, *Ostrinia nubilalis* (Hubner). Environ. Entomol. 3:718–720.

Sutter, G.R., and T.F. Branson. 1980. A procedure for artificially infesting field plots with corn rootworm eggs. J. Econ. Entomol. 73:135–137.

Tate, H.D., and O.S. Bare. 1946. Corn rootworms. Nebraska Agric. Exp. Stn. Bull. 381.

Taylor, L.R., and R.E. Berry. 1968. High altitude migration of aphids in maritime and continental climates. Proc. North Cent. Branch Entomol. Soc. Am. 23(1):69–70.

Tenhet, J.N., and E.W. Howe. 1939. The sand wireworm and its control in South Carolina coastal plain. USDA Tech. Bull. 659. U.S. Gov. Print. Office, Washington, DC.

Thomas, C.A. 1940. The biology and control of wireworms. Pennsylvania Exp. Stn. Bull. 392.

Thompson, L.S., and R.P. White. 1977. Effect of insecticides on European corn borer and yield of silage corn in Prince Edward Island. J. Econ. Entomol. 70:706–708.

Triplehorn, C.A. 1959. The possible effect of weather on incidence of corn leaf aphid infestation and damage. Proc. North Cent. Branch Entomol. Soc. Am. 14:28–29.

Tseng, C.T., W.D. Guthrie, W.A. Russell, J.C. Robbins, J.R. Coats, and J.J. Tollefson. 1984.

Evaluation of two procedures to select for resistance to the European corn borer in a synthetic cultivar of maize. Crop Sci. 24:1129–1133.

Tu, T.C., and R.E. Ford. 1971. Factors affecting aphid transmission of maize dwarf mosaic virus of corn. Phytopathology 61:1516–1521.

Uyemoto, J.K., and L.E. Claflin. 1981. Maize chlorotic mottle virus and corn lethal necrosis disease. p. 163–165. *In* D.J. Gordon et al. (ed.) Virus and viruslike diseases of maize in the United States. Ohio Agric. Res. Ctr. South. Coop. Ser. Bull. 247.

USDA. 1954. Chinch bugs. How to control them. USDA Leafl. 364.

––––. 1961. The armyworm and the fall armyworm—how to control them. USDA Leafl. 494. U.S. Gov. Print. Office, Washington, DC.

––––. 1962. The European corn borer and how to control it. USDA Farmers' Bull. 2084. U.S. Gov. Print. Office, Washington, DC.

––––. 1964. Grasshopper control. USDA Farmers' Bull. 2193. U.S. Gov. Print. Office, Washington, DC.

––––. 1966. Neotropical corn borer (*Zeadiatraea lineolata* (Walker). USDA Coop. Econ. Inst. Rep. 16(33):823.

VanDerSchaaf, P. 1969. Resistance of corn to laboratory infestation of the larger rice weevil, *Sitophilus zeamais.* J. Econ. Entomol. 62:352–355.

Vickery, R.A. 1929. Studies on the fall armyworm in the gulf coast district of Texas. USDA Tech. Bull. 138. U.S. Gov. Print. Office, Washington, DC.

Vinal, S.C. 1917. The European corn borer, *Pyrausta nubilalis* Hubner, a recently established pest in Massachusetts. Massachusetts Agric. Exp. Stn. Bull. 178.

––––, and D.J. Caffrey. 1919. The European corn borer and its control. Massachusetts Exp. Stn. Bull. 189.

Wahlroos, O., and A.I. Virtanen. 1959. The precursors of 6MBOA in maize and wheat plants: Their isolation and some of their properties. Acta Chem. Scand. 13:1906–1908.

Waiss, A.C., Jr., B.G. Chan, C.A. Elliger, B.R. Wiseman, W.W. McMillian, N.W. Widstrom, M.S. Zuber, and A.J. Keaster. 1979. Maysin, a flavone glycoside from corn silks with antibiotic activity toward corn earworm. J. Econ. Entomol. 72:256–258.

Walkden, H.H. 1950. Cutworms, armyworms and related species attacking cereal and forage crops in central great plains. USDA Circ. 849. U.S. Gov. Print. Office, Washington, DC.

––––, D.A. Wilbur, and H. Gunderson. 1954. Control of stored grain insects in the north central states. Minnesota Agric. Exp. Stn. Bull. 425.

Walter, E.V. 1957. Corn earworm lethal factor in silks of sweet corn. J. Econ. Entomol. 50:105–106.

––––, and A.M. Brunson. 1940. Differential susceptibility of corn hybrids to *Aphis maidis.* J. Econ. Entomol. 33:623–628.

Walton, R.R., and G.A. Bieberdorf. 1948. Seasonal history of the southwestern corn borer, *Diatraea grandiosella* Dyar, in Oklahoma; and experiments on methods of control. Oklahoma Agric. Exp. Stn. Tech. Bull. T-32.

Walton, W.R., and C.M. Packard. 1951. The armyworm and its control. USDA Farmers' Bull. 1850. U.S. Gov. Print. Office, Washington, DC.

Webster, F.M. 1913. The western corn rootworm. USDA Bur. Entomol. Bull. 8. U.S. Gov. Print. Office, Washington, DC.

Whitcomb, R.F., and R.E. Davis. 1970. Mycoplasma and phytarboviruses as plant pathogens persistently transmitted by insects. Annu. Rev. Entomol. 15:405–464.

––––, J.G. Tully, J.M. Vobe, and P. Saglio. 1973. Spiroplasmas and acholeplasmas: Multiplication in insects. Science 182:1251–1253.

Widstrom, N.W. 1974. Selection indexes for resistance to corn earworm based on realized gains in corn. Crop Sci. 14:673–675.

––––, W.D. Hanson, and L.M. Redlinger. 1975. Inheritance of maize weevil resistance in maize. Crop Sci. 15:467–470.

––––, W.W. McMillian, L.M. Redlinger, and W.J. Wiser. 1983. Dent corn inbred sources of resistance to the maize weevil (Coleoptera:Curculionidae). J. Econ. Entomol. 76:31–33.

––––, ––––, and B.R. Wiseman. 1979. Ovipositional preference of the corn earworm and the development of trichomes on two exotic corn selections. Environ. Entomol. 8:833–839.

––––, A.N. Sparks, E.B. Lillehoj, and W.F. Kwolek. 1975. Aflatoxin production and lepidopteran insect injury on corn in Georgia. J. Econ. Entomol. 68:855–856.

----, D.M. Wilson, and W.W. McMillian. 1984. Ear resistance of maize inbreds to field aflatoxin contamination. Crop Sci. 24:1155–1157.

----, B.R. Wiseman, and W.W. McMillian. 1972a. Genetic parameters for earworm injury in maize populations with Latin American germ plasm. Crop Sci. 12:358–359.

----, L.M. Redlinger, and W.J. Wiser. 1972b. Appraisal of methods for measuring corn kernel resistance to *Sitophilus zeamais*. J. Econ. Entomol. 65:790–792.

----, W.W. McMillian, and B.R. Wiseman. 1970. Resistance in corn to the corn earworm and the fall armyworm. IV. Earworm injury to corn inbreds related to climatic conditions and plant characteristics. J. Econ. Entomol. 63:803–808.

----, B.R. Wiseman, and W.W. McMillian. 1984. Registration of GT-R14 maize germplasm. Crop Sci. 24:626.

----, ----, ----, W.F. Kwolek, E.B. Lillehoj, M.D. Jellum, and J.H. Massey. 1978. Evaluation of commercial and experimental three-way corn hybrids for aflatoxin B1 production potential. Agron. J. 70:986–988.

----, W.J. Wiser, and L.F. Bauman. 1970. Recurrent selection in maize for earworm resistance. Crop Sci. 10:674–676.

----, ----, ----, K.J. Starks, W.W. McMillian, and B.R. Wiseman. 1975. Registration of GT-CEW-RS8 maize germplasm. Crop Sci. 15:738.

Wilbur, D.A., H.R. Bryson and R.H. Painter. 1950. Southwestern corn borer in Kansas. Kansas Agric. Exp. Stn. Bull. 339.

Wildermuth, V.L. 1917. The desert corn flea-beetle. USDA Bull. 436. U.S. Gov. Print. Office, Washington, DC.

----, and E.V. Walter. 1932. Biology and control of the corn leaf aphid with special reference to the southwestern states. USDA Tech. Bull. 306. U.S. Gov. Print. Office, Washington, DC.

Williams, W.P., P.M. Buckley, and V.W. Taylor. 1983. Southwestern corn borer growth on callus initiated from corn genotypes with different levels of resistance to plant damage. Crop Sci. 23:1210–1212.

----, and F.M. Davis. 1980. Registration of Mp703 germplasm lines of maize. Crop Sci. 20:418.

----, and ----. 1982. Registration of Mp704 germplasm lines of maize. Crop Sci. 22:1269–1270.

----, and ----. 1983. Recurrent selection for resistance in corn to tunneling by the second-brood southwestern corn borer. Crop Sci. 23:169–170.

----, and ----. 1984. Registration of Mp705, Mp706, and Mp707 germplasm lines of maize. Crop Sci. 24:1217.

----, and ----. 1985. Southwestern corn borer larval growth on corn callus and its relationship with leaf feeding resistance. Crop Sci. 25:317–319.

----, ----, and G.E. Scott. 1983. Second-brood southwestern corn borer infestation levels and their effect on corn. Agron. J. 75:132–134.

Wilson, R.L., J.L. Jarvis, and W.D. Guthrie. 1983. Evaluation of maize for resistance to black cutworm larvae. Maydica 28:449–453.

----, and D.C. Peters. 1973. Plant introductions of *Zea mays* as sources of corn rootworm tolerance. J. Econ. Entomol. 66:101–104.

Wiseman, B.R. 1985. Development of resistance in corn and sorghum to a foliar- and ear/panicle-feeding worm complex. Proc. Annu. Corn Sorghum Ind. Res. Conf. 40:101–104.

----, W.W. McMillian, and N.W. Widstrom. 1970. Husk and kernel resistance among maize hybrids to an insect complex. J. Econ. Entomol. 63:1260–1262.

----, ----, and ----. 1972. Tolerance as a mechanism of resistance in corn to the corn earworm. J. Econ. Entomol. 65:835–837.

----, ----, and ----. 1976. Wireworm resistance among corn inbreds. J. Ga. Entomol. Soc. 11:58–59.

----, R.H. Painter, and C.E. Wassom. 1967a. Preference of first-instar fall armyworm larvae for corn compared with *Tripsacum dactyloides*. J. Econ. Entomol. 60:1738–1742.

----, C.E. Wassom, and R.H. Painter. 1967b. An unusual feeding habit to measure differences in damage to 81 Latin-American lines of corn by the fall armyworm, *Spodoptera frugiperda* (J.E. Smith). Agron. J. 59:279–281.

----, N.W. Widstom, and W.W. McMillian. 1977. Ear characteristics and mechanisms of resistance among selected corns to corn earworm. Fla. Entomol. 60:97–103.

———, ———, and ———. 1983. Influence of resistant and susceptible corn silks on selected developmental parameters of corn earworm (Lep.:Noct.) larvae. J. Econ. Entomol. 76:1288–1290.

Wymore, F.H. 1931. The garden centipede. California Agric. Exp. Stn. Bull. 518.

Zuber, M.S., and F.F. Dicke. 1964. Interrelationship of European corn borer plant populations, nitrogen levels and hybrids on stalk quality of corn. Agron. J. 56:401–402.

———, G.J. Musick, and M.L. Fairchild. 1971. A method of evaluating corn strains for tolerance to the western corn rootworm. J. Econ. Entomol. 64:1514–1518.

14

Breeding Special Nutritional and Industrial Types

D. E. ALEXANDER

University of Illinois
Urbana, Illinois

Heritable variation in corn (*Zea mays* L.) is substantial not only for yield and other agronomic attributes, but for nutritional and industrial properties as well. The reader is referred to the second edition of *Corn and Corn Improvement* (ASA Monograph 18) for a detailed review of interactions among qualitative genes affecting nutritional quality of the kernel. In this chapter, the present status of breeding efforts aimed at modifying percent oil, protein, and starch, and protein quality and starch type in the corn kernel are up-dated. In addition, the status of breeding efforts on popcorn and sweet corn are reviewed.

14–1 HIGH OIL CORN

Concentration of oil in the kernel, henceforth referred to as oil content, varies widely in corn. Percent oil in the low oil population Burr's White was 1.2%, the high oil strain 21.3%, in the 87th generation of selection (J. W. Dudley, 1982, personal communication). Corn Belt dent inbreds typically range from 2.5 to 5.5% and Corn Belt commercial hybrids typically carry 4 to 5% oil. Although high agronomic quality, high oil content populations are ready for exploitation through breeding, a fundamental question exists: Should corn be bred for higher oil content? It can be argued that it is inherently self-defeating because synthesis of oil is energy-wasting compared to starch synthesis (an input of approximately two calories is required to create oil containing one calorie). Furthermore, the caloric content of oil is approximately 2.25 times as great as starch or protein on a weight basis. It would follow that high oil corn would yield less tonnage per hectare than lower oil corn providing each had equal photosynthetic and physiological capacities. Because corn is regularly bought and sold on a weight basis, few would be willing to produce and sell higher oil types if they produce less tonnage—unless a premium is paid.

High oil corn is an attractive possibility because of high caloric demands in feeding poultry (*Gallus gallus domesticus*), swine (*Sus scrofa*), and dairy cows (*Bos taurus*). Broiler diets regularly contain added oil. The full potential of bovine growth hormone in dairy cows will be more readily exploited if caloric intake is increased beyond that encountered with regular corn rations. Similar advantages can be expected in swine treated with porcine growth hormone.

The advantage, or disadvantage, of higher levels of oil in corn to processors is unclear. Those interested in alcohol, fructose, or industrial starch production may find the higher proportion of oil a disadvantage, particularly when vegetable oils are in surplus.

14–1.1 Methods and Effects of Selection

Progress as a consequence of differences in two methods of selection is shown in Fig. 14–1. The extended progress in the Illinois high oil strain, a derivative of an open-pollinated cv. Burr's White, is a product of a modified mass selection scheme (Dudley, 1977). In contrast, Alexho Synthetic (Misević et al., 1985) is a population produced by intermating 38 open-pollinated cultivars and synthetics. Six generations of phenotypic recurrent selection were carried out: Each generation several hundred selfs were made and gravimetric analysis made of bulked seed from each S_1 ear. The higher oil families were selected for recombination. In generations six through nine, bulk samples of seed from 136 to 493 ears were analyzed using nuclear magnetic resonance spectroscopy (NMR) (Alexander et al., 1967). From each of the 107 to 164 higher oil ears, 20 kernels were analyzed individually and the three highest oil kernels planted ear-to-row. Pollen was collected from all rows shedding on alternate days, bulked, and placed on silks of the best plant available in each row. A bulk sample of grain from each harvested ear was analyzed by NMR and

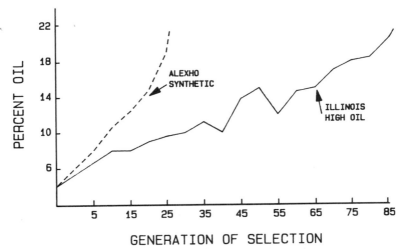

Fig. 14–1. Effect of selection for percent oil in two corn populations.

the higher oil ear, one from each surviving family subjected to single kernel analysis. This procedures, called the single-kernel method, has been repeated through generation 28 with modification in number of kernels analyzed per ear. (No fewer than 50 kernels per ear have been analyzed and no more than 3 kernels per family planted.)

Realized heritabilities for oil content are high. Misević et al. (1985) found they ranged from 0.66 during early cycles of selection in Alexho synthetic to 0.20 in cycles 14 to 24. Overall realized heritability was 0.27. Dudley (1977) reported similar values for the long-term selection experiment in the Illinois High Oil strain, ranging from 0.32 in the early nine cycles to 0.12 over cycles 53 to 76. In the strain selected for low oil, heritabilities for the same cycles were 0.50 and 0.15. Average gain in oil amounted to 0.43% per cycle over 25 cycles. Selection by the single-kernel method (Alexander et al., 1967) has continued and in cycle 27 mean percent oil was 21.2

Miller et al. (1981) reported on a high-intensity selection experiment involving Reid Yellow Dent, an open-pollinated cultivar. Phenotypic recurrent selection similar to that in Alexho Synthetic was carried out except on a larger scale and with higher selection intensity. Selection intensity within 400 families varied from 1/20 to 1/60. Percent oil increased from 4.0 to 7.7% in five cycles. Realized heritability amounted to 0.43. Additive variance remained virtually unchanged over cycles and dominance variance remained near zero suggesting further progress was possible. Yield of grain, plant and ear height, and days to half-silk over seven cycles remained unchanged, but moisture in grain at harvest was significantly greater in advanced cycles.

14–1.2 Performance of High Oil Corn

The effect of higher levels of oil on yield has been evaluated in many experiments. Alexander (unpublished data) found that yield declined from 8.5 to 6.3 t/ha as oil increased from 6.2 to 12.9% in cycles 0 and 22 in Alexho Synthetic. (Oil values were determined from grain produced in performance trials, therefore affected by xenia.) Silvela et al. (unpublished data) concluded that one percentage point increase in oil in Reid Yellow Dent, an open-pollinated cv., reduced yield by 248 kg/ha and an increase of 10% in the coefficient of inbreeding reduced yield by 457 kg/ha. In contrast, Miller et al. (1981) found yield was not depressed as a consequence of high-intensity selection in Reid Yellow Dent, a population in which inbreeding was minimal, and which cycle values ranged from 4.0 to 9.1%. Oil percentages were based on hand-pollinated seed and not from performance trials.

Performance of hybrids involving a standard inbred tester (B73) and inbreds originating from recurrent selection in high oil pools approaches that of standard hybrids (Table 14–1). Protein levels also tend to be somewhat higher than in lower oil hybrids. Miller et al. (1981) found

Table 14-1. Performance of high oil and standard hybrids. Urbana, 1984-1986.

	Yield	Oil	Water in grain	Protein in grain
	t/ha		%	
AEC_2 7 × B73	11.8	8.1	24	9.5
AEC_2 342 × B73	11.3	7.4	25	9.1
$UHOC_0$ 410 × B73	11.4	8.5	25	10.0
R806 × B73	11.2	7.1	24	9.2
Mo17 × B73	12.2	4.5	21	8.5

percent moisture in grain increased as percent oil increased in Reid Yellow Dent but time to half-silk remained unchanged. T. M. Sung (1985, personal communication) compared rate of water loss in a standard hybrid (Mo17 × B73, 4.5% oil) and a high oil hybrid (R806 × B73, 7% oil). Both flowered at the same time. Although the latter had significantly less water in the grain 38 d after anthesis, it was significantly higher (3 percentage points) at 80 d. Misević et al. (1985) followed moisture loss of nine single crosses ranging from 5 to 9% oil. He found that hybrids of 7 to 9% oil were higher in moisture 70 d after anthesis than those at the 5% level.

14-1.3   Feeding Value of High Oil Corn

Corns with higher levels of oil and lesser proportions of carbohydrate are obviously higher in energy because the calorie content of oil is approximately 2.5 times as great as that of carbohydrates.

Han et al. (1987) evaluated corn ranging from 4.8 to 14.4% oil in chicken (adult male) feeding trials. They found that the true metabolizable energy (TME) of 6.7% oil corn was approximately 4.5% higher than conventional corn with 4.8% oil. In trials with broilers, 8 to 22 d posthatching, they concluded, "Weight gain, gain-to-feed ratio, skin and plasma pigmentation were improved in chicks fed diets containing high oil corn compared to those fed conventional corn with the magnitude of response being highly correlated with oil content of the corn." High level skin and plasma pigmentation apparently arose as a consequence of higher levels of carotenoids in the higher oil types. Adams and Jensen (1987) emphasized that calorie/lysine ratio should be considered in formulating diets for growing swine. When optimally balanced, corn with about 7% oil resulted in 11% faster daily gain and 6% greater gain/feed ratio in pigs from 16 to 97 kg than similarly balanced rations containing 3.5% oil.

14-1.4   Oil Quality

Quality in corn oil is usually associated with the ratio of unsaturated to saturated fatty acids with the more unsaturated being most desirable, i.e., higher relative amount of linoleic (18:2) to oleic (18:1). Corn Belt corn typically has 60% linoleic, 20% oleic acid, 18% palmitic (16:0), and

2% stearic (18:0). Small amounts of linolenic (18:3) and trace amounts of other fatty acids also are produced.

Ratio of oleic to linoleic acids appears to be simply inherited and the breeding of types with high proportions of linoleic acid (70%) as well as those with low levels (30–40%) appears feasible (Poneleit and Alexander, 1965; Poneleit and Bauman, 1970).

Although peripheral to the breeding of high oil corn, tocopherol amount and kind is pertinent in that it is an oil soluble vitamin and also that it is an antioxidant that protects double bonds of unsaturated fatty acids from oxidation. The amount and kind of tocopherol (vitamin E) varies widely in corn embryos. Galliher et al. (1985) found a fivefold difference in amount of tocopherol among S_1 families of RSSSC. Broad-sense heritability was estimated to be 0.64. Strains essentially deprived of the α-isomer, others with essentially no γ-tocopherol also were isolated. It seems likely that types could be bred that have much higher concentrations of vitamin E with desired proportions of the γ- and α-isomers.

14–2   PROTEIN: QUANTITY AND QUALITY

Quantity and quality of protein in corn has received relatively little attention from breeders. Even though both are modifiable by breeding and are not particularly expensive to monitor, neglect is a consequence of concentration on attributes of immediate concern, i.e., yield, maturity, standability, etc. However, information on heritability of both amount and quality has been accumulating for many years, particularly about quantity.

A collection of historical papers concerning the Illinois long-term selection experiments (Dudley, 1974) provides perspective on breeding for both protein and oil.

14–2.1   Quantity

Dudley (1977) in a seminal paper reviewed progress for selection in the Illinois Chemical populations and provided a theoretical basis for genetic interpretation of the data. With reference to quantity of protein, he concluded that:

1. Seventy-six generations of mass selection had not exhausted genetic variance even though the mean of the last generation exceeded the mean of the original population by 139% (20 standard deviations).
2. Frequency of favorable (plus) alleles was <0.37 in the original cv. Burr's White.
3. A minimum of 122 loci differentiated the high and the low protein populations.
4. Realized heritability during generations 53 to 76 amounted to 0.15, a value comparable to 0.20 for the first nine generations. (The un-

expectedly high level of heritability encountered during the advanced generations may be a consequence of providing higher levels of N, thus permitting expression of favorable genotypes.)

Although the findings of Dudley are of particular interest to breeders involved with increasing protein levels in corn, they may be of greater influence on design of breeding for grain yield. If the original frequencies of favorable alleles ranged from 0.2 to 0.5, and as few as 50 and as many of 200 loci are involved, and further, that selection moved the mean by at least 20 standard deviations, then he argues that a more complex attribute such as grain yield should respond similarly to selection.

Dudley et al. (1977) found grain yield and percent protein to be negatively correlated (-0.70) in a series of nine hybrids of strains selected for oil and those selected for percent protein. The high negative, and significant, value may pertain only to these unusual types, i.e., involving ultra high and ultra-low protein levels. In experiments involving protein levels more nearly representative of standard corn (8–11%) the genetic correlations were not different from zero (Kauffmann and Dudley, 1979). Over 11 yr, genetic correlations between grain yield and percent protein in RSSSC ranged from -0.68 to $+0.34$ with a mean of -0.06 (J.W. Dudley, 1987, personal communication). Simultaneous selection for grain yield and percent protein in two populations (RSSSC and RSL) resulted in significant increases in both yield and protein and further, the gain of $C_1 \times C_1$ over $C_0 \times C_0$ was equal to the mean of the gains for the two populations (Kauffmann and Dudley, 1979). In RSSSC, results of six cycles of half-sib family index selection for yield and protein were compared with six cycles of stratified mass selection for grain yield with accompanying within block selection for protein. For both selection systems, significant gains in percent protein, kg protein ha^{-1}, and index value were found with no change in yield (J.W. Dudley, 1987, personal communication). Gains for both methods were essentially the same. Thus, percent protein can be increased without loss in yield, at least to the 11 to 12% level.

14–2.2 Quality

Ordinary corn has notoriously poor-quality protein primarily because it is low in two amino acids (lysine and tryptophan) and has an undesirable ratio of leucine to isoleucine. However, ruminants can use corn proteins to an advantage.

Although searches for higher-quality protein corn had been made earlier, it remained for Mertz et al. (1964) to find that the endosperm of the homozygous recessive mutant o_2 (*opaque-2*) was of high quality. The high quality resulted from a reduction in the proportion of zein and an increase in glutelins and globulins. Combinations of *opaque-2* and other mutants also were found to have desirable amino acid profiles but we know of no substantial breeding effort involving them.

Serious objections have been raised about the performance of *opaque-2* hybrids. Among them, yields are lower than comparable dent hybrids, they tend to have higher moisture levels at harvest and they can suffer more kernel damage during harvesting and handling than dent or flint types. However, reports on relative yields of *opaque-2* and dent types are mixed.

Glover (1976) reported that grain yields of *opaque-2* hybrids were 90.7% that of normal dent counterparts. Dry matter ceased to accumulate 7 to 10 d earlier than in the normal hybrids. Mertz (1986) reported that "agronomically superior *opaque-2* soft endosperm maize hybrids are now being produced commercially in the USA, South Africa and the USSR."

Efforts to breed vitreous endosperms in *opaque-2* backgrounds that presumably would resist harvest and handling damage have been successful (Wessel-Beaver and Lambert, 1982; Wessel-Beaver et al., 1985 Ortega and Bates, 1983; Kelly, 1985). Protein quality was usually lower in the more vitreous types. Wessel-Beaver et al. (1985) have suggested that simultaneous selection for hard endosperm and lysine/protein ratio should result in populations with good protein quality and satisfactory endosperm characteristics.

In the USA, a vastly greater effort is expended in breeding dent corns than *opaque-2* types. Consequently, one might expect *opaque-2* types to lag behind in overall performance. At any rate, production is still limited in the USA and is largely confined to farms which produce grain for on-farm feeding of swine. We estimate current acreage to be no more than 1 to 2% of total U.S. production.

Quality protein maize (QPM) performed well in many locations in Mexico and yields were ". . . . indistinguishable from yields of the best normal maizes" (Anonymous, 1987). Nuctricta, a high lysine open-pollinated cultivar released for commercial production in Guatemala in 1983 yields as well as a popular normal cv., ICTA B-1. Nuctricta is a hard endosperm-type similar to the International Center for Maize and Wheat Improvement (CIMMYT) cv. Tuxpeño-1 H.E.O$_2$.

14–2.3 Waxy Corn

Waxy corn, so called because of the dull, waxy appearance of its grain, was brought from China into the USA in 1908. Waxy, a recessive mutant, affects the synthesis of endosperm starches to the extent that only branched chain starch (amylopectin) is created to the exclusion of straight-chain starch (amylose). Ordinary corn is a mixture of branched chain and straight chain starches. The waxy corn is useful for industrial purposes in that it is homogeneous for starch type, thus making separation into distinct components unnecessary. (See Chapter 15 for a description of industrial uses.)

Breeding has centered on the backcross method using the better inbreds of the time and recovering waxy segregants in advanced generations.

Hence, waxy hybrids are usually counterparts of dent hybrids popular a few years earlier. If dent yields improve with succeeding years of breeding, it might be expected that waxy hybrids might not be as high yielding as contemporary dents. Abundant evidence exists that they perform well but little that they are superior to the best dents.

A new dimension has been added to waxy corns in that they may be nutritionally superior in ruminant diets. Baman et al. (1973) found waxy corn was superior to dent corn in the feeding of lambs (*Ovis aries*). Henderson (1974) reviewed a series of feeding trials with cattle and found three of nine experiments showed significantly greater daily gains for waxy corn rations. In one experiment, waxy rations produced significantly greater gain in body weight per unit of feed. In the eight other experiments, differences were not significant.

14–3   HIGH AMYLOSE

Normal corn possess amylose and amylopectin starches in varying proportions but usually contain 30 to 35% amylose. In contrast, waxy corn contains essentially 100% amylopectin. Vineyard and Bear (1952) described a mutant, designated as *ae,* which doubled amylose levels in the endosperm. Several breeding programs have focused on recovery of *ae/ae* segregants of elite dent inbreds. Commercial hybrids with levels of amylose ranging from 50 to 70% have been produced. In general, hybrids with highest percentages of amylose are lower in yield than those with lesser proportions of amylose.

The reader is referred to Chapter 15 for details on use of these corns.

14–4   POTENTIAL FOR BREEDING HIGHER STARCH CORN

Petroleum shortage, either potential or real, has created more interest in the production of ethanol from corn. A higher proportion of carbohydrates, and a corresponding decrease in protein, oil, fiber, and ash would result in greater production of ethanol per unit of grain. Although no direct data are available, indirect evidence suggests that proportion of starch can be modified by breeding. Strains possessing 4.5% protein, and others with 1% oil exist (Dudley, 1977). A reduction of protein to 6% and of oil to 3% in commercial hybrids seems to be a realistic goal. Thus, an increase of 4 to 5 percentage points in carbohydrate can be expected. Reduction of fiber and ash from existing levels seems unlikely and perhaps inadvisable because they make up no more than 3 to 4% of grain weight.

14–5 POPCORN

Popcorn is flint corn modified by selection to maximize popping expansion. High-quality types have pericarps that fragment into small, more acceptable pieces upon popping. Flavor and "mouth feel" are important qualities modifiable by selection. Quality is of paramount importance and is balanced against agronomic performance by breeders. Satisfactory yield, standability, disease and insect resistance are essential qualities that must be met.

Efforts to broaden the genetic base of popcorn by incorporation of dent corn germ plasm have met with mixed success. Inbreds from open-pollinated cv. South American and Supergold combine well, have excellent popping characteristics and agronomic qualities but have poor stalk quality compared to dent corns. Selection in segregating populations of dent × pop has been successful in improving stalk quality and yield but has resulted in poorer popping quality (W. L. Feist, 1983, personal communication).

The prime measure of quality is popping expansion. It increased greatly over the years, but direct comparisons are not easily made because methods changed over the years. Smith and Brunson (1947) reported expansion volumes as high as 30. Ashman (1964) reported popping expansion as high as 1183 in.^{3}/lb (42.7 cc/g) and in 1982 reported values as great as 44 cc/g. It would appear that substantial improvement has been brought about through breeding.

The Ga_1^S allele has been incorporated into widely used popcorn inbreds with the effect that they will not accept pollen from ordinary dents. As a consequence, outcrossing is eliminated in hybrid production fields and commercial fields do not contain rogue ears that reduce quality if mixed with a combine harvested crop.

Although popping expansion has been materially increased by breeding, non genetic factors are important in producing a high-quality product. Popping expansion is greatest in most hybrids if moisture level is at, or slightly below, 14%. Drying should be carried out with high-volume air movement and limited added heat. Kernel size has little effect on popping expansion. However, sizing is often carried out to meet specifications of the consumer. Large kernels tend to produce large flakes that withstand breakage but are less tender than small ones. Snack food producers prefer large kernels but home consumers accept smaller ones.

Most of the commercial crop of the USA today is harvested by combine, a change from hand or mechanical picking of the past. However, careless adjustment of combines and harvest while grain moisture is >18% or <15% inflicts damage that reduces popping expansion (Ziegler et al., 1984).

Popcorn acreage in the USA has ranged from 80.1 million ha in 1968 to 106.1 million ha in 1981, the last year USDA estimates were made. Typical production ranged from 200 000 to more than 300 000 annually.

Production probably has increased since the 1981 USDA estimates were made.

14-6 SWEET CORN

Sweet corn is a popular vegetable in the USA and ranks second in farm value for processing and fourth in commercial value among all vegetable crops (Boyer and Shannon, 1982).

Quality is of overriding importance in breeding programs—as in popcorn. Pericarp tenderness, sweetness, flavor, mouth feel, and perhaps aroma and appearance are to be considered by the breeder along with agronomic properties such as uniformity, yield, disease, insect resistance, etc.

A major factor influencing breeding has been the discovery that the recessive mutant, *shrunken*-2 (*sh₂*), effectively doubles the sugar content of kernels at the "roasting ear" stage (Laughnan, 1953) compared to the traditional vegetable corns homozygous for the recessive *sugary*-1 (*su₁*) allele. Furthermore, conversion of sugars to starches is slowed at ambient temperatures thus reducing the need for refrigeration after harvest.

Breeding programs have usually involved recovery of *shrunken*-2 versions of standard *sugary*-1 inbreds. Some of the more popular hybrids (Illini Xtra-Sweet, Honey n' Pearl, Florida Sta-Sweet) are genetically *sh₂/ sh₂ Su₁/Su₁*. The double recessive mutant has a severely defective endosperm at maturity and often fails to produce satisfactory stands particularly in cold wet soil.

Shrunken-2 corn is popular among home gardeners in the USA and as much as half may now be planted to them. Processors are beginning to use *shrunken*-2 hybrids and it can be expected that their use will increase. Standard *sugary*-1 corns are now largely replaced by *shrunken*-2 types in Florida winter production.

A second useful allele in vegetable corn breeding is sugary-enhancer (*se*) (Ferguson et al., 1978). Recessive homozygotes *se/se su₁/su₁* have approximately twice as much sugar at harvest as traditional sugary types, and have phytoglycogen levels that confer a "creamy" texture as *sugary*-1 types. although the degree of sweetness is similar to *shrunken*-2 corn, the sugars are converted to starch, as in conventional *sugary*-1 types, after harvest and therefore require refrigeration to maintain high quality.

In addition to the *shrunken*-2 and sugary-enhancer corn, breeders have investigated other combinations with improved seed quality. For example, hybrids of the genotype *su₁/su₁ Sh₂/sh₂ Se/se* segregate 9/16 conventional sugary kernels and 7/16 with heightened levels of sugar. The F_1 kernels germinate as well as conventional sugary types yet have elevated levels of sugar.

REFERENCES

Adams, K.L, and A.H. Jensen. 1988. High-fat maize in diets for pigs and sows. Anim. Feed Sci. Technol. 17:201–212.

Alexander, D.E., L. Silvela S., F.I. Collins, and R.C. Rodgers. 1967. Analysis of oil content of maize by wide-line NMR. J. Am. Oil. Chem. Soc. 44(10):555–558.

Anonymous. 1987. Quality protein maize. NRC, Natl. Acad. Press, Washington, DC.

Ashman, R.B. 1964. 1963 Hybrid popcorn performance trials. Purdue Univ., Agric. Exp. Stn. Res. Rep. 100.

————. 1982. 1982 Hybrid popcorn performance trials. Purdue Univ., Agric. Exp. Stn. Bull 403.

Baman, W.L., E.E. Hatfield, F.N. Owens, and J.D. Rinckner. 1973. Waxy corn and nitrogen sources for finishing lambs and steers fed all concentrate rations. J. Anim. Sci. 17(4):1010–1017.

Boyer, C.D., and J.C. Shannan. 1982. The use of endosperm genes in sweet corn improvement. p. 139–161. In J. Janick (ed.) Plant breeding reviews I. AVI Publ. Co., Westport, CT.

Dudley, J.W. (ed.). 1974. Seventy generations of selection for oil and protein in maize. CSSA, Madison, WI.

————. 1977. Seventy-six generations of selection for oil and protein percentage in maize. p. 459–473. In E. Pollak et al. (ed.) Proc. Int. Conf. Quant. Genet., Iowa State Univ., Ames. 16–21 Aug. 1976. Iowa State Univ. Press, Ames.

————, R.J. Lambert, and I.A. delaRoche. 1977. Genetic analysis of crosses among corn strains divergently selected for percent oil and protein. Crop Sci. 17:114–117.

Ferguson, J.E., A.M. Rhodes, and D.B. Dickinson. 1978. The genetics of sugary enhancer (se), and independent modifier of sweet corn (su). J. Hered. 69:377–380.

Galliher, H.L., D.E. Alexander, and E.J. Weber. 1985. Genetic variability of alpha-tocopherol and gamma-tocopherol in corn embryos. Crop Sci. 25:547–549.

Glover, D.V. 1976. Improvement of protein quality in maize. p. 69. In Improving protein quality in maize, Vol. 2. U.S. AID, Washington, DC.

Han, Y., C.M. Parsons, and D.E. Alexander. 1987. The nutritive value of high-oil corn for poultry. J. Poult. Sci. 66:103–111.

Henderson, H.E. 1974. Survey of recent beef cattle trials with waxey, high lysine and normal corn. p. 67–80. In Proc. 29 Annu. corn Sorghum Res. Conf. ASTA, Washington, DC.

Kauffmann, K.D., and J.W. Dudley. 1979. Selection idicies for corn grain yield, percent protein, and kernel weight. Crop Sci. 19:583–588.

Kelly, S.N. 1985. Genetic variability, correlations and selection response for kernel traits in two modified endosperm opaque-2 populations. Ph.D diss. Univ. of Illinois (Diss. Abstr. DES 86–00233).

Laughnan, J.R. 1953. The effects of the sh_2 factor on carbohydrate reserves in the mature endosperm of corn. Genetics 38:412–414.

Mertz, E.T. 1986. Genetic and biochemical control of grain protein synthesis in normal and high lysine cereals. World Rev. Nutr. Diet. 48:222–262.

————, L.S. Bates, and O.E. Nelson. 1964. Mutant gene that changes protein composition and increases lysine content of maize endosperm. Science 145:279–280.

Miller, R.L., J.W. Dudley, and D.E. Alexander. 1981. High intensity selection for percent oil in corn. Crop Sci. 21:455–457.

Misević, D., D.E. Alexander, J. Dumanović, and S. Ratković. 1985. Recurrent selection for percent oil in corn. Genetika 17(2):97–105.

Ortega, E.I., and L.S. Bates. 1983. Biochemical and agronomic studies of two modified opaque-2 mays populations. Cereal Chem. 60:107–111.

Poneleit, C.G., and D.E. Alexander. 1965. Inheritance of linoleic and oleic acids in maize. Science (3665): 1585–1586.

————, and L.F. Bauman. 1970. Diallel analysis of fatty acids in corn oil. Crop Sci. 10:338–341.

Smith, G.M., and A.M. Brunson. 1947. Hybrid popcorn in Indiana. Purdue Univ. Agric. Exp. Stn. Bull. 510.

Vineyard, M.L., and R.P. Bear. 1952. Amylose content. Maize Genet. Coop. News Lett. 26:5.

Wessel-Beaver, L., and R.J. Lambert. 1982. Genetic control of modified endosperm texture in opaque-2 maize. Crop Sci. 22:1095–1098.

––––, ––––, and J.W. Dudley. 1985. Genetic variability and correlations in a modified endosperm texture opaque-2 maize population. Crop Sci. 25:129–132.

Ziegler, K.E., R.B. Ashman, G.M. White, and D.S. Wysong. 1984. Popcorn production and marketing. Purdue Univ. Coop. Ext. Serv. Corn Handb. NCH-8.

15 Corn Marketing, Processing, and Utilization

STANLEY A. WATSON

Ohio Agricultural Research and Development Center
The Ohio State University
Wooster, Ohio

Corn (*Zea mays* L.), like other cereals, probably became established as a food crop in its region of origin, Central America, because it provided a storable form of food energy, could be planted and harvested periodically in a predictable manner, and was easily improved by mass selection. These virtues led to corn's cultivation and use as the basic food crop throughout aboriginal America, and in the Colonial Period, when subsistence agriculture was predominant. Even today in areas of Central and South America, Central and South Africa, Thailand, Indonesia, and parts of China, where subsistence agriculture is the norm, corn is a basic food. However, many people in the developed parts of these areas still prefer corn-based food items.

In the USA during the 19th century, when the population of predominantly European origin was rapidly expanding, demand for refined wheat (*Triticum aestivum* L.) products and animal-derived products also grew rapidly. Corn-based foods gradually became supplementary dishes in the menu but more recently have made a comeback in the form of ready-to-eat breakfast foods, snacks, and Mexican-type dishes. Sweet corn continues to be an important vegetable food in the USA. On the other hand, corn's greater productivity, excellent palatability, and high nutritional content for animals resulted in replacement of wheat, barley (*Hordeum vulgare* L.) and oat (*Avena sativa* L.) as the primary animal feed. An important reason for this shift was that yellow corn has become cheaper than wheat because of increasing knowledge of corn culture, especially in the fertile Central Prairie region.

The improvement of corn by breeding and use of fertilizers, herbicides, and insecticides has produced continuous increases in grain yield. This has resulted in an ever-increasing annual volume of corn produced in the USA (Table 15–1); yields have increased about 35% since 1976 and volume produced nearly doubled. Since, 1960 yields have doubled and production more than doubled (Leath and Hill, 1987). Farm and commercial elevator storage capacity is large and normally carries 10 to 20% of the prior year's crop into the next marketing year (Table 15–1).

Table 15-1. Production, supply, and prices of corn in the USA, 1974–1986.†

Year‡	Harvested area	Yield	Production	Storage 1 Sept.	Total supply	Storage as percent of production	Avg. farm price
	ha × 10⁻⁶	t/ha	——— t × 10⁻⁶ ———			%	$/t
1974/75	26.46	4.84	119.39	12.29	131.73	10.3	118.91
1975/76	27.36	5.81	148.34	9.17	151.56	6.2	100.01
1976/77	28.94	5.92	159.72	10.16	154.69	6.4	84.66
1977/78	28.98	6.11	165.21	22.50	187.76	13.6	79.54
1978/79	29.09	6.80	184.59	28.22	212.83	15.3	88.59
1979/80	29.30	7.37	201.35	33.12	234.49	16.4	99.23
1980/81	29.54	5.45	168.61	41.07	209.73	24.4	122.45
1981/82	30.15	7.33	206.20	26.26	232.48	12.7	98.44
1982/83	29.42	7.62	209.14	55.21	264.38	26.4	105.53
1983/84	20.84	5.46	106.03	79.24	185.32	74.7	127.97
1984/85	29.06	7.17	194.43	18.36	212.85	9.4	110.25
1985/86	30.39	7.94	225.14	41.86	220.55	18.6	92.54
1986/87	21.96	8.03	208.84	102.55	267.28	49.1	

† ERS (1985, 1986b).
‡ Defined as beginning 1 October, and ending 30 September through 1984/85. In July 1986, USDA redefined crop year as starting 1 September and ending 31 August, therefore 1986/87 numbers are not exactly comparable.
§ Conversion factors: ha × 2.471 = acres; t/ha × 15.933 = bu/acre; t × 1.1013 = tons.

However, in years when production and utilization have been erratic the system has carried over as much as 75% and as little as 6.2% of the previous year's crop. Excess storage from bumper crop of 1982 to 1983 was a great advantage in 1983–84 when production was less than half the normal expectation due to a combination of drought in the Midwest and extensive farmer participation in a government acreage reduction program. Animal feeding is by far the largest user of corn in the USA and in most developed countries. The USDA estimates shown in Table 15–2 indicate that since 1974, corn use for animal feeding has averaged 83% of domestic disappearance between 1980 and 1986, ranging from 79.3 to 87.9%. However, the corn equivalent of corn by-product feeds, amounting to about 2%, raises the average of corn fed to animals to about 85%. Corn growing has increased more rapidly outside the USA with the result that the USA now produces 44 to 48% of the total world corn crop in normal years compared with 60 to 70% 25 to 30 yr ago. In addition to corn raised for grain, more than 10⁸t of corn silage and forage are produced annually on 10 to 12% of the 33 to 34 × 10⁶ ha (acres × 0.4046) planted for all purposes (USDA, 1986).

The low price and ready availability of corn has resulted in the development of large volume industrial uses. Although corn dry milling began by grinding corn for food, the bulk of its products enter industrial applications. Corn is an excellent raw material for the production of chemicals by fermentation, but it has not been able to compete with petroleum for many years, except for a few specialties such as citric acid

Table 15-2. Disposition of U.S. corn crops, 1974–1986.†

Year‡	Domestic disappearance					Export	Total disappearance	Ratio: Exp./ total disappearance
	Wet milling§	Dry milling¶	Alcohol	Seed	Animal feed#			
					t × 10⁻⁶			%
1974/75	8.00	3.73	0.43	0.51	80.74	29.17	122.55	23.8
1975/76	8.51	3.88	0.38	0.51	90.63	43.45	147.38	29.5
1976/77	9.14	3.94	0.38	0.50	90.68	42.76	147.40	29.0
1977/78	10.03	4.06	0.38	0.50	95.08	49.45	159.50	31.0
1978/79	10.79	3.94	0.51	0.51	109.76	54.16	179.67	30.1
1979/80	12.06	4.06	0.51	0.51	114.47	61.76	193.37	31.9
1980/81	13.08	4.19	0.89	0.49	104.93	59.80	183.41	32.6
1981/82	15.10	4.14	0.89	0.37	106.68	49.94	171.23	29.2
1982/83	16.88	4.27	1.27	0.48	114.82	47.48	185.11	25.6
1983/84	18.79	4.16	1.27	0.49	94.85	47.36	166.91	28.4
1984/85	20.19	4.09	2.29	0.48	104.52	46.67	171.82	27.2
1985/86	21.33	4.06	2.79	0.48	104.13	41.27	173.84	23.7
1986/87	21.58	4.09	2.92	0.51				

† ERS (1985, 1986a, b).
‡ Defined as beginning 1 October, and ending 30 September through 1984/85. In July 1986, USDA redefined crop year as starting 1 September and ending 31 August. Therefore, the 1986/87 data are not exactly comparable.
§ Except alcohol.
¶ Includes alkaline cooked products.
# A residual term. Includes small unknown disposition.

and antibiotics. Although a significant volume of corn has been fermented to fuel alcohol in recent years, the process is not competitive without government support. Corn has been especially attractive for the manufacture of starch and sweeteners by the wet milling process, not only because of its price and availability, but also because the starch is easily recovered in high yield and purity, and because the by-products have significant monetary value. Milling processes separate corn kernels into the three basic parts shown in Table 15–3. In dry milling, the endosperm is the primary product which is further converted to food and industrial products. The pericarp and germ are separated and the corn oil recovered. The germ residue and pericarp become an animal feed ingredient. In the wet milling process, the specific components of each kernel part (starch, protein, oil, fiber, and solubles) are separated into relatively pure fractions that have a wide scope of specific uses. Alcohol (ethanol) is fermented from hydrolyzed purified starch obtained by wet milling. Alcohol is also made by cooking and fermenting whole ground corn. The residue remaining after removal of the alcohol is an excellent feed material. The amount of corn used to make the major products of the milling industries is given in Table 15–4. These materials enter many food products including bakery and dairy products, beverages, confections, etc. Industrial uses include paper products, construction materials, textiles, metal castings, pharmaceuticals, ceramics, paints, explosives, and countless others.

Table 15-3. Weight and composition of component parts of dent corn kernels from seven Midwest hybrids.†

Part		Percentage dry wt. of whole kernel	Composition of kernel parts, % db‡					
			Starch	Fat	Protein	Ash	Sugar	Unaccounted
Endosperm	Mean	82.9	87.6	0.80	8.0	0.30	0.62	2.7
	Range	81.8–83.5	86.4–88.9	0.7–1.0	6.9–10.4	0.2–0.5	0.5–0.8	
Germ	Mean	11.1	8.3	33.2	18.4	10.5	10.8	8.8
	Range	10.2–11.9	5.1–10.0	31.1–35.1	17.3–19.0	9.9–11.3	10.0–12.5	
Pericarp (Bran)	Mean	5.3	7.3	1.0	3.7	0.8	0.34	86.7
	Range	5.1–5.7	3.5–10.4	0.7–1.2	2.9–3.9	0.4–1.0	0.2–0.4	
Tip-cap	Mean	0.8	5.3§	3.8	9.1	1.6	1.6	78.6
	Range	0.8–1.1	--	3.7–3.9	9.1–10.7	1.4–2.0	--	
Whole kernels	Mean	100	73.4	4.4	9.1	1.4	1.9	9.8
	Range	--	67.8–74.0	3.9–5.8	8.1–11.5	1.37–1.5	1.61–2.22	

† Data of samples no. 1–6 and 8 in Earle et al., (1946).   ‡ db = dry basis.   § Composite.

Table 15-4. United States use of corn for wet and dry milling products and alcohol, 1979-1985.†

| Year | Wet milled products | | | | | Dry milled alcohol | | Dry milled/alkaline-cooked |
| | HFCS§ | Starch | Glucose dextrose | Alcohol | | | | |
				Fuel	Beverage	Fuel	Beverage	
				t × 10⁻³				
1979/80	3 556	4 445	3 302	254	508	0	508	4 064
1980/81	4 191	4 699	3 175	508	508	381	508	4 191
1981/82	4 826	4 699	3 429	1 397	762	635	254	4 140
1982/83	5 461	4 699	3 429	2 540	762	1 015	254	4 267
1983/84	6 477	4 826	3 683	3 048	762	1 016	254	4 166
1984/85	7 874	4 826	3 683	3 048	762	2 032	254	4 089
1985/86	8 382	4 826	3 810	3 556	762	2 540	254	4 064

† ERS (1985).   ‡ Beginning 1 October.   § HFCS = high fructose corn syrup.

A survey made by the Corn Refiners Association revealed that the average supermarket carries more than 1000 food items in which corn wet milling products or derivatives are ingredients.

15-1 CORN MARKETING

The corn grown by U.S. farmers is transferred to the final users through a sophisticated marketing network. Marketing involves physical facilities for drying and conditioning, handling, storing, transporting, pricing, and processing. Corn fed to animals averaged 47.8% of the total annual supply for the 6 yr, 1980 to 1985, (Tables 15-1 and 15-2) compared with 52.9% for 1970 to 1975 (ERS, 1985). This decrease is due largely to an 11.8% increase in harvested hectares and a 21.8% increase in grain yield per hectare with little change in grain-consuming animal units (USDA, 1986). Corn sold off the farm where it was grown (cash corn), therefore, amounted to 52.2%.

Country elevators that handle corn, numbering more than 5000, are the primary gatherers of corn sold off the farms, accounting for about 80% of the volume. About 15% of farm sales are made directly to sub-terminal or terminal elevators and about 5% to feedlots and other farmers (Leath and Hill, 1987). Country elevators supply most of the volume handled by subterminal and terminal elevators but also sell direct to processors. Country elevators also provide services for farmers including drying, storage, and blending of corn. Many also sell and apply fertilizers and pesticides. The marketing channel most used for farm sales varies with the logistics of each region, ranging from 64 to 94% through country elevators (Leath and Hill, 1987). Many grain-exporting firms own country, subterminal, and inland terminal elevators which ship unit trains of 100 or more cars directly to port elevators. River terminals ship corn directly by barges to port elevators. A dramatic expansion of large inland

and export terminal elevators in the 1970s to handle the surge in annual export corn sales from U.S. farms are being used to store surpluses of the 1980s.

Corn milling companies generally purchase corn through subterminal elevators, but depending on their location may make substantial purchases from country elevators and from farmers. Processors who utilize specialty types of corn such as waxy, amylomaize (high amylose), popcorn, white corn, or specific yellow dent hybrids having unique processing properties, cannot purchase them in commodity markets. These companies must purchase specialty corn by contracting directly with farmers, country elevators, or other agents. Contracts specify variety, purity, and a price above the listed commodity price for U.S. No. 2Y (yellow) on the day of delivery. Premiums for waxy corn average $9.84 to 11.81/t (25–30 cents per bushel) over No. 2Y. Amylomaize, which has a 35% lower grain yield than standard hybrids, requires a premium 50% above No. 2Y (M.L. McClachey, 1987, personal communication). These premiums compensate the farmer for extra care in isolation, storage, handling, delivery, and the elevator as "identity preserved" shipments.

In most parts of the USA, corn must be harvested at moisture levels too high for safe storage, therefore, the corn must be artificially dried for storage and transport (Herum, 1987). A survey of farm drying in Illinois, Indiana, and Iowa indicated that 50% or more of the corn crop is dried on the farm where it is grown (Anonymous, 1981). In all of the major producing states, about 65% of the corn produced is stored on the farm where it is grown; about 80% of the farm stored corn has been rapidly dried at elevated temperatures in various kinds of forced air dryers (Herum, 1987). Cultivars (hybrids) have been shown to differ with respect to rate of drying in the high-temperature dryers (Stroshine and Martin, 1986). The remainder is dried in the storage bins with ambient or low temperature air circulation (Leath and Hill, 1987). Mold development is often a problem in the bin drying systems because of low air flow and consequent slow-drying rate. Treatment with approved fungicides prior to binning may be a future alternative (D.G. White, 1986, personal communication).

Individual lots of corn sold off farms are diverse in genetic, physical, and chemical characteristics. Since processors and exporters prefer uniformity among lots, elevators perform the function of blending. Corn is marketed in accordance with a set of grading standards that include a set of characteristics that marketers have agreed are of universal importance (Table 15–5). These include moisture content (MC), bulk density termed test weight (TW), kernel damage by mold or insects (KD), heat damage (HD), broken corn (BC), and foreign material (FM). Different levels of these characteristics, except for MC are used to define numerical grades of 1 (best) to 5 and a sixth category of Sample Grade. The Standards recognize three classes, yellow, white, and mixed corn. There are special grade requirements for flint corn, flint-dent mixed, infested corn,

Table 15-5. United States grades and grade requirements for corn.†

| Grade | Minimum test wt. per bushel | Damaged kernels | | Broken corn and foreign material |
		Heat-damaged	Total	
	lb	%		
U.S. No. 1	56	0.1	3.0	2.0
U.S. No. 2	54	0.2	5.0	3.0
U.S. No. 3	52	0.5	7.0	4.0
U.S. No. 4	49	1.0	10.0	5.0
U.S. No. 5	46	3.0	15.0	7.0
U.S. Sample grade‡		--	--	--

† FGIS (1987c).
‡ U.S. Sample grade is corn that:
1. Does not meet the requirements for the grades U.S. Nos. 1, 2, 3, 4, or 5.; or
2. Contains eight or more stones which have an aggregate weight in excess of 0.20% of the sample weight, two or more pieces of glass, three or more crotalaria seeds (*Crotalaria* spp.), two or more castor bean (*Ricinis communis* L.), and four or more particles of an unknown substance(s), eight or more cockleburs (*Xanthium* spp.) or similar seeds singly or in combination, or animal filth in excess of 0.20% in 1000 g; or
3. Has a musty, sour, or commercially objectionable foreign odor; or
4. Is heating or otherwise of distinctly low quality.

and waxy corn. The Federal Grain Inspection Service (FGIS) must review the standards for each grain every 5 yr. The FGIS, 1987, gives the latest updating for all grains as mandated by recent legislation (Anonymous, 1986).

A lot of corn received at an elevator is sampled with equipment designed to give a representative sample (FGIS, 1980a). The sample is inspected to determine the level of grade properties (FGIS, 1980b), and grade determined based on the highest level of any one of the grade-determining factors. The elevator then attempts to comingle various lots to achieve the grade required by orders on hand, or to achieve preservation of the lot if it is to be stored. Most domestic buyers request U.S. Grade No. 2 but may buy lots of higher grade (lower quality) and apply discounts under the U.S. No. 2 grade level based on their experience with the effect of deficiencies for their particular use. Few, if any, buyers pay a premium for U.S. Grade No. 1. The U.S. grain grades and standards are administered by FGIS, a unit of the USDA. Grading for domestic markets is conducted by independent organizations certified by FGIS. Corn may be sold in the domestic market without grading at buyers request. Alternatively, a buyer may request, and pay for, an official inspection by FGIS.

All grain sold for export must have an official FGIS grade certificate obtained by inspection of a sample collected with an approved continuous sampler during loadout. Buyer pays on a "certificate final" basis and seller is not responsible for changes in grade during transit. Therefore, most buyers specify corn below 15.5% moisure content (MC) and free of live insects to prevent destructive changes during transit. Most export corn is purchased as U.S. no. 3 because of the higher level of BC in most lots by the time they reach the port due to breakage from the extra handling operations. More breakage also occurs during unloading and transfer to local carriers at destination ports. Paulsen and Hill (1977) have documented cases in which the BC content of shiplots of corn exported from the USA initially at 3 to 5% BCFM increased to 12 to 15% from the inland terminal elevators in the USA to unloading at destination ports. Sublots loaded into barges were as high as 20 to 22% due to nonuniform removal of BC and whole kernels from the holds. They determined that breakage was caused by impact of kernels during handling due to high levels of stress cracks in many of the kernels as discussed in section 15–2.4 (Foster and Holman, 1973).

15–2 CORN QUALITY

Differences in quality among corn kernels or lots fall into two main categories: (i) naturally inherited differences of structure or composition; and (ii) degradative differences due to physical or biological damage. The first type can be altered by breeding. The second type is often the result of careless handling and storage or to uncontrollable climatic or predator occurrences. Breeding can often provide a measure of resistance to the influence of both physical and biological damage. The importance of quality to the end user is different for each use and is determined by the user on the basis of the degree of economic harm experienced from poor quality, or the benefit gained from superior quality. A user can obtain any quality of corn he needs by selective purchasing. If the quality desired is not adequately defined by the U.S. Grades and Standards (Table 15–5), he can refuse to accept any lot of corn that has a higher level of defects (lower quality) in any one category than he wants, or assign such a high discount as to discourage undesirable quality from being offered. If the user has quality requirements that are different from the U.S. Grades and Standards, he must usually obtain it by "identity preserved" contracts as described in section 15–1. A user may also purchase commercial lots of different quality by applying special tests not included in the U.S. Grades and Standards, such as for aflatoxin or breakage susceptibility, to incoming loads and rejecting those that don't qualify or by applying a suitable discount or premium. All of these selective purchasing alternatives increase the price compared with the standard practice of relying on numerical grades. The following text describes some of these special quality parameters, but for a more complete review see Watson (1987b).

15–2.1 Moisture Content

The water or MC of corn grains is a natural component, but it is generally incidental to the conversion of the grain to useful products.

Only the dry substance can be converted into starch, corn flakes, or meat. Moisture has considerable influence on quality, but is not itself a quality factor. That is the reason MC was removed from the U.S. grading system as a grade-determining factor in August 1986 (FGIS, 1984). However, the MC of any lot of grain traded must be determined and recorded on the inspection certificate.

Moisture content influences texture of the kernel. Corn having MC above about 20 to 22% (wet basis) is easily cut and ruptured during harvesting (Herum, 1987). This property is optimized by the moisture tempering step in the temper-degermination (TD) dry milling process that adjusts the MC of corn to about 22% for most efficient germ release and recovery. Wet millers will often purchase freshly combined high moisture corn for immediate use because during steeping MC increases to about 45% for best wet milling. Below 12%, MC kernels are especially brittle. Feed manufacturers may prefer low moisture corn to improve grinding efficiency and because feed is not dried after preparation. All users, however, purchase corn for future use and must safely store it until needed for processing. Therefore, most corn purchased by processors is in the range of 12 to 15% MC to avoid mold damage to the corn during storage.

15–2.2 Mold Damage and Mycotoxin

That certain species of fungi are responsible for damage, heating, and burning of cereal grains during storage has been known with certainty only in about the last 25 to 30 yr, due largely to the research of Dr. Clyde M. Christiansen, Univ. of Minnesota, and his students (Christiansen and Meronuck, 1986). Only five species of *Aspergillus* and three of *Penicillium* are commonly found on grain damaged during storage. Six fungal species commonly grow on corn in the field to the extent that damage is noticed (Watson, 1987b). One of the species, *A. flavus*, the producer of aflatoxin, grows on corn both in the field and in storage. Corn, especially the germ portion, is a rich source of nutrient for fungi. The fungal specie that grows and becomes dominant on a particular lot of corn is determined primarily by the grain temperature and MC, or more correctly the relative humidity and temperature of the intergranular gas. The source and intensity of the fungal inoculum is usually of secondary importance because of the wide dispersal of spores of potential invaders. Field fungi require high kernel MC in the range of 22 to 23%, and seldom survive in storage (Christiansen and Sauer, 1982). Most damage by field fungi is done to the corn kernel by *Giberella zeae*, the ear rot fungus that is especially damaging in cold wet weather just before harvest, preceded by cool wet weather at silking time. This condition in 1972 in the U.S. Corn Belt resulted in severe damage to the corn crop (Tuite et al., 1974). *Giberella zeae* damages the kernel by interfering with kernel development causing it to be shrunken. A pink color develops starting at the tip with further invasion of the germ. In addition, this mold produces a toxin known as deoxynivalenol or vomitoxin which causes vomiting, uterus prolapse, and feeding refusal in swine. Feed manufacturers, dry millers, and distillers avoid lots of corn with heavy *G. zeae* infestation, but wet millers can use it if the discount is high enough to make up for the loss of recoverable oil in germ. Probably the most widespread disease of corn ears is *Fusarium* kernel rot caused by invasion of *F. moniliforme* (Shurtleff et al., 1976). Warm, moist weather just before harvest, such as frequently happens in the southeastern USA, disposes corn to this disease. Kernels have a salmon-pink to reddish brown discoloration beginning at the crowns of scattered groups of kernels over the ear. This kernel rot has been associated with a deadly disease of horses known as equine leucoencephalomacia (ELEM) but a specific toxin has not been identified (Haliburton et al., 1979).

Christiansen and Meronuck (1986) describe many cases in which grain, which was thought to be at safe MC, was severely damaged by storage molds. A MC of 15.5% is usually considered to be safe to store for 1 yr. However, *A. glaucus* and *A. restictus* will grow slowly at 14.0 to 14.5% MC. Moisture produced by respiration of these fungi can cause germination of spores of species that require a higher relative humidity (RH), and spoilage may accelerate. Corn lots entering an elevator from various sources will have differing MC's and differing histories of handling. They are blended and stored based on an average MC. However, there will be pockets of higher MC than the average and fungal growth may begin anywhere the MC and temperature are high enough for spore germination. High MC pockets can result from inadequate blending or by migration of moisture in response to temperature changes within a bin (Herum, 1987). Every fungal species has a minimum, optimum, and upper limit of growth, and they are oblivious to the average MC. *Aspergillus flavus* grows only above MC of 16 to 16.5% and at temperature above about 40 to 45 °C (Watson, 1987b). If corn is invaded by *A. flavus* in the field it will continue to grow in storage, and produce aflatoxin, but it is not able to compete with other mold species that overlap its lower MC growth limit. By culturing surface disinfected kernels from 2557 corn samples taken from farm bins in 27 states (Sauer et al., 1984) found *A. glaucus* in 84% of the samples with an average of 22% kernels invaded, and *A. flavus* in 35% of the samples but an average of only 1.2% of kernels invaded.

Mold invasion of corn causes deterioration of the germ as evidenced by brown to bluish coloration of the germ. Brown colors indicate mold damage before mycelium is observed, but the defect known as *blue-eye* is caused by accumulation of blue-green spores of *Penicillium* spp. or *Aspergillus* spp. on the surface of the germ under the pericarp. Damaged kernels category in the U.S. Grade Standards is primarily mold damage to the germ. Heat-damaged kernels are those that have become black due to extremely advanced mold damage and heating. As shown in Table 15–5, Grade No. 2 is allowed to contain a maximum of 5%, and No. 3 a maximum of 7% total damaged kernels. Wet millers place a high discount on damaged kernels because oil recovery from mold-damaged germs is very low (Freeman et al., 1970). Dry millers, snack food producers, and distillers generally avoid mold-damaged corn because of adverse effects on flavor of finished products, and in the case of dry millers, because germ breakage during milling results in higher oil content and poorer keeping properties of cornmeal. Feed mixers prefer corn of low damage because of rejection by animals and lower storage life. Seed producers cannot tolerate mold invasion of seeds because of reduced germination.

Aflatoxin was first identified in 1960 in moldy peanut (*Arachis hypogaea* L.) meal as an acute animal toxin and powerful carcinogen and linked to growth of *A. flavus* and *A. paraciticus* in the meal (Bodine and Mertens, 1983). It was soon demonstrated that these two organisms readily invaded corn and produced aflatoxin. At first they were thought to be only storage molds, but later were found in corn fields in southeastern USA and *A. paraciticus* in more tropical areas around the world. Animal toxicity was not observed below about 50 μg/kg (50 ppb). The USA and other governments enacted legislation limiting the level of aflatoxin to 10 to 20 μg/kg. Users of corn conduct surveys of incoming lots of corn by an ultra-violet lamp inspection method presumptive test followed by chemical analysis of suspect lots (Shotwell, 1983). Midwestern-grown corn is mostly free of aflatoxin because the mold requires high temperatures and droughty conditions for field invasion (Payne, 1983). Furthermore, little corn is stored in the high risk area of 18 to 20% MC where *A. flavus* grows rapidly (Herum, 1987). In years when aflatoxin is expecially prevalent in southeastern USA, and the one recent year (1983) when drought and high temperatures were prevalent in the Corn Belt, government agencies allowed corn to be fed to the more resistant animals, i.e., mature beef cattle (*Bos* spp.), sheep (*Ovis aries*), and swine (*Sus scrofa*), at levels of 100 μg/kg. Although many mycotoxins have been identified in isolated cases, only aflatoxin and vomitoxin have occurred in significant amounts.

15–2.3 Insects

Storey (1987) lists 18 insects that cause damage to corn. Most attack only stored corn but weevils also invade corn in the field in climates with warm winters. These storage insects are of three different habits, i.e., (i) those that develop inside the kernels, mainly weevils, a grain borer, and a moth; (ii) species that develop outside the kernel and live mainly on broken grain, which include five beetles and a moth; and (iii) species associated with high moisture grain and primarily consume the mold mycelium that grows on the grain, including six species of beetles (Coleoptera) and several species of mites (*Acarus* spp. and *Tyrophagus* spp.) (Christiansen and Kaufmann, 1974; Storey, 1987). Kernels damaged by these insects are included in the U.S. Grades and Standards under the Damage category. Insects also damage corn by the heat and respiration generated in their activity that also induces mold development. If unchecked by an insecticidal treatment, their rapid multiplication can quickly damage an entire lot of grain. Most stored-grain insects have a relatively short development period, a high rate of reproduction, and a long adult life. For this reason, all purchasers of corn, especially if it is to be stored or transported long distances, are careful to avoid infested lots or to apply an insecticide before storage or fumigate in storage. Storey et al. (1983) sampled 3000 farm bins of corn across 19 states and found one or more live stored grain insects in 79.9% of the samples. Twenty-four species or groups of species were found of which *Cryptolesetes* spp. (grain beetles) occurred in 57.7% of the samples. The second most prevalent was the Indian meal moth (*Plodia interpunctella*) at 27.9%. Weevils (*Sitophilus* spp.) occurred in 9.4% of the lots of farm-stored corn but among export shipments were the most frequent insect found in 14.4% of the shipments at a density of 5.8/1000 g.

The U.S. Grades and Standards have designated a lot of corn as "weevily" if a 1000-g sample contained two or more live internal developing insects, or one weevil and five other live grain storage insects (GSI), or no weevils and 15 other GSI (FGIS, 1980b). There was no limit on the number of dead insects even though the Food and Drug Administration has a limit of 50 insect parts of any origin per 100 g of foods, such as corn meal. However, in July, 1987, FGIS issued new rules as mandated by provisions in the Grain Qualtiy Act of 1986 (Anonymous, 1986). The new rules (FGIS, 1987c) replace the term "weevily" with "infested" as a special grade. These new rules, which are much less stringent than earlier proposals (FGIS, 1987b), provide that a shiplot of grain of 60 000 bushels (1524 t) will be considered infested with the same number of weevils or other live grain storage insects found in 500-g samples for every 2000 bushels (50.8 t) as in the former rules except that 10 instead of 15 other insects are the maximum allowed. Storey (1987) has described the problems and alternative methods for detecting insects levels in grain lots. He has also described the problems and alternatives of recent action by the Environmental Protection Agency in banning the use of liquid fumigants, formerly so widely used by farmers to eradicate insects in bins.

15–2.4 Mechanical Damage

Two kinds of mechanical damage to grain exists, external and internal. External damage is cuts and abrasions in the pericarp which can be of different depths, i.e., penetrating just through the epidermis or more deeply into the endosperm or germ. This type of damage usually occurs during harvesting and is caused by poorly adjusted combines, driving too fast, or harvesting at MC above 25%. Several studies of average combine operations (Ayers et al., 1972; Steele et al., 1969) revealed a range of from 12 to 66% of kernels with pericarp damage averaging 30 to 34%. Pericarp damage, especially over the germ makes a kernel much more vulnerable to mold invasion (Saul, 1968; Tuite et al., 1985). The latter authors, also Stroshine et al. (1986) found significant differences among hybrids in resistance to mold invasion by intact kernels. Although all damaged kernels were much more vulnerable to mold, hybrid differences were still apparent in the relative degree of invasion. Some exterior damage can be caused by birds or by insects in the field, or by grain-storage insects.

Internal damage is in the form of stress cracks in the horny endosperm and is caused by too rapid drying of the kernel (Thompson and Foster, 1968). Stress cracks are internal fissures that can be observed in kernels by a candling technique or by x-ray inspection. They are formed when shelled corn is dried from harvest MC to about 16% and are due to moisture differentials within the kernel during moisture removal or re-wetting of dried grain (Gustafson et al., 1983; White et al., 1982). Stress cracks are points of weakness which result in breakage when kernels are impacted against a hard surface.

15–2.5 Density

Density is a property of corn that is a measure of weight per unit volume and can be expressed either as bulk density or true density. True density is expressed as specific gravity compared with water as 1.0. It can also be measured against air using an air comparison pycnometer (Gustafson and Hall, 1970). Because the air method requires a large sample, some agronomists have used a simple density test of placing 100 weighed kernels in a cylinder of ethanol and measuring the volume replaced. Density is closely correlated with kernel hardness (Pomeranz et al., 1984).

Bulk density is more easily measured than specific density. It is a grade-determining factor known as *test weight* in the U.S. Grades and Standards (Table 15–5). It is expressed as pounds per Winchester bushel (lb/bu) in the USA and Canada and as kilograms per cubic meter (kg/m^3) in metric countries. Test weight is an important value for shippers or storers because it determines the size of the container needed for a given lot of grain. Test weight is affected by moisture content (Nelson, 1980), by the stage of kernel development when harvested, by the extent of mechanical damage (Hall and Hill, 1974), and by drying temperature (Hall, 1972). Its usefulness as a measure of quality has been debated frequently, but recent data shows that it is closely related to kernel hardness and to corn performance in dry milling (Stroshine et al., 1986; Paulsen and Hill, 1985). Most processors have relied on test weight as an index of kernel maturity characterized by plump, well-filled kernels for preferred processing quality. The epidemic of southern corn leaf blight (*Bipolaris maydis* Hisek and Miyake) in the U.S. Corn Belt in 1970 resulted in low test weight corn because of premature death of the plants. Severely blighted corn gave poor results in both dry milling and wet milling trials (Brekke et al., 1972). Wet millers have found that starch yield and other wet milling parameters were below optimum with corn samples having test weights below about 590 to 620 kg/m³ (46–48 lb/ bu). Dry millers have found unsatisfactory grit yields from corn having test weights below about 670 kg/m³ (Watson, 1987b).

15–2.6 Hardness, Breakage Susceptibility, and Broken Corn

Kernel hardness is an intrinsic kernel property that is generally measured by resistance to crushing or grinding (Pomeranz et al., 1984). It is an inherited characteristic that is modified by cultural conditions and postharvest handling. Intrinsic kernel hardness differences are due to differences in compactness of cell components, cell wall thickness, cell sizes, thickness of the protein matrix surrounding starch granules, pericarp thickness, but most of all to differences in the horny to floury (H/ F) ratios in the endosperm. A method of visually measuring areas of horny and floury endosperm on cross sections of sorghum [*Sorghum bicolor* (L.) Moench] (Kirlies et al., 1984) have been applied successfully to corn kernels (A.W. Kirlies, 1986, personal communication). Flint corn and popcorn types are hard, dent corns are intermediate, while flour corns, such as *opaque*-2, are soft. Corn dried slowly on the ear produces the hardest kernels because there are no endosperm stress cracks and hence low breakage susceptibility. The preferred methods of measuring hardness are use of specific types of mills to determine grinding time or power required. However, determining near infrared reflectance at 1680 λ on the ground material is well correlated with other indexes of hardness (Pomeranz et al, 1986).

Corn that is badly stress cracked produces a larger proportion of broken corn at every transfer point in a marketing chain because of impact against handling and storage or shipping equipment (Foster and Holman, 1973; Paulsen and Hill, 1977). Fiscus et al. (1971) found that breakage of commercially dried corn impacting a hard surface is an exponential function of velocity. Breakage susceptibility is increased as the rate of drying is increased by higher drying temperatures, by cooling rapidly after drying, and by drying from high-moisture levels in one pass to storage moisture levels (Gustafson et al., 1983). The persons who handle corn dried like that may take a discount at each successive marketing point for higher levels of broken corn and foreign material (BCFM) above the accepted level for No. 2 corn. Therefore, there has been a need for a quick method of detecting lots of the abusively dried corn at the first sale so as to assess the person responsible for its condition. Several instruments that give faster results than the previously accepted Stein breakage tester have been developed (Watson and Herum, 1986); one or two were acceptable but none has yet been produced for commercial use. A device known as the Ohio breakage tester, which combines the best features of previously tested instruments is being evaluated for possible future commercialization (F.L. Herum, 1987, personal communication).

A low degree of breakage susceptibility and greater intrinsic hardness are properties most prized by dry millers because such corn gives a higher yield of prime grits (Stroshine et al., 1986, Paulsen and Hill, 1985). Wet millers prefer nonstressed corn because corn dried at moderate temperatures gives better performance and because broken corn is screened out before steeping and goes into lower valued animal feed products. Feed manufacturers may prefer less hard corn because of lower energy requirements for grinding.

The U.S. Grade factors of broken corn and foreign material (BCFM) have been defined as all material passing a 4.8 mm (12/64 in.) round-hole sieve plus any material except corn which will not pass through the sieve. The BCFM is a a grade-determining factor (Table 15–5). The arbitrary screen size used in this separation has been questioned by Hill et al. (1982), who analyzed material passing through various size sieves. They found that material passing through a 2.4 mm (6/64 in.) round-hole sieve contained much of the dust and most of the fine foreign material. Based on these studies, and following a mandate in the Grain Quality Improvement Act of 1986 (Anonymous, 1986), FGIS has added a definition of Foreign Material (FM) to the corn standards as has been the rule for wheat, sorghum, and soybean [*Glycine max* (L.) Merr.] for many years. Foreign material in corn will include all material passing through a 2.4 mm (6/64 in.) sieve plus any noncorn material retained on the 4.8 mm (12/64 in.) sieve (FGIS, 1987c). All material passing the 4.8 mm sieve but retained on the 2.4 mm sieve is reported as broken corn (FGIS, 1987a). In this ruling, FGIS will not require separation of BC and FM but will require that the separate amounts be recorded for all shipments but the amount of FM will be reported only on nonexport certificates. The FGIS will accumulate data for several years to determine the feasibility of establishing separate limits for BC and FM (FGIS, 1987c).

Although broken corn has a feeding value about equal to whole corn, it has certain disadvantages that could be lessened by lower average reduction in breakage susceptibility. Corn dust, produced by abrasion of pieces of broken corn, is highly explosive in the presence of an ignition source and confined space. It has been responsible for destruction of many grain elevators and loss of life (Kameyana et al., 1982). Broken corn tends to accumulate in a core under the spout (hence the name spout line) when a bin or shiphold is being loaded. This uneven distribution results in uneven air flow through the corn and uneven drying when in-bin drying is being attempted. Wet corn in the center of the bin then becomes moldy, heating, and provides a breeding place for grain-storage insects. The presence of bin spouts in stored corn is the initial cause of much damage and lost grain when MC based on the average of the lot is thought to be at a safe level (Christiansen and Meronuck, 1986). When the broken corn is evenly distributed throughout the grain mass, air flow for drying or cooling is restricted (Herum, 1987). For these many reasons, grain quality would be benefited if all commercial corn was at a lower level of breakage susceptibility and hence lower BC.

15–2.7 Special Corn Cultivars

15–2.7.1 Food Yellow Corn

Regular yellow dent corn has a dominant place in world agriculture because it produces high grain yields, it is fairly easy to grind, whole kernels can be masticated by swine and cattle, it is highly digestible, it has a useful level of provitamin A, and it has received more intensive breeding interest than any other type. However for some uses, the standard types of hybrid yellow dent are not entirely suitable. The dry milling preference for harder kernels of uniform size, freedom from stress cracks and aflatoxin has been mentioned. The same properties are true for snack production and alkaline-cooked products (Mexican-type) foods, but further requirements include need for a white cob because the red glumes give the final product an undesirable color, kernels without prominent dents in the crown which tend to overcook in the alkaline processing, clean yellow color or white, and easy removal of pericarp after alkaline treatment. A yellow food corn hybrid yield trial and evaluation program has been established with partial funding provided by the Snack Food Association. Seed companies are invited to enter yellow hybrids that they believe will satisfy the needs of processors. Yield and agronomic properties are evaluated in most maturity zones by agronomists coordinated from the Univ. of Missouri (Darrah et al., 1987b). Process quality attributes are evaluated by scientists at Texas A&M University. There have been no significant attempts to breed yellow food hybrids until recently, but some of the larger snack food companies grow, under contract, hybrids which have specific processing properties.

15–2.7.2 White Corn

White corn has been important for many years for the production of white cornmeal or grits by dry milling, but development of white corn hybrids has lagged behind yellow hybrid development because of the small market for white corn seed. The Quaker Oats Company and the American Corn Miller's Federation have helped finance white corn breeding programs at some state agricultural experiment stations, but some of the hybrid corn companies now also have breeding programs. Yield and quality testing plots in all maturity zones have been coordinated for many years by agronomists at the Univ. of Missouri under sponsorship of the American Corn Millers Federation and the Quaker Oats Company, as described above for yellow food corn (Darrah et al., 1987a). Quality characteristics sought are pure white color, large uniform sized kernels, high specific density, hard endosperm, white cob, as well as the standard agronomic characters. Many good hybrids are now available for all areas. Annual total area harvested in the USA averages about 161 875 ha (400 000 acres) with an average yield of 5963 t/ha (95 bu/acre; S. Weaver, 1987, personal communication). Total production is therefore 965 243 t (38 million bu) amounting to about 23% of all corn used from dry milling and alkaline-cooked products (Table 15–4).

15–2.7.3 Waxy Corn

As discussed in Chapter 14, and under wet milling in this chapter, waxy corn contains starch granules that are 100% amylopectin (branched fraction) compared to 72% for regular cultivars. The U.S. Grades and Standards requires that waxy corn contain 95% or more waxy kernels as measured by an iodine staining test (FGIS, 1980b). Waxy seed corn is produced with 97% or higher waxy kernels. Production of waxy hybrids was begun by the Bear Seed Co., Decatur, IL in around 1940, but now about four companies are major producers of waxy hybrids. Desirable kernel quality characteristics are similar to those of regular yellow dent corn for wet milling, i.e., good yellow color, freedom from mold, low breakage susceptibility, and normal oil content (Freeman, 1973). Wet milling properties are about the same as for yellow dent type. Hybrids are now available with maturities of 93 to 119 d, and give grain yield and test weights about the same as regular hybrids (J.B. McKee, 1987, personal communication). Yellow waxy hybrids are preferred for starch processing in the USA, but white hybrids are preferred in Japan and parts of Europe where there is no premium for yellow gluten. A pure white starch is required in Japan where it may substitute for expensive waxy rice. A considerable volume of yellow and white waxy grain and seed are exported to Europe and Asia. The value of waxy corn in animal feeding is discussed in the section 15–3. Increased animal feeding plus the export market accounts for the steady growth of waxy corn hectarage now approximating 0.3 to 0.4 million ha (0.75–1 million acres).

15–2.7.4 High Amylose Corn

Corn containing starch having greater than the normal 27% of amylose (linear fraction) is known as high amylose corn or amylomaize (see Chapter 14 in this book). It is grown on limited acreage for production of high-amylose starch only. Custom Farm Seed of Momence, IL is the only breeder and producer of this corn type. Breeding to obtain kernel quality equivalent to regular yellow dent corn has been a continuing goal while maintaining amylose contents ranging from 55 to 75%. Amylomaize kernels are generally narrower than normal hybrid kernels, have a slight brown tarnish, and are produced at about 35% below normal grain yields. Production volume is not publicly known, but it is small. Wet milling of amylomaize is more difficult than yellow dent corn and starch yield is lower.

15-3   ANIMAL FEEDING

15-3.1   Corn Use and Processing for Feeding

From 1980 to 1985, 83% of the total domestic disappearance of corn in the USA was fed to animals. Even a greater proportion is used for animal feeding in other developed countries where less corn is used for food and sweetener production. Based on data presented by Ash et al. (1988), it can be estimated that 48.4% of total corn disappearance or 66.5% of domestic disappearance is fed to animals on the farms where the corn is grown. This amount will vary from year to year in response to the relative price of meat, corn, and other cereal grains. Sorghum, wheat, barley, and oat are also fed depending on regional availability and price in relation to corn (Riley, 1984). For example, in 1975 corn accounted for 86.7% of all grains used in manufactured feeds in the Corn Belt but dropped to 78.7% by 1984. In contrast, use of sorghum in the Corn Belt increased from 0.2 to 10.9% in the same time period.

Corn is recognized as giving the highest conversion of dry substance to meat, milk, and eggs compared to other cereal grains. The value of corn as a feed grain is because it is among the highest in net energy content, lowest in protein, and lowest in fiber content. This, as much as any of the grains, justifies the name "concentrate" because of the condensed form of its nutrients. Animals like it and eat it readily. Estimates made by ERS (1985) of corn distribution by type of farm animal averaged over two 6-yr periods, 1970 to 1975 and 1980 to 1985, are given in Table 15-6. Hogs were the largest consumers of corn in the 1980 to 1985 period at 34.6%, followed by beef cattle at 22.4%, poultry at 20.5%, and dairy cows at 18.0%. The change of American consumers eating less red meat for health reasons is supported by the large increase in broiler and turkey

Table 15-6. Comparison of corn consumed by animal groups in the USA.[†]

Class of animal	Six-yr avg.		Change	Ratio 1980-1985/ Total
	1970-1976	1980-1985		
	t × 10⁻⁶		%	
Hogs	28.5	36.7	+28.8	34.6
Dairy	13.8	19.1	+38.4	18.0
Beef[‡]	30.1	23.8	−20.9	22.4
Hens, pullets	8.5	8.7	+2.4	8.2
Broilers	5.7	10.5	+84.2	9.9
Turkeys	1.6	2.6	+62.5	2.4
(All poultry)	(15.8	21.8	+38.0	20.5)
Other livestock[§]	1.3	5.0	--	4.7
Total corn fed	89.5	106.4	+18.9	100

† ERS (1985)
‡ Includes other cattle on feed.
§ Includes unallocated and loss. Varied from 1.8 to 11.4 × 10⁶ t in 1980-1985 but only 1.0 to 1.4 × 10⁶ t in 1970-1975.

(*Meleagris gallopavo*) production and reduction in beef feeding. It is tempting to speculate further about the changes in corn use by the animal groups, but to do so without evaluating the actual meat, milk and egg production and consumption is risky because of the complexity of the equation. Health concerns of consumers, government regulations about food, food price interrelationships, relative prices among feed grains, farm profit margins, improved feed efficiencies and other changes in feeding regimes, government support programs for dairy herds, and other factors, all play a part.

Although some small hog and dairy farmers still feed whole corn, either shelled or on the ear, most of the corn fed to animals, whether premixed or fed directly is processed in some manner to improve acceptability or nutritional value (Jensen and Becker, 1965). Corn retained on the farm may be fed at harvest moisture content of 22 to 30% and can show as much as 9% greater feed efficiency over dry-rolled corn (Hale, 1984). Dry corn can also be re-wetted (reconstituted) before feeding to produce superior gains over dry corn. Water must be added in several increments over several days to achieve satisfactory wetting. Wet grain, whether at harvest moisture or rewetted can be preserved in storage either by ensiling in a low oxygen environment, or by addition of a fungistat such as propionic acid (Hall et al., 1974).

Methods of treating dry corn to improve feed efficiency besides rewetting, include cracking, fine grinding, rolling, and roll flaking with steam. Fine grinding, aside from easier blending with other ingredients, improves the feed efficiency for swine (Beeson, 1972). Pelleting improves feed efficiency of a corn-based mixed feed for swine by 10% (Jensen and Becker, 1965). More than 75% of the rations fed to broilers and turkeys, and 50% of the layer rations, are pelleted. Aside from advantages of ease of handling and the prevention of segregation of ingredients, pelleting, either as is or crumbled, provides a uniform diet for all animals in a pen. In addition, pelleted feeds improve feed consumption and growth rate in poultry and give improved feed efficiency (Allred et al., 1957).

The most effective method of processing corn for feeding beef and dairy cattle, especially on farms where large numbers of animals are fed, is steam flaking. In this process, corn is cooked for 15 min at 93 °C, then flaked through roller mills to a flake thickness of 0.8 mm (1/32 in.) Feed efficiency of corn is improved by 6 to 10%. Improvement is responsive to flake thinness, but also to the percentage of damaged kernels, time of storage, method and amount of drying, and the moisture content after cooking (Karr, 1984). In feeding sorghum, wet processing methods, including steam flaking, rewetting, or early harvest are essential for maximum results with cattle, giving 12 to 15% improvement over dry rolling (Hale 1984). With corn, dry rolling or grinding give good results (Beeson, 1972) at lower capital and operating costs than steam flaking (Schake, 1984) and are therefore most used by small operators.

Waxy corn has been investigated as a feed grain since about 1946

(Hanson, 1946) with variable but mostly positive results (often not statistically significant). Published feeding trials comparing waxy corn to regular corn on poultry, swine, lamb, and dairy and beef cattle have been reviewed by McDonald (1973) and Hicks (1979). They concluded that although some results gave no improvement or negative results, small but positive results were usually found. On the average, daily gain was greater and less feed was consumed per pound of live weight gain for the animals fed waxy corn. Many of the inconsistencies in results may have been due to poor control over quality of either the waxy or the regular corn used, and most did not make comparisons between isogenic hybrids. Nevertheless, many farmers have been growing and feeding waxy corn with positive results. Testimonials indicate increases in daily rate of gain with swine plus lower back fat and better grade. Dairymen are pleased with finding up to 12% increase in milk production and 10% increase in butter fat content. Beef cattle and sheep also are said to have shown profitable rate of gain and feed efficiency (Marking, 1987).

15-3.2 Formulated Feeds

Specialization in agricultural production has given rise to a feed industry which has shown remarkable growth in volume and sophistication over the past 60 yr. Sales of formulated feeds amounted to $10.5 billion in 1982 (USDC, 1984). Ash et al. (1988) have estimated U.S. production of all manufactured feed at 89.63×10^6 t (98.8×10^6 tons) of which 86.96% are classed as primary feed and 13.04% as secondary feeds (feeds made by adding a small amount of another ingredient to a primary feed). Primary feeds are of two types, complete feeds and supplements (including concentrates and premixes) to which a producer adds his own grain. The supplements amounted to 19.8% of all feeds and use about the same ratio of cereal grain to other ingredients as do complete feeds. Complete feeds were more important for poultry and dairy while supplements were used in larger volumes for beef and swine. Complete feeds made up 78.9% of the 1984 reported volume of primary feeds. The total number of feed mills in the USA in 1984 was 6600, but 27 of the largest mills ($>100 000$ tons annual capacity) produced 40% of the formulated feed volume (Ash et al., 1988). About one-third of the feed manufactured was fed to the producer's own livestock, but in the Southeastern states, where much of the broiler industry is located, 70% of the feed is fed to the producer's own livestock. By-product feeds from wet and dry milling of corn were used in feed formulation at a level of 1.9%, wheat mill feeds amounted to nearly 6%, and distillers feeds and brewers grains at 1.8% (USDC, 1984). Oilseed meals constituted 18.3% of primary feeds. Formerly the majority of feed was ground and fed in mash or meal form, but in 1984 53.1% was fed as pellets, up from 41.7% in 1975. An additional 4.2% was offered as cubes, 0.6% as blocks, and 5.6% in liquid form in 1984, leaving 36.5% fed in meal form (Ash et al., 1988).

Feed manufacturers use parametric linear computer programming in feed formulation (Enochian et al., 1971). With this method, the formulator uses weekly prices of all possible ingredients and determines their value on the basis of average composition for all needed nutrients in a particular formula. Ratios of ingredients are then adjusted to provide a feed product of desired composition at the lowest price. The new weekly formula is then transmitted to the computers that control blending of ingredients at the manufacturers plant(s). Practically all feed is now delivered in bulk carriers, generally trucks operating within a 50 to 75 mile radius of the mixing plant.

Manufacture of dog, cat, and other pet foods continues to expand and become more sophisticated. Sales in 1982 were $4.44 billion, up 44% from 1972 (USDC, 1984). These products provide convenience and good nutrition (Rhodes, 1975). Cooked and extruded corn or corn meal, cornflakes, corn gluten meal, and corn gluten feed are important ingredients in pet foods.

Although the major contribution of corn to any feeding system is energy production, its contribution to the protein content of feeds is estimated to be about 25% of total protein in complete foods. This estimate includes protein contributed by the corn by-product feeds. Corn protein is easily digested by all animals and has a high level of the S-containing essential amino acids, cystine and methionine. It is deficient in the essential amino acids, tryptophan and lysine, needed for optimum growth (Wright, 1987). Soybean meal is the major source of tryptophan and lysine, but is deficient in S amino acides. The achievement of a highly efficient animal agriculture owes its existence not only to a great expansion in the knowledge of nutrition in the last 50 to 60 yr, but also to the development of soybean as a major crop. Soybean not only took up the farmland released by the rapid expansion of corn yields, but have provided a low-cost companion feed material with corn. Soybean meal makes up about 17% of the volume of formulated feeds (USDC, 1984).

15–4 WET MILLING

The wet milling process, from its modest beginning about 1840, has developed into a highly sophisticated means of separating the components of the corn kernel by chemical and physical methods into a multitude of useful products. Since that date, the wet milling industry has experienced continued improvement in operating efficiency and product quality, continued expansion in variety and utility of products, and growing demand for its products. During the 10 yr from 1974 to 1984, corn used for wet milling increased 152% (Livezey, 1985). This phenomenal growth was made possible by development of a process for enzymatically converting glucose to fructose in 1961 (Hebeda, 1987). Sweetness equal to sucrose was achieved with introduction of a High Fructose Corn Syrup (HFCS) containing 55% fructose and 45% glucose in the late 1970s. Acceptance of this product for soft drinks accelerated production of HFCS in the early 1980s (Table 15–4) and in 1985 consumption of corn sweeteners for the first time exceeded sucrose consumption in the USA. (ERS, 1986f, 1987). Recovery of markets following the recession of 1982 to 1984, and participation by some wet milling companies in the government supported fuel ethanol programs has raised the utilization of corn by this industry to record levels. In the 1986–87 crop year, it consumed 21.58×10^6 t (850×10^6 bu) amounting to 10.3% of the corn produced or 16% of the domestic disappearance. Projections indicate that wet milling will utilize 25.4×10^6 t (1 billion bu) by 1990 (Corn Refiners Association, 1987). In the last 20 yr, the wet milling industry has adopted new technology resulting in plants that are highly automated and computer controlled (May, 1987). Since major markets for starch and sweeteners are nearly saturated, prices are highly competitive, and since major new product introductions are not close to commercialization, growth in the next decade will probably be closer to the pre-1970 average of 2 to 4% per year (Leath and Hill, 1987). This industry has reached a new plateau of maturity but through continued research and development of new markets, steady, undramatic growth can be expected.

Currently, 20 operating wet milling plants exist in the USA and probably over twice that number in other countries. Total world corn use in wet milling is not accurately known but may amount to as much as 50 $\times 10^6$ t.

15–4.1 The Process

The wet milling process is outlined in Fig. 15–1. The industry's raw material is shelled corn generally purchased as U.S. No. 2 or with appropriate cash discounts for any factors exceeding requirements for U.S. No. 2. Specialty corn-types, waxy and high amylose, are purchased by identity preserved contracts. Before the corn enters the plant, it is inspected for U.S. Grade factors, freedom from aflatoxin, insect, and rodent infestation; unfit shipments are rejected (Freeman, 1973). Accepted lots are thoroughly cleaned by screening and aspiration. Cleanings are added to the by-product feed. The clean corn is then steeped for 30 to 35 h at 47 to 35°C to soften it for the initial milling step. Steeping is more than just soaking corn in water. It is a complicated biochemical process (Watson, 1984). The corn is steeped in stainless steel tanks arranged in batteries of 8 to 12 steeps connected in series by pipes. Water is moved by pumps from one steep to another in a countercurrent relationship with respect to another in a countercurrent relationship with respect to the corn. Process waters are continually reused by operating the entire process in a countercurrent manner. Fresh water is introduced only at the final starch-washing step and works its way stepwise countercurrently to the flow of milled corn, picking up increasing levels of soluble materials. The resulting process water containing 1 to 2% solubles is dosed with 0.10 to

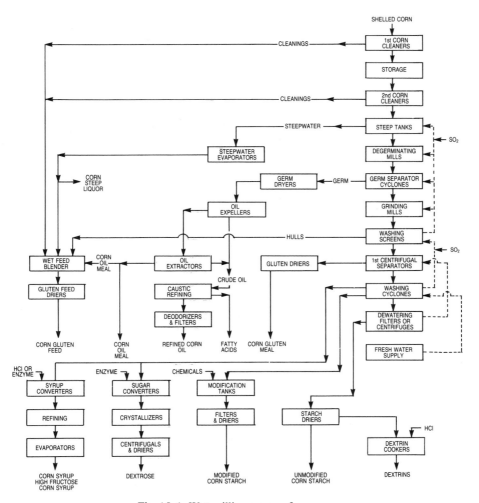

Fig. 15-1. Wet milling process for corn.

0.20% sulfur dioxide (SO_2) which is placed on the corn that has been in the battery the longest time, i.e., the corn that is nearly ready for milling. The oldest water is withdrawn at a solubles concentration of 5 to 7%, dry basis (db). It is evaporated to the thick, brown, corn-steep liquor, 50 to 55% dry substance, composed of protein, peptides, amino acids, lactic acid, and minerals. This fraction represents about 7.5% of the original corn dry substance. About half of this material was originally water soluble; the other half was solubilized during steeping by action of native grain enzymes and SO_2 on protein. The solubilizing action of SO_2 on endosperm protein is essential for softening the kernel for optimum starch recovery (Watson and Sanders, 1961). About half of the steepwater dry substance derives from the germ and half from the endosperm. Final steepwater contains 26% db of the lactic acid content derived by fermentation of sugar leached from the corn by indigenous lactic acid bacteria (Watson et al., 1955). The steep temperature is maintained between 47 to 53°C to favor growth of these bacteria. This temperature and the pH of 3.9 to 4.2 produced by the lactic acid inhibits growth of undesirable organisms.

The milling and separation steps are, of course, somewhat different for individual milling plants but, in general, all follow the steps shown in Fig. 15–1. They have been described in detail elsewhere (Watson, 1984; May, 1987). In the initial milling step, fully steeped corn at about 45% moisture (wet basis) is passed through an attrition (cracking) mill, along with some water, for the purpose of liberating germs with minimum germ breakage. Simultaneous to germ release about one-half of the kernel starch (prime starch) is released in this step. The germ fraction, which now contains about 50% oil (db), is separated from the denser components by flotation in continuously operated liquid cyclones. The germ is washed and dried in preparation for oil recovery.

The underflow from the liquid cyclones is further milled in vertical plate attrition-impact mills or in impact pin mills. However, one company recovers only the prime starch for further purification, while the remaining bound starch is saccharified and fermented to ethyl alcohol (Smith et al., 1966).

After the endosperm has been finely milled, starch and gluten particles must be separated from the residue. This is accomplished by passing the slurry over a series of screen-bend devices that are comprised of stationary curved metal surfaces perforated by precisely milled slots 70 to 80μ in width. At least one reslurry step is required to produce optimum starch yield. The fiber overflow is then usually dewatered in a continuous screw press and dried alone or in mixture with steepwater to produce corn gluten feed.

The starch and gluten particles in the screen underflow are separated in continuous centrifugal machines, usually of the disc stack nozzle-type. The lighter gluten particles are discharged with most of the water into the overflow while the heavier starch granules are discharged into the underflow. The gluten is concentrated and filtered using rotary vacuum filters. The filter cake is dried in flash or rotary hot air dryers to produce 70% protein corn gluten meal at a yield of 5.5 to 6.0% of corn, db. The recovered water is used for fiber washing or steeping.

The starch slurry must be further purified to a final protein content of about 0.3%. This is usually accomplished by diluting the starch slurry with fresh water and passing it through a series of liquid cyclones. The starch cyclones, 1 cm in diameter and 15-cm long, are assembled into a shell which provides for starch slurry introduction, purified starch underflow, and gluten and solubles overflow. The advantage of using the (5–7) cyclone units in series is that they accomplish gluten separation and starch washing simultaneously. The starch is washed countercurrently, finally being contacted with the fresh water entering the milling system (Fig. 15–1).

Starch may be dried by several different methods, but the most economical is with flash dryers. Starch slurry is dewatered by filtering or centrifuging and the cake discharged into stream of heated air. The starch is dried in only a few seconds; flash dryers operate at high volume and low cost. For the manufacture of hydrolyzed products or the manufacture of chemically modified starch products, finished starch slurry from the final cyclone stage is used directly. Although many of the specialized starches are sold in paper bags, most of the large tonnages of commercial starch is transported in hopper cars loaded and unloaded by air fluidization.

Continuing research and engineering developments have transformed the wet milling operation into a highly automated, continuous process (May, 1987). All phases of the unit operations are monitored by instruments which feed data into central control panels. The process may be operated from these control rooms by activating remote control valves, tank level controls and motor switches, and by automatic measurement of density and flow rates. The combination of continuous flow, precise control, closed stainless steel tanks, and careful sanitation has transformed "corn grinding" into a scientific food-processing operation. Continuous progress has been made over many years by the wet milling industry to minimize water and air pollution. Approximately 99% of the initial corn dry substance is recovered as useful products. The unrecoverable remainder is rendered harmless to the environment by modern sewage treatment and smoke abatement procedures.

15–4.2 Starch Products

The primary product of wet milling is starch. It is recovered in purified form in a yield of 67 to 69% of corn dry substance with a recovery efficiency of 93 to 96% of the contained starch. Nearly one-fourth of the corn starch produced is sold as starch products; more than three-fourths is sold as hydrolyzed products, corn syrups, and dextrose. Although starch sales (Table 15–7) increased since 1976, sweetener sales have increased more rapidly due to the impact of development of sweeter syrups. Total U.S. starch sales in 1982 were 2.485×10^6 t (5478.9×10^6 lb) of which corn was 91.75%, while other starches, including potato (*Solanum tuberosum*), tapioca (*Manihot utilissima* Pohl), wheat (*Triticum* spp.), and rice (*Oryza sativa* L.) starches, were 8.25% (USDC, 1984).

15–4.2.1 General Properties and Applications

Industrial corn starch is a fine white powder, 99% pure, containing only about 0.25 to 0.3% protein, <0.1% minerals, and 0.65% fat. The fatty components of starch are tightly complexed with the starch molecule

Table 15-7. Quantity of wet milling products sold.

Product description	Quantity		
	1976†	1982†	1986†
		1000 t	
Starch products§	2 489	2 281	2 211
Sweeteners, total			
Glucose syrups	2 144	2 302	3 226¶
Dextrose	575	580	NA
High Fructose corn syrup			
42% fructose	1 453	2 067	2 631
55% fructose¶	--	1 696	4 502
Corn oil (crude and refined)#	284	401	540
Corn gluten feed	2 263	3 905	4 389
Corn gluten meal	479	826	816
Steep liquor	NA	NA	150
Other by-products (Including seepwater)	260	480	NA
Exports not otherwise included	--	--	70
Total accounted for	9 947	14 538	17 995

† USDC (1984) except as noted.
‡ Data from Corn Refiners Assoc. (1987) plus 10% to account for wet millers not in the CRA.
§ Includes regular and modified starches, and dextrines.
¶ Includes a minor volume of 90 and 100% fructose products.
# ERS (1986d).

and are composed of 55 to 63% free fatty acids, 25 to 38% lysophospholipids and a small amount of other lipids (Morrison and Milligan, 1982).

Corn starch is an important manufactured product because of its usefulness in many industrial applications. Although a few uses depend on properties in the dry state, most applications relate to its properties as a cooked, hydrated paste. The industrial and food applications of corn starch are many and space in this chapter allows for only a cursory description. For more detailed information, the reader is referred to one of the comprehensive treatises available (Orthoefer, 1987; Smith and Bell, 1986; Whistler et al., 1984; Russell, 1973).

Corn starch occurs naturally in nearly spherical granules of 5 to 30 μ in diameter (avg. diam of 14μ). The granules are composites of crystalline and amorphous aggregates of two distinct molecular types, amylose and amylopectine, both of which are polymers of α-D-glucose. Amylose comprises about 27% of the corn starch granule. It is a linear polysaccharide composed of 1000 to 10 000 glucose residues connected by α-1,4 glucosidic linkages. The more abundant amylopectin, 73% of the granule, is a large bush-like molecule with short α-1,4 linked chains connected by α-1,6 glucosyl branching linkages (French, 1984).

Raw starch granules exhibit a maltese cross birefringence pattern when observed microscopically with plane polarized light. Their most striking characteristic is the ability to absorb water and swell within a narrow specific temperature range known as the gelatinization temperature range (GTR). At the beginning of the range a few granules lose birefringence and at the end-point temperature 98% of the granules have lost birefringence known as the birefringence end-point temperature (BEPT). The GTR is characteristic for each starch species but it is influenced by crop production environment (Freeman et al., 1968). Regular corn starch extracted from corn grown in the Midwest typically has a GTR of 62 to 72°C. Chemicals added to a starch slurry and/or chemical alteration of the starch granule can dramatically alter the GTR and the BEPT (Leach, 1965). Raw corn starch absorbs about one part water for two parts starch, but at the BEPT water absorption increased to 20-fold. As a result, the granule swells proportionally and continues to increase in volume as temperature is raised above the BEPT. In this condition, the granule is easily disrupted mechanically or is hydrolyticlaly degraded with acid or enzymes. A direct result of granule swelling is a parallel increase in starch solubility, paste viscosity, and clarity (Zobel, 1984; Leach, 1965).

Adhesion of the swollen granules and binding of water cause a large increase in viscosity. The application of shear to the swollen granules with continued cooking causes marked reduction in viscosity and increased clarity and solubilization. When the paste is cooled, viscosity again quickly increases to an even greater degree accompanied by increased opacity. The transformations are known as gel formation and retrogradation. These properties along with adhesiveness, film-forming ability, and digestibility combined with low cost, are what make corn starch such a useful material in the manufacture of food and industrial products.

Much of the research and development activity of major starch producers has been to modify starch in such a way as to optimize desirable and minimize undesirable properties for a particular commercial application. Most commercial starch products fall into one of the following categories; (i) unmodifed starch, (ii) acid-modified starch, (iii) dextrins, (iv) oxidized starch, (v) cross-linked starch, (vi) chemical derivatives of starch, and (vii) pregelatinized starch. Various combinations of these categories are also produced.

15–4.2.2   Unmodified Starch

Unmodified corn starch, also called *mill starch* or *thick-boiling starch*, is the largest volume and lowest cost industrial starch product amounting to about 60% of all corn starches produced. It is used where its properties of high paste viscosity, strong gels, and retrogradation are useful or can be tolerated. Charcoal briquette molding, beneficiation of bauxite ores, and dusting powder are examples. Paper and paper product manufacture comprise the largest industrial uses of raw starch, consuming about 60% of all starch sold. It is used as an internal binder in forming the paper sheet, as a coating to modify surface characteristics, and as an adhesive in manufacture of paperboard (Mentzer, 1984; Kennedy and Fischer, 1984). More than 22×10^6 t of paper and 25×10^6 t of paperboard were produced in 1982 and production is increasing at about 4.5% a year (USDC, 1984).

For most uses in paper, unmodified starch must be thinned by jet cooking or by enzyme thinning as the paste is made at the mill. This improves adhesiveness and increases production rate (Mentzer, 1984). Numerous chemical modifications of starch are manufactured to reduce paste viscosity, increase adhesiveness, increase retentiveness on fibers, and reduce setback to prolong working time. In food applications, chemical modifications are made to improve texture in foods, to increase clarity, to reduce gelatinization temperature, to improve emulsification properties, to increase solubility, etc. A starch can be made that will fit almost any use. New varieties are introduced every year which improve food quality and production efficiency (Moore et al., 1984; Smith and Bell, 1986).

15–4.2.3 Acid Modified Corn Starch

Granular acid-modified, thin-boiling starches are prepared by heating granular starch slurry below the GTR with acid. The random hydrolytic action is stopped by neutralization at a point that will give the desired paste thinness, and the starch is washed and dried. Cooked pastes of acid-modified corn starches have lower viscosities than mill starch but have a stronger gelling tendency. The lowered viscosity permits use of pastes at higher dry substance. In many uses, such as adhesives for paper lamination and clay coating, the starch must be incorporated at high solids content. In other uses, such as textile warp-sizing applications, where smooth, strong film coatings are needed to protect the fibers during weaving, acid-modified starches are preferred (Compton and Martin, 1967). The greater gelling tendency of acid-modified corn starches gives desired set and texture in gum confections (Wurzburg, 1970).

15–4.2.4 Maltodextrins and Pyrodextrins

"Dextrins" are degradation products of starch covering a wide range of properties and made by a variety of methods (Satterthwaite and Iwinski, 1973). Maltodextrins are prepared by the hydrolytic action of α-amylases on waxy (preferred) or regular starch pastes to the extent of producing 5 to 20 dextrose-equivalent (DE) products of complete solubility but little or no sweetness (Katz, 1986). Maltodextrins are instantly soluble in water, giving clear to hazy solutions of low viscosity. They are completely digestible and completely bland. They contribute body in frozen desserts, soups, etc.; they are excellent carriers for spray drying hygroscopic solids such as instant tea and coffee; they have excellent protective colloid action for fats and are major constituents of coffee whiteners; they are bland diluents for artificial sweeteners, etc. In dry mixes, low DE maltodextrins keep package contents free flowing.

Pyrodextrins are produced by the action of dry heat with or without the presence of (hydrochloric) acid. Pyrodextrin products have a wide range of properties and uses, but are used predominantly in the nonfood industries (Satterthwaite and Iwinski, 1973). The low conversion products, known as *white dextrins*, are made in a broad range of solubilities. Clarities of solutions increase and viscosities decrease with increasing solubility. The high-conversion yellow dextrins are completely soluble and produce clear, nonhazing solutions of low viscosity. Major applications for pyrodextrins are in adhesives for fabricating paper products of all kinds (Kennedy and Fisher, 1984) and for remoistenable gums such as on postage stamps and packaging tape, sizing and finishing textiles, thickeners for water-soluble, fabric-printing inks, and filler for rug backings. Use in foods is limited but is quite acceptable from a regulatory standpoint even though digestibility of the high conversion types is lower than starch. Uses are found in the pan coating of hard candy and to thicken emulsions.

15–4.2.5 Oxidized Starches

Another type of thin boiling starch, oxidized corn starch, is prepared by treating starch slurry with sodium hypochlorite solution. The hypochlorite treatment not only bleaches and causes limited hydrolysis but it also forms some carboxyl and carbonyl groups by oxidation of free hydroxyl groups (Rutenberg and Solarek, 1984). This results in a lower gelantinization temperature, improved ease of dispersion, improved paste clarity, and reduced setback or gel formation. Paste of oxidized starch, when spread in a thin layer, dries to a clear, adherent, continuous film providing the kind of properties desired for paper sizing, paper clay-coating adhesive, textile warp size for cotton and rayon, and laundry finishing, including aerosol spray starch. Lightly bleached starches find use in tableting certain pharmaceuticals such as aspirin and in some food uses such as batters and breadings. A small amount is used in manufacture of wallboard, and acoustical tile.

15–4.2.6 Pregelatinized Starches

The trend toward prepared home and bakery mixes, precooked foods, water-soluble laundry sizes, and many other convenience, items, require starch preparations that will form pastes in cold or warm water. These may be prepared by drying pastes on heated rolls, by spray drying, or by simultaneous pasting and drying on the rolls (Smith and Bell, 1986). Any type of modified starch may be prepared in this manner, but waxy starches are preferred because of easier reconstitution in water. These products are often difficult to disperse in water because all granule structure has been destroyed and particles tend to surface-paste with dry centers. Recently a granular, cold water swelling form has been developed by high-temperature treatment in an aqueous alcoholic solution (Eastman and

Moore, 1984; Smith and Bell, 1986) which simultaneously destroys the granule crystalline structure and removes free and complexed lipids (Jane et al., 1986). The instant solubility and different past viscosity properties may provide new applications for cornstarch.

15–4.2.7 Chemical Derivatives

Bifunctional reagents like glyoxal, epichlorohydrin, phosphorus oxy-chloride, and metaphosphates can react with 2 mol of hydroxyl to form linkages binding adjacent starch molecules. The degree of cross-bonding regulates the degree of swelling of the starch granule and the tolerance to viscosity loss in acidic conditions (Leach, 1965). Waxy starch must be cross-linked for use in foods to reduce peak viscosity and limit viscosity loss from shear and acidity while retaining the clarity and lack of setback. Cross-linked waxy starches are now used to thicken fruit pie fillings and prepared foods of all kinds. Heavily cross-bonded corn starch is used for dusting surgical gloves which must be autoclaved; the starch will not gelatinize but is slowly digested in the body (Wurzburg, 1970).

Monofunctional chemical reagents that react to form ester or ether linkages with hydroxyl groups in starch are a means of adding substituent groups which may radically alter the physical and chemical properties of starch. Most commercially produced chemically modified starches have a degree of substitution of <0.2, i.e., reaction with only one hydroxyl on every fifth glucose unit. A great number and type of chemical starch modifications are possible. For more details, the reader should consult Rutenberg and Solarek (1984), Orthoefer (1987), and Wurzburg (1986).

Hydroxyethyl starch, made by reacting ethylene oxide with starch, is probably the largest volume derivative. The hydroxyethyl group lowers gelatinization temperature and makes for stable pastes that produce clear, flexible films on drying (Rutenberg and Solarek, 1984). It is popular as a textile warp size and in liquid laundry starches. Hydroxyethyl acid modified corn starch is used in paper sizing and clay coating, and for thickening of high gloss printing inks. A highly substituted hydroxyethyl starch has been used as a blood plasma extender. Hydroxypropyl starch is FDA approved for use in thickening foods such as salad dressings.

Corn starches with cationic groups such as amino alkyl and quater-nary ammonium starches have found broad use as internal binders in paper manufacture (Russell, 1973; Mentzer, 1984). They disperse readily in hot water to give smooth, stable pastes. They are strongly absorbed by the negatively charged paper pulp and, although higher in price, can be used at dosages of 0.5% on a dry pulp basis compared with 2 to 3% for unmodified starch. The cationic starches are also useful as flocculating agents in purification of industrial water and ore benefication.

15–4.2.8 Waxy Starch

The waxy endosperm mutant (*wx*) was investigated by scientists at the Iowa Agricultural Experiment Station as early as 1936. They recognized that waxy corn starch properties were somewhat similar to those of tapioca starch and began to develop waxy hybrids. Wet milling possibilities were recognized by Hixon and Sprague (1944), and commercial production began soon thereafter (Shopmeyer et al., 1943). The wet milling properties of waxy corn (waxy maize) are similar to regular corn but starch properties are quite different from regular cornstarch. Waxy starch granules are similar in size and appearance to granules of regular corn starch but are composed entirely of the branched starch fraction, amylopectin (Shannon and Garwood, 1982). Waxy granules can be readily identified by observing a reddish purple coloration when stained with dilute I_2-KI solution instead of the intense blue color of regular starch or higher amylose starches. The unique properties of waxy starch pastes are attributable to absence of amylose. The GTR of waxy corn starch is a little higher than for regular starch; the swelling power when cooked at 95 °C is 2.66 times greater but with the same degree of solubiliziation. For this reason unsheared, waxy starch pastes exhibit high initial viscosity when freshly pasted but on shearing drop below the viscosity of similar regular corn starch pastes, especially under acidic conditions (Leach, 1965).

Waxy starch pastes are long and cohesive, whereas regular corn starch pastes are short and heavy bodied. Waxy starch pastes have a much greater degree of clarity than normal corn starch and tend to remain clear on cooling because of the absence of retrograding amylose. For the same reason, waxy starches do not gel on cooling but remain as fluid, redispersible sols. Waxy starch pastes, dried in thin layers, form translucent films that are readily redissolved. These properties make waxy corn starch useful in many food and industrial uses. However, in nearly all of these uses the properties must be modified by chemical or physical means to increase utility. The clarity and stability of amylopectin starch gels make them especially suitable for thickening fruit pies and many prepared, canned, and frozen foods (Wurzburg, 1970). Chemical cross-linking is necessary to restrict granule swelling and prevent viscosity breakdown on cooking; derivatization with phosphate, acetate, succinate, or hydroxypropyl groups increase paste clarity after repeated cycles of freezing and thawing (Rutenburg and Solarek, 1984).

Thin boiling, oxidized, and hydroxyalkyl modifications of waxy starch produce improved film clarity for textile sizing and certain types of paper coating. Waxy corn starch is the preferred starting material for maltodextrins because of improved water solubility after drying and greater solution stability and clarity. Waxy pyrodextrins have superior remoistening characteristics. Application for modified and unmodified waxy corn starches has continued to grow especially in response to consumer demands for more ready-prepared food items. Powell (1973) has provided a good review and a comprehensive list of applications for the waxy (amylopectin) starches.

15–4.2.9 Higher-Amylose Starch

The recessive endosperm mutant *ae* produces starch containing 55 to 60% amylose named *amylomaize* or high-amylose corn as described in Chapter 14 in this book. Subsequent breeding has produced modified *ae* types having up to 85% amylose. Amylomaize hybrids were initially developed by the Bear Seed Co., Decatur, IL, but are now produced by Custom Farm Seeds of Momence, IL. The commercial utilization was pioneered by two wet milling companies, National Starch and Chemical Corp. and American Maize Products Co., in the early 1960s. Wet milling of high-amylose corn gives lower starch yields than regular corn (Anderson et al., 1961).

Amylomaize starch granules are of two distinct types, spherical and irregular, and are smaller than normal starch granules. The BEPT is reported as 97 °C but they have a high, broad GTR (Shannon and Garwood, 1984). Some of the granules do not lose all birefringence even after prolonged boiling; swelling power is only one-fourth and solubles one-half that of regular corn starch at 95 °C (Leach, 1965). However, pastes prepared by jet steam cooking alone or in the presence of alkalies, salts, or formaldehyde can be handled commercially if not allowed to cool and can be used where tough, opaque films are valued. Hydroxyethyl and hydroxypropyl derivatives improve solution stability of amylomaize starch. Young (1984) has listed 56 applications of unmodified and chemically modified amylomaize starch. Its uses of greatest importance are sizing of glass fibers prior to weaving; a component of gummed candies; preparation of a clear, hot water dispersible, edible film for packaging foods, dyes, and other soluble materials; and coating paper to reduce water and fat absorption. Amylomaize starch sales are small but growing, especially in Europe.

15–4.3   Sweetener Products

The corn wet milling industry began in the mid-19th century as a producer of corn syrups, known for many years as glucose syrup or just glucose. Corn syrup has remained an important sweetener ingredient in foods, along with sugar. Corn syrups and crystalline glucose (dextrose) are less sweet than sucrose and therefore have normally brought lower prices. Glucose (dextrose) is the six-carbon monosaccharide that is the basic monomer comprising the starch molecule, and is the major source of energy in human and animal nutrition. The name *dextrose* refers to the crystalline commercial product. Wet milling companies now produce a syrup that has comparable sweetness to sucrose using an enzyme that isomerizes glucose to fructose. Coming at a time of scarcity and high price of sucrose in the early 1970s, the new high fructose corn syrup (HFCS) triggered a new round of expansion of wet milling facilities and entry of new producers into the business (Table 15–7). Since HFCS syrups can be produced and sold profitably at lower prices than sucrose, they have taken a significant share of the sweetener market. In 1985 to 1986, corn sweeteners for the first time in history, made up more than 50% of the U.S. sweetener market, an increase from about 10 to 11% prior to

1970 (Corn Refiners Association, 1987; Hebeda, 1987). This increase has been made possible due to U.S. government sugar crop support programs and import restrictions that maintain a price above world sugar prices.

15–4.3.1 Corn Syrups

In the time-honored method of manufacturing corn syrup, a 35 to 40% starch slurry is acidified with hydrochloric acid to 0.15 N and heated under pressure to 140 °C. Syrup properties are controlled by stopping the reaction by neutralization at the desired dextrose equivalent (DE). The hydrolyzate is purified by removing insolubles, decolorized by treatment with activated vegetable carbons, and in some cases deashed by passage over ion exchange resins. It is then evaporated to syrups with densities of from 40 to 46 ° Baume which correspond to 75 to 86% dry substance. The process is thoroughly described by Hebeda (1987).

Syrup properties are determined by the DE and by the sugar oligosaccharide components which can be analyzed by high performance liquid chromatography (HPLC) (Hobbs, 1986). Important functional properties include viscosity, sweetness, fermentabiliy, humectancy-hygroscopicity, colligative properties, and participation in the browning reaction. As DE increases, sweetness, fertmentability, and browning increase because of increases in dextrose, maltose, and maltotriose contents. Viscosity, an important property in many food systems, declines as DE increases. Following acid hydrolysis, saccharide composition can be further modified by treatment with various enzymes to produce desired functional properties (Hebeda, 1987).

The syrups consumed in largest volume at the present time are the standard low-priced 42 DE acid-converted syrup, and the 58 to 73 DE high fermentables noncrystallizing syrups produced for the brewing trade (Table 15–6). The latter syrups are made by converting a medium DE (40–50) acid syrup with a fungal diastase-type enzyme that will hydrolyze some higher saccharides (Newton, 1970). Syrups with high maltose are made from acid-thinned paste (15 DE) converted with malt. The enzyme technology now available permits manufacture of syrups with many different proportions of the sugars. Combinations of these products with or without sucrose provide an inifinite number of food applications.

The largest volume uses of corn syrup are in confections, followed by bakery and dairy products. Syrups provide a body to hard candies giving them chewiness and desirable mouthfeel without excessive sweetness; hygroscopicity of hard candy can be reduced by use of high maltose syrup (Frey, 1967). Corn syrups also act as foam stabilizers in marshmallows and provide desired humectancy to maintain plasticity, and they produce desirable viscosity in thick fruit syrups such as in canned peaches (Newton, 1970). Corn syrups are used in baking and in brewing as a source of fermentable carbohydrates. The more highly converted syrups produce freezing point depression for frozen desserts and osmotic concentration for food preservation. The lower converted products help control the number and size of sugar crystals in fondants, ice cream, icings, jams and jellies, and sheen in fruit preserves and pie fillings.

About 5% of the corn syrup sales are in nonfood uses such as bodying agents in inks, shoe polish, textile finishes, adhesive formulations, and pharmaceuticals; in tanning leather; as humectant in tobacco. Low (20–30) DE syrups can be dried (corn syrup solids) for use in foods where water input must be limited.

15–4.3.2 Dextrose

Fully converted starch hydrolyzates (95–96% dextrose) are now universally prepared from acid or enzyme (α-amylase) thinned starch pastes by incubation with amyloglucosidase, an enzyme of fungal origin (Hebeda, 1987). The hydrolyzate is refined and concentrated as for corn syrup and is introduced hot into crystallizers containing a large amount of seed crystals from a previous batch. The mixture is slowly stirred and cooled over a 3 to 4-d period. The crystals are recovered and washed in a basket centrifuge and dried (Schenk, 1986). It is also sold as a 71 dry wt. liquid and shipped in heated tankers. The anhydrous alpha form is produced by recrystallizing a solution of dextrose hydrate in a "strike" evaporator pan at 60 to 65 °C. Anhydrous dextrose is used in pharmaceuticals and food systems, such as dark, sweet, or milk chocolate products, and where the presence of water cannot be tolerated. The U.S.P. grade dextrose, which is used for intravenous feeding and other therapeutic uses, is produced by dissolving and recrystallizing centrifuge cakes to obtain high purity. Dextrose sales have declined slowly in the last 20 yr (Table 15–6).

Functional properties of dextrose include sweetness, fermentability, browning, and osmotic pressure. Dectrose crystals have a negative heat of solution and give a mouth-cooling flavor release. In dry or liquid form, dextrose is about 76 and 65 to 70%, respectively, as sweet as sucrose (Hanover, 1982).

Confectionery manufacture uses account for about 10% of the dextrose produced, mainly as a major component of tableted candies, chewing gum, gum confections, fondants, and hard candy formulations. Another large use for dextrose is in canning and frozen food packs, catsup, frozen desserts, prepared dry mixes, prepared icings, jams, jellies, and preserves, pickles, meats, soft drinks, wines, and malt liquors. The largest single use is in baked goods where the dextrose serves as a yeast nutrient, provides some sweetness, and produces crust browning.

It is used as a tableting aid and diluent, and large tonnages are converted yearly to sorbitol by hydrogenation. Sorbitol is used in the production of synthetic vitamin C and as an intermediate in other chemical syntheses. Dextrose is an excellent carbohydrate source in fermentations for citric acid, antibiotics, etc. (Hebeda, 1987).

15–4.3.3 High Fructose Corn Syrup

A corn syrup composed of 42% fructose (levulose) and 58% glucose (dextrose) is made by reacting fully converted starch hydrolyzate with the enzyme glucose isomerase, contained within cells of several different microorganisms. Whole cells or isolated enzymes are attached to solid particles, such as alumina, and the starch hydrolyzate is passed over columns of the immobilized enzyme for continuous isomerization. The syrup is refined before and after isomerization (Hebeda, 1987).

Since hydrolyzed sucrose solutions (invert syrup) are approximately 55% fructose, competition required development of equivalent corn syrups. This was accomplished chromatographically by passing 42% fructose syrup through columns of adsorbent containing Ca or other divalent anionic groups (Long, 1978), or a mineral adsorbent (Broughton et al., 1977). Fructose is retained on the adsorbent more strongly than glucose. Elution washes off glucose which is recycled to isomerization columns. Final elution is 90% fructose which is evaporated and sold as such (Young and Long, 1982) or, more generally, blended with 42% isomerate to produce a 55% fructose syrup. Additionally, pure crystalline fructose is now being commercially produced by chromatographic separation to obtain a 97% fructose fraction for crystallization (Hebeda, 1987; ERS, 1986e).

Properties of HFCS are similar to those of regular corn syrups but sweetness is its foremost property. Crystalline fructose is 1.8 times sweeter than sucrose and 2.4 times the sweetness of crystalline dextrose (Hanover, 1982). The 55% HFCS has the same sweetness as sucrose while the 90% HFCS is 6% sweeter, but sweetness perception is affected by temperature, pH, and concentration. Other studies have shown that sweetness comparisons in complicated food systems are often different from comparisons made from water solutions of sugars and are greatly affected by concentration. Hence, HFCS has equal sweetness to sucrose in some foods; in others it is less sweet. Thus, HFCS has found application in a wide variety of food systems such as confections, baked goods, table syrup, fountain syrups, sweet beverages, catsup and other condiments, pickles, etc. (Young and Long, 1982). A major marketing goal from the beginning was to obtain acceptance in all carbonated beverages. This goal was achieved in 1982 through improved quality standards, improved processing, and refining methods (Morris, 1984). Acceptance of HFCS for 100% of sweeteners by major bottlers gave a large boost to corn wet milling volume (Table 15–4) and produced a mature marketing environment capped by establishment of a futures market for HFCS on the Minneapolis Exchange in March, 1987 (ERS, 1986e).

15–4.4 Feed Products

Kernel components, mainly protein and fiber, remaining after recovery of the corn starch and corn oil in the wet milling process amount to about one-third of the original corn dry substance (Fig. 15–1). These materials are sold almost exclusively as ingredients in feeds for farm animals and pet foods (Wright, 1987). The corn gluten meal (CG) is standardized at 60% protein, and contains about 400 mg/kg in xanthophyll pigments at the beginning of a crop year. However, xanthophyll content drops gradually through the year due to oxidation in corn processed, reaching about 200 mg/kg of CG by the end of the season (Watson, 1962). Corn gluten meal is used primarily as a protein concentrate and pigment source in broiler chicken feeds (Kuzmicky, 1968) in areas where yellow skin is a desirable marketing attribute. It is important as a protein source high in essential S amino acids, methionine and cystine in poultry, swine, and pet rations (Wright, 1987). Soybean meal compliments the low levels of lysine and tryptophan in gluten meal while CG makes up for the deficiency of S amino acids in soy. In cattle and sheep, CG is only partially digested in the rumen providing essential amino acids through duodenal digestion (by-pass protein) (Klopfenstein et al., 1985). Corn protein purified in such a way as to have bland flavor is a potential source of vegetable protein for food in combination with soy and other proteins (Neuman et al., 1984).

The wet milling fraction, containing the corn pericarp or "fiber," is composed mostly of cellulose and hemicellulose plus residual starch and protein. It has a digestibility of 80% (total digestible nutrients, TDN) for ruminants and is sold by one wet milling company at a 10% protein level for ruminant and dairy rations. Several companies are refining the pericarp fraction to give a bland food fiber source containing up to 90% dietary fiber. Most of the wet milled fiber, however, is blended with steepwater and spent corn germ flakes or expeller cake and dried to 10% MC to produce corn gluten feed (CGF). This product has a standardized protein guarantee of 21% and finds use primarily as a major ingredient in dairy and beef cattle rations, but can also be used at up to 10 to 15% in laying chicken and swine rations, respectively. Versions of CGF having higher steepwater contents at up to 31.5% protein are available from several companies and may be more suitable for nonruminant animals because of a lower proportion of fiber. In recent years, wet CGF has been sold directly to cattle feed yards as a way to reduce air pollution and energy costs (Wright, 1987). Fortunately, CGF is highly regarded as a feed ingredient by the Dutch who import 80% of the U.S. production for European feeds. About 4.6×10^6 t of by-products were produced by the industry in 1986 compared with only 1.33 t in 1972.

Corn germ meal containing 22.5% protein is available from wet millers who solvent extract corn germ. It is useful in feeds as an absorbent for liquid ingredients such as molasses, fish solubles, choline, etc. Corn steep liquor or heavy steepwater is known officially as a feed ingredient by the name "condensed fermented corn extractives." It is sold to a limited extent as a component of liquid feeds for beef cattle, as a component in beef range blocks, and as a fermentation nutrient (discussed under Fermentation Industries, section 15–12). Corn steepwater is rich in phytin (hexaphosphoinositol) from which the vitamin, i-inositol, has been manufactured.

15–4.5 Corn Oil

Corn oil is commerically produced only from corn germ isolated by wet milling or dry milling. Because of this supply restriction combined with strong demand, corn oil usually commands a slightly higher price than the other two major vegetable oils, soybean, and cottonseed. The volume of corn oil produced has steadily increased over the last half century as wet and dry milling capacity has expanded. In 1972, the total corn oil volume reached 226 800 t (500 million lb); in 1986 the production had grown to about 612 123 t of (1.35 million lb) which 20% is exported. The dry milling process accounts for about 10% of the corn oil production. In the USA, corn oil is 4.3% of vegetable oil production and about 7.2% of domestic oil utilization (ERS, 1986c, 1986d).

Oil is recovered from corn germ by expelling, solvent extraction, or a combination of expelling and extracting as generally described by Reiners and Gooding (1970); Orthoefer and Sinram (1987). Wet milled germ is preferably expelled from an oil content of 50 to 60% down to 20 to 25% and finally extracted with hexane to a residual oil content of 1 to 2% in the spent corn germ flakes. Most dry corn mills recover oil only by extraction or sell germ to those who extract.

Crude corn oil is composed of 95% triglycerides. Minor components include free fatty acids, waxes, phospholipids, pigments, and odorous compounds, which must be removed by refining to achieve an acceptable food product. In outline, this process involves several steps: (i) forming the sodium soaps of the free fatty acids, (ii) removing the emulsion containing the soaps and the phosphatides by centrifugation, (iii) removing the waxes by chilling, (iv) removing pigments by contact with bleaching clays, (v) removing odors by high-vacuum distillation at 225 to 260 °C. The fatty acid fraction is recovered by heating the emulsion in the presence of sulfuric acid and is sold as an ingredient for use in beef and poultry rations (Orthoefer and Sinram, 1987).

Refined corn oil is 98% triglycerides in which the saturated constituent fatty acids are palmitic (16:0) 11.0%, stearic (18:0) 1.8%, and arachidic (20:0) 0.2%. The unsaturated fatty acids are linoleic (18:2) 60.9%, oleic (18:1) 25.3%, and linolenic (18:3) 1.1% (J.M. Hasman, 1986, CPC International, Union, NJ, personal communication). It is well known that variation in the ratio of the two principal fatty acids, oleic and linoleic, is due to genetic background as discussed in Chapter 14. The linoleic and oleic acid contents of commercial corn oil have gradually changed from 56 and 30% to the present ratio of 61 and 25% over a period of 40 yr (Weber, 1987; Reiners and Gooding, 1970) during which period total oil in corn processed at Illinois wet milling plants dropped from about 4.9 to 4.3%, apparently due to gradual changes in higher-yielding corn hybrids planted (Watson, 1987a).

The recognized acceptance of corn oil as a food oil is, in part, due to its flavor stability during storage and cooking, without added synthetic antioxidants. This stability is the result of an adequate level of natural antioxidants, the tocopherols, and a low level of linolenic acid (Weber, 1987). About 60 to 65% of the corn oil in the USA is consumed as salad or cooking oil (ERS, 1986d). Its bland flavor and high smoke point are mainly responsible for its popularity. Another reason for the popularity of corn oil is its high content of unsaturated fatty acids recognized by medical authorities (American Heart Association, 1968) as a dietary method of reducing blood cholesterol levels. The other large use, 30%, is in margarine. Corn oil margarine has grown from its introduction in 1957 to a major food item at about 11% of all margarine oils (ERS, 1986b). Other food uses are minor. The only part used industrially is the 7 to 8% removed from crude oil by refining.

15–5 DRY MILLING

The dry corn milling industry began as numerous small mills scattered across the country-side to supply whole ground corn meal to local clients for household uses. As the population became more urbanized, the demand for food products with longer shelf life resulted in the development of milling systems that produced low fat cornmeal by removal of germ. As the degermination dry milling process became more complex, mills became larger and fewer. Brekke (1970) reported that there were 152 dry corn mills in 1965 with daily capacity of 2268 kg (50 hundredweight). At last count (Anonymous, 1984a), the number of mills had declined to 88 in 1984. Of these, 66 were small mills in Southern states and California (two). Of the larger dry corn mills, 17 account for most of the output. Twelve of these are large mills with capacities between 254 and 1778 t/d (10 000–70 000 bu) for an annual grind of 2.82×10^6 t (111×10^6 bu), which is 92% of the reported industry capacity of 3.05×10^6 t (120×10^6 bu) (Alexander, 1987). Dry milling, unlike wet milling, has maintained a nearly constant production rate at 3.0 to 3.5×10^6 t (118–138 million bu) annual rate.

15–5.1 The Process

As mentioned previously, the normal dent corn kernel is comprised of the following parts: pericarp, tip cap, germ, horny endosperm, and floury endosperm (Table 15–3). The degerminated corn dry milling process, more accurately called the *tempering degerminating* (TD) system, is outlined in Fig. 15–2. This process is operated to make as complete a separation of these parts as is economically possible: (i) retaining the maximum amount of horny endosperm portion as discrete pieces; (ii)

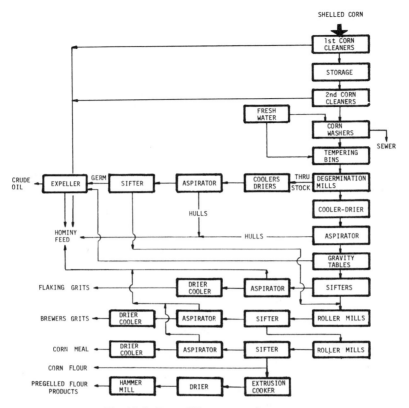

Fig. 15-2. Dry milling process for corn.

removing as completely as possible the germ and pericarp to give a low fat, low fiber product; (iii) recovering as high a percentage of the germ as large, clean pieces. Different steps in the separation process include cleaning, tempering by water addition, degerming, drying, cooling, grading, aspirating, grinding, sifting, and packaging. The corn used is usually purchased only after a sample has been inspected for freedom from aflatoxin, insects, mold, and in some plants, low breakage susceptibility (Watson, 1987b). The flow sheet (Fig. 15-2) shows how these steps are normally coordinated. However, this diagram is much simplified because separations are not perfect and fractions have to be remilled, reclassified, and resifted several times to try to achieve optimum yield and quality. Furthermore, mills differ markedly in the types of equipment used and preference for materials routing (Brekke, 1970; Alexander, 1987; Anderson and Watson, 1982).

The initial cleaning steps for the whole corn are of utmost importance because, although high-quality corn is purchased for food production, residual contamination must not be allowed to enter the process. Although not shown in Fig. 15-2., most mills use magnetic separators to remove tramp metal; scourers and aspirators to remove adhering dust, glume, and other light material; screens to remove large and small foreign material; water washing with flotation to remove cob pieces; and settlers to remove stones and nonferous metal. Some mills have used electrostatic separators to remove rat pellets the same size as corn kernels.

The cleaned corn must be tempered with water or steam to condition the corn for milling. The corn is moistened with water in an amount needed to bring the corn up to 20 to 22% moisture and held for a period of time (1–3 h) to allow the water to equilibrate through the kernel. Degermination may be accomplished in a variety of ways but the most popular, especially if flaking grits are desired, is with the Beall degerminator. Some companies use impact mills or granulators for degermination for different results with and without tempering (Brekke, 1970).

Discharge from the degerminator is dried to 15 to 18% moisture and cooled. It is sized over stacked coarse sifters or reels with the largest material +3.5 to +10 mesh passing through aspirators to remove free pericarps and thence to specific gravity tables where germs are separated from endosperm by difference in density. Endosperm fractions and impure germ-endosperm mixtures are passed through corrugated counter-rotating roller mills to remove adhering pericarp and/or germ pieces and flatten germ pieces for better screening. Each roller mill set is preceded by an aspirator to remove light material and followed by a sizing device, usually stacked screens of appropriate sizes for the stock being handled. The roller mills are set with differential speeds and a gap appropriate for the material it receives to minimize grit breakage. Endosperm fractions are finished in purifiers designed to remove fine pieces of fiber and are packaged according to grade at 12 to 14% moisture.

15–5.2 The Products

Finished germ, containing 18 to 27% oil depending on the mill configuration, is dried to 3% moisture and the corn oil expelled in standard oil expelling equipment followed by solvent extraction to a residual oil content of 1 to 2% (Brekke, 1970; Reiners and Gooding, 1970). The germ residue is blended with pericarp fractions, unseparable mixtures of endosperm, pericarp and germ, and corn cleanings to give a commodity feed item known as hominy feed (Table 15–8). This product is guaranteed to have a minimum level of 10% protein and 5% oil but generally averages 10.5% protein and 6.0% oil. Hominy feed is used as an ingredient of swine, ruminant, and poultry feeds as a source of energy and good-quality protein (Wright, 1987). Solvent-extracted germ has been processed to a germ flour containing 25% protein using a process developed by a USDA laboratory (Blessin et al., 1972). This material has become a useful, nutritious food ingredient.

A typical yield of products from dry milling are: hominy feed, 34%; corn oil, 2.0%; grits, meal, and flour, 60%; shrinkage, 4.0%. There are no

Table 15-8. Typical yields and products from dry corn milling.†

Product	Yield	U.S. Sieve Size	Fat	Protein
	%		%, db‡	
Hominy or cereal flaking grits	12	−3.5 + 6	0.7	8.4
Coarse grits	15	−10 + 14	0.7	8.4
Regular or medium grits	23	−14 + 28	0.8	8.0
Coarse or granulated meal	3	−28 + 50	1.0−1.2	7.6
Cones or dusted meal	3	−50 + 75	0.8−1.5	7.5
Corn flour	4	−75 + Pan	1.5−2.5	6.6
Corn oil§	2	--	100	--
Hominy feed	34	--	6.0	12.5
Shrinkage	4	--	--	--

† Brekke (1970).   ‡ db = dry basis.   § Solvent extracted.

definite specifications which closely define all products which can be manufactured, but the classifications generally accepted in the industry are shown in Table 15-8. The ratio among endosperm fractions varies with the quality of the corn, the milling conditions, and the orders the miller has to fill; most mills are quite flexible in the latter. Fat content is the most generally used criterion of purity. Fat values in Table 15-8 are minimum values and are affected by milling conditions and corn quality.

The grit fractions are all produced from the horny endosperm, have a bright yellow color or are clear white, and are free of dust and bran pieces. The miller usually tries to optimize yield of flaking grits because of premium price. Each hominy grit will become one corn flake. A common alternate distribution of products, depending on sales needs, is to produce brewers common grits by combining larger than 24-mesh material and milling so that 95% will pass 12-mesh. All material passing 24-mesh may be sold as cornmeal, but screen size up to 32-mesh is used in some mills. Quality of grits are judged on color, odor, fat content, and freedom from dust, pericarp, and insect fragments. Flour has long been considered a by-product which at times was put in feed. However, new uses have been found that have channeled all output into more profitable markets (Roberts, 1967).

Most mills make specialty products utilizing raw grits, meal, or flour. These raw materials are processed by cooking with steam to the desired degree of starch gelatinization, on flaking rolls or extrusion cookers, dried and ground as required by the user (Alexander, 1987). The degree of dispersibility of these products is conditioned by the particle size of the starting material, method, time, and pH of cooking, and degree of shear.

15-5.3 Uses for Corn Endosperm Products

Utilization of the approximately 2.857×10^6 t (6.299×10^9 lb; adjusted for noncorn ingredients) of dry corn products manufactured are distributed among human foods, beverages, pet foods, and industrial products are shown in Table 15–9.

Of the 1.86×10^6 t of endosperm products, 45% is used by the brewing industry. Although brewing is the single largest use, all food uses account for 39.3%. The most commonly recognized use, particularly in Southern states, is boiled grits served as a side dish with nearly all meals. Some people prefer the bolder flavor of yellow corn products especially in the northern USA, however, most people, especially in Southern states, prefer white grits; more than 80% of the table grits sold are white. Corn bread or corn muffins made from cornmeal have long been a favorite bread in all parts of the USA, and more recently these popular dishes have been offered as dry, self-rising mixes for easier preparation. Another favorite food is corn flakes. The flaking grits are cooked to a rubbery consistency with syrup, malt, salt, and flavoring added. After tempering, the cooked grits are flattened between large steel rolls followed by toasting in traveling ovens to a golden brown color (Rooney and Serna-Saldivar, 1987). Corn products are made into several other forms of ready-to-eat cereals alone or blended with other grain products (Fast, 1987).

The rapid growth of dry mix formulations and snack products of various kinds has increased demand for corn flour to the extent that mills sometimes must increase flour yield by milling larger sized fractions. Corn

Table 15–9. Estimated 1977 product volumes of the corn dry-milling industry.[†]

Application areas	Quantity
	$t \times 10^{-3}$
Brewing, total	838.98
Food, general	
Breakfast cereals and cooked grits	362.8
Mixes (pancake, cookie, muffin, etc.)	45.35
Baking	22.68
Snack foods	45.35
Other foods (breading, batters, baby foods, etc.)	34.03
Total	510.19
Fortified foods (PL 480), total	219.9[‡]
Nonfood	
Gypsum board	45.35
Building products (particleboard, fiberboard, plywood, etc.)	18.14
Pharmaceuticals/fermentation	90.70
Foundry binders	40.82
Charcoal binders	34.01
Other (paper, corrugating, oil well drilling fluids, etc.)	11.34
Total	240.36
Prepared pet foods[§]	49.43
Animal (Hominy) feed,[¶] total	997.70
Total	2 856.97

[†] Estimates based on unpublished data (Alexander, 1987).
[‡] Corn products represent 65 to 70% of total shipments, or 315 to 340 million lb.
[§] USDC (1984).
[¶] Data reported by Alexander (1973).

flour has been found to be particularly valuable as an ingredient of pancake mixes, baby foods, cookies, biscuits, ice cream cones, ready-to-eat cereals, batter breading mixes, and binders for loaf-type sandwich meats (Roberts, 1967). The high starch content of cornmeals and flour is important in giving a high puff in preparation of extruded snack products in which a delicate corn flavor is desired. On the other hand, isolated corn starch is most useful for snacks in which artificial flavors are to be added.

Industrial uses amount to about 13% of the dry-milled endosperm products. Most uses of corn flour are in processes where the more highly purified starches have no particular advantage even though they may be more effective on a weight basis. The major uses are foundry sand core binders, oil well drilling mud thickeners, and particle board manufacture which use pregelatinized corn flour. Unmodified corn flour is used in briquette binders; adhesive for gypsum board and other construction materials; refining and pelletizing ores; fermentation; and paperboard (Alexander, 1987). On the other hand, purified corn starches have the advantage that they can be chemically modified more specifically to fit a particular application and generally have greater adhesive power.

A food item of major importance to the dry miller in recent years has been corn-soy-milk (CSM) (Alexander, 1987) used under the Food for Peace Legislation (PL 480). This product is a mixture of 68% gelatinized corn meal, 25% defatted soy flour, 5% nonfat dry milk and 2% minerals and vitamins. A lower cost, but equally nutritious product called "corn-soy blend" (CSB) (the same as CSM except for omission of milk) has also been produced. The product has been made by companies under contract to U.S. Agency for International Development (U.S. AID). When the program began in 1966 until 1974, CSM and CSB have been distributed to more than 100 countries by the USDA. The high cost of dried milk caused a shift toward CSB in 1974. Alexander (1987) states that about 60 different products are being sent to impoverished people or local governments by private industry under contract with U.S. AID.

Corn endosperm products are also an excellent source of carbohydrate in fermentation as will be discussed in a later section. Brewers grits have long been used as a major brewing adjunct. Some breweries prefer to use a pregelatinized flake if cooking facilities are limited (Alexander, 1987).

15–6 OTHER CORN FOODS

15–6.1 Traditional Foods

Corn has been used in many parts of the world as the basic food item and people have found many distinctive ways to prepare it. For example, in the colonial and pioneer eras in the USA, traditional foods included Johnny cakes, a kind of corn bread, fried mush (cornmeal cooked, gelled,

largest popping volume for buttered popcorn, and "ball" which is preferred for carmel coating because of less breakage. These differences are partially inherited and partially due to popping temperature. Sales of regular and flavored popcorn amounted to $163 million in 1982 (USDC, 1984). Much raw popcorn is sold for home popping of which a growing segment is retailed in metalized paper containers for microwave oven popping. Prepopped popcorn is offered in many flavors and carmel coated.

15–6.4 Parching

Parched corn made by heating whole corn kernels on hot rocks, sand, or ashes was a trail food often used by North American Indians and pioneer hunters. The parched corn was also ground and used as gruels and porridges. Today, parched corn is a popular snack item knwon by the trade name Corn Nuts. For this product, the manufacturer prefers to use large flour-type kernels, developed from Corioco varieties from Peru. In preparation, pericarps are removed by a mild alkali treatment prior to toasting (Rooney and Serna-Saldivar, 1987).

15–7 FERMENTATION INDUSTRIES

Developments in the technology of growing microorganisms in pure cultures to produce specifically useful products has become a large and important industry in the last 35 to 40 yr in industrialized nations, especially the USA, Japan, and western Europe. Increasing volumes of corn and corn products are being used to produce a wide variety of chemicals and food and feed ingredients, as well as traditional beverages, and fuel ethanol (Perlman, 1973; Maisch, 1987). Cultures of yeasts, molds, bacteria, and actinomycetes are grown in deep fermentation tanks and their desired metabolic products recovered by a multitude of sophisticated methods (Casida, 1964). All microorganisms require carbohydrate as an energy source for growth. Corn, cornmeal, corn starch, corn syrup, dextrose, cane, and corn molasses may be used depending on the requirements of the particular organism and the method of recovery or desired purity of the end product. In the future, fermentation industries are expected to utilize increasing quantities of corn and corn products by utilizing new methods of improving performance of microorganisms by gene transfer and by development of continuous fermentation processes.

15–7.1 Beverages

Beer and distilled liquors are the leading beverage products with respect to volume production and utilization of corn in the USA. In other countries, the corn use in these beverages is limited. Maiden (1975) states that ingredients for average British beer are approximately 75.5% from malt, 5.5% from unmalted cereal adjuncts (barley, corn, and wheat), and 19% from brewing sugars and syrups. The British law does not specify any particular ingredients, while in Germany beer must be made from malted barley, hops, yeasts, and water. In 1982 the beer and liquor industries in the USA used 581.7 thousnad t (22.9 $\times$ 10^6 bu) of corn and corn products (USDC, 1984). This amounts to about 1.0 to 1.1% of the total corn usage in the USA. The figures for corn and corn products used in beer include common grits purchased from dry millers plus a small volume of corn starch grits supplied by wet millers. Starch grits are made from purified corn starch slurry by heating slightly before filtration to give a filter cake that dries in nondusting lumps or by compacting powdered starch on steel rolls. The use of corn grits reached a peak of nearly 2 billion lb in 1977, but since then their use has declined an average of 3.7% a year due to increasing use of rice and corn syrups (Alexander, 1987).

15–7.2 Beer and Malt Beverages

Beer manufacture is basically a process of treating malt to convert and extract the barley starch to fermentable sugars using the amylolytic enzymes present in malt (carefully sprouted and dried barley) followed by yeast fermentation. Demand for blander, less-satiating beers, especially in the USA, has permitted use of more refined carbohydrate sources of two types: (i) dry adjuncts, primarily dry milled corn or sorghum grits, unmalted barley, corn flakes, broken rice, refined corn starch grits, and dextrose; (ii) liquid adjuncts, namely corn syrups and liquid dextrose. The so-called "lite" beers use dextrose as adjunct since it leaves no unfermentable residues (Pyler and Thomas, 1986; Hebeda and Strylund, 1986).

The initial step in beer production is called *mashing* (Fig. 15–3). A malt-water slurry is slowly heated to extract the enzymes and initiate the digestion of starch and protein in the malt. Dry starchy adjuncts are cooked separately to gelatinize the starch and infused into the mash. Corn grits at a 30% level are said to produce a volatile aroma compound profile similar to that of an all malt beer (Pyler and Thomas, 1986). Corn flakes, pregelatinized by roll drying, can be added directly to the mash. When a starch-iodine test shows that all starch has been digested, the mash is filtered (lautered) and washed (sparged) to recover solubles. The extract (wort) is boiled to concentrate the solids, to sterilize and to precipitate excess proteins; hops is added during the boiling to provide the desired bitter flavor and to help precipitate protein. Clarified wort is a solution of 62 to 75% fermentable sugars, primarily glucose and maltose, plus dissolved proteins, minerals, vitamins, etc., extracted from the grain. Syrup and sugar adjuncts are added at this point (Hebeda and Stryland, 1986). The wort is cooled to 9 °C (48 °F), for lager beer (14 °C, 58 °F for ale) and inoculated with the appropriate brewers yeast. After about

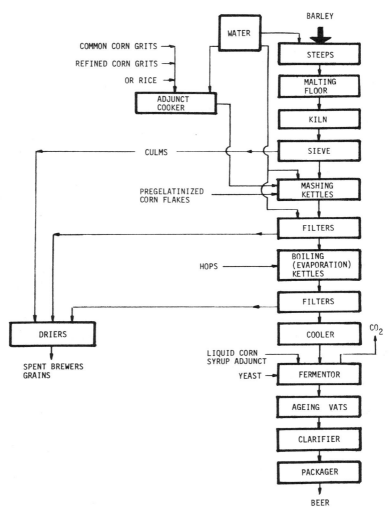

Fig. 15–3. The brewing process.

8 to 10 d, the yeast has converted the sugars to about equal parts ethyl alcohol and CO_2. The CO_2 is drawn off and compressed for later use in carbonation. Alcohol content averages 3.0 to 3.8% for most lager beers but may run up to 6.5% for some ales and stouts. In the final step, the beer is aged form 30 to 90 d at 0 to 1 ° C (32 to 34 °F), clarified, carbonated, and packaged.

High conversion and high maltose syrups have the same fermentability as normal malt wort, i..e., about 75 to 80%, and can replace all other brewing adjuncts at 30 to 48% of total extract, with no effect on flavor, aroma, or appearance. The syrup is added to the wort during boiling thereby eliminating the need for cooking and saccharifying the adjunct. Advantages are lower capital cost for brewery construction and expansion, and lower operating costs are realized by conducting high gravity fermentations. Other benefits from using liquid adjuncts are shorter fermentations, better color control, and greater uniformity (Hebeda and Strylund, 1986; Pyler and Thomas, 1986; Alexander, 1987). In Great Britain, the single-temperature mashing process of 65 °C makes the use of corn grits uneconomical, but high fermentable corn syrups are quite useful (Maiden, 1975). The use of corn syrup provides the brewing industry a low capital cost way to expand as it meets the growing total and per capita consumption of beer.

15–7.3 Wines

Although most of the sugar in wine fermentation comes from grapes (*Vitus* spp.), dextrose may be added prior to fermentation in eastern USA to compensate for lower sugar levels of eastern-grown grapes. Such supplementation is forbidden by law in California but is not needed because of the higher sugar content of California grapes. However, specially sweetened wines are made by adding sugar and dextrose. Sweet "pop"-wines and "wine coolers" sweetened with high-fructose corn syrup have achieved significant market penetration. Wine consumption in the USA is growing at an annual rate of 4 to 5% per year, and 90% of the consumed product is made in this country.

15–7.4 Distilled Liquors

In the manufacture of distilled liquors, corn is the major carbohydrate source for grain neutral spirits, corn whiskey, and bourbon. In the process, described in detail by Maisch (1987) corn is ground, then cooked (mashed) to gelatinize the starch. It is then cooled to 55 to 65 °C (131–149 °F) and mixed with about 2% malt based on weight of grain to convert the starch to the disaccharide, maltose. Distillers prefer malt over other enzyme sources because malt influences flavor. The converted mash is inoculated with selected strains of yeast, *Saccharomyces cerevisiae*, for 24 h at about 32 °C (90 °F) which produces 1 mol of CO_2 and 557 kJ (528 BTU) of heat energy for every mole of glucose converted to ethanol (ethyl alcohol). Maltose is hydrolyzed to glucose by maltase enzymes in the yeast. The CO_2 is recovered, condensed, and sold. The heat must be removed by cooling to maintain a constant temperature (Maisch, 1987). After fermentation is complete at 8 to 9% ethanol, the spent grains are removed and washed, and the wort distilled to recover the alcohol. The colorless distillate is aged for several years in white oak barrels (charred for bourbon; new for corn whiskey) to remove undesirable flavors. Bourbon is made with a mixture of grains, usually rye and corn, but corn must constitute 51% of the mash bill. Corn whiskey may be made from any corn material; corn, corn grits, corn starch, corn syrup, and corn sugar are the major raw materials. One company, The Grain Processing Corp., produces grain neutral spirits from wet milled corn endosperm (Smith et al., 1966).

The still bottoms from wort distillation are evaporated to recover solubles which are then dried with the spent grains to produce a valuable feed component called *distillers dried grains with solubles.* Some manufacturers dry and sell the two products separately but major production is in the combined form. This feed by-product contains 27% protein, 8% fat, 40% total (NDF) fiber, minerals, and vitamins. It is useful as a protein concentrate in a wide variety of animal feeds (Wright, 1987). A rule of thumb for yield of products from corn is one-third alcohol, one-third CO^2 and one-third feed by-products.

In 1983, the distilling industry produced 274.4 thousand kL (72.5 $\times$ 10^6 tax, gallons at 50% ethanol) of whisky and 100.5 thousand kL of gin and vodka in the USA (Anonymous, 1984b).

15–7.5 Fuel Alcohol and Chemicals

The biggest news in fermentation in the last decade is the development of a corn-based fuel alcohol industry in the USA as a response to nearly fivefold increase in cost of petroleum in the 1970s. Ethanol production by fermentation cannot compete with ethanol from petroleum priced under about $30/barrel because of the yield loss to CO_2. However, in an attempt to reduce petroleum imports, the U.S. government waived the 5 cents/gallon tax on gasoline containing 10% ethanol and has provided a variety of financial incentives for plant construction. Twenty-eight states have also given financial incentives ranging from 1 to 11 cents/gallon of alcohol but most states offer 3 to 5 cents/gallon (Gill, 1987). These subsidies, amounting to 50 to 80 cents/gallon of absolute (100%) ethanol, made for profitable production of ethanol from corn. Since the corn wet milling industry had excess starch conversion capacity and had only to add fermentation and distillation, they were able to begin making ethanol quickly. By 1984, wet millers were producing 75% of the 1.25 million kL (330 $\times$ 10^6 gal) of absolute ethanol. However, as the new whole-grain plants have come into production, the proportion produced by wet millers has declined (Gill and Allen, 1985). By 1986, 60% of all alcohol was produced by wet millers, 82.8% of which was fuel alcohol (ERS, 1986b). The USDA has estimated 7.366 $\times$ 10^6 t (290 $\times$ 10^6 bu) of corn will be used to produce about 2.84 million kL (750 $\times$ 10^6 gallons) of 100% ethanol and 2.21 $\times$ 10^6 t (2.436 $\times$ 10^6 tons) of high protein feed by-products. [This was calculated using a yield of 2.6 gallons of ethanol and 16.8 lb D.B. of feed by-products per bushel (Gill and Allen, 1985)]. A negative factor on profits from significant expansion of fuel ethanol from corn is the depressing effect increased feed by-product volume will have on feed price. Although there has been some resistance by motorists to use gasoline containing ethanol, it has become the cheapest anti-knock alternative as tetraethyl lead is phased out. Sales of "gasahol" (gasoline containing the maximum allowed level of 10% absolute ethanol) has grown about 1% a year and in 1986 amounted to 8 billion gallons, taking about 8% of the gasoline market. A new impetus to ethanol use in gasoline has come from data indicating that presence of oxygenated compounds in gasoline reduce carbon monoxide discharge from engines. California and Colorado are considering legislation requiring addition of oxygenated compounds of which ethanol is a leading contender (Gill, 1987).

The process for fuel ethanol production is similar to that used for beverage alcohol except that since flavor is not important, lower quality corn can be used, the starch conversion conducted with the lower cost commercial enzymes, and distillation done at higher efficiency. Production costs recently have been helped by low corn prices because corn accounts for 50 to 75% of the cost of ethanol. A low cost alternative to previously costly distillation methods of converting the 95/5% ethanol/ water azeotropic mixture to 100% ethanol required for motor fuel, is absorption of the water through a column of dehydrated corn grits (Ladish et al., 1984). The federal subsidy was due to expire in 1992, but has been restored in the tax reform legislation of 1986 (Gill, 1987).

The high price of crude oil in the 1970s, stimulated a great deal of research and speculation about volume production of certain chemical feedstocks by fermentation of corn or corn starch. Some of these chemicals such as acetone and butanol, were made by fermentation before petroleum became so plentiful. When petroleum became the lowest priced raw material for chemical production in the 1930s, fermentation chemical plants were shut down. However, some chemicals such as citric acid, glutamic acid, lysine, and food grade lactic acid, are made more economically by fermentation of corn, dextrose, or molasses. Two vitamins, riboflavin (B_2) and cobalmide (B_{12}) are made by fermentation using dextrose and corn steep liquor. Altogether, 20 to 25 chemical entities are made by fermentation (Perlman, 1973).

In the 1970s, when crude oil prices increased dramatically, much research was begun to revive and modernize fermentation methods for chemical manufacture. Much research, mostly unpublished, has been done using recombinant DNA or RNA methods to improve efficiencies of microorganisms or develop totally new forms which can be utilized in advanced fermentation techniques. In addition, numerous methods have been developed for attaching enzymes or whole cells to rigid media held in columns through which substrate can be passed for continuous conversion. The drop in oil prices from $30 to $8–10 a barrel in the early 1980s suspended much of this development, but the new technologies (Tsao, 1987), may make some processes much more competitive, especially if crude oil prices stabilize around $20/bbl or higher.

15–7.6 Antibiotics

Commercial antibiotic production by fermentation was established during World War II and has since grown to a large and important industry. The preferred carbohydrate sources are corn syrup, dextrose, corn starch, lactose, and sucrose. Corn, corn grits, or molasses are less preferred because of purification problems in recovery of the end products. Cornsteep liquor was early found to provide a ready source of soluble nitrogenous nutrients plus unknown growth factors that stimulate antibiotic production. Were it not for this stimulative effect of cornsteep liquor, the production of penicillin during World War II would have been seriously curtailed. The active ingredient in steep liquor has never been identified, so it continues to remain an important source of growth factors and readily available organic nitrogen in nutrient media for penicillin and other fermentations (El-Marsafy et al., 1975). About 15 kg of steep liquor (50% dry substance) and 20 kg of carbohydrate are needed for every kilogram of penicillin produced (Casida, 1964).

Total antibiotic production in the USA in 1982 had a total value of more than $1,689 million (USDC, 1984). Tetracycline is produced in largest volume followed by penicillin, neomycin, bacitracin, and streptomycin. Perlman (1973) lists more than 85 different antibiotics. A very large volume, predominantly penicillin, bacitracin, and neomycin, has been used as growth stimulant in animal feeds.

15–7.7 Enzymes

Enzymes, the specific active agents produced by microorganisms in all fermentations, are being produced in purified form for important commercial uses. Perlman (1973) has listed more than 60 commercial products. In many cases, whole corn or cornmeal supplies the carbohydrate for the production medium, and cornsteep liquor is an important ingredient. Production of enzymes of fungal or bacterial origin including α-amyase, gluco-amylase, and glucose isomerase have achieved high volume production to supply the demands of the rapidly growing HFCS market from cornstarch (Hebeda, 1987). Other enzymes have important uses in food preparation, detergents, meat tenderizers, cheese production, etc.

15–8 CORNCOB USE

Corn-growing produces about 18 kg of corncobs for every 100 kg of corn grain. Most cobs are left in the field but a cob conversion industry in the USA has developed as commercially feasible uses have been found. In 1979, about 1.1×10^6 t of cobs were used industrially. Nearly 700 thousand t were used as granular products. An additional 100 thousand t went into a variety of industrial applications including xylose production. An undetermined amount is used as feed for ruminant animals (Foley and Vander Hooven, 1981; Bagby and Widstrom, 1987).

Corncobs are structurally composed of: (i) inner and outer glumes (membranous structures subtending the kernels where they are attached to the cob); (ii) the woody ring of lignified conducting tissues, and (iii) the inner pith. The famous corncob pipes are made by grinding off the inner and outer soft layers followed by filling voids with gypsum and polishing the surfaces of the woody ring. However, pipes are made from special hybrids developed by the Univ. of Missouri and are grown on 2025 to 4045 ha (5000 to 10 000 acres) in one Missouri county. The entire annual world supply of 25 to 30 million pipes is made by three companies (M.S. Zuber, 1976 personal communication).

Most of the corncobs of commerce are the cobs that can be collected from the few farmers who still harvest corn with pickers. However, one company, The Andersons of Maumee, OH, pays a small premium to attract ear corn to supply their cob conversion business. Cobs dried to 10% moisture are ground, screened, and aspirated to separate the chaffy glumes, the woody ring pieces, and the soft pith (Foley and Vander Hooven, 1981). Cobs are extremely tough and difficult to grind. Woody portion granules are at the same time hard and absorbent. They are especially useful for blast polishing and cleaning of oil and other contaminants from metal stampings, and castings. Electrical parts can be cleaned without danger of removing insulation. Many finished metal parts are cleaned and deburred by tumbling with cob granules which produce almost no dust even under the most rigorous handling methods. The free-flowing, highly absorbent properties of corncob granules makes them useful as carriers for pesticides, fertilizers, vitamins, etc. More finely divided fractions are used in hand soaps, cosmetics, and animal litters. Foley and Vander Hooven (1981) list 49 chemicals for which corncobs have been a carrier and 46 different uses.

The pelleted chaff/pith portions are useful as absorbents for molasses in beef and dairy rations and for bedding laboratory animals. The pith has been used for removing oil spills from water surfaces with no added pollution effects.

Corncobs are composed of about 41% cellulose and 36% hemicellulose, 3% pectins, and 0.6% lignin (Foley and Vander Hooven, 1981). They have an ignition temperature of 205 °C (401 °F) and a net energy content of 18 800 kJ/kg (8088 BTU/lb). Since seed corn companies generate substantial quantities of corncobs, they have used them as a source of heat energy (Peart et al., 1981) but the ash has a critical melting point that can foul heat-exchange surfaces. However, Keener et al. (1985) have solved this problem by burning ground cobs in a fluidized sand bed burner at 75% efficiency. They have also found that ground corn, which has a heat energy of 18 740 kJ/kg, is equivalent to liquid propane at $0.80/ gallon in heat production for corn valued at $112.22/t ($2.85/bu at 15.5% MC).

An important use of corncobs is in production of furfural and its derivatives which have become important industrial chemicals. Furfural is produced on large scale by destructive distillation at a yield of about 8 to 10%. In this process, the corncobs are soaked with sulfuric acid and heated in a large retort. The hemicellulose is first liberated and hydrolyzed to constituent pentose sugars, xylose, 70 to 80%, and arabinose, 4 to 8% (Bagby and Widstrom, 1987). Further, heating with steam dehydrates the pentose molecule to give furfural, which is distilled and collected for direct use or conversion to other furan chemicals (Dunlop, 1973). The main chemical products for 1972 were as follows: furfural, furfuryl alcohol, tetrahydrofurfuryl alcohol, furan, and tetrahydrofuran. Over 102 thousand t (225 million lb) of furfural a year is produced using approximately 100 thousand t of corncobs, oat hulls, bagasse, and rice hulls. The acidified, charred residue has been used in plywood manufacture, but it mostly neutralized and used for fuel.

Furfural finds uses as a selective solvent in extraction of crude petroleum, purification of butadiene, and in the manufacture of grinding wheels. Furfuryl alcohol polymerizes to produce resins that are resistant to the action of acids, alkalies, solvents, and are relatively nonburning. These resins are used in many fabrication applications and may be copolymerized with urea and formaldehyde. Tetrahydrofurfuryl alcohol is useful as a solvent for dyes, resins, and lacquers, and is therefore useful in the paint and varnish industry. Tetrahydrofuran is a versatil nonaqueous solvent for many organic compounds and is an intermediate for other chemical products (Dunlop, 1973).

REFERENCES

Alexander, R.J. 1973. Industrial uses of dry milled corn products. p. 303–315. In Y. Pomeranz (ed.) Industrial uses of cereals. Am. Assoc. of Cereal Chemists, St. Paul.

————. 1987. corn dry milling: Process, products and applications. p. 351–376. In S.A. Watson and P.R. Ramstad (ed.) Corn: Chemistry and technology. Am. Assoc. of Cereal Chemists, St. Paul.

Allred, J.B., R.E. Frey, L.S. Jensen, and J. McGinnis. 1957. Studies with chicks on improvement in nutritive value of feed ingredients. Poult. Sci. 36:517–523.

American Heart Association. 1968. Diet and heart disease. Pub. EM379. Am. Heart Assoc., New York.

Anderson, R.A., C. Vojonovich, and E.L. Griffen, Jr. 1961. Wet milling high amylose corn containing 66–68% amylose starch. Cereal Chem. 38:84–93.

————, and S.A. Watson. 1982. The corn milling industry. p. 31–62. CRC handbook of processing and utilization in agriculture. Vol. 2, Part 1. CRC Press, Boca Raton, FL.

Anonymous. 1981. Survey of drying practices on Illinois Farms. Illinois Crop Rep. Serv. 1987.

Anonymous. 1984a. Grain storages. Milling Industry Directory Milling and Baking News 63 (Nov.) :623–665.

————. 1984b. Annual statistical review. Distilled Spirits Counc. of the United States, Washington, DC.

————. 1986. Title III. Grain quality improvement act of 1986. P.L. 99–641 Congr. of the United States, Washington, DC.

Ash, M., W. Lin, and N. Johnson. 1988. Selected characteristics of the U.S. Feed Manufacturing Industry, 1984. AGE 880121. Commodity Economics Div., USDA-ERS, Washington, DC.

Ayers, G.E., C.E. Babcock, and D.O. Hull. 1972. Corn combine performance in Iowa. p. 12–28. In Corn and soybean grain damage symposium. Ohio State Univ., Columbus.

Bagby, M.O., and N.W. Widstrom. 1987. Biomass uses and conversions. p. 575–586. In

S.A. Watson and P.E. Ramstad (ed.) Corn: Chemistry and technology. Am. Assoc. of Cereal Chemists, St. Paul.

Bedolla, S., and L.W. Rooney. 1982. Cooking maize for masa production. Cereal Foods World. 27:219–221.

Beeson, W.M. 1972. Effect of steam flaking, roasting, popping, and extrusion of grains on their nutritional value for beef cattle. p. 326–337. *In* Effect of processing on the nutritional value of feeds. NAS, Washington, DC.

Blessin, C.W., G.E. Inglett, W.J. Garcia, and W.L. Deatherage. 1972. An edible defatted germ flour from a commercial dry milled corn fraction. Cereal Sci. Today 19:224, 255.

Bodine, A.B., and D.R. Mertens. 1983. Toxicology, metabolism, and physiological effects of aflatoxin in the bovine. p. 46–50. *In* U.L. Diener et al. (ed.) Aflatoxin and *Aspergillus flavus* in corn. Alabama Agric. Exp. Stn., South. Coop. Ser. Bull. 279.

Brekke, O.L. 1970. Corn dry milling industry. p. 262–291. *In* G.E. Inglett (ed.) Corn: Culture, processing, products. AVI Publ. Co., Westport, CT.

––––, A.J. Peplinski, E.R. Griffen, Jr., and J.J. Ellis. 1972. Dry-milling of corn attacked by Southern leaf blight. Cereal Chem. 49:466–478.

Broughton, D.J., H.J. Bieser, R.C. Berg, R. Connell, D. Kourous, and R. Neuzil. 1977. High purity fructose via continuous adsorptive separation. Sucr. Belge 96:155–162.

Casida, L.E. 1964. Industrial microbiology. John Wiley and Sons, New York.

Christiansen, C.M., and H.H. Kaufmann. 1974. Microflora. *In* C.M. Christiansen (ed.) Storage of cereal grains and their products. 2nd ed. Am. Assoc. of Cereal Chemists, St. Paul.

––––, and R.A. Meronuck. 1986. Quality maintenance in stored grains and seeds. Univ. of Minnesota Press, Minneapolis.

––––, and D.B. Sauer. 1982. Microflora. p. 219–240. *In* C.M. Christiansen (ed.) Storage of cereal grains and their products. 3rd ed. Am. Assoc. of Cereal Chemists, St. Paul.

Compton, J., and W.H. Martin. 1967. Starch in the textile industry p. 147–162. *In* R.L. Whistler and E.F. Paschall (ed.) Starch: Chemistry and technology, Vol. 2. Academic Press, Orlando, FL.

Corn Refiners Association. 1987. 1987 Corn annual. Corn Refiners Assoc., Washington, DC.

Darrah, L.L., et al. 1987a. White corn 1986 national crop performance. Spec. Rep. 355. USDA-ARS, Univ. of Missouri, Columbia.

––––. 1987b. Food corn 1986 national crop performance. Spec. Rep 356. USDA-ARS, Univ. of Missouri, Columbia.

Dunlop, A.P. 1973. The furfural industry. p. 229–236. *In* Y. Pomeranz (ed.) Industrial uses of cereals. Am. Assoc. of Cereal Chemists, St. Paul.

Earle, F.R., J. J. Curtis, and J.E. Hubbard. 1946. Composition of the component parts of the corn kernel. Cereal Chem. 44:601–606.

Eastman, J.E., and C.O. Moore. 1984. Cold water soluble granular starch. U.S. Patent 4 465 702.

Economic Research Service. 1985. Feed outlook situation report. FdS-296 (May). USDA-ERS, Washington, DC.

––––. 1986a. Feed outlook and situation report. FdS-299 (March). USDA-ERS, Washington, DC.

––––. 1986b. Feed situation and outlook yearbook. FdS-301 (November). Washington, DC.

––––. 1986c. Oil crops outlook and situation report. OCS-10 (March). USDA-ERS, Washinton, DC.

––––. 1986d. Oil crops situation outlook yearbook. OCS-11 (July). USDA-ERS, Washington, DC.

––––. 1986e. Sugar and sweetener outlook and situation report. SSRY11N1 (March). USDA-ERS, Washington, DC.

––––. 1986f. Sugar and sweetener situation and outlook yearbook. SSRV11N2 (June). USDA-ERS, Washington, DC.

––––. 1987. Feed situation and outlook report. FdS-302 (May). USDA-ERS, Washington, DC.

El-Marsafy, M., M. Abdel-Aker, and M. El-Said. 1975. Effect of media composition on penicillin production. Starke 27:91–93.

Enochian, R.V., G.O. Kohler, and D.D. Kuzmicky. 1971. Evaluating research improvements on livestock feeds through parametric linear programming. Cereal Sci. Today 16:181–189.

Fast, R.B. 1987. Breakfast cereals: Processing grains for human consumption. Cereal Foods World 32:241–244.

Federal Grain Inspection Service. 1980a. Grain inspection handbook. Book 1. Grain sampling. FGIS, USDA, Washington, DC.

————. 1980b. Grain inspection handbook book II. Grain grading procedures. FGIS, USDA, Washington, DC.

————. 1984. Revision of the United States standards for corn, U.S. standards for sorghum, and U.S. standards for soybeans. Fed. Reg. 40:35743–35745 (12 September).

————. 1987a. Grain handling practices. Fed. Reg. 52:7880–7884 (13 March).

————. 1987b. Insect infestation in grain. Fed. Reg. 52:8455–8460 (18 March).

————. 1987c. Official U.S. standards for grain. Fed. Reg. 52:24414–24442 (30 June).

Fiscus, D.F., G.H. Foster, and H.H. Kaufman. 1971. Grain-stream velocity measurements. Trans. ASAE 14:162–166.

Foley, K.M., and D.I.B. Vander Hooven. 1981. Properties and industrial uses of corncobs. p. 523–543. In Y. Pomeranz and L. Munck (ed.) Cereals. A renewable resource. Theory and practice. Am. Assoc. of Cereal Chemists, St. Paul.

Foster, G.H., and L.E. Holman. 1973. Grain breakage caused by commercial handling methods. Marketing Res. Serv. Rep. 96b. USDA-ARS, Washington, DC.

Freeman, J.E. 1973. Quality factors affecting value of corn for wet milling. Trans. ASAE 16:671–678,682.

————, H. Heatherwick, and S.A. Watson. 1970. Evaluation of some grain quality tests for corn and effects of germ damage on wet milling results. p. 1–29. In Proceeding corn conditioning conference, AE 4251. Univ. of Illinois, Urbana.

————, N.W. Kramer, and S.A. Watson. 1968. Gelatinization of starches from corn (Zea mays L.) and sorghum [Sorghum bicolor (L.) Moench]: Effect of genetic and environmental factors. Crop Sci. 8:409–413.

French, D. 1984. Organization of the starch granule. p. 183–248. In R.L. Whistler et al. (ed.) Starch: Chemistry and technology. Academic Press, Orlando, FL.

Frey, R.R. 1967. Hard candy from high maltose syrup. U.S. Patent 3 332 783.

Gill, M. 1987. Corn-based ethanol: Situation and outlook. p. 30–37. In Feed situation and outlook report. FdS-302 (May). USDA-ERS, Washington, DC.

————, and E. Allen. 1985. Status of the U.S. ethanol market. p. 14–24. In Feed: Outlook and situation Report. FdS-297 (August) USDA-ERS, Washington, DC.

Gomez, M.H., L.W. Rooney, R.D. Waniska, and R.L. Pflugfelder. 1987. Dry masa flours for tortilla and snack food production. Cereal Foods World 32:372–378.

Gustafson, R.J., and G.E. Hall. 1970. Density and porosity of shelled corn during drying. Trans. ASAE 15:523–525.

————, D.A.Y. Mahmoud, and G.E. Hall. 1983. Breakage susceptibility reduction by short term tempering of corn. Trans. ASAE 26:918–922.

Hale, W.H. 1984. Comparison of 'wet' grain processing methods for finishing cattle. p. 90–98. In Proceedings of the feed grains utilization symposium (for feedlot cattle). Texas Tech. Univ., Lubbock.

Haliburton, J.C., R.F. Vesonder, T.F. Lock, and W.B. Buck. 1979. Equine leucoenchalomacia (ELEM): A study of Fusarium moniliforme as an etiologic agent. Vet. Human Toxicol. 21:348–352.

Hall, G.E. 1972. Test weight changes of shelled corn during drying. Trans. ASAE 15:320–323.

————, and L.D. Hill. 1974. Test weight adjustment based on moisture content and mechanical damage of corn kernels. Trans. ASAE. 17:578–579.

————, ————, E.E. Hatfield, and A.H. Jensen. 1974. Propionic-acetic acid for high moisture corn preservation. Trans. ASAE 27:379–382, 387.

Hanover, L.M. 1982. Functionality of corn derived sweeteners in formulated foods. p. 211–233. In G. Charalambous and G.E. Inglett (ed.) Chemistry of foods and beverages: Recent developments. Academic Press, Orlando, FL.

Hanson, L.E. 1946. Waxy corn versus non-waxy corn for growing fattening pigs fed in dry lot. J. Anim. Sci. 5:36–41.

Hebeda, R.E. 1987. Corn sweeteners. p. 501–534. In S.A. Watson and P.E. Ramstad (ed.) Corn: Chemistry and technology. Am. Assoc. of Cereal Chemists, St. Paul.

————, and C.R. Strylund. 1986. Starch hydrolysis products as brewing adjuncts. Cereal Foods World 31:685–687.

Herum, F.L. 1987. Harvesting and postharvest management. p. 83–124. *In* S.A. Watson and P.R. Ramstad (ed.) Corn: Chemistry and technology. Am. Assoc. of Cereal Chemists, St. Paul.

Hicks, D.R. 1979. Waxy corn. Univ. of Minnesota Bull. 43.

Hill, L.D., N.M. Leath, O. Shotwell, D. White, M. Paulsen, and P. Garcia. 1982. Alternative definitions for the grade factor of broken corn and foreign material. Univ. of Illinois Bull 776.

Hixon, R.M., and G.F. Sprague. 1944. Waxy starch of maize and other cereals. Ind. Eng. Chem. 34:959–962.

Hobbs, L. 1986. Corn based sweeteners. Cereal Foods World 31:852–857.

Hoseney, R.C., K. Zeleznak, and A. Abdelrahman. 1983. Mechanism of popcorn popping. J. Cereal Sci. 1:43–52.

Jane, J., S.A.S. Craig, P. Seib, and R.C. Hoseney. 1986. Characterization of granular water-soluble starch. Starke 38:258–263.

Jensen, A.H., and D.E. Becker. 1965. Effect of pelleting diets and dietary components in the performance of young pigs. J. Anim. Sci. 24:392–397.

Kameyana, Y., F.S. Lai, H. Sayama, and L.T. Fan. 1982. The risk of dust explosions in grain processing facilities. J. Agric. Eng. Res. 27:253–261.

Karr, M.R. 1984. Grain processing techniques and quality control. p. 99–112. *In* Proceedings of the feed grains utilization symposium (for feedlot cattle). Texas Tech. Univ., Lubbock.

Katz, F.R. 1986. Maltodextrins. Cereal Foods World 31:866–867.

Keener, H.M., J.E. Henry, S.L. Schonauer, and R.J. Anderson. 1985. Burning shelled corn as an alternate fuel. p. 60–62. *In* Ohio report, July-August. Ohio Agric. Res. Dev. Ctr., Wooster.

Kennedy, H.M., and A.C. Fischer, Jr. 1984. Starch and dextrins in prepared adhesives. p. 593–610. *In* R.L. Whistler et al. (ed.) Starch: Chemistry and technology. Academic Press, Orlando, FL.

Kirlies, A.W., K.D. Crosby, and T.L. Housley. 1984. A method for quantitatively measuring vitreous endosperm area in sectioning sorghum grain. Cereal Chem. 61:556–558.

Klopfenstein, T., R. Stock, and R. Bulton. 1985. Relevance of by-pass protein to cattle feeding. Prof. Anim. Sci. 1:27–32.

Koetz, R., and H. Neukom. 1977. Nature of bound nicotinic acid in cereals and its release by thermal and chemical treatment. p. 305–316. *In* T. Hoyden and O. Kvale (ed.) Physical, chemical, and biological changes in foods by thermal processing. Applied Sci. Publ., London.

Kuzmicky, D.D. 1968. Pigmentation potency of xanthophyll sources. Poult. Sci. 47:389–397.

Ladish, M.R., M. Voloch, M. Hong, P. Blenkowski, and G.T. Tsao. 1984. Ethanol dehydration. Ind. Eng. Chem. Process Des. Dev. 23:434–437.

Leach, H.W. 1965. Gelatinization of starch. p. 289–302. *In* R.L. Whistler and E.F. Paschall (ed.) Starch: Chemistry and technology. Vol. 1. Academic Press, Orlando, FL.

Leath, M.N., and L.D. Hill. 1987. Economics of production, marketing, and utilization. p. 201–253. *In* S.A. Watson and P.R. Ramstad (ed.) Corn: Chemistry and technology. Am. Assoc. of Cereal Chemists, St. Paul.

Livezey, J. 1985. Estimates of corn use for major food and industrial products. p. 12–15. *In* Feed outlook and situation report. FdS-296(May). USDA-ERS, Washington, DC.

Long, J.E. 1978. The second generation high fructose corn syrups. p. 16–19. *In* Corn annual Corn Refiners Assoc., Washington, DC.

Maiden, A.M. 1975. Carbohydrates in the brewing industry. Starke 27:82–90.

Maisch, W.F. 1987. Fermentation processes and products. p. 553–574. *In* S.A. Watson and P.R. Ramstad (ed.) Corn: Chemistry and technology. Am. Assoc. of Cereal Chemists, St. Paul.

Marking, S. 1987. Waxy corn: What's the real score? The Farmer (21, March) :50–52.

Matz, S.A. 1984. Snack food technology. 2nd ed. AVI Publ. Co., Westport, CT.

May, J.B. 1987. Wet milling: Process and products. p. 377–398. *In* S.A. Watson and P.E. Ramstad (ed.) Corn: Chemistry and technology. Am. Assoc. of Cereal Chemist, St. Paul.

McDonald, T.A. 1973. Waxy corn feeding trial results. p. 98–107. *In* Proceedings of the 28th corn sorghum research conference. ASTA, Washington, DC.

Mentzer, M.J. 1984. Starch in the paper industry. p. 543–574. *In* R.L. Whistler et al. (ed.) Starch: Chemistry and technology. Academic Press, Orlando, FL.

Moore, C.O., J.V. Tuschhoff, C.W. Hastings, and R.V. Schanefelt. 1984. Applications of starches in foods. p. 575–591. *In* F.L. Whistler et al. (ed.) Starch: Chemistry and technology. Academic Press, Orlando, FL.

Morris, C.E. 1984. Industry efforts upgrade HFCS. Food Eng. 1983 7:55–56.

Morrison, W.R., and T.P. Milligan. 1982. Lipids in maize starches. p. 1–18. *In* G.E. Inglett (ed.) Maize. Recent progress and technology. Academic Press, New York.

Nelson, S.O. 1980. Moisture-dependent kernel and bulk density for wheat and corn. Trans. ASAE 23:139–143.

Neuman, P.E., B.K. Jasberg, J.S. Wall, and C.E. Walker. 1984. Uniquely textured products obtained by co-extrusion of corn gluten meal and soy flour. Cereal Chem. 61:439–445.

Newton, J.M. 1970. Corn syrup. p. 25–30. *In* Symposium on the products of the wet milling industry in foods. Corn Refiners Assoc., Washington, DC.

Orthoefer, F.T., and R.D. Sinram. 1987. Corn oil: Composition, processing, and utilization. p. 535–552. *In* S.A. Watson and P.E. Ramstad (ed.) Corn: Chemistry and technology. Am. Assoc. of Cereal Chemists, St. Paul.

Orthoefer, F.T. 1987. Corn starch modification and uses. p. 479–500. *In* S.A. Watson and P.R. Ramstad (ed.) Corn: Chemistry and technology. Am. Assoc. of Cereal Chemists, St. Paul.

Paulsen, M.R., and L.D. Hill. 1977. Corn breakage in overseas shipments—Two case studies. Trans. ASAE 20:550–552.

––––, and ––––. 1985. Corn quality factors affecting dry milling performance. J. Agric. Eng. Res. 31:255–263.

Payne, G.A. 1983. Nature of field infection of corn by *Aspergillus flavus*. p. 16–19. *In* U.L. Diener et al. (ed.) Aflatoxin and *Aspergillus flavus* in corn. Alabama Agric. Exp. Stn. South. Coop. Bull 279.

Peart, R.M., H.R. Zack, and O.C. Doering. 1981. Corn cob gasification for corn drying. p. 338–341. *In* Agricultural energy, Vol. 2. Biomass energy in crop production. ASAE, St. Joseph, MI.

Perlman, D. 1973. The fermentation industries. Am. Soc. Microbiol. Newsl. 39:648–654.

Pomeranz, Y., Z. Czuchajowska, and F.S. Lai. 1986. Comparison of methods for determination of hardness and breakage susceptibility of commercially dried corn. Cereal Chem. 63:39–43.

Pomeranz, Y., C.R. Martin, D.D. Traylor, and F.S. Lai. 1984. Corn hardness determination. Cereal Chem. 61:147–150.

Powell, E.L. 1973. Starch amylopectin (waxy corn and waxy sorghum). p. 567–576. *In* R.L. Whistler and J.N. BeMiller (ed.) Industrial gums. 2nd ed. Academic Press, Orlando, FL.

Pyler, R.E., and D.A. Thomas. 1986. Cereal research in brewing: Cereals as brewing adjuncts. Cereal Foods World 31:681–683.

Reiners, R.A., and C.W. Gooding. 1970. Corn oil. p. 241–261. *In* G.E. Inglett (ed.) Corn: Culture, processing, products. AVI Publ. Co., Westport, CT.

Rhodes, H.E. 1975. Overview of United States pet food industry. Cereal Foods World 20:5–7.

Riley, J.G. 1984. Comparative feedlot performance of corn, wheat, milo, and barley. p. 19–35. *In* Proceedings of the feed grains utilization symposium (for feedlot cattle). Texas Tech. Univ., Lubbock.

Roberts, H. 1967. Corn flour from surplus commodity to premium product. Cereal Sci. Today 12:505–506.

Rooney, L.W., and S.O. Serna-Saldivar. 1987. Food uses of whole corn and dry-milled fractions. p. 399–430. *In* S.A. Watson and P.R. Ramstad (ed.) Corn: Chemistry and technology. Am. Assoc. of Cereal Chemists, St. Paul.

Russell, C.R. 1973. Industrial uses of cornstarch. p. 262–281. *In* Y. Pomeranz (ed.) Industrial uses of cereals. Am. Assoc. of Cereal Chemists, St. Paul.

Rutenberg, M.W., and D. Solarek. 1984. Starch derivatives: Production and use. p. 311–388. *In* R.L. Whistler et al. (ed.) Starch: Chemistry and technology. Academic Press, Orlando, FL.

Satterthwaite, R.W., and D.J. Iwinski. 1973. Starch dextrins. p. 577–599. *In* R.L. Whistler and J.N. BeMiller (ed.) Industrial gums. 2nd ed. Academic Press, Orlando, FL.

Sauer, D.E., C.L. Storey, O. Ecker, and D.W. Fulk. 1984. Fungal populations in U.S. farm-stored grain and their relationship to moisture, storage times, and insect infestations. Phytopathology 74:1050–1053.

Saul, R.A. 1968. Effects of harvest and handling on corn storage. p. 33–36. *In* Proc. 23 Annu. Corn Sorghum Ind. Res. Conf., Chicago. ASTA, Washington, DC.

Schake, D.E. 1984. Factors to consider in selecting the grain processing methods to use. p. 113–122. *In* Proceedings feed grains utilization symposium (for feedlot cattle). Texas Tech. Univ., Lubbock.

Schenk, F.W. 1986. Dextrose. Cereal Foods World (31:858–862.

Shannon, J.C., and D.L. Garwood. 1982. Genetics and physiology of starch development. p. 25–86. *In* R.L. Whistler et al. (ed.) Starch: Chemistry and technology. Academic Press, Orlando, FL.

Shopmeyer, H.H., G.E. Felton, and C.L. Ford. 1943. Waxy cornstarch as a replacement for tapioca. Ind. Eng. Chem. 35:1168–1172.

Shotwell, O.L. 1983. Aflatoxin detectin and determination in corn. p. 38–45. *In* U.L. Diener et al. (ed.) Aflatoxin and *Aspergillus flavus* in corn. Alabama Agric. Exp. Stn., South. Coop. Bull. 279.

Shurtleff, M.C., et al. 1976. A compendium of corn diseases. Am. Phytological Soc., St. Paul.

Smith, N.B., H.S. McFate, and E.M. Eubamks. 1966. Process for producing starch and alcohol. U.S. Patent 3 236 740.

Smith, P.S., and H. Bell. 1986. New starches for food applications. Cereal Foods World 31:724–727.

Steel, J.L., R.A. Saul, and W.V. Hukill. 1969. Deterioration of shelled corn as a measure of carbon dioxide production. Trans. ASAE 12:685–689.

Storey, C.L. 1987. Effect and control of insects affecting corn quality. p. 185–190. *In* S.A. Watson and P.R. Ramstad (ed.) Corn: Chemistry and technology. Am. Assoc. of Cereal Chemists, St. Paul.

––––, D.B. Sauer, and D. Walker. 1983. Insect populations in wheat, corn, and oats stored on the farm. J. Econ. Entomol. 77:1323–1330.

Stroshine, R.L., A.W. Kirlies, J. Tuite, J.F. Bauman, and A. Emam. 1986. Differences in grain quality among selected hybrids. Cereal Foods World 31:311–316.

––––, and J.H. Martin. 1986. Varietal differences in high temperature drying of maize in the midwestern United States. p. 470–480. *In* A.S. Mujamdar (ed.) Drying '86. Hemisphere Publ. Corp., New York.

Thompson, R.A., and G.F. Foster. 1968. Stress cracks and breakage in artificially dried corn. Marketing Res. Bull. 631. USDA-Agric. Marketing Serv., Washington, DC.

Tsao, G.T. 1987. Integrated processing schemes for the conversion of corn into chemicals. p. 354–356. *In.* Proc. 1 Annu. Corn Utilization Conf. 11–12 June. Natl. Corn Growers Assoc., St. Louis.

Tuite, J., C. Koh-Knox, R. Stroshine, F.A. Cantone, and L.F. Bauman. 1985. Effects of physical damage to corn kernels on the development of *Penicillium* species and *Aspergillus glaucus* in storage. Phytopathology 75:1137–1140.

––––, G. Shaner, G. Rambo, G. Foster, and R. Caldwell. 1974. The *Giberella* ear rot epidemic of corn in Indiana in 1965 and 1972. Cereal Sci. Today 19:238–241.

U.S. Department of Agriculture. 1986. Yearbook of agriculture 1985. U.S. Gov. Print. Office, Washington, DC.

U.S. Department of Commerce. 1984. 1982 census of manufactures. MC82–1–20D. Bureau of the Census, USDC, Washington, DC.

Watson, S.A. 1962. The yellow carotenoid pigments of corn. p. 92–100. *In* Proc. 17th Annual Hybrid Corn Res. Conf. ASTA, Washington, DC.

––––. 1984. Corn and sorghum starches: Production. p. 417–468. *In* R.L. Whistler et al. (ed.) Starch: Chimistry and technology. Acadamic Press, Orlando, FL.

––––. 1987a. Structure and composition. p. 53–82. *In* S.A. Watson and P.R. Ramstad (ed.) Corn: Chemistry and technology. Am. Assoc. of Cereal Chemists, St. Paul.

––––. 1987b. Measurement and maintenance of quality. p. 125–184. *In* S.A. Watson and P.R. Ramstad (ed.) Corn: Chemistry and technology. Am. Assoc. of Cereal Chemists, St. Paul.

––––, and F.L. Herum. 1986. Comparison of eight devices for measuring breakage susceptibility of shelled corn. Cereal Chem. 63:139–142.

––––, Y. Hirata, and C.B. Williams. 1955. A study of the lactic acid fermentation in commercial corn steeping. Cereal Chem. 32:382–394.

––––, and E.H. Sanders. 1961. Steeping studies with corn endosperm sections. Cereal Chem. 38:22–33.

Weber, E.J. 1987. Lipids of the kernel. p. 311–350. *In* S.A. Watson and P.E. Ramstad (ed.) Corn: Chemistry and technology. Am. Assoc. of Cereal Chemists, St. Paul.

Whistler, R.L., J.N. BeMiller, and E.F. Paschall (ed.) 1984. Starch: Chemistry and technology. Academic Press, Orlando, FL.

White, G.M., T.J. Ross, and C.G. Poneleit. 1982. Stress crack development in popcorn as influenced by drying and rehydration. Trans. ASAE 25:768–772.

Wright, K.N. 1987. Nutritional properties and feeding value of corn and its by-products. p. 447–479. *In* S.A. Watson and P.E. Ramstad (ed.) Corn: Chemistry and technology. Am. Assoc. of Cereal Chemists, St. Paul.

Wurzburg, O.B. 1970. Starch and modified starch. p. 20–24. *In* Symp. Proc. Products of the Wet Milling Industry in Food. Corn Refiners Assoc., Washington, DC.

————. (ed.) 1986. Modified starches: Properties and uses. CRC Press, Boca Raton, FL.

Young, A.H. 1984. Fractionation of starch. p. 249–284. *In* R.L. Whistler et al. (ed.) Starch: Chemistry and technology. Academic Press, Orlando, FL.

Young, L..S., and J.E. Long. 1982. Manufacture, use, and nutritional aspects of 90% high fructose corn sweeteners. p. 195–210. *In* G. Charalambous and G.E. Inglett (ed.) Chemistry in foods and beverages: Recent developments. Academic Press, Orlando, FL.

Ziegler, K.E., R.B. Ashman, G.M. White, and D.S. Wysong. 1985. Popcorn production and marketing. p. 1–6. *In* Iowa State Univ. Coop. Ext. Serv., Natl. Corn Handb., NHC-5.

Zobel, H.F. 1984. Gelatinization of starch and mechanical properties of starch pastes. p. 285–309. *In* R.L. Whistler et al. (ed.) Starch: Chemistry and technology. Academic Press, Orlando, FL.

16 Corn as a Livestock Feed

TILDEN WAYNE PERRY P.A.S.

Purdue University
West Lafayette, Indiana

Corn (*Zea mays* L.) is the most important feed grain produced in the USA. Annual production for the past 10 yr has approximated 200 Tg (200 million t). Of this total, 40 to 50% is fed to livestock directly as grain. Another 1.5 to 2 Tg (1.5–2 million t) of by-products of the wet and dry milling industries are utilized directly or in formulated feeds. An additional 130 Tg (130 million t) of whole plant silage is produced, consumption being confined almost entirely to ruminants. Grain usage by classes of livestock is presented in Table 16–1. Swine are the largest consumers of corn as grain. Usage, as a 20-yr average, amounts to 35.8 Tg (35.8 million t). Cattle on feed and other beef cattle account for 25 Tg (25 million t). Dairy cattle consume 19.7 Tg (19.7 million t) and all classes of poultry an additional 20.3 Tg (20.3 million t).

This chapter will present data on proximate chemical analyses for both whole grain and milling by-products. Information will be presented on grain usage and ration recommendations for the several classes of livestock. Attention also will be given to the role of silage under feeding or maintenance conditions.

Table 16–1. Corn consumption by various species of livestock in the USA, 1970 to 1985 (USDA, 1985).

Species	Year					
	1970	1973	1976	1979	1982	1985
	Tg					
Dairy animals	12.8	14.6	15.4	18.7	19.8	20.7
Cattle on feed	22.0	29.9	18.6	21.3	19.9	20.0
Other beef cattle	5.6	7.6	5.8	5.7	5.7	4.8
Hens, pullets, raised chickens	9.1	8.8	8.8	11.0	9.9	6.6
Broilers	6.0	5.9	6.8	9.3	10.1	11.9
Turkeys	1.5	1.7	1.6	2.4	2.5	2.9
Hogs	33.2	28.1	32.6	43.3	35.6	39.8
Other livestock, unallocated	1.1	1.1	1.5	3.1	11.4	1.8
Total, all livestock	91.3	97.7	91.1	114.8	114.9	108.5

16-1 CORN AS A FEED GRAIN

16-1.1 Composition of Corn Grain

Researchers at the Northern Regional Res. Lab of the USDA, (Earle et al., 1946) separated several samples of corn grain by hand into fractions representing the endosperm, germ, bran, and tip cap. The grain samples and the resulting fractions were analyzed for moisture, ash, N, oil, sugar, and starch (Table 16-2). The kernel fractions included 82% endosperm, 12% germ, 5% bran, and 1% tip cap.

In addition to the constituent parts of the corn kernel listed above, there is approximately 2.2% crude fiber, which is found primarily in the bran fraction of the kernel.

16-1.1.1 Starch

Starch, found for the most part in the endosperm fraction, consists of two types, namely amylose (about 27%) and amylopectin (73%). Both types of corn starch are comprised of D-glucose, except that amylose is a linear molecule whereas amylopectin is a branched molecule. Genetic manipulation has provided varying proportions of these two types of starch in selected strains of corn. For example, Bates et al. (1943) reported on a mutant corn type that produced amylopectin, exclusively, and was labelled as "waxy" corn because of its dull waxy appearing endosperm.

16-1.1.2 Protein

Protein, representing about 10% of the corn kernel dry matter, is of low biological value, as it does not supply the essential amino acids either in adequate quantities or in adequate proportions. Generally, the corn protein fraction is segregated into three or four types, based primarily on their relative solubility, i.e., 3% albumins (water soluble), 1.5% globulins (salt soluble), 47% prolamine, or zein (70-80% ethanol soluble) and 35% glutelin (NaOH soluble).

Mertz et al. (1964) reported a mutant gene which altered the amino acid composition of corn protein and which resulted in an increase in

Table 16-2. Average composition of whole, shelled corn and of component fractions (dry matter basis) (Earle et al., 1946).

Fraction	Kernel	Starch	Sugar	Protein	Oil	Ash
			%			
Whole kernel	100.0	71.5	2.0	10.3	4.8	1.44
Endosperm	81.9	86.4	0.6	9.4	0.8	0.31
Germ	11.9	8.2	10.8	18.8	34.5	10.10
Bran	5.3	7.3	0.3	3.7	1.0	0.84
Tip cap	1.1	--	--	10.7	3.9	1.95

Table 16-3. Amino acids in normal and *opaque*-2 corn kernels (Mertz et al., 1964).

Constituent	Normal corn	*Opaque*-2 corn
	%	
Protein	8.9	11.9
Amino acids		
Lysine	0.2	0.5
Tryptophan	0.1	0.2
Arginine	0.5	0.8
Valine	0.4	0.6
Glycine	0.4	0.6

the lysine content compared to "normal" corn. The typical analyses of the two types of corn are compared in Table 16-3.

The increases in lysine and tryptophan introduced by *opaque*-2 corn have been of interest to producers of monogastric animals such as pigs (*Sus scrofa*) and poultry since, in typical predominantly corn diets for these species, the first limiting amino acids are lysine and tryptophan. Generally speaking, strains of corn into which the higher lysine *opaque*-2 gene has been introduced have been lower in yield than normal corn. Thus the production of *opaque*-2 corn hybrids has been limited. In general, *opaque*-2 types of corn will produce only from 80 to 90% as much grain as normal corn on comparable areas of land.

16–1.1.3 Oil

Oil, comprising nearly 5% of the corn kernel (Table 16–1), has considerable commercial and human nutrition interest. The latter interest is due to its relatively high degree of unsaturation. Beadle et al. (1965) gave average values for the composition of corn oil as follows: 58.7% linoleic (C-18:2), 26.6% oleic (C-18:1), 11.5% palmitic (C-16:0), 2.2% stearic (C-18:0), 0.8% linolenic (C-18:3), and 0.2% arachidic (C-20:0). However, the relatively high degree of unsaturation is not desirable for swine feeding because of the tendency to produce oily or soft pork.

16–1.1.4 Ash

Ash, representing 1.44% of the kernel, has nutritional value. Note from Table 16–4 that corn is practically void of Ca. Furthermore, even though there is a much greater content of P (0.32%), much of its is relatively unavailable—perhaps up to 50% unavailable—to monogastric animals due to its relationship to phytate.

16–1.1.5 Stage of Maturity

Stage of maturity affects the composition of the corn kernel (Thornton et al., 1969). The increase in dry matter in the corn kernel from the early milk stage through early dough, mid-dent and maturity is due mostly to N-free extract plus a smaller amount from oil (Table 16–5). As percentage

Table 16-4. Mineral composition of corn grain (dry matter basis) (Crampton and Harris 1971).

Mineral	Percentage
Ca	0.03
P	0.32
K	0.35
Mg	0.13
Mn	7 (ppm)
Fe	0.004
Na	0.07
S	0.08

Table 16-5. Corn grain analysis as affected by stage of maturity (Thornton et al., 1969).

Nutrient	Concentration in dry matter			
	Early milk	Early dough	Mid-dent	Mature
Test wt., g/L	450	606	709	747
Dry matter, %	20.9	35.7	55.5	76.6
Crude protein, %	16.6	12.5	10.7	10.9
Oil, %	3.0	4.0	4.8	4.9
Crude fiber, %	5.4	3.3	2.5	2.1
Ash, %	2.8	2.3	1.7	1.5
Nitrogen-free extract, %	72.7	77.9	80.3	80.6
Starch, %	47.4	55.0	58.7	63.7
Cell wall constituents, %	27.7	24.6	16.3	13.9
Gross energy, kcal/kg	4560	4540	4590	4580

concentration in the dry matter, cell wall content, ash, crude fiber, and crude protein contents decline as the kernel matures.

Since the corn kernel may well represent 50% of the digestible energy in whole plant corn silage, corn grains must be in the dented and glazed stage at the time of silage harvest to achieve maximum yield of digestible nutrients. Furthermore, the stage of maturity between mid-dent and maturity is not as critical in achieving the maximum amount of digestible nutrients as the intervals of maturity prior to the mid-dent stage.

The color of yellow corn is due to the presence of a series of carotenoid pigments. The pigments of special interest are carotene, which is a precursor of vitamin A, and xanthophylls (lutein, zeoxanthin, etc.) which affect skin and shank color of broilers, yolk color of eggs as well as color of body fat.

16-1.1.6 Pro-vitamin A Value

The β-carotene molecule may be cleaved and one-half of the molecule has vitamin-A potency. In typical yellow corn, the β-carotene concentration is roughly equivalent to 2 IU of vitamin A per gram. However, animals vary in their ability to convert the β-carotene of yellow corn into physiologically active vitamin A. In addition, the carotene found in new corn gradually deteriorates under typical farm conditions. After about 1 yr most of the pro-vitamin A activity has been lost. Smith et al. (1963)

Table 16–6. Performance of finishing swine fed aged corn with and without supplemental vitamin A, on concrete floors or on pasture (Smith et al., 1963).

Treatment	880 IU vit. A kg diet	Daily gain	Daily feed	Serum vit. A	Liver vit. A	Level carotene in corn
		——— kg ———		μg/100mL	μg/g	mg/kg
Drylot (concrete floor)						
8-yr-old corn	–	0.65	2.2	9.5	1.4	0.33
8-yr-old corn	+	0.71	2.4	30.2	14.6	0.33
4-yr-old corn	–	0.71	2.4	11.3	1.3	0.79
4-yr-old corn	+	0.75	2.5	30.1	13.8	0.79
1-yr-old corn	–	0.66	2.3	19.8	3.6	1.78
1-yr-old corn	+	0.68	2.4	32.1	20.2	1.78
Pasture						
8-yr-old corn	–	0.66	2.2	31.3	31.2	0.33
8-yr-old corn	+	0.67	2.1	34.8	51.3	0.33

studied the feeding value of corn which had been in government storage for from 1 to 8 yr (Table 16–6).

Even 4-yr-old corn did not contain sufficient pro-vitamin A for maximum growth or for more than perhaps minimal blood levels, and certainly supported little liver storage. However, either supplemental vitamin A (880 IU/kg diet) or access to pasture appeared to correct the pro-vitamin A deficiency of the older corn.

16–1.1.7 Xanthophylls

Yellow corn derives much of its color from xanthophylls which have no pro-vitamin A activity. Xanthophylls, however, can be transferred from the grain to the body fat of animals consuming them. This effect is desirable in causing the body fat of chicken broiler carcasses to take on a yellow or golden color, and thus is pleasing to many people who purchase chicken for food. In contrast, yellow coloring in the fat of beef carcasses is undesirable. Generally, the xanthophyll consumed by a beef animal fed yellow corn, is sufficiently low that no yellowing of cattle body fat would be detectable. Much greater quantities of xanthophyll must be consumed by cattle to cause yellow body fat. This may occur in cattle which consume large quantities of xanthophyll-rich hay or haylage.

16–1.2 Corn for the Various Species of Livestock

Wherever corn is economically competitive, no other grain will compete as a livestock feed grain. Corn is relished by all species of livestock and only in the case of wheat for swine is any grain really competitive with corn. Because of its high starch-low fiber content, corn is one of the most concentrated sources of energy, containing more metabolizable energy—or total digestible nutrients—than any other feed grain. However, it is the lowest in protein of all feed grains. Corn is the only feed grain containing either β-carotene (pro-vitamin A) or xanthophyll in more than token amounts.

16–1.2.1 Swine

Where it is available, corn is accepted as the standard grain for swine. Except for wheat (*Triticum aestivum* L.), which is slightly more palatable and worth slightly more, corn is unsurpassed for swine. Table 16–7 presents the relative corn replacement value of several feedstuffs. Note that almost all feedstuffs fall behind corn.

Corn is such a high energy grain that swine will tend to overfatten rather quickly unless they are observed carefully and marketed at the optimal point in their maturation.

Since corn is predominantly an energy-type feed, it must be supplemented with protein (amino acids), minerals, and vitamins. Thus typical swine diets are referred to as "fortified corn-soy diets," implying that corn constitutes the principal ingredient (up to 85%) with soybean meal as a source of protein, plus minerals and vitamins, to meet the nutrient requirements for growing-finishing swine. Note, for example, how well a 16% protein diet consisting of corn and soybean meal—plus fortifying minerals and vitamins—fulfills the pig's amino acid requirements (Table 16–8). Although two of the amino acid levels are close to the minimal level, none show up as deficient in the corn and soybean meal combination.

Table 16-7. Relative swine feeding value of other feedstuffs compared to shelled corn (Ahlschwede et al., 1984).

Ingredient (air dry)	Feeding value relative to corn, %†
Alfalfa meal-dehydrated	45–50
Alfalfa hay sun cured	30–40
Animal fat, stabilized	210–220
Bakery surplus	75–90
Barley, 48 lb/bu	85–90
Beet pulp, dried	70–80
Corn, yellow	100
Corn, high lysine	100–105
Corn and cob meal	80–90
Corn grits by-product, hominy	100–105
Corn silage, 25–30% dm	20–30
Millet, proso	90–95
Milo, grain sorghum	95–100
Molasses, 77% dm	55–65
Oat, 36 lb/bu	80–90
Oat, high protein	90
Oat groats	110–115
Potato, 22% dm	20–25
Rye	90
Triticale	90–95
Wheat, hard	100–105
Wheat bran	60–65
Wheat aids	90–95
Whey, dry	100–110

† When fed at no more than the maximum recommended percent of complete diet.

Table 16–8. Corn-soy diets for swine and amino acid requirements (45-kg pig). Source of data: Crampton and Harris (1971).

Amino acid	Natl. Res. Counc. requirement	Corn	Soybean meal	15%† corn-soy diet
Arginine	0.18	0.43	3.07	0.78
Histidine	0.16	0.17	0.69	0.24
Isoleucine	0.44	0.43	2.31	0.68
Leucine	0.52	0.95	4.08	1.36
Lysine	0.61	0.17	3.33	0.61
Methionine + cystine	0.40	0.26	1.46	0.41
Phenylalanine + tyrosine	0.44	0.95	4.22	1.37
Threonine	0.39	0.35	2.15	1.08
Tryptophan	0.11	0.09	0.72	0.17
Valine	0.44	0.43	2.43	0.70

† 15% crude protein diet consisting of 83% corn, 14% soybean meal, and 3% minerals and vitamins.

From a nutritional point of view, corn need not be processed for swine, because they do an excellent job of breaking up the corn kernel. Because so many commercial swine producers feed complete mixed rations, much of the corn fed to swine is crushed or ground finely to facilitate mixing it with the other ingredients in the diet. Pelleting, roasting, crushing, cracking or other processing techniques improve the nutritional value of corn for swine very little.

Many years ago, it was quite common to offer corn to swine in the ear form and then to provide ad libitum a source of supplemental protein, minerals, and vitamins. This is not practical today since this technique of feeding corn does not lend itself well to complete mixed diet feeding. Another technique that once was common for feeding corn to swine was called *hogging down* corn in which the swine were turned into fields of standing unharvested corn and literally harvested the corn. Modern farming programs tend to dictate early fall plowing and hogging down corn does not lend itself well to early fall plowing.

16–1.2.2 Poultry

As in the case of swine, corn is the chief grain fed to poultry. Corn is not an indispensable grain for poultry and can be replaced on an equivalent nutrient basis by other grains. However, corn fits into poultry diets quite uniquely because of its xanthophyll and β-carotene content, in addition to its high-energy value. Naturally, corn as the only cereal feed grain containing β-carotene—or pro-vitamin A—provides a bonus from this standpoint. However, the β-carotene content of corn is not a major consideration since crystalline vitamin A is inexpensive and the pro-vitamin A value of corn declines in storage. After 1 yr in storage little pro-vitamin A remains. Xanthophyll, unique also to corn of the cereal grains, provides a yellow color which is desirable for the body fat, skin, and shank color of market broilers.

No processing technique applied to corn appears to improve greatly its nutritional value for poultry, although pelleting and subsequent crumbling slightly improves the nutirent value—at least for young broiler chickens. A high percentage of the poultry diets are fed as complete mixed diets, demanding that corn be ground in order to provide a relatively homogenous mixture. Where the grain is fed as a separate entity of the diet, as in the case of a scratch grain or in a hopper, there is little or no advantage to cracking the corn portion. In contrast, almost all other cereal grains need to be crushed or cracked in some manner for poultry.

Adequate energy intake becomes a problem in two classes of poultry, namely, the rapidly growing broiler and the heavy-producing laying hen. Because of corn's high energy content, it constitutes the principal energy grain for broilers and laying hens.

16–1.2.3 Beef Cattle

Corn is the number one grain for feeding beef cattle (*Bos* spp.), especially where maximum gain is desired. Under proper management it is possible to feed a no-roughage diet built around whole shelled corn plus supplemental protein, minerals, and vitamins. It appears the tip cap of whole shelled corn provides enough "scratch factor" to keep the rumen healthy and functioning. Lactic acidosis and foundering are possible on high corn diets, but corn is not as dangerous in this respect as wheat. The difference in the predisposition of corn or wheat to cause lactic acidosis appears to be attributable to the fact that wheat starch breaks down more readily than corn starch. Thus wheat-fed cattle have a more readily available and fermentable starch than corn-fed cattle.

Beef cattle benefit more from the processing of corn than probably any other species of farm livestock. Initial indications that this was true came from the discovery by the author of this chapter that ensiled high-moisture corn had from 8 to 12% greater feeding value for beef cattle than comparable dry corn (Beeson and Perry, 1958). Following this report, many other methods of processing corn were investigated. Soon it was shown that almost any heating method applied to corn would improve its utilization by beef cattle. In 1970, Perry et al. (1970) demonstrated the roasting of corn or heating it with dry heat to approximately 135 °C, which improved its feeding value at least 10% for beef cattle feeding.

Grinding of shelled corn was thought to be essential if beef cattle were to obtain the maximum nutrient value from it. However, researchers at the Univ. of Illinois (Hixon et al., 1969) reported feeding trials in which cattle fed whole shelled corn actually required an average of 7.5% less feed per unit gain than comparable cattle fed cracked shelled corn.

Most commercial cattle feeders follow the practice of steam-flaking shelled corn, and most other feed grains as well. This technique gives the greater utilization benefit from the heating of the grains as well as adding weight to the grain in the form of steam. Many commercial feedlots operate on the basis of the sale of feedstuffs by weight to their clients. Thus, the increased weight of moisture-laden steam-flaked grains might be more attractive to the feedlot owner than the decreased moisture content of grains that have been cooked with dry heat.

The harvesting of corn grain containing 25 to 28% moisture and ensiling it is one of the simplest methods of processing corn to achieve 10% greater utilization of it by cattle. Furthermore, this technique, has additional desirable attributes including: (i) at least 14 d earlier harvest with possibly better weather and earlier land preparation, (ii) no waiting in line at the marketing elevator and (iii) probably more dry matter harvested per hectare of land due to less lodging of stalks and less harvesting losses. However, there is an economic disadvantage to ensiling the entire corn needs for corn for a cattle-feeding enterprise during September and October. That economic disadvantage, of course, is that interest accumulates on the product stored in the ensiled high-moisture condition month after month. In contrast, most other processing techniques permit the feedlot owner to buy corn week-by-week or month-by-month, as needed, and no interest would accumulate since there is no stored corn.

16–1.2.4 Dairy Cattle

There are pros and cons to using corn as a dairy grain mix constituent. The good aspect is that it is one of the highest energy feed grains available. Since both genetics and the availability of bovine somatotropin are causing dairy cattle to produce ever-increasing quantities of milk, the problem of meeting their nutrient needs, especially for energy, is becoming greater. In other words, our technology for increasing milk production is growing faster than our nutritional knowledge. It is difficult to push enough feedstuff through the high-producing dairy cow to meet her needs. Because corn is one of the highest energy grains available, it will find its way into dairy cattle feeding programs. However, most dairy cattle nutritionists contend the dairy cow grain mix should be reasonably bulky, and the bulky aspect is achieved primarily by including some fibrous feeds such as oat (*Avena sativa* L.) or molasses feeds (molasses dried on oat hulls). As a rule of thumb, many dairymen prefer that the grain mix for dairy cows weigh only about 480 g/L (1 lb/qt) which is rather bulky.

For lactating dairy cattle, corn usually is fed in the ground form because they are thought to utilize the finer-sized particles of ground shelled corn, more efficiently than whole-shelled corn. In addition, the grinding of corn results in a particle size more consistent with the rest of the ingredients of the grain mixture.

With its relatively high level of xanthophyll, corn will contribute to the highly desirable yellow color of butterfat, especially for cows which do not have access to lush green pasture.

16–1.2.5 Sheep

Wherever corn is available and economically competitive, it is the number one grain utilized in lamb (*Ovis aries*) or ewe feeding. For sheep, a simple combination of shelled corn, alfalfa hay, or haylage and minerals represents a completely balanced diet. Sheep are possibly the only farm animal that do not benefit from the grinding or crushing of corn, at least in one or more aspects of their complete life cycle. Except for smooth-mouthed or aged toothless individuals there is no known nutritional advantage to grinding or cracking of corn for sheep.

Corn feeding fits well in a lamb finishing program. A daily diet of 700 g of shelled corn, 800 g of alfalfa hay, minerals, and possibly 50 g of linseed meal or soybean meal may be the most desirable feeding program available for finishing lambs. In the case of pregnant ewes, especially when pasture forage is not available, the feeding of 200 to 300 g of whole shelled corn per ewe per day during the last 42 d of gestation is recommended in order to decrease the incidence of parturient paralysis (also known as *pregnancy disease*).

Care must be exercised in feeding any concentrated feed grain, such as corn, to finishing lambs because of their tendency to develop enterotoxemia, also known as overeating disease. Lambs with this condition die in a short period of time. Apparently rich feeds in the digestive tract provide an attractive environment for bacteria which produce toxins which in turn cause enterotoxemia. Effective vaccines against enterotoxemia are available on the market at a reasonable cost. Although allegations have been made that heavy corn feeding results in wool loss in sheep, this has not been demonstrated under controlled experimental conditions.

16–1.2.6 Horses and Mules

Normally corn is not considered the no. one feed grain for horses (*Equus caballus*); rather oat is considered more desirable. However, much of this thinking is due to habit and general lack of information. Actually corn is an excellent horse grain. It is a much more concentrated form of energy than oat, and thus should not be substituted for oat in horse diets on an equal weight basis, but rather on an energy-equivalent basis. Oat contains only 70 to 75% as much energy as corn, or corn contains 130% as much energy as oat. Thus, from one-fourth to one-third less corn than oat, on a weight basis, would provide energy equivalency for horses and mules.

Generally, it is preferable to feed corn in the ear form or shelled form for horses and mules rather than in the ground form, unless their teeth are not in good condition. Ear corn is preferable to shelled corn since it requires horses to eat more slowly and to do a better job of chewing.

16–2   CORN AS A FORAGE CROP

When the entire corn plant is harvested and utilized as a livestock feedstuff, as in whole plant corn silage, it will surpass all other forage crops in average yield of dry matter and of digestible nutrients per hectare. Since the harvest of the corn plant can be 14 to 21 d earlier than when harvesting only grain, whole plant silage harvest lends itself well to a shorter growing season.

16–2.1   Proper Stage of Maturity for Silage-Making

Studies have been conducted (Perry and Caldwell, 1968) to determine the optimal time and/or stage of maturity of the corn plant for harvesting and ensiling (Table 16–9). Harvests of corn plants were made at biweekly intervals, starting in the early dough stage for the kernel (101 d post-planting) and extending through the winter for as long as 283 d post-planting. Each harvest was ensiled under limited O_2 conditions until it was opened for chemical analyses and cattle metabolism trials. Maximum yields of both dry matter (15.5–16.5 kg) and digestible dry matter (10.9–11.9 kg) per ha were obtained when the whole corn plant contained from 33 to 53% dry matter over a 28-d range (143 to 171 d postplanting). Thus, approximately a 30-d range in optimum time for maximum yield of digestible dry matter is possible when the whole corn plant is chopped and ensiled. A normal range of pH (3.8 ±) was obtained when the whole plant contained from 28 to 53% dry matter.

A highly digestible silage could be made even when the plant contained 80% dry matter (Table 16–9). However, two precautions should be noted here: (i) many of the leaves have been detached from the stalk

Table 16-9. Effect of maturity stage of harvest of corn silage on yield and digestible dry matter per ha. (Perry and Caldwell, 1968, Perry et al., 1968).

Days after plant-ing	Percent of dry matter	Silage pH	Dry matter	Yield†			
				Dry matter/ha	Max. yield	Digest. dry matter	Digest. dry matter/ha
			%	kg (× 1000)	——— % ———		kg (× 1000)
101	--	4.4	20	11.6	70	71	8.2
115	--	4.5	24	13.1	79	75	9.8
129	--	4.6	28	14.6	88	72	10.5
143	42	4.7	33	16.5	100	67	11.0
157	43	5.0	46	15.5	94	70	10.9
171	44	4.8	53	16.5	99	72	11.9
199	47	5.5	61	14.5	87	72	10.4
227	67	6.5	61	8.8	53	71	6.3
255	74	6.0	75	7.9	47	72	5.7
283	76	6.1	80	7.9	48	68	5.4

† Chemical analysis (dry matter basis): crude protein, 7.5 to 8.2%; ether extract, 2.4 to 3.5%; crude fiber, 19.4 to 22.9%; ash, 2.3 to 4.8%, N-free extract, 57.9 to 68%.

by the wind—giving rise to decreased dry matter yield per ha at the later harvest dates, and (ii) a higher pH (above 6) indicates less fermentation for the later-harvested corn plant thus a closer control of O_2 access is required to prevent spoilage. However, the digestibility of the dry matter was not affected by the stage at which the corn plant was harvested, chopped, and ensiled. This sustained digestibility of whole plant corn silage would lend itself to an early silo-filling followed by a much later re-filling of the same silage storage structure.

16–2.2 Varieties and Types of Corn for Silage-Making

16–2.2.1 Brown Midrib-3

The cellulose in the whole corn plant which must be broken down by the rumen microorganisms is chemically bound to lignin. Thus, the availability of cellulose as an energy source is dependent upon the lignin content as well as the manner in which it is combined with cellulose. The brown midrib-3 (bm_3) gene has been shown to reduce lignin content of the corn plant (Kuc and Nelson, 1964). Keith et al. (1981) studied the value of bm_3 corn silage in the diet of growing beef cattle and demonstrated that average daily gain for heifers fed bm_3 and normal silages was 1.03 and 0.90 kg ($P<0.10$) when no additional corn was fed. However, when 2% body weight of shelled corn was fed along with the silage, there was no advantage for the bm_3 silage (1.21 vs. 1.17 kg daily gain) (Table 16–10). The bm_3 silage contained 33% less lignin in Yr 1 (3.64 vs. 2.42% of dry matter) and 21% less in Yr 2 (2.73 vs. 2.14%). Other factors such as total protein and cellulose were not different between bm_3 silage and its normal genetic counterpart. Since the diets were offered according to appetite, cattle offered the bm_3 silage diet, without extra corn, tended to consume more dry matter than those offered the normal genetic counterpart silage. The major drawback to the production of bm_3 for silage-making is the much lower dry matter yield of current genotypes. Present lowered dry matter yields offset any nturitional advantage gained from the reduced lignin content of bm_3 silage. If bm_3-type silages could be developed which had yields comparable to their normal counterparts, then bm_3 silage could be attractive.

16–2.2.2 *Opaque*-2 Corn Silage

Due to the higher lysine content of *opaque*-2 corn, it attracted interest for monogastric animals. In addition, cattle trials were conducted (Thomas et al., 1975). Steers fed normal corn silage gained more rapidly (1.11 vs. 1.06 kg/d; $P<0.05$) than comparable cattle fed *opaque*-2 corn silage. In digestible energy studies, normal corn silage contained a higher percentage of energy digestibility (70.1) vs. 68.4%; $P<0.05$) than *opaque*-2 corn silage.

Table 16-10. Brown midrib-three compared to regular corn silage, with and without added grain (Keith et al., 1981).

Item	No. of cattle	Daily gain	Silage dry matter intake
		kg	
No added corn			
Yr 1 (232-d trial)†			
Bm_3 silage‡	12	0.90x§	5.9
Regular silage	12	0.82y	5.4
Yr 2 (154-d trial)†			
Bm_3 silage	12	1.03x	6.2x
Regular silage	12	0.90y	5.7y
Corn added, 2% body wt.			
Yr 1			
Bm_3 silage	12	1.03	2.7
Regular silage	12	1.01	2.5
Yr 2			
Bm_3 silage	12	1.21	2.1
Regular silage	12	1.17	2.1

† Average initial wt.: Yr 1, 242 kg; Yr 2, 227 kg.
‡ Bm_3 = Brown midrib-3.
§ Values in the same vertical column with differing letters vary ($P < 0.05$).

16-2.2.3 High Sugar Male-Sterile Hybrid Corn Silage

High sugar corn (HS-50) is a male-sterile double-cross which has been selected on the basis of its chemical constituents. Although a typical cob is found in the husk, only from 0 to 8 or 10 kernels of corn are found per cob. The stalk of HS-50 has been reported to contain more than seven times (3.81 vs. 0.50%) more total water-soluble carbohydrates than is found in a typically starchy dent stalk. Perry and Caldwell (1969) conducted metabolism trials to compare the two types of corn silage. Under equal rates of seeding (56 800 seeds/ha), the HS-50 corn yielded 6626 kg of dry matter per ha compared to 14 025 kg of dry matter for starchy dent corn. Chemical analyses of the silages showed greater protein (10.9 vs. 8.4%), greater crude fiber (30.3 vs. 21.3%), greater ether extract (5.1 vs. 3.5%), lesser N-free extract (49.3 vs. 61.7%) and lesser ash (4.4 vs. 5%) in the silage made from the male-sterile corn. The metabolism trial results showed higher protein digestibility (67 vs. 43.2%; $P<0.01$) and higher crude fiber digestibility (63 vs. 47.3%; $P<0.01$) for the male-sterile corn silage. However, since the dry matter yield for HS-50 corn was less than half that for regular starchy corn silage, no logical reason to conduct large scale feeding trials was found.

16-2.2.4 Blighted Corn as Silage

Infection of corn crops with southern corn leaf blight (*Helminthosporium maydis* Nisik &. Miy.) reduces yield and may affect the quality of derived feedstuffs. Typically, with the infestation appearing in mid- to late summer, the plant is killed before normal maturity. Ear filling is reduced and kernels are smaller than normal, test weights are low and the ears may become infected with fungi. The fungus has appeared to be nontoxic to animals. Caldwell and Perry (1972) conducted metabolism trials to compare the nutritive value of blighted corn silage (salvage) with normal corn silage. The blighted silage was brown in color and relatively dry when harvested (56.7 vs. 32.6% dry matter), although both were harvested at approximately the same time. Chemical composition of the two types of corn silage showed little difference with crude protein (8.1 vs. 8%), ether extract (3 vs. 2.1%), crude fiber (21 vs. 24%) and N-free extract (63 vs. 62%) being similar. In the metabolism comparisons, silage digesti_{bility} showed a difference ($P<0.5$) only in ether extract, which represents only a minor component (2–3%) of corn silage dry matter. These results indicate it is wise to salvage a corn crop infested with southern corn leaf blight by harvesting it as soon as possible and ensiling it for beef cattle feed.

16–2.2.5 Drought Corn for Silage

Drought damaged corn can be salvaged for cattle feed by ensiling it. Perry et al. (1984) reported feeding studies using drought damaged corn. Most of the stalks were <1.3 m in height (normal corn plant is 2 m in height or more), and even though cobs were present, many of them bore little or no grain. Silage dry matter harvested was 4.3 t/ha (normal silage would yield approximately three times that amount). In a cattle feeding comparison, growing-finishing beef cattle fed the drought damaged corn silage gained approximately as rapidly as those fed regular corn silage (1 kg/day). However, those fed the drought silage consumed more silage dry matter. Drought damaged corn may have an increased amount of carbohydrates stored in stalk and leaves thus partially compensating for reduced grain production. Thus, drought-stressed corn plant can be harvested and ensiled for cattle feed without adversely affecting cattle performance. In pursuing this route, it is important that sufficient moisture be available, either natural or added at the time of ensiling, to ensure adequate packing to prevent aerobic spoilage.

16–2.3 Corn Silage for Various Species of Livestock

16–2.3.1 Dairy Cattle

Whole plant corn silage is an excellent feedstuff for dairy cattle. It provides a succulent source of roughage which, because it is harvested and stored within a relatively short period of time will remain fairly uniform in quality and chemical composition since it was harvested and stored within a relatively short period of time. Typically, a dairy cow lactation diet will contain 2% of the cow's body weight daily as air-dry hay equivalent roughage. Thus, a 500-kg lactating cow might receive 10 kg of air-dry (90% dry matter) hay equivalent plus the amount of concentrates needed to meet her total nutrient requirements. Where corn silage is available, one-half of the air-dry hay equivalent is provided by silage; and since silage may contain only about one-third dry matter, in reality then 3% of the cow's body weight is fed as silage, plus 1% of her body weight as 90% dry matter hay.

When not handled properly, corn silage feeding can impart a distinct flavor and aroma to milk. However, it is not difficult to prevent such undesirable effects. Silage should be fed after milking, and the mangers should be cleaned regularly. Silage should not be left scattered on the floor, and the environment should be ventilated well.

16–2.3.2 Beef Cattle

Silage from well-matured corn plants in which the grain is dented and glazed fits well into many beef cattle programs. Each feeding situation should be examined to determine which program will provide the greatest return. A 1974 Univ. of Minnesota publication summarized research from 17 university experiments in which various ratios of corn and corn silage were fed to steer calves (Table 16–11). As the level of dietary dry matter was increased from 10% up to 80%, rate of daily gain decreased from 1.14 to 0.87 kg, and thus the length of time required for such calves to gain 300 kg was increased from 263 d up to 345 d. Thus, the total economics must be studied before a decision is made as to which level of corn silage best fits a particular feeding situation.

Generally, the feeding value of corn silage for beef cattle is highly dependent upon the ratio of corn to stover. A common guideline is that in whole corn silage, one-half of the available energy is contained in the grain portion whereas the other one-half is contained in the stalk, leaves, and cob. Thus, it is important that the corn plant be well-eared in order to make a reasonably high-energy silage.

When balanced for its protein and mineral deficiencies, corn silage

Table 16–11. Performance of steer calves fed various ratios of corn silage (summary of 17 university experiments).†

Item	Percentage of ration dry matter from corn silage							
	10%	20%	30%	40%	50%	60%	70%	80%
Daily gain, kg	1.14	1.13	1.10	1.07	1.04	0.99	0.93	0.87
Daily feed dry matter, kg								
Corn grain	5.9	5.3	4.7	4.0	3.3	2.5	1.3	1.0
Silage	0.7	1.4	2.2	2.9	3.7	4.4	5.0	5.5
Supplement	0.4	0.4	0.4	0.4	0.4	0.4	0.4	0.4
(Silage at 35% dry matter)	(2.0)	(4.0)	(6.2)	(8.4)	(10.5)	(12.4)	(14.1)	(15.7)
Feed dry matter/kg gain, kg								
Corn grain	5.1	4.7	4.2	3.7	3.2	2.5	1.8	1.1
Silage	0.6	1.3	2.0	2.7	3.6	4.4	5.3	6.3
Supplement	0.3	0.4	0.4	0.4	0.4	0.4	0.4	0.5
Days for 300-kg gain	263	265	273	280	288	303	323	345

† Developed from Univ. of Minnesota data (1974), Rep. B-195.

is an excellent roughage for wintering beef cows. Generally, beef cows tend to get too fat unless the amount of corn silage offered them is limited drastically. In most computer programs, corn silage will show up as being too expensive for wintering beef cows unless the level fed is limited.

A two-phase feeding program to make optimal use of corn silage in beef cattle growing and finishing diets is suggested. First, to predict how long the cattle will be on feed in order to reach the desirable market finish. Once the number of days is established, for example, 180 d, then the total number of days is divided into two equal periods. The first half of the feedlot period then becomes the "growing" phase, at which time the ratio of corn silage dry matter to shelled corn dry matter is 3:1, with sufficient supplemental protein, minerals, and vitamin A provided to balance the diet. Then during the last one-half of the feedlot period, the ratio is reversed to 1 part corn silage:3 parts shelled corn, on a dry matter basis, plus balancing protein, minerals, and vitamin A. Almost any age beef steer or heifer responds well to the above program, and it may well be the most economical program.

16-3   CORN BY-PRODUCTS

In order to understand the potential of the by-products of corn processing as animal feedstuffs, at least limited space must be given to describing the more important corn processing techniques.

16-3.1   Wet Milling of Corn

This process is used primarily in the production of corn starch. The process begins with the soaking of the corn kernel to soften the outer coat, or hull, so that the grain components may be separated into separate groupings. Sulfurous acid water may be utilized in this softening process which is known also as the *steeping process*. About 150 L of steeping liquid is utilized for each 100 kg of corn for approximately 36 h. Soluble matter generally amounts to 6% of the dry matter of the original corn, and such solids usually contain 35 to 45% protein, dry matter basis. Vacuum application will remove sufficient water that final condensed steep water solubles contain 35 to 55% solids.

The steeped corn next has the germ removed, and this resulting separation contains about 50% oil. Following the removal of the corn germ plus the steeping water, the main constituents are the starch, gluten and hulls; after screening out the coarse particles, the horny endosperm and hulls are ground to release the remainder of the starch. Eventually, the processing separates out the starch, the gluten and the hullls.

In the conversion of starch to sugars, the mother liquor from dextrose crystallization becomes corn molasses which is sold in competition with cane molasses. It must contain not <43% reducing sugars and not < 75% solids.

16-3.2   Dry Milling of Corn

This process consists primarily of separating the corn germ from the remainder of the corn kernel. General objectives of this technique include the removal of all germ and hulls, leaving the endosperm low in fat and fiber. (A more extensive discussion of corn milling will be found in Chapter 15 in this book.)

16-3.3   Fermentation and Distillation

This process consists essentially of the use of appropriate yeasts, molds, or bacteria on the carbohydrate-containing corn under controlled O_2 conditions to produce alcohol. The principal animal feedstuffs remaining after fermentation and subsequent distillation of the alcohol produced are corn distillers' grains, corn distillers' solubles, or a combination of the two called corn distillers' dried grains with solubles. When corn is utilized by the brewing industry, similar by-products remain for livestock feeding as exemplified by brewers' grains.

The typical chemical analyses for the more common corn by-products are listed in Table 16-12. Several by-products will be discussed.

16-3.4   Condensed Fermented Corn Extractives

Condensed fermented corn extractives often are identified as either heavy corn steepwater or as corn steep liquor. Feed regulation officials have developed standards to identify many feedstuffs. This product is

Table 16-12. Composition of by-products of the corn-processing industry (Crampton and Harris, 1971).

By-product	Dry matter	Dry matter analyses				
		Protein	Fiber	Ash	Ether extract	N-free extract
				%		
Wet milling industry						
Corn steep sols. (cond.)	94.3	22.8	0.0	8.2	1.6	67.4
Corn gluten feed	90.4	28.6	8.0	7.3	2.9	53.2
Corn gluten meal (41)	91.0	42.9	5.0	3.6	2.6	45.9
Corn gluten meal (60)	90.0	68.9	2.8	2.0	2.8	23.5
Corn germ meal	90.8	23.3	16.6	3.8	9.8	46.4
Corn solubles with corn germ and bran	94.9	33.4	5.5	10.3	1.3	49.5
Corn molasses	72.5	0.4	0.0	11.0	0.0	88.6
Distilling industry						
Corn dist. dried grains	93.8	29.7	13.4	2.4	9.9	44.6
Dist. dried grains with sols.	92.5	29.2	9.8	5.0	11.2	44.8
Corn dist. dried sols.	93.3	31.5	3.8	8.0	10.0	46.7
Dry milling industry						
Hominy feed	90.5	12.3	5.3	3.0	6.4	73.0

identified as follows: "Condensed fermented corn extractives are obtained by the partial removal of water from the liquid resulting from steeping or corn in a water and SO_2 solution which is allowed to ferment by the action of naturally occurring lactic acid producing microorganisms as practiced in the wet milling of corn."

Condensed corn fermentation extractives have been shown to have activity both as a source of many B vitamins and as a source of many benefits that cannot be attributed to the known vitamins. Normally, in the case of chicks, a level of 2.5 to 3% of the diet consists of sources of so-called unidentified growth factors (UGF) and condensed fermented corn extractives is an excellent source of UGF. Although condensed fermented corn extractives are as rich in N-free extract as cane molasses, they are used quite frequently in cattle feeding because of the level of natural protein and of price relationships. Since the balance of essential amino acids is not good, protein value is minimal for monogastric animals such as swine and poultry. It carries reasonably high levels of the mineral elements, K (2.4%), P(1.8%), and Mg (1%).

16–3.5   Wet Corn Gluten Feed

Wet corn gluten feed is defined as "that part of the commercial shelled corn that remains after the extraction of the larger portion of the starch, gluten, and germ by the processes employed in the wet milling manufacture of corn starch or syrup. It may or may not contain one or more of the following: fermented corn extractives, corn germ meal."

Wet corn gluten feed is an excellent feedstuff for cattle. Trenkle (1986a) showed that cattle fed up to 60% of their diet as wet corn gluten feed, replacing both corn and roughage, gained more rapidly than those not receiving wet corn gluten feed (Table 16–13). Feeding of either wet or dry corn gluten feed at 60% of the dietary dry matter appeared to provide adequate roughage for finishing cattle. Berger et al. (1985) reported similar

Table 16–13. Feedlot performance of yearling beef steers fed wet and dry corn gluten feed (147-d trials) (Trenkle, 1986a).†

Level of gluten feed	No. cattle	Daily gain	Daily dry matter intake	Dry matter/ kg gain
			kg	
Low silage	18	1.43	8.4	5.8
Medium silage	18	1.48	9.3	6.3
Wet corn gluten feed				
30%	18	1.59	9.6	6.1
45%	18	1.54	9.3	6.0
60%	18	1.53	9.0	5.9
Dry corn gluten feed				
30%	18	1.59	10.1	6.3
45%	18	1.46	9.8	6.7
60%	18	1.46	9.6	6.6

† 336 kg, initial wt.

results. In fact, when 70% of the dietary dry matter was supplied by wet corn gluten feed, removal of the standard 10% of the diet as corn silage resulted in a 5% increase in daily gain (1.33 vs. 1.26 kg per day).

Berger et al. (1985) recommended that wet corn gluten feed should constitute not more than 50% of the dry matter intake, and that dry corn gluten feed be limited to 25% of the dry matter intake.

Trenkle (1986b) reported tentative equations for calculating the value of corn gluten feed for finishing beef cattle and sheep. He proposed that at 30% of the diet, corn gluten feed will provide adequate supplemental protein, P, K, and S, and will have an energy value about 90 to 95% that of corn grain. In order to maintain this energy value of corn gluten feed when fed at higher levels, other contributors of roughage in the diet must be reduced or removed. Trenkle further suggested an economic value for corn gluten feed, when fed at no more than 30% of the dietary dry matter, and which is related to its protein and energy level as follows:

1. $(0.07 \times$ soybean meal price/ton$) + (14.08 \times$ corn price/bu$) =$ value of *wet* corn gluten feed/ton.
2. $(0.16 \times$ soybean meal price/ton$) + (32.64 \times$ corn price/bu$) =$ value of *dry* corn gluten feed/ton.

Trenkle suggested that a portion of corn gluten feed above 30% of the dietary dry matter provides only energy and has an economic value of:

1. $16.2 \times$ corn price/bu $=$ value of *wet* corn gluten feed/ton.
2. $35.9 \times$ corn price/bu $=$ value of *dry* corn gluten feed/ton.

The above equations do not take into account any storage, transporation, processing equipment, or management costs for corn, corn gluten feed, or soybean meal. The equations are based upon 88, 40, and 92% dry matters in corn, wet corn gluten feed and dry corn gluten feed, respectively. In order to comply with metric measurements, metric conversion are included: a bushel of corn (56 lb) $=$ 25.45 kg; a ton (2000 lb) $=$ 909 kg.

Loy (1986) presented summary tables based on the Trenkle (1986b) formulas (Tables 16–14 and 16–15). These values are based upon feeding no more corn gluten feed than that necessary to meet the protein requirements, and this probably would occur for growing beef cattle at 30 to 40% of the dietary dry matter.

Staples et al. (1984) and Hutjens et al. (1985) compared wet gluten feed (0, 20, 30, or 40% of he diet) for Holstein cows just past peak of lactation. Although milk yield (kg/d) was depressed linearly by additions of wet corn gluten feed to the diet (30.5, 29.9, 28.1, 28.1) yield of 4.0% fat corrected milk remained unchanged due to increasing milk fat percentage (2.86, 2.97, 3.15, 3.21). Milk solids-not-fat percentage and yield and milk protein percentage and yield were depressed linearly by addition of wet corn gluten feed to the diet.

Wet corn gluten feed probably does not fit as well in diet formulation for the monogastric animals (pigs and poultry) as with the ruminant

Table 16–14. Value of corn gluten feed as an energy source at varying corn prices (Loy, 1986).

| Corn price, cents/kg (dollars/bu) | Value of corn gluten feed, cents/kg (dollars/ton) | | | |
| | To replace corn | | To replace corn and roughage | |
	Wet	Dry	Wet	Dry
6.9 (1.75)	2.9 (26.43)	5.6 (60.75)	3.2 (29.40)	6.7 (60.90)
7.9 (2.00)	3.3 (30.20)	6.4 (58.00)	3.7 (33.60)	7.7 (69.60)
8.8 (2.25)	3.7 (33.98)	7.2 (65.25)	4.2 (37.80)	8.6 (78.30)
9.8 (2.50)	4.2 (37.75)	8.0 (72.50)	4.6 (42.00)	9.6 (87.00)
10.8 (2.75)	4.6 (41.53)	8.8 (79.75)	5.1 (46.20)	10.5 (95.70)
11.8 (3.00)	5.0 (45.30)	9.6 (87.00)	5.5 (50.40)	11.5 (104.40)

Table 16–15. Value of dry corn gluten feed as a protein supplement at varying corn and soybean meal prices (Loy, 1986).†

| Corn price, cents/kg (dollars/bu) | Soybean meal price, price/kg, cents (dollars/ton) | | | |
	16.5 (150.)	22 (200.)	27.5 (250.)	33 (300.)
5.9 (1.50)	8.0 (72.96)	8.9 (80.96)	9.8 (88.96)	10.7 (96.96
7.9 (2.00)	9.8 (89.28)	10.7 (97.28)	11.6 (105.20)	12.5 (113.28)
9.8 (2.50)	11.6 (105.60)	12.5 (113.60)	13.4 (121.60)	14.3 (129.60)
11.8 (3.00)	12.4 (121.92)	14.3 (129.92)	15.2 (137.92)	16.0 (145.92)

† Prices adapted by author according to Trenkle (1986b) formulas by converting bushels to kg (a 56-lb bushel = 25.45 kg) and tons to kg (a 2000-lb ton = 909 kg).

animals. Often complete mixed diets are fed to pigs and poultry, and the relatively high-moisture wet gluten feed has the tendency to mold quickly. Furthermore, monogastric animals do not digest the higher level of crude fiber as well as ruminant animals.

16–3.6 Dry Corn Gluten Feed

Dry corn gluten feed has a dry matter analysis similar to that for wet corn gluten feed on a dry matter-equivalent basis. Dry corn gluten feed can be substituted for corn in growing-finishing swine diets up to a maximum level of 25 to 30% without affecting rate of gain significantly, if attention is paid to maintaining optimal amino acid levels. Furthermore, up to 15 to 20% dry corn gluten feed may be incorporated into laying hen diets without affecting performance adversely (Parsons et al., 1985).

Research on dry corn gluten feed value for swine has been summarized in a bulletin put out by the Illinois Corn Growers Association (Hollis et al., 1985). Two different experiments with growing swine included, 0, 10, 20, or 30% dried corn gluten feed without affecting rate of gain significantly. In one of the two experiments, feed required per unit gain was increased on the higher dry corn gluten feed diets, whereas in the other, there was no effect on feed efficiency. The pelleting of dry corn gluten feed improved its value for swine and may have increased tryptophan availability. Generally, when dry corn gluten feed is used to substitute in swine diets for protein, as well as energy, one should check dietary levels of both lysine and tryptophan. Hollis et al. (1985) suggested that 100 kg of dry corn gluten feed is equivalent to 88 kg of corn plus 12 kg of soybean meal. From a chemical analysis point of view, swine diets appear to be adequate in P. However, since much of the gluten P is in the phytin form, and somewhat less available to the monogastric pig, at least one-half of the pig P requirement should be met with inorganic phosphorus, such as dicalcium phosphate.

16–3.7   Corn Gluten Meal

Corn gluten meal is the dried residue from corn after the removal of the larger part of the starch and germ, and the separation of the bran by the process employed in the wet milling manufacture of corn starch or syrup, or by enzymatic treatment of the endosperm. It may contain fermented corn extractives and/or corn germ meal.

Note in Table 16–12 two types of corn gluten meal are listed, namely 41 and 60% protein. The 41% protein meal is simply a combination of 60% protein corn gluten meal and corn gluten feed. Note also the higher crude fiber, ash and N-free extract content of the 41% protein corn gluten meal, as compared to the 61% protein meal. Since the trend is toward higher energy densities in broiler diets, the use of 61% protein corn gluten meal has increased over that of the 41% meal. Corn gluten meal is quite desirable in broiler diets because it contains practically all of the xanthophyll of the corn kernel, which gives the highly desirable yellow color to the body fat of broiler chicken carcasses. Once again, it is important to point out corn protein is quite low in the essential amino acids lysine and tryptophan. Therefore, corn gluten meal is desirable in poultry diets for its yellow color-imparting characteristics and not as a source of essential amino acids.

Corn gluten meal has been classified as somewhat less soluble in the rumen of the cow than soybean meal. Therefore, it has attracted attention as a "rumen by-pass" type protein. Other than its potential as by-pass protein, it has no special advantage for ruminants; and because of its poor balance of essential amino acids, it is not attractive for swine formulations. However, if economic relationships favored corn gluten meal for swine and if the essential amino acids were kept in balance, then it could be used for swine quite satisfactorily.

16–3.8   Hominy Feed

Hominy feed, obtained in the dry milling process, is a mixture of corn bran, corn germ, and a part of the starchy portion of either white or yellow corn kernels, or mixtures thereof, as produced in the manufacture of pearl hominy, hominy grits or table meal, and must not contain <5% ether extract.

Hominy feed has a protein level comparable to corn (11%); and with a minimum of 4% oil, it is an excellent energy feed. In fact, it may contain slightly more energy than corn. Because the germ protein is usually included in the hominy feed, it may have a slightly higher biological value protein than contained in the corn grain, with the concentration of lysine and tryptophan being nearly double those in corn grain.

16–3.9   Corn Distillers Dried Grains

Corn distillers dried grains are obtained after the removal of ethyl alcohol by distillation from yeast fermentation of corn, by separating the resultant coarse grain fraction of the whole stillage and drying it by methods employed in the grain distilling industry.

Corn distillers dried grains is relatively high in protein (27–30%) which is of rather low biological value, due to its lower levels of lysine and tryptophan. Because of its high fiber content (13%), it is a rather bulky feed. Thus, since the protein is of lower biological value and since it is a relatively bulky feedstuff, corn distillers dried grains is an excellent ingredient in dairy cow grain mixes. Normally, this product is not marketed in this form, but rather in combination with corn distillers dried solubles.

16–3.10   Corn Distillers Dried Solubles

Corn distillers dried solubles are obtained after the removal of ethyl alcohol by distillation from the yeast fermentation of corn, by condensing the thin stillage fraction and drying.

This product is used primarily as a source of unidentified growth factors for young poultry and for breeding poultry. Furthermore, it has value in beef cattle feeds, especially when it can be blended into liquid cattle supplements.

16–3.11   Corn Distillers Dried Grains with Solubles

Corn distillers dried grains with solubles (DDGS) is defined as the product obtained after the removal of ethyl alcohol by distillation from the yeast fermentation of corn, by condensing and drying at least three-fourths of the solids of the resultant whole stillage.

Corn distillers dried grains with solubles is a medium protein (29%), medium energy ingredient for monogastrics, but a high energy ingredient for ruminant animls. Thus, the dairy industry welcomes this ingredient in the diet whenever it is economically feasible. In addition, the poultry industry utilizes an appreciable amount of DDGS.

REFERENCES

Ahlschwede, W.T., M.C. Brumm, D.M. Danielson, A.J. Lewis, E.R. Peo, Jr., and D.E. Reese. 1984. Univ. of Nebraska swine diet suggestions. Univ. of Nebraska—Lincoln Coop. Ext. Serv. EC 84–210.

Bates, F.L., D. French, and R.E. Rundle. 1943. Amylose and amylopectin content of starches determined by their iodine complex formation. J. Am. Chem. Soc. 65:142.

Beadle, J.B., D.E. Rust, R.E. Morgan, and R.A. Reiners. 1965. Composition of corn oil. J. Am. Oil Chemist's Soc. 42:90.

Beeson, W.M., and T.W. Perry. 1958. The comparative feeding value of high-moisture and low-moisture corn with different additives for fattening cattle. J. Anim. Sci. 17:368.

Berger, L.L., J.C. Weigel, and S.G. Bidner. 1985. Corn gluten feed. Illinois Corn Growers Assoc., Bloomington.

Caldwell, D.M., and T.W. Perry. 1972. Nutritional value of blighted corn as silage or as grain. J. Dairy Sci. 55:1302.

----, and ----. 1971. Relationship between stage of maturity of corn plant at time of harvest for corn silage and chemical composition. J. Dairy Sci. 54:533.

Crampton, E.W., and L.E. Harris. 1971. Atlas of nutritional data on United States and Canadian feeds. NAS, Washington, DC.

Earle, F.R., J.J. Curtis, and J.E. Hubbard. 1946. Composition of component parts of the corn kernel. Cereal Chem. 23:504.

Goodrich, R.D., D.W. Crawford, M.L. Thoney, and J.C. Meiske. 1974. Influence of corn silage level on the performance and economic returns of steer calves. Univ. of Minnesota. 1974 Res. Dep. Rep. B-195.

Hixon, D.L., E.E. Hatfield, and P.E. Lamb. 1969. Whole shelled corn versus cracked corn in cattle finishing diets. Univ. of Illinois 1969 Beef Day Rep.

Hollis, G.R., R.A. Easter, J.C. Weigel, and S.G. Bidner. 1985. Corn gluten feed. Illinois Corn Growers Assoc., Bloomington.

Hutjens, M.F., J.C. Weigel, and S.G. Bidner. 1985. Corn gluten feed. Illinois Corn Growers Assoc., Bloomington, p. 6.

Keith, E.A., V.F. Colenbrander, T.W. Perry, and L.F. Bauman. 1981. Performance of feedlot cattle fed brown midrib-three or normal corn silage with various levels of additional corn grain. J. Anim. Sci. 52:8.

Kuc, J., and O.E. Nelson. 1964. The abnormal lignins produced by the brown midrib mutants of maize. I. The brown midrib mutant. Arch. Biochem. Biophys. 105:103.

Loy, D.D. 1986. Feeding corn processed by-products to beef cattle. *In* Proc. Cornbelt Cow-Calf Conf., Ottumwa, IA. 22 February. Iowa State Univ., Ames.

Mertz, E.T., L.S. Bates, and O.E. Nelson. 1964. Mutant gene that changes protein composition and increases lysine content of maize endosperm. Science 145:279.

Parsons, C.M., J.C. Weigel, and S.G. Bidner. 1985. Corn gluten feed. Illinois Corn Growers Assoc., Bloomington, p. 8.

Perry, T.W., and D.M. Caldwell. 1969. Comparative nutritive value of silages made from high-sugar male sterile hybrid corn and regular starchy corn. J. Dairy Sci. 52:1119.

----, and ----. 1968. The value of corn silage made from the corn plant at various stages of maturity. Purdue Univ. Agric. Exp. Stn. Res. Prog. Rep. 331.

----, ----, J.R. Reedal, and C.B. Knodt. 1968. Stage of maturity of corn at time of harvest for silage and yield of digestible nutrients. J. Dairy Sci. 51:799.

----, M.T. Mohler, and R.P. Lemenager. 1984. Drought corn silage for beef cattle. Indiana Beef Cattle Day Rep., p. 29.

Smith, W.H., R.A. Pickett, and W.M. Beeson. 1963. Effect of age of corn and vitamin A supplementation on the performance of growing-finishing swine. Purdue Univ. Res. Prog. Rep. 40.

Staples, C.R., C.L. Davis, G.C. McCoy, and J.H. Clark. 1984. Feeding value of wet gluten feed for lactating dairy cows. J. Dairy Sci. 67:1215.

Thomas, V.W., W.M. Beeson, and T.W. Perry. 1975. Effect of normal vs. opaque-2 vs. roasted normal corn and normal vs. opaque-2 corn silage for finishing beef cattle. J. Anim. Sci. 41:641.

Thornton, J.H., R.D. Goodrich, and J.C. Meiske. 1969. Corn maturity. I. Composition of corn grain of various maturities and test weights. J. Anim. Sci. 29:977.

Trenkle, A., 1986a. Feeding value of wet corn gluten feed when used to replace corn and roughage in a ration for yearling steers. Iowa State Univ. Beef Cattle Res. Rep., A.S. Leafl. R403.

----. 1986b. Evaluation of corn gluten feed. Prog. Rep. to Iowa Corn Promotion Board. Univ. of Iowa Press, Ames.

U.S. Department of Agriculture. 1985. Feed outlook and situation yearbook. p. 52–54. *In* Fd-S-298. U.S. Gov. Print. Office, Washington, DC.

SUBJECT INDEX

Aberrant ratio, 205
Abiotic disease, 747–749
  genetically-induced, 746–747
Abortion, 197–198, 208, 213, 215, 220
Abphyll, 374
Abscisic acid, 146, 178–179, 196, 354
Abscission, 184
Acid phosphatase, 190
Aconitase, 190
Action spectrum of mutation, 227, 232
Activator element, 114, 158, 160–161,
      200–201, 220, 223
Adaptive advantage, 24
Adaptive peaks, 13. *See also* Penetrance
Additive genetic variance, 479
Adenylate kinase, 190
Adherent leaf, 182
Aflatoxin, 814–815, 889
Africa, 39
Ageotropic roots, 183
Albescent seedling, 171–172, 178, 180
Albino seedling, 137, 139, 171–179
Alcohol
  annual production, USA, 883
  beverage, 927–930
  fuel, 883, 930
  process, 927–928
Alcohol dehydrogenase, 190, 193, 196, 211
Aldolase, 445
Aleurone, 38, 43, 53, 55–56, 58
  color
    blotched, 154, 158, 161
    inheritance, 114, 144, 148–170
    marbled, 155–156, 163
    mottled, 154–156, 163
    Navajo, 155, 163–164
    self-colored, 163
    stippled, 155, 163, 221, 234–235
  multilayer, 145
  tissue, 114, 139, 144–145
Alkaline cooked foods
  grain quality in, 896
  process of, 924–925
Allele
  metastable, 203
  paramutable, 43, 53–54, 59
  pattern, 162–163
Allelic complementation, 136, 141, 193
Allelic recombination (intragenic crossing-
      over), 288–289
Allelic series, 83
  a1, 151–152, 226, 233–236
  al, 172
  an1, 158
  anl, 153

B, 148, 153–155, 205
bt1, 141
bz1, 158
bz2, 158
c1, 148, 158, 167, 235
c2, 149, 159, 167
d1, 181
Ga1, 42, 44, 198
gl1, 234
in, 149, 159, 167
isozymes, 188–193
oy, 173, 178
P, 148–150, 160
pyd, 177
R, 148–149, 155–156, 158–159, 162–
      165, 203–205, 233–236
Rp1, 194
sh1, 141, 143
sh2, 141
su1, 142
transposable elements, 199–203
Tu, 185, 235
vp9, 174
w3, 174–175
wd, 177
wx, 143, 234–236
y1, 175, 179–180
yg2, 177
Allelism test, 85, 211–212
Allopolyploidy, 136, 281, 294
Allozyme loci, as markers, 449–450
Allyl alcohol, 198
Amargo maize, 195
Amazon Basin, 52–53
Amino acid
  analogues
    aminoethylcysteine, 378
    5-methyltryptophan, 378
    resistance, 358, 377–378
  inheritance, 137, 145
Aminopeptidase, 190
Amylase, 190
Amylomaize, 600, 886, 897, 911
Amylopectin, 875
  inheritance, 143, 198
Amyloplast, 143–144, 183
Amylose, 875
  inheritance, 142–143, 198
Anaerobic response, 141, 193, 196
Andes, 36, 43, 52, 56, 58
  Andean Complex, 36, 53, 56–57
  Andean races, 43, 52, 55–56, 58–59
Androgenesis, 164, 213, 223
Andromonoecy, 139, 181, 183–184
Andropogoneae, 9